A HISTORY OF CHEMISTRY

A HISTORY OF CHEMISTRY

BY

J. R. PARTINGTON

M.B.E., D.Sc.

EMERITUS PROFESSOR OF CHEMISTRY IN THE UNIVERSITY OF LONDON
FELLOW OF QUEEN MARY COLLEGE, LONDON

VOLUME TWO

LONDON
MACMILLAN & CO LTD
NEW YORK · ST MARTIN'S PRESS
1961

MACMILLAN AND COMPANY LIMITED
London Bombay Calcutta Madras Melbourne

THE MACMILLAN COMPANY OF CANADA LIMITED
Toronto

ST MARTIN'S PRESS INC
New York

PRINTED IN GREAT BRITAIN

PREFACE

THE present is the second volume of a work intended to be completed in four volumes. The third volume is in the press and the two will cover the period from about 1500 to about 1800, and so include the part of the subject which is probably of the greatest interest to many readers. It seemed desirable to publish these now rather than to wait for the completion of the material for the first and fourth volumes, now in a fairly advanced stage of preparation, which will deal with the earliest and latest periods. French chemistry, which falls largely into the eighteenth century, is treated in the third volume.

Since the books of Hoefer (1842–3; 2 ed. 1866–9) and Kopp (1843–7) there has been no comprehensive work based on original sources. The information they give has been considerably modified by research which has mostly been presented in periodical publications or monographs not easily accessible to chemists, and a new work incorporating such modifications and also carrying the subject to a later period should, therefore, be useful to many readers.

The present work is an enlargement of my book *A Short History of Chemistry*, first published in 1937 and reprinted, with revisions, five times to 1960. The treatment is more detailed and references are given to all the original sources, as many of which as was possible were used. Since Kopp's work, published more than a century ago, was also in four volumes, it is clear that a book of a reasonable size, bringing the subject up to date and also including full references (which were not given by Kopp), must aim at conciseness whilst at the same time being sufficiently detailed to be of real use. This has been achieved in the following ways:

(1) The reference material has been systematised in a way described on p. xi, and biographical details have been presented in a standard form at the beginning of each section, the places and dates of birth and decease being given as follows: 'Georg Ernst Stahl (Anspach, Bavaria, 21 October 1660–Berlin, 14 May 1734).'

(2) Digressions into general political and economic history, the history of learned societies, etc., topics usually called 'background material' and easily found in books and encyclopaedias included in all public libraries, may be omitted. A concise account of philosophical systems which profoundly influenced chemists, such as Descartes, however, must be included and the omission of this in previous works has often led to misunderstanding.

(3) Lavish use of illustrative material, adding largely to the size and cost of a book whilst not enhancing its real value, must be avoided.

(4) Extensive blocks of quotations, which are usually tedious to read, must be replaced by carefully selected portions, interspersed by explanatory text to relieve the monotony.

These guiding principles can all be criticised, but if they had not been followed the book would have swelled into more volumes and would probably have been less interesting and useful.

As far as possible the original sources have been used. Some modern Continental and American monographs not found in libraries available to me were priced beyond my means and, although I have mostly mentioned them, I regret that I have not been able to see them. Reprints of papers kindly sent to me by authors have been used and mentioned, and I hope that I shall continue to be favoured with them. The last two volumes of Prof. Thorndike's monumental work, which deal with the period of this volume from a different angle, were available only after my text was completed, but I have added references to them in all the appropriate places.

The period covered in the second and third volumes may seem rather remote to some young readers. As a young man I saw and heard Sir Henry Roscoe and he can be linked with earlier chemists as follows:

Roscoe	1833–1915	Stahl	1660–1734
Dalton	1766–1844	Boyle	1627–1691
Macquer	1718–1784	Van Helmont	1579–1644

This short chain brings us to the beginning of chemistry as a science.

CAMBRIDGE, *January 1961*

CONTENTS

LIST OF ILLUSTRATIONS

ABBREVIATIONS IN REFERENCES

In footnotes references are given to periodical publications in the order: year of publication, volume number in small roman numerals, page (see below). In some cases the title of a book or periodical is given in full. In other cases abbreviated titles are given, as in (*a*) below, or simply a number, as in (*b*). The full titles will be found in the lists of authors or publications beginning on p. xiii. Again, in separate chapters dealing with one person, a list of his publications in which they are denoted by numbers (or sometimes letters) is given towards the beginning of the chapter, and these abbreviations (*c*) are used throughout the chapter. In other chapters the titles are not abbreviated. Examples of the types of abbreviation are shown below:

(*a*) Sudhoff, *A. Nat.*, 1913–15, v, 198–201. See list of periodical publications for *A. Nat.*

(*b*) Lasswitz, (1), i, 343. See list of authors under Lasswitz, item (1).

(*c*) Van Helmont, ch. VI, p. 220, footnote 2 reads: 10, 22; 8, § 13; *Vb* 43, 47, 127. Items 10, 22 and 8 are works listed in the table on p. 215; *Vb* is the edition of Van Helmont's book listed on p. 213.

When the full titles of books or periodicals are given in the footnotes, these are not repeated in the lists of authors and abbreviations of titles of periodicals. Places of publication, unless otherwise stated, are London, Paris and Berlin for works in English, French and German. In some cases the place of publication of a periodical varied and the alternatives are not usually given. The size of a book is usually octavo (8°) unless otherwise stated.

LIST OF AUTHORS

ACR. Alembic Club Reprints. Edinburgh.

T. C. ALLBUTT. Greek Medicine in Rome, 1921.

BADEN POWELL. An Historical View of the Progress of the Physical and Mathematical Sciences from the Earliest Ages to the Present Time, 1834.

J. C. BARCHUSEN [BARCKHAUSEN]. Historia Medicinæ. Amsterdam, 1710.

P. BAYLE. Dictionnaire Historique et Critique. 4 vols. f°, Amsterdam, 1740.

J. BECKMANN. (1) A History of Inventions, Discoveries, and Origins, tr. W. Johnson, revised W. Francis and J. W. Griffith, 2 vols., 1846. (2) Beiträge zur Geschichte der Erfindungen, 5 vols. Leipzig, 1786–1805. (3) Vorrath kleiner Anmerkungen über mancherley gelehrte Gegenstände, 3 pts. Göttingen, 1795, 1803–6.

M. BERTHELOT. (1) Les Origines de l'Alchimie, 1885 (repr. 1938). (2) Collection des Anciens Alchimistes Grecs. 3 vols. 4°, 1887–8–8. (3) Introduction à l'Étude de la Chimie des Anciens et du Moyen Age. 1889. (4) Histoire des Sciences. La Chimie au Moyen Âge. 3 vols. 4°, 1893. (5) Archéologie et Histoire des Sciences. 1906.

C. L. and A. B. BERTHOLLET. Elements of the Art of Dyeing, tr. A. Ure. 2 vols., 1824.

Biogr. Univ. Biographie Universelle. 85 vols. 1811–62.

T. BIRCH. (1) History of the Royal Society. 4 vols. 4°, 1756–7.

BM. British Museum (Library), London.

BN. Bibliothèque Nationale, Paris.

H. BOERHAAVE. (1) Institutiones et Experimenta Chemicæ, sm. 8°, 'Paris', 1724. (2) Elementa Chemiae, 2 vols. 4°, Leyden, 1732. (3) A New Method of Chemistry, tr. P. Shaw and E. Chambers, 2 pts. 4°, London, 1727 (tr. of (1) with additions). (4) A New Method of Chemistry, 2 ed. by P. Shaw, 2 vols. 4°, London, 1741 (tr. of (2) with additions).

H. CARRINGTON BOLTON (see Browne, *J. Chem. Educ.*, 1940, xvii, 457, portr.). (1) A Select Bibliography of Chemistry 1492–1892 (Smithsonian Miscell. Collection no. 850), Washington, 1893. (2) I Supplement (*ib.* no. 1170), Washington, 1899. (3) II Supplement (*ib.* no. 1253), Washington, 1901.

O. BORRICHIUS. (1) De Ortu et Progressu Chemiæ, Dissertatio. sm. 4°, Copenhagen, 1668. (2) Hermetis Ægyptiorum et Chemicorum Sapientia. sm. 4°, Copenhagen, 1674. (3) Conspectus Scriptorum Chemicorum illustriorum. sm. 4°, Copenhagen, 1697.

W. T. BRANDE. A Manual of Chemistry. 6 ed., 2 vols. 1848.

LORD BROUGHAM. (1) Lives of Philosophers of the Time of George III. (In Works.) London and Glasgow, 1855, repr. 1872.

HARCOURT BROWN. Scientific Organizations in Seventeenth Century France. Baltimore, 1934.

J. CAMPBELL BROWN. A History of Chemistry from the Earliest Times. 1913 (2 ed. by H. H. Brown, 1920).

S. BROWN. Essays Scientific and Literary. 2 vols. Edinburgh, 1858.

J. BRUCKER. Historia Critica Philosophiæ, 2 ed., 6 vols. 4°, Leipzig, 1767 (66), the ed. used (1 ed. 6 vols. 4°, 1742–67).

ARABELLA BUCKLEY. Short History of Natural Science. 3 ed. 1883.

E. A. BURTT. The Metaphysical Foundations of Modern Physical Science. 1925.

CADET, see SPIELMANN.

A. L. CAILLET. Manuel Bibliographique des Sciences Psychiques et Occultes. 3 vols., 1912.

F. CAJORI. History of Physics. 2 ed. New York, 1929.

P. A. CAP. Études Biographiques pour servir à l'Histoire des Sciences, 2 vols., 1857–64.

Cat. Catalogue.

CUL. Cambridge University Library.

G. CUVIER. (1) Recueil des Éloges Scientifiques lus dans les Séances Publiques de l'Institut Royal de France, 3 vols., 1819–19–27. (2) Éloges Historiques (Bibliothèque Classique des Célébrités Contemporaines), 1860. (3) Histoire des Progrès des Sciences Naturelles, depuis 1789 jusqu'à ce jour, 2 vols., Brussels, 1837–8.

W. C. DAMPIER. A History of Science. Cambridge, 1946.

J. W. DANA and G. J. BRUSH. A System of Mineralogy. 5 ed. 1868.

F. DANNEMANN. Die Naturwissenschaften in ihrer Entwicklung und in ihrem Zusammenhang. 2 ed. Leipzig, 4 vols., 1820–21–22–23.

C. V. DAREMBERG. (1) Histoire des Sciences Médicales, 2 vols., 1870.

E. DARMSTAEDTER. (1) Berg-, Probir- und Kunstbüchlein. Mit Bibliographie und 12 Abbildungen. Munich, 1926.

M. DELACRE. (1) Histoire de la Chimie, 1920. (2) *Id.* in *Revue générale des Sciences*, 1924, XXXV, 704.

P. DIERGART. Beiträge aus der Geschichte der Chemie dem Gedächtniss von Georg W. A. Kahlbaum. Leipzig and Vienna, 1909.

DNB. Dictionary of National Biography.

J. B. DUMAS. (1) Leçons sur la Philosophie Chimiques professées au Collège de France en 1836, ed. Binau (*sic*), 1837. (2) 2 ed. by Bineau, 1878. (3) *ib.*, repr. 1937.

D. DUVEEN. Bibliotheca Alchemica et Chemica. 1949.

D. DUVEEN and H. S. KLICKSTEIN. A Bibliography of the Works of A. L. Lavoisier. 1954.

EB. Encyclopædia Britannica (ed. quoted).

Ency. Brit. Suppl. Supplement to the Third Edition of the Encyclopædia Britannica. 2 vols. in 4 pts. Edinburgh, 1801.

Ency. Méthod. Encyclopédie Méthodique. 166 vols. 1781–1832 (incompl.). In sep. departments, e.g. Chimie.

J. S. ERSCH and J. G. GRUBER. Allgemeine Encyclopädie der Naturwissenschaften und Künste. 167 vols. (incompl.). Leipzig, 1818–89.

J. EVELYN. Memoirs illustrative of the Life and Writings of John Evelyn . . . comprising his Diary, from the Year 1641 to 1705–6, and a Selection of his Familiar Letters, ed. W. Bray, 1870 (repr. of 2 ed., 1819).

J. FABRICIUS. Bibliotheca Graeca. 14 vols. 4°. Hamburg, 1718–28.

F. M. FELDHAUS. (1) Die Technik der Vorzeit. la. 8°, Leipzig and Berlin, 1914.

F. FERCHL and A. SÜSSENGUTH. (1) Kurzgeschichte der Chemie. Mittenwald, 1936. (2) tr. as A Pictorial History of Chemistry, 1939.

J. FERGUSON. Bibliotheca Chemica: Catalogue of the Alchemical, Chemical and Pharmaceutical Books in the Collection of the late James Young. 2 vols. la. 8°. Glasgow, 1906 (repr. London, 1954).

G. FESTER. Die Entwicklung der chemischen Technik bis zu den Anfängen der Grossindustrie. Ein technologisch-historischer Versuch. 1923.

J. C. FISCHER. Geschichte der Physik. 8 vols., Göttingen, 1801–8.

SIR MICHAEL FOSTER. Lectures on the History of Physiology during the Sixteenth, Seventeenth and Eighteenth Centuries (Cambridge Natural Science Manuals. Biological Series). Cambridge, 1901.

A. F. de FOURCROY. (1) Systême des Connaissances Chimiques et de leurs applications aux phénomènes de la nature et de l'art. 11 vols. 8°, 1801–2. (2) id., art. in Encyclopédie Methodique, Chimie, 1796, iii, 303–781 (ib., 1793, ii, is also quoted).

W. GANZENMÜLLER. Beiträge zur Geschichte der Technologie und der Alchemie, Weinheim, 1956.

T. GERDING. Geschichte der Chemie. Leipzig, 1869.

R. J. HARVEY GIBSON. Outlines of the History of Botany. 1919.

E. GILDEMEISTER and F. HOFFMANN. Die ätherischen Öle. Vol. i, 1928.

J. F. GMELIN. (1) Geschichte der Chemie seit dem Wiederaufleben der Wissenschaften bis an das Ende der achtzehnten Jahrhunderts. 3 vols., Göttingen, 1797–8–9.

N. GOBET. Les anciens Minéralogistes du Royaume de France; avec des Notes. 2 vols., 1779 (pagin. cont.).

F. A. C. GREN. Systematisches Handbuch der gesammten Chemie. 2 ed., 4 vols., Halle, 1794–4–5–6.

R. T. GUNTHER. (1) Early Science in Oxford, 14 vols., Oxford, 1923–45. (2) Early Science in Cambridge, Oxford, 1937.

H. HAESER. (1) Geschichte der Medicin. 2 vols., Jena, 1875–81.

A. HELLER. Geschichte der Physik. 2 vols., Stuttgart, 1882–4.

F. HOEFER. (1) Histoire de la Chimie, 2 ed., 2 vols., 1866–9. (2) ib., 1 ed., Histoire de la Chimie depuis les temps les plus reculés jusqu'à notre époque; comprenant une analyse détaillée des manuscrits alchimiques de la Bibliothèque Royale de Paris; un exposé des doctrines cabalistiques sur la pierre philosophale; l'histoire de la pharmacologie, de la métallurgie, et en général des sciences et des arts qui se rattachent à la chimie, etc., 2 vols., 1842–3. (3) Histoire de la Botanique, de la Minéralogie et de la Géologie, 1872. (4) Histoire des Mathématiques, 2 ed., 1879. (4) La Chimie enseignée par la Biographie de ses Fondateurs, 1865.

M. HOERNES. (1) Natur- und Urgeschichte des Menschen, Vienna and Leipzig, 1909. (2) Kultur der Urzeit, 3 vols., Leipzig, 1912.

A. W. HOFMANN. (1) Berliner Alchemisten und Chemiker. Rückblick auf die Entwickelung der chemischen Wissenschaft in der Mark. Rede gehalten zur Feier des Stiftungstages der Militärärztlichen Bildungsanstalten am 2 August 1882; 1882 (80 pp.). (2) Zur Erinnerung an vorangegangene Freunde. Gesammelte Gedächtnissreden, 3 vols., Brunswick, 1888.

J. HOOPS. Real-Lexikon der germanischen Altertumskunde, 4 vols., Stuttgart, 1911–19.

A. von HUMBOLDT. (1) Cosmos. tr. E. C. Otté and B. H. Paul, 4 vols., 1849–52. (2) Essai politique sur la royaume de la Nouvelle Espagne. 5 vols., 1811.

R. JAGNAUX. Histoire de la Chimie. 2 vols., 1891.

R. JAMES. Medicinal Dictionary. 3 vols. f°, 1745 (unpaginated).

C. G. JÖCHER. Allgemeines Gelehrten-Lexicon. 4 vols. 4°, Leipzig, 1750–1.

J. JUNCKER. (1) Conspectus Chemiae Theoretico-Practicae e Dogmatibus Becheri et

Stahlii. 2 vols. 4°, Halle, 1730–8. (2) Élémens de Chymie: suivant les Principes de Becker (*sic*) & de Stahl, tr. (from 2 Latin ed.) by Demachy, 6 vols. 12°, 1757.

G. W. A. KAHLBAUM, (ed.). Monographien aus der Geschichte der Chemie. 8 vols. Leipzig. 1897–1904.

M. H. KLAPROTH and F. WOLFF. Chemisches Handwörterbuch. 5 vols. and Supplement 4 vols. 1807–19.

A. C. KLEBS. Inunabula Scientifica et Medica. In *Osiris*, 1938 (publ. 1937) vol. iv.

C. KIESEWETTER. (1) Geschichte des neueren Occultismus, Leipzig, 1891. (2) Geschichte des Occultismus, 2 vols., Leipzig, 1895.

H. KOPP. (1) Geschichte der Chemie. 4 vols., Brunswick, 1843–4–5–7 (repr. in 1 vol. Leipzig, 1931). (2) Beiträge zur Geschichte der Chemie. 3 pts., Brunswick, 1869–75 (pagin. i and ii contin.). (3) Die Entwickelung der Chemie in der neuern Zeit. Munich, 1873. (4) Die Alchemie in älterer und neurer Zeit. Ein Beitrag zur Culturgeschichte. 2 pts., Heidelberg, 1886.

F. A. LANGE. Geschichte des Materialismus, Iserlohn, 1873, repr. 1882.

K. LASSWITZ. (1) Geschichte der Atomistik vom Mittelalter bis Newton. 2 vols., Hamburg and Leipzig, 1890 (repr. 1926). (2) *id.* in *Vierteljahreschrift für wissenschaftlichen Philosophie*, 1886, x, 166–89.

L. de LAUNOY. Minéralogie des Anciens. 2 vols., Brussels, 1803.

C. H. LA WALL. The Curious Lore of Drugs and Medicines (Four Thousand Years of Pharmacy). New York, 1927.

D. LECLERC [LE CLERC]. (1) Histoire de la Médecine. 3 pts. 4°, Amsterdam, 1702. (2) Nouvelle Édition, 4°, La Haye, 1729.

F. LENORMANT. Les Premières Civilisations. 2 vols. 1874.

J. G. LEONHARDI. Macquers Chymisches Wörterbuch. 6 vols., Leipzig, 1788–92.

M. B. LESSING. Handbuch der Geschichte der Medicin, 1838.

LENGLET DU FRESNOY. Histoire de la Philosophie Hermetique. Accompagnée d'un Catalogue raisonné des Ecrivains de cette Science. [Anon.]. 3 vols. 12°, 1742.

C. A. LOBECK. Aglaophamus sive de Theologiae mysticae Graecorum causis. 2 vols., Königsberg, 1829.

G. B. LIBRI. (1) Histoire des Sciences Mathématiques en Italie depuis la renaissance des lettres jusqu'à la fin du 17e siècle. 4 vols. 1838–41 (see p. 2).

E. O. VON LIPPMANN. (1) Abhandlungen und Vorträge zur Geschichte der Naturwissenschaften. 2 vols., Leipzig, 1906–13. (2) Entstehung und Ausbreitung der Alchemie. 3 vols., i and ii Berlin, 1919–31, iii Weinheim, 1954. (3) Beiträge zur Geschichte der Naturwissenschaften und der Technik, 2 vols., 1923 (Berlin)–53 (Weinheim). (4) Geschichte des Zuckers. 2 ed., 1929. (5) Geschichte der Rübe als Kulturpflanze, 1925. (6) Urzeugung und Lebenskraft, 1933. (7) Zeittafeln zur Geschichte der organischen Chemie, 1921. (8) Die Geschichte des Wismuts, 1930.

P. J. MACQUER. (1) Dictionnaire de Chymie [anon.]. 2 vols., 1766. (2) *ib.* 2 ed. 4 vols. 8°, 1778.

W. H. MAIGNE D'ARNIS. Lexicon ad Scriptores Mediæ et Infimæ Latinitatis, 1890.

J. J. MANGET. Bibliotheca Chemica Curiosa, seu Rerum ad Alchemiam pertinentium Thesaurus instructissimus, 2 vols. f°, Geneva, 1702.

J. E. MARSH. The Origins and Growth of Chemical Science, 1929.

I. MASSON. Three Centuries of Chemistry, 1925.

J. W. MELLOR. (1) A Comprehensive Treatise on Inorganic and Theoretical Chemistry. 16 vols., 1922–37.

MRS. MERRIFIELD. Original Treatises dating from the XII to the XVIII centuries on the Arts of Painting, etc. 2 vols., 1849.

J. T. MERZ. A History of European Thought in the Nineteenth Century. 4 vols. 1896–1914. 4 ed. (unchanged) Edinburgh, 1923.

MME. H. METZGER. (1) Doctrines Chimiques en France, 1923. (2) Newton, Stahl, Boerhaave, 1930.

E. VON MEYER. History of Chemistry, tr. G. McGowan. 3 ed., 1906.

E. H. F. MEYER. Geschichte der Botanik. 4 vols., Königsberg, 1854-5-6-7.

T. MEYER-STEINEG and K. SUDHOFF. Geschichte der Medizin, 1922.

J. P. (the Abbé) MIGNE. Patrologia Cursus Completus. Series Graeca (PG). Series Latina (PL).

J. C. W. MOEHSEN. (1) Geschichte der Wissenschaften in der Mark Brandenburg, besonders der Arzneiwissenschaft; von der ältesten Zeiten bis zu Ende des sechszehnten Jahrhunderts. 4°, Berlin and Leipzig, 1781. (2) Beiträge zur Geschichte der Naturwissenschaften in der Mark Brandenburg. 4°, Berlin and Leipzig, 1783.

Monographien, see Kahlbaum.

G. NAUDÉ. Apologie pour les grands hommes soupçonnez de magie. La Haye, 1653.

NBG. Nouvelle Biographie Générale. Ed. F. Hoefer. 46 vols. 1852–66.

NBU. Nouvelle Biographie Universelle: title of vols. i–ix of NBG; changed to avoid confusion with another work of the same title (also quoted).

M. NEUBURGER and J. PAGEL. Handbuch der Geschichte der Medizin. 3 vols., Jena, 1902-3-5.

WILHELM OSTWALD. (1) Lehrbuch der allgemeinen Chemie, 2 ed. 3 vols. Leipzig, 1910–11 and incomplete part of Vol. II, ii. (2) Elektrochemie, ihre Geschichte und Lehre, Leipzig. 1896.

OSTWALD's *Klassiker*. Klassiker der exacten Naturwissenschaften. Founded by W. Ostwald. Leipzig.

J. R. PARTINGTON. (1) Origins and Development of Applied Chemistry, 1935. (2) The Composition of Water, 1928. (3) A Short History of Chemistry, 1937, 3 ed. 1960. (4) A History of Greek Fire and Gunpowder, Cambridge, 1960. (5) A Text-Book of Inorganic Chemistry, 1921, 6 ed. 1961. (6) Advanced Treatise on Physical Chemistry, 5 vols., 1949–54.

JOHN PERCY (M.D., F.R.S., professor of metallurgy, Royal School of Mines). Metallurgy, 5 vols. (i Fuel, Fire-Clays, Copper, Zinc, Brass, etc., 1861; ii Iron and Steel, 1864; iii Lead, including Desilverization and Cupellation, 1870; iv Refractory Materials and Fuel, 1875, v Silver and Gold Pt. I (all publ.), 1880.)

H. W. PICTON. The Story of Chemistry, 1889.

PLINY. Historia Naturalis. Q. by book and chapter.

J. C. POGGENDORFF. (1) Biographisch-literarisches Handwörterbuch zur Geschichte der exacten Naturwissenschaften, sev. vols., Leipzig and Berlin, 1863–. (2) Histoire de la Physique. tr. E. Bibart and G. de la Quesnerie, 1883.

F. A. POUCHET. (1) Histoire des Sciences Naturelles au moyen âge, 1853.

J. PRIESTLEY. E & O = Experiments and Observations on Air, 3 vols., 1774-7.

T. PUSCHMANN. Handbuch der Geschichte der Medizin, Jena, 1903.

J. READ. (1) Prelude to Chemistry, 1936 (repr. 1939 unchanged except a footnote or so). (2) Humour and Humanism in Chemistry, 1947. (3) Through Alchemy to Chemistry, 1957.

T. A. RICKARD. Man and Metals. 2 vols. New York, 1932.

TH. A. RIXNER and TH. SIBER. Leben und Lehrmeinungen beruehmter Physiker

am Ende des XVI. und am Anfange des XVII. Jahrhunderts. 7 vols., Sulzbach,
  1819 (2 ed. 1829)–20–20–23–24–26–26.

H. E. ROSCOE and C. SCHORLEMMER. Treatise on Chemistry; q. by date and vol.

F. ROSENBERGER. Die Geschichte der Physick in Grundzügen. 3 pts. in 4 vols.,
  Brunswick, 1882–4–7–1890.

M. RULAND. Lexicon Alchemiæ. Frankfurt, 1612.

J. RUSKA. (1) ed. Studien zur Geschichte der Chemie, 1927.

L. F. SALZMAN. (1) English Industries in the Middle Ages. Oxford, 1923. (2) English
  Life in the Middle Ages. 1926.

G. SARTON. Introduction to the History of Science. 3 vols. in 5, Baltimore, 1927–31–47.

A. SAVERIEN. Histoire des Philosophes Modernes avec leurs Portraits, 8 pts., 12°,
  1760–73.

H. SCHELENZ. Geschichte der Pharmacie, 1904.

K. C. SCHMIEDER. Geschichte der Alchemie. Halle, 1832 (repr. Munich, 1927).

C. SINGER. (1) Science, Medicine and History. Essays on the Evolution of Scientific
  Thought and Medical Practice written in honour of Charles Singer, ed. E. A.
  Underwood. 2 vols., Oxford, 1953. (2) Short History of Biology. Oxford, 1931.
  (3) A Short History of Science to the Nineteenth Century. Oxford, 1941. (4)
  The Earliest Chemical Industry . . . the Alum Trade. f°, 1948. (5) Studies in
  the History and Method of Science. 2 vols., Oxford, 1917–21. (6) From Magic
  to Science. 1928. (7) Short History of Medicine. Oxford, 1928.

H. SOTHERAN. Annotated Catalogues of Works [for sale], q. by number of cat., date,
  number of item (or page).

J. R. SPIELMANN. Instituts de Chymie, tr. Cadet, 12 vols. 12°, 1770.

K. SPRENGEL. (1) Histoire de la Médecine, tr. A. J. L. Jourdain, revised E. F. M.
  Bosquillon, 9 vols., 1815 (i–vii)–32 (viii–ix). (2) Versuch einer pragmatischen
  Geschichte der Arzneykunde. 3 ed. 6 vols. in 7. Halle, 1821–40.

J. M. STILLMAN. The Story of Early Chemistry. New York, 1924.

F. STRUNZ. (1) Vorgeschichte und Anfänge der Chemie. Leipzig and Vienna, 1906.
  (2) Die Vergangenheit der Naturforschung. Jena, 1913. (3) Astrologie, Alchemie, Mystik. Munich-Planegg, 1928.

Surgeon Gen. Cat. Index Catalogue of the Library of the Surgeon General's Office.
  United States Army, Washington.

W. G. T. TENNEMANN. Geschichte der Philosophie. 11 vols., Leipzig, 1798–1819.

Theatrum Chemicum. Præcipuos Selectorum Auctorum Tractatus de Chemiæ et
  Lapidis Philosophici, etc., 6 vols. Strassburg (Zetzner), 1659–61.

THOMAS THOMSON. (1) History of Chemistry. 2 vols. 1830 (reprint, n.d.). (2) A
  System of Chemistry. 5 ed., 4 vols. 1817 (other eds. q. by year and vol.). (3)
  History of the Royal Society from its Institution to the end of the Eighteenth
  Century. 4°, 1812. (4) System of Chemistry of Inorganic Bodies. 1831. (5)
  Travels in Sweden. 1813. (6) Animal Chemistry. 1843.

L. THORNDIKE. A History of Magic and Experimental Science. 8 vols. London (i, ii)
  and New York (iii–viii). 1923–23–34–34–41–41–58–58.

F. UEBERWEG. (1) Grundriss der Geschichte der Philosophie, ed. K. Praechter.
  5 vols. 1923–8. (2) A History of Philosophy, tr. G. Morris and N. Porter. 2 vols.
  1872–4.

R. WATSON. Chemical Essays. var. eds.

M. E. WEEKS. Discovery of the Elements. 6 ed. Easton, Pa., 1956.

W. WHEWELL. (1) History of the Inductive Sciences. 3 ed., 3 vols., 1857. (2) The
  Philosophy of the Inductive Sciences. 2 vols., 1847.

J. C. WIEGLEB. Geschichte des Wachsthums und der Erfindungen in der Chemie. 3 vols. Berlin and Stettin. (1) in der ältesten und mittlern Zeit, 1792. (2) in der neurn Zeit, 3 vols. (I, i, I, ii and II), 1790–1. (3) Historisch-kritische Untersuchung der Alchemie. Weimar, 1777.

A. WOLF. A History of Science, Technology and Philosophy (1) in the 16th and 17th Centuries. 1935. (2) in the Eighteenth Century. 1938.

F. X. M. ZIPPE. Geschichte der Metalle, Vienna, 1857.

LIST OF PERIODICAL PUBLICATIONS

Abhl. Abhandlungen (with title following).

Abhl. K. Ges. Wiss. Gött. Abhandlungen der Königlichen Gesellschaft der Wissenschaften zu Göttingen. Göttingen.

Acta Acad. Mogunt. Acta Academiæ Electoralis Moguntinae Scientiarum Utilium quae Erfordiae est, Erfurt and Gotha, 2 vols. 1757–61; 12 vols. Erfurt 1776–95; Nova Acta 4 vols. 1799–1809.

Acta Acad. Petropol. Acta Academiae Scientiarum Imperialis Petropolitanae. St. Petersburg [Leningrad], 1777–82. Later — Nova Acta. See *Comment.*

Acta Physico-Med. Acad. Nat. Curios. See *Miscell. Acad. Curios.*

AdS, h, m. Académie Royale des Sciences, Paris, Histoire (h) and Mémoires (m).

AdS *Mém. div. Sav.* Mémoires présentés par divers Savants à l'Académie des Sciences, Paris.

Allgem. Journ. der Chemie; Allgem. J. Chem. Allgemeines Journal der Chemie.

A. Med. Archiv für die Geschichte der Medizin. Leipzig, 1907–43 (later Sudhoffs Archiv).

Amer Chem. Abstr. Chemical Abstracts. American Chemical Society. Easton, Pa.

A. Nat. Archiv für die Geschichte der Naturwissenschaften und der Technik. Leipzig 1909–20. Later as Archiv für Geschichte der Mathematik, der Naturwissenschaften und der Technik, 1927–31. Continued as QS (see this).

Angew. Chem. Angewandte Chemie.

Ann. Annalen der Chemie (1832–; at first, Annalen der Chemie und Pharmacie; later Justus Liebigs Annalen der Chemie). Heidelberg; Leipzig.

Ann. Chim. Annales de Chimie (1789–; in 1816–1913 Annales de Chimie et de Physique).

Ann. Gén. Sci. Phys. Annales générales des Sciences Physiques. Brussels. 1819–21.

Ann. Med. Hist. Annals of Medical History. New York. 1917–.

Ann. Phil. Annals of Philosophy. 1813–26.

Ann. Sci. Annals of Science. 1936–.

An. Soc. Quim. Argentina. Anales de la Sociedad Química Argentina. Buenos Aires. 1913–.

Arch. della R. Soc. Rom. di Storia Patria. Archives della R. Società Romana de Storia Patria. Rome.

Archeion. See *Archivio.*

Archiv Gesch. Philos. Archiv für Geschichte der Philosophie. 1888–1932.

Archives. Archives internationale d'histoire des sciences, 1947–(contin. of Archeion).

Archivio. Archivio di Storia delle Scienze. 1927 (cont. as Archeion).

Arhiv Hem. Farm. Arhiv za Hemiju i Farmaciju. Zagreb.

Atti R. Accad. Torino. Atti della Reale Accademia delle Scienza di Torino. Turin.

B.A. Rep. British Association for the Advancement of Science. Reports of Meetings. 1832–.

Beitr. Beiträge (with title following).

Bibl. Brit. Bibliothèque Britannique. Geneva.

Bibl. Univ. Bibliothèque Universelle. Geneva.

Bonon. Comment. De Bononiensi Scientiarum et Artium Instituto atque Academia Commentarii. Bologna.

Brit. Med. J. British Medical Journal.

Bull. Acad. Roy. Belg. Bulletin de l'Académie Royale de Belgique. Classe des Sciences. Brussels.

Bull. Acad. Roy. Méd. Belg. Bulletin de l'Académie Royale de Médecine de Belgique. Brussels.

Bull. British Soc. Hist. Sci. Bulletin of the British Society for the History of Science.

Bull. Hist. Med. Bulletin of the History of Medicine. Baltimore.

Bull. Inst. Hist. Med. Bulletin of the Institute of the History of Medicine. Baltimore. 1933-. Continued as *Bull. Hist. Med.*

Bull. Johns Hopkins Inst. Med. Hist. Bulletin of the Institute of the History of Medicine, Johns Hopkins University. Baltimore. 1939-.

Bull. Soc. Chim. Bulletin de la Société Chimique de Paris [de France].

Bull. Soc. Encourag. Bulletin de la Société d'Encouragement pour l'Industrie Nationale.

Bull. Soc. Philomath. Bulletin des Sciences, par la Société Philomathique.

Chem. Age. Chemical Age. 1919-.

Chem. and Ind. Chemistry and Industry. (Society of Chemical Industry.)

Chem. News. Chemical News. 1860-1932.

Chem. Weekbl. Chemisch Weekblad. Amsterdam.

Chem. Ztg. Chemiker Zeitung. Cöthen.

Comment. Acad. Petropol. Commentarii Academiae Scientiarvm Imperialis Petropolitanae. St. Petersburg [Leningrad], 1726-46, with Novi Commentarii, 1747-75; see *Acta.*

Compt. Rend. Comptes Rendus hebdomadaires des Séances de l'Académie des Sciences. (Paris.)

Crell's *Ann.* Chemische Annalen. Ed. L. F. F. von Crell. Helmstädt. 1784- (each annual vol. divided into two parts I and II).

Crell's *Beytr.* Beyträge zu den Chemische Annalen. Ed. Crell. Helmstädt. 1785-99.

Crell's *N. chem. Archiv.* Neues Chemisches Archiv. Ed. Crell. Leipzig. 1783-91, 1798.

Crell's *N. Etdeck.* Auswahl aller eigentümliche Abhandlungen aus den neusten Entdeckungen der Chemie. Ed. Crell. 1785-6.

Dingl. J. Dingler's Polytechnisches Journal. 1820-1931.

Edin. J. Sci. Edinburgh Journal of Science. Edinburgh.

Edin. Med. J. Edinburgh Medical Journal.

Ency. Méthod. Encyclopédie Méthodique (in sections, e.g. *Chimie*). 1781-1832.

Ephemer. [*Acad.*] *Nat. Curios.* See *Miscell. Acad. Curios.*

Fortschr. Min. Krist. Petr. Fortschritte der Mineralogie, Kristallographie und Petrographie. Jena.

Gentleman's Mag. Gentleman's Magazine.

Hist. Acad. Berlin (HAB). Histoire de l'Académie Royale des Sciences et des Belles-Lettres de Berlin (includes Mémoires).

Hist. Acad. des Sciences. See AdS.

Ind. Eng. Chem. Industrial and Engineering Chemistry. Easton, Pa.

J. Chem. Educ. Journal of Chemical Education. Easton, Pa.

J. Chem. Soc. Journal of the Chemical Society (London).

J. Chem. Phys. J. f. Chemie. Journal für Chemie und Physik. Ed. J. S. C. Schweigger. Nürnberg; Halle.

J. Chim. Phys. Journal de Chimie Physique.

J. de Méd. Journal de Médecine.

J. de Phys. Journal de Physique.

J. des Savants. J. Sçav. Journal des Savants (Sçavants).

J. Franklin Inst. Journal of the Franklin Institute. Philadelphia.

J. Hist. of Med. and Allied Sciences. Journal of the History of Medicine and Allied Sciences. New York.

J. Iron and Steel Inst. Journal of the Iron and Steel Institute.

J. Mines. Journal des Mines.

J. Lit. Sci. Art. See *Quart. J.*

J. pr. Chem. Journal für praktische Chemie. Leipzig.

J. Sci. Arts. The Journal of Science and the Arts (Royal Institution, London). 1816–19. Continued as *Quart. J.*

J. Soc. Chem. Ind. Journal of the Society of Chemical Industry.

J. Soc. Glass Technol. Journal of the Society of Glass Technology. Sheffield.

J. Warburg Inst. Journal of the Warburg Institute.

KAH. Kongliga Svenska Vetenskaps-Akademiens Handlingar. Stockholm.

Lychnos. Lychnos. Lärdoms historiska Samfundets Årsbok. Uppsala. 1936–.

Manch[ester] Mem. (or *Proc.*). Memoirs (or Proceedings) of the Manchester Literary and Philosophical Society. Manchester.

Med. Chirurg. Trans. Medico-Chirurgical Transactions.

Med. Phys. J. Medical and Physical Journal, containing the Earliest Information on the Subjects of Medicine, Surgery, Pharmacy, Chemistry, and Natural History.

Mem. Acad. Turin. Memorie della Reale Accademia di Scienza di Torino. Turin.

Mém. couronnés et autres mémoires publ. par l'Acad. Roy. Brussels. Mémoires couronnés et autres mémoires publiés par l'Académie Royale des Sciences . . . de Belgique. Brussels.

Mém. Soc. Arcueil. Mémoires de Physique et de Chimie de la Société d'Arcueil.

Mém. Soc. Roy. de Médec. Mémoires de la Société Royale de Médecine.

MGM. Mitteilungen zur Geschichte der Medizin und der Naturwissenschaften. Hamburg and Leipzig.

Miscell. Acad. Curios. Miscellanea curiosa sive Ephemerides Medico-Physicæ Germanicæ Academiæ Naturæ Curiosorum, Nürnberg (see p. 317). Later vols. are entitled *Acta* and *Nova Acta.*

Miscell. Berolin. Miscellanea Berolinensia. Berlin.

Monit. Scientif. Moniteur Scientifique.

Monatsh. Monatshefte für Chemie. Vienna.

Naturwiss. Die Naturwissenschaften, Leipzig.

Nicholson's J. Journal of Natural Philosophy, Chemistry, and the Arts. Ed. W. Nicholson.

N. Jahrb. Min. Monatsh. Neues Jahrbuch für Mineralogie. Monatsheft. Stuttgart.

Nova Acta Acad. Curios. See *Miscell. Acad. Curios.*

Nova Acta Acad. Petropol. See *Acta Acad. Petropol.*

Nuov. Cim. Il Nuovo Cimento. Pisa and Bologna.

Obs. Phys. Observations sur la Physique, sur l'Histoire Naturelle et sur les Arts.

Pharm. J. Pharmaceutical Journal.

Pharm. Ztg. Pharmazeutische Zeitung, Berlin, 1855–.

Phil. Collect. Philosophical Collections. See p. 553.

Phil. Mag. Philosophical Magazine.

Phil. Trans. Philosophical Transactions of the Royal Society of London.

Philos. Rev. Philosophical Review. Boston and New York, 1892–.

Proc. Cambridge Antiquar. Soc. Proceedings of the Cambridge Antiquarian Society.

Proc. Cambr. Phil. Soc. Proceedings of the Cambridge Philosophical Society.

Proc. Chem. Soc. Proceedings of the Chemical Society (London).

Proc. Roy. Inst. Proceedings of the Royal Institution of Great Britain. 1851–.

Proc. Roy. Soc. Edin. Proceedings of the Royal Society of Edinburgh.

Proc. Roy. Soc. Proceedings of the Royal Society of London.

Proc. Roy. Soc. Med. Proceedings of the Royal Society of Medicine (London).

QS. Quellen und Studien zur Geschichte der Naturwissenschaften und der Medizin, Leipzig, 1931–.

Quart. J. Lit. Sci. Arts. Quarterly Journal of Literature, Science and the Arts (Royal Institution of Great Britain). 1819–30.

Rev. Scient. Revue Scientifique. 1863–.

Rev. gén. Sci. Revue générale des Sciences Pures et Appliquées. 1890–.

Rev. Univ. des Mines. Revue Universelle des Mines. Liége.

Roy. Soc. Cat. (Sci. Papers). Catalogue of Scientific Papers, collected and published by the Royal Society of London, 1867–1925.

Samml. chem.- u. chem. techn. Vorträge. Sammlung chemischer- und chemisch-technischer Vorträge. Stuttgart.

School Sci. Rev. School Science Review.

Schweiz. Min. Petr. Mitt. Schweizerische mineralogische und petrologische Mitteilungen . . . Zürich.

Sci. Progr. Science Progress. 1894–.

Sitzb. Österr. Akad. Wiss. Phil.-hist. Kl. Sitzungsberichte der Österreichischen Akademie der Wissenschaften. Philol. histor. Klasse. Vienna, 1947–.

Skrifter Vidensk. Selsk. Christiana. Mat. naturv. Kl. Skrifter utgitt av det Norske Videnskaps-Akademii. Christiania [later Oslo].

Smithsonian Misc. Coll. Smithsonian Miscellaneous Collections. Washington.

Taylor's Sci. Mem. Scientific Memoirs selected from the Transactions of Foreign Academies etc. Ed. R. Taylor. 5 vols. 1837–52.

Times Lit. Suppl. The Times Literary Supplement.

Trans. Inst. Chem. Eng. Transactions of the Institution of Chemical Engineers.

Trans. Newcomen Soc. Transactions of the Newcomen Society for the Study of the History of Engineering and Technology.

Trans. Roy. Geol. Soc. Cornwall. Transactions of the Royal Geological Society of Cornwall. Penzance, etc.

Verhl. K. Nederl. Akad. Wet. Afd. Letterkd. Verhandelingen der Koninklijke Akademie van Wetenschappen. Afdeeling Letterkunde. Amsterdam.

Veröffl. d. Kommission f. neuere Geschichte Österreichs. Veröffentlichungen der Kommission für neuere Geschichte Österreichs. Vienna.

Z. angew. Chem. Zeitschrift für angewandte Chemie. Leipzig.

Z. f. Bücherfreunde. Zeitschrift für Bücherfreunde.

Z. gesamte Naturwiss., Z. ges. Naturwiss., Z. f. Naturwiss. Zeitschrift für die gesamte Naturwissenschaft. Brunswick, Berlin, 1935–40.

Z. [für des] gesamte Schiess-u. Sprengstoffwesen. Zeitschrift für das gesamte Schiess- und Sprengstoffwesen. Munich.

Z. hist. Theol. Zeitschrift für historische Theologie.

Z. f. Instrumentenkunde. Zeitschrift für Instrumentenkunde.

Z. techn. Phys. Zeitschrift für technische Physik. Leipzig.

Z. physiol. Chem. Zeitschrift für physiologische Chemie (Hoppe-Seyler). Strassburg.

CHAPTER I

EMPIRICAL PRELUDE

Leonardo da Vinci

Leonardo da Vinci (Vinci, nr. Florence 15 April 1452 (O.S.) — Cloux, nr. Amboise 2 May 1519)[1] besides being a great artist, an expert musician, an accomplished civil and military engineer, and architect, was a man of very varied scientific ability, but by no means superficial. He was an extraordinarily acute observer, seeing things in natural objects which would elude nearly everybody. Before 1490 he was in the service of Duke Lodovico Sforza in Milan and in 1502 became military engineer to Caesar Borgia. Leonardo's importance was first appreciated when the contents of a large collection of manuscripts, mostly disconnected notes for his own use, became known. These are written with the left hand in mirror writing, mostly in 1490–1518, and contain many drawings. They were left on his death at Cloux and bequeathed to Francesco Melzi, who died in 1570.[2]

The manuscripts were dispersed after 1570. Some were cut up by Pompeo Leone and were made up into a large codex, called *Codice Atlantico* (on account of its size) containing 402 sheets, which came to the Ambrosian Library in Milan. On the conquest of Italy by Napoleon this and twelve other manuscripts were taken to Paris in 1796. The *Codice Atlantico* was restored to the Ambrosian Library in 1815 but the other twelve manuscripts were retained by the Institut in Paris, where they still remain. Venturi (see below) counted

---

[1] Two notarial documents dated 1457 and 1469 say Lionardo (*sic*), 'son of Ser Piero and the Charterina, now donna d'Achattabriga di Piero del Vaccha da Vinci' was born in 1452; a document in the hand of Antonio, Ser Piero's father (d. *c.* 1464), says Lionardo was born on 15 April, 1452. He was born in a house on the Borgo da Vinci, not in Vèlla de Anchiano. Sarton, *Isis*, 1952, xliii, 125.

[2] Carra de Vaux, *Léonard de Vinci*, Paris, 1910; J. W. Draper, *Conflict of Religion and Science*, 1875, 233; P. Duhem, *Études sur Léonard de Vinci*, 3 ser., Paris, 1906–09–13; Eastlake, *Materials for a History of Oil Painting*, 1847, i, 321 f.; Feldhaus, (1), 1914, 620 (list of MSS.); id., *Ruhmsblätter der Technik*, Leipzig, 1910, 29 f., 622; id., *Leonardo als Techniker und Erfinder*, Jena, 1922; I. B. Hart, *Mechanical Investigations of Leonardo da Vinci*, 1925; Heller, (1), 1882, i, 222; Marie Herzfeld, *Leonardo da Vinci der Techniker, Forscher und Poet*, Jena, 1926; Hoefer, (1), 1869, ii, 92; Humboldt, (1), 1849, ii, 446, 661, 703, 732; Jähns, *Geschichte der Kriegswissenschaft in Deutschland*, Munich and Leipzig, 1889, i, 286; *Leonardo da Vinci and his Works. Consisting of a Life . . . by Mrs. C. W. Heaton and an Essay on his Scientific and Literary Works by C. C. Black*, 1874; Lippmann, (1), 1906, i, 346; E. MacCurdy, *Leonardo da Vinci's Note-books, arranged and rendered into English*, 2 vols., 1938 (ref. to as 'MacCurdy'); E. Muntz, *Leonardo da Vinci, Artist, Thinker and Man of Science*, 2 vols. 4°, 1898; Partington, (4), 174; Poggendorff, (2), 66; A. Prandi, *Rev. Univ. des Mines*, 1953, ix (no. 9), 693–724 (plates); J. P. Richter, *The Literary Works of Leonardo da Vinci* (tr. mostly by Mrs. R. C. Bell), 2 vols. 4°, London (printed Leipzig), 1883 (ref. to as 'Richter'), enlarged and revised by J. B. and I. Richter, 2 vols. 4°, OUP, London, 1939; E. Solmi, *Leonardo da Vinci*, tr. E. Hirschberg, Berlin, 1908; J. A. Symonds, *Renaissance in Italy. The Fine Arts*, 1897, 227 f.; Thorndike, v, 16; Ueberweg, (1), 1924, iii, 61; Uzielli, *Ricerche intorno a Leonardo da Vinci*, 2 vols., Rome, 1896.

the manuscripts as 14, taking an 18-page appendix to MS. B as a separate one. The Paris manuscripts were published in facsimile, transcript, and French translation in 1880–91.[1] The *Codice Atlantico* was published in facsimile, transliteration, and Italian text by the Accademia dei Lincei in 1894–1904.[2] Other manuscripts published are the Arundel manuscripts 263 in the British Museum,[3] a manuscript which belonged to the Earl of Leicester and formerly at Holkham Hall, Norfolk, but later sold to America, which contains part of the treatise on 'the nature of water',[4] manuscripts in Windsor Castle (Fogli and Quaderni MSS.) mostly on anatomy, the Forster MSS. in the Victoria and Albert Museum, South Kensington,[5] two manuscripts on flight (*Sul Volo*) in the Royal Library, Turin, and the Fatio Collection, Geneva. These have been published in facsimile and transliteration, in several large folio volumes.[6] A survey of the manuscripts is given by MacCurdy[7] and a summary of dates (1473–1518) by Feldhaus.[8]

Many had access to Leonardo's note-books, and there is material from them in Cardan's *De Subtilitate* (1550) and *De Rerum Varietate* (1557) (p. 10).[9] Attention was drawn to the manuscripts taken to Paris and to Leonardo's scientific work by Venturi,[10] Amoretti[11] and Count Guglielmo Libri,[12] who had access to the Paris manuscripts and purloined some of them; he was accused, left for London, and in 1850 was condemned by default.

Libri thought that Leonardo, a century before Francis Bacon, was fully conversant with the Inductive Method, advocated a direct appeal to observation and experiment, and was probably the first to attempt a systematic explanation of the whole of natural phenomena on the basis of experience. Unlike Bacon, he was convinced of the great value of mathematics, and had studied the works of Archimedes. Leonardo gives a list of books including Avicenna, Roger Bacon and Vitruvius, whom he quotes.[13]

Duhem and Thorndike laboured to show that Leonardo held many Aristotelian ideas, e.g. of the order of arrangement of the elements[14] and much of his thought to be original can be found in Nicolas of Cusa[15] and in Scholastic authors such as Albertus Magnus, Buridan, Albert of Saxony, Themo the Jew, and Blasius of Parma. His geological and palæontological views, however,

[1] *Les manuscrits de Léonard de Vinci, publié en fac-similes . . . , avec transcriptions littérale,* etc., C. Ravaisson-Mollien, 6 vols. f°, Paris, 1881–83–88–89–90–91.
[2] *Il Codice Atlantico di Leonardo da Vinci nella Biblioteca Ambrosiana de Milano,* 6 vols. f°, Milan, 1894–1904.
[3] *Léonardo da Vinci, Sciences physico-mathématiques . . . manuscrits inédites, reproduit d'après les originaux conservés au British Museum, London,* 4 vols. 4°, Paris, 1901 (100 copies printed).
[4] *Il Codice di Leonardo da Vinci della Biblioteca di Lord Leicester in Holkham Hall,* ed. G. Calvi, f°, Milan, 1909 (for R. Ist. Lombardo di Scienze e Lettera), facsim., transcr., notes and index.
[5] *Problèmes de géometrie et d'hydraulique,* 8°, Paris, 1901; *Trattato del Modo e Misura del Acqua,* 4°, Bologna, 1828.
[6] *I Manoscritti e i Disegni de Leonardo da Vinci,* Rome, 1923–1941.
[7] i, 43–57.   [8] (1), 1914, 622.   [9] Duhem, 1906, i, 229.
[10] *Essai sur les ouvrages physico-mathématiques de Léonardo de Vinci,* 4°, Paris, 1797, 56 pp.; *Notices de quelques articles . . . tirés de l'essai sur les ouvrages physico-mathématique de Léonardo da Vinci,* in *Ann. Chim.,* 1797, xxiv, 150; *Nicholson's J.,* 1798, ii, 84 (air and flame).
[11] *Memorie storiche su la vita, gli studij, e le opere di Leonardo da Vinci,* 8°, Milan, 1804.
[12] (1), 1838, ii, 40; 1840, iii, 11–58.
[13] MacCurdy, i, 225; ii, 570, 572, 577; the *De Architectura* of Vitruvius was printed in 1486, works of Archimedes not until 1543–4.
[14] MacCurdy, i, 393.   [15] Duhem, 1909, ii, 97 f.

are largely original and are like those later held by Palissy (1510–90).[1] The lack of references to authorities and of order in the writings depends on the fact that they were not intended for publication; in some intended for publication Leonardo notes that they must be carefully arranged.[2] His careful studies of plants and animals, his excellent anatomical observations based on dissections, and his sound and quantitative studies of hydraulics, put Leonardo above the authors opposed to him by Duhem and Thorndike (neither an experimental scientist). Leonardo said:[3]

'Those who are inventors and interpreters between Nature and Man as compared with the reciters and trumpeters of the works of others, are to be considered simply as is an object in front of a mirror in comparison with its image when seen in the mirror, the one being something in itself, the other nothing.'

His great mechanical inventiveness (he anticipated the submarine, the aeroplane, the military tank, and the use of poison gas in warfare, which he regarded as 'most bestial madness')[4] also puts him in a different place. An able technician, he stands out in his work on hydraulics, gun casting[5] and ballistics; he sketched in perfect detail a great number of pieces of machinery both large and small. He invented water bellows,[6] a lamp with constant oil level,[7] a mercury siphon clock[8] and a steam gun.[9] His extensive writings on statics and dynamics[10] are, as Duhem showed,[11] less original than was supposed, but his studies of flight, leading to designs and experiments on aeroplanes,[12] are highly original. He clearly adumbrated the Theorem of Least Action (Maupertuis, 1744): 'every action done by nature is done in the shortest way'.[13] He insisted that instruments should be as simple as possible and not unnecessarily complicated by subsidiary parts.[14] He had some ideas of capillary attraction and described the coalescence of liquid drops.[15]

Leonardo opposed the views that winds are formed by the twelve signs of the Zodiac, or by vapours raised upwards by heat and pressed down by cold; he thought the congregation of humidity scattered through the air, which comes together for the creation of clouds, and similarly the breaking up of clouds to form the dispersed humidity of the air, both form wind. Water boiling in a pot over a fire makes a wind in the chimney, and boiling water enclosed in a vessel with a small aperture escapes with great force like a wind. He denied that vapour in the air is pushed down by cold.[16]

The colour of air is blue; this is not its own colour but that of heated moisture evaporated into the minutest imperceptible particles which beams of sunlight attract and make luminous against the intense darkness of outer space. Excessive moisture makes the air white. This agrees with the blue colour of smoke from dry wood, which becomes grey on rising in the atmosphere; smoke from green wood is not blue because it is not transparent and is heavily

[1] Duhem, 1906, i, 39, 246; 1909, ii, 283; MacCurdy, i, 327.
[2] MacCurdy, i, 62; ii, 58.   [3] MacCurdy, 1938, i, 61.   [4] MacCurdy, 1938, i, 24, 34.
[5] Feldhaus, 1910, 112; MacCurdy, ii, 206, 403; Richter, ii, 22.
[6] MacCurdy, ii, 164.   [7] Ib., ii, 167.   [8] Ib., ii, 169.   [9] Ib., ii, 188.
[10] Ib., i, 523–624: movement and weight.
[11] Cf. I. B. Hart, Archives, 1951–3 (1956), xxviii, 105–29.
[12] MacCurdy, ii, 423–520.
[13] Ib., i, 79, 90.   [14] Ib., i, 71.   [15] Ib., i, 394–5; ii, 110.   [16] Ib., i, 414 f.

charged with moisture. 'I say that the atmosphere acquires its blue colour from particles of moisture which catch the luminous rays of the sun.'[1] Leonardo was familiar with structure colours in the feathers of birds, on the surface of old glass, in oil films on water, etc., but confused them with the dispersion colours in light refracted by diamonds.[2]

Leonardo distinguished between common heat and the radiant heat from the sun, which can be reflected by a mirror and refracted by drops of water, and does not heat water in passing through it.[3] He still held Aristotle's views on the four elements and their positions, thinking that if fire, the rarest element, could be strongly compressed it might become as dense as water or even earth,[4] and that air is convertible into water and vice versa.[5] He was sceptical about the 'materialisation' of spirits, arguing that they cannot coexist with air.[6] All heat in the universe comes ultimately from the sun.[7] He speaks of hatching eggs in ovens.[8] In distillation, liquids such as mercury combine with fire, which rises to join its own element (above the atmosphere) and carries them with it, but in the receiver the liquid falls to join its own element (water, below the atmosphere) and the heat rises.[9]

The saltness of the sea is not due to the scorching action of the sun, or to the sun drawing off the finer and sweeter parts and leaving the coarser and bitter parts, since marshes and ponds drying up do not become salt. Neither is it a sweat of the earth, since springs penetrating the earth are not salty. It is due to springs in the earth dissolving mineral salt and carrying it to the sea. Salt is also extracted from ashes and burnt refuse by water and is contained in the urine and excretions of animals.[10] Salt is contained in all created things, and since there will be animals for ever, the stock of salt in the world must pass unchanged through their bodies.[11] Leonardo prepared for some purpose a salt by burning human excrement.[12]

Fresh water is lighter than salt water since it rises higher in a piece of linen dipped into it than salt water in a similar piece.[13] Leonardo thought that water rises from the depths of the sea to the summits of the highest mountains, pours through the broken veins to the shallow parts of the sea, and so in course of time the whole element circulates.[14] He compared the densities of liquids by balancing columns in a U-tube.[15] Water becomes denser as it becomes colder until it freezes.[16] Salt water filtered through clay leaves its salt behind.[17] Distilled water can be made cheaply in large quantities by adapting a still to a kitchen cooking-stove.[18]

Pouchet[19] had noticed the many drawings of chemical apparatus in the *Codice Atlantico*. These include filters,[20] a cylindrical furnace,[21] an athanor furnace with stills,[22] (see Fig. 1) alembic heads,[23] various chemical appara-

[1] *Ib.*, i, 418–21; with experiments; ii, 307.
[2] *Ib.*, ii, 299. [3] *Ib.*, i, 304. [4] *Ib.*, i, 302. [5] *Ib.*, i, 393, 397.
[6] *Ib.*, i, 154. [7] *Ib.*, i, 84, 295. [8] *Ib.*, i, 179. [9] *Ib.*, i, 193.
[10] *Ib.*, ii, 63–5. [11] Richter, ii, 189. [12] *Ib.*,ii, 13.
[13] *Ib.*, ii, 191; MacCurdy, ii, 63. [14] MacCurdy, ii, 102. [15] *Ib.*, i, 555.
[16] *Ib.*, ii, 34; not 'when it freezes' as Thorndike, v, 30, says. [17] Richter, i, 323.
[18] *Ib.*, i, 323; MacCurdy, ii, 584. [19] (1), 1853, 508 f.
[20] *Il Codice Atlantico*, Tavole, II, 289 Ra, plate DCCCCXXXXVIII.
[21] *Ib.*, Tav., II, 306 Rc, pl. MXXIII. [22] *Ib.*, Tav., 335 Rb, pl. MCXXI.
[23] *Ib.*, Tav., II, 400 V, pl. MCCCLXIX.

tus,[1] a mixing mill,[2] and a furnace with pots on an inclined support with a flue underneath (like the cascade concentrator for sulphuric acid).[3] Leonardo complains that his German assistant Giovanni (Johann) spent his time shooting and using Leonardo's work-rooms and apparatus to produce inventions of his own (textile working), about which he was very secretive.[4]

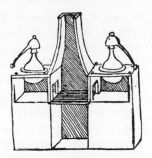

Leonardo describes some chemical tricks such as making white wine purple by adding galls and vitriol,[5] a sympathetic ink of oak galls and vitriol powders spread on paper, which can be written on with a pen moistened with saliva,[6] and making a room seem filled with fire by evaporating brandy and kindling the fumes.[7] Green fire is made by soaking verdigris in oil of turpentine and filtering.[8] Leonardo, knowing the work of his predecessors, made

FIG. 1. DRAWING OF A CHEMIST'S FURNACE, WITH TWO ALEMBICS.

MADE BY LEONARDO DA VINCI. From the *Codex Atlantico*, Milan.

his own paints and varnishes — not always with good results, as the state of some of his pictures shows.[9] He extracted the colour from blue flowers by alcohol.[10] His contemporary, Pomponio Gauricio of Naples, also included chemistry among the subjects which should be known to sculptors.[11]

Leonardo invented a lamp chimney to carry off air vitiated by combustion, i.e. exhalation (esalamento) from the flame, and for bringing fresh air to the flame,[12] and invented a lamp with constant oil level.[13] He was aware of the common participation of air in the maintenance of life and flame, comparing life with a flame, and had very accurate views on the structure of flame and on the relation of flame and air. He gave a description and pictures of a candle flame showing the blue inner cone of unburnt gas.[14]

Where a flame is produced a current of air is generated which serves to make the flame luminous. The fire constantly destroys the part of the air which nourishes (nutrica) it and would form a vacuum if more air did not stream in to fill it. When air is not able to support flame, nothing else can live in it; no animal can live in a place where a flame cannot burn. The blue centre of a candle flame forms a nucleus of smoke, since the air which enters into the composition of a flame cannot penetrate there; the air reaches the surface of the flame, condenses there in nourishing the flame, into the composition of

[1] *Ib.*, Tav., I, 80 Rb, 132 Vb, pls. CCXXXIX, CCCCV.
[2] *Ib.*, Tav., I, 60 Rb, pl. CLXXIV.   [3] *Ib.*, Tav., I, 32 Ra, pl. XC.
[4] MacCurdy, ii, 542.   [5] Richter, i, 324; MacCurdy, ii, 174.
[6] MacCurdy, ii, 173.   [7] Richter, i, 325.   [8] MacCurdy, ii, 197.
[9] Richter, i, 315 f., 323 (list of chemicals); ii, 19 (smalt); MacCurdy, ii, 383 (also distilled turpentine, etc.).
[10] MacCurdy, ii, 295.
[11] Gauricius, *De Scvlptvra*, in Ioannis ab Indagine, *Introdvctiones Apotelesmaticæ* . . . *accessit Pomponii Gvaricii* . . . *Tractatvs*, sm. 8°, Urselli (Zetzner), 1503, 372.
[12] *Il Codice Atlantico*, Tavole, I, 145 Vc, 165 Vc, plates CCCCLVIII, DXXXVIII.
[13] MacCurdy, 1938, ii, 167.
[14] *Il Codice Atlantico*, Tav., II, 237 Va, 270 Va, pls. DCCLXXXIX, DCCCCIX; MacCurdy, i, 149, 403.

which it enters, and leaves an empty space which is again filled with air. The light of a candle is proportionally less as it is placed in a colder spot.[1]

Leonardo studied the composition of bronzes for gun casting; some tin can be replaced by lead.[2] The most suitable bronze for guns contains 6 to 8 per cent of tin.[3] He also describes a method of making steel.[4] What he calls Greek fire is a gunpowder made from willow charcoal, saltpetre, spirit of wine (aqua vitæ), sulphur, pitch, frankincense, and camphor boiled together and spread over Ethiopian wool (lana etiopica).[5] Poison gas warfare was anticipated in asphyxiating sulphur bombs;[6] a German (sic) poison gas consisting of fumes of burnt feathers, sulphur, and realgar (arsenic sulphide), lasts seven or eight hours.[7] A poisonous gas (fumo mortale), blown by smith's bellows, is made from arsenic, sulphur and realgar (the remedy being rose water).[8] Bacterial warfare is anticipated by venom of toads, slaver of a mad dog, and tarantula spiders. A poisonous dust for throwing on ships contains verdigris, or chalk mixed with poison; care should be taken that the wind does not blow it back, and the nose and mouth should be covered with fine wetted cloth.[9]

Making large pearls is described in the same way as in the Byzantine chemical works (Vol. I). Some chemical notes describe the preparation of aqua fortis from equal weights of Roman vitriol, saltpetre, cinnabar (? colcothar) and verdigris; it is used to dissolve copper, the solution being evaporated to a paste, spread over a 'figure', and this covered with earth (?) and heated. Pyrites contains copper if it gives a green solution with aqua fortis: 'precipitate this with saltpetre (?) and soft soap.' A depilatory is made from lime and orpiment.[10]

Leonardo was anti-clerical but not demonstrably anti-religious;[11] he was perhaps a non-Christian pantheist. He held the Jewish Qabbalistic view that man, composed of the four elements and with bodily structures which can (fancifully) be compared with parts of the world, is a microcosm; he 'has been called by the ancients a lesser world', and 'the term has been rightly applied'.[12] The earth is a star.[13] Leonardo, at first accepting the Ptolemaic theory, later adopted that of Copernicus.[14] He was generally opposed to superstition; necromancy is even worse than alchemy.

Alchemy does at least work with simple products of nature and performs things, such as making glass, which nature cannot do of herself, lacking organic instruments; necromancy, although 'the sister of alchemy', is a mere 'ensign or flying banner, blown by the wind' and 'the guide of the foolish multitude'.

[1] Venturi, Essai, 1797, 16; Heaton and Black, 1874, 172; MacCurdy, i, 402–4, 409; Libri says Leonardo recognised that air has a small density, diminishing with rise of temperature, and that he believed in the possibility of producing a vacuum artificially.
[2] Richter, ii, 22; MacCurdy, ii, 405.   [3] Richter, ii, 24.   [4] MacCurdy, ii, 412.
[5] Richter, ii, 280; MacCurdy, ii, 186, 194, 207, 217 (both translations are incorrect); Jähns, 1889, i, 286.
[6] MacCurdy, ii, 198.   [7] MacCurdy, ii, 201; Paris Institut MS. B, 63 v.
[8] Ib., ii, 210, 217.   [9] Ib., ii, 210, 217–19.
[10] MacCurdy, ii, 582; Achillo Marazza, Leonardo, Saggi e Ricerche, Instituto Poligrafico dello Stato, Rome, 1954, 47 (chemistry; merely a list of synonyms).
[11] MacCurdy, i, 37; Richter, ii, 127, 283; Thorndike, v, 35.
[12] MacCurdy, ii, 21.
[13] Richter, ii, 144, 156, 162; not 'compared to a star', as Thorndike, v, 32, says.
[14] MacCurdy, i, 29: 'the sun does not move.'

Those who wish to grow rich in a day will live a long time in poverty, 'as happens and will to all eternity happen to the alchemists, the would-be creators of gold and silver, and to the engineers who think to make dead water stir itself into life with perpetual motion, and to those supreme fools, the necromancer and the enchanter.'[1] Leonardo was acquainted with the frauds of alchemists:[2]

I bugiardi inter pitri di natura affermano lo argento vivo essere commune semenza a tutti i metalli, non si ricordano che la natura varia le semenze, secondo la diversitá delle cose che essa vole produrre al mondo.

The false interpreters of nature declare that quicksilver is the common seed of every metal, not remembering that nature varies the seed according to the variety of the things she desires to produce in the world.[3] 'O speculators about perpetual motion, how many vain chimeras have you created in the like quest? Go and take your place with the seekers after gold.' Nature, however, creates gold in the earth, and 'she will show you veins of gold spreading through the stone, the blue lapis lazuli'.[4] Gold is 'begotten of the sun inasmuch as it has more resemblance to it than to anything else that is, and no created thing is more enduring than gold'. Nature does not produce gold from mercury or sulphur of any kind, but only by the fire or heat of nature giving life to the world.

'And consider carefully this ramification of the gold, and you will see that the extremities of it are continually expanding in slow movement, transmuting into gold whatever they come in contact with; and note that therein is a living organism which it is not within your power to produce.'[5]

Leonardo had a good knowledge of anatomy, physiology, and botany. The heart is the most powerful muscle.[6] The blood is warmed by the motion of the heart; this thins the blood and changes it into air, and would change it into fire if the blood were not cooled by the cold air drawn into the lungs by respiration. Since the lungs cannot send air into the heart to cool the blood there, some air is generated from the blood in the heart, and this evaporates from the blood at the extremities of the capillary veins on the skin, exhaling from them in the form of perspiration.[7] Leonardo's anatomical knowledge was gained by dissections (which were unfavourably regarded by the Church in Rome), and his anatomical and physiological studies were intended to enable him to paint men and animals with perfect detail.[8]

He seems to have been the first to make anatomical wax castings (of the cerebral ventricles), an art not used by anatomists till long after his time.[9] His medical knowledge was based on Galen; disease is due to a discord of the four elements in the body and medicine must aim at remedying the conflict of the elements.[10] He says: 'keep clear of the physicians, for their drugs are a kind of

[1] *Ib.*, i, 86, 88.   [2] *Il Codice Atlantico*, f. 76 *v*; Milan, 1894, i, 168.
[3] Richter, 1939, ii, 250; MacCurdy, i, 327.
[4] MacCurdy, ii, 173.   [5] *Ib.*, i, 151; from Windsor MS. B 28 *v*.
[6] MacCurdy, i, 195.   [7] *Ib.*, i, 175.
[8] A. Castiglioni, Leonardo da Vinci Anatomista y Fisiologo, *Publ. Cultura de la Univ. de los Andes*, no. 22, Merida, 1952 (slight); L. Binet, *Léonarde de Vinci anatomiste et physiologiste*, Paris, 1953.
[9] MacCurdy, i, 103, 189.   [10] *Ib.*, i, 227.

alchemy concerning which there are no fewer books than there are medicines'
(or 'about medicine').[1] Although he emphasised that the blood moves (comparing it with the movement of water in the earth), he had no idea of the
general circulation.[2]

Leonardo studied botany so that he could paint plants correctly.[3] He knew
that humus is formed in soils from decayed vegetable matter, making an experiment to prove that this forms 'a blend of rich fat substance and broken bits
of all sorts of things', and not pure earth; this is changed into 'a rich ooze'
which 'feeds the roots of plants'.[4] Libri says Leonardo knew that plants can
improve bad and vitiated air and suggested that they use it for nourishment,
and he believed that fossils are remains of living beings and not 'sports of
nature'.

ECK OF SULZBACH

Paul Eck of Sulzbach, who apparently lived in the fifteenth century, is the
otherwise unknown author of a short Key of the Philosophers (*Clavis Philosophorum*).[5] He mentions the formation of a silver 'tree' (afterwards called arbor
Diana)[6] by the action of mercurous nitrate on a solution of silver nitrate. He
dissolved 1 oz. (loth) of silver in 2 oz. of aqua fortis and added 8 oz. of mercury
dissolved in 6–8 oz. of aqua fortis, 'when you will see marvellous things; you
will see the production of delightful growths, hillocks and bushes which suddenly move and grow (elevatur in delectabilissimas excrescentias, monticulos
et arbusta, et subitor movetur et vivit).[7] In a chapter called increase of calx
(*Augmentatio cinerum*) he mentions, according to Hoefer, the increase in
weight of mercury on calcination but, as Ferguson says, the passage is very
obscure. He took (in November, 1489) fixed weights of distilled mercury and
silver and calcined them in four vessels, when in eight days six pounds became nine (quatuor vasa comprehendunt sex libras quæ in diebus octo aug-
mentantur tribus libris).[8] The increase would be much too large for the
reaction $2Hg + O_2 = 2 HgO$, and Hoefer seems to have read too much into the
passage. Jörgensen,[9] who confirmed that silver amalgam oxidises on heating in
air more easily than mercury, showed that the confused description refers to
mixing various quantities of calx and mercury so that, in the end, nine pounds
of material are obtained from six. The phrase 'spiritus unitur corpori'[10] quoted
by Hoefer seems to refer to the combination of aqua fortis with mercury
(aqua animata) and not to oxygen.

[1] *Ib.*, i, 229; Richter, 1939, ii, 106.   [2] MacCurdy, i, 29.
[3] Richter, i, 203 f.; MacCurdy, i, 317; G. de Toni, Le Piante e gli Animali in Leonardo
da Vinci, *Publ. Inst. Stud. Vinciani in Roma*, iv, Bologna, 1923.
[4] MacCurdy, i, 337.
[5] *De Lapide Philosophico Tractatvs Gemine, prior, Anonymi, posterior Pauli Eck de Sultzbach,
scripti . . . editi à Ioachim Tanckio . . .* Francofvrti, Typis Mathiæ Beckeri, sm. 8°, M. DC.
IV (1604) (39 pp., p. 20 blank, p. 21 sep. tp. *Clavis Philosophorum, Pauli Eck de Sultzbach, qui
vixit Anno Christi 1489 . . .*, M. DC. IIII; Tanck's preface, pp. 22–3, is dated April, 1603),
Theatrum Chemicum, 8°, Strassburg, Zetzner, 1659, iv, 998–1014 (reprint of prefaces and both
treatises); Gmelin, (1), i, 513 (16–17 cent.?); Lenglet du Fresnoy, iii, 155; Hoefer, (1), i, 471;
Ferguson, i, 232.
[6] Kopp, (1), iv, 199.   [7] 1604, 24; 1659, 1007.   [8] 1604, 29; 1659, 1009.
[9] *Samml. chem. u. chem.-techn. Vorträge*, 1909, xiv, 131.   [10] 1604, 32; 1659, 1011.

CARDAN

Jerome Cardan (Girolamo or Geronimo Cardano; Hieronymus Cardanus) (Pavia 24 September 1501 — Rome 21 September 1576)[1] was descended on the paternal side from a noble family of Milan; his parents were separated and Jerome, who had weak health, was harshly treated by his father, acting as a domestic servant until he went to school at the age of 19. At 23 he went to the University of Padua, where the students chose him as their rector. His poverty he mitigated by play at chess, a game of which he was always very fond, losing a fortune in play in 1554 and selling his wife's jewels. At 24 he graduated as doctor. Plague and civil war drove him to Sacco (between Padua and Venice), then to Milan, where he practised medicine in miserable circumstances.[2]

In 1552 Cardan was called to St. Andrews as physician by the Archbishop of Scotland, John Hamilton, whom he cured after the local physicians had failed, and this gave him a great reputation.[3] He was professor of mathematics at Milan in 1534-6, and of medicine in 1543, in medical practice in Milan in 1553-8, and professor of medicine at Padua (1559), Bologna (1562-70), and Rome, where he died.

Cardan's mathematical discoveries are important, but 'Cardan's method' for the solution of cubic equations was communicated to him by Tartaglia in confidence, which he betrayed by publishing it as his own. In mechanics, the Cardan shaft and the Cardan suspension are well known.

Cardan had a profound knowledge of ancient science and a keen and penetrating mind, but was vain, credulous, and superstitious. He had visions from his youth and was 'illuminated' in 1529 and 1573-5. Morhof says his powerful genius and remarkable intuition were mingled with foolish knowledge, his periods of genius alternating with intervals of foolishness. Libri thought that if we did not possess his autobiography, we should never believe that a man of such science could show such folly. Hoefer says 'il mêle les observations les plus exactes aux théories les plus insoutenables'. Cardan believed in magic, which he says was taught at Salamanca in his time,[4] in engraved gems,[5] and in

[1] Cardan in his De Propria Vita Liber, ed. G. Naudé, Paris, 1643; Opera omnia, 1663, i, 2; tr. Jean Stoner, London (printed U.S.A.), 1931; says: ortus sum Anno MDVIII Cal. Octobris; in his De Utilitate ex adversis capienda libri IV; Opera omnia, 1663, ii, 112: natus sum Anno Salutis millesimo quingentesimo primo . . . die vigesimo tertio Septembris; the portrait in De Subtilitate, dated 1553, has 'aged 49', suggesting that he was born in 1504. Morley says the date 1500 occurs only once and 1501 is correct, and Eckman agrees.
[2] Burckhardt, The Civilisation of the Renaissance in Italy, pt. iv, ch. 5, 1944, 204; A. Bellini, Gerolamo Cardano e il suo tempo, Milan, 1947 (Studii di Storia della medicina, vol. VIII); review by Wickersheimer, Archives, 1951, xxx, 819; L. Durey, La médecine occulte de Paracelse . . . J. Cardan, etc., Paris, 1900; J. Eckman, 'Jerome Cardan', Bull. Hist. Med., Baltimore, Suppl., 1946 (bibl.); Haeser, (1), 1881, ii, 120; Heller, (1), 1882, i, 323; Hoefer, (1), 1866, i, 94-6; Kiesewetter, (1), 115; Lessing, 1838, 330; Libri, (1), 1840, iii, 167-80; Morhof, (1), P. II, bk. i, ch. xv, §3, 1747, ii, 109; Henry Morley, The Life of Girolamo Cardano of Milan, Physician, 2 vols., London, 1854; Poggendorff, (2), 1883, 71; Rixner and Siber, 1820, ii; Rodwell, Chem. News, 1864, x, 195; Sardou, NBU, 1854, viii, 686; Sprengel, (1), 1815, iii, 272; Thorndike, v, 563-79; Ueberweg, (1), 1924, iii, 41; W. G. Waters, Jerome Cardan, a Biographical Study, London, 1898.
[3] J. D. Comrie, History of Scottish Medicine, 2 ed., 1932, i, 180-7.
[4] Cardan, De Subtilitate, lib. xviii-xix (De mirabilibus, De daemonibus), 8° Basel, 1560, 1218.
[5] Cardan, De Varietate, bk. xvi, chs. 89-90.

astrology, casting horoscopes, including one for King Edward VI of England, predicting a long life for him, although the king died the year after, which Cardan found should have happened after correcting his arithmetic.[1] He was much influenced by Neopythagorean and Neoplatonic teachings, but apparently had no knowledge of Paracelsus.

Cardan was a voluminous writer on a great variety of subjects. His works were published by Charles Spon (Lyons; 1609–84), a French physician of German origin, in ten large folio volumes,[2] containing 138 treatises divided by the editor into philological, logical, moral, physical, mathematical, musical, astronomical, astrological, onirocritical, medical (vols. 6–9), and fragments.

Cardan's most important works for our purpose are his *De Subtilitate libri XXI* (1550)[3] and *De Rerum Varietate libri XVII* (1557),[4] the tenth book of which is on chemistry. In what follows the *De Subtilitate* is denoted by *S*, and the *De Rerum Varietate* by *V*, with the page reference to the *Opera omnia*, 1663, vol. iii, unless otherwise stated. *S* is not divided into chapters, the 100 chapters in *V* run consecutively through the eighteen books.

The relation between natural magic and experimental science had been emphasised in 1489 by Petrus Garsia, bishop of Ussellus in Sardinia, in criticising Pico della Mirandola. He said:

'Moreover, to assert that such experimental knowledge is science or a part of natural science is ridiculous, wherefore such magicians are called experimenters rather than scientists. Besides, magic, according to those of that opinion, is practical knowledge, whereas natural science in itself and all its parts is purely speculative knowledge.'[5]

Cardan's *De Subtilitate* and *De Rerum Varietate* were on the Spanish Index of 1559 but were freely cited outside Spain. He was personally in trouble with the Inquisition in 1570 and 1571.[6] The *De Subtilitate* was violently criticised by Julius Caesar Scaliger.[7] Cardan answered Scaliger in the fourth edition of his *De Subtilitate*.[8]

Cardan[9] had said that bees are too busy flying about to carry eggs around; they are spontaneously generated from honey. Scaliger[10] pointed out that spontaneous generation implies putrefaction, that honey is a preservative, and that other flying insects generate normally. Scaliger, however, believed in

---

[1] Thorndike, v, 572.

[2] *Hieronymi Cardani Mediolanensis Opera omnia in decem tomos digesta. Curâ Caroli Spon*, 10 vols. f., portrait, Lyons, 1663.

[3] f°, Nürnberg, 1550, and later much enlarged editions, f°, Basel, 1554, etc., to 4°, Basel, 1664; *Opera omnia*, 1663, iii, 357 f.; the only translation is: *Les livres de la subtilité*, sm. 4°, L'Angelier, 1556 (by R. LeBlanc), reprinted 1566 and 1584; Libri, (1), 1840, iii, 117, says the work was little read.

[4] f° and 8°, Basel, 1557 (Sotheran *Cat.* 789 (1924), 340, no. 4560) and later revised and enlarged editions, 1558, 1581; *Opera omnia*, 1663, iii.

[5] *Petri Garsia . . . in determinetiões magistrales côtra conclusiones apologiales Ioannis Pici Mirandulani*, f°, Rome, 1489 (BM); Thorndike, iv, 501.

[6] Thorndike, vi, 148.

[7] *Exotericarvm Exercitationvm Liber Quintus Decimvs, de Subtititate, ad Hieronymum Cardanvm*, 4°, Paris, 1557, and later eds. The title suggests that Scaliger had written fourteen previous books on the subject, which is not the case. The *Doctrina vera Alchymiæ atque Artis Metallicæ* attributed to Scaliger by Kopp, (1), iii, 120, is by Gratarolo; Ferguson, i, 341; ii, 325.

[8] f° and 8°, Basel, 1560: addita insuper Apologia adversus Calumniatorem, qua Vis horum Librorum aperitur.

[9] *S*, 8°, 1560, 546.   [10] Ex. CXI; f. 260 r.

spontaneous generation in producing rains of frogs.[1] In discussing the supposed property of goat's blood in softening diamond, Scaliger[2] says recent authors, who detest occult properties and call them the asylum of ignorance, made the blood act on diamond because of an analogy which is a common principle of them; yet, says Scaliger, what is this but an occult property (quid aliud est principij communis analogia, quàm proprietas occulta?).

Scaliger mentions cobalt (cobaltun) for colouring glass;[3] *zaphera* quam manganesem vocant Itali[4] — perhaps pyrolusite; *rusma* for removing hair, made from quicklime and arsenic sulphide;[5] bismuth (cassiteri, quod Angli vocant, glaciale);[6] sugar and manna (zuccara uocant Arabes: Indi proximi uoce, Igara).[7] He repeated[8] the story in Pliny[9] that if the flesh of poultry is mixed with gold in a state of fusion it will absorb the metal and consume it, thus showing that it acts as a poison upon gold.[10]

Thorndike[11] thought Scaliger's criticisms had some effect in reducing credulity generally; his book, however, is unjust to Cardan, making much of printer's errors which Cardan had corrected in editions published before Scaliger wrote, and Scaliger's book as a whole breathes a defiant violence quite uncalled for in scientific criticism. Sir Thomas Browne,[12] said: 'If Cardan saith that a Parrot is a beautiful Bird, Scaliger will set his Wits o' work to prove it a deformed Animal.'

The eighteenth book of Cardan's *De Subtilitate* is a collection of 'marvels' and tricks. A pyrophoric stone (pyrophilium lapidum) is made from human blood putrefied, evaporated, and calcined (phosphorus?).[13] Among human marvels he mentions change of sex, living a long time without food, and the emission of sparks from the hair (electric sparks).[14] A magic candle with colour, odour, motion, and decrepitation (candela colore, odore, motu et strepitu admirabilis) is made with 1 part of saltpetre, 1/5 of myrrh, common oil and spurge juice (lactis lathiridis), 1/10 of sulphur, and 1/2 wax.[15]

Cardan's *De Gemmis et Coloribus*,[16] *Historiæ lapidum, metallicorum et metallorum*[17] and *Somniorum Synesiorum*[18] contain very little of chemical interest. His medical works were published in 1559.[19]

Cardan modified Aristotelian physics by accepting only three elements: earth, water and air, since distillation of bodies gives only these; fire is not a substance but a form of motion; cold is mere absence of heat and all three elements (including air) are cold; dryness is absence of moisture. Hence the four qualities are reduced to two, heat and moisture,[20] and dryness is absence of moisture. He distinguished between electric and magnetic attractions,[21]

[1] Ex. CCCXXIII, f. 434.   [2] Ex. CCCXLIV, 8 (de adamante, & hirci sanguine), f. 455 v.
[3] Ex. CIII, 20, f. 165.   [4] *Ib.*, CIII, 23, f. 166.   [5] *Ib.*, CXIIII, 4, f. 178.
[6] *Ib.*, CCXX, f. 181 v.   [7] *Ib.*, CLXIIII, f. 225 v.   [8] *Ib.*, LXXXVIII, f. 134.
[9] *Hist. Nat.*, xxix, 25.   [10] Basso also accepted this; Thorndike, vi, 388.
[11] vi, 283.   [12] *Christian Morals*, ii, 3; *Works*, ed. Sayle, 1927, iii, 468.
[13] *S*, xviii; 8°, 1560, 1170.   [14] *V*, viii, 43; 8°, 1557, 560-1.   [15] *V*, x, 49; p. 193.
[16] Basel, 4°, 1585; *Opera*, 1663, ii, 552.   [17] *Opera*, 1663, x, 520-32.
[18] *Somniorvm Synesiorvm, omnis generis insomnia explicantes, Libri IIII. Qvibvs accedvnt, . . . De libris proprijs. De curationibus & prædictionibus admirandis. Neronis encomium. Geometriæ encomium. De uno. Actio in Thessalicum medicum. De secretis. De gemmis & coloribus* [in part II, 308], etc., 4°, 2 vols. in one, Basel, Henric. Petri, 1562.
[19] *Opuscula quaedam artem medicam exercentibus utilissima*, f°, Basel, 1559.
[20] *S*, ii, de elementis, pp. 372-5; *V*, i, 1-2 (ignis vires et alimenta); x, 49, p. 192: docuimus ignem non esse substantiam, sed summam caliditatem substantiae corrruptricem.
[21] *S*, v; 8° Basel, 1560, 373.

discussed the causes of odours and tastes,[1] telegraphy by night,[2] snow crystals,[3] sympathetic, coloured and indelible (linseed oil and carbon) inks,[4] many ingenious machines, and a letter lock.[5] He said[6] the force of thunderbolts had been exceeded by recent bronze cannon (machinæ) which threw a 60 lb. iron shot 5000 paces and throw down a whole tower at one blow. He describes Greek fire from Marcus Græcus (Gracchus) and gives recipes for gunpowder: 3 saltpetre, 2 willow charcoal, 1 sulphur for large guns, 10 : 3 : 2 for medium, and 10 saltpetre, 1 sulphur, and 1 charcoal of hazel-nut tree wood without knots for small guns; purified saltpetre is necessary.

A short chapter on chemistry (chymica)[7] is mildly critical: three things are requisite to the chemist, something to desire, something to hope for, and some means of realising the hope (quid optandum, quid sperandum, et quomodo habendum quod speratur); the third is the most difficult. The visions of the alchemists (chimistæ) are classed with the vain hope of witches and the miserable.[8] It is denied that gold and silver can be distilled or a water made of either, but the extraction of an oil of other metals by finely powdering them and distilling with vinegar is described, and the process, which is very long and difficult, can be used with gems and pearls. Cardan was told that such a nostrum enabled a man to live 124 years.[9] He attempted a solution of the Sibylline oracle[10] as ἀρσενικόν.

Earthy bodies (mista sub terra) are divided into four genera: earths, juices, stones, and metals, and the varying action of heat on mixtures of these gives eleven species of compound bodies. Three kinds of mixture are distinguished: *mistio*, *krasis*, and *coacervatio*, corresponding roughly to our chemical combination, solution, and mechanical mixture, respectively, and based on Aristotle (Vol. I).[11] Among the earths Cardan mentions fossil or stone coal (carbones fossiles seu lapidei) as burnt in London and Scotland, and recently (i.e. about 1555) imported to France.[12] He thought that the vasa murrhina of the ancients (see Vol. I) were 'to-day called porcelain (quæ hodie vocantur Porcellanæ)', which is made from a fine, light, and fatty clay, well kneaded together for a long time.[13]

Metals grow in the earth and have a kind of life; the magnet also lives. The metals have special tastes.[14] The seven metals are associated with the planets and there are also seven primary colours.[15] Electrum, which is a mixture of gold and silver, is associated with planet Mercury (see Vol. I). Cardan mentions a mass of 200 lb. of native copper found in Hispaniola. Artificial steel, including damascened, is made from pure iron and marble. Tin is not a natural but an artificial product and contains silver: it is used for organ pipes. The chemists claim to convert mercury into gold and silver; an apothecary of Trevigo (tarvisanus) claimed to have discovered a process which he showed to the Doge and the learned men of Venice. The chemists can give colour and

[1] V, iii, 14; p. 38 f.: mixtorum proprietates.   [2] S, xvii, 8°; Basel, 1560, 1057.
[3] S, xxi, p. 663; V, xv, 71, p. 278.   [4] V, xiii, 63 f., pp. 251 f., 255 f.
[5] S, xvii (lock, 8°, 1560, p. 1075).   [6] S, ii, pp. 376, 379; Basel, 1560, 103, 107.
[7] V, x, 51, pp. 205 f.; cf. S, bks. vi, xvii; 8°, 1560, 421, 1041.
[8] V, xvi, 93; 8°, 1557, 1087.   [9] V, x, 50; 8°, 1557, 687–8.
[10] V, x, 51; 8°, 1557, 714.   [11] S, v; pp. 434, 438.   [12] V, v, 17, p. 47.
[13] S, v; 8°, 1560, p. 341.   [14] S, v, pp. 440 f.; vii, pp. 474 f.   [15] V, iii, 14, p. 42.

weight, but not subtlety (subtilitas), firmness (firmitas) or internal structure (structura interna); mercury cannot be changed into gold, and still less silver. A man of Milan was able to dip his hands, moistened with water, into melted lead. Although metals are said to be generated from mercury and sulphur, these materials are not found where metals occur, and metals are really congealed waters. The metals can be burnt to water, especially when mixed with orpiment and heated under the earth in a vase or over boiling water.[1] Seals are made as amulets from the appropriate metals with the signs of the planets.[2]

Mercury, found in Bohemia, is a poison and causes paralysis. It perforates all metallic vessels and when heated in a sealed glass vessel it bursts it. When mixed with heated sulphur it forms cinnabar. Sublimed silver (argentum sublimatum; really mercuric chloride) is made by subliming a mixture of mercury with vitriol (atramentum sutorium) in a glass vessel. Red precipitate (argentum coctum rubrum vocant Præcipitatum) is made by dissolving mercury in the liquid (i.e. nitric acid) distilled from equal parts of alum and vitriol and half the weight of salt (probably nitre), evaporating the solution to dryness, heating the residue till red fumes appear (fumus et vas rubescant), grinding, heating again, and stirring till the solid becomes as red as minium (red lead). 'Marcasite' (marchesita, i.e. bismuth) is mixed with lead to make printing type (notularum pro typis); other semi-metals are cadmia, cobalt (cobaltum) and antimony (antimonium).[3] 'Bisemutum', hitherto unknown (hucusque incognitum) is intermediate between lead and tin (white lead) and antimony is a fourth kind of lead.[4] Metals and minerals produce various coloured flames (ignis autem purus albus est . . . magis metallis aut metallicis ob id talia mutare colorem flammae solent).[5]

Lead on conversion into white lead (cerussa) and on burning (to red lead or litharge) increases in weight by one thirteenth:[6]

It does this because the celestial heat is dissipated, for it is certain that nothing is added and yet it increases, as is for the same reason seen in animals, which become heavier on death on account of the departure of the soul.[7] It is clear that metals and stones themselves live.

Clarius idem fit experimento: nam plumbum cùm in cerussam vertitur, ac uritur, tertiadecima parte sui ponderis augitur. Hoc fit, quia calor ille cœlestis evanescit: nam certum est adjici nihil, et tamen crescit. Cum igitur par ratio etiam in animalibus videatur, quæ graviora morte finut, quoniam exhalante anima secum calor etiam, ac quicquid ab illo est elaboratum, evanescit, manifestum est corpora metallica et lapides ipsos etiam vivere.

This explanation was repeated by George Pictorius, at first a schoolmaster in Freiburg in Breisgau, then (1540) town physician in Ensisheim in Alsace.[8] Scaliger[9] ridiculed the idea of a 'soul' escaping from a metal, and said the increase in weight is due to the destruction of particles of air included in the metal, which hence becomes heavier, as crude bricks on baking:

[1] S, vi, pp. 452 f., 457 f.   [2] S, xviii, p. 646; V, xvi, 89 f., pp. 307 f.
[3] S., v, pp. 446 f., 448.   [4] S, v, pp. 452 f.
[5] V, x, 49, p. 193.   [6] S, v, p. 440.
[7] Pliny, vii, 18, says 'the bodies of all animals are heavier when they are dead than when alive, they also weigh more when asleep than when awake'.
[8] *Physicarum Quæstionum*, Basel, 1568; q. by Thorndike, vi, 403.
[9] *Exotericarum Exercitationum*, Ex. ci, c. 18, Ex. civ, c. 17; 4°, Paris, 1557, ff. 152 v, 164 v; quoted in full in Gobet, *Essays de Iean Rey*, Paris, 1777, 72–3.

Al plumbum absumptis partibus aereis gravius fit. Qua de caussa later quoque coctus crudo gravior. At contra, arundo combusta levior fit. Plumbum quoque aiunt augescere. Calcem in fornace tecta videmus adeo turgescere: ut tigna atque tegulus sustolleret.

Jean Bodin (1530–96)[1] also raised the question:

Why does lead reduced to a calx in the reverberatory fire become heavier, while other things become lighter? Is it not because the lighter aerial essence is driven away by the fire, and the calx of lead therefore becomes more compact?

Cur plŭbum in calcem redactum ignea reuerberatione ingrauescat, cum cætera fiant leuiora? An quia aërea vis leuior ab ignibus fugatur, ac propterea calx plumbi solidior fit?

The idea that the loss of lighter parts increases the weight of a body re-appears in Galileo's *Il Saggiatore*.[2]

'. . . how very fallacious an argument it is to say this body has not lost weight ac-cording to the balance, therefore no part of it has been lost, since it can be that some of it is lost and its weight is not diminished but even sometimes increased; this will always happen when that which is lost and taken away has a smaller specific gravity (*men graue in specie*) than the medium in which it is weighed . . . particles of a substance less heavy than the air separate from them, which, when it alone is removed, would leave that body heavier than before.'

Cardan describes sal ammoniac, the most bitter of salts, obtained from vol-canoes, made artificially, and also found under sand; alkali (sal cali); saltpetre (sal nitrum) generated by decay, which consists of fine and dry particles and is grown anew in the earth after five to six years.[3] When saltpetre from old walls is thrown on glowing coals it causes a rapid combustion and flame by gener-ating a wind (*flatus*):[4]

contigit ut jam quasi extinctus, in flammam accensus erumpat, ob salsedinem murorum et halinitrum quod muris vetustis adhaeret, et lignorum cariem; quodcunque enim flatum gignit e pruna, flammam excitare solet.

Flame is ignited air:[5]

est enim flamma nihil aliud quam aër accensus . . . ergo flamma non eadem unquam manet, sed perpetua generatione altera alteri succedit.

Copperas (cuperosa) is formed by the efflorescence of misy (a kind of pyrites). An oil (sulphuric acid) is made by distilling vitriol (chalcanthum, vitriolum).[6] Oil of sulphur (sulphuric acid) is made by collecting the fumes of burning sulphur on a glass vessel called a nola:[7]

fumus qui colligitur dum refrigeratur, oleum efficitur, ut expertus sum. Opus est autem vase unico tantum vitreo, quod nolam vocant.

In discussing the properties of mixtures, Cardan says urine becomes clear on heating, but glass opaque (devitrification).[8] He calls seven times rectified spirit of wine 'ether':[9]

---

[1] *Vniversæ Natvræ Theatrvm* (Lyons, 1596, 263–4; Frankfurt, 1597 (same pagin.).
[2] 4°, Rome, 1623, 175; *Opere*, ed. Alberi, Firenze, 1843, iv, 313; *Opere*, ed. Nazionale, Firenze, 1890–1909, vi, 333; Partington and McKie, *Ann. Sci.*, 1937, ii, 365; for various issues of *Il Saggiatore*, see Sotheran *Cat.* 786 (1923), no. 3171, p. 241.
[3] *S*, v, p. 444 f.   [4] *V*, x, 49, p. 194.   [5] *S*, ii; 8°, 1560, 86.
[6] *S*, v, p. 445.   [7] *S*, viii, p. 493.   [8] *V*, iii, 14, p. 35 f.
[9] *Liber de vitali aqua seu de aethere*; *Opera*, 1663, ii, 601.

experimentum docet aquam ardentem quo saepius fuerit destillata, eo tenuiorem et acutiorem esse, adeò ut septies destillata, statim ardeat, et degustari minimè possit.

He seems to mention cochineal (imported from America in the 16 cent.),[1] and tapioca (hyuca);[2] he describes the fabulous barnacle geese[3] and the virtues of the bezoar stone (pazar lapis)[4] which came from India and was a concretion found in goats.[5] He elsewhere says that no true gems are generated in the sea (which would exclude pearls) or in animals (which would exclude bezoars).[6] He agreed with Rondelet against Aristotle that some fish breathe air,[7] but agreed with Aristotle that bees make only the honey-comb from flowers, the honey being formed from dew.[8]

In chapters on distillation[9] Cardan describes and figures the apparatus, including an arrangement of two alembics as vasa mutua, reciproca vasa; and the water bath (balneum mariae). He describes the distillation of alcohol (aqua ardens) in an alembic with a very long neck, and the preparation of an elixir from it. He deprecates the excessive use of distilled waters (spirits) in his time, and says they may contain poisonous particles of copper and lead from the metal stills.[10] He gives the preparation of oil of bricks.[11] Before Boyle (see p. 548) Cardan used distilled human blood in medicine.[12]

In his *De propria vita*, written in 1575, Cardan says that in his *De Subtilitate* and *De Rerum Varietate* he had not delved into such questionable arts as poisoning, chemistry, incantations and invocations of demons, although he had dealt with the properties of things and natural magic.[13] He nevertheless composed an early treatise on toxicology.[14] In this he deals with poisons formed by putrefaction and corruption (i.e. ptomaines). There are five kinds of corruption: rancid, mucous, acid, and two kinds without names (nisi marcorem in siccis, velut lapidibus et ossibus: atque humidis, velut malis punicis). He deals with poisons absorbed from air and water,[15] the symptoms of poisoning,[16] the methods of cure,[17] poisoning by mercury,[18] and a list of poisons and their antidotes.[19] He denied that blood can putrefy in the living body.[20]

PORTA

Giambattista della Porta (Naples; 1535–4 February, 1615),[21] of an old noble family, was very precocious and at the age of fifteen had written the first three books of his natural magic (*Magia Naturalis*). This is a collection of superstitions, recipes and out-of-the-way scraps of information from a great variety

[1] S, ix; 8°, 1560, 648: tinctura purpurea nova pro serico.   [2] S, xii, p. 563.
[3] V, vii, 36, p. 108 f.   [4] S, vii (De lapidibus), p. 469.
[5] Somn. Scip., 1562, ii, 325 (De gemmis et coloribus).   [6] V, v, 18; 8°, 1557, 174.
[7] V, vii, 37; 8°, 1557, 387.   [8] V, vii, 25; 8°, 1557, 243.
[9] S, xvii, p. 615; V, x, 50, p. 194.   [10] De methodo medendi, sect. i, cap. 12; Opera, vii, 207.
[11] V, x, 50.   [12] Thorndike, vi, 292, q. Aldrovandus, Monstrorum Historia, 1642, 310.
[13] Thorndike, v, 564.   [14] De Veneris Libri tres; Opera, 1663, vii, 275.
[15] Opera, vii, p. 285.   [16] Ib., p. 310.   [17] Ib., p. 326.
[18] Ib., p. 338.   [19] Ib., p. 350.
[20] Contradicentia medicorum, bk. iv, chs. 6, 26; Opera, vi, 688, 706.
[21] Price, in the preface to the reprint of Porta, Natural Magick, New York, 1957, says 'it has been admirably demonstrated by Rosen', The Naming of the Telescope, New York, 1947 (a work not available to me), that Porta was born between 7 December 1534 and 6 July 1535; the usual date is 1538, but Ferguson, ii, 216, gives 1545.

of authors which, especially in its later extended form in twenty books, was exceedingly popular and was translated into Italian, French, Spanish, English, German and (so Porta says in the preface) into Arabic.[1] He visited many places in Italy, France, Germany and Spain, reading in libraries (where he found many unpublished manuscripts) and getting information from learned men and artificers, and by correspondence. In his house he had a museum of natural curiosities and a collection of apparatus, especially optical, and he had some talent as an experimenter; the garden of his villa contained rare plants. In his house he founded in 1560 a scientific society, the Accademia de' Secreti,[2] membership of which required some medical or physical discovery, but the suspicions of Pope Paul V were aroused and Porta was summoned to Rome. He was released, it is said, on condition that he dissolved the society and ceased to study dangerous sciences.[3]

The Accademia de' Lincei was founded in Rome in 1603 by Count Federigo Cesi (then aged 18) under the protection of Cardinal Barberini and lasted until 1651. The members met in Cesi's house, had a botanic garden, a cabinet of natural history, and a rich library. The Academy published the description of the natural products of Mexico written by Francisco Hernandez.[4]

Porta enjoyed a great reputation; he was fêted in Rome and in 1610 was admitted a member of the Accademia de' Lincei. He wrote some poems and meritorious plays, and besides his *Magia Naturalis* a treatise on the supposed relations between plants and animals[5] and works on optics, pneumatics, fortification, etc. He was also a capable mathematician. He rarely names his sources, beyond classical authors, which makes it difficult to decide how much in his works is due to himself.[6]

Porta's *Coelestis Physiognomoniae libri sex* (Naples, 1603) is astrological, although in the preface he says he had been taught by the Church to abhor astrology as much as he once had pursued it. A posthumous *Della chirofisonomia*, translated from a Latin MS. by Pompeo Sarnelli (1677), had the title altered to distinguish it from superstitious chiromancy.[7] Porta's *De Aeris Transmutationibus libri IIII*[8] deals with meteorology, the saltness of the sea, etc., and recognises the existence of poisonous exhalations different from air. Porta's works on physiognomy and chiromancy were prohibited by the Holy Office. He was denounced to the Inquisition for using the aid of demons but successfully defended himself.[9] His *Magia Naturalis* was 'purged' by the censor, of which he complains in the preface of the 1561 edition.

Porta's most celebrated work is that on Natural Magic (*Magia Naturalis*), which went through a great number of editions (Lehmann says over 30) and is a storehouse of very miscellaneous lore (Ea pandimus quae tacuerunt diu, vel

[1] E. H. F. Meyer, iv, 439; Poggendorff, (2), 77.   [2] Gliozzi, *Archives*, 1950, iii, 536.
[3] Poggendorff, (2), 214.   [4] Partington, *Ann. Sci.*, 1955, xi, 1; anon., NBU, 1854, ix, 502.
[5] *Phytognomonica . . . octo libris contenta*, 4°, Naples, 1588, 320 pp. +xiv ll.
[6] *Notice historique sur la vie et les œuvres de J.-B. Porta, Gentilhomme Napolitain, par* [G. H.] D[uchesne], Paris, An IX (1801) (BM 612. g. 18); Gmelin, (1), i, 319; Haeser, (1), 1881, ii, 122; Heller, 1882, i, 306; Kiesewetter, (1), 1891, 130; A. Lehmann, *Aberglaube und Zauberei*, tr. Petersen, Stuttgart, 1908, 234; Libri, (1), 1841, iv, 108–38, 327; NBG, 1862, xl, 841; Rodwell, *Chem. News*, 1863, viii, 186; Thorndike, v, 68; vi, 156, 162 f., 282, 418 f.
[7] Thorndike, vi, 162–3.
[8] 4°, Rome, MDCXIV (BM 528. d. 20; colophon dated 1610); Sotheran *Cat.* 832 (1932), 322 (no. 4462) gives 1 ed. sm. 4°, Rome, 1610, but NBG, 1862, xl, 843, gives 4°, Naples, 1609.
[9] Thorndike, vi, 150, 156, 418.

scientis invidia, vel nescientis inscitia).[1] It incorporates all the old fables from Pliny, etc., without criticism. The first issue was in four books,[2] dedicated to Philip II of Spain, who became king in 1556:

I. Magiae Natvralis sive De Miracvlis Rervm Natvralivm Libri IIII . . . , Napoli Apud Matthiam Cancer, M.D. LVIII, 4° (described in catalogues as f°), xvi + 163 pp. Other eds. in BM are: 8° Antwerp, 1561; 16° Lyons, 1561; 16° Antwerp, 1564; I have used an ed. sm. 8°, Antwerp, 1585. Other eds. mentioned are Antwerp, 1560, 1562, 1576; Lyon, 1564, 1569, 1591. An ed. of 1555 mentioned by Leclerc is said by Duchesne, p. 212, not to exist. French tr., Paris, 1570, Rouen, 1631 (reprinted in Paris, n.d. [1900]; Lyon, 1650; Italian tr., sm. 8°, Venice, 1650 (Sotheran *Cat.* 773 (1919), no. 131, as 18°), 1562 (Sotheran *Cat.* 780 (1922), no. 706), 1638 (?), 1665 (Sotheran *Cat.* 789 (1924), no. 5941); German, Naturliche Magie, 8°, Magdeburg, 1612 (not seen). The date 1567 always quoted by Kopp (1), is that of some edition in four books quoted by Gmelin, (1), i, 319–22 who actually used an edition of 1597 in 20 books.

Domenico Pizimenti (the translator of the Greek alchemical works, Vol. I) was Porta's classical master and claimed to be the actual author of the first form (4 books) of the *Magia Naturalis*, according to Guibert,[3] who says both Porta in Naples and Pizimenti in Rome told him they had transmuted mercury into silver by heating it in a pot with a toad until the parched toad soaked up most of the mercury and was finally consumed by fire, but they were unable to repeat the experiment successfully.

A much enlarged edition in twenty books was first published in 1589,[4] dedicated to Julius Baboli of Ragusi; approbation dated Naples, 9 August, 1588:

II. Magiae Natvralis libri XX, ab ipso Authore expurgati, et super aucti, 4°, Neapoli, M.D. LXXXVIIII (1589), Apud Horatium Salvianum, engr. t.p. with portrait on verso, xvi, 363 pp. (last blank). BM 719. l. 3. (2.) (imperfect); BN Cat., 1937, cxli, 147 (303 f., titre à encadrement, fig. portr.; incorrectly descr. as f°); other eds. in BM 8°, Frankfurt, 1607, and Hannover, 1619; 12°, Leyden, 1651 (the ed. I have used; engr. t.p. dated 1650), and Amsterdam. Other eds. described are Frankfurt, 1591, 1597; 12°, Hannover, 1644; 8°, Rouen, 1650. Hoefer, (1), ii, 96, incorrectly gives 1584 for first ed. English tr.: Natural Magick by John Baptista Porta A Neapolitane: in Twenty Books . . . , 4°, London, T. Young and F. Speed, 1658, engraved t.p. (portrait), (an ed. sm. f°, London, for John Wright, 1669, has been mentioned); facsim. repr., New York, 1957, 1958. German tr.: Magia Naturalis, oder Hauss- Kunst- und Wunder-Buch . . . von allen Fehlern . . . gereinigt, 4°, Nürnberg, 1713.[5] Italian tr.: Di i miracoli et margvigliosi effett dalla natura prodotti, 8°, Turin, 1882.

Porta says in the preface that the books cost him an immense amount of labour and that he obtained by correspondence information from books he was unable to consult personally. In the following account, references to the edition in *four* books (1585) are to books in small Roman numerals (e.g. ii); to the edition in *twenty* books (1651) in large Roman numerals (e.g. XII);

---

[1] Pref. to edit. in xx books.
[2] Not three, as NBG, 1862, xl, 842, says, adding that the fourth book first appeared in the Antwerp ed. of 1560 or 1561; Feldhaus, (1), 1914, 810, said the only copy was in Berlin, Kgl. Bibliothek, but there is a copy in BM, 7003. eee. 17, and two in CUL; three copies were offered for sale in 1919: Sotheran *Cat.* 773 (1919), nos. 128–30, price £6–6–0; Poggendorff, (2), 77, says there was an earlier ed. of 1553?, which is not now known to exist, Libri that the ed. of 1558 was the earliest he had seen.
[3] Guibert, *De Interito Alchymia Metallorvm Transmvtatoriæ*, 8°, Toul, 1603, pt. ii, 132.
[4] Duchesne, 214, says 1588, but the BN copy he quotes is 1589; he says eds. of Antwerp, 16°, 1576 and 1585, are non-existent.
[5] Sotheran *Cat.* 780 (1922), no. 719, says it is the only one; Kiesewetter gives 8° Sulzbach, 1680, and 4° Nürnberg, 2 vols., 1715.

chapters are in Arabic numerals (e.g. 12) in both cases. Page references are to the editions named here.

Campanella[1] says Porta tried to revise the study of ancient magic, but only exoterically, since he had no real knowledge of the active causes. Porta united a real talent in physics (particularly optics) with a belief in occult forces and the doctrine of signatures (which was in great favour with Paracelsus). It is possible that his *Natural Magic* was familiar to Francis Bacon.[2]

In the edition in four books, these deal, respectively (without general titles), with: (i) magic, spiritualism, sympathy, etc., in general; (ii) the production and improvement of fruits and experiments with fruits; fireworks, inks, poisons, etc.; (iii) the extraction of waters and oils, sublimation, metals, glass, imitation gems, etc.; (iv) optical experiments and the virtues of gems.

In the edition in twenty books the superstitious material was toned down somewhat. In the preface Porta complains that he had been called a sorcerer (magum veneficum) and a French author (who was a Protestant and not, like himself, a good Catholic) had said Porta's book should be burnt because it included an unguent of witches; this, however, Porta says, was taken from writings of praiseworthy theologians. Anyway, it had passed the censor. The twenty books deal with the causes of wonderful things (magic, sympathy and antipathy, etc.), the generation of animals by putrefaction, mixed breeds, etc., the production of new plants by putrefaction, grafting, etc., increasing household stuff (preserving fruit on trees, in oil, etc., bread from various things, wines, vinegars, oils), transmuting metals or chemical experiments (bk. v), counterfeiting gems, the magnet (Porta denies that garlic weakens its force, and he gives many new experiments), medical experiments, beautifying women (hair dyes, cosmetics), distillation, perfumes, fireworks, tempering steel, cookery, fishing, fowling and hunting, invisible writing and counterfeiting seals, burning-glasses, static experiments (e.g. parting water from wine), pneumatic experiments, and finally 'chaos' (miscellaneous experiments). There is much of practical interest in the book, but it is mostly a compilation and the author was devoid of critical faculty.

Tin is made to imitate silver by boiling with mercury in a cucurbit, when it loses its 'cry' and softeness;[3] it is calcined by heating with common salt or saltpetre;[4] mirrors are made from amalgamated tin or from an alloy of tin, antimony, and copper.[5] Mercury is adulterated with half its weight of a mixture of lead and bismuth (marchesita), when it remains liquid but forms a 'tail' on flowing.[6]

Silver calx (silver chloride) is made by grinding silver amalgam with common salt and distilling off the mercury in a retort (in obtorte vitreo vase); or by dissolving silver in aqua fortis and precipitating with salt dissolved in water. It melts like wax (uti ceram) on heating.[7] A silver tree is made (ut argentum vivum in arborem excrescat) by putting mercury in a solution of silver nitrate:

---

[1] *De Divinatione*, bk. iv, ch. 1; q. by Kiesewetter, (1), 1891, 175.   [2] Thorndike, vi, 421.
[3] iii, 8, p. 230.   [4] iii, 2, p. 209.   [5] iv, 18–19, pp. 279 f.; XVII, 23, p. 620.
[6] V, 2, p. 246.   [7] iii, 2, p. 208.

quod ad se argentum attrahet, et diei spatio ab imo pullulabit arbor speciosissima, capillacea, veluti ex subtilissimis aristis compacta, totumque vas replebit.

A gold tree is similarly made with a solution of gold in aqua regia.[1]

Gold is separated from silver by fusing with stibnite or antimony (stibium, antimonium) in a crucible (crucibulum) and pouring into a greased iron cone, when the gold settles to the bottom and the upper part on cupellation gives silver, with a little loss.[2] Silver is separated from solution in aqua fortis by putting in copper plates, when it settles like a cloud (in nubes formas),[3] or like fleeces of wool (in formam velleris).[4]

Metallic calces are reduced (in pristinum revertuntur) on heating with chrysocolla (borax), tartar, alum, yolk of egg, alkali (sal alchali), sal ammoniac (ammoniacum), saltpetre (sal nitrum) 'and what is called soap' (et quem saponem vocant).[5] Stibnite (antimony sulphide) is reduced to metallic antimony or regulus (quod vocant chymistae *regulum*) by heating with tartar and saltpetre.[6] Iron is converted into copper (ferrum in aes commutare) by alum and vitriol (alumen et atramento sutorio) contained in waters of the Carpathians, and is whitened by heating with pyrites and arsenic.[7] Mercury is 'congealed' by heating with arsenic crystals and tartar in a closed copper globe (argenti vivi congelatio cum aeneis pilis).[8]

Although the transmutation of metals which are not too dissimilar (non tamen eorum quae maximo distent intervallo, sed quae cognata et vicinia sunt) is philosophically possible, yet vulgar and ignorant persons (rudes homines et idiotae) labour at making imitation gold (sophistico auro praeparando) and delude themselves.[9] Copper may be deceitfully coloured to resemble other metals, e.g. like silver by means of litharge or arsenic, or (in a conjuring trick) by rubbing it with a moist powder of sal ammoniac, alum, saltpetre and silver dust;[10] or by rubbing it with a mixture of silver powder (precipitated by copper from a solution of silver in aqua fortis), tartar, and common salt,[11] but the products will not stand the test. An obviously fraudulent process for increasing the weight of a gold vessel with silver and lead is given.[12] The temper colours of steel are described.[13] The preparation of imitation gems (de gemmis adulterandis) is dealt with in detail.[14] First the preparation and purification of soda (sal sodae) from the kali plant, potash (sal tartari) from tartar, and rock crystal (crystallus) or calcined and powdered flint (silex), best from the Thames, are described. To make the paste (pastilli), five parts each of soda and potash and double the weight (horum duplam) of powdered crystal or flint are fritted in a reverberatory furnace (in reverberationis fornacem) and then fused in a Valencia crucible for six hours at the highest temperature in a small kind of glass furnace, eight feet square, with two chambers, one containing the fuel.

---

[1] V, 5, p. 253. Metal 'trees' were described by Eck of Sulzbach (1489?), *Theatrum Chemicum*, 1659, iv, 1007; see p. 8; Richard Eden (1562), J. O. Halliwell [-Phillips], *A Collection of Letters*, 1841, 5 (silver); 'Basil Valentine', *Chymische Schrifften*, Hamburg, 1740, 850; see ch. V; and Becher, *Grosse Chymische Concordantz*, part iii, no. 26: Leipzig, 1755, 329: arbor vegetabilis Philosophorum.

[2] V, 9, p. 262. [3] V, 10, p. 264. [4] V, 12, p. 264. [5] iii, 3, p. 213.
[6] V, 7, p. 257. [7] iii, 6, p. 327. [8] V, 5, p. 251. [9] iii proem., p. 201.
[10] V, 3, p. 246. [11] VI, 12, p. 284. [12] V, 8, p. 258. [13] XIII, 6, p. 497.
[14] VI, 1 f., 265 f.

To make a clear glass free from bubbles some white lead is added. The colouring materials are described. Sapphires are imitated by fusing with cobalt (zaphara), amethysts with manganese (manganesi), topaz with iron oxide (ferrei croci), emerald with burnt copper (aes combustum), chrysolite by adding burnt copper to topaz glass.

In the earlier work[1] crystal and tartar only are used for making the paste; ruby is made by adding orpiment, emerald with burnt copper, prasius with this and iron oxide, chalcedony with silver calx, sapphire with cobalt (caerulea terra illa quam figuli zapharum vocant), topaz by melting tin calx with sand, purple paste with manganese. A sapphire is turned into a 'diamond' by strongly heating it in iron filings. Enamels (smalti) are coloured like gems but are opaque, powdered brick, gypsum, etc., being added.

In the later work,[2] white enamel is made from tin oxide melted with litharge and glass, blue enamel (smalta) contains cobalt. The *giallolini* specified for making a yellow enamel[3] is Naples yellow, or lead antimoniate.[4]

Porta describes many incendiary mixtures, including some, e.g. quicklime with colophonium and magnet; or sulphur, nitre (salnitri vocati repurgati), camphor, and quicklime, after the style of the earlier recipes of Julius Africanus and Marcus Græcus.[5] Various compositions of gunpowder are given, e.g. 4 saltpetre, 1 sulphur and 1 willow charcoal; the saltpetre must be freed from common salt by refining; better powder is made with 6 or 8 parts of saltpetre instead of 4, but thorough mixing is essential. A 'silent' powder (sine strepitu) which will throw a ball with little noise is made by mixing gunpowder with 'glue or butter of gold' (auri glutinum & butyrum), but Porta refrains from giving the composition, lest the mixture should come into impious hands for wicked use (ne ansam impiis male operandi præbeamus).[6] A gun fires ten balls stratified with powder and lighted at the mouth.[7] Hand grenades, rockets like shrapnel, underground mines filled with gunpowder, and mines under water, are all familiar to Porta.[8]

An incendiary composition for a rocket contains rosin, pitch, varnish, frankincense, camphor, sulphur, saltpetre, aqua fortis, oil of nitre, and gunpowder;[9] various fire-balls (igneæ pilæ) for shooting from guns,[10] compositions burning under water,[11] metal shells filled with gunpowder,[12] underground mines,[13] a composition taking fire in the sun and a 'scalding oil'[14] are all described. A 'most burning water (aqua ardentissima)' is alcohol.[15] An ancient perpetually burning candle enclosed in a glass vial was said to have been found about 1550, still burning, in a Roman sepulchre near Naples,[16] 'but,' Porta adds, 'whoever saw a burning candle shut up tight in a glass vessel?'. Although he once opened a cucurbit in which he had made a chemical experiment and a flame issued from it, he had forgotten what it contained. Smoke bombs contain white arsenic.[17]

[1] iii, 16–18, p. 248 f.   [2] VI, 8, p. 277 f.   [3] VI, 8, p. 277.   [4] Wiegleb, (1), 1792, 230.
   [5] ii, 9 f., pp. 106 f., 129 f.; XII, 2, 10, pp. 465, 479: ignis qui dicitur Græcus; 'M. Graccho'; Partington, (4).
[6] XII, 3, p. 466.   [7] XII, 4, p. 466.   [8] XII, 4 ff., pp. 467 f.
[9] XII, 4, p. 468.   [10] XII, 5, p. 469.   [11] XII, 6, p. 471.
[12] XII, 7, p. 474.   [13] XII, 8, p. 476.   [14] XII, 10, p. 479.
[15] XII, 11, p. 483.   [16] XII, 13, p. 486.   [17] XII, 12, p. 485.

Olive or linseed oil distilled gives a very volatile and inflammable oil.[1] A curious trick is to fill a room with alcohol vapour by boiling spirit of wine in a dish over hot charcoal; when a person enters with a lighted taper the whole air takes fire. Sugar candy crushed between the teeth seems to emit sparks (videbuntur ex ore scintillae movere).[2]

Some recipes for discouraging 'gate crashers' include a napkin dusted with dry powdered vitriol and galls, handed to the parasite when he has wetted his hands and face, which when wiped with it become black as coal.[3] Various kinds of invisble writing (including that on eggs, which were smuggled into the Inquisition prisons), sympathetic inks, including the use of iron vitriol and galls,[4] inks which can be developed, those which fade after a time (useful for legal documents), and methods of writing on the skin of messengers are all described. There are useful directions for counterfeiting seals (by taking impressions of them), opening sealed letters by tearing off the paper under the seal and then repairing it again with white gum tragacanth, etc. These and other diplomatic arts were well developed in Italy.

Rabelais in his *Pantagruel and Panurge* gives several sympathetic inks (some perhaps imaginary): solution of sal ammoniac, hold to fire; juice of tithymallus, put in water; onion juice, hold to candle; blood of red toads or green earth frogs, rub with milk of a woman giving suck to her eldest daughter; dew found on the herb alcakengy or winter cherry, rub with ash of a swallow's nest; gall of raven, rub with ear-wax; juice of garden spurge, dip in vinegar; ambergris, rub with fat of bat or flittermouse; stone alum, put in basin of fresh water.

Cosmetics for whitening the skin include preparations from snails, lead salts, calomel, and corrosive sublimate[5] — which rotted the skin. Faces beautified with white lead turn black in the sulphur fumes in Puteoli.[6]

Volcanic sal ammoniac (ammoniacus sal) found in the mountains of the Campagna (in Phlegræis montibus) is formed by the condensation of sulphurous vapours (fumus sulphuris in salem ammoniacum congelatur). It is purified by dissolving the volcanic earth in hot water, filtering and evaporating, when a salt is found not different from sal ammoniac (nil (ut spero) ab ammoniaco diversum). Porta says this is a discovery of his own. Kopp said this is the first mention of volcanic sal ammoniac in a European author.[7]

Porta tried to prove that air can be converted into water (quomodo ex aëre aqua fit) by the deposition of moisture on the outside of a glass vessel containing a cooling mixture of ice and crude nitre (repleatur salnitro impuro, solazzo vulgo dicto, et glacie).[8] He describes the preparation of soap (smegmata sapones vulgo dicti) by boiling oil or fat with alkali causticised with lime, and how hard soap may be thrown out of solution by the addition of common salt.[9] A 'quintessence' of chicken is made by macerating the flesh in water, filtering through linen and evaporating in a phial to a solid (ex carnibus quintum esse extrahere).[10]

Porta describes an apparatus for obtaining fresh water by the distillation of sea water,[11] and discusses in detail the old experiment of Aristotle (see Vol. I)

[1] XII, 10, pp. 479 f.   [2] XII, 11, p. 482.   [3] XIV, 13, p. 524.
[4] ii, 12, p. 177; XVI, 1 f., p. 544.   [5] IX, 9, pp. 371 f.   [6] IX, 30, p. 396.
[7] X, 20, p. 444; Kopp, (1), iii, 241.   [8] XX, 2, p. 650.   [9] XI, 7, p. 458.
[10] X, 13, p. 425.   [11] XX, 1, p. 644.

for converting salt water into fresh water by sinking a wax vessel in the sea. He thought the effect was produced by filtration through the pores of the wax (per cerae poros salsedo corpulenta magis neget introitum), although he mentions that Solinus had explained the sweetening of sea water by filtration through clay (marina aqua argilla si percoletur, dulcescit). He found by experiment that salt water is not made fresh by percolation through ten vessels of earth, although a friend told him he had succeeded with twenty. Leo Baptista Alberti (1404–72, in Florence) said that a well-stopped earthen pot put into salt water will fill with potable water, but Porta found that the water which percolated was always salty. Porta describes the preservation of fruits in wine, honey, or salt water, in jars sealed with pitch, or in sawdust;[1] the preparation of artificial wines from fruits and the distillation of an aqua vitæ (whisky) from fermented wheat or barley;[2] the preparation of various kinds of vine-gar;[3] the fortification of weak wine by adding brandy (aqua vitae);[4] and the artificial incubation of eggs in Cairo.[5]

Aqua ardens (alcohol) is made by distilling good, strong, black wine with quicklime, tartar, salt, and sulphur in a chemical glass (vitriis chimistarum organis ut docebimus). The product can be burnt on the hands and does not feel very hot (ardet in manibus detenta, nec comburit multum).[6] The strongest spirit is made by tying parchment over the mouth of the cucurbit, when only alcohol vapour passes through to the condensing head and falls into the receiver. The residue in the receiver is the dead body of the wine (vini cadaver). Distillation in steam on a large scale is described.[7] Highly rectified spirit is Paracelsus's quintessence (quintam essentiam Paracelsi ... aquæ vitæ educere).[8]

Porta devoted much attention to the distillation of 'waters' and oils, 'an invention of later times'.[9] He describes the separation of a distilled oil from the water which comes over with it either in a conical funnel with the orifice stopped with the finger, or in 'a most ingenious' apparatus consisting of a receiver with a swan-neck bent upwards from the bottom, from which the heavier part of the distillate runs.[10] This is probably the first description of the so-called 'Florentine receiver' which was re-invented much later by Homberg and others.[11] He describes the preparation of oils etc. by distillation 'per descensum';[12] a worm-tube (anguineos flexus, 'serpentine') cooled by water;[13] a tall vertical column with a head on the top; a zig-zag column;[14] and a vertical column with three delivery tubes of different heights, which would allow of fractional distillation.[15] All this apparatus was known in Italy before Porta's time.[16]

This section also describes the preparation of magisteries and tinctures,

---

[1] IV, 1–13, pp. 227 f.; mostly from Columella, see Vol. I.   [2] IV, 21, p. 221.
[3] IV, 22, p. 226.   [4] IV, 23, p. 229.   [5] IV, 26, p. 237.
[6] ii, 10, p. 113.   [7] X, 3, p. 412.   [8] X, 13, p. 423.
[9] iii, 1, p. 203 f.; X, 1 f., p. 397 f., with illustrations.   [10] X, 7, p. 411–12.
[11] Gildemeister and Hoffmann, 1928, i, 249 f.   [12] X, 4, 9, 12, pp. 404, 414, 422.
[13] X, 3, p. 403.   [14] X, 8, p. 414.   [15] Hoefer, (1), ii, 106.
[16] Berthelot, *Science et Morale*, 1897, 367; for early reflux apparatus, see Galates, *Chem. Ztg.*, 1910, xxxiv, 619; on pelicans, Kout, *ibid.*, 853, R. J. Forbes, *Short History of the Art of Distillation*, Leiden, 1948.

tincture of gold being extolled but no method given for making it.[1] A clyssus is defined as the extraction of the spirits of every part of a plant united into one common entity; the parts may be distilled in several cucurbits joined to a common head.[2] Porta frequently mentions the matras (*matarazzo*) and retort (*retorto, obtorto*).[3]

A red oil of sulphur made by boiling sulphur in oil of tartar (concentrated potassium carbonate solution), evaporating to dryness and allowing the solid to deliquesce, would be concentrated potassium sulphide solution.[4] Oil of vitriol (oleum vitrioli) is made by distilling vitriol (ferrous sulphate), first calcined in an earthen pot, in a well-coated (multiplici luto loricatam) glass retort (obtortam vitream) by a strong heat (et liquabitur vas); 3 lb. of vitriol give 1 lb. of oil.[5] The preparation of oil of sulphur (oleum sulphuris), usually credited to Libavius (ch. VII), is described:[6] a vessel containing burning sulphur is suspended in a glass bell which is hung over a vessel to catch the drops condensing on the bell from the moist fumes in it:

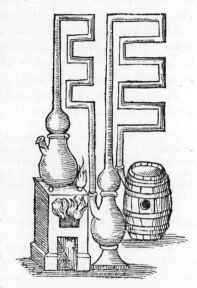

Fig. 2. Still with Columns and
Condensers.

From Porta, *Magia Naturalis*, 1589.

Vas vitreum habeto oris ampli et concavum, in companae formam, ubi luto illeueris, pede ferreo suspendatur filo, inferius autem amplum receptaculum locato, ut è marginibus campanae extillans oleum recipiat, cujus medio terreum, vel ferreum accommodetur vas sulphure conditum: ignem tunc succendito, et dum comburitur, aliud recentius superindatur: nam dum uritur, consumeritur erigeus se fumus, vasisque feriens fundum, humectio exhalationibus corporescit, et reciprocans in oleum coalescit ac inde dilabitur.

Porta recommends the acid so made for use in cleaning and whitening the teeth, which were oftened blackened by taking mercury;[7] this treatment would remove what was left of them. A water or oil of salt, known to very few, is made by strongly heating bricks, quenching them in salt solution, and then heating very strongly (this would be hydrochloric acid):[8]

'Aquam, vel oleum ex sale elicere. A paucis cognitum. Salem mineralem assumito, in obtortam vitream indito, luto triplici loricatam, ac benè exiccatum, & reverberationis furno accommodato, loco vbi optimè, & exquisitè flammæ eluctentur.' The ignited residue is dissolved in water and: 'in liquidum salem ignitos lateres extinguunt, & lateres postea vehementissimo igne distillant, vt in oleo lateritio.'

Water for separation of silver (aqua separationis argenti) which is nitric acid

[1] X, 14, 15, pp. 428–35. [2] X, 18, p. 439.
[3] X, 2, 6, pp. 402, 409; *De Distillatationibus*, 1609, 44, 104 f., 114 (in vas obtortum), 119, 120 and fig. (retortum vas), 129, etc.
[4] X, 19, p. 440. [5] X, 20, p. 443.
[6] iii, 1, p. 205; X, 20, p. 443; *De Distillationibus*, 1609, 116 and fig. [7] IX, 25, p. 391.
[8] X, 20 (De Aqvis Fortibvs), Naples, 1589, 197; unchanged in ed. 8°, Hannover, 1619, 407; in Leyden, 1651, 442, the middle part is altered. The 1589 description is given in the text.

is made by distilling nitre (halinitrum) and alum in a thrice-luted glass retort (vasis triplici luto muniatur) and collected in a large well-luted receiver
(a small one will burst). To clarify it, silver is dissolved in it by heat and
the acid poured off from the residue (silver chloride).[1] Oil of camphor was
made by heating camphor with aqua fortis.[2] A strong water (which would be
aqua regia) obtained by distilling nitre, vitriol, sal ammoniac, and cinnabar
is used for making hair yellow, although it burns it.[3] Porta only just mentions
aqua regia as a solvent for gold.[4]

Porta published a special work on distillation, which is an expansion of the
section in the *Natural Magic*:

(i) Io. Bap. Portae Neapolitani De Distillatione lib. IX. Quibus certa methodo,
multipliciq; artificio, penitioribus naturae arcanis detectis, cuiuslibet mixti in propria
elementa resolutio, perfectè docetur, 4° Romae M. DC. VIII. Ex Typographia Reu.
camerae Apostolicae (BM 528. d. 20), pp. xx, 154, vi (portrait on p. x); dedicated to
Marquis Cesi (founder of the Accademia de' Lincei); preface dated Naples, 20 July
1604.
(ii) De Distillationibus libri IX; sm. 4°, Strassburg, 1609, viii ll., 149 pp., V pp.,
portrait on reverse of title. German tr., Ars distillatoria, 4°, Frankfurt, 1611.[5]

It deals in successive books with the names of the vessels used in the various
processes (fancifully compared with animals and birds) and the degrees of heat;
distillation of waters; oils of flowers, exotic plants, resins, and woods; strong
waters (aqua regia, water or oil of vitriol, oil of sulphur (with figure of apparatus),[6] oil of tartar, oils of mercury, bricks, salt, and talc, the extraction of the
virtues of substances (*aqua vitae essentia* is alcohol),[7] clyssus (with a figure of a
multiple-headed alembic), and expressed oils. In methods of distilling per
descensum by the heat of the sun (per solis calorem), the cucurbit is exposed
to the direct rays of the sun, or to the rays focused by a concave mirror, and
the product collected in a receiver below.[8]

In his *Natural Magic* Porta gives detailed information about poisons, some
of it curiously enough in the part on cookery (aquinariae artis).[9] He mentions
a decoction of belladonna (herba belladona vocata) in wine which, given three
hours before a meal, renders the guests incapable of swallowing (ut assumptos
gulo cibos glutire nequeat), a joke which could easily have fatal results. In the
book on trapping animals (De Acupio),[10] he describes a wolf poison made with
aconite (Aconitum lycoctonum), powdered glass, quicklime and arsenic, made
into pills with honey, which could be used for other purposes than poisoning
wolves. In his book on medical experiments (De medicis experimentis)[11] he
mentions a mixture of hemlock juice (cicutæ succo), hyoscyamus seeds,
mandragora, and opium, with musk to disguise the smell, which is put in a
closed lead box and allowed to ferment for some days; if this is opened for a
short time under the nose of a sleeping person it will cause him to lose his
senses, but he will feel no ill effects on waking (nec doli suspicio). If the dose
is prolonged, however, the subject will lose his reason (eadem plantæ quæ

[1] X, 20, p. 441.   [2] X, 11, p. 421.   [3] IX, 1, p. 364.   [4] X, 14, p. 434; X, 21, p. 442.
[5] Duchesne, summary of book, 216–31.   [6] 1608, 118.   [7] 1608, 131.
[8] 1609, 29–32.   [9] XV, 11 chapters, p. 526 f.   [10] XIV, 13 chapters, p. 501 f.
[11] VIII, 14 chapters, pp. 332–61.

somnum inducunt, si paulo plus propinentur, dementant),[1] and a further dose would presumably have a fatal result.

Food powdered with stramonium or belladonna gives rise to remarkable hallucinations, the persons believing themselves to be animals, some swimming on the ground like fish, others pecking the ground like geese, others eating grass like cattle, etc.[2] In Porta's time, the art of the poisoner flourished in Italy, and a large number of mineral, vegetable and animal poisons were in use. He says in his preface that he had described many hurtful things which could be used harmfully by wicked men, but a desire to benefit posterity prevented him from concealing the most noble secrets of nature, although some of the most magnificent and excellent he had veiled by 'transposing and depressing words' or intentional obscurity, so that they would be 'intelligible only to ingenious readers'. His recipe for cooking and serving a goose alive throws light on the cultured Renaissance society of Porta's time.[3]

Porta's *Natural Magic* contains a number of observations of interest in the history of Physics, e.g. the camera obscura without lens (also attributed to Leonardo da Vinci and others)[4] but probably first described by Ibn al-Haitham (*c.* 965–1039), and the camera obscura with lens,[5] said to have been described by Daniel Barbaro.[6] A supposed description of the magic lantern by Porta[7] is said to be some effect produced by a concave mirror. The optical trick shown on the title-page of the 1651 Leyden edition of the *Magia Naturalis* (completely misinterpreted by the artist in the German translation, 1713) is described in Dee's translation of Euclid (1570):[8] the point of a sword is moved towards a concave mirror, when the real image of the sword appears to issue from the mirror. Fish can be caught by attracting them to the light from a candle in a glass vessel sunk in the water.[9] The observations on magnets contain some interesting material. (Gilbert's *De Magnete* was published twelve years after Porta's book.)[10] Some experiments on the weights of metals in air and water[11] gave inaccurate specific gravities (which Porta did not calculate), the correct figures being given in brackets: gold 14 (19·4), silver 10·4 (10·4), lead 7·75 (11·4), iron 6·3 (6·0), brass 4·3 (8·5), copper 4 (8·9), marble 3·5 (2·7).

Books on Poisons

A great deal of interest was taken in Porta's time in Italy on poisons. Besides his descriptions there is a whole literature on the subject. Burckhardt[12] said that in the time of the Borgias 'the death of any powerful man was seldom or never attributed to natural causes'. They used a white powder which acted at the end of a definite period and was identified with a 'venenum atterminatum' given by the Prince of Salerno to the Cardinal of Aragon; the poison with which the painter Rosso Fiorentino killed himself (1541) was a powerful acid.

[1] VIII, 1, p. 335.   [2] VIII, 2, p. 337.   [3] ii, 13, p. 126; XIV, 9, p. 516.
[4] Poggendorff, (2), 1883, 79.   [5] XVII, 8, p. 591.
[6] *La Practica della Perspettiva*, l. 4°, Venice, 1568, 192; Sotheran *Cat.* 783 (1923), p. 85.
[7] XVII, 6, p. 589.   [8] *Diary of Dr. John Dee*, 1842, 29.   [11] XVIII, 8, p. 630.
[9] XV, 5; 1651, p. 533.   [10] VII, 1–56; 1651, 286–332.
[12] *Civilization of the Renaissance in Italy*, bk. vi, ch. 2; 1944, 277.

Poisoned letters and poisoned furniture were also in use. Lorenz Beheim, prefect of artillery for Caesar Borgia, wrote a recipe for a slow poison, accompanied by a conjuration of the Devil.[1]

The first treatise on poisons to be printed is said[2] to be by Ferdinand Ponzetti,[3] but a work *De Venenis* by Sante Ardoino (Saintes de Ardoynis), finished in 1426, was printed in 1492[4] and was reprinted with Ponzetti's.[5] Ponzetti's work is partly theoretical and somewhat critical, although it accepts the story of the basilisk, which he thought killed by exhalations rather than its glance; it prescribed the bezoar stone (generated from tears shed by stags),[6] powdered emeralds, and crocodile fat.[7] Dead basilisks were reported to have been seen by Mercurialis in a collection of the Emperor Maximilian; and by Encelius (p. 64) whose specimen had been killed by a shepherd in the forest of Luckenwald.[8]

A well-known work on poisons by Jacques Grevin (Clermont Beauvois, 1539—Turin, 1570)[9] includes his French translation of Nikandros, quotes ancient authors, also Agricola, Cardan, and Mattioli, and deals mostly with poisonous animals. If the basilisk is poisonous it is by emanation; some gems may cure if taken internally in powder but not by suspension. Grevin criticised the admiration of the medicinal virtue of antimony which is a poison (Loys de Launay had said it had a malignity because of its affinity with lead but this was removed by chemical treatment) and borax has no virtue in purifying it, nor is its calcination beneficial.[10] Grevin did not deny great virtues in metals and many secrets yet unknown, and approved of the alchemical extraction of oils and quintessences if made by qualified masters.

Albertus Scheligius in his digest of the lectures by Hieronymus Mercurialis at Padua,[11] says wearing arsenic over the heart is beneficial when plague is about and drinking water is helpful to those who have taken arsenic. He gives three methods for detecting poisoned foods at table: sweating of serpent's horn, brass dishes changing colour, and loss of colour of an emerald in a ring.

BACCIUS

Andrea Baccius (or Baccio), of St. Elpidio in the Anconian Marches, was professor of botany in Rome (1567–1600), then physician to Pope Sixtus V, but dissipated his fortune and was pursued by his creditors till he sought

---

[1] Thorndike, v, 472.

[2] Thorndike, v, 472: ch. 21 on 'Poisons, Fascination, and Hydrophobia'.

[3] *Libellus de Venenis*, f°, Rome, 1521 (BM 546. c. 9).

[4] *De Venenis*, f°, Venice, 1492 (BM IC 22657, old 542. k. 11. (2.)).

[5] As *De venenis libri tres*, f°, Basel, 1562, BM 547. k. 14.

[6] An idea of Avenzoar; La Wall, 109.

[7] Thorndike, v, 474.   [8] Thorndike, v, 480; vi, 310.

[9] *Deux Livres des Venins* . . . , 8°, Antwerp, 1567–8, BM 432. b. 16. (1–2); tr. Martius, *De Venenis libri duo*, 8°, Antwerp, 1571, BM 778. d. 13.

[10] *Discours sur les vertus et facultez de l'antimoine, contre ce qu'en a escrit maistre Loys de Launay*, 8°, Paris, 1566 (not seen); *Le second Discours sur les vertus et facultez de l'antimoine*, 8°, Paris, n.d. [1567] (BM 546. b. 9); Chassang, NBG, 1858, xxii, 1; in the second work (1567) Grevin called de Launay an 'empirique'.

[11] *De venenis et morbis venenosis . . . ex voce excellentissimi Hieronymi Mercurialis . . . in libros duos digesti opera Alberti Scheligii Vbarschauiensis*, Venice, 1584 (BM 7509. h. 22), also eds. of 1601, 1618; Thorndike, v, 479.

asylum with Cardinal Ascagnio Colonna.[1] He lectured on poisons in Rome in 1585 and wrote a book on them,[2] saying that the unicorn's horn sweats when near poison, and a candle in a holder of a vulture's foot is extinguished. The gem aëtites prevents one from swallowing poisoned food. Baccius also wrote on gems (he is quoted by Boetius de Boot, see p. 101), the unicorn, the beast alce, etc., in a superstitious manner,[3] also on wines,[4] but his most interesting work from our point of view is that on mineral waters and baths, which went through several editions.[5] Following ancient authors, he supposed that mineral waters contain sulphur, salts, alum, and metals.[6] He treats of saline waters,[7] waters containing soda (de salnitratis aquis),[8] alum,[9] vitriols (de atramentosis aquis),[10] bitumen[11] and petroleum (petroleum Mutinense),[12] various mineral waters,[13] including chalybeate waters, also those supposed to contain lead and tin,[14] gold,[15] Belgian waters containing zinc (ex cadmia naturali),[16] and chrysocolla and ochre.[17] The sections on acid waters[18] include material from de Heer's *Spadecrene* (see ch. VI).

BOOKS OF SECRETS

Antoine Mizauld (Mizaldus) (Montluçon, Bourbonnais *c.* 1510–Paris 1578), physician and astrologer, a friend of Oronce Fine and physician of Marguerite de Valois, was esteemed in his time;[1] he wrote many works:

(1) Arcanorum naturae sylvula, 1555 (2 books); (2) De arcanis naturae libelli quatuor, 16°, 1558 (4 books), BM 974. a. 23; (3) Centuriae novem rerum memorabilium utilium et iucundorum, 8° Paris, 1566; enlarged as Memorabilium utiliu ac iucundorum centuriæ novem in aphorismos arcanorum . . . digestae, 8°, Paris, 1567 (BM 1170. c. 1. (1.)); Memorabilium aliquot naturæ arcanorum sylvula . . . libellus duobus complectens, 12°, Paris, 1554 (BM 8460. aa. 16. (3.), 1555?; De arcanis naturæ libelli quatuor, Paris, 1558 (BM 974. a. 23); Memorabilivm, sive Arcanorvm omnis generis, per Aphorismos digestorum, Centuriæ IX. Et, Democritvs Abderita, De rebus Naturalibus & Mysticis. Cum Synesii, et Pelagii Commentarijs. Interprete . . . Dominico Pizimentio Vibonensi, 12°, Cologne, Birckmann, 1572, 1573 (BM 1169. a. 4), 1574; Centuriæ IX. Memorabilium, Vtilium, ac Iucondorum in Aphorismos Arcanorum omnis generis. . . . Accessit his Appendix nonnullorum

---

[1] NBU, 1853, iv, 44; Thorndike, v, 484; vi, 315.

[2] *De Venenis et Antidotis* προλεγομενα, 4°, Rome, 1586 (BM 957. l. 23); NBU gives 4°, Rome, 1590.

[3] *Le XII pietre pretiose, le quali per ordine di Dio nulla santa legge, adornauano i vestimenti del sommo Sacerdote . . . Discorso dell' alicorno, e delle sue singolarissime virtù. Et della gran bestia detta alce da gli antichi,* 4°, Rome, 1587 (BM 956. g. 2); tr. by Gabelchover, with notes, *De gemmis et lapidibus pretiosis,* 8°, Frankfurt, 1603 (BM 987. b. 20); on unicorns and fabulous beasts, *De monocerote seu vnicornu, eiusque admirandis viribus et vsu, tractatus . . . a Wolfgango Gabelchouer . . . latine redditus . . . accessit alicus, de magna bestia, ab antiquis alce, Germanis Ellend vocato, eiusque vngulæ . . . viribus et vsu libellus,* 8°, Stuttgart, Marcus Fuersterus, 1598 (BM 976. e. 20), viii ll. 131, 39 pp. viii ll. index; *L'Alicorno. Discorso . . . nel quale si tratta della natura dell' alicorno, & delle sue virtu, excellentissime,* 4°, Florence, 1582 (BM 976. e. 19. (1.)).

[4] *De Naturali Vinorum Historia,* f°, Rome, 1596.

[5] *De Thermis Libri Septem,* f°, Venice, 1571 (BM 33. f. 5), 1588 (BM 456. f. 13); f°, Basel, 1622 (BM 34. f. 5); *De Thermis Andreæ Baccii Elpidiani . . . libri septem . . . accessit nunc liber octavus. De nova Methodo Thermarum explorandarum . . . editio novissima,* f° in 6's, Padua, Sumptibus Jo. Baptistæ Conzatti, 1711 (with index; BM 778. i. 18; the ed. quoted).

[6] 1711, 30 f.	[7] *Ib.,* 154 f.	[8] *Ib.,* 164.	[9] *Ib.,* 166.
[10] *Ib.,* 178.	[11] *Ib.,* 180.	[12] *Ib.,* 183.	[13] *Ib.,* 187f.
[14] *Ib.,* 204 f.	[15] *Ib.,* 207.	[16] *Ib.,* 216.	[17] *Ib.,* 217 f.

[18] *Ib.,* 220 f., 338 f.

Secretorum, Experimentorum, Antidotorumque . . . Seorsum excusa, Harmonia cælestium corporum & humanorum, dialogis vndecim Astronomice & Medice . . . Item Memorabilium aliquot naturæ Arcanorum Syluula . . . libellis II. complectens, 16°, Frankfurt, Wecheli, 1592 (BM 1169. a. 9. (1–3)), 1613 (BM 1169. a. 11. (1–3)); Mizaldus Redivivus, sive, Centuriæ 12 Memorabilium, 12°, Nürnberg, 1681 (BM 1169. a. 21); (4) Alexikepus, seu Auxiliaris hortus, 8°, Paris, 1565 (BM 988. e. 9); 1574 (BM 957. i. 20); tr. by La Caille as Le Jardin Medicinal enrichi de plusieurs et divers Remèdes et Secrets, 8°, Paris, 1578 (462 pp.); (5) Secrets de la Lune, 8°, Paris, 1571 (BM 718. d. 27. (1.)) (deals with the correspondence of the sun and moon with animals, stones, plants, etc.).[1]

Mizauld is one of the authors cited by Aldrovandi[2] as saying that horses' hoofs facilitate the fusion of copper, and oil of tartar removes spots from the face or from iron.

Nicolaus Cabeus, a Jesuit, in his commentary on Aristotle's *Meteorologica*[3] thought the fourth book should come after the second book on *Generation and Corruption* (see Vol. I); he dealt with the three alchemical principles.[4]

Alexis of Piedmont, a cleric of the Gesuati (not to be confused with the later Jesuits)[5] who was perhaps born about 1471, wrote a collection of secrets said to have been first published in Venice in 1555.[6] According to Ferguson, the preface by Sansovino in Jeronimo Ruscelli's *Secreti Nuovi* (Venice, 1567) says the book was given by Ruscelli to the press under the name Donno Alessio of Piedmont, but Ferguson did not think the book was by Ruscelli. The title of this book (not available to me) is given by Thorndike as: Girolamo [or Jeronimo] Ruscelli, *Secreti nuovi di marvigliosa virtu I quali continouando e quelli di Donno Alessio cognomine finto del detto Ruscelli*, Venice, 1567, but he does not say that he had seen it. Ruscelli (Viterbo, *c.* 1520?–Venice, 1566), born in poor circumstances, was a linguist, poet, and historian, who founded an academy (dello Sdegno) in Rome, then went to Venice as reader for the printer Valgrisio.[7]

The second edition of the first part (Ferguson thought it was the first edition — he was often wrong in this way) of Alexis appeared in 1557.[8] The second part appeared in 1558,[9] the third in 1559,[10] and the three together in 1563.[11] The French translation by Christofle Landré appeared in 1557,[12] the English (from the French) by William Ward in 1558,[13] the German by Wecker

[1] NBG, 1861, xxxv, 708; Thorndike, vi, 216.
[2] *Musæum Metallicum*, Bologna, 1648, 107, 817.   [3] 4 vols. f°, Rome, 1646.
[4] Thorndike, vii, 422.
[5] Eastlake, *Materials for a History of Oil Painting*, 1847, 6 f.
[6] Darmstaedter, (1), 1926, 180 (copy in Munich Staats-Bibliothek); Beckmann, (1), i, 475; Ferguson, i, 22; *id.*, *Proc. Roy. Soc. Med.*, 1930, xxiv, 225–46; *id.*, *Isis*, 1931, xvi, 492; 1933, xviii, 459; Thorndike, vi, 215; in a catalogue of Davis and Orioli now lost (*c.* 1925) an ed. of Rome, 1540, was given; Hendrie, *Theophilus*, 1847, pp. xxxvi, 168; Duveen, 15–17; Ferguson published many inaccessible papers on books of secrets, e.g. *Books of Secrets*, 1914 (36 pp.; slight); *Some Early Treatises on Technological Chemistry*, and Supplements, read to the Phil. Soc., Glasgow, 1886–1916 (CUL 8340. c. 165).
[7] NBG, 1863, xlii, 913.
[8] *De' Secreti del reuerendo donno Alessio Piemontese*, 4°, Venice, 1557 (BM 42. f. 19); also 4° (and 8°?), Lucca, 1557 (Hendrie).
[9] 8°, Milan, 1558.   [10] 8°, Milan, 1559.   [11] 8°, Venice, 1563, also 1674.
[12] *Les Secrets de reueren signeur Alexis Piemontis, Traduit d'Italien en François*, 4°, Antwerp, Plantin, 1557, 1559; 16°, Paris, 1573; 8°, Rouen, 1691.
[13] *The Secretes of the Reuerende Maister [Mayster] Alexis of Piedmont*, 4°, London, 1558–59, 1562–66, 1568–6–9, 1580–78; 1615–4.

in 1575,[1] and the Latin by Wecker in 1560.[2] The above editions are in the British Museum, but many others are listed.[3] Later editions of the work contain a fourth part, described in the English translation (1569) as 'A Book conteining six hundred foure score and odd experienced Medicines'.

Johann Jacob Wecker (Basel 1528–Colmar 1586) was professor of logic (1557) and Latin (1560) in Basel, then qualified in medicine and in 1566 went as town physician to Colmar.[4] His book of secrets, *De Secretis Libri XVII*, 8°, Basel, 1582, went through many editions (the last in 1753) and translations. He also wrote antidotaries: *Antidotarivm Speciale*, 4°, Basel, 1577; *Antidotarium Generale et Speciale*, 4°, Basel, 1595, 1601,[5] 1617, and other editions and translations. Book iii[6] deals with chemical operations and distillation, with many figures of apparatus.

Leonardo Fioravanti (Bologna; ? –4 September 1588), a physician who sailed to Africa with the Spanish fleet, then settled in Bologna, receiving a doctor's degree and the title of count, invented a balsam supposed to cure poisoning by arsenic, the preparation of which he described.[7] Besides other works he wrote on caprices of medicine,[8] the treasure of human life,[9] and a compendium of secrets[10] which (and translations) appeared in several editions, some as late as 1647. He is quoted as 'Empyricus Venetus' by Aldrovandi[11] for the medical use of lapis lazuli and sapphires. His *Capricci* has woodcuts of distilling apparatus. The fourth book of the *Tesoro* deals with the medical uses of the philosophers' stone,[12] secrets and magistery of antimony,[13] a discourse on mercury and its great use in the *galliche infermità*,[14] l'alume di rocca,[15] alum of tartar (?, alume di feccia),[16] distillation of vinegar in the alembic (per lambicco),[17] the preparation of iron amalgam (malgama di marti) by boiling iron, mercury, tartar, and vitriol with rain water, sale elebrot and armoniaco;[18] a 'very beautiful secret of the moon', used for 'augmenting' silver and made by fusing orpiment, arsenic, iron filings, and tartar,[19] and 'recetta rubicondissima alchimica'.[20] Fioravanti was one of the few followers of Paracelsus in Italy.

Signora Isabella Cortese compiled a collection of mineral, medical, artificial, alchemical, and cosmetical recipes, dedicated to the Archdeacon of Ragusa.[21]

---

[1] *Artzney Buch . . . Auss Welscher vnd Lateinischer Sprache in Teutsch gebracht . . .*, Basel, 1575.

[2] *Alexii Pedemontani de secretis libri*, 8°, Basel, 1560.

[3] Ferguson said there were 69 to the date 1691. A French translation not listed by Ferguson (who gives Rouen 1614, 1627, and 1691) in my possession is that of Rouen, 8°, Iacqves Caillove, 1661, 705 pp. and index, in two parts.

[4] Jöcher, iv, 1839; Ferguson, ii, 533.   [5] Duveen, 612.   [6] 1617, 117 f.

[7] Gmelin, (1), i, 301; Sprengel, (1), iii, 369; Hoefer, (1), ii, 127; NBG, 1856, xvii, 722; Ferguson, i, 276 (more favourable); Thorndike, vi, 217.

[8] *Capprici Medicinale*, 8°, Venice, 1561 (Thorndike; BM has 1565, 1568, 1582).

[9] *Il Tesoro della Vita Humana*, 8°, Venice, 1570 (BM 1170. d. 4) and 1582 (portr.; the ed. quoted).

[10] *Del Compendio dei Secreti rationali intorno della Medicina, Cirurgia et Alchimia libri cinque*, 8°, Venice, 1564 (BM).

[11] *Musæum Metallicum*, f°, Bologna, 1648, 871, 973.   [12] Ch. 2, f. 272.

[13] Ch. 19, f. 283.   [14] Ch. 20, f. 283 v.   [15] Ch. 22, f. 284 v.   [16] Ch. 26, f. 286.

[17] Ch. 37, f. 292.   [18] Ch. 89, f. 317.   [19] Ch. 90, f. 318.   [20] Ch. 91, f. 318 v.

[21] *I Secreti de la Signora Isabella Cortese . . . appartenenti a ogni gran Signora*, 8°, Venice, 1561, viii ll., 207 pp. (BM 1038. c. 4. (2.) and other eds. and trs. (German, 1592, 1596); Thorndike, vi, 218; Ferguson, i, 179.

She says man surpasses nature with oil of scorpions, potable gold, etc., and includes ten precepts in alchemy of Chirico, abbot of Cologne, who warns against reading Geber, Arnald of Villanova, and Lull.

Physicians discussed the question as to whether certain things acted in an occult manner or 'from a property of their whole substance'. Giovanni Francesco Olmo (Ulmus) of Brescia treated fully of this.[1] He denied the sweating of unicorn's horn in presence of poison, but prescribed powdered human skull for epilepsy.

Tommaso da Ravenna (Thomas Janothus)[2] discussed the virtues of stones and herbs, demons of the air, holding the hand in fire without injury, a recipe for infernal fire revealed to Paracelsus by a demon of the sphere of fire, and other 'marvellous secrets of nature'.

Gerónimo Cortés of Valencia[3] gave recipes for aqua ardens, making sea water drinkable, vinegar, squeezing an egg into a bottle, invisible ink, kindling fire in water, etc.

Hippolitus Obicius of Ferrara,[4] an opponent of Sanctorius (p. 442), included chemistry (*Chemica ars*) as a branch of natural magic, believed in occult virtues, cited Wecker and Levinus among recent authors, and wrote a treatise (*Iatrostronomicon*) on astrological medicine.

Giovambatista Birelli of Siena wrote a text-book on alchemy[5] dedicated to Cosmo di Medici. This includes a 'life of Hermes' with a portrait,[6] and deals with metals, gems, chemical apparatus and operations, lutes, pigments, varnishes, dyes, perfumes, mineral acids, salts, etc., with curious woodcuts. Birelli believed in transmutation, but his book contains many practical processes, derived from old sources and workshop secrets. There are some crude illustrations of apparatus adapted from the *Alchemiæ Gebri Arabis* (Nürnberg, 1545), and of the plants lunaria or borissa (with human-headed flowers) and celidonia.[7] There are descriptions of a tower furnace,[8] cupellation,[9] the seven planetary metals,[10] bismuth (marcasite),[11] aqua vitae,[12] oil of gold (apparently gold chloride),[13] and a reverberatory furnace with a dome.[14]

An author formerly much quoted but now forgotten is Ludovicus Coelius

---

[1] *De iis quæ in medicina agunt ex totius substantiæ proprietate*, 8°, Augustæ, 1576 (BM 547. d. 27. (1.)); *De occultis in re medica proprietatibus libri quatuor*, Brescia, 1597 (BM 543. b. 6. (1.)); Thorndike, vi, 230.

[2] *Idea del Giardino del Mondo ove oltre molti secreti marvigliosi di natura*, sm. 4°, Venice, 1593 (BM 43. d. 31. (2.)); Thorndike, vi, 428.

[3] *Phisonomia y varios secretos de naturaleza*, Cordova, 1601; Zaragoza, 1603; enlarged, Tarragona, 1609 (120 ll.) (BM 7383. f. 8, the BM has eds. of Alcala, 1612; Madrid, 1675; Barcelona, 1681, 1750 (?); Paris, 1850, 1958); Thorndike, vi, 166, 428, gives Tarragona, 1610, 1614; for his mathematical works see Jöcher, i, 2119.

[4] *De nobilitate medici contra illius obtrectatores dialogus triparitus*, Venice, 1605 (BM), Mainz, 1619; Thorndike, vi, 429; Jöcher, iii, 1008.

[5] *Opere. Tomo primo. Nell qual si tratta dell' Alchimia . . . con la vita d'Hermete*, 4°, Florence, 1601; at the end he says: 'Io, Giouambatista di Giuseppe Birelli Senese ho composto dett' Opera d'Alchimia a benefizio vniuersale'; German tr. by Peter Uffenbach, *Alchimia Nova. Das ist Die Güldene Kunst Oder Aller Künsten Gebärerin*, 4°, Frankfurt, 1603; Gmelin, (1), i, 502, mentions Italian eds. of 1602 and 1661, and Ferguson, i, 107, a reissue of the German tr., 1654, and a Latin tr., Copenhagen, 1654.

[6] 1601, p. 551; 1603, pp. 292, 725. [7] 1601, pp. 215–17. [8] Bk. i, c. 33.
[9] Bk. i, c. 47. [10] Bk. i, c. 55. [11] Bk. i, c. 103; it gives no information about it.
[12] Bk. ii, c. 11. [13] Bk. ii, cc. 25–9. [14] Bk. iii, c. 2.

Rhodiginus (Ludovico Ricchieri or Richerius) (Rovigo 1450–Padua 1523).[1]
He forged some fragments of Apuleius,[2] and is said to have derived the word
'archemia' (an alternative to alchemia) from ἀργυρίον χημεία.[3]

[1] *Lectionum Antiquarum Libri XVI*, f°, Basel, Frobenius, 1517, BM 632. l. 5; *Lectionum Antiquarum libri XXX recogniti ab auctore atque locupletati ut tertia plus parte auctoris sint redditi*, f°, Basel, 1542, BM C. 77. e. 5; f°, Frankfurt, 1599, 1666; the last 14 books were added in 1542 by Camillus Richerius and I. M. Goretti; Jöcher, iii, 2053.

[2] Schwabe, in Pauly and Wissowa, *Real-Encyclopädie der classischen Altertumswissenschaft*, ii, 258.

[3] Kopp, (2), i, 81.

CHAPTER II

TECHNOLOGICAL TREATISES

BIRINGUCCIO

Of the private life of Vanoccio (or Vanuccio) Biringuccio (Siena 1480–
Rome 1538/9) very little is known. As a young man he entered the service of
the Tyrant of Siena, Pandolfo Petrucci, with whose varying fortunes he
periodically rose and sank. Biringuccio's extensive knowledge of metallurgy
and technology, improved by a visit to Germany, included such politically
useful branches as gun casting, the manufacture of gunpowder, and making
false coin. In later life he served the Duke of Parma, Duke Alphonso I of
Ferrara, and the Republic of Venice, and he seems to have had considerable
military skill. He died in the service of the Pope as director of the arsenal.[1]
His richly illustrated work was first published in 1540:[2]

De la Pirotechnia. Libri. X. Dove Ampiamente si tratta non solo di ogni sorte &
diuersita di Miniere, ma anchora quanto si ricerca intorno à la prattica di quelle cose di
quel che si appartiene à l'arte de la fusione ouer gitto de metalli come d'ogni altra
cosa simile à questa. Composti per il. S. Vanoccio Biringuccio Sennese. Con Priuilegio
Apostolico & de la Cesarea Maesta & del Illustriss. Senato Veneto. MDXL. (1540), 8°
(always, like the following, described as sm. 4°) viii ll., 168 ff. Colophon: Stampata
in Venetia per Venturino Rossinello.

2 ed.: Pirotechnia. Li dieci libri della Pirotechnia. Nelliquali si tratta non solo
la diuersita delle minere, ma ancho quanto si ricerca alla prattica di esse: ẽ di
quanto s'appartiene all'arte della fusione ouer getto de metalli, e d'ogni altra
cosa a questa somigliante. Composti per il S. Vannuccio Biringuccio, nobile
Senese...8°, MDL (1550) viii ll., 168 ff., i l. At end: In Vinegia, per Giouan
Padoano, i l. engr.

Later eds. are 3 ed., Venice, 1558–9 (1558 on title); 4 ed., Venice, 1559 (nvovamente
corretta et ristampata), 5 ed. Bologna, 1678. French translation (inexact) by J. Vincent,
La Pyrotechnie ov Art dv Fev, 4°, Paris, 1556, 1572, Rouen, 1627. The section on 'The
generation of metals and mines' is translated in Rychard Eden, The Decades of the
Newe Worlde, 4°, London, 1555, ff. 326 v.–341 v.; the section on gun casting in: Traité
de la fabrication des bouches à feu de bronze au XVIe Siècle en Italie ... Traduit de
l'Italien par Rieffel, Paris, 1836 (tr. of extracts from Books V–VII and notes on Biringuccio). German translation by O. Johannsen: Pirotechnia. Ein Lehrbuch der chemisch-
metallurgischen Technologie und des Artilleriewesens aus dem 16 Jahrhundert, übersetzt und erläutert, Brunswick, 1925 (xvi, 544 pp., 86 illust.). English translation, with
notes by C. S. Smith and M. T. Gnudi: The Pirotechnia of Vannoccio Biringuccio,
New York, The American Institute of Mining and Metallurgical Engineers, 1942.

[1] McKie, Nature, 1949, clxiii, 627.
[2] I. Guareschi, Luigi F. Marsigli ... con appendice sur Vannoccio Biringucci, 4°, Turin, 1915
(medallion portrait of Biringuccio, p. 33); O. Johannsen, Biringuccio und seine Pirotechnia, in
Beiträge zur Geschichte der Technik und Industrie, 1926, xvi, 153–61; A Mieli, Isis, 1914, ii,
90–9; Zietz, J. Chem. Educ., 1952, xxix, 507; a new edition of the Pirotechnia begun by A.
Mieli, Bari. 1914, was not completed.

Several illustrations from Biringuccio were reproduced by Zacharias a Puteo.[1] Hoefer[2] said 'Biringuccio has not the classical erudition of Agricola; he is little acquainted with antiquity. But he has good sense and sagacity and is concerned to combat the pretensions of the alchemists'.

The book is essentially practical; it covers the whole field of metallurgy and is the first printed work to do this, but it deals also with applied chemistry, gunpowder, military arts, and fireworks. Theory is not wholly neglected but plays only a minor part. Like Agricola, Biringuccio is severely but unfairly critical of Albertus Magnus. He was acquainted with Agricola's *Bermannus* (1530) but this contains very little relevant material.

The *Pirotechnia* describes and pictures reverberatory furnaces,[3] describes the liquation of silver from copper by means of lead,[4] and has important descriptions of bell casting and cannon founding.[5] Biringuccio is named by Agricola (*De Re Metallica*, 1556) as one of his sources.[6] Biringuccio regarded metals as compound bodies formed from the four elements by fermentation and decoction; he does not use the theory that metals are formed from mercury and sulphur.[7] He condemned alchemy.[8] He was one of the first to consider the fact that lead increases in the fire by 8 to 10 per cent of its weight, which seemed to him wonderful since the nature of fire is to consume substances; his explanation[9] was as follows:

... ogni graue tende al centro, & ogni corpo quanto e piu denso piu e nella sua spetie graue. Et di questa tal composition di piombo essendoli leuato dal fuocho come a metallo mal misto, quelle parti aquee & aeree & richiuso ogni sua porosita naturale in laquale soleua entrare laere, quale per sua natura & potentia lo teneua in certa leggerezza suspeoo nela sua regione che essendo cosi condotto recascha tutto come cosa abbandonata & morta in se medesimo, & cosi viene a restare piu nela sua ponderosita, come ancho el semigliante si dimostra aduenire a vn corpo de vno animal morto, qual con effetto piu assai pesa che viuo.

... every heavy body tends to the centre, and every body increases in specific gravity as it becomes more compact. And of this composition of lead, when the watery and aerial parts have been removed by the fire, like badly mixed metal, and all its natural pores have closed up, in which the air was wont to enter, which by its nature and power held it in some lightness when the body is suspended in it, and when this air has been thus driven forth, the whole falls like a thing left to itself and altogether dead and so comes to be greater in weight, as also the like is shown to occur in a dead animal body, which indeed weighs much more than when alive.

The two theories given by Biringuccio from some unknown source (perhaps Leonardo da Vinci) are separately advocated by Cardan (1550) and Scaliger (1557), to whom they are commonly attributed (p. 13).

The Prologue of the *Pirotechnia* deals with the signs of the occurrence of minerals, among which is abundance of water (since metals are formed from water) and tests for minerals by evaporating the water, tasting the residue and

[1] *Officina Chymica Fornacium, Vasorum, Ac Instrumentorum ad Destillationem pertinentium*, 4°, Venice, Ad Bibliothecam Leonis Aurati, 1611 (134 woodcuts), BM (with two other works by Puteo); Duveen, 489.
[2] (1), ii, 51.   [3] 1540, 51 *v*, 102 *v*.   [4] 1540, 54 *v*.   [5] 1540, 74 *v*–118 *v*.
[6] Wiegleb, (1), 165; Partington, *Chem. and Ind.*, 1935, liv, 490; *Isis*, 1935, xxiv, 121; (4) 117, 173, 316; Lippmann, (1), i, 598; (3), i, 136; ii, 202.
[7] 1540, 1 (there are 8 unpaged leaves first).
[8] 1540, 5 f.: vna volonta vana, & vn pensiero imaginato impossibile.
[9] Bk. i, ch. 4; 1540, 14 *v*; the text of the last ed., 1678, 53, differs in spelling and punctuation; the punctuation in the French tr. is inaccurate; Partington and McKie, *Ann. Sci.*, 1937, ii, 363.

subjecting it to the 'ordinary assay by fire'. Book I deals with gold, silver, copper, lead, tin, iron, steel (which he thought was very pure iron) and brass (*ottone*; *orchal* in the French translation), made in Flanders, Cologne, Paris and Milan from copper and calamine (*giallamina*). Biringuccio does not mention zinc or bismuth, although he mentions[1] Agricola, the later editions of whose *Bermannus* mention both (pp. 49, 51).

Biringuccio in his section on gold refers to its medical uses. It can be extracted by amalgamation, the mercury in the amalgam being pressed out through leather and the gold purified by melting with borax, saltpetre (sal nitro) or black soap. He has a long disquisition on alchemy; he disbelieves in it and does not think transmutation was or ever will be effected (non solamente non credo che sene trovi, ma che alcun mai con verita ne vedesse anchor che molti dhaverne veduto dichino; in the French transl.: non seulement ie ne croy pas qu'on en trouve, mais qu'il n'y eust homme iamais qui en veist.). Some silver ores contain copper, iron, arsenic and mercury.[2] Copper is hot and dry.[3] Tin foil is thinner than paper.[4]

Biringuccio gives an important account of the manufacture of steel (acciaro) in Brescia. It is made by fusing cast iron with marble dust or other fusible stones, which purify the iron (il marmo pesto, o altre pietre fusibili per lequali si purga) on a hearth composed of clay and charcoal, and putting into the molten cast iron solid lumps of 30–40 lb. of 'the same metal', which are turned round regularly until they become pasty. They are then cut up and the pieces returned to the bath for the same treatment until they are converted into steel.[5] This process consists in immersing masses of wrought iron in a bath of molten cast iron containing excess of carbon from the charcoal used in melting. Agricola copied the description almost word for word (p. 52). An earlier German work, *Von Stahel und Eysen*, printed by Cammerlander, Strassburg, 1539, gives recipes for hardening and tempering steel similar to those in Theophilus (Vol. I).[6]

The semi-minerals (mezzi minerali) described in Book II are mercury, sulphur, antimony, marcasites (golden and silvery pyrites, from which no metal is obtainable; Agricola knew that pyrites contain a metal; see p. 48), vitriols (Cyprian, Babylonian, Roman, and German), alum; arsenic, orpiment, and realgar; common salt, saltpetre, sal ammoniac, and sal alkali (soda); calamine (giallamina), zaffre (zaffara),[7] and manganese (*sic*); magnet (calamita); ochre, bole, emery, and borax (borrace); azure (lazzuro) and green azure (malachite); rock crystal (cristallo) and various gems (on which Biringuccio promised to write a separate treatise); glass (with a fair account of its manufacture, including its decolorisation with pyrolusite), lead and tin enamels, and counterfeit gems.

Mercury (argento vivo) is obtained by distillation, since it flies away from

---

[1] Bk. I, ch. ii   [2] Bk. I, ch. ii.   [3] Bk. I, ch. iii.
[4] Bk. I, ch. v: plus subtil que papier, French tr., 42.
[5] Bk. I, ch. vii; 1540, 18; Percy, *Metallurgy of Iron and Steel*, 1864, 807, 879.
[6] Williams, *Technical Studies in the Field of the Fine Arts*, Fogg Museum of Art, Harvard Univ., 1935, iv, 63–92, tr.
[7] H. C. and L. H. Hoover, tr. Agricola *De Re Metallica*, 1912, 112, say Biringuccio was the first to mention zaffre (see 51).

its enemy fire. Biringuccio gives three processes of extraction: (i) burning the ore (cinnabar) in a small furnace and condensing the vapour in a chamber containing green branches; (ii) heating the ore in a large pot covered with another; (iii) (he was told) distilling in a pot covered with a bell with a spout (an alembic; he gives a figure). Mixed with sal ammoniac and distilled it forms a white sublimate like snow but corrosive and a deadly poison; distilled with sulphur it forms cinnabar.

Sulphur is purified by subliming native sulphur in two pots with short necks with a common receiver. The melted sulphur in the receiver is allowed to solidify to a cake or poured into moulds of cane, wood, or terra-cotta (to make roll sulphur). Very pure crystals of sulphur are found native and this kind is called 'live sulphur (solfo vivo)'. Sulphur is used for bleaching wax and preparing an oil of great virtue, hot and drying (caldo e molto disecchativo) — sulphuric acid (see p. 24). Antimony (antimonio, i.e. the native sulphide, stibnite), found in Italy and also imported to Venice from Germany, gives a metal which is silver-white but as brittle as glass. The alchemists extract from stibnite a blood-red oil said to give silver the colour of gold.

Alum (alume di Roccha — Biringuccio says the origin of the name is unknown but it is probably derived from the Arabic name for Edessa, al-Ruhā') — was made at Tolfa from an earth (alunite, $K_2SO_4, 3 Al_2 (SO_4)(OH)_4$)[1] which was roasted for ten to twelve hours, but not too much, since fire consumes its virtue. The pieces were then stacked like stones in a wall, and the heap sprinkled with water night and morning and three times a day. It was then boiled with water in cauldrons and the solution crystallised in oak vats. This process was introduced by John de Castro from Constantinople and Smyrna after the Turkish conquest (1453).[2]

Biringuccio clearly distinguishes soda (nitrum) from saltpetre (sal nitri). He describes the formation of saltpetre on walls and in caves[3] and its extraction from manurial soil of nitre beds,[4] this being lixiviated and filtered. The solution is purified by boiling with a lye of quicklime and wood ashes (which would precipitate deliquescent calcium salts) and clarified with alum before crystallising. Another method of purification is the addition of a little sulphur to the fused salt (when the potassium sulphate formed would precipitate the deliquescent calcium nitrate as sulphate on recrystallisation).[5]

A work on saltpetre by Guillain (1625) is mentioned by Gobet[6] and a description of making saltpetre was given by Thomas Henshaw.[7] A work on saltpetre[8] was composed by William Clarke (Swainswyke near Bath c.

[1] Roscoe and Schorlemmer, Treatise on Chemistry, 1923, ii, 751.
[2] Pii secundi Pontificis Max. Commentarii Rervm Memorabilivm, f°, Frankfurt, 1614, bk. vii, p. 185; G. Zippel, L'allume di Tolfa e suo commercio, in Arch. della R. Soc. Rom. di Storia Patria, 1907, xxx, 5; Mercati, Metallotheca, f°, Rome, 1717, 53, 79, and plate; Patterson, Ind. Eng. Chem., 1926, xviii, 634; C. Singer, The Earliest Chemical Industry, 1948, 193 f.
[3] Bk. ii, ch. 8.   [4] Bk. x, ch. 1.
[5] Partington, (4), 175, 316.
[6] 1779, ii, 900.
[7] In Sprat, The History of the Royal-Society, 4°, 1667, 260.
[8] The Natural History of Nitre: or, A Philosophical Discourse of the Nature, Generation, Place, and Artificial Extraction of Nitre, with its Vertues and Uses, sm. 8°, London (E. Oats), 1670.

1640–Stepney 24 April 1684)[1] and a treatise by Günther Christoph Schelhamer (Jena, 1649–Kiel, 1716).[2]

Biringuccio has a long chapter on gunpowder (polvara),[3] giving various compositions from saltpetre, sulphur, and charcoal (heavy guns 3 : 1 : 2, medium guns 5 : 1 : $1\frac{1}{2}$, arquebuses and pistols 10 : 1 : 1 or $13\frac{1}{2}$: $1\frac{1}{2}$: 2). In grinding, it is moistened with ordinary water, vinegar or spirit of wine being useless. Noiseless powder is a lie. Sir Thomas Browne[4] says he tried adding mercury and sal ammoniac (1 oz. to 1 lb. of nitre), or opium, and found them ineffective; he adds that Porta had specified a mixture of borax and butter (see p. 20).

Book III of Biringuccio deals with the preparation of ores for smelting and with assaying. It describes the separation of lead from copper by liquation and of gold and silver from other metals by cupellation (con la coppella), the fused metal in the large cupel being blown by large bellows. It also describes how to make small cupels of bone ash in moulds, and the forms of furnaces, and gives a detailed account of charcoal burning both in meiler and in pits.[5]

Book IV[6] deals with the separation of gold and silver. It describes in considerable detail the preparation of nitric acid (acqua acuta) from a mixture of equal parts of saltpetre and pure alum with one eighth the total weight of sand, calcined flints (?) or brickdust (tutto o mancho di rena, o de calcincinacci, o di matton pesti) filled into a luted glass vessel (boccie). The head (capello) was then luted on with a lute of ashes and white of egg, and the nose of the alembic (al naso del lambiccho) luted to the receiver (recipiente). The furnace, the construction of which is accurately described, was fired with wood and charcoal. The distillation was continued for an hour after the water (acid) had ceased to come over and the receiver had cooled. The receiver was then well cooled with a wet cloth and the luting broken.

The acid was purified (from chlorine, which would dissolve gold) by adding a little silver, which it 'turns into water', and decanting from the white precipitate (silver chloride). The gold-silver alloy is treated with the acid, when the silver dissolves and the gold deposits as a black powder (renella negra). The silver is best recovered from the clear liquor by boiling to dryness and heating the residue to redness, when the silver is left and is purified by melting with borax, nitre or black soap.[7] The purification of gold by fusion with stibnite is also described. There is a good description of the cementation process by heating the laminated metal with common salt and brickdust for purifying gold (modo de cimentare loro) from silver and base metals, which is perhaps the earliest full description of the process.[8]

Book V is on alloys (de leghe) and Book VI deals with casting (del arte del

---

[1] Ferguson, i, 161, says a tract on nitre was published by Sir Thomas Chaloner, junr., *A Shorte Discourse of the most rare and excellent Vertue of Nitre*, sm. 4°, London, 1584, ff. ii, 22 (BM 778. e. 56).

[2] *De Nitro cum Veterum tum Nostro Commentatio*, sm. 8°, Amsterdam, 1709.

[3] Bk. x, ch. 2.   [4] *Pseudodoxia Epidemica*, bk. ii, ch. 5; *Works*, ed. Sayle, 1927, ii, 271.

[5] 1540, 60 v–63 r.   [6] 1540, 63 v–73 r.

[7] The precipitation of the silver as chloride with salt water, followed by cupellation, is described in the *Probir-Büchlein*, c. 1518; Frankfurt, 1574, 41.

[8] Stockdale, *Sci. Progr.*, 1924, xviii, 476.

gitto), with full details of the moulds for casting bronze, the various compositions of bronze, casting various types of cannon (*artigliarie*) and bells, with an
entirely new process for the latter.[1] Books VII–VIII deal with casting and
foundry work, reverberatory and wind furnaces and boring cannon. Evelyn[2]
saw the great gun foundry at Venice; 'there is one cannon weighing 16,573 lbs.
cast whilst Henry the Third dined, and put into a gally built, rigg'd, and fitted
for launching within that time'. One forge had 13 furnaces.

Book IX gives the first description of the amalgamation process for the extraction of silver from its ores,[3] by grinding in a manual mill with sublimate,
verdigris, common salt, vinegar and mercury.

Book IX has a section on chemistry (del arte alchimica), including distillation, and various kinds of apparatus, and is illustrated (including what is said
to be the first use of a coil condenser).[4] The products include nitric and sulphuric acids, aqua regia and empyreumatic and volatile oils. Sulphuric acid
can be distilled from vitriol and in a second way an oil can be drawn from
sulphur by burning it under a bell (incensione medesima messo sotto una
campana aperta e aconcia che golgha tutto el fumo e per il lambicho gocciando
lo stilli nel recipiente). Book IX also describes the making of niello (silver
coloured black with sulphide, known in antiquity),[5] metal work such as
hardening files, tempering steel, beating gold leaf and wire drawing, gilding,
and making pottery.

Book X is on pyrotechny — the only one justifying the title of the whole
treatise. It describes incendiary mixtures after the style of Marcus Græcus,
who is named (Marcho graco), with some additions,[6] the purification of saltpetre and making gunpowder, the bombardment of fortresses, underground
mines and fuses (used at Naples in 1503), fireworks, petards, and iron cannon
balls.[7] The sections on saltpetre, gunpowder, mines, bombs, and fireworks in
Whitehorn's *Certain Waies for the Ordering of Souldiers in Battelray*, 1560, are
mere translations of Biringuccio, some of his illustrations being also pirated.[8]

BUDÉ AND SAVOT

The use of nitric acid (aqua medicata quam Chrysulcam vocant) for parting
gold from silver was described in 1514 by Guillaume Budé:[9] *aqua chrysulca*:
Quae autem aqua vim habet chrysulcam (id est auri ab argento abstrahendi).
The use of aqua fortis (eau de depart) is said to have been introduced into Paris
by Le Cointe, who made a great fortune and left the process as a secret monopoly to his son. The latter sold the secret to the Paris Mint. It was probably
used in Venice from about 1500 with Spanish silver containing gold and later

---

[1] Partington, *Isis*, 1935, xxiv, 121.   [2] *Diary*, June 1645; ed. Bray, 1870, 167.
[3] Bk. ix, ch. 11; Kopp, (1), iv, 198.   [4] 1540, 128 *v*.
[5] Conybeare, *Ann. Phil.*, 1822, iv, 364–70; *Quart. J. Lit. Sci. Arts*, 1823, xiv, 22–40.
[6] Bk X, ch. 9: modi di comporre varie compositioni di fuochi quali il vulgo chiama fuochi
lavorati.
[7] Romocki, *Geschichte der Explosivstoffe*, Berlin, 1895, i, 187, 250; Partington, (4).
[8] Smith and Gnudi, *Biringuccio*, 1942, xxiii.
[9] *De Asse et partibus ejus. Libri quinque*, Venundantur in aedibus Ascensianis, Paris, 1514,
f. lv.

in Holland.[1] The name chrysulca is from the Greek χρυσός (chrysos), gold, and ἕλκω (helko), I draw out.[2] The process was described by Louis Savot (Saulien, Bourgogne, 1579–Paris, 1640), physician to King Louis XIII:[3]

Quoy que l'argent soit tout dissoult & reduit en eau, au moins à l'apparence de la veuë, on l'en retire toutesfois, en rabattant premierement & adoucissant la force de l'eau forte, par le moyen de l'eau commune qu'on mesle parmy, & y iettant par apres dedans des pieces de cuiure, lesquelles ont ceste proprieté particuliere d'attirer à soy tout l'argent qui estois dissoult avec l'eau forte, lequel par le moyen du cuiure se tourne en poudre blanche, pour se joindre & attacher au cuiure, si bien que par ce moyen l'or & le cuiure se trouvent separez d'ensemble.

S'il y a du cuiure dissoult dans l'eau forte, on l'en retire par le moyen du fer, de mesme que l'argent s'en retire par le moyen du cuiure, le cuiure attiré par le fer, & separé de l'eau se mesle parmy le fer, & le teint en couleur de franc cuiure.

Savot says the alchemists thought that vitriol dissolved in water transmuted iron into copper, but this is only because it contains copper (noanmoins ce n'est que le cuiure dissoult dans le vitriol, comme dans l'eau forte, qui a reprins son premier estat & consistens du cuiure par le moyen du fer); and he adds that Nic. Guibert had proved this in his *Alchymiae Interitus* directed against Libavius (see p. 268).

Savot deals with the compositions of ancient coins and medals,[4] three kinds of tin,[5] refining gold by cementation and by antimony,[6] refining silver by cupellation with lead, and the spitting of silver (argentum pustulatum),[7] and whether gold and silver can be perfectly refined.[8] Particularly interesting are his sections on zinc and brass.[9] Brass is probably the old orichalcum, aurichalcum, or electrum, but chalcolibanus was a resin; Agricola was wrong in saying orichalcum was black copper, since it was described as silvery-white. Savot thought the pseudargyros of Strabo (see Vol. I) was either brass or more probably zinc or speautre (quoting Linschot, ch. xvii, on calaëm).[10] He describes cadmia, tutia and spodium, and says the crocus aurichalcum of Ruland[11] is cadmia. He quotes Festus on brass and Scaliger on the orichalcum of Mexico,[12] and discusses the Corinthian copper, hepatizon, and pyropus of Pliny, saying Cæsalpinus was wrong on hepatizon,[13] and he also deals with the alloy potin.

The treatise on coinage by Jean Boizard, councillor at the Cour des Monnaies in Paris,[14] described the production of coins from an alloy of gold and silver, which could be misused, and its reprinting was forbidden—yet it appeared in three editions.

ACOSTA

A simplified modification of the amalgamation process, only mentioned by Biringuccio, as carried out in the silver mines of Potosí in South America, is

[1] Jagnaux, ii, 401. [2] Kopp, (1), iii, 206.
[3] *Recherches sur la Métallurgie des Anciens*, 1627, reprinted in Gobet, 1779, ii, 813–900 (848–849); Hoefer, (1), ii, 66 (in full).
[4] Gobet, 839, 867. [5] *Ib.*, 821–33. [6] *Ib.*, p. 850. [7] *Ib.*, 854, 864.
[8] *Ib.*, 859. [9] *Ib.*, 872–88. [10] *Ib.*, 883. [11] 1612, 176.
[12] *Ib.*, 890; this is platinum. [13] *Ib.*, 893.
[14] *Traité des monnaies, de leurs circonstances et dépendances*, 12°, Paris, 1692, 2 ed., 2 vols. 12°, 1711, 3 ed. 1723; NBU, 1853, vi, 482.

first described in detail by the Jesuit, Joseph de Acosta.[1] It consisted in grinding the ore with salt brine and mercury for nine to twenty days (more rapidly if heated), washing the amalgam, squeezing out some of the mercury in a cloth, and distilling off the mercury from the amalgam in earthenware retorts. This so-called 'Mexican process', which is still in use, was introduced into Schemnitz in 1780–5 by Baron von Born (see p. 731).

BARBA

The amalgamation process used at Potosi is also described by Alvaro Alonso Barba, a Spanish priest said to have been born in 1569 in Lepe, a small township of Andalusia, who lived about 1609 at Tarabuco, a market-town in the province of Chareso, eight miles from Plata, in South America. In 1615 he was curate at Tiaguacano (or Tiguanoco) in the province of Pecayes, and in 1617 lived at Lepas in Peru. For many years he had the living of the church of St. Bernard in Potosí.[2] He gave a detailed account of the ores and minerals of South America in his book (composed at the command of Don Juan de Liçaraçu) on the art of metals (1640):

El Arte de los Metales, en quo[3] se enseña el verdadero beneficio de los de Oro y Plata por Açogue, el modo de fundir los todos, y como se han de refinar . . . 4°, Madrid, 1640, iv, 122 pp., approbation dated Potosi, 15 March 1637. Reprinted 1729, 1770.

The work was kept secret in Spain but a copy was obtained by Edward Montague, first Earl of Sandwich (1660), when ambassador extraordinary to Spain, who translated two of the five books into English in 1669:

The First Book of the Art of Mettals, In Which is Declared the manner of their Generation; and the Concomitants of Them. . . . The Second Book of the Art of Metals, Wherin is Taught the Common Way of Refining Silver by Quicksilver. . . . Translated in the Year 1669, By the R. H. Edward Earl of Sandwich, sm. 8°, London, 1670; with same title 1674 (two books);[4] A Collection of Scarce and Valuable Treatises upon Metals, Mines, and Minerals . . . Being, a Translation from the Learned Albaro Alonso Barba . . . and the Observations of Several Ingenious Persons of our own Country, founded on many Years Experience, sm. 8°, London, 1738; reissued, 1739, 2 edit. 1740; also containing: A Discovery of Subterranean Treasure . . . founded on the Experience of Mr. Gabriel Plattes (t.p. dated 1738 in 1739 edition) and: Rara Avis in Terra or the Compleat Miner . . . with an Explanation of the Miners Terms of Art, by Thomas Houghton (t.p. dated 1738 in 1739 edition);[5] El Arte de los Metales, translated from the 1640 Madrid edition by R. E. Douglas and E. P. Mathewson, London, 1923, 276 pp. (a complete translation).
Traité de l'Art Métallique, 12°, Paris, 1730 (BN; abridgment by Hautin de Villars). Métallurgie ou l'Art de tirer ou de purifier les Métaux, 2 vols. 12°, Paris, 1751 (BN, transl. by 'Gosford', i.e. Lenglet Dufresnoy) and La Haye, 1752.
Berg-Büchlein, Darinnen von der Metallen und Mineralien Generalia und Ursprung, . . . ausführlich und nutzbarlich gehandelt wird, tr. by I[ohann]. L[ange]., 8°,

[1] Historia natural y moral de las Indias, 4°, Seville, 1590, lib. iv, caps. 5, 9 f., 12 f., pp. 203 f., 218 f., 225 f.: de el arte que se saca el Azogue y se beneficia con el la plata; Histoire natvrelle et moralle des Indes, tant Orientelles qu'Occidentelles, tr. Regnault, 8°, Paris, 1600, l. iv, 5–13, pp. 136–50; The Natvrall and Morall Historie of the East and West Indies . . . , tr. E. G[rimstone?], 4°, London, 1604, 216, 232 f., 241 f.
[2] Thomson, (1), i, 223; Thorndike, vii, 258–61.   [3] que in later eds.
[4] Phil. Trans., 1674, ix, 187; Ferguson, i, 70, says the two books were first issued in 1674.
[5] Ferguson, i, 170.

Hamburg, 1676; Frankfurt, 1726, 1739; Vienna, 1749, 1767; a long summary of Barba's work is given by Gmelin[1] and Hoefer.[2]

Barba's work is in five books. The first (34 chapters) deals with the generation of metals and things accompanying them; the second (24 chapters) with the extraction of silver by mercury; the third (16 chapters and 13 figures) with the process he discovered in 1607 for the extraction of gold, silver and copper by boiling with salt solution and mercury in a copper vessel; the fourth (22 chapters and 48 figures) with the extraction of these metals by fusion; and the fifth (15 chapters and 13 figures) with the refining and separation of these metals.

Barba accepted the heavens as a universal cause but thought the association of the metals with the planets was a 'vain curiosity', and in any case there are more than seven metals; bismuth (bisamuto), a metal which is a mean between tin and lead, had recently been discovered in the mountains of Hungary, and there may be more metals still.[3] He accepted, however, antipathies and sympathies between metals and minerals.[4] There are strong waters (agua fuerte) which separate gold and silver (i.e. nitric acid),[5] and even convert gold into water (i.e. aqua regia).[6] He is non-commital on the claims made for potable gold.[7] The metals are generated from sulphur and mercury, by the influence of the heavenly bodies according to some.[8] Barba illustrates a balance in a glass case.[9]

The Mexican Amalgamation Process

Cinnabar, or native mercury sulphide, called by the natives *limpi*, sometimes mixed with native mercury, occurs in Mexico and Peru (rich deposits at Huancavelica) and was worked before the Spanish conquest,[10] e.g. in the mines at Chilapan, being used for paint.[11] Remains of pre-Columbian (Inca) mercury furnaces were found at Huanvelica and other places and they were perhaps in use in Mexico and Chile. The clay retorts were bottle-shaped, the large clay receivers globular and air cooled.[12]

Herrera[13] says of mercury 'the Indians know it not but the Romans carried it from Castile in stone [ore] and from it got mercury'. A chapter dealing with gold, silver, and quicksilver[14] gives a description of the Potosí mines with their four seams (rich, centeur, tinne, and mendieta).[15] The section on mercury[16] says the Indians mined cinnabar (*limpi*) for use in painting their own and their idols' bodies and faces, but did not know mercury. The ore was found in Huancavelica in Peru, etc., the Spaniards discovering the mines in 1566–7

[1] (1), i, 747.   [2] (1), ii, 305 f.   [3] Bk. i, ch. 22.   [4] Bk. iii, ch. 2.
[5] Bk. v, ch. 7.   [6] Bk. v, ch. 14.   [7] Bk. i, ch. 26: se queden con la obscuridad.
[8] Bk. i, chs. 18–20.
[9] Bk iv, ch. 9; 1770, p. 147; Guzmán, *Anales de la Real Sociedad Española de Físca y Química*, Madrid, 1936, xxxiv, 495.
[10] Acosta, *Histoire natvrelle et moralle des Indes*, 1600, bk. iv, chs. 9–12, pp. 146 f.; Humboldt, (2), iv, 109 f., 119 f.
[11] Humboldt, (2), iii, 303; Browne, *Isis*, 1935, **23**, 406 (417).
[12] Neumann, *Z. angew. Chem.*, 1921, xxxiv, 161.
[13] 'Description of the West Indies', in *Purchas his Pilgrimes*, London, 4 vols. f°, 1625, iii, 894; on p. 855 it is said the work was printed from a poor English translation from Spanish in Hakluyt's papers. Samuel Purchas, Thaxted, 1577–London, 1628.
[14] *Ib.*, 1625, iii, 941 f.   [15] *Ib.*, 944–6.   [16] *Ib.*, 949–50.

when Henrique Guarces, a Portuguese, recognised the ore, which was then carried to Mexico for use in silver refining. Mercury so made was used at Potosí from 1571.

In the process described by Acosta and Herrera the cinnabar was stamped and heated in luted clay pots over a grass fire, the mercury condensed on the upper part being removed when cold after opening the pot. Neumann thought the process so primitive as to be a relic of that used by the Incas, which Lippmann[1] doubts. Extraction of gold by amalgamation was unknown before the Spanish conquest.[2]

The mercury in skin bags was carried by sea to Ariqua, and then on the backs of sheep [pack-llamas] to Potosí. The powdered silver ore was ground with salt and water, mercury 'rained' on through holland, and the mixture stirred over a furnace. Previously, a cold process lasting twenty days was used. The washed amalgam was squeezed in cloth bags to remove liquid mercury and the solid amalgam heated in a pot over a violent fire, a conical hood condensing the mercury, which ran off by a pipe. The silver was assayed on a cupel, the very small globule being put by forceps on a very delicate balance, the process being very nice and accurate.

The amalgamation process is usually said to have been introduced into Mexico in 1554 by Bartholomew of Medina, a native (or inhabitant) of Seville; the original documents are lost, one account says Bartholomew brought with him 'a German . . . who knew how to purify silver minerals with mercury'.[3]

A *Compendium and Description of the West Indies*, written about 1628 by Fray Antonio Vázquez de Espinosa (Jarez, 1570–Seville, 1630), a Carmelite missionary who travelled in Mexico and Peru, returning to Spain in 1622, also describes the preparation of mercury from cinnabar and the amalgamation process.[4]

PLICTHO

In the same year as Biringuccio's book, the first book on dyeing, *Plichtho*, appeared:[5]

Plictho de Larte / de tentori che insegna / tenger pãni telle banbasi / et sede si per Larthe magiore / come per la comvne, Venice, MDXL (colophon).
Plico Dell Arte / del Tingere Tvtte / le Sorte di Colore. / Divisio in Tre Parti. / Prima per imparar a tinger Pani de Lana, & / Telle, Bombaci in vari colori. / Il

[1] (2), ii, 180.   [2] Browne, *Isis*, 1935, xxiii, 406 (418).
[3] Carracido, in Diergart, 1909, 314 f.; Humboldt (2), iii, 270; iv, 52 f., gives 1557, as from documents published in Madrid in 1646; U. J. Paoli, L'età aurea della metallurgia ispano-coloniale, in *Archivio*, 1926, vii, 95, 226; 1927, viii, 83, 200, 364, 375 (index), 496 (bibl.). F. A. Schmidt in G. Agricola's *Mineralogische Schriften*, Freyberg, 1806, i, said the amalgamation process was introduced into Mexico by Bartholome Medina in 1552. Thomson, (1), i, 223, says Pedro Fernandes de Velasco introduced a method of extracting gold and silver from their ores by means of mercury into Mexico and Peru in 1566. Hoover, Agricola's *De Re Metallica*, London, 1912, 300, says it is not certain whether the process was an importation from Europe (which may be presumed) or was re-invented in Mexico.
[4] Tr. by Clark, *Smithsonian Misc. Coll.*, 1942, cii, pp. 1–862; 6000 quintals of mercury used annually, over 300,000 quintals of cinnabar being roasted, 531, 540 f. (Potosí), 622 (cupellation), 625 (amalgamation), 627 (assaying on cupel), 166, 237 cochineal, 173 cane sugar; see excellent index.
[5] Singer, *The Earliest Chemical Industry*, 1948, 73.

C

Secondo Libro Tratta il modo / Di tingere tutte le sorte di sede in variate sorte di colori. / Il Terzo Trattasi Bellisimi secreti / di tinger Pelle in varij & diversi colori, & il modo di Conzar / Corami da Scarpe: Et in perfete Conze opera vt- / tilissima a chi di tal arte si dileta. / Con Privilegio. / In Venetia. M. DC. XI. / Appresso Alessandro Vecchi. Sm. 8°, 102 pp., i l. index.[1] BM 1044.c.23.

French tr.: Suite du Teinturier parfait, ou l'art de teindre les laines, soies, fils, plaux, poils, plumes, etc., comme ils se pratique à Venise, Gênes, Florence, et dans le Levant, et la manière de passer en chamois toute sorte de peaux: traduite de l'Italien, Paris, 1716.

The books deals with dyeing in various colours, including scarlet with kermes (grana over kermes), or crimson (color cremesino maestro Rainando Fiorentino)[2] or perfect crimson (chremesino parfetto),[3] or vermilion (vermiglio),[4] or scarlet (fare lana de scarlatto grana).[5] It gives recipes for various mordant liquors containing Roman vitirol, alum (lume de piuma), etc.,[6] gum water (acqua de goma)[7] and quick dyeing (?, teintura de scorcione).[8] It describes the distillation of aqua fortis (nitric acid) from saltpetre and Roman vitriol (Recipe salnitro, vitriol Romano & lambica),[9] also a water to dye in all colours (a fare acqua per tenger in ogni colore. Recipe vitriol Romano, lume de piuma oueto lume scagliola. Sal agromiago: queste uuol esser lire 2. Cinaprio lire 1. Et sanne acqua per lambico).[10] It gives a recipe containing orpiment (oropigmento).[11] It does not mention indigo or true cochineal.[12]

A book on inventions, De inventoribus rerum, by the historian Polydore Vergil (Urbino, 1470?–1555?), who became Archdeacon of Wells (1508) and was naturalised in 1510, appeared first in 1499 in three books, and after 1521 in eight, and went through a great number of editions (e.g. 1671) and translations.[13] It is composed of extracts from ancient authors and is of little interest.

Jean Taisnier (b. Hainault, 1509), physician, poet, musician, lawyer, and astrologer, in 1562 listed gunpowder, artillery and cannon balls as beneficial inventions, mentions a diving bell (cacabo) he saw in 1538, and says sea water can be made fresh by straining through wax or passing it backwards and forwards through a stone channel filled with pebbles.[14]

AGRICOLA

Georg Bauer, Latinised as Agricola, born at Glauchau in Saxony (Glauchau, 24 March 1494 (not 1490)–Chemnitz, 21 November 1555), studied at the University of Leipzig and took the B.A. degree. He taught classics from 1518 in the Municipal School at Zwickau, becoming Principal in 1520. In 1522 he became a lecturer at Leipzig, but in 1524 he studied medicine at Bologna, Venice, and probably Padua, and probably took the M.D. On his return to

---

[1] Wiegleb, (1), 1792, 178, gives the title Plictho de Larte but the date 1548; he and Gmelin, (1), i, 358 (Plichtho, Plicto, Pletho, Plycto, Venice, 1540, 1548) and Berthollet, 1824, i, 22 (calls it Mariegola, 1429, enlarged 1510) says the author was French, John Ventura Rosetti; the BM Catal. and Fester, 1923, 59 ('Maniegola dell' arte dei Tintori . . . erschienen 1429') attribute it to Giovanni (G.V.) or Bonaventura Rossetti; J. L. Lawrie, A Bibliography of Dyeing and Textile Printing, comprising a List of Books from the Sixteenth Century to the Present Time, 1946, London, 1949.

[2] 1611, 9, 64.   [3] 1611, 67.   [4] 1611, 47.   [5] 1611, 32.   [6] 1611, 16 f.
[7] 1611, 18.   [8] 1611, 33.   [9] 1611, 20.   [10] 1611, 16 v.   [11] 1611, 50.
[12] On S. American dyes, incl. cochineal, see G. A. Fester, Isis, 1953, xliv, 13.
[13] Hand List of Editions of Polydore Vergil's De Inventoribus Rerum, ed. from a MS. of Ferguson's by Fulton, in typescript, New Haven, 1944 (BM Ac. 2692. meg. (5.)); D. Hay, Polydore Vergil. Renaissance Historian and Man of Letters, 1952 (BM 10634. k. 20); Thorndike, vi, 148.
[14] NBG, 1865, xliv, 785; Thorndike, v, 580.

Germany in 1526 he settled in a mining district in Bohemia, where he made an intense study of mineralogy. After a residence in Joachimsthal, he became in 1533 town physician, and in 1546 burgomaster, of Chemnitz, where he died. Agricola used every opportunity of seeing and studying all kinds of mining and metallurgical processes as physician to the miners and spent all his means in pursuing such studies, the Dukes of Saxony several times coming to his aid. Duke Maurice, Elector of Saxony (to whom his *De re metallica libri XII* is dedicated) excused him taxation and gave him a pension.

Agricola's only medical book is on the plague,[1] which he thought was caused by a special heavy and pestilential air, originating in putrid exhalations, together with a state of the sky producing exhalations and generating mice, frogs, and insects spontaneously, although bad food may also vitiate the humours. The treatment is Galenical. Galen also recognised stagnant waters as containing seeds of the plague ($\lambda o\iota\mu o\hat{v}$ $\sigma\pi\acute{\epsilon}\rho\mu\alpha\tau\alpha$).[2]

Agricola had a good classical education and his works are written in good Latin in a quiet and dignified style contrasting sharply with the coarse verbosity of Paracelsus. Erasmus in a letter dated 1529 prefixed to Agricola's *Bermannus* (1530) said of his book: visus sum mihi valles illas et colles, et fodinas et machinas non legere, sed spectare. Agricola, although a medical man, took no part in the bitter discussions on the use of chemical remedies in medicine which arose out of Paracelsus's teachings and practice: his works deal solely with technical matters. He was probably not acquainted with the writings of Paracelsus, very few of which had appeared before Agricola's last years. By plentiful quotations from Classical authors, and painstaking attempts to give Latin equivalents of German mining terms (often with pedantic detail), Agricola 'humanised' a field which had little attraction to scholars, and made it respectable. Agricola died at Chemnitz but, since he was a Roman Catholic and Saxony was strongly Protestant, he could not be buried there. After five days, his body was taken to Zeitz and interred in the Cathedral.[3]

Agricola's earliest works were a Latin grammar (1520), two religious tracts (1522), part of a joint revision of the Greek text of Galen (1525), and a work recommending a European union against the Turks and the restoration of

[1] *De Peste Libri Tres*, 8°, Basel, 1554.   [2] Galen, *Opera*, ed. Kühn, 1824, vii, 289.
[3] Bayle, *Dictionnaire historique et critique*, f°, Amsterdam, 1740, i, 99; M. L. Becker, *Manch. Mem.*, 1924, lxviii, 41; E. Darmstaedter, *Georg Agricola (1494–1555). Leben und Werk*, Munich, 1926 (96 pp., 12 figs.; *Isis*, 1928, x, 144); Ferguson, i, 9; Fischer, *N. Jahrb. Min. Monatsh.*, 1944, A, 113–225; Risch, *ib.*, 226–40; Fourcroy, *Ency. Méthod., Chimie*, 1796, iii, 323; *Georgius Agricola 1494–1555*, Deutsche Akademie der Wissenschaften, Berlin, 1955 (362 pp., 23 plates, a collection of essays); portrait in J. Sambucus, *Icones Veterum aliquot ac Recentium Medicorum Philosophorum, quæ elegiolis suis editæ*, Antwerp, 1574, reprod. in Darmstaedter (1926) and in Fischer (1944); Gmelin, (1), i, 366; I. B. Hart, *Scientia*, 1932, lii, 311; H. Hartmann, *Georg Agricola*, Stuttgart, 1953 (134 pp.); Hoefer, (1), ii, 38 (says mistakenly A. was born in Chemnitz; on t.p. of A.'s *De Re Metallica* he is called Kempnicensis Medicus); R. Hofmann, *Dr. Georg Agricola: ein Gelehrtenleben aus dem Zeitalter der Reformation*, Gotha, 1905; H. C. and L. H. Hoover, tr. of Agricola, *De Re Metallica*, London, 1912, intr.; H. Hyman, *Metal Industry* (London), 1924, xxv, 388; G. H. Jacobi, *Der Mineralog Georgius Agricola*, Werdau i/S. [1889]; Karsten, *System der Metallurgie*, Berlin, 1831, i, 121; J. H. Pepper, *Playbook of Metals*, 1861; A. D. Richter, *Vita Georgii Agricolae*, Annaberg, 1755 (not seen); Sarton, *Isis*, 1929, xiii, 113; 1931, xv, 227; Saverien, 1773, viii, 1; Thomson, (1), i, 219; O. Vogel, *Stahl und Eisen*, 1916, xxxvi, 405; Wiegleb, (1), 1792, 164.

Greece.[1] He wrote a work on the weights and measures of the ancient Greeks and Romans:

Liber Qvinqve de Mensuris & ponderibus, 8°, Paris, 1533; sm. 4°, Basel, Froben, 1533; enlarged, f°, Basel, Froben, 1550 with t.p.: De mensuris & ponderibus Romanorum atque Græcorum. Lib. V. De externis mensuris & ponderibus. Lib. II. Ad ea, quæ Andreas Alciatus denuo disputavit de mensuris & ponderibus, brevis defensio. Lib. I. De mensuris, quibus intervalla metimur. Lib. I. De restituendis ponderibus atq; mensuris. Lib. I. De precio metallorum & monetis. Lib. III. . . .
(Colophon: Basiliæ Apud Hier. Frobenium et Nic. Episcopium Anno M.D.L. Mense Martio; 340 pp., 8 ll., BM 604. h. 1. (1.); the others works appeared first in this edition.)

An abridgement was printed in some editions of Vitruvius.[2] Another work on ancient money is by François Garrault.[3] A work by Agricola mentioned by Bayle, *De traditionibus Apostolicis*, does not seem to have been published. Bergman's statement[4] that Agricola wrote before 1500 is incorrect.

Agricola's first work on mining and mineralogy is his *Bermannus*, 1530 (for convenience in references the works are designated by Roman numerals):

I. Bermannus sive de Re Metallica, sm. 8°, Basel, Froben, 1530, pp. 1–130 (followed by *Rerum metallicarum appellationes*, pp. 131–5); tr. as *Gespräch vom Bergwesen . . . in das Teutsche übersetzet, mit . . . Anmerkungen . . . versehen von J. G. Stör*, Rothenburg an der Fulda, 1778: the work is quite different from the *De Re Metallica Libri XII*, first published in 1556, no. VII below.

It is in the form of a conversation in which Bermannus, a miner (really named after his friend Lorenz Bermann, d. 1533)[5] and two Italian physicians, Nicolaus Ancon and Johannes Naevius, discuss mines and minerals. At the end is a small glossary of German mining terms with Latin equivalents by Petrus Plateanus (a schoolmaster at Zwickau), which was much enlarged in later works of Agricola, when it was called *Interpretatio Germanica vocum rei metallicae* and supplemented by a *Nomenclatura Latina Graecaque Germanice reddita*, attached to the *De Natura Fossilium* (see below), and a *Nomenclatura secunda*. The *Bermannus* gathered together much unsystematic and empirical knowledge of the miners. It was reprinted in 1546 with an enlarged list of synonyms and four new works:

De ortu & causis subterraneorum Lib.V De natura eorum quae effluent ex terra Lib. IIII De natura fossilium Lib. X De veteribus & nouis metallis Lib. II Bermannus, sive De re metallica Dialogus. Interpretatio Germania uocum rei metallicæ, additio Indice fœcundissimo, f°, Basel, Froben, 1546, 487 pp. xxvi ll. index; BM 604. h. 1. (2.); each work has a sep. t.p. and dedic. to Duke Maurice of Saxony but is paginated continuously (incl. blanks): 5–82, 83–164, 165–380, 381–414, 415–68, synonyms 469–87; 2 ed., f°, Basel, 1558.

II. *De ortu et causis subterraneorum libri V*

This is mostly on geology. It gives an approach to the modern theory of ore

---

[1] *Oratio de Bello adversus Turcam suscipiendo*, 4°, Basel, 1538; 8°, Leipzig, 1594.
[2] Vitruvius, *De Architectura*, 4°, Lyons, 1552 (BM 559. c. 1.); *Epitome in omnes Georgii Agricolæ de Mensvris et Ponderibvs Libros, per Guilielmvm Philandrvm Castilionivm*, in Vitruvius, *De Architectvra*, ed. J. de Laet, Amsterdam, 1649, 240–52.
[3] *Mémoires & Recueil des nombres, poids, mesures, & monnoyes anciennes & modernes*, 8°, Paris, 1595, q. by Gobet, 1779, i, 15.
[4] Bergman, *Essays*, Edinburgh, 1791, iii, 114; Wiegleb, (1), 1792, 164.
[5] Hofmann, 1905, 35.

deposits and rejects the old idea — still believed by Boyle (p. 506) — that rock crystal is formed from water by intense frost (satis intelligimus ex sola aqua non gigni lapidem ullum), mentions Hecla as an active volcano and explains the origin of minerals and certain rocks as due to a petrifying juice (*succus lapidescens*).[1]

III. *De natura eorum qui effluent ex terra, libri IIII*

This deals with water, mine gases, volcanic eruptions and exhalations.

IV. *De natura fossilium libri X*[2]

In this Agricola describes the minerals and rocks known to the ancients and those since discovered, divided into five classes: earths, concrete juices, stones, minerals or semi-metals, and metals. The remarks on crystal form, cleavage, hardness, weight, colour, lustre, and other properties, served as a model for all later descriptions of minerals, so that Werner called Agricola 'the father of mineralogy'.[3] The section on gems repeats some obsolete material. Aldrovandi[4] quotes Albertus Magnus, Hermolaus Barbarus, and Agricola[5] for Pliny's statement that the diamond is softened by goat's blood, Aldrovandi adding that 'our dealers in gems think this false and ridiculous (etiamsi hoc gemmarii nostri falsum et ridiculum existimant).'

Agricola's description of a crystal as in the form of a compressed cylinder 'but the striae of both the upper and lower portions intersect in such a way that they produce ridges in the centre that also have the form of a rhomb (ita se intersecant, ut plures in earum medio fiant eminentiæ, quibus omnibus item rhombi cot figura)'[6] is probably the first description of a vicinal form on a crystal.[7]

V. *De veteribus et novis metallis libri II*

This is the first history of metals, with accounts of mining, and containing anecdotes (not to be found elsewhere) respecting the ways in which celebrated German mines were discovered.

These works describe volcanic action, sea-shells, mineral waters, caverns yielding various exhalations, etc., some passages dealing with astrology and alchemy. There is an attempt to classify minerals and ores and provide them with Latin names. Peter Weiss (Albinus) (Schneeberg? — Dresden, 1 August 1958), professor of poetry and mathematics in Wittenberg, composed a history of mines based on Agricola's works.[8]

There was an early Italian translation of Agricola's tracts.[9] The *Bermannus*

---

[1] *De Re Met.*, 1657, 505, 511, 513, 543; Hoover, 1912, 46.
[2] Agricola, *De] Natura Fossilium (Textbook of Mineralogy)*, tr. from the First Latin Edition of 1546 by M. C. Bandy and J. A. Bandy, Geological Soc. of America, *Special Paper 63*, New York, 1955 (240 pp.).
[3] Jacobi, 1889, 33.
[4] *Quadrupedorum*, Bologna, 1621, 701; q. by Thorndike, vi, 285; cf. *Musaeum Metallicum*, Bologna, 1648, 19.
[5] IV, vi; 1657, 620.   [6] IV, v; 1657, 611.   [7] Bandy, 1955, 100.
[8] *Meissnische Bergk-Chronica ... Beschrieben durch Petrvm Albinvm ...*, 2 vols., f°, Dresden, 1589–90 (BM 455. c. 17. (1, 2.); NBU, i, 634.
[9] *Di Georgio Agricola De La generatione de la cose, che sotto la terra sono ...*, Recato tutto hora dal Latino in Buona Lingua volgare, 8°, Vinegia, 1550.

was translated into German by F. A. Schmidt[1] and all the tracts by E. Lehmann.[2]

In a work on subterranean animals first published in 1549:

> VI. De Animantibvs subterraneis Liber, sm. 8°, Basel, 1549 (Frobenius); 8°, ed. J. Sigfrid, Wittenberg, Typis Meisnerianis: Impensis Z. Schurer, 1614

Agricola gravely describes salamanders living in fire, and good and evil spirits of mines, including Kobolds which mimic men (ut etiam Graeci vocant Cabalos, quod hominum sunt imitatores), and some which kill men with their breath (asphyxiating gases?), and there is some superstitious lore in his other works.[3]

Agricola's most famous work published in 1556, a year after his death (the preface is dated 1550) is the *De Re Metallica Libri XII*:

> VII. Georgii Agricolae De Re Metallica Libri XII. Qvibus Officia, Instrumenta, Machinæ, ae omnia deniq; ad Metallicam spectantia, non modo luculentissimè describuntur, sed & per effigies, suis locis insertas adiunctis Latinis, Germanisq́; appellationibus ita ab oculos ponuntur, ut clarius tradi non possint. Eivsdem De Animantibvs Svbterraneis Liber, ab Autore recognitus: cum Indicibus diuersis, quicquid in opere tractatum est, pulchrè demonstrantibus, f°, Basel, Frobenius, 1556 (pp. x, 502 misnumb. 538, lxii, ii colophon).

Further editions, all in folio at Basel, are of 1561 (Frobenius), 1621 (L. König) and 1657 (E. König).[4] The last, including other works by Agricola, is the one I have used:

> Georgii Agricolæ Kempnicensis Medici ac Philosophi Clariss. De Re Metallica Libri XII. Quibus Officina, Instrumenta, Machinæ, ac omnia denique ad Metallicam spectantia, non modo luculentissimè describuntur; sed & per effigies, suis locis insertas, adjunctis Latinis, Germanisq́ue appellationibus, ita ob oculos ponuntur, ut clariùs tradi non possint. Quibus accesserunt hâc ultima editione. Tractatus ejusdem argumenti, ab eodem conscripti, sequentes. De Animantibus Subterraneis. Lib. I. De Ortu & Causis Subterraneorum. Lib. V. De Natura eorum quæ effluent ex Terra. Lib. IV. De Natura Fossilium. Lib. X. De Veteribus & Novis Metallis. Lib. II. Bermannus sive de Re Metallica, Dialogus. Lib. I. Cum Indicibus diversis, quicquid in Opere tractatum est, pulchrè demonstrantibus. Basileæ, Sumptibus & Typis Emanuelis König. Anno M. DC. LVII. (vignette on t.p., vii ll., 708 pp., xlvi ll. (1 blank); poor paper, usually browned).

It is dedicated to the Elector Maurice and the 1657 edition has a short preface on the composition of metals by Cornelius Martini (1567–1621), professor of Logic in Antwerp, a Lutheran who studied in Germany. An unsatisfactory German translation was published in 1557:

> VIIa. Vom Bergwerck xii Bücher dariñ alle Empter, Instrument, Gezeuge, unnd alles zü disem handel gehörig, mitt schönen figuren vorbildet, und klärlich beschriben seindt, erstlich in Lateinischer sprach, durch . . . Georgium Agricolam . . . verteüscht, durch . . . Philippum Bechium, . . . Getruckt zü Basel durch Jeronymus Froben, unnd Niclausen Bischoff, im 1557. jar, leaf with device follows; gothic letter, signs. a₄, a–u, w–z, A–S6=4 prel. ll. +pp. i–ccccxci +Vocabulary, Colophon and device, 6 ll., 270 woodcuts, incl. folding yard

---

[1] *Georg Agrikola's Bermannus*, Freyberg, 1806.
[2] *G. Agricola's aus Glauchau Mineralogische Schriften übersetzt*, 4 pts., Freyberg (p. 3 in 2 vols.), 1806–07–09–12.
[3] Pouchet, 1853, 512 f.   [4] Sotheran *Cat.* 806 (1927), no. 13960 f.; Hoover, 1912, xv, 593.

measure at p. 101, large circular diagram between pp. 104–5; monogram H.R.M.D. in some cuts accompanied by the figure of a dagger.[1] Also f°, Frankfurt, 1580; f°, Basel (L. König), 1621.

VII*b*. Zwölf Bücher vom Berg- und Hütten-wesen. . . . In neuer deutscher Übersetzung bearbeitet von Carl Schriffner unter mitwirkung von Ernst Darmstaedter, etc., herausgegeben und verlegt von der Agricola-Gesellschaft beim Deutschen Museum, f°, Berlin, 1928, xxxii, 564 pp.[2]

An Italian translation by Michelangelo Florio is dedicated to Queen Elizabeth:

VII*c*. Opera de Giorgio Agricola de L'Arte de Metalli . . . Tradotti in lingua Toscana da M. Michelangelo Florio Fiorentino, f°, Basel, Frobenius, 1563, 542, vi pp.

An English translation by H. C. and L. H. Hoover with valuable notes is:

VII*d*. Georgius Agricola De Re Metallica Translated from the First Latin Edition of 1556, with Biographical Introduction, Annotations and Appendices, f°, London, 1912 (pp. xxxi, 640, i); repr. New York, 1950.

In his account (the first published) of the divining rod (*virgula divina*) Agricola is sceptical,[3] but the efficacy of the forked hazel twig was warmly defended by William Pryce.[4] Agricola criticises alchemy in the preface (dated 1550) of the *De Re Metallica*, and two works on alchemy attributed to him[5] are neither his nor on alchemy.[6] In this preface Agricola mentions 'the art of chemistry, if it is an art (de arte chymica, si modo ars est)', and gives the names of several Greek chemical authors (Vol. I), probably from the St. Mark's manuscript which he saw at Venice. He cannot decide whether the alchemists ever really carried out transmutation (res in dubium vocatur). An intelligent study of the works of the alchemists would have saved him from blunders in the chemical portions of his own writings, in which he relied too much on Classical and Medieval authors who knew nothing of chemistry, except Albertus Magnus, whom he criticised sharply.

The *De Re Metallica* is illustrated with quaint woodcuts, said to have been drawn by Basilius Wefring (or Wehring) of Joachimsthal;[7] some are signed RMD, perhaps Rudolph Manuel Deutsch. Some closely resemble those in Biringuccio's work, and were probably copied from it, others had been published, with a brief text, by Sebastian Munster.[8] Singer[9] said the text and figures were, 'I am sure, by more than one hand, and the latter part is inferior to the former', but this is improbable. Agricola knew less about the subject of the last part and copied more from Biringuccio without understanding him.

Agricola mentions a large number of minerals, many for the first time,[10] and describes and illustrates numerous mining and metallurgical processes, many of which are still in use. The separate parts of the machinery are shown. The first six books deal with: (1) reasons for the study of mining and metallurgy,

---

[1] Hartmann, 1953, 35 (facsim. of t.p.); Sotheran *Cat.* 806 (1927), no. 13967 f.
[2] *Isis*, 1929, xiii, 113; Schuster, *A. Nat.*, 1928–9, xi, 337.   [3] *De re met.* lib. ii; 1657, 26.
[4] *Mineralogia Cornubiensio*, f°, London, 1778, 113; J. W. Gregory, *Annual Reports of the Smithsonian Institution*, 1928 (1929), 325–48; T. M. Riddick, *Proceedings American Philosophical Society*, 1952, xcvi, 526–34; Thorndike, viii, 495 (Gassendi accepted it for finding water but questioned its use in finding veins of metals, and Boyle's attitude was similar).
[5] Schmieder, 269; Kopp, (4), i, 41.   [6] Ferguson, i, 8.   [7] Jacobi, 1889, 29.
[8] *Cosmographiae Universalis lib. VII*, f°, Basel, 1552, 430–7.
[9] (4), 1948, 227, 320; *Isis*, 1950, xli, 131.   [10] Identifications in Hoover, VII*d*, 108 f.

(2) the qualities a miner should possess, the divining rod, and the choice of a locality (which should be near a forest and water), including the signs of metals such as the sickly appearance of trees (already in the Prologue to Biringuccio's *Pirotechnia*), (3) veins and ore deposits, (4) the officials of mines, and conditions of labour (which were good), divisions of boundaries (claims), (5) surveying, timbering, tunnelling, etc., and the occurrence of ores (including a large number of names of minerals), and (6) tools, drainage and pumps, machinery, and diseases of miners. The fifth book describes the stratification in the Harz mountains, seventeen different strata being revealed in sinking a shaft to the copper ore; the general law of stratification is usually ascribed to Woodward in 1723.[1]

Book 7 deals with methods of assaying (experiendarum rationes) of ores, e.g. mercury by distillation, gold by cupellation with lead (which must be free from silver, such as lead from near Villach), with descriptions of balances (in cases) and weights, furnaces, crucibles (including graphite), scorifiers, cupels of wood ash and bone and horn ash, and muffles, together with the compositions of various fluxes (*additamenta*) and cement powders.[2] The processes include scorification of pyritic ores, and the use of the touchstone and standard 'touch-needles' composed of alloys of gold, silver, and copper. It mentions the coloured 'fumes' emitted by various minerals in a furnace. The book is an advance on previous ones of the subject.[3] The works chemist will sympathise with the direction that the laboratory should have no door, 'lest anyone coming in at an inopportune moment might disturb his thoughts.'

Book 8 deals with the preparation of ores by sorting, stamping, grinding, washing and roasting (the first adequate description), and the amalgamation process for gold. The roasting removes sulphur, bitumen and arsenic. Book 9 treats of smelting furnaces and bellows, the preparation of mercury by distillation *per descensum* and in retorts, and its purification; stibnite and bismuth purified by liquation, and the separation of precious metals from the *matte* obtained by smelting pyrites (panes ex pyrite conflati) by melting with lead in a furnace, and it is noteworthy that Agricola mentions the collection of dust from the furnace fumes in a settling chamber. The production of steel is described (from Biringuccio).

Book 10 deals with the separation of gold and silver[4] by (i) the old process of cementation (Vol. I), (ii) fusion with sulphur or stibium (antimony sulphide), and (iii) 'parting' with nitric acid (aqua valens). It describes the preparation of nitric acid by distilling saltpetre with vitriol (ferrous sulphate) and alum in a coated retort connected with a receiver by a luted joint with a vent-peg. There is a description of a large cupellation furnace for silver with a dome-shaped roof over a circular hearth composed of wood ashes from which the alkali had been extracted by water, and a detailed description of the cupellation process with lead, litharge being obtained. Agricola[5] says a mine of silver had been dis-

---

[1] Whewell, 1857, iii, 411; on Agricola's priority see Wolf, (1), 1935, 354 f., 486 f.
[2] Stockdale, *Sci. Progr.*, 1924, xviii, 476.
[3] Glossary of early German assaying terms in Hoover, VIId, 220.
[4] Percy, *Metallurgy of Gold and Silver*, 1880, 303, 317, 325, 377, 388, 439, 561.
[5] V, ii; 1657, 675.

covered in Scotland; argentiferous ore was later discovered in Stirlingshire but it is doubtful if any silver was mined in Scotland in Agricola's time. Several recipes for cement powders as alternatives to the old mixture of brick-dust and salt are given and Agricola is the first to specify the addition of saltpetre.[1] He speaks of 'coating', perhaps glazing, the inside of a clay crucible with litharge (spuma argenti obductum).

Book 11 describes the separation of silver from copper by 'liquation' of the alloy with lead. The silver-lead alloy sweating out of the mass on heating was then cupelled. The residual copper was freed from lead by melting with free admission of air to oxidise the lead to litharge, and then 'poling' the molten copper by thrusting in a pole of hazel wood.[2] The whole process, including the working up of the slags, is still used in Germany.

Book 12 (the last) deals with the technical production of salts (succi concreti, concrete juices), common salt by solar evaporation in ponds and by boiling, saltpetre, alum, and vitriol (vitriolum), also the preparation and purification of sulphur, and the manufacture of glass, including the blowing in copper moulds. It is largely copied from Biringuccio, but without understanding him, and the illustrations are often not described in the text.

Agricola explains that metals contain earth and water; in gold the earth is of small quantity, pure and perfectly combined with the water, so that the metal is not calcined on heating, whilst in base metals the earth is copious, less pure and well tempered, so that the earth is burnt by intense heat and the unprotected moisture is expelled (quia terra est multa et minus pura, minusque bona temperatio, idcirco ipsa ignis violentia intereunt. Nam cum terra flammis accensa fuerit, humorem exhalant).[3] He also frequently gives the 'alchemical' theory of the formation of metals from mercury and sulphur, from Avicenna and Albertus Magnus.

Brass (orichalcum) is made from copper and mineral calamine (ex aere et cadmia fossili fit), or the latter is by some substituted by the zinc oxide (German Ofenbruch) deposited in brass furnaces (sunt qui in cadmiae fossilis locum cadmiam fornacum substituunt).[4] Agricola was acquainted with metallic zinc, which he calls conterfe.[5] In 1546[6] he distinguished between cadmia fossilis or lapis calaminaris (German Calmei) and cadmia metallica, German Kobelt, apparently metallic zinc. The mention in the later edition of Bermannus[7] of zinc (. . . effoditur, multo etiam major Raurisi misti quod zincum nominant: quodque specie differt à pyrite) is not in the 1530 or 1546 editions, and zincum here seems to mean the ore rather than the metal. Hoover[8] says the passage was added to the revised editions of Bermannus and De Natura fossilium, both of 1558. The latter[9] speaks of heating cadmia to cause it to sublime (in the same way as quicksilver) in a suitable vessel, when 'a black, brown, or grey body is formed, which the chemists call cadmia sublimata';

[1] Hoover, VIId, 460.
[2] Biringuccio, iii, 8; 1540, 59 v, mentions the poling of the metal with a piece of chestnut wood 'or an iron bar'.
[3] II, v; 1657, 527.
[4] II, v; IV, ix and x; 1657, 527, 647, 658.
[5] Kopp, (1), iv, 117; Jacobi, 1889, 37.
[6] II, Basel, 1546, 476.
[7] 1657, 689.
[8] VIId, 409.
[9] 1657, 658.

cognate with it is 'a mixt' (*mystum*) which the Noricans and Rhetians call *zincum*'. This is very vague.

The name *Kobelt* or *conterfe* (cf. ψευδάργυρος, Vol. I) occurs in the un-paged *Nomenclatura secunda*.[1]

In describing the furnaces at Goslar[2] Agricola says: 'in catinum defluit liquor quidam candidum . . . deinde ex fornace in catinum defluit stannum, hoc est mistura plumbi nigri cum argento', i.e. a mixture of lead and silver; but in the list of technical words[3] he says: 'liquor candidus primò è fornace de-fluens cũ Goselariæ excoquitur pyrites, kobelt: què parietes fornacis exudant, conterfey.'[4] This was zinc, first clearly described by Löhneyss (see p. 108).

The names gunderfai (=contrefey) or cyprium (perhaps in the sense of electrum or brass) occur in the *Buch der Natur* of Konrad of Megenberg (*c.* 1350; the first German book on natural history);[5] his chief source was Thomas of Cantimpré (13 cent.) (see Vol. I).

There is much confusion in Agricola's descriptions of zinc, cobalt, and arsenic minerals.[6] He calls zinc blende a useless galena (galena inanis, Blende).[7] He mentions the white vitriol (atramentum candidum) of Goslar,[8] i.e. zinc sulphate.

White vitriol may be mentioned by Hildegard of Bingen (A.D. 1098–1179) (see Vol. I). It appears in the oldest tax list of Strasbourg (1401) as Galician stone (Gallizenstein) for use in varnishes and as a mordant.[9] The origin of the name 'Galician stone' was unknown to Kopp,[10] who says green vitriol was often called 'green Galician stone'; Lippmann thought it was derived from Galicia in Spain, which has a shrine of St. James of Compostela, and has tin mines. The 'yellow coperose' mentioned in English medical works of about 1400[11] was probably not white vitriol but effloresced and partly oxidised green vitriol, although it is said[12] that white vitriol was made at Raibl in Carinthia before 1400. It was made from 1500 at Goslar from blende by Christopher Sander.[13] Beckmann[14] says it was made in Rammelsberg in or before 1564.

Agricola's references to cobalt are obscure, but he knew that a colour (i.e. zaffre) was made from the residues from bismuth ores (ex portiori parte

---

[1] 1657, f. γ1 *r*: *kobelt* quem parietes fornacis exudant, *conterfe*; see also *ib.*, β4 *v*: cadmia, *kobelt*; *Bermannus*, 1530, 61, says: Cobaltum nostri uocant, non multũ differẽs à pyrite, and, p. 134, situlus =kobel. See also Maigne d'Arnis, 1890, 527 (Cobali . . . génies des montagnes dans les légendes allemandes'); Ruland, 1612, 158 (Cobationis fumus, ist Kobolt), 271 (Koboltum vel kobaltum vel colletum est metallica materia . . . cadmia lapis . . . ein raubendt Schwebel der in Rauch das Gut Ertz wegführt); Berthelot, (3), 245 f.; Lobeck, 1829, 1312 (κόβαλος); Lenormant, 1874, i, 114; Hoops, ii, 456.
[2] VII, ix; 1657, 329.   [3] 1657, unpaged, p. 13 after p. 708.
[4] i.e. zinc.   [5] Ed. Schulz, Greifswald, 1897, 411.
[6] Dawkins, *Chem. and Ind.*, 1949, 515.
[7] *Rerum metallicarum interpretatio*; 1657, f. Nn 5.   [8] IV, iii; 1657, 589.
[9] Schulte, *Geschichte des mittelalterlichen Handels und Verkehrs zwischen Westdeutschland und Italien*, Leipzig, 1900, i, 689, 697; q. by Lippmann, *Chem. Ztg.*, 1923, xlvii, 2, 41, 131; (2), ii, 225; (3), ii, 91.
[10] (1), iv, 122.
[11] Schöffler, *Lexikalische Studien zur mittelenglischen Medizin*, Halle, 1919, 31; q. by Lippmann, (2), ii, 225.
[12] Gmelin, (1), i, 117.
[13] Gmelin, (1), i, 386, who mentions, ii, 606, its preparation from zinc and sulphuric acid by Pott in 1745.
[14] (1), ii, 38.

metallum, e viliore pigmenti quoddam genus non contemnendum conficiunt)[1] and says: Recrementum plumbi cinerei (i.e. bismuth), Zaffera, so blaw ferbet.[2] He mentions bismuth as bisemutum in the *Bermannus* (1530) and says it is different from lead and tin. In the *De Natura Fossilium* (1546) he calls it plumbum cinereum (ash-coloured lead) or bisemutum. In the *De Re Metallica* (1556) he describes its occurrence with silver in the mines of Schneeberg, its extraction by liquation (quin stibi in catinis excoctum), its truly metallic character, and its use alloyed with tin for making printer's type (si aliqua portio additur in plumbum album, libraria fit temperatura), or an alloy of ½ lb. bismuth and 16 lb. of tin, which is hammered into platters, plates, and dishes, the English adding more bismuth and making from the alloy articles resembling silver. A pigment is made from bismuth (the oxide, bismuth ochre ?).[3] According to Agricola, bismuth was regarded as unperfected silver (metallici nostri tectum argenti ipsum dicere consueverunt):[4] the German miners called bismuth the 'roof of silver' (tectum argenti), thinking that it was silver beginning to form but not yet completed. When they found a vein of bismuth they said: 'Alas, we have come too soon' (dicunt se cito nimis venisse).[5] In his complimentary poem at the beginning of Agricola's *De Re Metallica* (1657) Fabricius says: Ignotum Graiis est Hesperiisque metallum, quod Bisemutum lingua paterna vocat.

The mineral called 'wolf's foam' (lupi spuma), which is black and looks like tinstone but is barren and gives no tin, is probably wolframite (ferrous tungstate).[6] Agricola describes four kinds of 'magnet': (i) magnes, (ii) magnetis, (iii) lapis Heraclius, and (iv) sideritis. Only the 'male' kind attracts iron. Magnetis does not attract iron but is very like silver and chemists mix it with copper to make a metal like silver.[7] He perhaps means some arsenical ore. He[8] regarded pyrolusite as identical with the magnet (magnes): it 'attracts' impurities from glass as well as iron (in se liquorem vitri trahere creditur, ut ad se ferrum allicit; tractum autem purgat, et ex viridi vel luteo candidum facit).

Agricola says Spanish white (tin oxide ?) is made from tin, and white lead from lead by means of vinegar vapour (ex candido autem facta, vocatur album Hispanicum, ex nigro, cerussae nomen retinet).[9] Spanish green (Grünspan oder Spanschgrün quod primo ab Hispanis ad Germanos sit allata)[10] is verdigris (viride aeris). Agricola quotes Galen as saying that lead sheets increase in weight after years (plumbeas tegulas . . . multo graviores, aliquot post annis, inveniunt ii qui prius pondus notarunt).[11]

Agricola gives a clear but concise description of the manufacture of tinplate

[1] I, 1530, p. 127 (cobaltum), 132 (cobaltum = cobalt); 1546, 466–7 (cobaltum); 1657, 693.
[2] *Rerum metallicarum interpretatio*; 1657, f. Nn 6 r.
[3] I, 1546, 339 (bisemutum, plumbum cinereum), 1646, 447 (bisemutum), 476 (German, Bismut); IV, i, viii, xi, 1657, 575, 644 (plumbum cinereum, nostri vocant Bisemutum), 645 (type metal), 647 (alloys), 657; II, v, 1657, 526; VII, i, ii, v, ix, 1657, 1, 29, 78, 326, 349.
[4] I; 1657, 693.
[5] E. König, *Regnum Minerale*, 4°, Basel, 1686, 80; Thomson, (4), 1831, i, 604.
[6] IV, v; 1657, 609; Kopp, (1), iv, 78; Dana and Brush, *System of Mineralogy*, London and New York, 1868, 601.
[7] IV, v; 1657, 603 f., 608.   [8] VII, xii; 1657, 471.
[9] IV, vii; 1657, 645.   [10] *Rerum metallic. interpretat.*; 1657, 703.
[11] II, v; 1657, 519; Galen, *Opera*, ed. Kühn, xii, 230 (see Vol. I), says that lead sheets stored in cellars in impure air increase in bulk and weight.

(which is not mentioned by Biringuccio). Polished iron is immersed in melted tin covered with tallow (fabri ferrarii ad liquidum plumbum candidum addentes sevum, opera ex ferro incoquunt, eo prius tantummodo polita).[1] Agricola mentions native iron (ferri massae puri et grana quaedam parva quod Albertus novit).[2] He[3] regarded steel (acies, chalybs, στόμωμα) as pure iron, refined from slag (ferrum saepius liquefactum et a recrementis purgatum), and describes the process of manufacture (copied from Biringuccio) by melting iron with charcoal in a blast of air and stirring with an iron bar, the mass like dough being beaten under a hammer and reworked.[4] Swedish iron is the best (ferrum Suedorum præstans).[5] Agricola's accounts of the metallurgy of iron are much behind the English practice of his time.[6] He mentions cast iron only as a half-way product to wrought iron, whilst in gun casting in Sussex in 1543 as much as three tons was cast from a double furnace.[7]

Pyrites (Kis) is of various colours;[8] the light coloured pyrites gives green vitriol on roasting (atramentum sutorium subviride ... nascitur e pyrite pallido),[9] whilst copper pyrites (pyrites aerosus) gives blue vitriol (melanteria).[10]

In an early work[11] Agricola gives a long account of mercury (argentum vivum), saying that it is not congealed except through the chemist's art (nisi arte chymica), that the Moors keep it in basins covered with hides, that its proper container must be of metal (iron ?), solid rock, or glass, since it penetrates earthenware or wood, and that it is used to cure a mange (scabie) called 'French' in Italy and 'Spanish' in France, this use producing salivation. The metal itself is not poisonous but if properly treated by a chemist (in sui generis vas à chymistis impositum) it rises on heating as a 'mercury sublimate' (argentum vivum sublimatum) which is as corrosive as quicklime and even destroys this. He later[12] gave (from Biringuccio) five methods of making mercury, with a full description of the distillation apparatus; distillation per descensum, in alembics, in a vaulted chamber in which the mercury condenses on green trees, and other methods using pots and condensing the mercury on a lid or a superimposed pot.

Agricola describes the preparation of alum both from alunite and by roasting pyritic shales, urine being added to the solution to be crystallised (which would give ammonium alum), and of vitriol (atramentum sutorium, vitriolum), which he supposed contained more 'earth' than alum but was a salt, not an earth (nulla ratione terra dici potest. Ita etiam de sale judicandum est); it is described in the section on salts.[13] He mentions the excellent refractory Waldenburg potters' clay, and also glazed pottery; the pure white kind of clay is found

---

[1] IV, ix; 1657, 649.
[2] I; 1657, 694–5; Albertus Magnus, De Mineralibus, bk. iv. ch. 7; Cologne, 1569, 367: ut grana quaedam nigra in terra invenitur.
[3] V, i; IV, vii; 1657, 645, 669.   [4] VII, ix; 1657, 341.
[5] 1657, index, f. η4 v, incorrect reference to text, as often.
[6] Percy, Metallurgy of Iron and Steel, 1864, 809.   [7] Becker, 1924, 50.
[8] Rerum metallicarum interpretatio; 1657, f. Nn 5 verso; IV, x; 1657, 659.
[9] I; II, v; 1657, 520, 689 f.   [10] IV, iii; 1657, 589.
[11] IV, viii; 1657, 642–3.   [12] VII, ix, 1657, 344.
[13] VII, xii; II, iii; IV, iii; 1657, 456 f., 511, 590; on alum manufacture see Beckmann, (1), 1846, i, 180 (alum works in Constantinople, Smyrna, etc. in 15 cent.), and Singer, (4).

in Eisleben, the Waldenburg kind and that of Ipsen (made into triangular crucibles), are grey, others (used for muffles catillos), are yellow and red.[1]

Fluorspar and its use as a flux are clearly described (lapides sunt gemmarum similes, sed minus duri; fluores ... nostri metallici appellant ... siquidem ignis calore, ut glacies solis liquescunt et fluunt. Varii autem et jucundi colores eis insident. . . . Dum metalla excoquuntur, adhiberi solent, reddunt enim materiam in igne non paulo fluidiorem).[2] Various kinds of common salt[3] are mentioned, and a full account of the manufacture of salt from brine is given, including clarification by adding ox-blood and beer during the boiling.[4] Agricola mentions the use of artificial sal ammoniac (sal ammoniacus) as a flux in tinning (aes aut orichalcum, aut ferrum incoquendum argento aut stanno, aut stanno argentario, aut plumbo candido, prius illinitur aceto, in quo sal ammoniacus factitius fuerit resolutus. Mox in argentum liquidum, aut in aliud ex metallis jam commemoratis imponitur).[5]

Agricola spent two years in Venice, where he saw the famous glass works (vitrariae officinae omnium celeberrimae). The alkali used was native soda (nitrum) or ash of the soda plant (herba salsa), but an alkali (potash) can be extracted from the ash of any kind of wood.[6] He has a long account of glass manufacture, saying that some use three furnaces, some two, and others only one. When three furnaces are used, the material is melted in the first, remelted in the second, and cooled in the third. When two furnaces are used, the first is used to melt the material partially (fritting) and the second for melting. Those who use one furnace, which has three chambers, melt the material in pots (the description is confused). The blowing with a pipe, rolling on a marble, gilding, and painting are mentioned. He does not mention lime as added in making glass.

FIG. 3. A SALT WORKS.
From Agricola's *De Re Metallica*, 1556.

Borax (nitrum factitium hodie ex nitro fossili, quod Arabice vocat Tincar)[7] is mentioned, and perhaps microcosmic salt (sal ex urima decocta confectum).[8]

[1] IV, ii; 1657, 579.

[2] I, 1530, 125, 132 (fluores = German Flusse); 1657, 701; Partington, *Manchester Mem.*, 1923, lxvii, 73.

[3] IV, iii; 1657, 584.

[4] VII, xii; 1657, 446 f.; W. Brownrigg, *The Art of Making Common Salt*, London, 1748, 53, 293, plate V (Fig. 3); Partington, *Everyday Chemistry*, 1957, 306–8.

[5] IV, ix; 1657, 649.   [6] VII, xii; 1657, 471; Lippmann, (1), ii, 343.

[7] IV, iii; 1657, 587.   [8] VII, vii; 1657, 186.

Agricola (following Biringuccio) distinguished soda (nitrum) from saltpetre (halinitrum) and described (mostly from Biringuccio) the manufacture and refining of saltpetre.[1] Saltpetre is extracted by water from a dry and somewhat fatty earth (ex terra sicca et subpingui) stratified with a mixture of ashes and quicklime, the solution being evaporated to half, poured off from the earthy deposit, filtered through sand, mixed with some lye, evaporated and allowed to crystallise. The saltpetre is purified by recrystallisation. The residual earth is then mixed with twigs and sprinkled with saltpetre mother liquor, and after 5 or 6 years it is again extracted. The part played by the organic matter was not understood. Agricola describes in detail the distillation of nitric acid (*aqua valens*) by distilling saltpetre with vitriol or vitriol and alum in luted alembics, and the production of aqua regia from this by addition of sal ammoniac; he gives several recipes, which he obviously did not fully understand.[2] He describes the distillation of native sulphur in small retorts, and from pyrites in pots with perforated bottoms,[3] its use in making gunpowder for new instruments of war (novi tormenta generis), a sad invention (pessimo invento); also sulphur matches for use with flint and steel (sulfuratis ellychniis, cum silicis et ferri conflictu elicimus ignem, arida ligna et candelas accendimus. . . . Constat autem ea ellychnia sulfurata vel ex funiculis stupeis aut canabinis, vel ex ligna exilibus sulfure obductis).[4]

Agricola had little interest in organic compounds, but he was acquainted with nearly pure succinic acid, from the distillation of amber (Arabic kahrabe), when one obtains an oil, a black bitumen, a black earth, and a white sublimate like salt (partim denique in candidum quiddam . . . similitudinem . . . speciemque salis).[5] What he calls 'Melilites, Honigstein', was not the mineral (aluminium mellitate) now called by that name, which was first described by Werner (1789).[6] Agricola mentions the name petroleum as a new one (liquidum bitumen . . . nunc vocatur petroleum);[7] *Oleum petroleum* is in a Vienna apothecary tax of 1440;[8] the chief European source was Mount Zibio (or Gibio) near Modena.[9] Agricola was familiar with British coal, called fossil carbon (quem aream carbonum appellant) and found, for example, in Scotland (in Britanniae parte . . . Scotiam appellamus).[10] A coal mine at Dysart in Scotland, which he says was on fire, was still burning in Black's time.[11] Agricola also mentions a

[1] VII, xii; 1657, 451 f.
[2] VII, x; 1657, 354 f.; cf. Biringuccio, p. 36.
[3] VII, xii; 1657, 466.
[4] IV, iii; 1657, 593.
[5] IV, iv; 1657, 599; in Wiegleb, (1), 1792, 214; Tschirch, *Helvetica Chimica Acta*, 1923, vi, 214; MGM, xxiii, 17.
[6] II, iv; IV, v; *Rerum metallicarum interpretatio*; 1657, 514, 606, 706; Dana and Brush, *System of Mineralogy*, 1868, 750.
[7] IV, iv; 1657, 594.
[8] Schelenz, 1904, 352.
[9] Francesco Ariosti, *De Oleo Monti Zibinii*, Copenhagen, 1690, Modena, 1698 (MS. of 1462, Florence); a broadsheet on the petroleum of 'Montesible' and its medicinal properties was issued in 1480 by Guillaume Grangier, notary to the Grand Duke of Tuscany, republished (Antwerp ?, 1540–50 ?) by Charles de Minne; Weil, *Cat.* 16 (1950), no. 1 and reproduction.
[10] IV, iv; 1657, 597.
[11] Black, *Lectures on Chemistry*, Edinburgh, 1803, ii, 490.

burning coal mine in Zwickau (Saxony).[1] An underground coal fire started in
Benwell near Newcastle about 1643 is still burning.[2]

Agricola regarded camphor as a pure variety of bitumen extracted by heat
from earth resin and petroleum, and not of vegetable origin (a fact well known
in his time).[3] He uses the name *tartar* for the deposit from wine (faex vini
sicca, quam tartarum vocant), and says it was used as a flux.[4]

Agricola's *De Re Metallica* is a classic of mining and metallurgical technology. Much of it is entirely new. For chemical information he had only the
writings of Paracelsus and the alchemists; the *Alchemia* of Libavius (1597) was
published long after his death.

Mining Superstitions

Mention has been made (p. 46) of Agricola's description of mine goblins.
There is an account of these by François Garrault, Intendant Général of
finance in Champagne and Treasurer of Épargne, in a book on silver mines in
France.[5] He says the main reason why the mines in France and Germany were
abandoned was the existence in them of spirits (esprits métalliques) in the
form of horses of light colour and proud look, the breath and whinnying of
which killed the poor miners. In the pit called Couronne de Rose at Annaberg,
the spirits killed twelve miners at once. There are other spirits, like workers in
black robes, who lift the miners to the top of the mine and then let them drop
down. The goblins (follets), which are less dangerous, appear dressed as
miners; they are 2 ft. 3 in. high and come and go in the mine, seeming to work
but achieving nothing (combien qu'il n'expedient rien). The Greeks call them
κοβάλος because they are imitators. They do no harm if not irritated: 'mais,
au contraire, ils ont soin d'eux et de leur famille, jusques au bestial, qui est
cause qu'ils n'en sont effrayez, mais conversent ensemble familierement.'
There are six kinds of mine spirits, the most dangerous having a black cowl
(qui ont ce capeluchon noir) engendered of a bad and thick humour. Their
malice may be averted by fasts and prayers. The Romans, says Garrault, had
continued to work their mines because they disregarded the inconvenience of
the workers, who were criminals condemned to penal servitude for life (aussi
ils n'y employoient qu'hommes abandonnez, desquels la vie estoit condamné
dicts *servi poenae*). This reminds us of the gloomy picture of service in mines
in Egypt given by Diodorus Siculus.[6] Garrault also refers to the bad air in
mines.[7]

The famous adventuress the Baroness Beausoleil in a pamphlet addressed
to Cardinal Richelieu reproduced much of this material on mine goblins as

[1] IV, ii; 1657, 505.
[2] J. Durant, *Phil. Trans.*, 1746, xliv, 221, no. 480 (letter to Boyle, February 1674); L.
Hodgson, *ib.*, 1676, xi, 762, no. 130 (dated May 1676); R. L. Galloway, *Annals of the Coal
Trade*, 1898, i, 163.
[3] III, i; IV, iv; 1657, 537, 594.
[4] IV, ix; 1657, 648.
[5] *Des Mines d'Argent trouvees en France*, 1579 (NBG, xix, 539 says 1574); in Gobet, 1779, i,
1 f., 23 f., 34.
[6] iii, 11; see Vol. I.
[7] Gobet, i, 47.

from her own personal observation.[1] In Cumberland in the 18 cent. the coal miners had seen the small tools used by the dwarfs.[2]

Mines

The Thuringian mines were exploited under Charlemagne, those of the Harz in 968. The Erzgebirge mines were in active operation in the 16 cent., those of Mansfeld, Hesse and Thuringia in the 15 cent.[3]

From the Middle Ages, particularly in Germany and the tin mines in England, miners were privileged communities, 'almost independent states', with unusual rights, exempt from ordinary taxation and military service, and with their own courts and parliaments.[4] Each of the three main fields of lead mining in England, Derbyshire, Cumberland and the Mendips, had its system of mine-courts, and code of laws and punishments.[5] The iron miners, less skilled, were not organised as a whole, but in the Forest of Dean a body of 'free miners', with their own court, had entire control of the iron mining.[6]

The Rammelsberg pyrites were worked from 1577, first by Nesler, a smelter from Joachimsthal; they were washed, roasted, washed to extract the copper vitriol, then smelted for matte, washed again for vitriol, and finally melted with lead made from litharge. The alloy was then liquated.[7] The discovery of silver ore at Goslar in 965 started the mining industry in the Harz mountains.[8] Rammelsberg, according to Agricola,[9] is named after a horse Ramelus, who turned up silver ore there with his hoof. Silver ore was found at Joachimsthal at the beginning of the 13 cent.; in Silesia, east of Meissen, gold was discovered about the same time. The first miners in the Harz are said to have been Franks from Franconia to the south. Silver was found at Schneeberg in 1460. Schemnitz in Hungary has the name of a German town and German miners probably migrated from Saxony into Bohemia and Hungary as well as Servia.[10] The Rammelsberg district was unproductive until 1450 at least;[11] Goslar was the principal town in the Harz near the Rammelsberg mines, in the southern part of old Saxony. Rickard[12] says 'to Cornwall and Saxony we owe the beginnings of the real art of mining', Cornwall probably being earlier.

The silver mines at Joachimsthal (Bohemia) were opened at the beginning of the 16 cent. and silver coins (later called Thaler, the origin of dollar) were

[1] *La Restitvtion de Plvton*, 1640; in Gobet, i, 339–441 (mostly astrological); Hoefer, (1), ii, 60, quotes the passage from a reprint in Alonso Barba, *Métallurgie*, Paris, 1751, ii, 60. Jean de Châtelet, baron de Beausoleil et d'Auffenbach, was born in Brabant about 1578 and wrote a Latin alchemical *Diorismus veræ Philosophiæ de Materia prima Lapidis*, 1627 (30 pp.; repr. in Gobet, i, 259–458; it deals mostly with the Archeus). Martine de Berterau, Baroness de Beausoleil, was born in Touraine or Berry about 1578 and also wrote *Ueritable declaration . . . des riches & inestimable thresors nouuellement descouverts dans le Royaume de France*, 1632 (in Gobet, i, 295–308), passports, etc. (in Gobet, i, 441–52). On the Beausoleils see Vibert, *Annales de Chimie Analytique*, 1943, xxv, 205.
[2] Hutchinson, *The History of the County of Cumberland*, 1794, ii, 58.
[3] Jagnaux, 1891, ii, 356; see also the brief sketch in Wiegleb, (1), 1792, 162 f. (from A.D. 677); Gmelin, (1), i, 180 f., 371–459; Hoefer, (1), i, 370, 492; ii, 58; and a few scraps in Sarton, iii, 217.
[4] M. B. Donald, *Elizabethan Copper: the History of the Company of Mines Royal*, 1955.
[5] Salzman, (1), 1923, 41 f., 55 f.; (2), 1926, 236; R. Watson, *Chemical Essays*, 1796, iii, 207, 251; H. O. Hofman, *Metallurgy of Lead*, New York, 1918, 1.
[6] Salzman, (2), 1926, 235 f.   [7] Jagnaux, ii, 356.
[8] Rickard 1932, ii, 507 f.   [9] V, i; 1657, 671.
[10] Rickard, 1932, ii, 521 f., with further information.   [11] *Ib.*, 525.   [12] *Ib.*, 531.

first struck there in 1519.[1] Hoernes[2] says the silver mines in the Harz were worked in the time of Otto the Great (A.D. 962).

In Roman Britain the wealthy had solid silver table ware.[3] The ambassadors of Frederick II were astonished to see cooking pots of unalloyed silver, 'a thing that seemed to all [the Germans] superfluous', in the Palace of Westminster in 1235 when they went for his bride Isabella of England,[4] and a Venetian in 1500 found as many silver vessels in shops in the Strand alone as would exceed those of Milan, Rome, Venice, and Florence together. (The chief centre of the goldsmiths was not the Strand, but Lombard St. and Cheapside).[5]

Lead mining in the Mendips was continued after the departure of the Romans in 410 and extensively in the 11 cent. The ore was broken with hammers (mechanical stamps were used from the 16 cent.), washed in buddles or troughs and smelted in furnaces, the commonest being the rough stone 'bole' like a lime kiln with holes below for natural wind-draught. These were soon supplemented by 'fornelli', like a blacksmith's forge, with bowl-shaped stone hearths 12–18 in. deep with bellows blast. As fuel, brushwood was used in boles, charcoal or peat in fornelli or hearths. In Derbyshire in 1557 6 tons of lead were made in one 'boyle' of 2 days and nights in a bole. The 'hutte furnace' used in Devon produced silver (by cupellation ?); the 'turn hearth' in the Mendips could be adjusted to face the wind. Cupellation (carried out by the Romans in Silchester and in Wales) was on bone-ash hearths, in Devonshire and Derbyshire with spent tan bark as fuel, the metal being blown from the side. In 1297 there were 5 skilled assayers in Devon.[6]

Tin and Tinning

The Saxons probably worked British tin but the industry is not mentioned in the Domesday Book. Smelting was first carried out in open fires, then in boles like those used for lead, then in more substantial furnaces in buildings. The ore was broken, washed, and smelted, the tin being cast into stamped blocks (100 lb. in Devon, 200 lb. in Cornwall), afterwards remelted and cast into strakes (rectangular lattices) for retail sale. Authentic history begins about 1150.[7] Merret[8] and W. Pryce[9] describe the mining of tin and the smelting in stone 'castles', 6 ft. high, containing strata of ore and charcoal, blown with two large bellows. Tin mining began in Altenberg, Saxony, on a large scale in 1436–40 and a little later at Amberg in the Palatinate.[10] A primitive method of smelting used in Spain (Zamora) was carried out with tinstone and charcoal in

---

[1] Zippe, 1857, 171.   [2] 1909, ii, 215.

[3] A. Weigall, *Wanderings in Roman Britain*, 1926, 83, 227.

[4] Kantorowicz, *Frederick II*, 1931, 407.   [5] Salzman, (1), 1923, 137 f.

[6] Salzman, (1), 1923, 41 f., 55 f., 60 f.; R. Watson, 1796, iii, 207–336, gave an interesting account of the ore and lead smelting and desilvering; also, *ib.*, 337 f., the manufacture of white and red lead.

[7] G. R. Lewis, The Stannaries, A Study of the English Tin Miner, *Harvard Economic Studies*, 1908, iii (299 pp.); *id.*, *Vict. County History of Cornwall*, 1906, i, 522–63; Salzman, (1), 1923, 70 f., 78, 81.

[8] *Phil. Trans.*, 1678, xii, 949, no. 138.   [9] *Mineralogia Cornubiensis*, f°, London, 1778, 131–6.

[10] Schulte, *Die grosse Ravensburger Handelsgesellschaft*, Stuttgart, 1923, ii, 199; q. in Lippmann, (2), ii, 228; C. G. Bapst, *L'Étain*, 1884, 121 f.; Trautmann, q. in MGM, 1930, xxix, 88.

a clay cylinder 2 ft. by 10 in., on a masonry support like a chair; wind and bellows were combined.[1]

Large quantities of tin were exported from England to Venice and Florence in the 15 cent.[2] A Venetian visitor to London in 1550 was impressed by the fine tin (pewter) table ware.[3] The best tin in Florence contained not more than $\frac{1}{2}$ oz. lead per lb., the common sort up to 4 oz.[4] and English tin was always considered the purest on the Continent. There was an export duty in 1300[5] on British tin which supplied all the tin used until the 13 cent., when the Bohemian mines began to be worked;[6] the so-called 'Venetian' tin was only refined (adulterated ?) there.[7]

The first mention of German tin is by Thomas of Cantimpré (c. 1240)[8] and Albertus Magnus,[9] who says it is softer than English. The first mention of tin from the East Indies is in Castanheda[10] (1552) as calem[11] (although this may mean zinc).[12] Leo Africanus (d. 1526) mentions tin cups for lemonade in Cairo[13] and they are still used in Syria.[14] Tin was mined in Mexico and Peru in the 16 cent.[15]

Tinned iron is mentioned by Chaucer about 1390 (*The House of Fame*, iii, 392: 'a pillar that was of tynnéd yren cleer').

The tinning of iron (*stagnare ferro*) is mentioned in a Florentine document of 1406,[16] but the tin of the Erzgebirge was probably used in Agricola's time in the adjacent Bohemia and Saxony. Tinplate is commonly said to have been invented in Bohemia in the 14 cent. and to have been introduced into Saxony by an agent of the Duke of Saxony in 1620.

Griffiths says[17] tinning must have been used in England before 1525, since Henry VIII passed an act of parliament against the importation of foreign tinware; it was perhaps in use to some extent in the Norman period. The Emperor Ferdinand gave a privilege to Freiherr Hans von Ungnad in Steiermark in 1551 for twenty years to make sheet iron (schwarzes Blech) and 'verzinnen zu lassen'. An English customs document mentions tinned nails from Germany in 1483. Mathesius (*Sarepta*, 1578) says: 'mit dem geschmeidigen Zihn vherzihnet man Stahel und Eysen.'[18] The date 1620 for the introduction of tinplate into Germany is thus probably too late.

The process was seen in Saxony (Bohemian tin being used) about 1665 by Andrew Yarranton, who was sent from England to learn the method with an interpreter and was very civilly received; on his return excellent specimens of

[1] Boyd Dawkins, *Early Man in Britain*, 1880, 410; J. Phillips, *Phil. Mag.*, 1849, xxxiv, 247.
[2] Gmelin, (1), i, 179.
[3] Salzman, (1), 1923, 140 f.: 'pewter was an essentially English art'.
[4] A. Doren, *Studien aus der Florentinischen Wirtschaftsgeschichte*, Stuttgart, 1901–8, ii, 626.
[5] E. G. Nash, *The Hansa*, 1929, 23.   [6] Beckmann, (1), ii, 226.
[7] Merrifield, 1849, ii, 895.   [8] Ferckel, in Ruska, (1), 1927, 77.
[9] *De Mineral.*, iv, 4; 1569, 341.   [10] See Partington, (4), 234.
[11] See p. 528.
[12] Yule and Burnell, *Hobson-Jobson*, 1903, 145.
[13] E. Reitemeyer, *Beschreibung Ägyptens im Mittelalter*, Leipzig, 1903, 229.
[14] E. S. Stevens [Drower], *Cedars, Saints and Sinners in Syria*, [1926], plate opp. p. 216.
[15] Gmelin, (1), i, 446, 468, 753; Humboldt, (2), 1811, iii, 308, 325; iv, 105, Prescott, *Conquest of Mexico*, bk. i, ch. 5; bk. iv, ch. 2; Browne, *Isis*, 1935, xxiii, 406.
[16] Doren, iii, 104.   [17] *J. Soc. Chem. Ind.*, 1931, l, 431.
[18] Cohen, in Abegg, *Handbuch der anorganischen Chemie*, Leipzig, 1909, III, ii, 541, with refs.

tinplate were made in England but political obstacles put a stop to the work until it was resumed in Pontypool, South Wales, by John Hanbury about 1720 or earlier.[1]

Bismuth

One of the earliest mentions of bismuth (wysmud-ertz) is in the *Berg-Büchlein* attributed to Rülein von Calw (1505) (see p. 66),[2] but it seems to be mentioned in older chronicles of Schneeberg; and in medieval paintings in the Nürnberg Museum the ground is a layer of bismuth; the technique may be as old as the 14 cent.[3] In the 17 cent. bismuth was confused with antimony:[4] Wissmatt / Conterfin, ist Jouis [=tinny] Geschlecht / Ist ein vnzeitige Frucht / darumb macht es grossen Unwillen, under the heading Antimonium; or with tin,[5] in England 'tin glass'.[6] Ruska[7] thought the name was from the Arabic ithmid (stibnite), but Lippmann[8] said it is 'unquestionably of German origin', from wis mât, white mass, 'a silver-white metal'. Bismuth is not silver-white but pink, and the name bismuthum is early.

Mathesius[9] derives the name from Wiesen, a meadow, the colour of a pink clover meadow in bloom being like that of metallic bismuth (es bläet wie ein schöne Wisen / darauff allerley farb blumen stehen). He says the metal was used in Milan work called conterfey and, mixed with antimony, in casting metal type (braucht man es zu Meilendischer arbeit welche man conterfey nennet / vnd die Buchdrucker giessen ire buchstaben drauss / mit spiessglass vermengt). Mathesius has a good deal to say about bismuth and evidently had a detailed knowledge of it. He[10] uses the name wismat for a kind of cadmia (zinc oxide ?: cadmia tuciam nennen wismat), as well as for bismuth.[11] Bodin[12] thought bismuth (bisemutum) was a mixture of tin and lead.

Cobalt

Blue glass (vitrum saphireum) is mentioned by Theophilus (10 cent.?) and probably (as saphirus) by Heraclius (8–9 cent.?) (see Vol. I). Suger of St. Denis (1081–1151) mentions the expensive but beautiful 'sapphire' glass

---

[1] *England's Improvement by Sea and Land. To outdo the Dutch without Fighting, to Pay Debts without Moneys . . . by Andrew Yarranton, Gent.*, 2 pts. 4°, 1677, 1681 (with many plans, charts, etc.), ii, 148 f. (The Improvement of our Iron and Tinn, by Converting and Making it into Plates, commonly called Tinn-Plates); Parkes, *Manchester Mem.*, 1819, iii, 347; *id., Chemical Essays*, 1823, ii, 572 f. (life of Yarranton, 576 f.); Beckmann, (1), ii, 227; Vogel, *Chem. Ztg.*, 1909, xxxiii, 1297; Feldhaus, (1), 105; Mantell, *Tin*, New York, 1929, 240; Griffiths, *J. Soc. Chem. Ind.*, 1931, l, 431; R. Watson, 1796, iv, 203 (dates Yarranton's book 1698); on Hanbury, see Gibbs, *Ann. Sci.*, 1950, vi, 390; 1951, vii, 25, 43, 113.

[2] Darmstaedter, (1), 1926, 118; *Isis*, 1928, x, 143–4; Hoover, *Agricola* (VIId), 1912, 433.

[3] Lippmann, (1), i, 247; *id., Geschichte des Wismuts zwischen 1400 und 1800*, Berlin, 1930 (42 pp.).

[4] Ruland, 1612, 44.

[5] De Mayern MS. Sloane, q. by Eastlake, *Materials for a History of Oil Painting*, 1847, 537; Ruland, 1612, 468: wismat ist leprosum non tractabile, vel malleabile, rude stannum.

[6] Scaliger, *Exotericarvm Exercitationvm*, 4°, Paris, 1557, CXX, f. 181 v: cassiteri, quod Angli vocant, glaciale; Boyle, *The Origine and Virtues of Gems*, 1672; *Works*, 1744, iii, 227: tinglass (taken for the bismuth of the ancient mineralists); *ib.*, i, 501; ii, 250; v, 103 (bismutum, bismute or tin-glass; bismuth, which seems to be the same mineral that we, in English, call tin-glass).

[7] *Das Steinbuch des Aristoteles*, Heidelberg, 1912, 175.

[8] (2), i, 642; *id.*, (8), 1930.   [9] *Sarepta*, f°, Nürnberg, 1571, 100 v f.

[10] *Ib.*, 109 r.   [11] *Ib.*, 106 r.   [12] *Vniversæ Natvræ Theatrvm*, Lyon, 1596, 256.

(saphirorum materia) in his church windows[1] and there seems little doubt
that it was made as early as the 12 cent.[2] Cobaltum for colouring glass is mentioned by Scaliger;[3] his *Zaphera*[4] (siderea Zaphera, quam manganesem vocant
Itali) had been confused by Cardan[5] with pyrolusite, which gives a purple
colour.

Hommel[6] says kobelt meant all kinds of metallurgical residues. The cobalt
minerals from which zaffre is made occur in the Erzgebirge with bismuth ores.
Mathesius (see p. 62) also says that a beautiful blue colour is made from bismuth residues (Wismuthgraupen).[7]

According to Bergman[8] cobalt blue (smalt or zaffre) was first made by
Sebastian Preussler in Bohemia in 1571 and by John Jenitz and Joseph Harren
in Saxony in 1575. Another account credits Peter Weidenheimer of Schneeberg with the production of smalt, and its use in colouring glass to the glassmaker Christopher Schürer of Platten.[9] Beckmann[10] has another story which
seems to have come from Lehmann.[11] Lehmann says that between 1540 and
1560 Christoph Schürer, a glassmaker of Platten (Bohemia), went to Neu-
deck, where he set up his business. At Schneeberg on a visit he collected some
pieces of the beautifully coloured Kobolten, and he tried them in his furnace.
Finding that they melted, he mixed some with the glass (paste) and obtained a
beautiful blue glass, at first used only by local potters, but later sent by way of
Nürnberg to Holland, where glass-painting was much cultivated. Zippe[12] said
the Schürers were in his time a 'sehr verzweigten' family which in the 15 cent.
imported glass-making from Venice to Bohemia. The preparation of cobalt for
glass and pottery was especially developed in Holland.

There is little doubt that cobalt glass was known long before Schürer's
time and that it was probably an Italian, not a German, invention, since it is
described in a work by Antonio of Pisa (where glass making was famous in the
14 cent.), who flourished in the 14 cent. He says it was made from chafarone
(zaffre) coming from Germany.[13]

Iron

Although iron was made extensively in England in the Roman period (Vol.
I) there are no traces of Saxon workings. In the 11–12 cents. the industry was
expanding and in the 13 cent. the Forest of Dean had a monopoly, although
Kent and Sussex were becoming rivals. Iron was also worked in Cleveland,
Furness Abbey, Northampton, Rutland, and Derbyshire. Charcoal (sometimes mixed with peat) was used. The furnace was a short cylinder of stone
lined with clay. Bellows were worked by water power in the 15 cent. (1496). In

---

[1] Migne, *Patrologia Latina*, 1854, clxxxvi, 1237–8.
[2] Ganzenmüller, 1956, 167 f.; Chesneau, *Bull. Soc. Encourag.*, 1933, cxxxii, 609.
[3] *Exotericarvm Exercitationvm*, 1557; CIIII, 20, f. 165.   [4] *Ib.*, CIIII, 23, f. 166.
[5] Cardan, *De Subtilitate*, 8°, Basel, 1560, 387.   [6] *Chem. Ztg.*, 1912, xxxvi, 918.
[7] *Sarepta*, f°, Nürnberg, 1571, 100–101, 110; see also p. 63.
[8] *Essays*, Edinburgh, 1791, iii, 124.   [9] Fester, 1923, 73.
[10] (1), i, 483, q. Klotzsch, *Sammlung zur Sächsischen Geschichte*, iv, 363.
[11] *Geschichte des Farbenkobolds, I Theil*, Königsberg, 1761, 14; Bergman, *op. cit.*, in a different account says arsenic was prepared from minerals in 1564 by David Heidler in Bohemia
and by Hieronymus Zurch in Meissen.
[12] 1857, 253.   [13] Ganzenmüller, 1956, 71 (77).

the 16 cent. the furnace was a truncated cone 24 ft. diam! and 30 ft. high, with a bowl-shaped hearth of sandstone, and with a powerful blast cast iron was obtained. The ore was broken, washed, and roasted, and was stratified with charcoal, and (before cast iron was made) the iron was in the form of blooms. These were refined by heating on a hearth (strynghearth) and hammered.[1]

Proposals to use coal, peat, etc. (but not coke), instead of wood or charcoal in smelting iron and other metals, etc., were made in a patent of 1611 by Simon Sturtevant,[2] but in a few months the grant was withdrawn and another issued in its place to John Rovenzon, an assistant to Sturtevant.[3] Dud Dudley (1599–1684), son of Lord Dudley and a collier's daughter, was brought down from Balliol College, Oxford, to supervise a furnace and two forges belonging to his father at Pensnet in Worcestershire, where (under a patent taken out by his father in 1621) he made, he says, iron of good quality with pit coal.[4] It is fashionable now to doubt whether Dudley made good iron with mineral coal (he does not mention coking).[5] Darby senr. of Coalbrookdale first used coke for smelting, perhaps in 1718.[6]

The oldest type of blast furnace seems to have been the Osmund or Ösemund furnace (the derivation of the name is unknown; perhaps from åfsumd, bloom) used in Sweden, an oblong rectangular structure blown from the side, cone-shaped inside; it is described and illustrated by Swedenborg.[7] This furnace produced a bloom of malleable iron. The so-called Stückofen might be described as one conical Osmund furnace inverted on another. It also produced blooms but the conditions in it were favourable for the production of a highly carburised iron which could be fused in the furnace, and hence produced cast iron.[8]

Blast furnaces are said to have been in operation in Namur in 1340 and near Liége in 1400; the use of cast iron may have developed independently in England in the Weald in Sussex, where the use of the blast furnace soon led to this region being the outstanding iron-producing district in England. The oldest English cast iron is a 14-cent. slab in the church at Burwash in Sussex. The oldest English cannon had an inner chamber of cast iron, a breech-loading mortar of the 15 cent. at the latest was in the Rotunda at Woolwich. Iron casting in England may have originated in the Sussex weald.[9] The Burwash slab is older than the 15-cent. casting in Siegen, Prussia, where casting iron was said to have originated.[10] O. Johannsen[11] gives an advertisement of a Merckiln

[1] Salzman, (1), 1923, 23–32.   [2] *Metallica or The Treatise of Metallica*, 1612.
[3] *A Treatise of Metallica*, 1613.
[4] *Mettallum Martis: or, Iron made with Pit-coale, Sea-coale, &c*, 1665; reprinted, with Sturtevant and Rovenzon, by T. Simpson, Wolverhampton, 1854.
[5] T. S. Ashton, *Iron and Steel in the Industrial Revolution*, Manchester, 1951, 10; R. A. Mott, *The History of Coke Making*, Cambridge, 1936; A. and N. Clow, *Ann. Sci.*,1956(1957), xii, 85.
[6] Ashton, 1951, 29; *Trans. Newcomen Soc.*, 1926, v, 9; J. W. Hall, *ib.*, 1; Rickard, 1932, 893.
[7] *De Ferro*, Dresden, 1734; O. Johannsen, *Geschichte des Eisens*, Düsseldorf, 1925, 36 f., 58 (import to Germany), 88; Thunberg, *Chem. Ztg.*, 1921, xlv, 323.
[8] J. Newton Friend, *Iron in Antiquity*, 1926, 204; Rickard, 1932, 885.
[9] M. A. Lower, *Sussex Archaeological Collections*, 1849, ii, 178–220; C. Dowson, *ib.*, 1903, xlvi, 1–62; J. S. Gardner, *Archaeologia*, 1898, lvi, 133–64 (Burwash slab, etc.); Rhys Jenkins, *Trans. Newcomen Soc.*, 1921, i, 16–33; White, *Speculum*, 1940, xv, 141–59; T. T. Read, *Trans. Newcomen Soc.*, 1940, xx, 119; T. S. Ashton, *Iron and Steel*, etc., 1951, 3; E. Straker, *Wealden Iron*, London, 1931.
[10] Percy, *Metallurgy. Iron and Steel*, 1864; Ashton, 1951, 4.   [11] 1925, 75, 78.

Gast, living in Frankfurt just before A.D. 1400, for casting small hand guns and other guns of iron (er kan clein handbussen und andere bussen uz jsen gyeszen). Johannsen says the process was to melt iron scrap in a shaft-furnace (bell-maker's furnace) with tin and stibnite as fluxes. In 1400–50 cast iron was made directly from the ore in blast furnaces (Hochofen). He dates the introduction of cast iron into Sussex 'by Walloons and Germans about 1500'.[1] The German cast iron chimney-pieces and grave-slabs he illustrates date from 1497 but are mostly later; he illustrates only a very late (1636) English one.[2] The blast furnace used in Italy in Brescia about 1450 is described in the technical romance *Architettura* of Filarete.[3] Large double bellows worked by a water wheel are mentioned in a Latin poem by Nicolas Bourbon in 1517, describing charcoal burning and iron smelting in the territory of Vandoeuvre on the banks of the River Barse.[4] The cast iron guns of Gustavus Adolphus of Sweden (1594–1632) were famous.[5]

The cementation process for making steel was apparently invented in England, patents being taken out in 1614,[6] although a claim for Liége has been made. The conventional belief of its origin in Germany lacks foundation.[7]

MATHESUIS

Some additional information on German mining and metallurgy is given by the Lutheran pastor of Joachimsthal, Johann Mathesius (Mattesius) (Rochlitz, Meissen, 24 June 1504–Joachimsthal, 18 October 1565, or 7 October 1564, or 8 December 1568) in a book of sermons interspersed with facts likely to interest his flock.[8] Red and white 'zinck' in Freyberg and 'gelff stein gallen' in Hungary[9] were probably zinc ores. The ninth sermon is on Zihn, pley glet, Wismut and Spiessglass (antimony).[10] Wulfrumb, welche die Lateiner Wolff-schaum, ettlicher Wolffshar heissen,[11] is already in Agricola, as is also Mispickel.[12] Of bismuth, he says it looks like a white pyrites (sih er einem weissen kiss), sometimes of cubical form like marcasite, easily fusible and mixes with tin, making it soft and deformed (lesset sich gern im fewer vberweltigen, im

[1] *Ib.*, 104.   [2] *Ib.*, 78 f.   [3] Johannsen, 1925, 65.
[4] Jagnaux, ii, 228 f.   [5] Johannsen, 1925, 99.
[6] Rhys Jenkins, *Trans. Newcomen Soc.*, 1922–3, iii, 16–27, and discussion 27–32; Desch, *Isis*, 1927, ix, 134.
[7] D. Brownlie and de Laveleye, *J. Iron Steel Inst.*, 1930, cxxi, 455–76, with discussion.
[8] *Sarepta, darinn von allerley Bergwerck unnd Metallen was ir eygenschafft und natur, und wie sie zu nutz und gut gemacht, guter bericht gegeben . . . Auff ein newes mit fleisz durchsehen*, f°, Nürnberg, 1571 (BM 443. h. 7); *Bergpostilla, oder Sarepta . . . Jetzund mit fleisz widerumb durchsehen, corrigiert, und gemehret mit einem newen Register, und kurtzen Summarien . . . Sampt der Joachimsthalischen kurtzen Chroniken bisz auff das 1578 Jar*, f°, Nürnberg, 1578 (BM 695. k. 1); 2 pts. 4°, Leipzig, 1618 (BM 452. a. 33), and with new t.p., 1620 (BM 726, e. 2); the ed. quoted here is 1571 or 1578 (foliation identical); Bergman, *Essays*, 1788, ii, 315, gives 1562 as the first ed., Lippmann, (2), i, 598, 1555, but quotes from an ed. of 1587. Jöcher, 1751, iii, 289–90, says J. Mathesius's life was published by J. B. Mathesius in 1705. Poggendorff, (1), ii, 81–2, gives eds. f°, Nürnberg, 1562, 1564, 1578, 1587; 4°, Freiberg, 1679. Fischer, 1802, iii, 244, mentioning the last (without page ref.), says Mathesius knew a man who could 'raise water with fire', perhaps an anticipation of a steam engine. Mathesius's book has no index but the marginal titles are helpful. I have altered the Roman numerals of the folios into ordinary figures.
[9] *Sarepta*, 28 r; Bergman, *Essays*, 1788, ii, 315.
[10] *Ib.*, 95–96 v.   [11] *Ib.*, 99 v.   [12] *Ib.*, 100 v.

schmeltzen menget er sich vnters zihn, vnd macht es mürb vnd vngestalt). It was named (from its iridescent appearance — very characteristic of bismuth) after a meadow in bloom (es habens die alten bergleut wismut genennet, das es blüet wie ein schöne Wisen).[1] Bismuth (wismut) is dealt with in some detail;[2] it is said to be used with antimony in casting type (die Buchdrucker giessen ire buchstaben drauss, mit spiessglass [antimony] vermengt; sie sollen hart bley oder Wismat[3] mit Spiessglass vermischet). He says 'mini (minium) auff Hebraisch Mercurius heisset'. Lead 'sol wachsen vnd zunemen' in moist places.[4] Printing, he says, was 'zu Strassburg erfunden im 1440' by Johann Guttenberger — but he spoils his historical credibility by making Berthold Schwartz, 'ein Münch', the discoverer of gunpowder and inventor of guns.[5] Antimony sulphide (Spiessglass) in the fire turns into lead (i.e. metallic antimony); 'wird zu bley'.[6] The purification of gold with antimony[7] and of silver by cupellation (blicksilber)[8] are mentioned. 'Bleyschweiff oder plumbago' is apparently not graphite, since it is 'einem gelblicht metall voller schwebels (a yellowish metal full of sulphur)'.[9]

Brass (messing, messig) is made from zinc ore (galmey).[10] A brass fountain pen (schreibffedern voller dinten mit sich füren) is mentioned.[11] Brass is made by mixing copper with calamine and covering with powdered glass before melting. From 4 parts of copper, 5 of brass are obtained with calamine of Aix but not so much with the red and white calamine from Eisenlau.[12] The origins of the German name Messing, the English name brass (A.S. braes), mod. Greek τούντζι etc., have been discussed.[13]

Different kinds of pyrites (kiss) are mentioned,[14] also the magnet and the compass.[15] A general disquisition on smelting[16] shows a good knowledge of the subject. Mathesius mentions cobalt (cobelt, kobelt — he thought the name was derived from Cabul).[17] It seems to have been arsenical cobalt, although he still calls it *cadmiæ lapis* or *cadmiæ fossiles*: die Deutschen nennen den schwartzen Teufel, und die alten Teufels huren und Cadartin, alte vnd schwartze cobel, die vihe vnd leute mit ihrer zauberey vnnd gift vnd gaben schaden thun ... kobelt ist vnd bleibet dennoch gleichwol ein wildes vnd gifftiges metall ... bissweilen ist er ... gleich zu scherben ... daher wir er poculum mortis nennen' (i.e. fly-poison).[18]

The conversion of iron into copper by the action of copper vitriol, and the preparation of ink from copperas[19] are mentioned. Sulphur is the father of

---

[1] *Ib.*, 101.   [2] *Ib.*, 99 *v*–100 *v*.
[3] *Ib.*, f. 106 *r*, where wismat is bismuth; the wismat, f. 109 *r* is not bismuth, but cadmia tuciam nennen wismat, i.e. white zinc oxide.
[4] Cf. Agricola, p. 51, from Galen.   [5] *Ib.*, f. 106 *r*; Partington, (4), 91.
[6] *Sarepta*, f. 106 *v*; Pliny says this, see Vol. I.   [7] *Ib.*, f. 141 *r*.
[8] *Ib.*, 149 *v*–150 *r*.   [9] *Ib.*, 101 *v*.   [10] *Ib.*, 104 *v*, 110 *v*, 141 *r*.   [11] *Ib.*, 104 *v*.
[12] Neumann, *Z. angew. Chem.*, 1902, xv, 515; Hommel, *Chem. Ztg.*, 1912, xxxvi, 905, 918.
[13] Schrader-Jevons, *Prehistoric Antiquities of the Aryan Peoples*, 1890, 201; Schrader, *Real-Lexikon der Indogermanischen Altertumskunde*, Strassburg, 1901, 178, 539 f.; Diergart, *Z. angew. Chem.*, 1901, xiv, 1297; Neumann, *ib.*, 1902, xv, 516; Bucher, *Geschichte der technischen Kunst*, 1893, iii, 45.
[14] *Ib.*, 110 *v*.   [15] *Ib.*, 141 *r*.   [16] *Ib.*, 148.   [17] *Ib.*, 28 *v*, 109–110.
[18] *Ib.*, 28 *r*, 109–10; Hoover, *Agricola* (VIId), 1912, 214; Thomson, (2), 1802, i, 201.
[19] *Ib.*, 155 *r*.

metals, which are composed of it and mercury.[1] A true alchemist (ein rechter Alchimist) makes spirit and quintessence (spiritus et quintum essentiam).[2] Saltpetre (salniter, haloniter), borax (borras), alum,[3] and the manufacture of common salt at Halle,[4] mine gases (schwaden und gifftigen dunsten und bosen wetters)[5] and the manufacture of glass,[6] all call for mention. Mathesius discussed metals in an academic exercise at Wittenberg in 1540[7] in which he criticised Pliny's statement (xxxiii, 19) that only gold is found native; he says that metals have certain laws and relations to one another (which proves that the world was not formed by chance); and argues from the scarcity of precious metals in his time, as compared with antiquity, that the earth has grown sterile from human injustice rather than because (as some said) it was in its last stages.

ENTZELT

Christopher Entzelt (Encelius), also a pastor (1520–1586), a native of Saalfeld in Thuringia, compiled a small book on metals and stones[8] with a commendatory letter of Melanchthon dated 1551. Entzelt acknowledges his debt to Agricola, but (since he was more interested in the medicinal uses of metals, stones, gems, and minerals) he cites Pliny, Dioskourides, and Serapion oftener, repeating ancient and medieval traditions and beliefs, although he recognised that Dioskourides is out of date on the subject of ink.[9] He gives many German names (with index) and mentions German mines. He complains[10] that Albertus Magnus was not diligent enough in scrutinising mines and ores and had listened too readily to chemists (*chimisti*), and[11] censures him for belief in magic, although he himself quotes properties of stones little short of magical. He repeats that bezoar stones (see p. 97) are the solidified tears of stags[12] and says he had seen a dead basilisk killed in a forest near Luckenwald,[13] but he adds little or nothing to the marvellous stories of Pliny, Albertus Magnus and other earlier reputable authors. He tabulates and classifies much of his material and takes pains to clear up doubtful points.

Entzelt deals concisely with the metals (formed from sulphur as father and mercury as mother),[14] including bismuth (wysemut, plumbum cinereum) also called mythan or conterfein because it was used to make vases imitating silver; it was unknown to the Arabs or the chemists.[15] His plombagine is galena.[16] Cobalt is a sort of cadmia so called after black demons in mines.[17] Rock crystal is snow hardened by intense frost.[18] He deals concisely with misy,[19] sory,[20] orpiment,[21] sandarach,[22] alum,[23] pumice[24] gypsum,[25] native and manufactured

---

[1] *Ib.*, 123 r.   [2] *Ib.*, 155 r.   [3] *Ib.*, 116–18.
[4] *Ib.*, 125.   [5] *Ib.*, 139 v.   [6] *Ib.*, 186 v, 195 f.
[7] *Quaestio de rebus metallicis recitata a Mag. Iohanne Matthesio die 23 Sept. 1540*; in *Corpus Reformatorum*, ed. Bretschneider and Bindseil, 1842, x, 729–32; Thorndike, v, 396.
[8] *De Re Metallica, hoc est, de Origine, Varietate, & Natura Corporum Metallicorum, Lapidum, Gemmarum, atq; aliarum, quæ ex fodinis eruuntur, rerum, ad Medicinæ usum deseruientium, libri III*, sm. 8°, Frankfurt, Hæred. C. Engolph, 1557 (8 ll., 271 pp.; 1 l. blank, 3 fold. tables, 1 l. blank); Gmelin, (1), i, 364; Ferguson, i, 240; Thorndike, vi, 308.
[9] ii, 38, pp. 144–5: de atramento librario; ii, 1, p. 73 is on atramentum, sutorium seu vitriolum.
[10] i, 20, pp. 30–1.   [11] iii, 71, p. 265.   [12] iii, 49, p. 235.   [13] iii, 54, p. 244.
[14] i, 1; ii, 2 f.; pp. 5, 27 f.   [15] i, 30, p. 60.   [16] i, 34, p. 66.   [17] i, 21, p. 33.
[18] iii, 18, p. 202.   [19] ii, 3, p. 81.   [20] ii, 5, p. 84.   [21] ii, 7, p. 91.
[22] ii, 8, p. 94.   [23] ii, 9, p. 97.   [24] ii, 10, p. 99.   [25] ii, 41, p. 141.

common salt[1] and soda and saltpetre.[2] He refers to coal (lithanthrax, steinkol), which he says was known to Theophrastos,[3] and says a kind of bitumen found in Saxony is called *thorff*.[4] Diamond he describes among combustible minerals.[5] The chapters on bitumen and naphtha[6] are mostly from classical and Arabic authors but mention that white naphtha is petroleum.

Perez de Vargas

A treatise in eight books by the Spanish author Perez de Vargas:

De Re Metallica En El Qual Se Tratan Muchos Y Diversos Secretos del conocimiento de toda suerte de minerales, de como notables se deuen buscar ensayar y beneficiar, con otros secretos e industrias por el magnifico cauallero Bernardo Perez de Vargas . . . sm. 8° (sometimes called 12°) Madrid, 1569–68 (pp. xxxviii (2 blank), 206 leaves, colophon, blank).[7]
Traité Singulier de Métallique, contenant divers secrets touchant, la connoissance de toutes sortes de Métaux & Minéraux. . . . Traduit de l'Original Espagnol de Perez de Vargas, imprimé à Madrid en 1568 in 12 [*sic*]. Par G. G., 2 vols., 12°, Paris, 1743.

is largely a compilation from Biringuccio and Agricola, who are mentioned.[8] It was considered important enough to justify a French translation in 1743. The author has nothing to say of the Spanish exploitation of the mines of America which was occurring in his time.[9] Book I draws largely from Albertus Magnus and deals with alchemy as a possible science. Book II gives the composition of metals on the old theories; their first principles are dryness and moisture, as well as sulphur and mercury, and the proportions of these explain fusibility, malleability, colour, taste, etc. Gold is the most perfect metal because its dryness and moisture are in the correct ratio.[10] The cause of combustibility is an unctuous humidity mixed with a dry earth (humidad vntuosa mezclada con substancia terrestre seca)[11] and sulphur is of this nature. Book III deals in eight chapters with the metals gold (chs. 1 and 2), silver, copper, which with an earth called *gialamina* (calamine) gives brass;[12] lead tin, iron, steel, and brass. Book IV deals in fifteen chapters with the semi-metals mercury,[13] sulphur, antimony (Antimonio o Alcohol) which is used to make bell metal, a common Venetian process,[14] marcasite, vitriols, alum, arsenic (which is so poisonous that those mining it must keep their mouths filled with vinegar),[15] salt, sal ammoniac, alkali and saltpetre, calamine, zafera and manganese,[16] the latter being earthy black in colour and infusible by itself, but melting with the components of glass and giving it a colour of clear water, purifying green or yellow glass and making it white, and in itself useful to glass makers and potters. There are descriptions of the magnet, ochre, azure, glass, crystal, and gems.[17]
Books V to VII are mere summaries of Agricola's *De Re Metallica*, dealing

---

[1] ii, 11–12, pp. 101–6.   [2] ii, 15, p. 109   [3] iii, 13, pp. 187, 193.
[4] ii, 25; iii, 15; pp. 130, 194.   [5] iii, 10, p. 177.
[6] iii, 14, 15; pp. 188–94; tr. in *J. Franklin Inst.*, 1927, cciii, 806–9.
[7] Gmelin, (1), i, 364, mentions a work by J. A. de Villa-Feina, *Quilatador de la Plata, Oro y Piedras, conforme a las Leyes Reales*, 4°, Valladolid, 1572.
[8] Bk. iii, ch. 3; Hoefer, (1), ii, 57, incorrectly says not.
[9] See p. 41.
[10] From Biringuccio, *Pirotechnia*, bk. i, ch. 1.   [11] Bk. ii, ch. 5; 1569, 26 r.
[12] Bk. iii, ch. 4: *gialumina* or *chalemic* in the French tr., i, 120.   [13] Bk. iv, ch. 2.
[14] Bk. iv, ch. 8; 1569, 41 v.   [15] Bk. iv, ch. 8.   [16] Bk. iv, ch. 10.   [17] Bk. iv, ch. 15.

with mines, saltpetre, assaying, smelting and separating metals, without illustrations. Book VIII contains 'Secrets', a collection of recipes for niello, tempering steel (including files), engraving on metals with aqua fortis (the metal being waxed), gilding metals with gold amalgam, and alchemical secrets (de algunos secretos Alquimicos), with figures of distillation apparatus.[1] The French translation has a plate with the figure of the rectifying column from Brunschwig (see p. 85) which is not in the Spanish edition. The recipes are all in the old traditions of the technical treatises and books of secrets. Iron is made as soft as lead by rubbing with oil of bitter almonds, wrapping in a mixture of wax, benzoin and soda, covering the whole with a lute of horse-dung and powdered glass, and leaving over coals during the night until the fire goes out.[2]

Assaying Booklets

Previous to Agricola's *De Re Metallica* and known to him were Biringuccio's *Pirotechnia* (1540) and some small German works on assaying.[3]

The *De necessariis observantiis scacarii* (*Dialogus de scaccario*; scacarium = chamber of finances) of Richard Fitzneal, Treasurer to Henry II and Richard I, d. bishop of London 1198, written about 1178,[4] and the *De Monetarum* (1355–8) of Nicole Oresme,[5] are said to show a knowledge of assaying, which is a very old process.[6]

One anonymous work on assaying was attributed by Darmstaedter to Ulrich Rülein von Kalbe, Mayor of Freiberg, who is mentioned by Agricola in the preface and at the end of the fourth book of his *De Re Metallica* as Calbus Fribergius.[7] A *Berg-Büchlein* (1505) is said by Darmstaedter to be the earliest German work on the subject, and a *Probier-Büchlein*, containing technical and medical recipes, went into a very large number of editions.

The first dated edition of the *Bergbüchlein* is Augsburg, E. Ratdolt, 1505.[8] Sisco thinks an undated edition is older and more authoritative, but it may be a second printing of a lost original. Pieper gives facsimiles of the title-pages of all known editions.[9] He thinks the author is Ulrich Rülein of Calw in Swabia (not one of the two places called Kalbe near Magdeburg in Saxony), who became B.A. in 1487 and M.A. and M.D. in 1490 at Calw, was town physician in Freiberg (1497–1519), taught mathematics in Leipzig (1491–7), also medicine after 1519, and died in 1523.

The *Probier-Büchlein* went through a great number of editions. Darmstaedter thought the earliest, without place or date, was published in 1518,

---

[1] Bk. viii, ch. 6 f.   [2] Bk. viii, ch. 4; see Hoefer, *loc. cit.*

[3] G. H. Jacobi, *Der Mineralog Georgius Agricola*, Werdau i/S. [1889], 46; E. Darmstaedter, (1), 1926; *Isis*, 1928, x, 143; Hoover, *Agricola* (VIId), 1912, 610 f.; Cohen, *Isis*, 1951, xlii, 55; McKie, *Pharm. J.*, 1955, clxxiv, 117; Gmelin, (1), i, 364, mentions a work by C. Schreittmann, *Docimasticæ Metallicæ*, 8°, Frankfurt, 1578.

[4] Sarton, (1), ii, 467; *Isis*, 1934, xxi, 358.   [5] Sarton, (1), iii, 1494.

[6] Partington, (1), *passim.*; *Proc. Chem. Soc.*, 1959, 241.

[7] Fischer, *N. Jahrb. Min. Monatsh.*, 1944A, 203 (portr.).

[8] A. Daubrée, *J. des Savants*, 1890, 379–92, 441–52; Sisco, *Isis*, 1952, xliii, 337–43; 1957, xlviii, 370–1 (figures in Daubrée); Daubrée owned a copy but made his translation from the 1539 ed. of Steiner; Hoover's statements, *Agricola*, VIId, 1912, 610–12, are incorrect.

[9] W. Pieper, *Ulrich Rülein von Calw und sein Bergbüchlein*, Berlin, 1955, q. in *Isis*, 1957, xlviii, 370.

Sisco and Smith date it after the first dated edition of 1524:[1] *Probierbüchlein tzu Gottes Lob*, Magdeburg, Hanss Knappe jr., 1524 (71 ll.). Sisco and Smith list twelve other issues, mostly with the title *Probierbüchlein auff Gold Silber Kupfer* with slight variations:[2]

Probier Büchlein Auff Goldt / Silber / Ertz vnnd Methal / mit vil köstlichen Alchimistischen Künsten / Sampt aller zugehör / auch Instrumenten darzu dienstlich . . . , 8°, Frankfurt, 1574, 79 ll. (colophon: Getruckt zu Franckfort am Meyn / Bey Christian Egenolffs Erben / In Verlegung D. Adami Loniceri / M. Johannis Cnipij / vnd Pauli Steinmeyers . . . M.D. LXXIIII.

Different from the above are:

A. Probierbuch, publ. S. Zimmermann, printed M. Manger, Augsburg, 1573 (x, iv, 172, ii, i errata, viii index) probably the only edition, critical of alchemy; the style is better than that of the others; it mentions zinc and seems to know of the Mexican amalgamation process for the extraction of silver from ores.
B. Probierbüchlein. Frembde vnd subtile Künst . . . vormals im Truck nie gesehen . . . Durch Ciriacum Schreittmann, Franckf. Bey Chri. Egen. Erben, 1578 (my copy) and 1580 (viii ll. 86 pp. i l.), which describes balances and weights fully.[3]
C. Bergwerck vnd Probirbüchlein, für die Bergk vnd Feuerwercker, Goltschmid, Alchimisten und Künstner. Gilbertus Cardinal vonn Soluiren vnnd scheydungen aller Metal. Polirung allerhand Edelgesteyn. Fürtreffliche Wasser zum Etzen, Scheyden vnd Soluiren. Verhütung vnd rath für gifftige dämpffe der Metal, 8°, Frankfurt (C. Egenolph), 1533 (39 ll.), 1535; the last work is by Ellenbog (see p. 69).[4]

D. Of more interest is a work by Modestin Fachs, master of the mint of the Prince of Anhalt, written not later than 1567:

Probier Büchlein / Darinne Gründlicher bericht vormeldet / wie man alle Metall / und derselben zugehörenden Metallischen Ertzen und getöchten ein jedes auff seine eigenschafft und Metall recht Probieren sol. . . . Durch weylandt H. Modestin Fachsen . . . , 8°, Leipzig, Berwald, 1595 (xvii, v, 236, ix; BM, bound with a pamphlet by Fachs dated 1568, printed 1595.[5]

The preface by Modestin Fachs is dated 1567 and the book was published by his son Louis Wolfgang Fachs. In this is a passage to which Jean Rey[6] drew attention saying that in the process of cupellation the total weight of the vessel, cupel, metal, and lead increases:[7]

Wie es zugehet das wann man ein Ertz probieret und man wiegt erstlich den Probier Scherben das Bley das Ertz unnd die Capelle und wenn man alsdenn das Ertz probieret hat und die Schlacken-probier Scherben und Werck wider wieget das dieselben Stück mehr wegen als erstlich.

[1] Sisco and Smith, *The Bergwerk- and Probierbüchlein*, New York, American Institute of Mining and Metallurgical Engineers, 1949; *Archives*, 1950, iii, 768; Cohen, *Isis*, 1951, xlii, 54; Sisco, *ib.*, 1952, xliii, 337.
[2] *S.l.* 1527, 89 pp.; *s.l.e.a.* (? after 1524); Strassburg, 1530; Augsburg, 1534, 1546; Nürnberg, 1549; *s.l.e.a.* (BM, Augsburg, J. Schonsberger, 1510 (!); Sisco and Smith, 1550, two issues); Nürnberg, 1564; Augsburg, 1565.
[3] Ferguson, ii, 227, 341.
[4] Ferguson, i, 100.
[5] The BM has also editions of 1669, 1678, and 1689, Leipzig; Ferguson, i, 261, describes an ed. Leipzig, 1622, and mentions by report eds. of 1636, 1671 and 1680, Leipzig, and 1669, Amsterdam. Baumer, q. by Ferguson, mentioned 19 eds.; Gobet, 1779, i, 391, gives eds. of 1569, 1595, 1664; Gmelin, (1), i, 365; Bergman, *Essays*, Edinburgh, 1791, iii, 118; Darmstaedter, (1), 1926, 191.
[6] *Essays*, Bazas, 1630, 115.   [7] *Probier Büchlein*, Preface.

This passage, as Rey said, is quoted in Latin by Libavius:[1]

vt cùm vena examinatur explorato prius pondere testæ, copellæ, plumbi, & venæ, examine absoluto ponderatis iterum testis copellis, scoriis & stanno [=lead-tin alloys, a mis-translation of 'Werck'] deprehendantur hæc grauiora illis, cùm tamen multum de plumbo, aliisque impuritatibus per ignem sit absumptum.

BOOKS OF RECIPES

Several small books of recipes appeared in German in the 16 cent. and were often reprinted and translated into English, French, Dutch, Danish, and Italian. Some of them may have been used in the *Probier-Büchlein*.

1. Rechter Gebrauch d'Alchimei, mitt vil bissher verborgenen, nutzbaren vnnd lustigen Künsten, Nit allein den fürwitzigen Alchimismisten, Sondern allen kunstbaren Werckleutten, in vnd ausserhalb feurs. Auch sunst aller menglichen inn vil wege zugebrauchen . . . , 4°, 1531 (Frankfurt, C. Egenolph ?) xxvii numb. ll., 1 l. blank).[2]
2. Alchimia. Wie man alle farben wasser, olea, salia, vnd alumina, damit mann alle corpora, spiritus vnd calces preparirt, sublimirt vnd fixirt, machen sol . . . , sm. 4°, Strassburg, Camerlander, 48 leaves; later eds. (with slightly varying title), e.g. 1570 (with preface by Kertzenmacher); Alchimia, Das ist Alle Farben, Wasser, Olea, Salia, vnd Alumina, damit man alle Corpora, Spiritus vnd Calces Præparirt, Sublimirt vnd Fixirt, zubereyten . . . , 8°, Frankfurt, 1613 (130 pp.).[3]
3. Alchimi und Bergwerck. Wie alle farben, wasser, olea, salia und alumina, damit mañ alle corpora, spiritus und calces prepariert, sublimirt, und fixirt, gemacht sollen werden, lert das erst buch. Das ander buch zeygt an, wie mañ dise ding nütze, auff das Sol und Luna werden mög. Und vom soluiren auch scheydung aller metal, Polirung aller handt edel gesteyn, Fürtreflichen wassern zum etzen, scheyden und soluiren, und zuletst wie die gifftige dämpff der metal zu verhüten, auss Archilao, Koleno &c eyn kurtzer begrieff, 4°, Strassburg, Jacob Cammerlander, 1534, 44 ll.;[4] with slightly different title, sm. 8°, Augsburg, H. Steyner, 1546 (with Kertzenmacher's name in preface), and in P. Gertz, Des berühmten Alchimisten, Petri Kertzenmachers, Alchimia, Das ist, Alle Farben . . . Ein kurtzer Bericht, wie die giftigen Dämpffe zu verhüten, *s.l.*, 1720.[5]
4. Artliche kunste mancherley weyse Dinten vnd aller hand Farben zubereiten, Auch Goldt vnd Silber sampt allen Metallen, ausz der Feder zu schreyben, . . . , sm. 4°, Nürnberg, Simon Dunckel, 1531; later eds., e.g.
4a. Kunstlüchlein. Auff mancherley weiss Dinten und aller handt Farben zu bereyten. Auch Goldt und Silber, sampt allen Metallen auss der Federn zu schreiben . . . Etliche zugesetzte Kunststücklein vormals in druck nie aussgangen. . . . Gedruckt zu Cöllen, Bey Peter von Brachel, 12°, 1616, 43 pp. This deals with inks and writing and illuminating on parchment, engraving on weapons, etc.
5. Carlo Lancilotti, Guida alla Chimica, Che per suo mezo conduce gl'Affezionati alle Operazioni sopra ogni Corpo misto Animale; Minerale, ò Vegetabile. Dimostrando come s'estraggono i loro Sali, Ogli, Essenze, Magisterij, Mercurij &c. con il modo di fare varij Colori, Belletti, & altri rari Secreti . . . , 12°, Venice, 1674, pp. (x), 326 (xviii).[6]
Valentin Boltz of Rufach in Upper Alsace translated Latin, preached, wrote plays,

---

[1] *Syntagmatis selectorum undiqvaqve et perspicue traditorum alchymiæ arcanorum*, Frankfurt, 1595, 225; *id.*, *Alchemia*, 1597, Appendix, *Ars probandi mineralia*, 219.
[2] Ferguson, ii, 246; *id.*, *Some Early Treatises on Technological Chemistry*, Glasgow, 1888, and 5 Supplements, 1894, 1910, 1912, 1913, 1916 (privately issued); *id.*, *Histories of Inventions and Books of Secrets*, 6 parts, Glasgow, 1883–90, and Supplements 1894–? (privately issued).
[3] Ferguson, i, 19, who thinks the author was Peter Kertzenmacher.
[4] Duveen, 317; for the last part, see p. 69.
[5] Duveen, 244 (109, iii ll., 8 woodcut plates in red; Gurney, *Cat.* 26 (1960), no. 362).
[6] Duveen, 336; for *Opusculi Diversi del Lancillotti* (*sic*), 12°, Modena, 1677, see Ferguson, ii, 6; a collection of small Italian and other recipe books is BM 1038. d. 35.

and composed an *Illuminirbuch*.[1] It deals in three main divisions with medicines, varnishes, and colours; the use of colours in painting; and recipes for inks, etching, dyeing horn, bone and feathers, lutes, etc.

ELLENBOG

Ulrich Ellenbog (Feldkirch, 1440–Memmingen, 1499), physician to the bishop of Augsburg (1470–78), wrote in 1473 a treatise on the poisonous vapours of metals and acids.[2] It is probably the first work on industrial hygiene. The advice to keep windows open to avoid poisoning by charcoal fumes is good, but the remedies (smelling musk, wormwood wine, etc.) for poisoning by vapours of lead, mercury, and antimony, and of aqua fortis, verdigris, and sal ammoniac, are useless.

Later accounts of the toxicology of metallic furmes are by Agricola (p. 48), Martin Pansa;[3] Leonard Ursinus;[4] Samuel Stockhausen (of Goslar),[5] J. F. Suchland of Clausthal,[6] and Bernardino Ramazzini.[7] Ramazzini deals with pneumoconiois and other diseases of miners, lead poisoning in potters, silicosis in stone-masons, diseases among metal workers, and 'diseases of learned men'. Ellenbog's tract was reprinted in the *Bergwerck und Probir-Büchlein*, Frankfurt, 1533, 1535, and in many other works, sometimes anonymously. Conrad Heingarter (*c.* 1470) had warned the Duke of Bourbon against poisonous metallic fumes such as those of mercury and other metals, and the sublimations of alchemists.[8]

After this rather dreary material it is a relief to take up the study of a man of genius whose writings belong to the treasures of French literature.

PALISSY

Bernard Palissy (Agen district in Lot-et-Garonne (?) *c.* 1509/10–Paris (the Bastille), 1589/90; his place and date of birth are uncertain) after working ten or

[1] *De coloribus eorumque præparatione, Mixturis*, Basel, 1547; *Farbbüch oder Illuminierbuch*, 12°, Basel, 1549 (372 pp.); *Illuminirbuch, Künstlich alle Farben zumachen vnnd bereyten*, . . . *s.l.*, 1566 (BM 1042. c. 41. (1.); perhaps printed by Egenolff, ff. [2], 60 [6, Register]); Frankfurt, 1589 (BM 1043. b. 41. (2.)); Frankfurt (printed in Darmstadt), 1613 (BM 787. c. 2. (2.)); Strassburg, 1630; Hamburg, 1645 (BM 1043. b. 41. (3.)), all sm. 8°; Danish tr., sm. 4°, Copenhagen, 1648 (BM 1044. d. 9. (1.)); sm. 8°, Erfurt, 1661 (BM 786. a. 47. (3.), incomplete); Ferguson, *Some Early Treatises on Technological Chemistry, Suppl. V*, Glasgow, 1916 (privately printed).
[2] *Von den gifftigen Besen Tempffen Vn[d] Reüchen der Metal / als Quicksilber Bley vnd anders*, 8°, *s.l.e.a.* [Augsburg, Melchior Ramminger, 1524], 4 ll.; facsim. Munich, 1927, with introd. by Zoepfel, in *Münchener Beiträge zur Geschichte und Literatur der Naturwissenschaft und Medizin*, ed. Darmstaedter, Sonderheft II; Carozzi, *Lancet*, 1931, ii, 809, 997; tr. Barnard (from 1927 text), *ib.*, 1932, i, 270; revised tr. by Ernst, in A. H. Whittaker and D. J. Scobin, *Industrial Medicine*, May, 1941 (8 pp. reprint used).
[3] *Consilium peripneumoniacum: das ist, Ein getrewer Rath in der* . . . *Berg und Lungensucht*, 4°, Leipzig, 1614 (BM 546. g. 9. (2.)).
[4] *Disputatio de morbis metallariorum*, 4°, Leipzig [1652], (BM 1179. g. 7. (16.)).
[5] *De Lithargyri fumo noxio morbifico ejusque metallico frequentiori morbo vulgo dicto Die Hütten-katze oder Hütten-rauch, cum appendice de montano affectu asthmatico metallicis familiare die Bergsucht*, 2 pts., Goslar, 1656 (BM 1170. c. 21, no t.p., title from Haller).
[6] *De paralysi metallariorum*, Utrecht, 1693.
[7] *De Morbis Artificiorum Diatriba*, 8°, Modena, A. Capponi, 1700 (viii, 360 pp.); 2 ed. Utrecht, 1703; Padua, 1713, and in his *Opera Omnia Medica et Physica*, 4°, London, 1717; English tr. by W. C. Wright, 1940.
[8] Thorndike, iv, 380.

twelve years as a journeyman glass-painter went to live at Saintes, and there, about 1540, after seeing a painted cup (perhaps of majolica or faience from Italy) he resolved to discover the secret of enamelling pottery. After years of intense work in which he and his family were reduced to such poverty that he was obliged to burn his furniture for fuel, his efforts were crowned with success in 1557. His glazed ware, representing plants and animals coloured in high relief, made him famous, and although as a Huguenot he was imprisoned in Bordeaux in 1562 he was soon released by royal edict. In 1564/6 he set up a workshop in the Tuileries, the ruins of which were found in 1865. In 1572 he was specially exempted from the massacre of St. Bartholomew. In 1575-84 Palissy lectured to learned audiences on natural history, chemistry, and agriculture, exhibiting specimens and charging a modest fee, but in 1588 he was again arrested on the instance of Matthieu de Launay, and although d'Aubigné says Henri III visited him in prison, he refused to become a Catholic and died in the Bastille. Although far in advance of his time in scientific ideas he had no influence on their development and until comparatively recently his writings were unknown.[1]

I. Recept veritable, par laqvelle tovs les hommes de la France povrront apprendre a mvltiplier et avgmenter levrs thresors . . . , 4°, Rochelle, 1563 (BN), 1564 (BM C. 31. e. 21).[2]

II. Discovrs admirables de la natvre des eaux et fonteines tant natvrelles qv'artificielles des metaux, des sels et salines, des pierres, des terres, du feu et des émaux. Avec plvsievrs avtres excellents secrets des choses naturelles. Plvs, vn traité de la marne, fort vtile et necessaire, pour ceux qui se mellent de l'agriculture. Le tovt dressé par dialogves, esquels sont introduits la theorique et la practique, 8°, Paris, Chez Martin le Ieune, 1580 (BM 1171. d. 3).[3]

III. Œuvres de Bernard Palissy, revues sur les exemplaires de la Bibliothèque du roi, avec des notes; Par M. Faujas de Saint Fond, et des Additions par M. Gobet. A Paris, Chez Ruault, Libraire, rue de la Harpe. Avec Approbation & Privelége du Roi, 4°, 1777 (pp. lxxvi, 734: the first issue is said to have a dedication to Benjamin Franklin, suppressed in the second). This ed. contains *Déclaration des abus et ignorance des médicins* which appeared in Lyon, 1557, as by Pierre Braillier[4] and is included in the BM copy of II.

[1] L. Audiat, *Bernard Palissy: Étude sur sa vie et ses travaux*, Paris, 1868; Bessmertny-Heimann, *Archeion*, 1936, xviii, 166; P. Bouty, *Bernard Palissy (Les artistes célèbres)*, Paris, 1886 (56 pp.); A. Brongniart, *Traité des Arts Céramiques*, 2 ed., Paris, 1854, ii, 60; Bucher, *Geschichte der technischen Künste*, 1893, iii, 460; Cap, *Œuvres complètes de Bernard Palissy*, 12°, Paris, 1844; *id.*, *Études Biographiques*, Paris, 1857, i, 20; Chaptal, *Elements of Chemistry*, 1791, ii, 90; E. Dupuy, *Bernard Palissy*, Paris, 1902; EB[14], 1930, xvii, 148 (dates 1510–89); *Enciclopedia Universal Ilustrada Europeo-Americana*, Barcelona, 1920, xli, 346 (portr.); Fisquet, NBG, 1862, xxxix, 89; E. and É. Haag, *La France Protestante*, Paris, 1858, viii, 69–97; A. B. Hanschmann, *B. Palissy, der Künstler, Naturforscher und Schriftsteller als Vater der induktiven Wissenschaftsmethode des Baco von Verulam*, Leipzig, 1903; Hoefer, (2), 1843, ii, 72; *id.*, (1), 1869, ii, 67–92 (recognition of Palissy's services, calling him 'un des plus grands hommes dont la France peut s'enorgueiller'); A. Lamartine, *Jeanne d'Arc suivi d'une étude sur Homère et Bernard de Palissy*, Brussels, 1852, 201 f.; Larousse, *Grand Dictionnaire Universel*, 1874, xii, 67; Leroux, *La Vie de Bernard Palissy*, Paris, 1927 (portr.); I. Levine, *Francis Bacon*, 1925, 148; H. Morley, *The Life of Bernard Palissy, of Saintes, his Labours and Discoveries in Art and Science, with an Outline of his Philosophical Doctrines, and Translation of illustrative Selections from his Works*, 2 vols., London, 1852 (1855, 1869, 1878); Parkes, *Chemical Essays*, 2 ed., 1823, ii, 90, 594; Thorndike, v, 596; Venel, art. 'Chimie', in Diderot's *Encyclopédie*, repr. in *Ency. Méthod., Chimie*, iii, 295.

[2] Morley, 1852, ii, 205, says this and one in the BN, are the only two copies known, but Dupuy, 1902, 337, mentions one of 1564 in the Bibliothèque de l'Arsenal.

[3] Morley, 1852, ii, 206, says this is very rare; I and II were republished in an altered ed. in 1636, 2 vols., 8°, Paris.

[4] Thorndike, v, 465, says it is by him

IV. Oeuvres complètes de Bernard Palissy, édition conforme aux textes originaux imprimés du vivant de l'auteur; avec des notes et une notice historique, par Paul-Antoine Cap, 12°, Paris, 1844 (xxxix, 437 pp.).[1]
V. Oeuvres complètes de Bernard Palissy publiées d'après des textes originaux, avec une notice historique et bibliographique, par Anatole France, 8°, Paris, 1880. (The text is practically Cap's with substitution of j for i and v for u, in places.)
VI. Les oeuvres de Maistre Bernard Palissy. Nouvelle édition revue sur les textes originaux par B. Fillon, avec une Notice historique, bibliographique et iconologique (96 pp.) par Louis Audiat, 2 vols. la. 8°, Niort, 1888; contains a Palissy MS. first publ. in 1862: Devis d'une Grotte pour le Roye Mère.

Palissy's *Ordonnance de la grotte rustique de monseigneur le duc de Montmorency*, La Rochelle, 1563, was reprinted in 8°, Paris, 1919 (BM 07816. c. 18). Translations of many parts of his works are given by Morley.

Whilst important in the history of literature and the technical arts, the works of Palissy contain little of direct interest to chemistry, and no actual discovery can be attributed to him. He ridicules the alchemists,[2] although it was an alchemist, J. F. Böttiger (1682–1719), who succeeded in 1709 in making porcelain, which was beyond Palissy.[3] Palissy[4] says he wasted forty years 'scratching the earth' in reading the works of Geber, the *Roman de la Roze* and *Raimond Lule*, and he had available the *Miroir d'Alchimie* (1557; see Vol. I), a work of 1551 entitled *De la transformation métallique*, containing a *Bref discours des admirables vertus de l'or potable* . . . by Gilles de la Tourette, and *Une apologie de la très utile science d'Alchimie*. The style of the *Opuscule très excellent* . . . attributed to Denys Zacchaire (1567) (Vol. I) may[5] have given Palissy the idea for his account of his efforts to make enamelled pottery. In another place Palissy says he learnt alchemy 'by the teeth'. He was not, of course, exempt from some popular superstitions and beliefs, although his attitude towards astrology was cool. Thorndike is hard pressed to find good examples in Palissy in support of his favourite thesis, and a mere experimental scientist reading Palissy will probably get a favourable opinion of him. Palissy condemns readers of books[6] and his treatise on clay[7] is the work of a practical potter; yet Brongniart, an authority on ceramics, says[8] that if Palissy had paid more attention to theory he would have spared himself time and trouble; such theoretical views as he puts forward, although indicating 'a spirit of observation', have 'little foundation'. This seems to be too severe.

Dupuy[9] shows that Palissy borrowed (mostly without acknowledgment) from the French translations (he knew no Latin) of Cardan, Dioskourides, Pliny (through the *Propos rustique* of Noël du Fail, 1547), Isidore of Seville (by oral tradition), the *Lapidaire* of ψ-Mandeville, Vincent de Beauvais (as excerpted in *L'image du monde* and the *Trésor* of Latini), Pierre Belon, Jean Bullant, and other authors. Palissy seems to ascribe to himself two observations which he had read in Vitruvius, one on the expansion of water on

[1] Morley, 1852, ii, 208, says this is a better edition than III.
[2] *Traité des métaux;* III, 1777, 315; IV, 1844, 188 f.
[3] Schmieder, 1832, 471; Kopp, (4), i, 129; Bucher, *Geschichte der technischen Künste*, iii, 533; E. Kalkschmidt, *Die Goldmacher Joh. Fr. Böttger und die Erfindung des europäischen Porzellans*, Stuttgart, 1926.
[4] *Discours admirable*, preface; IV, 1844, 130; Morley, ii, 101.   [5] Dupuy, 148 f., 154.
[6] *De l'art de terre*; III, 1777, 5; IV, 1844, lxxiii, 129; Morley, 1852, ii, 97.
[7] *Des terres d'argile*; III, 1777, 38; IV, 1844, 298.   [8] 1854, ii, 61.   [9] 1902, 156 f.

heating and the other on the aeolipile;[1] his account of the Corinthian capital is taken almost bodily from a summary of Vitruvius in French published in 1559.[2] Thorndike says he knew Latin, but Palissy implies that he did not.

Palissy shines as a close and accurate observer of natural objects, a man of eminent common sense, and an original and laborious experimenter. He advocated that observation and experiment are the only sure way of acquiring knowledge of nature. In this he had been anticipated by Roger Bacon (Vol. I), but he anticipated some ideas in the *Novum Organum* (1620) of Francis Bacon, who visited Paris in 1576 with Sir Amyas Paulet and lived there three years. He *may* have heard Palissy lecture and seen his museum, but he says nothing about this. In a lost tract, *Temporis partus maximus*, which in 1625 he said he had published about forty years before (*c.* 1585), Bacon *may* have been directly influenced by Palissy, but this is only conjecture.[3]

Palissy offered to explain difficult parts of his *Discours admirable* and to make models for those who could not carry out the directions in it.[4] The various parts of the work are entitled (pagination of 1580 ed.): des eaux (1); de l'alchimie, des metaux (84); de l'or potable (138); du mitridat (148); des glaces (156); des diverses sortes des sels, vegetatifs ou generatifs (163); du sel commun (179); des pierres tant communes que precieuses (193); des diverses terres d'argile (254); de l'art de terre, des esmaux et du feu (266); de la marne (295–361). In what follows, these treatises are quoted by their separate names. In the preface Palissy refers to a museum or cabinet in which he had collected a large number of *labelled* specimens of mineral products, from which more could be learnt in a few hours than by reading books for fifty years. His audience in his lectures comprised physicians (including Ambriose Paré), canons, lawyers, dukes and nobility,[5] and in some ways his museum and lecture room foreshadowed the Royal Institution in London.[6] The 'Monsieur de Ruisi'[7] may be Nicolas Rasse des Noeux, the king's surgeon,[8] but he is mentioned in the same place as 'Monsieur Race'. Palissy's works are mostly dialogues between 'Theorique' and 'Practique', in which the former is always refuted. They were practically unknown in France until the 18 cent., although Hugh Platt[9] gave an account of them. Palissy is mentioned by Mersenne[10] and C. Sorel.[11] Reaumur[12] praised his observational power and his style.[13] Palissy was mentioned by a large number of authors in the 18 cent.[14]

In the treatise on water and fountains[15] Palissy says thermal springs have

---

[1] Vitruvius, *De Architectura*, i, 6.   [2] Dupuy, 176 f., 180.
[3] Hanschmann, 1903; Allbutt, 1921, 576 f.; W. Frost, *F. Bacon und die Naturphilosophie*, Munich, 1927, 453, regards Hanschmann's view as too speculative.
[4] IV, 1844, 134.   [5] *Des pierres*; IV, 1844, 270 f.
[6] Dupuy, 1902, 212 f.   [7] *Des metaux*; IV, 1844, 219.
[8] Leroux, 1927, 67.
[9] *Jewell House of Art and Nature*, 1594, pt. ii, see p. 102.
[10] *Questions théologiques, physiques, morales et mathématiques*, Paris, 1634.
[11] *La Science universelle*, 4 vols., Paris, 1635–44; new ed., 1668, BM 1135. f. 2–5.
[12] AdS, 1720, h 5, m 400.
[13] On the latter, and his peculiar words, see Dupuy, 1902, 235 f., and glossary, 277 f.
[14] List in III; Audiat, VI, 1888, I, cxviii f.
[15] *Des eaux et fontaines*; III, 1777, 239 f.; IV, 1844, 150 f.; Morley, 1852, ii, 124; *Resources: A Treatise on 'Waters and Springs' written by Bernard Palissy in 1557*, tr. E. E. Willett, Brighton, 1876 (39 pp.).

been heated by subterranean fires of sulphur, coal (charbon de terre), ignited by falling or moving rocks, and peat and bitumen. Earthquakes are caused by subterranean fires, water and air (he mentions the aeolipile). The medicinal virtues of mineral waters are due to dissolved salts, since salt preserves fish, etc. Spa waters are not hot but, as physicians say, contain iron, and many French waters would be just as good. Terrestrial waters come ultimately from rain and not from the sea. Palissy suggested boring for water (artesian wells) and explained the effect of rocky strata below sands carrying water; water never rises above the level of its source. He recognised that water dissolves minerals from the earth and explained the cause of goitre by such impurities in the water. In another treatise[1] he says the rainbow is formed by sunlight shining on drops of water.

His treatise on stones[2] and his *Recepte véritable*[3] describe experiments on the crystallisation of salts, and speculations on the formation of rocks, which have some resemblance to those of Avicenna (Vol. I). His treatise on marl[4] mentions its use as manure, already well known to the Romans (Vol. I), and the works on salts[5] state that plants extract salts from the soil: there is much simple agricultural lore in his *Recepte véritable*.[6] Manures return to the soil salts taken out by crops; they lose these salts when exposed to rain.[7] The presence of salts in plants is shown by burning them; *sal alcaly* is formed by burning salicor in Narbonne and Saintes, or fern (*fougere*).[8] Salts are present in fruits, e.g. grapes, since wine lees form on burning corrosive tartar like the alkali from salicor;[9] these are used by the alchemists to whiten copper.[10] Palissy thought the tannin of oak bark was a salt,[11] but he correctly classed copperas (couppe rose), vitriol, nitre, sal ammoniac (armoniac), salt of tartar and borax (bourras) among salts.[12] Metals and stones contain salts, since they are reduced to ashes on burning, and quicklime contains an alkaline salt.[13] Palissy thought quartz crystals had been deposited from water like the similar crystals of salt-petre;[14] stalactites are deposited from some kind of salt dissolved by water in percolating through the earth.[15] Precious stones are formed from waters in the earth[16] and their colours are due to metallic parts, e.g. copper in emerald and cobalt (*saphre*) in turquoise. Glass is not corroded by moonbeams, but by rain dissolving its saline part, and glass also contains water.[17]

Various salts (common salt, saltpetre, alum, copperas, etc.) dissolved in water crystallise out separately by reason of a peculiar attraction of like particles, like a magnetic force or the (electric) attraction of amber or jet.[18] There are two waters, one common and exhalative and the other essential, congelative and generative, which flows concealed in streams, etc., and forms crystals, minerals and salts, just as animal sperm forms organised beings. From ashes of plants a glass clear as water can be formed, the exhalative water having been driven off in the fire. Wood and shells have been metallised, and

---

[1] *Des Metaux*; IV, 1844, 204. [2] *Des pierres*; III, 1777, 54; IV, 1844, 261.
[3] IV, 1844, 45. [4] *De la marne*; III, 1777, 141; IV, 1844, 325.
[5] *Des sels divers*; *Du sel commun*; III, 1777, 203 f.; IV, 1844, 241.
[6] III, 1777, 489; IV, 1844, 1 f. [7] IV, 18, 23 f. [8] *Ib.*, 19. [9] *Ib.*, 20.
[10] *Ib.*, 41. [11] *Ib.*, 21. [12] *Ib.*, 22, 53. [13] *Ib.*, 31 f. [14] *Ib.*, 45.
[15] *Ib.*, 47. [16] *Ib.*, 51 f. [17] *Ib.*, 50 f. [18] *Des Metaux*; IV, 211, 221.

fossil fish in Mansfeld reduced to metal (pyrites) by mineral water.[1] Palissy showed marcasite crystals attached to a piece of slate which must have been deposited from water,[2] just like fossil shells, and since crystals of various ores have shapes like salt crystals he thought they were formed from salts dissolved in water, although a kind of oil may have contributed to the formation of metals and formed their 'sulphur' on coagulation. He thought metals felt a kind of sympathy and voided excrements as well as took nourishment; common sulphur is such an excrement, like turpentine from pines.

Sir Thomas Browne[3] explained the deposition of crystals as due to a 'mineralising spirit' present in the solution, or a 'retreat into their proper solidities' of the dissolved salts. In his treatise on salts[4] Palissy says they are innumerable, everything having its specific salt, including metals: he mentions copperas, nitre, vitriol, alum, borax (borras, which he elsewhere[5] says is white, crystalline, and a secret preparation), sugar (sucre), sublimate, saltpetre (salpestre), sal gemme, salicor, sal alkali, tartar and sal ammoniac. Every soluble, odorous and sapid material is a salt, including the tannin of oak bark. Salt is a cement for all things (vn mastic qui lie et mastique toutes choses),[6] it gives sonority to metals, aids generation, gives transparency, etc., etc.[7]

Palissy repeats his theory of manures (see p. 73), which supply, not common salt, but 'des sels vegetatifs'.[8] Birds peck old mortar to get the lime from it.[9] After giving uses of salts, Palissy says:[10] 'ie ne suis point capable de descrire l'excellence des sels, ny leurs vertus merueilleuses', and gives a long definition of a salt. He was acquainted with the action of alum as a mordant by attracting the dissolved colour and fixing it to the fabric.[11]

The treatise on common salt[12] describes the manufacture of 'solar' salt in Saintes ('aux isles de Xaintonge'). Palissy was a member of the tax (gabelle) commission there. The evaporation was carried out in 'meadows' connected with an 'iard' (English, yard) or receptacle, which is filled in March, and the evaporation carried out in the three or four hottest months.

The work *De la dignité et utilité du sel* which he mentions[13] is by Jean de Marcoville, a physician.[14] The treatise on stones[15] says they do not grow by a vegetative action but by a congelative augmentation, like melted wax solidifying on a mass of solid wax, from salts carried in water and dissolved from the earth, by crystallisation:

les pluyes qui passent au travers des terres prennent les sels qui sont aussi inconnus, lesquels sels ou matieres metalliques sont fluentes et se laissent couler avec les eaux qui entrent dans la terre jusques à ce qu'elles ayent trouvé quelque fonds pour s'arrester: et si elles s'arrestent sur une carriere ou miniere de pierre, lesdites matieres estant liquides passent au travers des terres, et ayans trouve lieu pour s'arrester se viennnent à congeler et endurcir et faire un corps et une masse pour l'autre pierre.[16]

He got this idea by a visit to a stalactite cavern: 'nous vismes distiller l'eau qui

---

[1] IV, 216 f., 218 f.; Morley, ii, 177 f.   [2] IV, 206, 213, 215 f.
[3] *Pseudodoxia Epidemica*, bk. ii, ch. 1; *Works*, ed. Keynes, 1928, ii, 88.
[4] *De Sels Divers*; IV, 241.   [5] *Des pierres*, IV, 286.   [6] *Ib.*, 244.
[7] See also the summary in *Du Sel commun*, IV, 260.   [8] IV, 246.   [9] *Ib.*, 248.
[10] *Ib.*, 250.   [11] *Ib.*, 249.   [12] IV, 1844, 251 f.   [13] IV, 258.
[14] Dupuy, 1902, 173.   [15] *Des pierres*; IV, 261 f.   [16] *Ib.*, 263.

se congeloit en nostre presence'.[1] He had over a hundred pieces of fossil wood and had been told of fossilised men.

Salts have some affinity (*affinité*) for one another,[2] so that vitriol can do nothing but convert into copper the things which it finds. He had also seen wood converted into metal (pyrites?) in the earth by means of copperas. He explains[3] the petrifaction of shells by infiltered water as follows:

Et estant en terre, par leur vertu salsitive on fait [les coquilles] attraction d'un sel generatif, qui estant joinct avec celuy de la coquille en quelque lieu aqueux ou humide, l'affinité desdites matieres estant jointes à ce corps mixte ont endurcy et petrifié la masse principalle.

Palissy denies Cardan's statement[4] that stones have vegetative souls and the belief that fossils were dispersed by the Deluge.[5] In 1686, Emanuel König, a rational author very well informed on recent publications, believed that minerals are growing plants buried in the earth.[6] Marcasite crystals must have been deposited from water like salt crystals, but stones must have taken the shape of the mould in which they were deposited.[7]

Iron, lead, silver and antimony produce yellow colours in glazes and the colours of gems are due to metallic constituents entering when the earthy part solidified,[8] although yellow Lorraine glass (for windows) is coloured with rotten wood (bois pourry) and dyers use a herb called gaude (weld). The only thing he knew[9] which coloured stones blue was *saphre* (i.e. cobalt) 'a mineral extracted from gold, silver and copper', which, although grey itself, forms a beautiful blue with glass; hence lapis lazuli may also contain cobalt. Chrysocolla (which he thought was the ancient borax) is a salt formed by water passing through copper mines. Some blues are made with copper, but this is 'by accident, not by nature'.[10] The transparent selenite, like talc, called *hif*, is found in the plaster works at Montmartre; most of its substance is water, and it may be calcined like other plaster. Hard stones are formed only where there is much water; opaque stones contain admixed earth, which has sometimes settled out in the lower part.[11]

The treatise on clays[12] explains that clay (terre d'argile) had been called an adherent (tenante), glutinous, and viscous earth (une terre visqueuse, grasse et glueuse), but it mixes with water and is hence not oily or viscous. It would be better to call it pasty earth (terre pasteuse). There is a good classification of earths into refractory, fusible, etc., black earths which burn white, yellow earths which burn red, etc. Good drying is necessary before clay objects are fired, otherwise they burst: the exhalative humour must first be driven out slowly, otherwise 'a thunder is engendered' from the heat and moisture, like natural thunder. By adding sand, the pores are made larger for the moisture to escape and this is done by the Paris potters. Clays vary considerably and one is 'toujours apprentif à cause des natures inconnuës és diversitez des terres'.[13]

---

[1] *Ib.*, 266. [2] *Ib.*, 267. [3] *Ib.*, 275.
[4] *De Subtilitate*, see p. 12; Palissy's use of Cardan was quite extensive, Dupuy, 156.
[5] *Ib.*, 272 f.; his discussion is the basis of modern geology, A. Buckley, 1883, 214.
[6] *Regnum Minerale*, 4°, Basel, 1686, 16 f.
[7] *Des pierres*; IV, 282. [8] *Des pierres*; IV, 285.
[9] Perhaps from the French translation of Biringuccio, 1556, see p. 32; Dupuy, 1902, 77
[10] *Ib.*, 288. [11] *Ib.*, 293. [12] *Des terres d'argile*; IV, 298 f. [13] *Ib.*, 301–4.

The famous treatise *De l'art de terre*[1] contains the story of Palissy's early struggles and failures as a potter, and his final success in making painted ware, a kind of faïence. He discusses whether he should reveal his secrets or not, giving examples of trades which have ceased to provide their practitioners with a living because the processes have been too freely revealed, and he finishes by giving practically no information at all, saying only:[2]

Les esmaux dequoy ie fais ma besongne, sont faits d'estaing, de plomb, de fer, d'acier, d'antimoine, de saphre, de cuiure, d'arene, de salicort, de cendre grauelée, de litarge, de pierre de Perigord [manganese dioxide]. Voila les propres matieres desquelles ie fais mes esmaux.

Coloured enamels had been used before by della Robbia in Italy.

In his *Traité de la marne*,[3] Palissy calls his 'generative water' a 'fifth element',[4] which is carried along with common exhalative water in streams, rivers, etc., and when in repose forms stones, etc. He announces his theory of artesian wells[5] (voire des eaux pour faire puits, laquelle bien souuent pourroit monter plus haut que le lieu où la pointe de la tariere les aura trouvées), and says there are bands (bans) of earth, sand, stone, and clay in the earth. Palissy reserved his practical processes for his own uses and discoursed only on generalities.[6]

Metals are composed of mercury (argent vif), sulphur, and also some salt which aids their congelation.[7] But the red colour of gold is probably due to antimony, not sulphur, since a little antimony colours a large quantity of mercury yellow.[8] In his treatise on metals and alchemy[9] Palissy says the opinion of the multiplication, generation and augmentation of metals is 'plus inueteree en la ceruelle de plusieurs hommes que nulle des autres opinions'. Three kinds of practitioners of alchemy are blameless: (1) the rich (seigneurs) who pursue it for recreation; (2) the physicians (physiciens, medicins) who wish to understand the natures; and (3) those who have the power and believe it possible but do not wish to abuse it. The thousands of others, incapable by ignorance and lack of experience, who lack means, abuse outer tinctures and sophistications of metals. Alchemists and false coiners had protection in high places.[10] Their tricks are exposed. Metals and minerals grew from seeds made at the Creation, each producing only its own species:[11]

c'est l'oeuvre de Dieu que de semer la matiere des metaux et leur donner l'accroissement, et aux hommes de les recueillir, purifier et examiner, fondre et mallier . . . les semences des metaux sont semences divines . . . inconnuës aux hommes, voir invisible . . . les semences des metaux et de tous mineraux et de toutes pierres ont esté créées en un mesme jour, . . . les metaux sont engendrez d'une eau, à sçavoir d'eau salée, ou pour mieux dire d'un sel dissout.

Since metals are formed from a salt dissolved in water they cannot be generated by fire. In a dialogue[12] 'Theory' says there is no harm in trying to tinge silver into gold by oil of antimony or oil of gold, or in taking fine copper

---

[1] IV, 306–24.   [2] *Ib.*, 321.   [3] IV, 325 f.   [4] *Ib.*, 332.
[5] *Ib.*, 341.   [6] Allbutt, 1921, 566.   [7] *Recepte verit.*; IV, 53.
[8] He may be thinking of the formation of cinnabar with antimony sulphide?
[9] III, 311–60; IV, 188–223; Morley, ii, 153 f.   [10] IV, 199.
[11] IV, 192 f., 203.   [12] *Des Sels divers*; IV, 249.

and removing its phlegm or red tincture so as to give it the colour of silver. 'Practice' retorted that thousands had wasted time and means on this and achieved nothing.

Palissy[1] denied the medicinal value of potable gold, mentioning Paracelsus (probably through Roch le Baillif)[2] as 'monarque entre les medicins'. Antimony is not a metal but a kind of marcasite or the 'commencement of metal', and a dangerous poison. Only bodies capable of putrefaction can be digested in the stomach and gold is not. In a short essay[3] Palissy criticised the theriac, composed of a great number of drugs (Vol. I). He believed in Aristotle's theory that water in wells is colder in summer than in winter because the warmth in the air 'produces its contrary', i.e. antiperistasis.[4]

PICCOLPASSO

The earliest known monograph in a European language on the potter's art is that of Cipriano Piccolpasso (Castel Durante; 1524–21 November 1579), a military architect and brother of a potter:

Li tre libri dell'arte del vasaio nei quai si tratta non solo la practica ma brevemente tutti gli secreti di essa cosa che per sino al di d'oggi è stata sempre tenuta ascosta, del cavaliere Cipriano Piccolpasso Durantino. The Three Books of the Potter's Art which treat not only of the practice but also briefly of all the secrets of this art, a matter which until to-day has always been kept concealed. By Cavaliere Cipriano Piccolpasso of Castel Durante, text and tr. by B. Rackham and A. van de Put, London (Victoria and Albert Museum), 1934, xxii, 85 pp., 80 plates (no index).

The work was more or less completely printed in Italian in 1857 and 1879, and in French in 1860 or 1861; the Victoria and Albert MS. is dated in a different hand 1548, but the original was probably written in 1556–9. The author sometimes did not understand what he was describing and has the Renaissance tendency to labour the trivial and obvious; there is some fulsome flattery of his patron Guidobaldo II, Duke of Urbino. Parts of it are based on Biringuccio, who is said not to have dealt adequately with the glazes,[5] but the order of treatment is much inferior to Biringuccio's or Agricola's.

The work is mostly concerned with (i) maiolica (for which Castel Durante was famous), covered with a ruby lustre containing cuprous oxide and a golden lustre containing silver, and (ii) faïence (Delft) wares, covered with white opaque tin glaze, introduced into Italy in the 14 cent. if not earlier from the Near East, perhaps by way of Spain; in Piccolpasso's time it was somewhat outmoded. The lead-glazed ware made at Bologna and elsewhere (sgraffiato ware) is not described in detail. At that time potters were using various coloured glazes, including a blue from cobalt (zaffre) and a bright yellow (zalulino) from antimony.

The first book deals with clays, the potter's wheel (turned with the foot),

---

[1] De l'Or potable; III, 361; IV, 224.

[2] Premier Traicté de l'Homme, et son essentielle Anatomie, auec les Elemens, & ce qui est en eux: De ses Maladies, Medecine, & absoluts remedes és Tainctures d'Or, Corail, & Antimoine; & magistere des Perles: & de leur extraction, 8°, Paris, 1580, 62 pp. viii ll. (BM 784. d. 10. (2.)).

[3] Du Mitridat ou Theriaque; III, 375; IV, 231.

[4] IV, 238; see Vol. I, and Boyle, p. 510.   [5] 1934, I, 23.

plaster of paris moulds, and wood and iron tools. Soils containing *genga* yield white clay; a chalky clay (*terra creta*) is mentioned, and the washing, levigation, and beating of the clay ready for the wheel are described. The second book deals with glazes and pigments, grinding mills worked by hand, asses, or water power, kilns, firing, and special processes for making lustred maiolica. Tartar (*taso*) is burnt in heaps (producing an unpleasant smell) to a white ash which must be kept in closed vessels. For the properties and uses of tartar the author quotes Dioskourides; burnt tartar is called lees (*feccia*). A frit of sand and lees is *marzacotto* and various proportions are specified:[1]

sand	30	30	30	30	
lees	12	10	4	9	or unburnt tartar 7 (!)

The marzacotto is similar to the *martiacocta* mentioned by Scaliger[2] as made from alkali (chali) or else burnt tartar, alum, sand, and lead, to which 'cassiteri, quod Angli vocant, glaciale' (i.e. bismuth) is added. This would be a glaze. The marzacotto is heated in pots in the kiln until it is as hard as a stone: it would be potassium silicate. The best white silvery sand is from San Giovanni in Tuscany.[3] In Venice, Levant ashes [sucla] were used.[4]

Piccolpasso then describes the burning of tin.[5] The best Flanders tin [from Cornwall] is melted in an iron ladle, poured into a wooden bowl and beaten with a wooden pestle (*pestel*), when it will turn into ashes (in cenare); or it is poured through a linen jelly-bag (which would not give calcined tin). In the calcination (*calcinatione*), good block tin (stagnio di massa) is mixed with 6 or 7 times its weight of lead, or old pewter (*peltri*) is mixed with 4 times its weight of lead. The metal is melted on the hearth of the reverberatory furnace (il fornello di Reverbero) and the dross raked off to the side with an iron hoe, hence the process is called the drag (trainello). Some throw bits of sulphur on the fire to assist the calcination. Burnt lead (*piombo abrugiato*), which is reddish (litharge), is made similarly.[6]

There are recipes for coloured glazes,[7] some being used in his brother's works, some in the March (*della Marca*, perhaps Ancona), and others in Venice. The white glaze contains calcined tin and lead (e.g. 30 tin and 100 lead); a colour without gloss is made from 40 lb. sand, 20 lb. lees, 8 oz. of azure and 4 oz. of burnt copper (*ramia*). Some compositions include antimony (*antimonio; stimmi over stibio*) for the properties and uses of which Dioskourides is quoted. It is found in Siena and the Maremma, but the best came from Venice. Calcined iron rust (best from anchors) is *ferraccia*.[8] *Zaffara* 'called by us *azurro*', was obtained from Venice; manganese (*il manganese*; i.e. pyrolusite) is found all over Italy and used wherever glass is made.[8] Compositions for glazes are:

Green					*Yellow*			
antimony	1	3	2	2	ferraccia	$\frac{1}{2}$	2	$1\frac{1}{2}$
ramina	4	6	6	3	lead	$1\frac{1}{2}$	5	2
lead	1	2	3	3	antimony	1	3	2

[1] 1934, pp. 29, 31, 38.
[2] *Exotericarvm Exercitationvm*, Paris, 1557, Exerc. CCXX, f. 181 *v*.
[3] 1934, 30.   [4] *Ib.*, 50.   [5] *Ib.*, 32.   [6] *Ib.*, 35–6.   [7] *Ib.*, 32–3, 38.   [8] *Ib.*, 34.

Light Yellow

antimony	lb.	1	2	4	2
lead	lb.	1½	3	6	3
lees	oz.	1	1	1	1
common salt	oz.	1	½	0	½

To make light yellow some add Alexandrian tutty (*tutia allesandrina*).[1] These mixtures obviously need melting with the *marzacotto*. A firing kiln is rectangular with a hearth and a barrel roof, holes in the floor and roof for the flames from the fire to pass through, and four spy-holes in one side for examining the inside.[1] It is started as follows: 'Invoking the name of God, take a handful of straw, and with the sign of the cross light the fire of dried wood.' Firing continued for twelve hours.

After describing the mill for grinding the glaze, the author gives recipes[2] for whites, and marzacottos (which now contain tin and lead). *Colore* is a white coating or painted surface, mostly tin enamel, but for Castillo ware pipe-clay; below its recipe is one for its glaze (*la sua coperte*) made from marzacotto and lead,[3] so that this is a clear glaze applied (*copertare*) over the *colore* after painting, the application of the enamel (*bianco*) itself being called glazing (*invetriare*):

Ordinary White					*The Glaze*			
Marzacotto	30	32	31		Lead	17	16	8½
Tin	12	12	11		Sand	20	20	10
					Lees	12	13	6
					Salt	8	9	4

In other cases the marzacotto has a composition similar to the above glaze, but with tin instead of lead. A pale blue *colore* contains a little zaffre, either with or without tin:

Lees	lb.	5	4	Tin	12	
Sand	lb.	5	5	Marzacotto	10	
Lead	lb.	2	3	Sand	8	
Zaffre	oz.	1	1*	Blue	3	
Salt	oz.	1	1			

* P. 49 has lb. in mistake for oz.

Black				*Maiolica Red*			
						A	B
Burnt copper	1	0		Red earth	oz.	3	6
Manganese	1	1		Armenian bole	oz.	1	0
Sand	6	12		Ferretto of Spain*	oz.	2	3
Lead	10	12		Cinnabar†	oz.	0	3
Black Zaffre	0	1					

* Calcined copper. † Probably ferric oxide.

The descriptions are obscure: 'If you desire to stain it, copper is taken away, then the staining is done, pouring upon it Ferrarese white mixed with a little glaze, which will appear liquid and rich.'[4] It is never clear whether the outer

---

[1] *Ib.*, 39.   [2] *Ib.*, 44–51.   [3] *Ib.*, 47.   [4] *Ib.*, 50.

clear glaze (coperta) is put on in a second firing, or directly on top of the painted white enamel. In making a golden maiolica glaze, the second (B above) maiolica red composition is mixed with a Carlino (a silver coin, a weight) of calcined silver (*mesti un Carlino di Argento calcinato*); *argentum ustum*, according to Libavius[1] was made by heating silver amalgam and Roman vitriol in a cavity between two bricks. For maiolica, the kiln was square, and was lighted 'always in the blessed name of God', the fire being very smoky (as the illustration shows). The fired maiolica was soaked in a tub of lye (*lessia*) to clean the surface which was then polished with a dry cloth. The surface would have a film of copper or silver, reduced by the smoky fire.[2]

Book three deals with grinding colours, painting designs on the surface of the glazing and the second (?) firing to fuse on the glaze, and gives some stock designs. The *colore* (glaze) is ground with water on a porphyry or in a mortar or in a mill (a circular stone revolving and also turning round over a stone base by means of a crank mechanism as in Biringuccio). A cream of ground glaze and water was kept stirred with the hand, and the biscuit ware dipped in it in ways which (as well as the method of coating the interior of pots) are described in detail. The pieces were then put on a table suspended so that it could be turned, and the surface painted with brushes of ass's or goat's hair or mouse whiskers,[3] a separate brush being used for each. Red is difficult, Armenian bole with red vinegar, painted over light yellow, being perhaps the only good way.[4] *Pignatte* or *pentole* is a white ware invented by the Duke of Ferrara; the glaze is:

lead	lb.	3	21	20
sand	lb.	2	7	8
ferraccia	oz.	1½ lb.	1	1

It is applied twice as thickly as others, and the painting is with black and blue zaffre. The ware is then ready for firing.

The pieces are put in a sagger (*case*), flat ware on stilts like chess pawns but pointed; if pots are inverted the glaze is scraped from the rim. 'In the name of Jesus Christ the setting of the kiln is begun.'[5] When the stacking is complete, 'prayers are offered to God with all the heart'[6] and the firing begun, 'remembering always to do all things in the name of Jesus Christ.' The fire must appear equally bright through all the four spy-holes, otherwise it is increased where it is needed; it lasts twelve hours. When the kiln is cooler, the inside can be inspected by putting a piece of wood on an iron rod through a spy-hole, when it kindles and illuminates the interior. 'Amongst all the things sought after in this art, keeping clean the colour and having a good eye for the fire seem to me to be of great importance.'[7]

GESNER

Conrad Gesner (Zürich; 26 March 1516–13 December 1565), professor of Greek at Lausanne (1537) and of physics and natural history (1541) at

---

[1] *Alchymia*, 1606, 47.   [2] Piccolpasso, 53.   [3] *Ib.*, 61.
[4] *Ib.*, 64.   [5] *Ib.*, 67.   [6] *Ib.*, 69.   [7] *Ib.*, 57.

Zürich, was a voluminous writer.[1] There is an extensive set of his works in the Gesner Collection, Zentralbibliothek, Zürich. His work on fossils and stones:

De omni Rervm Fossilivm Genere, Gemmis, Lapidibvs, Metallis, et hvivsmodi libri aliqvot, pleriqve nvnc primvm editi. Opera Conradi Gesner, 8°, Tiguri, Jac. Gessner, M.D.LXV. Contents: Kentmani Dresdensis Medici Nomenclaturæ Rerum fossilium. Eiusdem Calculorum qui in corpore ac membris hominum uinas eūtur. De Metallicis rebus ac nominibus observationes variæ & eruditæ ex Schedis Georgij Fabricij quibus ea potissimùm explicantur quæ Georgius Agricola præteriit. Seuerini Gœbelij . . . de Succino libri II. prior Theologicus, posterior physicus & medicus. Valerij Cordi de Halosantho seu Sperma Ceti liber. S. Epiphanij . . . de duodecim gemmis . . . Liber Graecus & Latinus. Fr. Ruei medici Insulani De Gemmis aliquot. Hic recte iungetur in idem volumen Conradi Gesneri De rerū fossilium . . . cum iconibus plurimis. (BM 987. b. 20 does not contain any illustrations or any work by Gesner); contents in Migne, *Patrologia Græca*, XLI, ix f.; 8, 95, 1 blank; 2, 22 f.; 3 31 f.; 2, 36 f. (last blank); 3, 37 f.; 4, 28 f.; 2, 85 f.; 7, 169 f.; numerous woodcuts; the work of Gesner is no. 8, De rerum fossilium, lapidum et gemmarum maxime, figg. et similitudinibus, liber cum iconibus plurimis.

contains a description and picture of a lead pencil made with English graphite (worked at Borrowdale from about 1550): stylus inferius depictus ad scribendum factus est, plumbi cujusdam genere, in mucronem derasi, in manubrium ligneum inserti.[2] The blacklead pencil, however, is mentioned by Theophilus Presbyter (10 cent.; Vol. I). Gesner's book describes and illustrates a dish of 'porcellana' or 'majorica' (majolica), a white ceramic with painting in blue, very hard and solid.[3] The first description of true porcelain ('porcelaine') which he saw in Cairo and was told came from the Indies (des Indes; really from China) was given by Pierre Belon (p. 94).[4] Rauwolf (d. 1596) saw porcelain cups used for coffee in Aleppo in 1573.[5]

The work of Rueus (François de la Rue, Lille, 1520–85) had been published[6] with some passages deleted by the censor. Gesner regretted this and added some passages from another book by Rueus on astrological images to fill the gap.[7] The work by Fabricius[8] quotes the *Genialium Dierum Sex* (Rome, 1522, BM 90.e.5) of Alessandro Alessandri of Naples (1461–1523) for a plant having leaves of pure gold, and says Osiander (the editor of Copernicus, who was himself interested in medicine) wore a gold chain on his neck to prevent infection by leprosy.[9]

Gesner published anonymously an illustrated work on distillation (based on Brunschwig and Ulstadius):

Thesavrvs Evonymi Philiatri, De Remediis Secretis. Liber Physicus, Medicus Et partim etiam Chymicus, & œconomicus in uinorum diuersi saporis apparatu, medicis &

[1] Benedicenti, q. in *Isis*, 1929, xiii, 257; Cap, *Études Biographiques*, 1864, ii, 47; Ferguson, i, 313; ii, 36; Saverien, 1773, viii, 15 (portr.); Thorndike, vi, 307, and index, 672; R. Wolf, *Biographien zur Kulturgeschichte der Schweiz*, Zürich, 1858, i, 15.

[2] Gesner, 1565, 104; Feldhaus, 106; *id., Z. angew. Chem.*, 1918, xxxi, 76; C. A. Mitchell, *J. Soc. Chem. Ind.*, 1919, xxxviii, 383T; E. A. Voice, *Trans. Newcomen Soc.*, 1949–51 (1956), xxvii, 131–41.

[3] 1565, 113.

[4] *Les Observations de Plvsievrs Singvlaritez . . .* , 1553, bk. ii, ch. 71, p. 315.

[5] Prandtl, *Chymia*, 1953, iv, 115; Hoefer, NBG, 1862, xli, 715.

[6] *De gemmis aliquot iis praesertim quarum divus Ioannis Apostolos in sua Apocalypsi meminit,* 8°, Paris, 1547.

[7] Thorndike, vi, 303.   [8] Gesner, 1565, f. 2 r–v.

[9] *Ib.*, f. 4 r: aureum cathenam collo gestauit ne lepra inficeretur.

pharmacopolis omnibus præcipue necessarius . . . , sm. 8°, Zürich, per Andream Gessner. F. & Radolphum Wyssenbachium, 1552, 576 (misnumb. 580) pp., 24 ll. (Ferguson, i, 315; Duveen, 245); Zürich, 1554 (576 misnumb. 580 pp., 20 ll.); 16°, Lyons, 1555 (pp. (8), 498, (38)); sm. 8°, Venice, no printer's name, 1556 (567 pp., (41) pp. index; my copy); Italian tr. by Pietro Lauro, Tesauro di Evonomo Filatro De Rimedi Secreti, 8°, Venice, Fratelli, 1556 (152, (16) ll., Duveen, 246), 1560; English tr. by Peter Morwyng, 'felow of Magdaline Colleadge in Oxford', A new booke of destillatyon of waters, called the Treasure of Evonymvs Whereunto is added a profitable table or Index . . . , 4°, London, 1559 (Ferguson, i, 315), 1565 (Ferguson, i, 314); French tr. by Barthélemy Aneau, Trésor de Euonime Philiatre des Remedes Secretz, 8°, Lyons, 1555, 1558, 1559; German tr. by Johann Rudolph Landenberger, Ein Köstlicher Theürer Schatz Euonymi Philiatri . . . , sm. 4°, Zürich, getruckt bey Andrea und Jacobo den Gessneren gebrüder, 1555[1] and Zürich, 1608,[2] with title: Köstlicher Artzneyschatz dess . . . Evonymi Philiatri. The second part, ed. Caspar Wolf, was publ. posthumously as: Euonymus. Conradi Gesneri . . . de Remediis secretis Liber secundus nunc primum opera et studio Caspari Wolphii . . . in lucem editus, 8°, (Zürich, 1569) (Duveen, 247). It was tr. by Liébaut as Quatre Livres Des Secrets de Médecine, et de la Philosophie Chimique. Faicts François par M. Jean Liebaut Dijonnois, Docteur Médecin à Paris. Esquels sont descrits plusieurs remedes singuliers pour toutes maladies . . . : traictees bien amplement les maniers de destiller eaux, huiles, & quintes essences de toute sorte de matieres, preparer l'Antimoine & la poudre de mercure: . . . 8°, Paris, 1573, 1579;[3] Engl. tr. by George Baker as: The newe Iewell of Health, wherein is contayned the most excellent Secretes of Phisicke and Philosophie, deuided into fower Bookes. In the which are the best approued remedies for the diseases . . . : treating very amplye of all Dystillations of Waters, of Oyles, Balmes, Quintessences, with the extraction of artificiall Saltes, the vse and preparation of Antimonie, and potable Gold . . . , 4°, London, 1576, pp. xxiv, 258 ll., black letter, 4 full p. woodcuts (CUL Adams 7. 575); 2 ed., The Practise of the Old and New Physicke . . . , 4°, 1597 (BM 46. m. 2).

Gildemeister and Hoffmann[4] say *evonymus*, εὐώνυμος, was the spindle tree, φίλος ἰατρός, 'the doctor's friend'. The book contains some new material, describes the plants to be distilled (Gesner was a botanist), the furnaces and apparatus, also the methods of making the quintessences of wine, of plants, animals and of minerals, quoting Arnald of Villanova, Lull, Ulstadius, Bulcasim (Abu'-l-Qāsim, Vol. I), etc. Gesner also wrote on petroleum, bitumen and amber.[5] His posthumous work on the scorpion (*De Scorpione*) was published in Zürich, 1587, by his friend Caspar Wolf,[6] who said it contained marvels and prodigies; scorpions are formed from decaying crabs.[7]

Books on Distillation

Michale Puff (1400–73) of Schrick, an Austrian village, wrote a treatise on distillation the title and dates of which are given differently by all who refer to it.[8] I have not been able to see it. It mentions that oil should sink in brandy, a

[1] Sotheran *Cat.* 917 (1957), no. 995. [2] Ferguson, i, 314.
[3] Duveen, 358. [4] 1928, i, 56.
[5] *De bitumine et cognatis ei Naphtha (id est, vulgi petroleo) Pissasphalto et Electro Corollarium*, 1565, with Gobelius, *De succino*; q. by Thorndike, v, 466.
[6] Thorndike, vi, 291. [7] Pliny, ix, 51, said serpents were formed so.
[8] Kopp, (1), iv, 278; Verzeichnuss der ausgebrannten Wasser, 1483; Ferchl and Sussenguth, *Pictorial History of Chemistry*, 1933, 52: Von den gebrannten Wassern, 1474 (fig.); Forbes, *Short History of Distillation*, 1948, 83, 108, 389: Hienach volget ein nüczliche materi von manigerley ausgepranñten wesser, Augsburg, 1478, 1479, 1483, etc.; Klebs, *Osiris*, 1937, iv, 295: Von den ausgebrannten Wassern, Augsburg, 1477, 1478, 1479, 1481 (3 issues), 1482 (3 issues), 1483, 1484, 1496; Strassburg, 1481 (2 issues); and others, 21 in all to 1500; Duveen, 537: Von den aussgepranten Wassern, In welcher mass man die nutzen und prauchen sol, zu gesunthayt der menschen, 4°, Augsburg, 1521 (12 ll.); Hirsch, *Chymia*, 1950, iii, 138.

test used by Ulstadius and later authors, including C. J. Geoffroy in 1718. In England during the Middle Ages the brewers were mostly women,[1] and on Puff's title-page a woman is shown operating the still. Almost until to-day women domestics were in charge of the 'still-room', which had become a store for jams, etc. In a picture in a work *Eaux Artificielles*, Lyon, 1483, and many later eds.,[2] the woman with the distilling apparatus is also shown. Some authors give Puff the name 'Schrick', which is really his birthplace.

Petrus Andreas Matthiolus (Siena, 23 March 1501–Trent, 1577)[3] M.D. Padua, published a Latin edition of Dioskourides with a commentary[4] which has a good account of distillation apparatus (with illustrations). In his letters[5] he says a young physician of Prag, Andreas de Blavven, told him that potable gold can be made by dissolving gold in aqua fortis (aqua regia?) or salt of human skull, and is probably to be identified with the elixir; human hairs make metals ductile. Matthiolus distilled salts from two human skulls, he prescribed mercury internally, and prepared an oil from scorpions.[6] He was criticised by Melchior Guilandini (d. 1598), a German whose real name was Wieland, professor of botany at Padua[7] who described ever-burning lamps filled with some alchemical liquor, specimens of which, still burning, had been found in Italy. He also wrote on papyrus.[8]

BRUNSCHWIG

Hieronymus Brunschwig (*c.* 1430–1512/13) of Strassburg (whose real name is said to have been Saler)[9] wrote a book on surgery[10] and one on distillation in two parts:

1. Liber de arte destillandi de Simplicibus. Das buch der rechten kunst zü distilieren die eintzigē ding, f°, Strassburg, J. Grueninger, 1500, 212 leaves.

2. Liber de arte Distillandi de Compositis. Das buch der waren kunst zü distillieren die Composita vñ simplicia, vnd ds Buch thesaurus pauperū ... f°, Strassburg, 1507, 344 leaves.[11]

3. The vertuose boke Of Distyllacyon of the waters of all maner of Herbes, with the fygures of the styllatoryes, Fyrst made and compyled by the thyrte yeres study and labour of ... Master Jherom bruynswyke ... sm. f°, London, 18 April, 1527 (138 ll., 1st English ed.); 1528 (?); 3 ed., 1530 (?) (138 ll.), tr. by Laurence Andrew.

[1] Salzman, (2), 1926, 76.　　　[2] Hirsch, *Chymia*, 1950, iii, 131, 141.
[3] Thorndike, vi, 224, calls him Pierandrea Mattioli.
[4] *Commentarii in sex libris Pedacei Dioscoridis Anazarbei de Materia Medica. Post diversarum editionum collationem infinitis locis aucti: De ratione destillandi aquas ex omnibus plantis; et quomodo genuini odores in ipsis aquis conservari possint*, f°, Venice (Valgrisius), 1570; E. H. F. Meyer, iv, 366, says the commentary first appeared in Italian, Venice (Bascarini), 1544.
[5] *Epistolarum medicinalium libri quinque*, f°, Prag, 1561; Frankfurt, 1598; q. by Thorndike, vi, 224.
[6] Lippmann, (3), i, 133.
[7] *In C. Plinii maioris capita aliquot ut difficillima ... commentarius varia ... ubi Matheoli errores non pauci deteguntur*, Lausanne, 1576, q. by Thorndike, vi, 279.
[8] *Papyrus, hoc est commentarius*, 4°, Venice, 1572; Partington, *Ann. Sci.*, 1955, xi, 14.
[9] Moehsen, (2), 1783, 202; the name is also given as Brunswyck, Brunschwygk, Braun-schweyg, Braunschweig, etc. He is usually dated 1450–1534, but F. Hommel, *A. Nat.*, 1928, x, 155–7, showed that he was earlier.
[10] *Das ist das buch der Cirurgia Hantwirck der Wundartzny*, Strassburg (J. Grüninger), 1497, and later eds.; *The Book of Cirurgia by Hieronymus Brunschwig. With a study on ... Brunschwig and his Work*, by H. E. Sigerist, sm. f°, Milan, 1923 (facsim. of 1497 ed.).
[11] Editions in Duveen, 105–7. There was a Flemish translation: *Die distellacien eñ virtuyten der waterē*, f°, Brussels, T. Van de Noot, 1517 (104 ll., BM).

4. Das Buch zu Distilieren die zusamen gethonen ding: Composita genant: durch die einzigen ding, un das buch Thesaurus Pauperum genant, für die armen yetz von neuwem wider getruckt . . . , f°, Strassburg, Grüniger, 1532 (288 ll.; 3 ed.).[1]

Brunschwig describes the distillation of spirit from wine, mead, and fermented fruit juices, and the distillation of plants, roots and flowers. *Quinta essentia* is used by him to denote aromatic and empyreumatic oils, distilled vinegar, and other products of distillation. The *Cirurgia* is said by Haeser to be the first to treat in detail of gunshot wounds, which were thought (like gunpowder) to be poisoned; an earlier work on them is Pfolspeundt, *Bündth-Ertzney*, 1460. Lorenz Fries (Laurentius Frisius) of Colmar, perhaps of Dutch descent,[2] called Brunschwig a coarse peasant living near the fish market in Strassburg.[3]

Ulstadt

Philipp Ulstadt (Ulstadius) of Nürnberg taught medicine at Fribourg in Switzerland and published a work on distillation, etc. with the title *Coelvm Philosophorvm sev De Secretis Natvrae Liber* (1525 and many later editions). The name *coelum philosophorum* was used by ψ-Lull for alcohol (Vol. I). The book is based on Brunschwig, Lull, Rupescissa, Arnald of Villanova, Albertus Magnus, etc.[4]

All editions of the book are rare; the very rare first edition, LXIII leaves, colophon (Epilogus), LXII v: Exactũ Friburgi Heluetiorum VI. Kalendas Marcias. Anno dñi. 1525, another issue, described as Denuo reuisus & castigatus, Friburgi, M.D. XXV, with LVII leaves, and the ed. of 1526, LXIIII leaves with errata leaf, and colophon: Excusum . . . Argentoragi (*sic*), arte & impensa Iohannis Grienynger Anno . . . M.D. XXVI. Pridie nonas Martias, are all in my possession. Editions in the BM are: f°, Strassburg, P. Grienynger, 1526 (new no. 8908. h. 18), 1528 (717. i. 2. (1.)); *s.l.e.a.* (Strassburg ?, 1530 ?) Denouo revisus et castigatus (717. i. 2. (4.)); 8°, Paris, 1544 (8908. a. 53), Lyon, 1553 (1036. a. 6); 12°, Augustæ Trebocorum, 1630 (1033. b. 5), and the German tr. Coelum Philosophorum. Von Heimlichkeit der Natur, f°, Frankfurt, 1551 (7943. h. 7), and 8°, Strassburg, 1630 (1033. c. 8. (4.)). There are also eds. in 8°, Lyon, 1533; Augustae Trebocorum, 1543, 1544. French tr., Le Ciel des Philosophes, 8°, Paris, 1547. The later eds. (e.g. 1544) have very long titles; Thorndike, v, 542. Ulstadius also wrote on the plague: De Epedemia Tractatus, 8°, Basel, 1526 (BM new no. 1167. c. 41); 8°, Paris, 1543 (Duveen, 591). A letter to Cornelius Agrippa in 1531 mentions 'in cœlo suo physico Dominus Ulstadius'.[5]

[1] The books are rarely found complete. Gmelin (1), i, 166; Lessing, 1838, 565; Haeser, (1), 1881, ii, 158; Gildemeister and Hoffmann, 1928, i, 44; *id.*, *The Volatile Oils*, 1913, i, 39; E. H. F. Meyer, iv, 287 (says many cuts in vol. i are from *Hortus sanitatis*, Mainz, Faust and Schoyffer, 1485, but some improved and some new ones added); F. Hommel, *A. Nat.*, 1927, x, 155–7; *Isis*, 1928, xi, 178; Parish, *J. Franklin Inst.*, 1927, cciii, 781; A. Brunschwig, *Ann. Med. Hist.*, 1929, i, 640; A. J. V. Underwood, *Trans. Inst. Chem. Eng.*, 1935, xiii, 34; Hirsch, *Chymia*, 1950, iii, 130, gives as eds. of the *Liber de arte distillandi* ('large book') Strassburg, 1512, 1515, 1519, 1521, 1528, 1531, 1532; Brussels, 1517 (BM); London, 1527, 1528 (?), 1530 (?); Frankfurt, 1533, 1535, 1536; and of the *Liber de arte distillandi de simplicibus* ('small book'), Strassburg, 1500, 1509.
[2] *Spiegel der Artznei*, Strassburg, 1518, perhaps the oldest book on internal medicine in the German language.
[3] Thorndike, v, 432; anon. [C. G. A. Schmidt], *Laurent Fries de Colmar médecin astrologue géographe*, Nancy [1888], 54 pp. (BM).
[4] Gmelin, (1), i, 165; Hoefer, (1), i, 472; Gildemeister and Hoffmann, 1928, i, 35; Ferguson, ii, 482; Duveen, 591; Atkinson and Hughes, *J. Chem. Educ.*, 1939, xvi, 103; Thorndike, v, 541.
[5] Agrippa, *Epistolae*, vi, 32; in *Opera*, ii, 995.

Ulstadius says in the preface that in his time the works of Lull were in few hands (ad paucorum enim manus pervenisse video). He shows a distilling apparatus with a water bath heated by a flue from a fire in a room below, with four regulating dampers, giving a secret heat (ignem secretum). Ulstadius has several chapters on potable gold, made by dissolving gold leaf in a 'water', presumably aqua regia since he gives another method of making it 'absque aqua forte', but the recipe is not intelligible.[1] He describes refining gold by cementation fairly clearly. His potable gold seems to have been gold leaf triturated with honey and other materials, but he also calls spirit of wine (quinta essentia vini) potable gold.

FIG. 4. EARLY ALCOHOL STILLS SHOWING RUDIMENTARY RECTIFYING COLUMNS (FROM BRUNSCHWIG, 1500).

The *Coelum Philosophorum* gives recipes for spiced wines, claret, hypocras, etc., and describes the preparation of spirit of wine (aqua vitæ) by distilling wine in an alembic with the neck packed with sponges soaked in oil, and alembics for 'circulation' (refluxing), which was thought to enrich the wine in spirit. The strength of the spirit was tested by pouring it on linen and lighting it, when all should burn away (statim cum ipsa aqua comburatur).

The picture (Fig. 4) of the distilling column in which the operator is estimating the temperature-gradient by touch[2] was misunderstood by Sudhoff,[3]

---

[1] 1525, f. xxxvii.
[2] 1525, f. III *v* (Forma Fvrni); Partington, *Everyday Chemistry*, 1929, 505.
[3] *A. Nat.*, 1914, v, 282.

who thought the *whole* tube should be cooled by water. A picture of an alembic with a series of aludels in which various fractions could be collected is shown in a 14-cent. Bologna MS. of Albini di Moncalieri.[1]

Johannes Petrus Arlunus:

> Index operis Io. Petri Arluni Patricii mediolanensis De Faciliori Alimento Summula. De Faciliori alimento tripartius cõmentarius. De Potu balnearum cõmentarius. De Lotii difficultate cõmentarius. De Articulari Morbo. . . . De Spirandi difficultate. . . . De Seminisfluore. De Febre quartano. . . . De Suffusione, Milan, 1532, G. Pontius V. Gauoti . . . impendio, roman type, 116 ff. (BM 544. k. 1).[2]

praised the alchemical remedy of the quintessence or potable gold,[3] perhaps following Ulstadius.

Ryff

Walter Ryff (Ruff, Reiff, Rivius, etc.), a Strassburg physician whose *Reformierte Apotheke* (1563) contains the first account in German of the French essential oil industry founded early in the 16 cent.[4] and who also wrote on astrological medicine and edited works of Arnald of Villanova, ψ-Lull, and Albertus Magnus,[5] compiled a book on distillation:

> New Vollkoñen Distillier:buch Wohlgegrundete künstlicher Distillation . . . hernach durch . . . Gvaltherum Ryff . . . , f°, Strassburg; 1597, 217 ff. (BM 717. b. 38. (1.), with MS. notes by Turquet de Mayerne ?); New gross Distillier-Büch wolgegrundeter künstlicher Distillation. Gvaltheri H. Ryff . . . , f° in 6's, Frankfurt, Egenolffs Erben, 1596, 197 ff., 284 woodcuts.

much of which is taken from earlier works of Adam Lonicer (or Lonitzer) (Marburg, 10 October 1528–Frankfurt, 29 May 1586) and Philipp Hermann,[6] a Paracelsan. Lonicer's book:

> Naturalis Historiæ Opus Novum . . . , 2 vols. f°, Frankfurt, 1551 (BM 456. b. 8); Kreuterbüch von allerhand Bäumen . . . Kreutern . . . und Gewürtzen . . . Auch Distillierens Bereytschafft . . . , f°, Frankfurt, 1560, 1564, 1593, 1630; Ulm, 1679, 1737 (all in BM).

gave the oldest recipe in Dutch for gin (aqua juniperi, geneverbessenwater).

Rossi

Geronimo Rossi of Ravenna (1539–1607), physician to Pope Clement VII, wrote a compendium on distillation:

---

[1] Sudhoff, *A. Nat.*, 1914, v, 198–201.

[2] The titles in the index at the commencement are not very obviously reproduced in the text; e.g. in the index, f. BB1 *r* it is said: Medicamentorum in tenuissimas partes attritio cunctis necessaria conditio exigitur, ut in humanum corpus propriam actionem efficiunt, but this suggestion of homoeopathy was, apparently, not followed up in the text. Jöcher, 1750, i, 545, mentions a *Vinumne mixtum an meranum noxiis junctuarum doloribus magis conveniat*, Perugia, 1573, by Arlunus.

[3] *Op. cit.*, 1532, De lotii difficultate, ff. LXIIII *v*–LXV *r*; Thorndike, v, 542.

[4] Gildemeister and Hoffmann, 1928, i, 50.   [5] Ferguson, ii, 306; Thorndike, v, 442, 560.

[6] *Een Constich Distilleerbouck* . . . , 8°, Hague, 1597 (BM 1035. e. 1); Amsterdam, 1622 (BM *ib.*); Forbes, *Short History of Distillation*, 1948, 159, 379, gives eds. of Antwerp, 1552, 1558, and 1566.

Hieronymi Rvbei Ravenn. De Destillatione Liber, sm. 4°, Ravenna, 1582 (222 pp.); De Destillatione, Hieronymi Rvbei Ravenn. Liber: In quo Stillatitorum liquorum, qui ad Medicinam faciunt, methodus ac uires explicuntur: Et Chemicæ artis ueritas, ratione, & experimento comprobatur . . . , 8°, Basel, 1585 (4 ll., 290 pp., 3 ll. index; for other eds., 1582, 1584, 1599, 1604, see Duveen, 518).

He describes the preparation of distilled oil of roses, which had been made on the large scale in Persia and other places in the East (Vol. I).[1] Baptista Porta[2] says it is most difficult to extract, and only small amounts were obtained. It is mentioned in a German apothecaries' price list of 1614.[3]

OTHER WORKS ON DISTILLATION

Remaclus (or Remaclius) Fuchs (or Fusch) (Limburg, 1510–Brussels, 1587) compiled a manual of distilled waters then in practical daily use.[4] The work of John French (Broughton near Banbury, 1616–Boulogne, 1657), army surgeon, translator of Glauber (see ch. X), etc.,[5] is largely compiled from Brunschwig's *Liber de arte Distillandi de Compositis* and from Glauber's works; it is extensively illustrated and contains many medical recipes. It describes lamp furnaces, sublimation and calcination. Donato D'Eremita[6] wrote on the elixir.

Jacques Besson, of Grenoble or Dauphiné, was interested in mathematics, mechanics, medicine, and chemistry. He was professor at Orleans in 1569 but died before his *Théâtre des instruments mathématiques et méchaniques* (ed. F. Béroald, f°, Lyon, 1578) was published. His interest in geology is shown in his treatise on springs[7] in which he says pure earth was originally white, tasteless, and inodorous; the ocean was salt from the first and the earth was then also salty and not yet sweetened by vegetation on its surface. Rivers flowing into the sea are supplied by rain and evaporation in an equal amount; springs on mountain sides descend from rainfall and do not rise through subterranean channels contrary to nature. Mountains are worn away and re-formed. Subterranean waters are contained in caves, produced by pressure of mountains or hollowed out by penetrating winds or rain water. The best water for drinking is rain water, but the water should be agitated and aerated; spring water is

[1] *De Dest.*, 1582, 136.   [2] *De Distillationibus*, Strassburg, 1609, 76.

[3] *Valor sive Taxatio omnium materium medicarum . . . quae in officina pharmacentica swinphordiana venundantur*, Giessen, 1614; q. by Roscoe and Schorlemmer, *Treatise*, 1885, III, i, 671, who refer to Langlès, *Recherches sur la Découverte de l'Essence de Rose*, 1804, and F. A. Flückiger and D. Hanbury, *Pharmacographia: A History of the Principal Drugs of Vegetable Origin*, 1874; the name attar ('otto') is the Arabic *itr*, perfume; the Eastern name is *itrgul* (Persian gul = rose).

[4] *Historia omnium aquarum quae in commune hodie practicantium sunt usu, vires et recta eas distillandi ratio*, 8°, Venice, and Paris, 1542; Gmelin, (1), i, 328; Thorndike, v, 544; for other works.

[5] *The Art of Distillation: Or, a Treatise of the choicest Spagyrical Preparations, Experiments, and Curiosities, performed by way of Distillation. . . . To which is added also The London-Distiller* [sep. pagin.], London, 4°, 1651 (191 pp.), 1653–2 [sic], 1664, 1667; Ferguson, i, 292; *Ind. Eng. Chem.*, 1936, xxviii, 677.

[6] *Dell' Elixir Vitae*, sm. f°, Naples, 1624 (xii, 182 pp., 19 full p. engr.); *Antidotario*, sm. f°, Naples, 1639, Lyon, 1668; Catalogue of Works on Alchemy and Chemistry. Exhibited at the Grolier Club, New York, 1891, no. 35; Lenglet du Fresnoy, iii, 147; Gmelin, (1), i, 577; Duveen, 176.

[7] *L'art et science de trouver les eaux et fontaines cachées soubs terre*, 4°, Orléans. 1569; Thorndike, v, 588–96.

next, river water last. He advises filtration through sand. Cisterns should have at the bottom some pure sand or pebbles, or a bottle of good vinegar closed with lime slaked in oil.

Besson published a work on distillation[1] in which he gives a list of herbs, seeds, and aromatics to be distilled, describes the furnaces and vessels, says how oils can be extracted from greasy woods, gums, and harder materials, and how the oil is separated from the aqueous humour in the distillate. The composition of a most fragrant balsam is described. Twenty-two questions are then answered in a scholastic style; in the thirteenth it is said the oil of a simple is 'a certain unctuosity or *humidum radicale* which gives being to the object in which it resides no less than does form itself.' When it is removed only dregs (faeces) remain. The unctuosity of a simple, or its fragrance, is not a fifth essence, as it is sometimes obtained from cold seeds or herbs with a thick juice and not only from dry and hot species.

Johannes Antonius Campesius, who quotes Ulstadius, wrote a book[2] in four chapters with illustrations of distillation apparatus. The reflux (reflex) distillation of mercury is said to convert it into water, which when digested with oil in a sealed vessel heated on an iron plate over a philosophical candle forms an elixir for making artificial gold and silver, more medicinal than the natural. Aurum potabili is made by distillation of red wine. The delivery tube from the cucurbit is called a *colubrum*. The author speaks of 'propter quod dicitur Cœlum nostrum'[3] as if he were Ulstadius. The philosophers' stone is prescribed for diseases, for the restoration of radical humidity, ad coitum facientia, and all infirmities of the body.

Conrad Khunrath (brother of the more famous Heinrich Khunrath, p. 645) a physician of Leipzig who lived some time in Schleswig-Holstein and Denmark, wrote[4] on the distillation of wine, sea-water, urine, honey, wax, resins, etc. Khunrath's book was used by Libavius (see ch. VII). Johann Sigismund Elsholtz (Frankfurt a.d. Oder, 26 August 1623–Berlin, 28 February 1688) wrote a *Curious Distillatory*[5] which also contains experiments in metals

---

[1] *Iacobi Bessoni De absoluta ratione extrahendi olea et aquas e medicamentis simplicibus accepta olim a quodam empirico postea vero ab eodem Bessono locupleta et rationibus experimentisque confirmata*, sm. 8°, Zürich, Andream Gesnerum iuniorem, 1559, 42 pp. (BM 1033. e. 2. (2.)), with a preface by Conrad Gesner, who mentions a discussion of metals by Besson; later eds. in Latin; appendix to Libavius, *Praxis Alchymiae*, Frankfurt, 1604; French tr., with Latin and French in parallel columns: *Art et Moyen parfaict de tirer huyles et eaux de tous les Médicamens simples et oleagineux*, Paris, 1571, 1573; Gmelin, i, 330; NBU, v, 820; Thorndike, v, 589.

[2] *Directorium Summae Summarum Medicinae, ad Administrandum Divinam Medicinam seu Lapidem Philosophorum in aegritudinum curâ*, printed in Ulstadius, *Cœlum Philos.*, 1630, 198–230.

[3] *Cœlum Philos.*, 1630, 217.

[4] *Medulla Destillatoria et Medica. Das ist, Wahrhafftiger eigentlicher gründtlicher bericht, wie man den spiritum Vini . . . Künstlich Destilliren, nachmals in Quintam Essentiam, zur höchsten exaltation bringen soll . . .*, 2 vols. 4°, Schleswig, pref. dated Schleswig, 1594 (publ. 1596?; author's name only in initials C. C[onrathus]. L[ipsiensis].); a second part was publ. in 1605, after Khunrath's death, and reprinted in 1614; many eds. with varying titles: Hoefer, (i), ii, 105; Ferguson, i, 461 (to which add 5 ed., Hamburg, 1623); Sotheran *Cat.* 800 (1926), no. 11194.

[5] *Destillatoria Curiosa: das ist: curiose und nachdenksame Destillir-Kunst*, 8°, Berlin, 1674, 12° Nürnberg, 1683; tr. by Thomas Sherley, *The Curious Distillatory: or, The Art of Distilling Coloured Liquors, Spirits, Oyls, &c., from Vegitables, Animals, Minerals, and Metals . . .*, sm. 8°, London, Boulter, 1677 (viii ll., 111 pp.); Ferguson, i, 238; for the tract on phosphorus, see p. 372.

and minerals (ch. iv), on animals (ch. v), and on vegetables (ch vi, with a figure of distillation apparatus with adapters), lignum nephriticum with experiments (ch. x),[1] and true cinnamon (ch. xiv). A recipe (ch. xvi) for a metal like Rhine gold, from which rings and medals can be made, says copper amalgam is first made by heating mercury, rust of brass, salt, and vinegar in an iron frying pan, then it is made into balls which are melted with turmeric root and cadmia.

CESALPINO

Andrea Cesalpino (Andreas Cæsalpinus) (Arezzo, 1519–Rome, 23 February 1603), professor of botany and medicine in Pisa, First Physician to Pope Clement VIII, succeeded Aldrovandi (p. 92) as director of the Botanic Garden in Bologna.[2] He has been credited with an understanding of the circulation of the blood before Harvey's publication of *De Motu Cordis* (1628). Cesalpino says:[3] huic sanguinis circulationi ex dextro cordis ventriculo per pulmonis in sinistrum eiusdem ventriculum optimi respondent ea quae ex dissectione apparent. The passage has been much discussed and it is now thought that Cesalpino understood by 'circulatio' a to-and-fro movement 'like that in chemical distillation' (in actual fact 'circulatio' was a *continuous* refluxing process with an alembic) and not a general circulation.[4]

He still believed that some blood passed through the septum of the heart (denied by Vesalius in 1543), that the veins brought aliment to the heart to be converted into spirit, which was diffused through the body by the arteries (which contain spirit as well as blood). The theory of circulation was criticised by Nicolaus Taurellus of Montbéliard (1547 1606), professor at Altdorf, in a book with the derisive title 'Alps of Cheese' (*Alpes Caesae, hoc est, Andr. Caesalpini Itali monstrosa et superba dogmata discussa et excusa*, Frankfurt, 1597). Cesalpino believed in spontaneous generation; even man could be produced from putrid matter but it would be foolish to think that the rational soul could be so produced. He thought the nerves came from the heart, not the brain and spinal medulla, and agreed with Aristotle that the heart is the seat of the soul and the centre of sensory and motor activities. He agreed with Aristotle that the seat of animal heat is the heart; what fills the left ventricle and streams in the arteries is not blood but something different, yet formed from blood, a *substantia* or *elementum*, or *ignis, faculus aethereus*, its motion being *efflare* (ignem animalium effluere per arterias . . . Conclusit igitur optime natura aethereum faculum in cordis ventriculis).

The *Quaestionum Peripateticarum* was republished as *Tractationum Philosophicorum tomus unus*, Geneva, 1588 (BM 526. n. 6). A supplement appeared as *Appendix ad libros de plantis et quaestiones peripateticas*, 4°, Rome, 1603, the book on plants in sixteen books, *De Plantis*, 4°, Florence, 1583 (BM 447. b. 2. (1.)) being famous. Cesalpino also published *Quaestionum Medicarcum Libri II*, 4°, Venice, 1593.

Cesalpino's most interesting work from our point of view is that *On Minerals* (1596) in three books, in which he shows a sound knowledge of

[1] See Partington, *Ann. Sci.*, 1955, xi, 1.

[2] Libri, 1841, iv, 99; NBU, 1854, ix, 436; Rodwell, *Chem. News*, 1864, x, 195; Hoefer, (1), ii, 51; U. Vivani, *Vita ed Opere Andrea Caesalpino*, Arezzo, 1922 (portrs.); Thorndike, vi, 325–38.

[3] *Quæstionum Peripateticarum*, bk. v, chs. 3–4; 4°, Venice, 1571, 1593, 116 f., 125 *v*; NBG, 1854, ix, 437, says it was first publ. in Florence in 1569.

[4] Haeser, (1), 1881, ii, 249; Sprengel, (2), 1827, iii, 88; Daremberg, 1870, ii, 593; Gunther, (1), 1926, iii, 125; Thorndike, vi, 328; Bayon, *Ann. Sci.*, 1938, iii, 59, 83, 435; 1939 (1940), iv, 65, 329; Franklin, *ib.*, 1941, v, 57; on a supposed statement on pulmonary circulation by Ibn al-Nafīs (d. A.D. 1289) see Sarton, ii, 1099; Elgood, *A Medical History of Persia*, Cambridge, 1951, 335.

ancient and contemporary material.[1] In the first book he explains from Aristotle that metals are vapours condensed by cold (metalla sunt vapores a frigore congelati), and distinguishes minerals from vegetables in that the former do not putrefy and form no aliment suitable for the nourishment of animals. He explains the presence of shells in some stones as resulting from the withdrawal of a previous sea, a theory previously held by Leonardo da Vinci.[2] Mineral waters, some hot enough to cook eggs, are produced by the combination of bodies which are burnt inside the earth (fontes calidi exeuntes mixtionem corporum, quæ intra terram comburuntur, significant).[3] He mentions sal ammoniac (sal Armoniacum), called by some Sal Armeniac, or Nusader (the Persian name) and said to be made from camels' urine:[4]

Sunt qui in Armenia fieri testantur ex urina Chamelorum unde Armeniacus vocatur. Posteriores salem Armoniacum interprætati sunt apud Serapionem quod Huxander seu Nusader vocat.[5]

The manufacture of alum in the Papal works near Tolfa in the territory of Rome is described:[6]

A soft and white stone, or a hard and red stone [an aluminous schist], give two kinds of alum, a white and a red. The stone is calcined in a furnace, sprinkled for some days, and then boiled, with water. Then, having separated the impurities, the liquors are concentrated in cauldrons and cooled in wooden vats, when angular and transparent crystals the size of nuts separate (concrescit in ligneis receptaculis ad similitudinem crystalli angulosum nucis crassitudine pellucidum). The Roman alum was much prized by dyers since it is free from soluble iron salts, the red colour being due to a quite insoluble ferric oxide, and the process is still worked at Tolfa.

The theory of many chemists that metals are composed of sulphur as a masculine seed, and mercury, coagulated in various purities and proportions is given without comment; it is said that oleum sulphuris (sulphuric acid) is made by burning sulphur under a glass bell and has the same virtues as oil of vitriol (oleum chalcanthi).[7]

The second book deals with limestone, marble, precious stones, salts, etc. It says that mineral bodies assume regular geometrical forms on crystallisation: nitre, alum, vitriol and white sugar (which is not, of course, a mineral) become hexagons, octagons, cubes, etc., and 'one asks with astonishment why the same bodies always crystallise in the same forms'.[8] The lynx stone, said to be the coagulated urine of the lynx, is like amber; a kind found near Naples grows mushrooms when watered.[9] It is said that cobalt (zaffer) is used for colouring glass but Cesalpino was ignorant of its nature (lapis vitrum tingens colore caerulea, et si plusculum addatur, inficit nigredine, Zafferam vocant).[10]

---

[1] *De Metallicis Libri tres Andrea Caesalpino Avctore. Ad Sanctissimvm Dominvm Nostrvm Clementem VIII Pont. Max. Romae, Ex Typographia Aloysii Zannetti, M.D. XCVI. Svperiorom Permissv.*, 4°, Rome, 1596, pp. xvi, 222, colophon; *De Metallicis Libri tres Andrea Caesalpino Aretino, Medico & Philosopho auctore, Noribergae, Recusi curante Conrado Agricola, M.D. CII*, (4°, Nürnberg, 1602). Both eds. have the same pagination, including the incorrect pagination from p. 180.
[2] Whewell, (1), iii. 406.   [3] Bk. i, ch. 7.   [4] Bk. i, ch. 20, p. 51.
[5] The name huxader is used by Serapion, *Practica . . . De Temperamentis Simplicium*, f°, Venice, 189 v.
[6] Bk. i, ch. 21; Roscoe and Schorlemmer, *Treatise on Chemistry*, 1923, ii, 751; Singer, (4), 139, 241; see Mercati, p. 92.
[7] Bk. i, ch. 28.   [8] Bk. ii, ch. 19, p. 96.   [9] Bk. ii, ch. 45, p. 134.   [10] Bk. ii, ch. 55, p. 153.

The third book deals with metals. It gives a recipe from Albertus Magnus for tempering iron (steel) in radish-juice mixed with earthworms.[1] It says[2] it is curious that lead burnt to ash in a furnace increases in weight by 8 to 10 per cent., as the metallurgists testify. This is caused by the soot condensing in the pores. The ashes can be reconverted into lead, but of less weight, hence the burning does not increase the lead but diminishes it, and the increase is in the dross. On exposing lead in a damp place, however, its weight increases, as Galen says,[3] and the substance of the air produces the rust (*sordes*) on the lead, augmenting its substance:

. . . magis admiratione dignum est, quod vstum in fornace, donec cinis fiat, crescit ejus pondus octo aut decem pro singulis centenarijs ut Metallici testantur . . . accedit fuligo ignis . . . in poris condensatur . . . et cineribus Plumbi, vnde pondus augetur. . . . Si iterum cinis fundatur vertitur quidem in Plumbum, sed admodum diminuta mole, reliquium in recrementum transit. Vstione igitur non augetur Plumbum, sed minuitur . . . aere substantia efficit veluti sordem circa Plumbum, unde augetur eius substantia.

Lead is like 'soap which washes gold and silver (est enim veluti sapo ad sordes abstergendas auri et argenti)' by cupellation (qui modus purgandi Cupella appellatur); a yellow pigment from tin is called Giallolinum;[4] this may be lead antimonate (Naples yellow).

Plumbago (lapis molybdoides), a shining slippery black stone which stains the hands and called Flanders stone, since it comes from Belgium, is used for drawing:[5]

Puto autem Molybdoidem esse lapidem quendam in nigro splendentem colore Plumbeo, tactu adeo lubrico, et perunctus videatur, manusque tangentium inficit colore cinereo, non sine aliquo splendore Plumbeo: vtuntur eo pictores coticulis in cuspidem excisis, ad figuras designandas; appellant autem lapidem Flandriæ, quia ex Belgia affertur.

Stibnite is a stone like black lead (aliter est lapis Plumbo similis, quod Stimmi [misprinted Stimni] Græci vocant, Latini Stibium; vulgo Antimonium).[6] Metallic antimony is mixed with bismuth (found in Germany) to make metal type; it is hard and brittle:[5]

Eundem reperiri tradunt in Germania, vbi Bisemutum vocant, quem assumunt cum stibio, mistura liquefacta ad formandos Characteres, quibus impressores librorum vtuntur, materia admodum dura ac frangibili.

Chemists make a red oil from stibium (ex eo Chimistæ conficiunt oleum rubicundum); it can also be burnt to ash with evolution of fumes, and then melted with borax and sal ammoniac and poured over sheet copper or marble (vsto donec luteus quidam fumus exieret, & in cinerem conuersum fuerit: quem addita portione Boracis, aut salis Armoniaci conflant, & fundunt super æris laminam aut marmor).[7]

Cinnabar was mined near Goeritz in Idria as a friable red stone as heavy as lead, containing brilliant droplets of mercury and called native cinnabar (cinabriam natiuum). Mercury (argentum vivum) is obtained from it by

---

[1] Bk. iii, ch. 6, p. 182; see Vol. I.   [2] Bk. iii, ch. 7, p. 184 (misnumb. 180).
[3] See p. 51.   [4] Bk. ii, ch. 62, p. 161; Bk. iii, ch. 7, p. 185.
[5] Bk. iii, ch. 8, p. 186.   [6] Bk. iii, ch. 9, p. 187.   [7] Bk. iii, ch. 8, p. 188.

heating in earthen vessels, from which the mercury runs into underground receivers (in subiecta vasa sub humo condita).[1] From it is now prepared red precipitate by dissolving in nitric acid, evaporating and heating (præparatur hodie cum aqua acuta coctum, donec in cinerem redigatur, qui siccatus in igne colorem rubicundum contrahit, Praecipitatum vocant); and by subliming with sal ammoniac (corrosive) sublimate in white crystals like sugar but intensely poisonous are obtained (per sublimationem præparatur cum sale Armeniaco, ascendente in igne vtriusque substantia, & congelata in similitudinem Sacchari, quod vulgo Sublimatum vocant, venenum est acerrimum exedens). Salivation is produced by the use of mercurial ointment (made by rubbing mercury with lard) in the cure of venereal disease:

Confluere magnam vim pituitæ ad os, vnde totum corpus expurgetur in morbo Gallico . . . sed aliquando lingua ex confluxu pituitæ adeo intumescit, vt contineri in ore nequeat: & processu temporis vt plurimum incidunt ægrotantes in prauas distillationes, anhelationes, & cordis palpitationes.[2]

MERCATI

Michele Mercati (San Miniato, Tuscany, 8 April 1541–Rome, 25 June 1593), superintendent of the Vatican gardens, then Papal physician, wrote a *Metallotheca* which was published in 1717–19 by Lancisi:

Michaelis Mercati Samminiatensis Metallotheca. Opus Posthumum . . . studio Joannis Mariæ Lancisii Archiatri Pontificii illustratum, f°, Rome, 1717 (pp. [i–xii], xiii–lxiv, 378 [16], engr. t.p., f.p., portr., 5 pl. and engravings in text); Appendix ad Metallothecum Vaticanam, f°, Rome, 1719 (fold. pl., Regestum [iv], portr. Lancisi, 2 t.ps., pp. 53 [1]).

He was a pupil of Caesalpinus, whose *De Metallicis* was intended as a supplement to Mercati's work, which was unfinished on his death.[3] It mentions the use of manganese, unknown to the ancients (manganensis cùm veteribus ignotus fuerit), for colouring glazes (vasa maganonizet) and whitening green and yellow glass.[4] Mercati's account of the manufacture of alum, although based on Agricola's, is better. His book has a large folding plate of the ancient alum works in the Solfatara at Pozzuoli.[5] He published a tract in Italian on the plague in Rome, 1576.[6]

ALDROVANDI

Ulisse Aldrovandi (Ulysses Aldrovandus) (Bologna; 1520–1605) professor of philosophy and medicine in Bologna, spent his means in publishing several large folio volumes of a work on natural history at Bologna and left a mass of manuscript material, some published subsequently. He died in poverty in a hospital;[7] some of his manuscripts and botanical collections were burnt as fuel. His published works comprise (all f°, Bologna):

[1] Bk. iii, ch. 11, pp. 191–3.   [2] Bk. iii, ch. 11, pp. 194–5.
[3] Thorndike, vi, 334.   [4] 1717, i, 148.
[5] 1717, 53 f., 79; Singer, (4), 1948, 172, 234; Patterson, *Ind. Eng. Chem.*, 1926, xviii, 634.
[6] Thorndike, vi, 210.
[7] Bayle, 1740, i, 150; Saverien, 1773, viii, 37 (portr.); Libri, 1841, iv, 103 (says b. 1522); Belmin, NBU, 1852, i, 740; Thorndike, v, 249; vi, 258, 276; *Intorno alla vita e opere di Ulisse Aldrovandi*, Bologna, 1907 (several authors).

Ornithologiae Libri XII, 3 vols, 1599–1634
De Quadrupedibus Solidipedibus, 1616
Quadrupedum Omnium bisulcorum Historia, 1613, 1621
De Quadrupedibus digitatis viviparis et . . . oviparis, 1637
De Reliquis Animalibus, 1606
De Piscibus et Cetis, 1613
De Animalibus Insectis, 1602, 1638 (767 pp.)
Serpentum et Draconum Historiae, 1640
Monstrorum Historia, 1642
Musaeum Metallicum, 1648.
Another volume on trees, Dendrologia naturalis, was also issued, f°, 1668, but does not properly form part of the set.

Several of these were republished in Frankfurt (1616–29; *Dendrologia* 1671, 1690). Aldrovandi's books are scholarly and useful; the one of direct interest to us, which is often cited, is *Musaeum Metallicum*, compiled some forty years after the death of Aldrovandi by Bartholomaeus Ambrosinus from a manuscript *Geologia ovvero Fossilibus*, which is said to use the name 'geology' for the first time in its modern sense. The work is divided into four sections: on metals, earth, concrete juices (*succi concreti*), and stones (minerals, rocks, and fossils). It includes the medicinal properties of rocks, minerals, and gems. In most cases it gives synonyms, places of occurrence, uses, mythology, medical virtues, etc., classical, medieval and modern authors being quoted. It is possible that some additions were made by the editor.

Aldrovandi[1] says astrologers and chemists (chymici) associate the planets with metals and parts of the body, but this idea had been exploded by Scaliger; yet he says later that the moonstone suspended from the neck by a thread of silver (a metal associated with the Moon) produces the same effect as the Moon.[2] The bezoar stone, which is Jovial, if carved with the image of a scorpion when the Moon is in Scorpio, resists the stings of scorpions.[3] Recent physicians (medici) infer from the fact that gold is best purified by antimony that man the microcosm may be purged of noxious humours by antimony, and this is confirmed by experience.[4]

Paracelsus had reported that a magnet was strengthened by repeatedly igniting it and quenching it in an oil made from crocus of iron and the best steel, but Baptista Porta found it lost its magnetism, and had also found false the statement that a magnet ceases to attract iron if anointed with garlic or in presence of a diamond, unless the latter was counteracted by goats' blood.[5] Yet Porta had obtained the gem from the head of a toad by putting it on a purple cloth and angering it by blows.[6] Aldrovandi was shown eggs laid by a cock but he doubted if they would hatch basilisks.[7]

Aldrovandi's works contain a great store of ancient and modern superstition and occultism (rather over-emphasised by Thorndike), and he was in trouble with the Inquisition in 1549 and 1571, but escaped imprisonment. In 1615 the government of Bologna petitioned Rome for the return of some of his books,

[1] *Mus. Met.*, 1648, 3, 9, 11.
[2] *Ib.*, 685; he quotes Gaudentius Merula, who wrote a *Memorabilia* (1546) and is cited on the magnet by Gilbert; Thorndike, v, 546.
[3] *Mus. Met.*, 808.   [4] *Ib.*, 191, ref. to Paracelsus and Johannes de Rupescissa.
[5] Aldrovandi, *Mus. Met.*, 1648, 557, 948.   [6] *Ib.*, 810: de bufonite.   [7] Thorndike, vi, 283.

but without effect.[1] Aldrovandi set the fashion for modern authors in compiling long lists of authorities but omitting to mention those mainly used, e.g. Conrad Gesner on animals.[2]

BELON

Pierre Belon (la Soultière, *c.* 1517–assassinated in the Bois de Boulogne, Paris, April 1564) wrote on the mines of Siderocapsa (in Macedonia)[3] but is better known for the book written after his travels in the East (1546–9).[4] He also wrote on antiquities[5] with a section (*De medicato funere*) on mummies and bitumen (*mumia*). In his first work[6] he distinguishes clearly between saltpetre and Egyptian nitrum (soda), sold in Cairo at 10 livres per maidin and used for dyeing and making glazes. He says 'il n'y a une seule scintille de Nitre en tout le pays des Chrestiens'.

CESI

Bernard Cesi (Caesius) (Mantua, *c.* 1581–Modena, 4 September 1630), a Jesuit professor of theology at Modena and Parma, compiled a work on mineralogy (he seems to have been the first to use this name in the modern sense) which was published posthumously.

Mineralogia, sive Natvralis Philosophiæ Thesavri, in qvibvs metallicæ concretionis medicatorúmque fossilium miracula, terrarum pretium, colorum & pigmentorum apparatus, concretorum succorum virtus, lapidum atque gemmarum dignitas continentur, f°, Lyons, 1636, pp. 626 and index; NBU, 1854, ix, 503 (d. 14 September); Thorndike, vii, 254–7; Möbius, *Jenaische Zeitschrift für Medizin und Naturwissenschaften*, 1944, lxxvii, 216.

It is mostly compiled from classical and medieval authors. It gives[7] some classifications of minerals, etc.: Aristotle (fossils, metals); Theophrastos (metals formed from water, stones from earth); Galen (earths, stones, metals); Albertus Magnus (stones, metals, 'middle' minerals); Avicenna (stones, metals, sulphurs, salts); Gregory Reisch (stones, salts, metals); Agricola and Cardan (earths, concrete juices, stones, metals). It lists numerous supposed properties of gems.

CANEPARIO

Pietro Maria Canepario (Petrus Maria Caneparius) of Crema, professor of medicine in Venice, composed a book on inks[8] in which he describes pyrites,

---

[1] Thorndike, vi, 153.   [2] Thorndike, vi, 259.

[3] *Description des Mines de Siderocapsa*, 1546–9 (made by order of François I); in Gobet, 1777, i, 53.

[4] *Les Observations de Plvsievrs Singvlaritez & Choses Memorables, trouués en Grèce, Asie, Judée, Égypte, Arabie & autres Pays estranges redigée en trois livres*, sm. 4°, Paris, 1553 (210 ll.); 1554 (211 ll.); Latin, *Plvrimarvm Singularivm*, 8°, Antwerp, 1589; with wood engravings of plants and animals; Hoefer, NBU, 1853, v, 295.

[5] *De Admirabili Opervm Antiqvorvm*, sm. 4°, Paris, 1553.

[6] *Les Observations*, 1555, bk. ii, ch. 71, p. 316.   [7] P. 129.

[8] *De Atramentis Cujuscunque Generis. Opus sanè novum, Hactenus à nemine pormulgatum: In sex Descriptiones digestum*, sm. 4°, Venice, 1619 (Ferguson, i, 139, quotes other eds. he had not seen; Beckmann, (3), 1795–1806, 175 f. said this was the first ed.; Jöcher, i, 1622, gives an ed. of Rotterdam of 1618, but this is probably a mistake for 1718); sm. 4°, London, 1660, the ed. used, xvi, 568 pp.

cadmia, magnesia, marcasite, vitriols, the preparation of inks and ink powders, and the preparation and uses of oil of vitriol.[1] He distinguished the modern 'chalcitis' from the ancient, and misy and sory, refuting 'Agricola and his sect',[2] describing sutorium, chalcanthum, stillatitium and stalacticum, 'now called coparosa',[3] ancient inks and printer's ink made from varnish, soot, and linseed oil or nut oil, encaustic, secret writing, etc.,[4] coloured inks from flowers, the ancient purple, and crimson (colore cremesino). It includes a chapter on brazil wood (de Brazilio, Verzinove Ligno tinctorio), which came from Tamasin, a town in the province of Brasil, in 'Provincia Indiæ'.[5] It also deals with mineral colours and pigments, spagyric or chemical medicines prepared by alchemy, the kinds of fire, the anatomy of vitriol and the preparation of oil of vitriol, etc., all copiously interspersed with classical quotations.[6]

IMPERATO

Ferrante Imperato, a pharmacist in Naples who founded a botanic garden and a collection of minerals, and corresponded with Guillandini, Meranta, and Aldrovandi, compiled an account of minerals, plants and animals, the part on minerals and metals being based on Theophrastos, Paracelsus, Agricola, and Biringuccio.[7] Book xii deals with furnaces,[8] bk. xiii with salts (including sal ammoniac and saltpetre),[9] bk. xiv with bitumens and naphtha (from Belloni),[10] bk. xv with sulphur, arsenic, mercury and metals,[11] bks. xvi–xvii with minerals, mining and smelting (from Agricola),[12] bk. xviii with the separation of metals,[13] bk. xix with the separation of metals by solution (parting with acid) and cementation (from Biringuccio),[14] and bk. xx with the separation of silver and copper by lead.[15] Bk. xxi deals with transmutation (from Paracelsus),[16] bk. xxii with stones and gems (from Theophrastos),[17] bk. xxiii with the gems of India (from Andrea Corsali),[18] and bk. xxiv with the shapes of gem crystals.[19] The account of stones in bk. xxv[20] mentions graphite as a kind of talc (gleba piombina, il graffito dello piombino) and tartar as a stone (pietre tartare).[21] Bk. xxvi deals with litharge, haematite, etc.,[22] and mentions pyrolusite as 'manganese'.[23]

His son Francesco Imperato, of Naples, also published a work on fossils and hieroglyphics on stones[24] and fourteen discourses on gems, pyrites, the mineral bezoar (a specimen of which had been given to his father by a physician), etc.[25] Johann Chesnecopherus (1581–1635), professor at Uppsala, published a

---

[1] Thorndike, vii, 250–2.   [2] 1660, 133, 140.   [3] Ib., 161, 177.
[4] Ib., 251 f.   [5] Ib., 309.   [6] Ib., 383–568.
[7] Dell' Historia Natvrale di Ferrante Imperato Napolitano Libri XXVIII. Nella Qvale Ordinamente si Tratta della diuersa condition de miniere, e pietra, Con alcune historie di Piante & Animali, f°, Naples, 1599 (xii ll., 791 pp., fold. plate); f°, Venice, 1672; Latin, 4°, Cologne, 1695; it is frequently quoted by Beckmann, (1); the p. refs. here are to the 1599 ed.
[8] P. 348.   [9] P. 372.   [10] P. 402.   [11] P. 425.   [12] Pp. 449, 469.
[13] P. 493, bisemuto, p. 519.   [14] P. 520.   [15] P. 543.
[16] P. 568; the quintessence or 'ethre', p. 571.   [17] P. 582.   [18] P. 626.
[19] P. 640.   [20] P. 674.   [21] P. 691.   [22] P. 694.   [23] P. 704.
[24] De fossilibus opusculum . . . multa quae hieroglyphice per fossilia noviter interpretantur, Naples, 1610 (BN S. 5525); Thorndike, vii, 247, who says, ib., 249, it was reputed that the true author of Ferrante's book was Nicolaus Antonius Stelliola.
[25] Discorsi intorno a diverse cose naturali, Naples, 1628; Thorndike, vii, 248.

disputation on concrete juices (salts), and precious earths.[1] Jerome Bock (Hieronymus Tragus) in his herbal (*Kreutterbuch*, 1560) refers to alchemical authors for the use of the herb lunaria (Botrychium lunara, called Martagon by the alchemists) in transmutations.[2]

PHARMACY

Antonius [Musa] Brasavola (Ferrara; 16 January 1500–6 July 1555; the name Musa was given him by King François I of France) studied at Padua, Bologna, and Paris, took the doctorates of law, medicine, and theology, taught logic, natural philosophy, and theory of medicine at Ferrara, and then became physician to Pope Paul III. He was, therefore, a man of great learning. His book on medical simples was composed in 1534 and is in the form of conversations between Brasavola, an old apothecary, and a herbalist:

Antonii Mvsae Brasavoli Ferrariensis. Examen omnium Simplicium medicamentorum, quorum in officinis usus est, f°, Rome, Bladi de Asula, 1536 (BN Te¹³⁸. 65); Antonii Mvsae Brasavoli Ferrariensis, Examen omnium Simplicium medicamentorum, quorum in officinis usus est. Addita sunt insuper Aristotelis Problemata, quæ ad stirpium genus, & oleracea pertinent, 8°, Lyons, Apud Ioannem et Franciscvm Frellaeos Fratres. M.D. XXXVII, italic type, xii ll., 529 pp. (530–42 Aristot. Problemata, viii ll., colophon, and index) (BM 1168. e. 1); the Lyons printers, leaf after p. 542, explain that the book is printed from a copy of the Rome ed. supplied by Benedictus Curtius Symphorianus. Thorndike says the Rome ed. has a fuller index. All refs. in the text are to pp. of the Lyons ed.

The book was annotated by Aloysius Mundella of Brescia, physician, professor of botany in Rome and from 1545 director of the Botanic Garden at Padua:

Aloysii Mvndellae Brixiensis . . . Epistola medicinales . . . Eiusdem annotationes in Antonij Musæ Brasavolæ simplicium medicamentorum examen, Basel apud Mich. Ising, Colophon: Ex Brixia tertio Calend. Ianuarij, M.D. XXXVIII, BM 1165. b. 1; q. here as Mundella.[3]

Brasavola's book deals with plants (pp. 1–149), seeds (150–99), fruits (200–34), roots (235–305, including two kinds of *turbit*, p. 267), barks (305–22), woods (322–30, including guaiacum, p. 326, but not lignum nephriticum), liquids (331–4), concrete juices, including two kinds of manna (334–41), sugar (saccharum, saccharum Candum made in Venice, Taberzet, and sal Indus) (341–6), opium (352), aloes (353), scammony, etc. (356), dragon's blood (360), cinnabar (362), camphor (363), gums (myrrh, stacte, styrax liq., euphorbium, sagapenum, opoponax, ammoniacum, styrax) (366 f.), pitch (*pix*) and resin (375 f.), gum arabic, etc. (382), charabe (392), amber (397), bones (414–17), metals (417–34), stones (434–45), gems (445–50), earths (450–85), salts (486–90), miscellaneous (490–5), fats, including human (498–503), marrow (*medullis*) (505), lungs and testicles (505–7), and oils (508–29, including oil of vitriol, p. 513). From this rich feast we select a few scraps.

In the miscellaneous drugs he mentions (p. 490) 'tutia à Germanis utrunque Nix appelatur', and (p. 495) 'tartarum, German Wein stein'. Of oil of vitriol

---

[1] *Disputatio physica decima octava de succis concretis et terris pretiosis*, 4°, 1625, BM B. 236. (3.); Thorndike, vii, 252.
[2] Thorndike, vi, 292.   [3] On Brasavola and Mundella, Thorndike, v, 445.

he says (p. 513) 'Albucasis & alij recentes modum conficiendi ostendunt', thus wrongly supposing it to be known to Abu'-l-Qāsim (Vol. I). He had seen in a shop in Venice some *reuponticum* answering to Dioskourides' *rhaponticum*; it is not the present *rhabarbarum*, and the present *reuponticum* or *rhaponticum* is most like the *centaurium majus* of Dioskourides (pp. 4–11).[1] Mundella (p. 509) thought rhubarb is the Greek rhaponticum, and Champier (36 r) that this is the rheubarbarum of Avicenna and the Arabs. Brasavola accused the Arabs of curtailing the materia medica (45) but they introduced a few new simples, such as nux methel, nux vomica, and nux Indica (219, 231). Mesuë should not be criticised because he says things not found in Greek authors (429), and Avicenna mentioned the smell of pitch (*picis*), whilst the Greeks did not (457). Guillaume Dupuis of Blangy-sur-Ternsise, who became professor at Grenoble, also defended Mesuë on the uses of aloes and rhubarb.[2]

Brasavola says camphor was unknown to Dioskourides, Pliny, Galen, and Paul of Ægina, and was first mentioned by the Arabs, unless it is in Aëtius (363), and the Greeks had no special name for gum arabic (382–3); Champier (74 v) said it was Dioskourides' 'tragacantha'. Brasavola (360) still accepted Pliny's story of the origin of dragon's blood (Vol. I); in a long discussion (361, 431) he tried to distinguish between dragon's blood and cinnabar; the last is quite different from minium which is a poison, and from cinaprium, which is made artificially in Venice from mercury and sulphur (432). The dragon's blood sold for use in medicine or by painters, he says, is probably the drop or tear of a tree and was brought to Venice not long before he wrote.

The vexed question of the nature of dragon's blood was discussed by Juan Fragoso, physician and surgeon to Philip II of Spain, in a book on spices.[3] He said it was the gum or tear of a bush growing in the Canaries with a flower like a dragon. It is the true cinnabar of the ancients and does not dissolve in wine or alcohol, unlike the adulterated kind made from brazil wood and resin or some other gum. At that time the origin of amber (which was confused with ambergris from the sperm whale) was still undecided.[4] Champier (30 v) said larch-tree resin was sold for terebinth but Brasavola (378) reported that true terebinth was now imported in round lumps from Cyprus to Venice. The 'confection of alkermes' often mentioned by 17-cent. authors was a syrup made from rose water, sugar, apple juice, raw silk, and kermes insects according to a prescription of Mesuë.[5]

The 'Oriental' bezoar came from Persia or India[6] and several varieties were

---

[1] Symphorien Champier, *Castigationes seu emendationes Pharmacopolarum*, Lyons, 1532, 35 r, had so identified it.

[2] *Guilhelmus Puteanus Blangiacus medicus civis Gratianopolis, Ionnis Mesue medici aloën aperire ora venarum, aliaque similia non pauca dicenda, adversum Ioan. Monardum & Leonardum Fuchsium, aliosque neotericos multos medicos Defensio ad simplicium medicamentorum facultates noscendas non parum utilis*, 8°, Lyons, Germanum Rose, 1537, BM 778. a. 1. (1.).

[3] *Discursos de las cosas aromaticas arboles y frutales y de otras muchas medicinas simplices que se traen de la India Oriental*, 8°, Madrid, 1572, iii, 15, f. 49 r (BM 546. c. 12); *Aromatum fructuum et simplicium aliquot medicamentorum ex India utraque et Orientali et Occidentali in Europam delatorum*, tr. Israel Spachius, Strassburg, 1600; Thorndike, v, 469.

[4] Thorndike, v, 470.   [5] Vol. I; Ray, *Historiæ Plantarum*, f°, London, 1688, ii, 1392.

[6] Engelbert Kaempfer, *Amœnitatum Exoticarum Politico- Physico-Medicarum Fasciculi V, Quibus continentur Variæ Relationes, Observationes & Descriptiones Rerum Persicarum & Ulterioris Asiæ*, 4°, Lemgo, 1712, Fasc. II, § 111: Lapis Bezoar, pp. 391–406.

described. The 'Occidental' bezoar came from the West Indies, etc.[1] Garcia da Orta[2] and Monardes correctly recognised that the bezoar stone is a concretion found in the stomachs or intestines of certain wild goats. The true Persian bezoars were extremely expensive and probably never reached Europe, where imitations were made. Tests for the true bezoar were described.

The bezoar was supposed to be an antidote to poison and to possess wonderful curative virtues, hence chemical remedies were described later as 'bezoardic'. The name *bezar* or *bezoar* is Spanish-Portuguese, and has been derived through the Arabic *bādizahr* or *bāzhar* from the Persian *pādzahr*, from *pād*, antidote or preserving from, and *zahr* or *zahir*, poison (although other derivations have been given); it occurs in al-Idrīsī (*c.* A.D. 1150).[3] The bezoar was used medicinally mostly with unicorn's horn, coral, and gems. The Royal Museum at Copenhagen in 1696 had a large collection of oriental and occidental bezoars.[4]

Johann Benedictus Silvaticus (or Sylvaticus), born in Milan, professor of medicine in Pavia, wrote a dissertation on unicorn's horn, bezoar stone, emeralds, and pearls, in which he is sceptical of the medical virtue of the first three but defends the use of pearls in fevers.[5]

Brasavola says the Greeks knew nothing of mace, which is mentioned by Serapion, Isaac Judaeus and Avicenna; the Portuguese found whole forests of it (Brasavola, pp. 319–22); they also found that sandal wood, first noted by the Arabs, grew abundantly in Calcutta (325), as well as forests of lignum aloes in Sumatra (323); Bresavola, and Champier (lii r) said it rarely reached Europe. Although Champier (68 r) had said sugar (*saccharum*) was the same as the ancient *sal Indicum*, Brasavola (343) said it was perhaps unknown to Galen. Mundella (1538, 1 f.) also admitted that the Arabs had discovered new drugs. Brasavola (453 f., 459) defined *mumia* as the remains of an embalmed body and the same as bitumen judiacum (Jew's pitch); Mundella (1538, 639–40) said it was detestable, and used bitumen or petroleum instead. Brasavola used gems as amulets or powdered for internal use, coral being especially valuable, but the right kind should be used (436 f.); he drew the line at believing the *lapis lyncurium* was congealed lynx urine, since Count Tasso kept two of them and the earth on which they urinated never congealed (436–8). Mundella discussed gems (1 f., 69 f.) and disapproved of powdering them, since brass abraded from the pestle and mortar might mix with them (36).

Brasavola names four kinds of alum found in shops (459–62): alumen rochæ,

[1] Monardes, *Dos libros. El vno trata de todas las cosas q̃ traē de nras Indias Occidētales. . . . El otre libro, trata de . . . la piedra Bezaar . . .* , 8°, Seville, 1565; Partington, *Ann. Sci.*, 1955, xi, 1.

[2] *Colloqios dos simples, e drogas he cousas mediçinais da India . . .* , 4°, Goa, 1563; *Colloquies on the Simples & Drugs of India*, tr. C. Markham, 1913; bk. i, ch. 45.

[3] Meyerhof, *A. Nat.*, 1930, xii, 234; Laufer, *Sino-Iranica*, Chicago, 1919, 525.

[4] C. Bauhin, *De Lapidis Bezaar orient. et occident. cervini item et Germanici Ortv, Natvra, differentijs, veroque Vsu*, sm. 8°, Basel, 1613 and 1625 (288 pp.); Neumann, *Chemistry*, tr. Lewis, 1759, 532; H. Fühner, *Janus*, 1901, vi, 317, 351 (bibl.); W. G. A. Robertson, *Ann. Med. Hist.*, 1926, viii, 240–8; Thorndike, iv, 224; v, 316, 474, 476; vi, 235, 311, 323, 335.

[5] *De unicornu, lapide bezaar, smaragdo, et margaritis, eorumque in febribus pestilen. usu*, 4°, Bergamo, 1605 (BM 546. i. 12.); Thorndike, vii, 242; Jöcher, iv, 959; Pliny, viii, 31, gives the unicorn (*monoceros*) as an Indian animal; Philostratos, *Apollonios of Tyana*, iii, 2, says cups made from its horn confer immunity from poison; it was thought to sweat on the approach of poison.

zucharinum, plumæ, and scaiolæ (found in gypsum mines) (464). Alum
comes from German mines (the Papal monopoly is not mentioned). What he
calls *alumen catinæ*, used to purify glass, is made by burning the dried herb
called *cali* by the Arabs, when the vapour forms sal alkali and the ash hardens
into alumen catinum (really soda). Alumen zuccharinum, used by women to
whiten and purify their faces, is made from liquid alum, rose water, and white
of egg. The last two kinds were unknown to the ancients, who gave the name
alumen scissile to alumen plumæ (462). Sal gemmæ (rock salt), so called
because it shines like a gem, is rarely found in large masses (486); sal armoni-
acus is not called armeniacus from Armenia as Pandectarius[1] said, but ammoniacus from the oracle of Ammon, where it is found under the sand (488).
Sal nitrum, called by the Germans 'salczpeter', is not the ancient nitrum
(488; Mundella, 1538, 644), and its use in gunpowder is deplored. Sal naph-
thicus was unnecessary in pharmacy (489, Mundella, 645: common salt from
petroleum wells). The translators of Serapion, Pandectarius, etc., had translated the Arabic *Zeg* (Zāj) as vitriolum, whilst it is vitriolum romanum
(Galen's *misy*), ordinary vitriolum being the ancient chalcanthum. Chalcitis
and chalcanthum had been confused, although Galen said that chalcanthum
becomes chalcitis after a long time (466–72; Mundella, 1538, 641, said they
had the same qualities and could be used indifferently). Zeg is the same as
atramentum or ink (Arabic zāj = vitriol), and Brasavola distinguished writing
and printing inks (469–72).

He included auripigmentum (orpiment), sandaracha or risigalum (realgar)
and arsenigal among the gums (387–9?). The chemists call them yellow, red,
and white arsenic, respectively, but are wrong in saying the last is made in
Venice by burning auripigmentum, since it is a mineral, and Agricola in
Bermannus is wrong in saying sandaracha does not smell of sulphur, since it
does if rubbed in the hand. Star of earth is the name of talc and of the herb
lunaria, which opens at night and reflects moonbeams, so that people run
away, thinking they saw the devil; it is used in sorcery and by chemists for
fixing mercury. The alchemists seek for blue, green, or yellow talc, which cannot be found, and 'wear out their lifetime in false nonsense' (483–5: in falsis
nugis).

Among metals Brasavola includes quicksilver (uiuum argentum eius loco
receptum est), and 'silver sublimate' (argentum sublimatum),[2] unknown to the
ancients, prepared according to Albucasis from chalcanthum, mercury, and
vinegar, to which sal armoniacum was now added. It can be bought in Venice.
He wished this poison had never come to light; no simple is so poisonous; it
kills in less than half an hour, burning the vitals like fire, especially those
round the heart. He once touched it with his tongue, which swelled up. In its
preparation, the fumes have killed or mutilated the operators or afflicted them
with apoplexy. Women in Italy use it to whiten the skin, but this is wrinkled,
their teeth decay, their breath takes a bad odour, and they die suddenly of
apoplexy. A decoction in moderate quantity cures scabies (scabiem) in three
days, unless it is the noxious kind. It was formerly used for syphilis, but

---

[1] Matthaeus Silvaticus, *Liber pandectarum medicinæ*.   [2] Corrosive sublimate.

mercury[1] is now preferred (430–1). Rascally barbers try to cure everything with mercury, but kill more than they cure (422). Since gold is only pure mercury condensed with the purest part of sulphur, it is as injurious as other metals, although capons cooked with gold coins were prescribed; the medical use of gold was very rare among the ancients (418–19).

Johann Thomas Freige (Fregesius) (Freiburg in Breisgau, 1543–Basel, 16 January 1583), a Jesuit and Ramist, professor of ethics in Basel[2] in his *Quæstiones Physicæ*, Basel, 1579, opposed astrology but accepted sympathy and antipathy and occult influences. He discussed cinnabar, cinnamon, unicorn and rhinosceros horn, the basilisk, emerald and jasper, and the softening of diamond by goat's blood. A work on cosmetics by André Le Fournier[3] or Furnerius is cited by Gesner[4] for distilled waters, including one distilled from puppies (ex catulis) to prevent the growth of hair.

FALLOPPIO

Gabriello Falloppio (Fallopius) (Modena, 1523?–Padua, 1562), professor of anatomy at Padua, described minerals.[5] His lectures on mineral waters given in Padua in 1556 were published posthumously together with his lectures on minerals given in 1557.[6] Fanestri says he hesitated to publish them until he saw editions of a *Secreti* falsely attributed to Falloppio.[7] Falloppio's book on mineral waters criticises Savonarola (Vol. I) and others for their statements about minerals found in springs. It gives (f. 34 *v*) a picture of a still and (28 *v*–30 *v*) a chemical examination of water 'per elambichationem' according to 'modern physicians'. One spring said to contain copper did not, various others did not contain iron. Lead can hardly be contained in springs, but alum might be (36 *v*). Some said a bath near Reggio contained camphor and smelled of it; Savonarola said it contained alum and salt or nitre; Menghus of Faenza (who wrote more learnedly than others on baths) that it contained salt and alum; Falloppio found in it salt and nitre in about equal quantities, with a little marble or chalk (80 *v*): he mentions that the waters are exported to Naples and even France and Spain without loss of their virtue. Falloppio mentions (119 *v*) a druggist of Treviso who made gold from mercury in the presence of the college and senate of Venice and so became famous. He deceived the senators, was punished, and reduced to poor circumstances. The senate had previously issued a decree against alchemy, but Ewald von Hogheland,[8] who mentions the incident from Cardan and others, says the Venetian coiners were forbidden

[1] Ointment. [2] Jöcher, ii, 737; Thorndike, vi, 186.
[3] *La decoration d'humaine nature et a ornement des dames*, 1530 (BM 1174. d. 2).
[4] *Euonymus, De Remediis Secretis*, Venice, 1556, 109, 294, 302, 345.
[5] *De Compositione Medicamentorum*, 4°, Venice, 1570; Gmelin, (1), i, 303, 331; Ferguson, i, 262; NBG, 1856, xvii, 66; Thorndike, v, 548; vi, 208, 218 (Falloppia).
[6] *De medicatis aqvis atque fossilibvs . . . ab Andrea Marcolino Fanestri medico ipsius discipulo amantissimo collectus*, 4°, Venice, 1564 and (with same foliation) 1569, 176 ll.
[7] Ferguson, i, 262, says this was publ. in Italian in 1566 and 1578, Thorndike 1563 (?), 1565; German tr., *Gabr. Fallopii (sic) wunderlicher . . . Secreten*, 8°, Frankfurt, 1588 (?), 1641 (474 pp.; BM 1038. d. 8). It is generally regarded as spurious.
[8] *Historiæ aliquot transmutationis Metallicæ*, Cologne, 1604, 24, 27.

by decree of the senate to inquire whether the gold they minted was natural or artificial.[1]

LAPIDARIES

It has been seen (Vol. I) that the ancient books on gems were of two kinds: those following the tradition of Theophrastos in dealing with the physical properties on a scientific basis, and those of the type of the lapidary ascribed to Orpheus, in which the interest was solely in their supposed magic powers. This division continued more or less during the Middle Ages, although in such works as the *De Mineralibus* of Albertus Magnus both interests were represented.[2] In the period now under discussion both lines of interest were still continued.

Camillo Leonardi or Lunardi (Camillus Leonardus), a physician and astrologer of Pesaro, published a lapidary dedicated to Caesar Borgia.[3] A 'key' to it was published by Petrus Constantius Albinius, of Villanova.[4] Leonardi traces the history of science and magic to Adam, Noah, and the Magi; it was corrupted by the Greeks but restored by Trithemius and Cornelius Agrippa. Magic is an art which teaches the properties and abstruse operations of elements and compounds. Three with the magical four produces the perfect seven — which might apply to the three alchemical principles and the four elements. He deals with the generation and physical properties of gems and the detection of counterfeits, but is more concerned with occult properties. His book is mainly a compilation from Albertus Magnus and others but it mentions saltpetre (nitrum) and gunpowder. It gives extracts from a ψ-Aristotle.[5]

Anselmus Boëtius de Boodt (Bruges; *c.* 1550–1632), physician to Rudolph II, wrote a work on gems:

Gemmarvm et Lapidvm Historia, Qua non solum ortus, natura, vis & precium, sed etiam modus quo ex iis, olea, salia, tinctura, essentiæ, arcana & magisteria arte chymica confici possint, ostenditur. Opvs Principibvs, Medicis, Chymicis, Physicis, ac liberalioribus ingeniis vtilissimum. Cum variis figuris, Indiceq; duplici & copioso, 4°, Hanoviæ [Hanau] Typis Wechelianis apud Claudium Marnium & heredes Ioannis Aubrii [1609] (portr., x ll., 288 pp., viii ll.); Tertia Editio longe purgissima, ed. Toll and J. de Laet, with de Laet's text and tr. of Theophrastos, *De Lapidibus*, 8°, Leyden,

---

[1] Thorndike, v, 548–9.

[2] J. Evans, *Magic Jewels of the Middle Ages and the Renaissance, particularly in England*, Oxford, 1922.

[3] *Speculum Lapidum*, 4°, Venice, 1502; 8°, Paris, 1610, 247 pp., portr., with Petrus Arlensis de Scudalupis, 'priest of Jerusalem', *Sympathia Septem Metallorvm, ac Septem selectorvm Lapidvm ac Planetas*, to p. 499, and index; Leonardi, *The Mirror of Stones*, 8°, London, 1750; Ferguson, ii, 26; J. Evans, *Magic Jewels*, 1922, 141; Thorndike, vi, 298, 324; Morhof, (1), bk. i, ch. xi, § 11; 1747, i, 99, says: Petri Arllusi de Scudalupis Opus de sympathia septem metallorum, septem lapidum & septem planetarum, Madriti primum, hinc Romæ in folio, sub initium hujus [17th] saeculi editum. . . . Est quidem in Gallia illud recensum minori forma, sed totius mutilum, nulliusque pretii.

[4] *Magia Astrologica, hoc est Clavis Sympathiæ septem Metallorum et septem selectorum Lapidum ad Planetas*, 8°, Paris, 1611 (BM 718. b. 15. (2.); reprinted, 8°, Hamburg, 1716; NBU, 1852, i, 631; Thorndike, vi, 324, 464.

[5] *Lapidarius de novo ex Græco traductus*, Merseburg, 1473; Klebs, 48; tr., *Virtu di alcune pietre*, Milan, 1491–5, Klebs, 338; *Stein-Büchlein, Tugend der Edelsteine*, Erfurt, 1498, Klebs, 310; extracts from it by way of Camillus are given by King, *Natural History of Precious Stones and Precious Metals*, 1883, 5, 28, who was unable to see it.

1647; French tr. by François Bachou, Le Parfaict Ioaillier, Ou Histoire Des Pierres . . .
nouveau enrichi de belles Annotations, Indices & Figures. Par André Toll, sm. 8°,
Lyon, 1644. Other eds. are described.

De Boodt also wrote botanical works.[1] After a dedication to Rudolph II and a
preface, the book gives a list in alphabetical order of 648 gems, stones, and
minerals, and a list of 19 authors (including Pliny, Dioskourides, Galen,
Epiphanius, Albertus Magnus, Matthiolus, Cardan, Agricola, Gesner,
Libavius, and Quercetanus; others are named in the text). There is a scale of
hardness of three degrees,[2] a table showing the relation of weight and value of
diamonds,[3] and a graph for use with a compass.[4] De Boodt accepts the four
elements and three principles, and discusses the atomic theory.[5] He has a
little on the ways of distinguishing true from false gems and on making imitations in coloured pastes,[6] but the chemical material mentioned in the title is
confined to the preparation of lapis lazuli for use as a pigment,[7] making tinctures of gems and corals,[8] and the distillation of amber.[9] There is plenty of
superstitious material. The stone found in hemispherical form about the eyes
of crabs when they are changing their shells reduces stone in the bladder to a
powder which is voided in the urine, and also purges ulcers and wounds;
chemists reduce it to an essence or liquor, e.g. by distilling with vinegar.[10] The
toad stone and stones produced by lightning and by the hissing of snakes (as in
Pliny) protect from poison or lightning.[11] The existence of the unicorn's horn,
to which great virtues against poison were attributed, is doubted; the specimens
he had seen were stones or fossilised woods.[12] A little-known version of de
Boodt's work is contained in a later edition of a book by Sir Hugh Platt (or
Plat) (1552–after 1611; knighted 1605):

> The Jewell House of Art and Nature. Conteining diuers rare and profitable Inuen-
> tions, together with sundry new Experimentes in the Art of Husbandry, Distillation,
> and Moulding. Faithfully and familiarly set downe, according to the Authors owne
> experience, by Hugh Platte, of Lincolnes Inne, Centleman [sic], sm. 4°, London,
> Peter Short, 1594 (in three parts with separate title-pages and pagination): Diverse
> new and conceited experiments (xvi, 96 pp., folding diagram of apparatus), Diuerse
> new sorts of Soyle (60 pp.), Diuers Chimicall Conclusions concerning the Art of
> Distillation (pp. 1–47, 48 blank), The Art of Molding and casting (pp. 49–68), An offer
> of certaine new inventions . . . (pp. 69–76).

It contains accounts of salt manufacture, manures, working metals (including
niello), mechanical inventions (first announced in a broadsheet in 1592), etc.
It was reprinted (sm. 4°, London, Elizabeth Alsop, 1653, viii, 232 pp.) with
A Rare and Excellent Discourse of Minerals . . . by D.B. (i.e. de Boodt, although
Lee says it is Arnold de Boot, or Boate, a Dutch physician who, with his
brother Gerard, was in England and Ireland). A copy (1594) in Chetham's
Library, Manchester, has notes by a user and a handbill of a London merchant,

---

[1] NBU, 1853, vi, 665; F. M. Jaeger, *Chem. Weekbl.*, 1918, xv, 628; *id.*, *Historische Studiën*,
Groningen, 1919, 99; J. Evans, *Magic Jewels*, 1922, 154; J. E. Hiller, *Archeion*, 1933, xv, 348–
368 (portr.); *id.*, *Annales Guébhard-Severine*, 1935, xi, 74; *id.*, *QS*, 1941–2, viii, 1–215 (nearly
complete tr., indexes of authors quoted and minerals).
[2] 1609, 27.   [3] 1609, 65.   [4] 1609, 233.   [5] 1609, 9.
[6] 1609, 29–33, quoting Baptista Porta.   [7] 1609, 141.   [8] 1609, 156–8.
[9] 1609, 165.   [10] 1609, 175.
[11] 1609, 240: de chelidonia, brontia, et ombria: the brontia were belemnites.
[12] 1609, 209–15.

Gosling, 1628, pasted on to p. 69, on Platt's invention of balls of coal slack and clay, which Ferguson says was given in a pamphlet by Platt in 1603 (4°, 15 folios).[1] A different person was Gabriel Plattes (dates unknown) who wrote:

A Discovery of Subterraneall Treasure, viz. of all manner of Mines and Mineralls from the Gold to the Coale . . . The Art of Melting, Refining and Assaying of them . . . with a perfect way to make colours that they shall not stayne nor fayde . . . , sm. 4°, London, J. Okes for J. Emery, 1639; 2 ed. 1653, 3 ed. 1679; with other works, in a Collection of Scarce and Valuable Treatises upon Metals, Mines, and Minerals, 12°, 1738 and 1740.

It contains (ch. vii) the first description in English of the parting of gold and silver with nitric acid. Plattes is said to have died of starvation in a London street.[2] He wrote another (quite different) work:

Discovery of Infinite Treasure, hidden since the Worlds Beginning. Whereunto all men, of what degree soever, are friendly invited to be sharers with the Discoverer, G.P., sm. 4°, London, 1639, Printed by I. L. and are to be sold by George Hutton, within the Turn-stile in Holborne (the only issue, but the imprint varies in different copies; BM; Sotheran Cat. 907 (1954), 31, no. 321 (as above); DNB incorrectly gives it as another issue of the previous work.

Robert de Berquem who published on the West Indies[3] is different from Ludwig van Berquen of Bruges who is said to have invented the polishing of diamonds with diamond dust in 1456 (gems had been polished in Nürnberg in 1385).[4] De Boodt says something of diamond polishing. According to P. Grodzinski[5] this is first described by Benvenuto Cellini (1568) but the earliest detailed account, with illustrations, is by A. Felibien (1676). T. Nicols of Jesus College, Cambridge, published *A Lapidary*, 1652: 2 ed. *Arcula Gemmea*, 1653; 3 ed. *Gemmarius Fidelius, Or the Faithful Lapidary*, 1659. John Ray (1627–1705)[6] published:

A Collection of English VVords Not Generally used, with their Significations and Original, in two Alphabetical Catalogues, The one of such as are proper to the Northern, the other to the Southern Counties. With Catalogues of English Birds and Fishes: And an Account of the preparing and refining such Metals and Minerals as are gotten in England, sm. 8°, London, 1674 (xiii, 148 (misnumb. 178) pp.)

He describes the smelting of silver in Cardiganshire and of tin in Cornwall, the iron furnace, wire work at Tintern, and making red lead, vitriol, alum, and salt.

The Marquis Marco Antonio de la Fratta e Montalbani (Bologna; 1630–30 April 1695), member of a famous Bolognese family, travelled in Germany, Hungary, Poland (where he was made a marquis) and the coasts of the Adriatic, studying mineralogy. He published three works:

(1) Practica Minerale, trattato del marchise Antonio della Fratta et Montalbano, 4°, Bologna, 1670 (dedicated to the Duke of Parma); (2) Catascopia minerale ovvero esploratione o modo di far saggio d'ogni miniera metallica, 4°, Bologna, 1678; (3)

---

[1] S. Lee, DNB, 1949–50, xv, 1293; Ferguson, ii, 206; Parkes, *Chemical Essays*, 1823, i, 450, 608.

[2] Ferguson, i, 170; ii, 207.

[3] *Les Merveilles des Indes Orientales Et Occidentales Ou Nouveau Traitté des Pierres precieuses & Perles*, sm. 4°, Paris, 1661.

[4] Feldhaus, (1), 1914, 954; see also Theophilus Presbyter. Vol. I.

[5] *Trans. Newcomen Soc.*, 1951–3 (1956), xxviii, 203–5.

[6] C. E. Raven, *John Ray, Naturalist*, 1942.

Dell' acque minerali del regno di Ungheria, 4°, Bologna, 1687; U. G. Paoli, *Archeion*, 1935, xvii, 353–78 (illustr.); P in NBG, 1861, xxxvi, 79, says b. 1630, dates (1) 1678, (2) 1676, and says (3) was printed in Venice.

The *Practica* describes the amalgamation process for extracting silver, the parting of gold and silver by aqua fortis, of silver from copper by lead, the crystallisation of vitriol, assay and cupellation furnaces, weights, etc. Biringuccio (who is quoted) and Agricola are used for text and illustrations.

ERCKER

Lazarus Ercker was born about 1530 at Annaberg, educated at Wittenberg, became warden of the mint at Annaberg, and in 1555 assay master to the Elector of Saxony at Dresden, who had a laboratory. He is the author of a MS. *Probierbüchlein* (1556). He was created chief assay-master over senior men, whose jealousy led him to go as warden of the mint and later mine master to the Duke of Brunswick at Goslar (1558–66), and assayer and finally chief consultant under the Emperors Maximilian II and Rudolph II (who knighted him in 1586) in Bohemia, from 1568 till his death, probably in 1594.[1]

He composed a book on ores and assaying which makes use of Agricola's *De Re Metallica* but omits the discussion of mining and to some extent smelting, but is much more precise and practical on assaying methods:

Beschreibung Allerfürnemisten Mineralischen Ertzt vnnd Berckwercks arten . . . Durch Lazarus Erckern, f°, Prague, 1574 (colophon dated M.D. Lxxiiij; in the BN copy the colophon has M.D. Lxxiij (1573), with an extra j added later by hand; reprinted Frankfurt, 1580, 1598, 1629 (134 pp., iii f.; should have 41 woodcuts).

This was enlarged and issued with a different title:

Aula Subterranea Domina Dominantium Subdita Subditorum. Das ist: Unterirdìsche Hofhaltung . . . oder Gründliche Beschreibung derjenigen Sachen so in der Tieffe der Erde wachsen . . . , 4°, Frankfurt, 1672 (vii, 332, ii pp.), 1684; f°, 1703, 1736 (should have 44 woodcuts). Books iii–v in the 1684 ed. used are paginated separately, i and ii are continuously paginated.

This was translated by Sir John Pettus of Suffolk, who was then in the Fleet Prison and gave it a punning title:

Fleta Minor. The Laws of Art and Nature, in Knowing, Judging, Assaying, Fining, Refining and Inlarging the Bodies of confin'd Metals. In Two Parts. The First contains Assays of Lazarus Erckern . . . in V Books. . . . The Second contains Essays on Metallic Words, as a Dictionary to many pleasing Discourses, f°, 1683, 1686 (with alt. t.p.). The 44 illustrations have been re-drawn, with the men in English costume.

Modern translation: Lazarus Ercker's Treatise on Ores and Assaying, translated from the German Edition of 1580, by A. G. Sisco and C. S. Smith, Chicago, 1951, with introduction and notes.

In the unpaged 'Essay on Metallick Words' in his *Fleta Minor* Pettus says of black lead (plumbago): 'Of late, it is curiously formed into cases of Deal or Cedar, and so sold as dry Pencils, something more useful than Pen and Ink', but these had been described and illustrated by Conrad Gesner in 1565 (see

[1] P. R. Beierlein, *Lazarus Ercker*, Berlin, 1955, q. in *Isis*, 1957, xlviii, 367; Armstrong and Lukens, *J. Chem. Educ.*, 1939, xvi, 553.

p. 81).[1] In a section on Load-Stone Pettus describes and illustrates a curious contrivance of a sundial, magnet, and scales, to show the weather, but how it works he does not say.

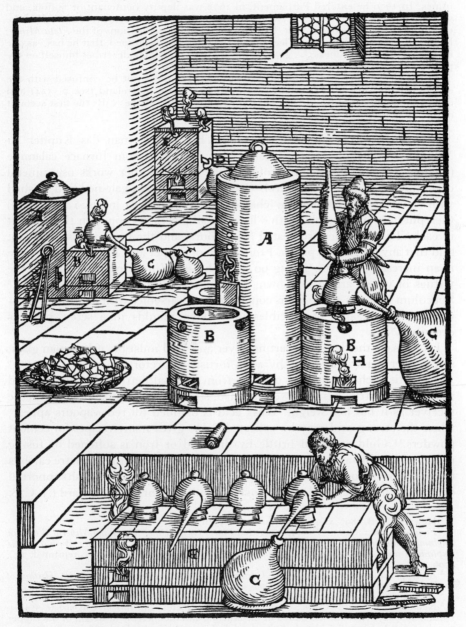

FIG. 5. ERCKER. FOUR TYPES OF FURNACES FOR DISTILLING NITRIC ACID.

AB THE TOWER FURNACE (ATHANOR) WITH SIDE-CHAMBER BH. C GLASS RECEIVERS. D EARTHENWARE RECEIVER. G GALLERY FURNACE WITH HEADS OF FOUR ALEMBICS. ED AND AB (ON LEFT) SMALLER FURNACES. F SECOND CONDENSER.

[1] E. A. Voice, *Trans. Newcomen Soc.*, 1949–51 (1956), xxvii, 131–4.

John Pettus (1613–90), knighted by Charles I in 1641, was taken prisoner by Cromwell and imprisoned in Windsor Castle for fourteen months. He exerted himself to save the life of Charles I and subsequently furnished money to Charles II, but lived on good terms with Cromwell, and in 1651 was appointed deputy governor of the royal mines. In 1670 he entered Parliament, in 1672 was deputy lieutenant of Suffolk, and served in the war with Holland. He impoverished himself by payments on behalf of the crown and died in absolute want. In 1683, in one of his dedications of the *Fleta Minor*, he informs the Warden of the Fleet Prison, where he was confined, that he has, 'as one memorial of your kindness . . . given it the name of Fleta'. He describes himself on the portrait in the *Fleta Minor* as 'Auratus Infletatus 1679'.[1]

Pettus also wrote an account of mining law.[2] He must not be confused with the economist Sir William Petty (1623–87), tutor to Boyle in Ireland (see p. 524) and one of the founders of the Royal Society, who gave what Parkes calls the first account of dyeing in English.[3]

Ercker gives a description of making brass (Wie man das Kupffer zu Messing macht)[4] in Hesse, Goslar, and the Harz from furnace calamine (Galmey . . . aus den Schmeltzöfen) from Goslar. Other works use mineral calamine from Ach in the Tirol. Goslar calamine was calcined and washed with charcoal-ash (Kohlnesch; 'charcoal dust' incorrectly in Sisco and Smith) then put in small crucibles with 8 lb. of small pieces of copper on the top of it in each. The crucibles are heated for 9 hours, and the brass is cast. It is not said that any charcoal is put in. From 64 lb. of copper and 46 of calamine there is an increase of 26 lb., giving 90 lb. of brass.[5] Zinc (Speauter, Zinck), the virtues of which are little known, precipitates other metals from solutions.[6] Speculum metal is made from copper, tin and arsenic, with or without antimony.[7] The making of crucibles in wooden moulds in a screw press is described.[8]

Ercker says the flasks for parting silver and gold must be of Venetian glass, since other glass is attacked by aqua fortis: iron retorts may also be used.[9] Aqua fortis (Scheidwasser) is distilled from 4 lb. saltpetre and $4\frac{1}{2}$ lb. calcined vitriol: if the vitriol has been well calcined, so much water must be put into the receiver as it has lost weight. Weak acid is distilled till red vapours appear, when the strong acid may be collected.[10] He gives many recipes for cement powders.[11] Gold rendered brittle by tin, lead or iron is softened by fusing under a layer of saltpetre.[12] Book 5 deals with saltpetre: the saltpetre earth is tested by lixiviation and evaporation of the solution in a weighed dish supported on a triangular piece of sheet iron over a candle.[13] Christian Berward ('J. C. &

[1] Hewins, DNB, 1896, xlv, 111; Ferguson, i, 245; ii, 185.

[2] *Fodinæ Regales. Or the History, Laws And Places Of the Chief Mines and Mineral Works in England, Wales, and the English Pale in Ireland. As also of the Mint and Mony. With a Clavis Explaining some difficult Words relating to Mines &c.*, f°, 1670, Pt. i (History) reprinted, 12°, 1706.

[3] An Apparatus to the History of the Common Practices of Dying (sic), in Sprat, *History of the Royal Society*, 1667, 284; Parkes, *Chemical Essays*, 1823, i, 18.

[4] *Aula*, 1684, iii, 49; *Treatise on Ores*, 1951, 254, with a valuable note, not in the 1574 ed.

[5] Neumann, *Z. angew. Chem.*, 1902, xv, 515; Spielmann, *Instituts de Chymie*, tr. Cadet, 1770, i, 268, says charcoal was added in the crucible and the increase in weight of the copper was $\frac{1}{3}$ at Aix-la-Chapelle, Namur $\frac{1}{5}$, England $\frac{1}{3}$, Goslar 'de près du double' (? $\frac{2}{3}$), Sweden 'hardly $\frac{1}{2}$'.

[6] *Aula*, 1684, Annot. to iv, 95.

[7] *Aula*, 1684, ii, 57; see Newton, p. 470.

[8] *Aula*, 1684, i, 84.   [9] *Aula*, 1684, ii, 138 f., 145 f.

[10] *Ib.*, ii, 156.   [11] *Ib.*, ii, 181 f.   [12] *Ib.*, ii, 192.   [13] *Ib.*, v, 100.

Assess. jud. Metal.') compiled a metallurgical dictionary[1] (bound at the end of Ercker's *Aula Subterranea*):[2]

Interpres phraseologiae metallurgicae. Oder Erklärung der fürnembsten Terminorum und Redearten, welche bey den Bergleuten, Puchern, Schmeltzern, Probirern und Müntzmeistern etc. in Benennung ihrer Profession Sachen, Gezeugs, Gebäude, Werckshafft, und Instrumenten gebräuchlich sind . . . , f°, Franckfurt, Zunner, 1673 (ii, 47 pp.).

LÖHNEYSS

Georg Engelhard von Löhneyss, who describes himself in the dedication of his book to Friederich Ulrich Duke of Brunswick and Lüneberg as 'Berghauptmann', was a nobleman at the court of the Elector Augustus of Saxony and entered the service of Heinrich Julius of Brunswick-Wolfenbüttel in 1583, he himself designed the plates etc. for his book and had them printed at his own press; the plates were engraved by Joachim Wichmann, of Hamburg (who signed pls. 5 and 11 and initialled others). Löhneyss also wrote a book on horses (*Von Zeumen, c.* 1588). Morhof[3] calls him Christopher Löhneyss, who was a politician, and in the British Museum catalogue is confused with Georg.[4] Löhneyss published a work dealing with mining, metallurgy, mining law, and book-keeping:

1. First issue with engraved t.p. only: Bericht vom Bergwerck, wie man dieselben bawen und in güten wolstande bringen sol, sampt allen dazu gehörigen arbeiten, ordning und Rechtlichen processen beschrieben durch G. E. Löhneyss (f° in 6's, *s.l.e.a*, xxi, 343 pp., 16 engraved plates; BM 443. h. 25, 443. h. 26 (2 copies), MS. entry in Catalogue has 'Zellerfeld, 1617'; sheets K and L numbered partly by pages and partly by leaves; this is the edition quoted).
2. The second edition (1690) has this engraved t.p. and a second long t.p.: Georg Engelhard von Löhneyss . . . Grundlicher und aussführlicher Bericht von Bergwercken . . . , Stockholm und Hamburg. In Verlegung Gottfried Liebzeits Buchhändlers. Gedruckt in Leipzig bey Christopff Günthern / Im Jahre Christi 1690 (f° in 6's, xxi, 343 pp., 16 plates (not the same impressions as in the first ed., e.g. pl. 3 is 'No. 3' but only '3' in first ed.); BM 460. a. 16.

About a fifth of the book is taken without acknowledgment from Ercker.[5] Löhneyss was an opponent of alchemy, saying the alchemists could colour metals but could not make a new thing or change a metal (ein new Wesen zu machen und eine Metall zu verändern, haben sie noch nicht beweist).[6] He gives an account of refining gold by antimony (wie man das Goldt durchs Spiessglass giessen und fein machen sol),[7] of the preparation of sulphur and vitriols (victril), including white (zinc vitriol), and of alum, in Goslar,[8] mentioning that iron is converted into copper by the 'sharp water', and he has a long and detailed account of making and refining saltpetre.[9] He also describes in great detail the preparation of aqua fortis (Scheidewasser) by heating 4 lb. of saltpetre, and 4¼ lb. of calcined vitriol, or 3 lb. of saltpetre, 3 lb. vitriol, 1 lb. burnt alum, and 2 lb. calcined flints in a coated glass retort, and its purification (from hydrochloric acid) by adding a solution of silver in a small portion of it. Aqua regia is made by distilling it (after purification with silver!) with common salt.[10]

[1] Ferguson, i, 243–4.   [2] 1684, sep. t.p., iii, 68 pp. (pref. by Ercker).   [3] (1), 1732, ii, 403.
[4] Ferguson, ii, 42.   [5] Schroeter, *Schweiz. Min. Petr. Mitt.*, 1942, xxi, 313.
[6] *Bericht*, 1617, 25.   [7] *Ib.*, 153.   [8] *Ib.*, 328 v–332.   [9] *Ib.*, 333–40.   [10] *Ib.*, 123–8.

Zinc

Löhneyss gives the first description of the extraction of zinc at Rammelsberg (Goslar):[1]

'When the smelteries are in operation, there collects on the front wall under the furnace, in the gaps not filled with mortar, and between the slate stones, a metal called by the smelters Zinck or Conterfeht, and when they knock on the front wall this metal runs out into a trough which they put under. This metal is white like tin but harder and less malleable (ungeschmeidiger) and it rings like a little bell. They could collect much more of it if they would take the trouble, but it is little valued and the servants and smelters take no trouble to get it; but as much as collects without danger in the wall, so much they knock out, but not all in the cavity. They only collect it if promised a tip (Trinckgeld), when they knock it out. They make more at some times than others, sometimes nearly two pounds, at others not more than three or four ounces (drey oder vier Loth). This metal by itself is of no use, since it is as brittle as cast bismuth, but if it is mixed with tin it makes it harder and more beautiful, like English tin. The alchemists make much request for this zinc or bismuth (haben eine grosse Nachfrage nach diesem Zinck oder Wissmuth).

Although Löhneyss here confuses zinc and bismuth, he gives in another place[2] a method of testing true bismuth ore (wie man Wismutertz probieren sol), the residue after melting out the very fusible bismuth being 'Graupen', used to colour glass blue.

Bergman[3] and Beckmann[4] say the cadmia (Ofenbruch) of Rammelsberg was thrown away until Erasmus Ebener (or Ebner) of Nürnberg (privy-councillor of Julius Duke of Brunswick in 1569), who died at Helmstädt in 1577, showed that it could be used instead of mineral calamine to make brass. Beckmann, who takes 1617 as the date of Löhneyss, said this would be in 1557, but other old authors, he says, made it 1548, 1550, or 1559. After this, says Beckmann, the managers of the Harz works collected and used the old refuse heaps. Metallic zinc was used in Germany to make brass in 1673, since in that year Morhof[5] says this was made by mixing copper and zinc (cum è cupro & zinco inter se justa proportione commistis, substantia oritur, quæ flavo colore . . . componi possit). Wiegleb[6] says the emperor Frederick had white vitriol (zinc sulphate) works at Raibl, Carinthia, in 1330; Beckmann says it was made at Rammelsberg about 1564 or earlier.

Stahl[7] describes in more detail than Löhneyss the production of zinc in Goslar. He says the stone walls were cooled by water, and the fused metal, dislodged by hammering, was shaken down and prevented from burning by coal dust. On cooling it is melted over a gentle fire and cast into pigs. By improper operation, the metal is lost. Practically the same account is given, from per-

[1] *Bericht*, 1617, 83 v; Beckmann, (1), ii, 42; Henckel, *Pyritologia*, 8°, London, 1757, 190; Percy, *Metallurgy*, 1861, i, 519; K. B. Hofmann, Zur Geschichte des Zinks bei den Alten, in *Berg- und Hüttenmannische Zeitung*, 1882, xli, 479, 483, 503, 515, 528, 542; tr. in Sisco and Smith, 1951, 271.

[2] *Bericht*, 173.   [3] *Essays*, 1787, ii, 316.

[4] (1), ii, 37.

[5] *De Metallorum Transmutatione*, Hamburg, 1673, 73.

[6] (1), 1792, 170; Kopp, (1), iv, 122, doubted this.

[7] *Metallurgiae Pyrotechnicae*, Halle, 1700; in *Opusculum Chymico-Physico-Medicum*, Halle, 1715, 791 f.; tr. in Geoffroy, *A Treatise of the Fossil, Vegetable, and Animal Substances . . . in Physick*, 1736, 210–12; and James, 1745, iii, art. Zinc.

sonal observation, by Neumann.[1] Swedenborg[2] reported that an internal slab of stone was built in the Goslar furnaces to protect the metal from the blast and 140–50 cwt. of zinc was produced annually, although only 4 or 5 lb. was obtained in each operation. In the meantime zinc was being imported from the Far East (see Vol. I).

Van Linschoten, who visited the Malacca coast in 1579, saw at Parak a metal resembling tin which was called *calaem* (alhier vintmer veel Calaem 'twelck is gelijck Tin; 'tselfde comt oock van Gundsalan).[3] De Laval[4] who visited India, reported that in the Indian islands money was made from iron and also from *calin*, which is white like tin but harder and more beautiful. The Portuguese also coined this metal in India. The metal was highly prized throughout the whole of India. Libavius,[5] who refers to Linschoten, says a large quantity of the metal calaem was captured in a Portuguese ship from Malacca by the Dutch the year before (devectum anno) and a specimen of it was given to him by his friend Dr. Doldius of Nürnberg.

Savot[6] also reported that the Dutch captured a Portuguese ship from Malacca carrying a metal called *speautre* (où on le nomme speautre) in Paris, where (among other places) it was sold. Whether this zinc came from India or China is not clear (see Vol. I). Beckmann[7] says in his time zinc came from China, Bengal, Malacca, and the Malabar coast.

François Valentyn (Dordrecht, April 1666–*c.* 1725), a Protestant pastor in Amboina, spent most of his life in the East Indies, of which he wrote a large description[8] in which[9] he gives as shipped from Malacca in 1605, 4500 pikal (1 pecul Chinese = $133\frac{1}{3}$ lb. avoir,) of 'Tintenaga[10] or Speauter', i.e. zinc, along

---

[1] *Chemical Works*, tr. Lewis, 4°, 1759, 122–3.

[2] *Regnum Subterraneum sive Minerale de Cupro et Orichalco, Opera Philosophica et Mineralia*, Dresden and Leipzig, 1734, 382–3.

[3] *Itinerario . . . van J. H. van Linschoten naer Oost ofte Portugaels Indien 1579–1592*, ed. H. Kern, Hague, 1901, i, ch. xvii, p. 72 (*ib.* 71: Brandewijn want is gedistileert water dat uyt die Indiaensche Noten comt (Goa)); the note on p. 72 says Calaem, from Arabic quala'ī, is 'tin', but here it is zinc. The passage is on p. 78 of the reprint of 1955. Jan Huygen van Linschoten (Haarlem, 1563–Enkhuyzen, 8 February 1611) sailed from Lisbon to Goa in 1583 and stayed there for five years. His work was printed in three parts (the second before the first) in Dutch, Amsterdam, 1595–6; a Latin tr. (Frankfurt, also Amsterdam) in 1599; the English tr. in 1598; repr. (Book I only): The Voyage of John Huyghen van Linschoten to the East Indies, ed. Burnell and Tiele, Hakluyt Society, 2 vols., London, 1885; i, 103–4: 'From Queda following the Coaste South south east 40. miles, till you come under 4 degrées and a half, lyeth a town named Pera [Perak]: there is found much Calaem, which is like tinne, there commeth likewise of the same from Gunsalan a place lying upon the same coast North north west, from Queda 30. miles under 8. degrées and a halfe, from Pera 30. miles, along the coast South east and by south, lyeth the towne and fortresse of Malacca. . . .' These places are all in the Malay Peninsula and the zinc may have come from India or China.

[4] *Voyages de François Pyrard de Laval, contenant la Navigation aux Indes Orientales . . . Nouvelle edit.*, . . . , 4°, Paris, 3 pts., 1679, 164; q. by Beckmann, *Litteratur der älteren Reisebeschreibungen*, 3 pts., Göttingen (I, 1807, II, i, 1809, II, ii, 1810), II, i, 115 f., 124; who adds: So sagt auch Vincent le Blanc voyage I. p. 211. u. 221 es sey so weiss als Silber und schmeltze-wie Zinn. Ich halte Calin für Zink, welches in Indien früher als in Europa gewonnen ist.

[5] *Commentationum . . . ,* 4°, Frankfurt, 1597; *Commentatiorvm Alchemiæ, Pars Secunda*, Frankfurt, 1606, 18.

[6] *Recherches sur la Metallurgie des Anciens*, 1627; in Gobet, 1779, ii, 883.   [7] (1), ii, 44.

[8] *Oud en Niew Oost-Indiën*, 5 vols. (in 8) f°, Dordrecht and Amsterdam, 1724–4–6–6–6; all except the first have different titles, the fifth, 1626, V, i, has the title *Beschryvninge van Choromandel . . . Malakka . . . Ceylon . . . Malabar . . . Japan*, etc.; the author spells his name as given (not Valentijn) and describes himself as 'Onlangs Bedienaar des Goddelyken Woords in Amboina'.

[9] 1626, V, i, 329 (for 'Tin' (*sic*), 311).   [10] A misprint for tiutenaga.

with other Chinese goods such as camphor, vermilion (Waejers), porcelain (porcelyn), Radix China, and silk (zyde). Valentyn[1] also mentions as exported from China to Batavia: *een soort van metaal calin genaand dat zeer weinig van zilver verschied* (a sort of metal called calin very little different from silver). A. Rogerius[2] reports that in India in Akbar's time (emperor 1556–1605) taxes were paid (in pagodas, gold coins) in temples on copper, brass (geel Koper), tin, mercury, vermilion, alum, camphor, sulphur, and spiauter (zinc).

Nehemiah Grew[3] mentions, from information given him by Samuel Clark, Surveyor of the King's Warehouse in the Port of London, 'Tuetenage. A sort of Speltar, as many Experiments shew. Hereof Parallelepipedon Vessels are made in Japan, wherein their Thea is brought over.' Tutenague is the Portuguese name for zinc.[4] The so-called 'bronzes' from Benin in East Africa (16–17 cents.), the casting technique of which is thought to show European influence although the foundation is purely African, really consist of alloys of copper, lead, and zinc in varying proportions,[5] and metallic zinc may have been used in their preparation.

Isaac Lawson[6] says zinc is a bluish-white semi-metal, coming from the East and Germany; that from England may be confused with bismuth (zincum corpus semimetallicam, coloris ex albo caerulei, semimalleabile, ex Oriente et Germania. Quidam dicunt quoque ex Anglia, ut vereor, ne confundant cum Bismutho). When strongly heated it burns and produces a white powder (*nihilum album*). Isaac Lawson seems to have been born in Scotland; he was a pupil of Boerhaave in Leyden and presented a dissertation on zinc in 1737 for the degree of M.D. He returned to Holland later in life and died in Oosterhout in 1747.[7] Bergman[8] says: 'It is not known how zinc is extracted in China. A certain Englishman, who several years ago took a voyage to that country for the purpose of learning the art, returned safely home, indeed, and appears to have been sufficiently instructed in the secret, but he carefully concealed it. We find afterwards that a manufactory had been established at Bristol, where zinc is said to be obtained by distillation per descensum.' This may refer to Lawson (for whom Cramer was operator), but zinc was made in Bristol fifty years before Lawson took his M.D. in Leyden and this industry could hardly have been introduced by him. That zinc was made in Bristol (still a centre of the English zinc industry) in 1685 is shown by a letter to Robert Plot by W. Cole, 25 March, 1685, saying the metal from the calamy (calamine) mines was exported in large quantities to Sweden to harden brass; the Bristol plumber

[1] *Op. cit.*, 1726, IV, i, 249.

[2] *De Open deure tot het verborgen Heydendom*, 4°, Leyden, 1651; ed. W. Caland, Hague, 1915, 121.

[3] *Musæum Regalis Societatis. Or a Catalogue & Description of the Natural and Artificial Rarities Belonging to the Royal Society And preserved at Gresham Colledge*, f°, 1681, 386.

[4] Yule and Burnell, *Hobson-Jobson*, 1903, 932.   [5] *Nature*, 1898, lviii, 224.

[6] *Dissertatio Academica sistens Nihil*, 4°, Leyden, 1737, 7 (BM 541. f. 9. (6.) and B. 380. 12).

[7] Boulger, DNB, 1892, xxxii, 291; Pryce, *Mineralogia Cornubiensis*, London, 1778, 46; John Campbell, *Political Survey of Britain*, 2 vols., 4°, London, 1774, ii, 35 (zink); Cronstedt, *An Essay towards a System of Mineralogy*, 1788, ii, 785; R. Watson, *Chemical Essays*, 1796, iv, 34; T. E. Lones, *Zinc and its Alloys* [1919], 4–5; Hulme, *J. Inst. Metals*, 1930, xliii, 355; J. M. Dawkins, *Zinc and Spelter*, Zinc Development Association, Oxford, 1950 (35 pp.); H. Hamilton, *The English Brass and Copper Industries to 1800*, 1926, 333–49.

[8] *Essays*, 1788, ii, 317.

who gave Cole the information was confident that the artificers knew how to make the metal (zinc) malleable but kept it secret.[1]

Pryce, and Watson, say that Lawson, 'observing that the flowers of *lapis calaminaris* were the same as those of zinc, and that its effects on copper were also the same with that semi-metal, never remitted his endeavours till he found the method of separating pure zinc from that ore.' Campbell says Lawson died too early to derive any benefit from his discovery. Lawson's dissertation is quoted by Pott.[2]

Henckel[3] in 1737 said that zinc is made from calamine by means of plumbago, 'en les mêlant à parties égales avec un peu de charbon, & les poussant à très-grand feu dans un vaisseau de terre un peu épais'. The hope of making it had been realised in England, since an Englishman recently arrived from Bristol said he had seen it succeed in that country. Bergman says Anton von Swab (see Vol. III) extracted zinc by distillation from its ores in Westerwick in Dalecarlia, but not on a large scale, and that Marggraf published a method of carrying out the process in 1746 (see p. 726).

Watson, after saying that the extraction of zinc from calamine was known in England before von Swab's work, adds: 'though this gentleman, unless I have been misinformed, instructed the late Mr. Champion of Bristol, either in the use of black jack [blende] for the same purpose as calamine, or taught him some improvements in the method of obtaining zinc from its ores. . . . The manufactory, however, of zinc was not established at Bristol till about the year 1743, when Mr. Champion obtained a patent for the making of it. About 200 tons of zinc are annually made at the place where the manufactory was first set up.' Watson then gives an account of the process, which he saw about 1766, when it was 'a great secret'. The zinc vapour was allowed to pass from a crucible, in which the zinc ore and carbon was heated, through an iron tube passing through the bottom of the crucible, from which drops of molten zinc fell into a crucible below.[4] The process was fully described by Percy[5] and was used until about 1865, the product being impure.[6]

Calamine was found in the Mendips in Queen Elizabeth I's time; previously it was imported from Sweden. The Queen invited foreign miners to England; she founded the Society of Mines Royal and the Society for the Minerals and Battery Works in 1567; in 1564 she made a grant to Christopher Schutz and an Englishman, of all mines, minerals and subterranean treasures (except alum and copperas) found in England or in the English pale in Ireland, specifying gold, silver, copper, tin, lead, quicksilver, and cadmia or lapis calaminaris, and 'all manner of ewres or oares simple or pure, mixt or compounded, for latten [brass], wire or steel etc.' There are remains of Roman brass foundries in

---

[1] Oxford Ashmole ms. 1813; Gunther, (1), 1939, xii, 284–5.
[2] *Dissertations Chymiques*, Paris, 1759, iii, 405, 415, 449, 492, 496, 499; iv, 466; Watson, *Chemical Essays*, iv, 34, says he had never seen it; Beckmann, (1), 43, had not seen it, and Gmelin, Kopp, Hoefer, and Lippmann are silent on Lawson.
[3] De Zinco, in *Acta Physico-Med. Acad. Nat. Curios.*, Nürnberg, 1737, iv, Obs. LXXX, pp. 308–12; tr., Dissertation sur le Zinc, *Oeuvres*, 4°, Paris, 1760, ii, 494–7.
[4] Watson, *Essays*, 1796, iv, 38.
[5] *Metallurgy. Fuel . . . Zinc; Brass*, 1861, 520, 550.
[6] Lones, 76.

England. The abundant calamine deposits in Wales were used only as road metal until about 1718.[1]

The name *latten* (French *laiton*) for brass occurs in a 12–13 cent. Latin chemical work containing many Arabic words (laton vel eramin)[2] and may be derived from *electrum*.[3] Latten was known in England in 1272, when the monument of Henry III in Westminster Abbey was made (perhaps from imported brass) by William Torel. The Somerset calamine was found in 1566 and the first true brass made from it was shown in 1568. John Brode, a London goldsmith, claimed to have made the first good brass from copper and calamine in a works at Isleworth in 1580–90.[4] Latten also appears in a 15-cent. document referring to a fraudulent London goldsmith.[5] The name calamine occurs in Albertus Magnus[6] for a mineral which converts copper into brass (convertunt cuprum in aurichalcum per pulverem lapidis qui calamina vocatur). It may be derived from cadmia through the Arabic (and Syriac) al-qalīmiya.[7]

WEBSTER

John Webster (Thornton-on-the Hill, Yorkshire, 3 February 1610– Clitheroe, Lancashire, 18 June 1682) wrote a work on metals dedicated to Prince Rupert with chapters on alchemy,[8] in which he collects a great deal of information from old and contemporary authors (including German) and adds personal observations. He does not seem to mention Boyle's *Sceptical Chymist*. He learnt chemistry when a young man from a Hungarian alchemist, John Huniades, in Whitechapel. He was convinced by a number of authors and from his own observations that metals grow in the earth from a juice called *Gur*.[9] Webster knows practically nothing of bismuth or zinc,[10] not having seen either. Lapis lazuli or armenus, he says, was used in England to make blue starch;[11] it was perhaps azurite. He quotes Paracelsus, Basil Valentine, and Van Helmont. Webster is best known for his attack on belief in witchcraft[12] in which he refers to Van Helmont's 'unparalleled stories' of *injecta*, or large foreign bodies finding their way inside the human body, which he felt compelled to believe as related by 'a person of unquestionable veracity', whose experiments had been vouched for by Boyle.[13]

BATE

John Bate described how 'To make Ice that will melt in fire, but not dissolve in Water. Take strong water made with saltpeter, allum, and oyle of

---

[1] Pennant, *Tours in Wales*, 1883, i, 84, 102–3.

[2] *Liber Sacerdotum*, Berthelot, (4), 1893, i, 197, 209.   [3] Berthelot, (3), 55, 275.

[4] Lones, 116.   [5] Salzman, (1), 1923, 139.   [6] *De Mineralibus*, bk. iv, ch. 6.

[7] Salmasius, *Homonymis Hyles Iatricae*, f°, Utrecht, 1689, 223; Berthelot, (4), ii, 128.

[8] Porter, DNB, 1899, lx, 125; Ferguson, ii, 532; Morhof, (1), 1747, ii, 402; *Metallographia: Or, An History of Metals. Wherein is declared the signs of Ores and Minerals . . . and the discussion of the most difficult Questions belonging to Mystical Chymistry, as of the Philosophers Gold, their Mercury, the Liquor Alkahest, Aurum potabile, and such like . . .* , 4°, London, 1671 (388 pp.). On Huniades see Taylor and Josten, *Ambix*, 1953, v, 44, 115.

[9] Gobet, 1779, i, 276, from letters of Boerhaave, says this was an idea of Agricola's.

[10] Ch. 27.   [11] Ch. 28, p. 346.

[12] *The Displaying of Supposed Witchcraft . . .* , f°, London, 1677.   [13] Thorndike, viii, 577.

tartar, of each, one pound. Infuse them together, then put into them a little *aqua ardens*, and it will presently coagulate them, and turne them into ice.' This is a precipitation of dissolved salts by adding alcohol.[1]

LEMNIUS

Levinus Lemnius (Lieven Lemse) (Zierikzee, Zeeland; 20 May 1505–1 July 1568), said to have been a pupil of Vesalius, Gesner, and Dodoens, published a jumble of miscellaneous observations:

Occulta Naturæ Miracula … duobus libris explicata … , 8°, Antwerp, G. Simonem, 1559 (BM 8705. a. 2.; xvi ll., 192 ff.); De Occvltis Natvræ Miraculis Libri IIII, 8°, Cologne, 1573 (BM 1170. d. 2); De Miracvlis Occvltis Naturæ, Libri IIII. Item de Vita cvm anima et corporis incolvmitate recte Institvenda Liber vnvs, 8°, Antwerp, Plantin, 1574 (CUL M. 18. 38) and 1581 (CUL M. 17). Thorndike, vi, 393, mentions eds. of Antwerp, 1561, 1564 (4 books ment. by Andreas), 1567; Ghent, 1570; Cologne, 1581; Jena, 1588; Frankfurt, 1590, 1593, 1598, 1604, 1611, 1628 (5 books), 1640, 1655; Amsterdam, 1650; Leiden, 1666; Italian tr., Venice, 1560, 1563, 1567; French tr., Lyons, 1566, Paris, 1567 and 1575; German tr., 1586, 1592, 1593, 1601; English tr., 1650. Zeitlinger, in Sotheran *Cat.* 852 (1938), nos. 1499–1500, says it was on the Spanish Index; parts of it are semi-obscene and *stercus* is often mentioned; these parts are omitted in the Latin eds. Other works of his on astrology were published in 1591–6 and 1626, with a tract on herbs and trees in the Bible, together with the works of Rueus (see p. 81); other works mentioned in Valerius Andreas, *Bibliotheca Belgica*, 3 ed., Louvain, 4°, 1643, 608–9.

Lemnius[2] describes the distillation 'per alembicum' of brandy (Aqua vitae seu Vinum ardens & causticum, vulgò Brandewijn); he says its flame does not burn the hand, and gives the test of burning a linen cloth soaked in it (linteũ liquore illo madefacto, ac flâmae admouete, si confestim inardescit illæso intactoq; linter, efficassima est). Also[3] 'argentum vivum quod Belgis à mobilitate Quicksilver dicetur', and the preparation of 'puluis præcipitatus' by heating it with vitriol (chalcanti), alum, and saltpetre (salis nitri). He mentions the 'compas',[4] 'Pistolettes' (pistols),[5] potable gold,[6] the manufacture of salt,[7] soap (smegma, Belgice Seepe),[8] and potash (kali).[9] Lemnius[10] mentions the use of saltpetre (sal nitrum, vulgo Salpeeter) in cooling wine, so that it becomes so cold that the teeth cannot bear it:

Æstivis mensibus ne vinum in congijs citò vapescet, aut calore perfundatur, sed inter propinandũ frigescat, in labro aque gelida oppleto collocentur vrcei, aut capaciore pocula; deinde Sal nitrum, vulgo Salpeeter, insternatur: tanta frigiditate vinum imbui continget, vt eam vix dentes tolerent. Huius autem qualitas illum in bombardis strepitum efficit; nullo autem sonitu, nec tam validè explodi glandem continget, si is eximatur.

[1] *The Mysteryes of Natvre and Art: conteined in foure severall Tretises; the first of water workes the second of Fyer workes, the third of Drawing, Colouring, Painting, and Engrauing, The fourth of divers Experiments … by J. B.*, London, sm. 4°, 1634 (BM) 155; the first ed. was in 1631 (Sotheran *Cat.* 773 (1919), p. 4); 'second edition', 1635; Davis, *Isis*, 1931, xvi, 87; 3 ed., 1654: *The Mysteries of Nature and Art. In four severall Particular Parts. Water-works; Fierworks; Drawing, Colouring Limming, Paynting, Engraving and Etching; Sundry Experiments.*
[2] Bk. ii, ch. 34, 1559 f. 158; Bk. ii, ch. 24, 1574 or 1581, 222.
[3] Bk. ii, ch. 35, 1559. f. 160; Bk. ii, ch. 25, 1574 or 1581, 225.
[4] Bk. iii, ch. 4, 1574 or 1588, 297.   [5] *Ib.*, p. 301.   [6] Bk. iii, ch. 6, 1574 or 1581, 309.
[7] Bk. iii, ch. 9, 1574 or 1581, p. 319.   [8] *Ib.*, p. 322.   [9] *Ib.*, p. 324.
[10] Bk. ii, 1559, f. 189; 1574 or 1581, p. 265.

Cooling by saltpetre and water is mentioned by Zimara (d. 1532), a Neapolitan commentator of Aristotle and Averroës,[1] and is fully described in 1550 by Blasius Villa Franca, a Spanish physician in Rome.[2] The use of salt-petre for cooling water was known much earlier in the East; it is described by Ibn abī-Uṣaybiʿa about 1242,[3] and the method was used in India.[4]

[1] *Problematum Liber*, in *Trinum Magicum*, ed. L. Cæsar, Frankfurt, 1609: Problem 102, p. 146: Quaesiuit Dominatio vestra, propter quod vinum positum in vase constituto in aqua, salenitro commista maximè refrigerescit?

[2] *Methodvs Refrigerandi ex Vocato salenitro vinvm, Aqvamqve Ac potus quoduis aliud genus, cui accedunt uaria naturalium rerū Problemata, non minus iucūda lectu, quam necessaria cognitu,* sm. 4to., Rome, 1550 (45 ff., 1 l.; colophon dated 1550; BM 1033. h. 3. (3)), f. 20 r., with figure of a tub containing a cooling mixture with a spherical flask in it; Jöcher, iv, 1607, gives an ed. Venice, 4°, 1553; on the history of artificial cooling see Beckmann, (1), ii, 142 f.; Lippmann, (1), i, 110; Partington, *Ann. Sci.*, 1955, xi, 1 (10–11).

[3] Partington, (4), 311.

[4] *Ā'īn-i Akbarī* of Abu-'l-Faḍl (completed in 1595), tr. Blochmann, Calcutta, 1873, i, 55.

CHAPTER III

PARACELSUS

One of the most curious personalities of the sixteenth century was the man afterwards called Theophrastus Bombast von Hohenheim or Paracelsus.[1]

[1] Melchior Adam, *Vitæ Germanorum medicorum: Qui seculo superiori, et quod excurrit, claruerunt*, Heidelberg, 1620, 28–39; Barchusen, *Historia Medicinæ*, Amsterdam, 1710, 401–41; Boerhaave, (1), 1724, i, 25; *id.*, (3), 1727, 22; *id.*, (4), 1741, i, 37; Brande, 1848, I, xxiv (chemistry began in the medical and pharmaceutical writers of the XVI cent., 'who rescued it from the hands of the alchemical pretenders, and gave it a place and character of its own.'); S. Brown, 1858, i, 131; Brucker, 1766, iv, 646–73 (summary from Croll); Cap, 1857, i, 1; Chevreul, *J. des Savants*, 1849, 663 (665–72); E. Darmstaedter, (1) *Arznei und Alchemie. Paracelsus Studien*, in *Studien zur Geschichte der Medizin*, ed. Sudhoff and Sigerist, Leipzig, 1931, xx (77 pp.) (alchemy); (2) *id.*, *Janus*, 1933, xxxvii, 1, 48, 109; T. L. Davis, *J. Chem. Educ.*, 1928, v, 671 (Boerhaave's account of Paracelsus and Van Helmont); L. Durey, *La médecine occulte de Paracelse . . . J. Cardan*, etc., Paris, 1900; Escher, in Ersch-Gruber, 1838, ser. iii, XI, 285; J. Ferguson, *Bibliographia Paracelsica*, Glasgow (privately printed), 1877–96, parts I–VI (set in BM); A. Franck, (1) *Paracelse et l'Alchimie au XVIᵉ siècle*, in *Collection d'ouvrages relatifs aux Sciences Hermétiques*, ed. J. Lermina, Paris, 1889; (2) *id.*, *Mysticisme et l'alchimie, Paracelse*, in his *Philosophie et Religion*, Paris, 1867; W. Ganzenmüller, *Angew. Chem.*, 1941, liv, 427; *id.*, *Beitr.*, 1956, 300–14; Gmelin, (1), i, 197 f.; K. Goldammer, *Paracelsus. Natur und Offenbarung*, Hannover, 1953 (review by Pagel, *Archives d'Hist. Sci.*, 1954, vii, 214); F. Gundolf (a pseudonym), *Paracelsus*, Berlin, 1928; Haeser, (1), 1881, ii, 71–106 (favourable: date of birth 1490 or 1491); J. Hargrave, *The Life and Soul of Paracelsus*, 1951; F. Hartmann, *Life of Paracelsus*, London, 1887, 1895; Hoefer, (2), 1843, ii, 9; (1), 1869, ii, 5; O. T. Hult, *Lychnos*, 1936, i, 182 (portr., also of John Oporinus; extracts from Peter Payngk, *Rapsodia vitæ Theophrasti Paracelsi*); C. G. Jung, *Paracelsica: Zwei Vorlesungen*, Zürich, 1942; G. W. A. Kahlbaum *Theophrastos Paracelsus, ein Vortrag*, Basel, 1894 (70 pp.); H. Kayser, *Schriften Theophrasts von Hohenheim gennant Paracelsus. Ausgewählt und herausgegeben*, Leipzig, 1921; Kiesewetter, (1), 1891, 40 f.; A. Koyré, *Mystiques, Spirituels Alchimistes du XVIᵉ siècle allemand* (Schwenkenfeld, Sebastian Franck, Paracelsus, Weigel), *Cahiers des Annales*, x, Paris, 1955; D. Leclerc, (2), 1729, 792; Lessing, (1), 1838, 359–403; (2), *id.*, *Paracelsus, sein Leben und Denken*, Berlin, 1839 (Neuarbeitung, Nürnberg, 1937); R. E. Liénard, *Paracelse, sa vie son œuvre, étude historique et critique*, Lyon, 1932; Lindroth, *Lychnos*, 1941, vi, 191; K. F. H. Marx, *Zur Würdigung des Theophrastus von Hohenheim*, Göttingen, 1842, in *Abhl. K. Ges. Wiss. Gött.*, 1843, i, 73–212; E. H. F. Meyer, 1857, iv, 423; F. Mook, *Theophrastus Paracelsus, eine kritische Studie*, Würzburg, 1876 (bibl. of works of Paracelsus); Morhof, (1), P. II, lib. i, cap. xv, § 16 (plane sylvestris . . . Gloria tamen Germani; many theological works then unpublished); *ib.*, P. II, lib. ii, pt. i, cap. 16; Lübeck, 1747, ii, 118, 249–54; H. M. Pachter, *Paracelsus: Magic into Science*, New York, 1951; W. Pagel, *Isis*, 1948, xxxix, 44; 1951, xlii, 244; *id.*, *Paracelsus. An Introduction to Philosophical Medicine in the Era of the Renaissance*, Basel, 1958 (refs. to recent literature; bibl. of works of Paracelsus, 31); *id.*, *Bull. Hist. Med.*, 1959, xxxiii, 480; Partington, *Nature*, 1941, cxlviii, 332; W. Ramsay, *System of Inorganic Chemistry*, 1891, 6, 8; Rixner and Siber, 1819 (2 ed. 1829), i; Saverien, 1769, vii, 1; A. Schierbeck, Paracelsus, in *Biologisch Jaarboek uitgegeven door het Koninklijk Natuurwetenschappelijk Genootschap Dodonaea te Gent*, Antwerp, 1937, iv, 138–70 (incl. chemistry; *Isis*, 1938, xix, 218); Schroeter, *Schweiz. Min. Petr. Mitt.*, 1942, xxi, 313 (Paracelsus as a mineralogist; useful bibl.); Schlueter, *Ann. Med. Hist.*, 1935, vii, 274; Sherlock, *Ambix*, 1948, iii, 33 (P.'s chemical knowledge defective); Sprengel, (1), 1815, iii, 284–333; *id.*, (2), 1827, iii, 430–92; F. Spunda, Paracelsus, in *Menschen, Völker, Zeiten*, ed. Kemmerich, Vienna and Leipzig, 1925, vi; G. Sticker, *Paracelsus. Ein Lebensbild*, in *Nova Acta Leopoldina*, (1), 1941, x, No. 66, 29; (2), 1941, x, No. 69 (conversation of P. with King Ferdinand I, in a Vienna MS.); J. M. Stillman, *Paracelsus, his personality and influence as physician, chemist and reformer*, Chicago, 1920; *id.*, 1924, 308; Anna M. Stoddart, *The Life of Paracelsus*, London, 1911; F. Strunz, (1) *Theophrastus Paracelsus, sein Leben und seine Persönlichkeit: ein Beitrag zur Geistesgeschichte der deutschen Renaissance*, Leipzig, 1903; (2) *id.*, *Paracelsus: eine Studie*, Leipzig, 1924; (3) *id.*, *Archeion*, 1932, xiv, 76–87; (4) *id.*, *Theophrastos Paracelsus. Idee und Problem seiner Weltan-*

Paracelsus was born in Einsiedeln in Switzerland. Bombast (and never Bombastus, even in the Latinised name) is said to have been, in the form Bambast or Banbast, the name of a family of Hohenheim, and Paracelsus a Latinised form of the latter;[1] other names (Philippus Aureolus) have no authority. The statement that he belonged to the Hohenheim family which had a castle near Stuttgart (which was sold to the Spaet family in 1432) is probably untrue, the Paracelsan coat of arms, on which this claim rests, being

ALTERIVS NON SIT, QVI SVVS ESSE POTEST.

EFFIGIES PHILIPPI THEOPHRASTI AB HOHENHEIM: ÆTATIS SVÆ, XLVII.

OMNE DONVM PERFECTVM À DEO: IMPERFECTVM À DIABOLO.

FIG. 6. PARACELSUS, 1493–1541, LEANING ON HIS SWORD, THE HILT OF WHICH HE REGARDED AS A TALISMAN.

spurious.[2] That he was born in Appenzell, or Sihlbrücke (Teufelsbrücke), and that his mother (probably a native of Einsiedeln) belonged to the family of Ochsner, are doubtful legends. His date of birth is usually taken as 1493

schauung, Salzburg and Leipzig, 1937; K. Sudhoff, (1) Versuch einer Kritik der Echtheit der Paracelsischen Schriften: Theil I. Bibliographia Paracelsica, Berlin, 1894 (repr. Graz, 1958); Theil II. Paracelsus Handschriften gesammelt und besprochen, Berlin, 1899; id., (2) Paracelsus. Ein deutsches Lebensbild aus den Tagen der Renaissance, Leipzig, 1936; Süssenguth, Pharm. Ztg., 1937, lxxxii, 859; W. P. Swainson, Theophrastus Paracelsus, 1919 (also in Three Famous Alchemists, ed. Waite, 1939); T. Thomson, (1), i, 140 (from Sprengel); Thorndike, v, 9, 416, 438 f., 604, 617 f., 625 f.; vi, 85, 712; Titley, Ambix, 1938, i, 166; Ueberweg, (1), 1924, iii, 122; F. P. Weber, Medical Magazine, April, 1917; K. H. Weimann, A. Med., 1957, xli, 154 (Paracelsus MSS.); R. Wolf, Biographien zur Kulturgeschichte der Schweiz, Zürich, 1860, iii, 1–50 (said by Haeser to be one of the best accounts).
    [1] Kopp, (4), i, 33 f.; Marx (Bombast doubtful).   [2] Pagel, 1958, 8.

(various months are given); 1494, also proposed, is less probable.[1] In 1502, the family moved to Villach in Carinthia.

Paracelsus (a Swiss) always regarded himself as German: 'zum ersten danken wir Gott dass ich ein geborner deutscher Man bin.'[2] His father, Wilhelm von Hohenheim, a practising licentiate in medicine who had studied in Tübingen and migrated to Switzerland, taught him medicine and some mineralogy and chemistry. Van Helmont[3] says the father was the illegitimate son of a German knight. Paracelsus (as his portraits suggest) was reputed to be a eunuch.

In 1516 Paracelsus was acquainted with Siegmund Füger, a chemist and mine-owner of Friedberg and Schwarz.[4] The 'abbot of Spanheim' named by Paracelsus as one of his teachers (probably only through his books)[5] was identified by Sudhoff[6] with a Count Sponheim, Abbot of St. Paul, near Villach, but there is little doubt that Paracelsus meant Trithemius.[7] The other names he mentioned are of doubtful or unknown identity. Paracelsus says that in his youth he suffered from poverty, and that he not only studied in schools but also wandered about Europe picking up scraps of information from peasants, barbers, chemists, old women, quacks, and magicians.[8] He is supposed to have made a special study of mines, minerals and metallurgy, to have known many alchemists and to have visited Constantinople in 1520 and have met there an alchemist Solomon Trissmosin or Trismosin (whose real name is said to have been Pfeiffer), who taught him how to make the philosophers' stone.[9] Paracelsus seems to have practised as an army surgeon in 1522 but his supposed travels to Tartary, etc., are fictitious; he says himself that he was never in Asia or Africa.[10] He probably derived his 'occult philosophy' largely from his contemporary Cornelius Agrippa.[11] It is certain that he visited Alsace, Southern Germany, Switzerland, Tyrol, Bohemia, and Austria; his other travels are doubtful but he may have visited other countries under Venetian influence in his capacity as an army surgeon.[12] The surgeons stood below the physicians in estimation, and Paracelsus's enmity towards qualified practitioners of medicine may have been connected with this. He issued a protocol at Basel in 1527 claiming that he had graduated M.D. at Ferrara and an indication in the archives of Verona is said to show that he received a medical degree there,[13] but Pagel thinks it is very doubtful if he ever had any

---

[1] Pagel, 1958, 6 f.

[2] *Opera*, Geneva, 1658, ii, 325 (gratias primum Deo ago, quòd me, natum Germanum voluit); Rixner and Siber, 1829, i, 5; the passage may be spurious.

[3] Tartari historia, i; *Ortus Medicinæ*, 1652, 187: Equitum Teutonicorum Magistri nothus.

[4] Liénard; Sticker; the family is said to have been unconnected with the Fuggers of Augsburg; Stillman, 1920, 13.

[5] *Chirurg. mag.*, tract., iii, cap. 1; *Opera*, 1658, III, i, 66; Van Helmont, *loc. cit.*; Sprengel, (1), iii, 288; Stillman, 1920, 13, 28 f.

[6] *Janus*, 1922, xxvi, 118.   [7] Pagel, 1958, 8.

[8] *Grosse Wundartzney*, 1536; *Opera*, 1658, III, i, pref.; Strunz, 1903, 28, 31; Stillman, 1920, 77.

[9] Van Helmont, *loc. cit.*; Jöcher, iii, 1245; Trissmosin, *Aureum Vellus oder Guldin Schatz*, 4°, Rorschach, 1598, sect. II; Ferguson, ii, 469.

[10] Liénard; D. Leclerc, 1729, 792; Rixner-Siber, i, 7; Strunz, (1), 1903, 32; Sticker, (1).

[11] Lehmann, *Aberglaube und Zauberei*, tr. Petersen, Stuttgart, 1908, 230.

[12] Pagel, 1958, 13–14; Paracelsus, *Sämtliche Werke*, ed. Strebel, St. Gallen, 1944, i, 284.

[13] Koyré, 48.

medical degree; when he settled in Strasbourg in 1526 he was enrolled in the guild of grain merchants, not of doctors.[1] In his will,[2] published in 1574 by Michael Toxites (Bogner, or Schütz) and regarded by Van Helmont[3] as a forgery but probably genuine, he calls himself a doctor *Liberalium Artium* as well as of medicine, another degree probably self-conferred. He read very few books, fearing to spoil his originality; on his death he left some theological works and one printed and seven manuscript volumes of medical treatises.[4]

In March 1527, on the recommendation of Oecolampadius (Hausschein), he was appointed medical officer of health (Stadtarzt) in Basel, a municipal and not a university appointment, which did not require a medical degree. He was allowed to lecture, which he did in German, not in Latin (of which his knowledge was imperfect).[5] Boerhaave,[6] says Paracelsus was not a professor but merely licensed by the magistrates to practise physic and lecture two hours a day on his own books. He proposed to examine and supervise the apothecaries, which made him very unpopular with these tradesmen.[7]

Sebastian Franck, who knew him well,[8] says Paracelsus in a lecture of 20 or 24 June, 1527, began by burning the works of Avicenna (a large and expensive book). This has been denied,[9] but could have been an imitation of Luther's burning of the Papal bulls and decretals at Wittenberg in 1520, although Paracelsus was nominally a Catholic throughout his life.[10] He himself says he publicly burnt the work of Platearius, which is smaller and cheaper than Avicenna's.[11] Another story is that he burnt the works of both Galen and Avicenna (together worth a small fortune) in a brass pan with sulphur and nitre (they would be too bulky to burn alone), saying that their authors were in like circumstances (sumsit vas æneum cum igne, immisit sulphur et nitrum, et simul Galenum, Avicennam et Arabes conjecit in ignem, dicens, sic vos ardebitis in Gehennâ).[12] Bergman's statement[13] that Paracelsus was professor of chemistry at Basel is incorrect; he never lectured on this subject.[14] His lectures were very unconventional and gave great offence to the physicians at Basel, whom he is said to have invited to a lecture on the greatest secret in medicine (or on fermentation), which he began by uncovering a pan of excrement, whereupon his audience fled in anger, Paracelsus shouting after

[1] Liénard, 56 f., 117; Strunz, 1903, 42; Schlueter, *Annals of Medical History*, 1935, vii, 274; Thorndike, iv, 593; v, 439; Strebel, 1944, i, 43; F. M. G. de Feyfer, *Janus*, 1941, xlv, 196; Pagel, 1958, 10.
[2] Printed at the end of the *Opera*, 1658, iii; tr. in Stillman, 1920, 175 f.
[3] Arcana Paracelsi, *Ortus Medicinæ*, 1652, 627.
[4] Stillman, 1920, 178; Marx, 1843, 142 f., gives a list of authors quoted by Paracelsus, all of whom he regarded as much inferior to himself.
[5] Strunz, 1903, 46.   [6] (3), 1741, i, 38.   [7] Strunz, 1903, 50.
[8] Pagel, 1958, 40.   [9] Thorndike, v, 438.   [10] Pagel, 1958, 20.
[11] Liénard; Rixner-Siber, 1829, i, 11; Kahlbaum, 49; Strunz, 1903, 10; Stillman, 1920, 161.
[12] Boerhaave, (1), 1724, 33; (3), 1727, i, 25; Paracelsus's own words in his *Paragranum*, pref., *Opera*, 1658, i, 183, probably suggested this story; Moehsen, (2), 1783, 67, omits the sulphur and nitre.
[13] *Essays*, Edinburgh, 1791, iii, 111.
[14] Hoefer, (1), 1869, ii, 9; Wiegleb, (1), 1792, 157; Sticker, 1941, x, no. 66; Haller, *Bibliotheca Medicinæ Practicæ*, 1777, ii, 2, is responsible for the statement that Paracelsus lectured on chemistry in Basel from 1527.

them: 'If you will not hear the mysteries of putrefactive fermentation, you are unworthy of the name of physicians.'[1]

Paracelsus's successful treatment of the Basel printer Frobenius (who died soon after) brought him in contact with Erasmus, with whom he corresponded.[2] Paracelsus soon put an end to his appointment in Basel. He engaged to cure the Canon Cornelius Lichtenfels of Basel of gout for a fee of a hundred guldens, gave him three pills, and as these gave relief (probably by acting as an opiate) Paracelsus demanded his fee. The Canon sent him six guldens as the considered value of his services and the three small pills (tres murini stercoris pilulas, as Oporinus called them). Paracelsus lost his case when he sued the canon before the magistrates, and abused the latter; acting on the advice of his friends, he quitted Basel hurriedly in February 1528, and thereafter wandered through Alsace, Germany, Bohemia, Vienna, Hungary and other places, writing books and practising medicine. His life was very restless and even when he had some opportunity of settling down he soon moved on.

There seems to be no doubt that Paracelsus felt himself 'called' to reform medicine and that he thought he could do this. His failure, the contempt for his teachings shown by the medical men of his time and most of his students, a scurrilous attack upon him posted in public places in Basel, and the necessity for his flight in disgrace, left an indelible stamp on his character. The coarse and bitter invective in the introduction to his *Paragranum*,[3] a passage frequently quoted, was published after his death and might have been toned down if he had revised the work for the press:

Mir nach / Avicenna, Galene, Rhasis, Montagnana, Mesue, &c. Mir nach / vnd nit ich euch nach / Ihr von Pariss / ihr von Mompelier / ihr von Schwaben / ihr von Meissen / ihr von Cöln / ihr von Wien / vnd was an der Thonaw vnd Rheinstrom ligt / ihr Insulen im Meer: Du Italia, du Dalmatia, du Athenis, du Griech / du Arabs, du Israëlita, Mir nach / vnnd ich nicht euch nach / ewrer wird keiner im hindersten Winckel bleiben / an den nit die Hunde seichen werden: Ich wird Monarcha, vnd mein wird die Monarchey sein . . . wie gefelt euch Cacophrastus?[4] diesen Dreck müsst ihr essen . . . ich würde sie vnnd ewern Porphyrium, Albertum, &c. in meinem Dreck tauffen.

He also said[5] the monarchy of all the arts belonged to him, prince of philosophy and medicine, chosen by God to extinguish all the fantasies, falsehoods, and presumptions of the Greek and Arabic physicians and their followers. Marx[6] thought the crude language was rarely used in the genuine works (he took the *Paragranum*, undoubtedly genuine, as spurious); it was common at the time, and sounded worse in German than in Latin. We must not forget that Paracelsus had to contend, almost single-handed, with a whole army of conventional physicians well dug in, and to dislodge them called for no little violence.

On leaving Basel, Paracelsus went to Colmar, Esslingen, Nürnberg (1529), Beratzhausen (1529–30, where he wrote the *Paragranum*), St. Gall (1531,

---

[1] Waite, *Lives of the Alchemystical Philosophers*, 1888, 139.
[2] Letters in *Opera*, 1658, i, 485.
[3] *Opera*, Strassburg, 1603, i, 199; Thomson, (1), i, 145; Stillman, 1920, 69.
[4] He had been called Cacophrastus in a pamphlet circulated after the death of Froben in October, 1527; Pagel, 1958, 21.
[5] *De tinctura physicorum; Opera*, 1658, ii, 116.   [6] 1843, 99, 101.

where he completed the *Paramirum*), Appenzall, Innsbrück, Ulm, and Augsburg (1536). He wrote the *Philosophia Sagax*, a very superstitious work, in Bavaria and Bohemia (1537), and after visiting Pressburg, Vienna, and Carinthia (1538), he came to rest in Salzburg, where he died on 24 September 1541, Boerhaave[1] says 'in an inn at the sign of the White Horse, on a bench in the chimney corner'. His tomb at Salzburg has an inscription calling him a great physician (insignis medicinæ doctor); another inscription put up in 1752 also makes him a great alchemist (tantam orbis famam ex auro chimico adeptus est).[2] Prayers are still said before his tomb.[3] A legend due to Sömmerring that Paracelsus died a violent death was disproved by C. Aberle,[4] who showed that the injuries to the skull were caused by exhumation.

His factotum, Oporinus (Johannes Herbst) (1507–68), a printer, and for a brief period (1534) professor of Greek at Basel, and Dessenius, said Paracelsus often spent the night drinking in taverns with peasants and seldom undressed, sleeping on the floor, and visiting his patients the next day, and that he was intoxicated when he dictated his books.[5] Oporinus says Paracelsus was little interested in religion and seldom said his prayers, but it has become fashionable to call him a deeply religious man and a good Catholic;[6] he composed in 1532–3 a large mass of religious writings (in which he confers upon himself still a third degree, Doctor of Theology), now in course of publication.[7] He seems (in spite of what Strunz says) to have been a heterodox pantheist, and a book[8] attributed to him attacks the Pope.[9] According to Franck[10] Paracelsus was not a pantheist, since he differentiated God from Nature, but he does sometimes confuse them.[11] His spiritualism may have been derived indirectly from the *Celestial Hierarchy* of ψ-Dionysios.[12] All the works of Paracelsus were on the Rome *Index* of 1599. The printing of the works was forbidden by the city council of Nürnberg in 1530 at the instigation of the medical faculty of Leipzig.[13]

It was thought that Oporinus was spiteful because Paracelsus would not teach him how to make the philosophers' stone (which he could hardly do, since he did not know it), and although fond of drink Paracelsus is said by a pupil never to have been more than 'reasonably merry (gemeiniglich lustig)'.[14] Van Helmont, who gives some details of the life of Paracelsus,[15] says the usual accounts of this 'ornament of Germany' were not worth a nut.

[1] (3), 25.   [2] Rixner-Siber, i, 33 f.; Haeser, (1), ii, 76.   [3] Kahlbaum, 1894, 11.
[4] *Grabdenkmal, Schädel und Abbildungen des Theophrastus Paracelsus*, Salzburg, 1891; Liénard, 56 f.
[5] Oporinus's letter of 26 November 1555, is printed in Sennert's *De Chymicorum cum Aristotelicis et Galenicis Consensu ac Dissensu*, ch. 4; *Opera*, 1666, i, 188; Kopp, (2), iii, 132; Bauer, *Chymie und Alchemie in Österreich*, Vienna, 1883, 14, thought the letter was not genuine, but Pagel, 1958, 29, has no doubt that it is.
[6] Strunz, (1), 1903, 11, 77, 87, etc.
[7] Liénard, 50; Stillman, 1920, 142; Sticker, 1941, (1), 84.
[8] *Expositio Vera Harum Imaginum Nurenbergae Repertorum ex fundatissimo Magiæ Vaticinio deducta*, 1570; Duveen, 451.
[9] Thomson, (1), i, 154; Rixner-Siber, i, 44; Stillman, 1920, 143.   [10] 1889, 26.
[11] *De Mineralibus*, i; *Opera*, 1658, ii, 342: Is solus est omnia in omnibus: is est rerum prima materia, is est rerum ultima materia, is est omnia; Sprengel, (1), iii, 304; Strunz, (1), 1903, 24. Spunda, 1925, 73.
[12] Thorndike, i, 546.   [13] Thorndike, v, 380.   [14] Stillman, 1920, 132 f.
[15] *Tartari historia; De magnetica vulnerum curatione*, ch. 51 f.; *Ortus Medicinæ*, 1652, 186, 603.

Unfavourable opinions of Paracelsus and chemical medicine were expressed by Erastus (see p. 156). Paracelsus was also violently attacked as a limb of Satan and the world's worst liar by Nicolas Guibert.[1] Conring[2] opposed Paracelsus and alchemy, and Dessenius[3] was especially severe; he calls Paracelsus: Magus insuper monstrosus, superstitiosus, impius & in Deum blasphemus quemadmodum ex ipsius execrabilibus scriptis ... aperte cognoscere potest, and used such words as mendacissimus, infandus impostor, ebriosus, monstrum horrendum.

The charge of blasphemy may have arisen from Paracelsus's idea that, as the stars poison men on the earth, the imagination of men influences the stars and even to some extent restrains the acts of God.[4] His beliefs in magic, sorcery, evil spirits, witchcraft, necromancy, etc., are expounded in his genuine works *Philosophia Sagax*,[5] and *Paradoxorum*, including astrology, divination, and (in the part *Archidoxis Magica*) the preparation of engraved talismans.[6] Spunda says these parts of Paracelsus's writings are usually passed over since the index to this volume of Huser's edition is defective. The talismans were criticised as superstitious by Godelmann in 1591, but approved by Belot in 1619.[7]

Melanchthon (1497–1560), an opponent of alchemy, seems to be attacking Paracelsus when he said in 1531 that medical empirics who are actors rather than physicians derive their medicines from magicians, Jews, apothecaries, barbers and midwives, and pretend to diagnose from the urine (this sounds like Thurneisser, see p. 152). Melanchthon's pupil Joachim Cureus (1532–1573) says his master would sometimes speak harshly of Paracelsus and his followers, and Cureus, while allowing a place in natural philosophy for true chemistry, in 1527 compared Paracelsus with Manes and censured the impiety of those who, 'armed with alchemical or rather diabolical juggleries and monstrous sophisms, overthrow arts propagated in a continuous series from the first antiquity of the human race'.[8]

Johann Georg Godelmann (1559–1611), a German Jesuit lawyer, in a discussion of hyperphysical diseases said Paracelsus went too far in advising magic cures, and his books are full of superstitions rather than natural amulets. Godelmann had seen a magician cure the sick by using diabolical names, and he regarded the use of the weapon-salve as diabolical, rejecting the authority of Avicenna, Pomponazzi, and Paracelsus on the action of the stars on images.[9] Tycho Brahe (1546–1601) called Paracelsus 'the incomparable philosopher and physician of the Germans'.[10] The picture of Tycho's observatory (1587) shows distillation apparatus in the background.[11]

Guinther of Andernach (Johann Winter) (Andernach nr. Coblenz, 1487–Strassburg, 4 October 1574), well known as a translator of Greek medical

---

[1] *Alchymia ratione et experientia*, Strassburg, 1603 (see p. 268); Thorndike, vi, 245.
[2] *De Hermetica Ægyptiorum vetere et Paracelsicorum Nova Medicina*, Helmstädt, 1648, 177 f.
[3] *Bernardus Dessenius Cronenbergius, Medicinae veteris et rationalis ... defensio*, Cologne, 1573, 202–9.
[4] Spunda, 1925, 70, 78, 81.
[5] *Opera*, 1658, ii, 522–644; Spunda, 1925, 116 f., 139 f. — a good objective account.
[6] *Opera*, 1658, ii, 645–718.   [7] Thorndike, v, 536; vi, 508.
[8] Thorndike, v, 380–1, 440.   [9] Thorndike, vi, 536.   [10] Thorndike, vi, 85.
[11] A. Wolf, (1), 1935, i, 127; Lawrence, *Movements in European History*, Oxford, 1925, 233.

authors, in his book on ancient and modern medicine[1] says Paracelsus was not the first chemist, since he was preceded by Zosimos (Zoysimus), Blemidas, Olympiodoros, and Hebes Mesuë, but he deserved credit for making spirits, sublimates, and the quintessence (nec non sublimes quoq; spiritus facultates, & quintæ quasi essentiæ ex ijsdem eliciuntur). Guinther mentions remedies sought from the *Qabbalah* and demons (ex Cabella, dæmonibus) and reports that some said that so long as a cure was effected, it mattered little whether God or the devil was responsible for it (Quinetiam hodie extant, qui nihil referre dicunt, Deus ne, an malignus spiritus ægrotos à morbis liberet vindicétque: unò remedia grauissimorum affectuum à nullo nisi dæmonum coniuratore, vel spiritu tam maligno, quàm bono comparari posse: quasi naturalium rerum scientia ad huiusmodi vitia non potens satis efficáseque esse possit). Guinther was for a time regius professor in Paris, but went back to Germany in the Wars of Religion. In his seventieth year he began to study chemistry and became a Paracelsan. In the above work he says only chemical remedies can cure the gravest diseases and Paracelsus had good grounds for departing from Galenism. The three principles were superior to the old four elements.[2]

Sir Thomas Browne[3] said: 'many would be content that some would write like Helmont and Paracelsus; and be willing to endure the monstrosity of some opinions, for divers singular notions requiting such aberrations.' Naudé[4] thought that Paracelsus, 'the zenith and rising sun of all the alchemists', who made magic one of the four pillars of medicine and included much superstitious material in his *Philosophia sagax*, was just a charlatan.

Boerhaave[5] says the real merit of Paracelsus lay in his skill in surgery, and his use of metallic remedies, opium, and especially mercury; 'the rest was empty smoke, and idle ostentation'; he was able to cure the venereal disease, which baffled the ordinary physicians, as well as leprosy, scabies, ulcers and dropsy, and hence he attained a great reputation:

remediis paratis ex mercurio, et ex opio, crebro usus et audacter, sanavit lepram, luem veneream, scabiem, ulcera, hydropes leviores, dolores; quae sane mala per medicos ad sanationem perduci haud poterant: quum vim argenti vivi ignorarent; opium, ut quarto gradu frigidum, pertimescerent ignari.[6]

Freind[7] called him illiterate and fanatical. Sprengel,[8] who mentions that Paracelsus believed that his knowledge came by divine revelation rather than by study, could find no really new principle in his works. 'His greatest merit is that of having recommended mineral remedies in place of useless syrups and decoctions, of having observed several interesting phenomena in nature, and having studied a large number of remarkable diseases, particularly those which enter the domain of surgery.'

Marx[9] says that nearly all the unfavourable opinions of Paracelsus go back

[1] *Ioannis Gvintherii Andernaci . . . de Medicina veteri et noua tum cognoscenda, tum faciunda Commentarij duo*, f°, Basel, Henricpetrina, 1571, 867 pp. and index (BM 773. m. 20); pref. to Maximilian II, f. *₊* 2 v; Thorndike, vi, 219.
[2] Sprengel, (2), 1827, iii, 508.
[3] *Christian Morals*, ii, 5; *Works*, ed. Sayle, 1927, iii, 471.   [4] 1653, 278.
[5] (3), 1727, 29.   [6] Boerhaave, (2), 1732, i, 21; Darmstaedter, 1931; Liénard, 1932, 96.
[7] *Opera omnia*, 1733, 375.   [8] (1), 1815, iii, 297, 332.   [9] 1842, 111, 119, 151 f., 160 f.

to Oporinus and Erastus. He was 'a German man, a German physician', and a Catholic, although he admired Luther; it is impossible to get rid of occult and superstitious elements from his genuine works, but they were a feature of his time. Later historians of medicine are partly favourable[1] and partly unfavourable.[2] Most recent writers give Paracelsus credit for his brave attempts to introduce a much-needed reform in medicine, but agree that his knowledge was insufficient and his method unsuited to ensure success in that capacity.[3]

A Paracelsus Gesellschaft issued an *Acta Paracelsica* (Munich, 1930–32), with a supplement 'Nachweis zur Paracelsus-Literatur' by Sudhoff. The British Museum has a large collection of books by, and about, Paracelsus. The Trew library at Erlangen had 117 volumes of his German and Latin works, and the Hering collection in the Hahnemann Medical College, Philadelphia, has 191 Paracelsus items.

Marx[4] thought only those works were genuine which weae dedicated to some person, gave the place of composition, and were signed 'Theophrastos von Hohenheim' (which reduced their number to ten items). It was fashionable in Germany to condemn as spurious many works having a superstitious or other unworthy character, but most recent specialists (such as W. Pagel) accept them as genuine. Not only his works, but Paracelsus himself was full of contradictions. Hoefer[5] in a description which cannot be improved, said:

'Picture to yourself a man who, in certain moments, gives evidence of a remarkable penetration, and in others raves in the most pitiable way possible; a man who, at one time, devoted to the progress of science, proclaims the absolute authority of experience, and thunders the most violent anathemas against the theories of the ancients; yet at another time, like a lunatic, seems to converse with demons and believe in their absolute power. Fasting in the morning, drunk in the evening, presenting exactly every idea in the order in which it came to his mind, such is Paracelsus.'

Discounting the extravagant praise in writers such as Sudhoff we might agree that Paracelsus had genius and some real achievements to his credit (der zu allen Zeiten so verschieden beurteilte, doch sicher geniale und an wirklichen Verdiensten nicht arme Paracelsus),[6] but Davy[7] said Paracelsus's 'enthusiasm almost supplied his want of genius'. From our point of view, he represents a step forward from alchemy. He administered a rude shock to the conventional alchemists, and by his blustering profusion of abusive rhetoric he pushed aside their unintelligible jargon by one even less comprehensible but more modern and in nearer relation to reality.

In spite of his wandering life, Paracelsus wrote (or dictated) a great number of books.[8] Their number has been given as 364 and Gmelin[9] gives 122 titles as of chemical interest. Only a few were issued in the lifetime of Paracelsus, but he left a mass of manuscripts, which were passed on by Oporinus to Bodenstein and Toxites. All the printed and manuscript material which he could collect was assembled and printed under the editorship of Johann Huser of Waldkirch, Baden, physician in Glogau. Some of the manuscripts were auto-

[1] Mook, 1876, 5 f.   [2] Daremberg, 1870, i, 356, 361–464.
[3] Stillman, 1920, 80, 115.   [4] 1843, 92 f.   [5] (2), 1843, ii, o.
[6] H. Boruttau, *A. Med.*, 1909, ii, 301 (312).   [7] *Elements of Chemical Philosophy*, 1812, 18.
[8] Mook; Sudhoff, (1), 1894–9; Ferguson, 1877–96.   [9] (1), i, 238, 240 f.

graphs, of others Huser gives the names of the owners; some, he says, had been altered. Huser's edition, in an unpleasant Swiss dialect of German, was published in Basel in 1589–90, with the patronage of the Archbishop of Cologne:

I. Bucher und Schriften des Edlen Hochgelehrten und Bewehrten philosophi und medici Philippi Theophrasti Bombast Hohenheim Paracelsi genannt . . . auss den Originalien, vnd Theophrasti eigner Handschrifft, souiel derselben zu bekommen gewesen . . . durch Iohannem Hvservm Brisgoivm. Basel, Conrad Waldkirch, 1589–90, 10 vols. 4°. This, regarded as authoritative, is very rare (I have seen only vols. i to iv). It was reprinted (not without faults) as:

II. Opera Bücher vnd Schrifften, 2 vols. f°, Strassburg, 1603 and 1616; Chirur-gische Bücher vnd Schrifften, 2 pts. f°, 1605 and 1616.[1]

III. An edition in modern German with notes by B. Aschner (4 vols. 1926–32; BM) was not completed.[2]

IV. Sämtliche Werke. I Abt., medizinische, naturwissenschaftliche und philoso-phische Schriften, ed. (vols. vi and vii with W. Matthiessen) K. Sudhoff, 14 vols., Munich and Berlin, 1922–33 (i 1929, ii 1930, iii 1930, iv 1931, v 1931, vi 1922, vii 1923, viii 1924, ix 1925, x 1928, xi 1928, xii 1929, xiii 1931, xiv 1933); Abt. II, Theologische und Religionsphilosophische Schriften, ed. K. Goldamer, Wiesbaden, IV, i, 1955, V 1957, VI 1959. This is the definitive edition, but the order has been 'arranged'.

V. Sämtliche Werke in Zeitgemässer kurzer Auswahl, ed. J. Strebel, 8 vols., St. Gallen, 1944–9 (chemistry in viii, 237–378).

VI. Schriften: ausgewählt und herausgegeben von J. Kayser, Leipzig, 1921.

The *Grosse Wundarzenei* was translated into Latin as *Chirurgia Magna in duas tomos digesta, Josquino Dalhemio Ostrofranco Medico Latinitate donata*, f°, 3 pts. in 1, Strassburg (printed by Perna in Basel), 1573, and another surgical work translated by G. Dorn as *Chirurgia Minor, quam alias Bertheoneam intitulavit*, 3 vols. f°, Strassburg (printed by Perna in Basel). An edition of 26 works in Latin was published in 1575 (2 vols., Basel, Perna, 1700 pp.) before Huser's edition in German. A Latin trans-lation of the complete works, based on Huser's German text, was edited by Zacharias Palthenius, *Operum Medico-Chimicorum*, 11 vols. 4°, Frankfurt, 1603–5, but the best Latin edition is that edited by the Geneva physician Frederick Bitiskus:

VII. Avr. Philip. Theoph. Paracelsi Bombast ab Hohenheim Medici ac Philosophi celeberrimi, Chemicorúmque Principis, Opera Omnia Medico-Chemico-Chirvrgica, 3 vols. f°, Geneva, Sumptibus Ioan. Antonij, & Samuelis De Tournes, 1658, with a long preface defending Paracelsus, and index. Vol. I, portr. (quite different from that in I), xvii ll., 828 pp., xx ll.; Vol. II, xiii ll., 718 pp., xvi ll.; Vol. III, i, 212 pp., xvi ll.; ii, 119 pp., iv ll., 18 pp. This ed., which is the one I used (IV appeared long after this chapter was written) is not always completely correct,[3] but I believe all I have taken from it is trustworthy. An incomplete English tr. of VII, with some spurious works, is:

VIII. The Hermetic and Alchemical Writings of . . . Paracelsus the Great, now for the first time faithfully translated into English. Edited, with a Biographical Preface, Elucidatory Notes, a copious Hermetic Vocabulary and Index, by A. E. Waite, 2 vols. 4°, London, 1894.

IX. Selected Writings, ed. Jolande Jacobi, tr. N. Guterman, London (pr. U.S.A.), 1951 (illustr.; useful list of contents of Sudhoff's ed., 307–16; incl. trs. of some theological writing. Some works of Paracelsus were translated into Arabic about 1659 by Ṣāliḥ Halabī.[4] Sudhoff in his edition arranged the works in the order of the supposed dates of composition (which he gives).

[1] Contents in Rixner-Siber, 1829, i, 37–44.
[2] *Isis*, 1928, x, 149; 1929, xii, 362.
[3] Escher, 1838, 285 f.; Sudhof, (1), 1894, 588 f.; Liénard, 12.
[4] Massignon, in Festugière, *La Révélation d'Hermès Trismégiste*, 1944, i, 385; P. Richter, *A. Nat.*, 1913, vi, 294–304 (ibn Salām, d. A.D. 1669).

The works referred to in the text, with approximate dates, are listed below; those marked with an asterisk are usually regarded as spurious.

1 Paramirum de Quinque Entibus omnium morborum (part 1520; 1531–5)[1]
2 Paramirum aliud, quod partibus quinque absolvitur
3 Fragmenta varia ad Medicinam Physicam pertinentia
4 Paragranum in quo columnæ quatuor (Philosophia, Astronomia, Alchymia et Proprietates Medici) describuntur (1530)
5 Paragranum alterum
6 Fragmentum ad Paragranum pertinens
7 Labyrinthus Medicorum (1537–41)
8 De Morbis Tartareis (1537–41)
9 De Morbis ex Tartaro oriundis (1525–7)
10 De Causis Morborum Tartareorum
11 Fragmenta quædam de peste et de tartaro
12 De viribus membrorum (with fragmcnt. De conservatione quatuor elementorum in homine) (1526–7)
13 De tribus primis Essentiis
*14 De Pestilitate (4 tracts)
15 De Peste
16 Liber quatuordecim Paragraphorum (1527–8)
17 Liber Sextus in Medicinis
18 Liber Septimum in Medicinis
19 Liber Nonus in Medicinis de contractis membris (1525–6)
20 Undecim tractatus
21 De Podagricis (c. 1520)
22 De Caducis (1530)
23 De Morbis metallicis et mineralibus (1531–5)
24 Practica particularis de Lithiasi
25 De Urinarum ac Pulsum judiciis
26 De Modo Pharmacandi (1527)
27 Archidoxorum (1525–7) 9 books (10th spurious)
28 De Vita Longa (1526–7)

29 De Præparationibus mineralium et metallorum (1526–7)
30 De Natura Rerum libri nonem (1525–6)
*31 De Tinctura Physicorum
*32 Coelum Philosophorum sive Liber Vexationum (? Fixationum)
*33 Thesaurus Thesaurorum Alchimistarum
34 De Metallorum transubstantionibus et Cæmentis (1526–7)
35 De Gradationibus
36 De Projectionibus
*37 Manuale de Lapide Philosophico medicinale
38 De Gradibus et Compositionibus (1527) (a different work from no. 35)
39 Herbarius Theophrasti
40 De Naturalibus Rebus (1537–41) (a different work from no. 30)
41 Philosophiæ ad Athenienses
42 Fragmentum Principii Operis Anatomiæ
43 Philosophiæ de generationibus Elementorum 4 bks.
44 De Generatione Hominis
45 Liber Meteorum
46 De Mineralibus (1526–7)
47 De Naturalibus Aquis
48 Paradoxorum (Philosophia Magna), 20 parts
49 De Occulta Philosophia
50 De Imaginibus
51 Quinque tractatus alii Philosophiæ
52 Astronomia magna (Philosophia Sagax) (1537–8)[2]
53 Azot sive de Ligno et Linea Vitæ
54 Archidoxis Magicæ
55 Chirurgiæ magnæ, 5 parts (1536)
56 Chirurgiæ minoris (Bertheoneæ) (1528)
57 Spital Buch (1529)
58 De tumoribus, pustulis, ac ulceribus morbi gallici (1528)

Two works of special interest are *De Natura Rerum* and *Archidoxis*, separate editions of which appeared:

De natura rerum libri septem. De natura hominis libri duo, Opuscula verè aurea. Ex Germanica lingua in Latinam translata per M. Georgium Forbergium Mysum, 8°, Basel, P. Perna, 1573 (BM 1032. b. 18. (4.)). Nine Books of the Nature of Things, tr. by J. F[rench]., with his tr. of Sendivogius (see p. 426), sm. 4°, London, 1650; 8°, 1674.

Although Sudhoff questioned the authenticity of the *De Natura Rerum*, which

[1] New tr. by Leidecker, *Bull. Inst. Hist. Med.*, 1949, *Suppl.* xi (69 pp.).
[2] Considerable portions in Paracelsus's own MS. were used by Huser; Kayser, 108,

he supposed was written (if genuine) about 1527, Darmstaedter[1] thought it genuine but written about 1537. Of two manuscripts of it, one contains only books 1–7 and the other only books 8–9. Pagel[2] says there are reasons to believe that it is not a genuine product of the pen of Paracelsus, but its basic doctrine of putrefaction as generation is Paracelsan.

De summis Naturæ mysteriis Commentarij tres, tr. G. Dorn, 8°, Basel, P. Perna, 1584, BM 1032. b. 18. (5.); contains De Spiritibus Planetarum, De Occulta Philosophia, De Medicina cœlesti siue de signis Zodiacii & Mysteriis eorum (title incorrect in Thorndike, v, 628).

Paracelsus His Aurora, & Treasure of the Philosophers. As also the Water-Stone of the Wise Men; describing the matter of, and manner how to attain the Universal Tincture, faithfully Englished and published by J[ohn]. H[ester]. Oxon., 12°, London. Printed for Giles Calvert and are to be sold at the Black Spred Eagle, at the West end of Pauls, 1659.

Paracelsus, His Archidoxis, Or, Chief Teachings; Comprisen in Ten Books, Disclosing the Genuine Way of Making Quintessences, Arcanums, Magisteries, Elixirs, &c. Together with his Books Of Renovation and Restauration. Of the Tincture of the Philosophers. Of the Manual of the Philosophical Medicinal Stone. Of the Virtues of the Members. Of the Three Principles. And Finally his Seven Books Of the Degrees and Compositions of Receipts, and Natural Things, Englished by J[ohn]. H[ester]. Oxon., sm. 8°, London, 1661, and 1663 (Printed for Lodowick Lloyd, and are to be sold at . . . the Castle in Cornhill).[3]

In the sixteenth century medicine was generally very backward. The Latin works of Arabic authors such as Avicenna, Mesuë and Averroës, mainly commentaries on the works of Galen, were authoritative, and all independent thinking was frowned upon. Disease was regarded as a visitation from God or the Devil or the stars, or else from a disturbance of the four humours, and the materia medica was that of the Arabs, together with the superstitious and disgusting remedies which had come down from antiquity. Paracelsus and his followers believed in peculiar essences attached to the body, recognisable by signatures and stimulated by a 'magnetic force' acting on the vital force of the body. 'Magnets' prepared from human blood and excrements, material bases of the spirits and called 'mummies', were prepared from human blood by putrefaction in an egg-shell closed with isinglass and put under a sitting hen till the chickens were hatched from the other eggs; the fleshy mass found in the egg was then placed in a baker's oven till the bread was baked, and kept for use. Dried toads and lizards were thought to absorb poison from the body. Moehsen says the use of superstitious medicines, elixirs of gold and tinctures of pearls and corals, amulets, talismans, plants gathered at a particular phase of the moon in magic clothing, etc., was prevalent in Germany even in the 18 cent.[4] Sprengel[5] says that Paracelsus's medical system was based not so much on mysticism as on the grossest superstitions (auf den gröbsten Aberglauben), and the story that Paracelsus said: 'if God will not help, the Devil

---

[1] *Janus*, 1933, xxxvii, 109 (115).   [2] 1958, 115.

[3] An *Abrégé de la Doctrine de Paracelse et de ses Archidoxes*, 12°, Paris, d'Houry, 1724 (not seen) is said to be by the alchemist François Marie Pompée Colonne (Paris, c. 1649–1726), who wrote several works on alchemy; NBG, 1855, xi, 296.

[4] Moehsen, (1), 1781, 13; T. J. Pettigrew, *On Superstitions connected with the History and Practice of Medicine and Surgery*, 1844; J. Nohl, *The Black Death*, tr. C. H. Clarke, 1926, 79 f., 95; La Wall, 1927; Thorndike, v–vi.

[5] (2), 1827, iii, 493.

will', comes through Zwinger, who knew him well.[1] As Thorndike[2] said, he had 'so to speak, to move in a fourth dimension and continually watch his step at that.'

Paracelsus said that medicine is very dependent on magic[3] an attitude which had been characteristic of Arnald of Villanova (Vol. I).[4] He believed in healing through faith, but only of Christians; Jews, Turks and Saracens must be given medicines.[5] He also made extensive use of ligatures and charms which had come down from antiquity through Alexander of Tralles.[6] While in Italy he no doubt picked up some notions of gnosticism:[7] 'heaven is man and man is heaven, and all men one heaven and heaven but one man',[8] the 'mother principle' (=Sophia), the powers of the stars, demonology, etc., but these were probably derived partly from popular superstition and partly from such works as the *Occulta Philosophia* of Agrippa of Nettesheim. He had some knowledge of the *Qabbalah* (which he regarded as a Persian doctrine perverted by Jews),[9] particularly the micro-macrocosm theory, which is fundamental in all his works.[10] His Neoplatonic ideas were perhaps derived from Marsilius Ficinus,[11] but, as Sprengel[12] recognised, the basis of his philosophy, physiology ('if he can be said to have had any'), anatomy, pathology, and pharmacology is the Jewish *Qabbalah* (which again he probably derived from Agrippa's work, in circulation in manuscript before its publication in 1531). The Jewish doctrine of 'correspondences' between the greater and lesser worlds had been developed in great detail and related to astrology by Ramon Lull in his *Ars Brevis* (Vol. I).[13] Lull was singled out for special condemnation by Paracelsus.

Paracelsus coined a large number of new names, probably with the intention of puzzling and irritating the conventional physicians and making his writings impressive: pagoyus, undimia, aniadus (an astrological botany), limbus, azoth, cagastric, iliastric, tartarus, archeus, alcola (urinary deposit), divulsio (sediment), anatomy (signature of a thing), gotaronium, roades, etc. He was fond of such speeches as: 'Da besehet ihr den blauen Himmel und lüget und trüget, dass ihr selbst müsset Zeugnis geben, dass der meiste Theil nichts ist, denn Rätherey und Gedünken und Wähnen und keine Kunst'.[14] in criticising uroscopy (Seichsehen) instead of a chemical examination — which he fails to specify. His 'anatomy' is a sort of astrology and 'alchemy' is the art of bringing out the stars of metals. His pupils and admirers compiled dictionaries of his barbarous terminology,[15] e.g. Michael Toxites,[16] Gerhard Dorn,[17] Martin

[1] Pagel, 1958, 49.   [2] v, 628.
[3] De virtute imaginativa, in (48); VII, ii, 493; Rixner-Siber, 1829, i, 187.
[4] Thorndike, ii, 858.   [5] Rixner-Siber, 1829, i, 195 f.
[6] Thorndike, ii, 579.   [7] Pagel, 1958, 204–13.   [8] *Paragranum*; VII, 1658, i, 201.
[9] *Philos. Sagax*, i: Probatio in Scientiam Nectromantiam, VII, 1658, ii, 565: Gabanala.
[10] Pagel, 1958, 213–17.
[11] Pagel, 1958, 218–27; Sudhoff in Meyer-Steineg and Sudhoff, 1922, 270.
[12] (1), iii, 307; (2), iii, 447, 452 f., 458 f., 462 f., 467, 477 f., 491; Jacobi, 1951, 28, 200, etc.
[13] F. A. Yates, *J. Warburg Inst.*, 1954, xvii, 115–73; Pagel, 1958, 242.
[14] Sprengel, (2), iii, 477; from *Paragranum 2*.
[15] Sprengel, (1), iii, 296; Waite, VIII, ii, 348.
[16] *Onomastica II. I Philosophicum medicum et synonymum. II Theophrasti Paracelsi: hoc est eorum vocum quarum in scriptis eius solet usus esse, explicatio*, 8°, Strassburg, 1574.
[17] *Dictionarium Theophrasti Paracelsi, continens obscuriorum vocabulorum quibus in suis scriptis passim vtitur*, 8°, Frankfurt, 1583 and 1584.

Ruland,[1] J. F[rench],[2] Roch le Baillif de la Rivière [Riverius],[3] and William Johnson.[4]

German mysticism is a thing apart. Its founder, Meister Eckhart (1260–1327), nominally a Thomist, taught that God is indeterminate, the world proceeds from God by divine self-revelation, and in the return of things to God there is a progress to a higher intuition. He was really a pantheist, and similar views were held by Nicolas of Cusa (Vol. I).[5] Jakob Böhme (1575–1624) ('Behmen' in English authors), born in a peasant home, founded his mysticism on the Bible and Paracelsus. He was studied by Newton and by John Pordage, the translator of Willis (see p. 305). His ideas, a mixture of current folklore and Neoplatonism, also influenced Kant, Schelling, Oken, and Hegel.[6]

Spirit must distinguish itself from non-spirit in order to be, this inner differentiation beginning in God and reproducing itself in consciousness; it is the principle by which the world evolved. Böhme explained the etymology of sulphur as 'sul', active and 'phur' passive. He was familiar with mystical alchemy but completely ignorant of chemistry, using chemical terms which he did not understand; he attributed human sensations and divine personalities to minerals. A work on alchemy attributed to him is said by Kopp to be spurious.[7]

De Wulf[8] thought that Neoplatonic mysticism was a German characteristic, going back even to Albertus Magnus but strongly emphasised by Thierry of Freiburg and Meister Eckhart, and was opposed to scholastic philosophy. Eckhart's idea that 'God is not complete without my love' appears in Paracelsus.

Paracelsus's philosophy, which is nebulous and of little real interest,[9] is mostly a development of the speculations of the Jewish *Qabbalah*.[10] He sought divine 'seals' and 'signs' in Nature, and identified the mind with the 'internal knowledge' possessed by natural objects, which can be 'overheard' by research, union with the object being the aim of the philosopher and physician. His

---

[1] *Lexicon Alchemiæ sive Dictionarium Alchemisticum, cum obscuriorum verborum et rerum Hermaticarum, tum Theophrast- Paracelsicarum Phrasium*, 4°, Frankfurt, 1612.

[2] *A Chymical Dictionary explaining hard places and words met withall in the writings of Paracelsus, and other obscure Authors*, included in his tr. of Sendivogius (p. 427), sm. 4°, London, 1650; 8°, 1674.

[3] *Dictionariolum vocum quibus in suis scriptis usus est Paracelsus*, in VII, iii, app., 13.

[4] *Lexicon Chymicvm. Cum Obscuriorum Verborū[m], et Rerum Hermeticarum, tum Phrasium Paracelsicarum, in Scriptis ejus: et aliorum Chymicorum, passim occurrentiam, planam explicationem continens*, 18°, London, 1652; second part, 1653 (containing *Vita Paracelsi*), *Vocabula Chimica in priore Libro omissa, multis Vocabulorum Chymicorum Characteribus adjectis e Basilio Valentino, Theophrasto Paracelso, Oswaldo Crollio, aliisque Auctoribus Chymicis collectis*; new ed., 2 vols, 12°, Frankfurt and Leipzig, 1678; complete in Manget, i, 217–91. A good list is given by Kayser, 1921, 484–545.

[5] Sarton, iii, 568; *The Works of Meister Eckhart*, tr. C. de B. Evans, 1924.

[6] Windelband, *History of Philosophy*, 1893, 447; Kingsley, *Alexandria and her Schools*, 1854, 52, 84.

[7] *Idea Chemiæ Boehmianæ Adepta oder Abriss der Bereitung des Steins der Weisen*, Amsterdam, 1680 or 1690, and later eds. to *Jak. Böhmes kurze und deutlich Beschreibung des Steins der Weisen*, Amsterdam, 1747; G. von Harless, *Jakob Böhme und die Alchemisten*, Berlin, 1870 and 1882; Ueberweg, 1924, iii, 144; Hoefer, (1), ii, 326; S. F. Mason, *A History of the Sciences*, 1953, 282; Kopp, (1), ii, 238; (4), i, 212; Ferguson, i, 111; Lippmann, (2), i, 680; H. L. Martensen, *Jacob Boehme*, tr. T. R. Evans, revised by S. Hobhouse, 1949; R. D. Gray, *Goethe the Alchemist*, Cambridge, 1952, 38, 269, and index, 306; H. Grunsky, *Jacob Boehme*, Stuttgart, 1956, 178 f.; *The Signatures of Things* was publ. in the Everyman series; his *Seraphinischen Blumengartlein* is full of the wonderful properties of the 'edlen hochteuren Steines des Weisen', the theory of signatures, etc.

[8] *Philosophy and Civilization in the Middle Ages*, Princeton, 1922, 290 f.

[9] Brucker, 1766, IV, i, 677–85; Stillman, 1920, 34; Liénard, 1932; Lasswitz, 1890, i, 298 f.; Koyré, 1955; Pagel, 1958, 50–125.

[10] Pagel, 1958, 137 f., 213 f.

belief in magic, if 'protoscientific' as Pagel[1] calls it, has hardly 'a scientific and modern ring'. His astrology is traditional even if enriched with new names, and the supposed correspondences between the stars and parts of the body is late Neoplatonic. References of diseases and drugs to particular stars[2] 'play an important part' in his biology and pathology. Each disease was endowed with a body.[3]

The *Philosophy of the Athenians*[4] has been regarded as an extract from the *Philosophia Sagax*; it was widely read. It deals with the 'mysteria' of things: cheese is a 'mysterium' of maggots, a star is a 'mysterium' of caterpillars, etc., all descended from a 'Mysterium Magnum' or mother of things. This and the *Philosophia Sagax*, until recently thought to be spurious, are the main sources used in Koyré's account of the doctrine of Paracelsus, 'Mélange de mystique, de magie, d'alchimie. Très belle toutefois.'

The four elements contain spirits which may attach themselves to man in the processes of witchcraft. Thunder is the 'fruit' of the stars. The 'real' elements are spiritual. Every object is coagulated smoke, but each has its own smoke. Wood is smoke from Derses, herb is smoke from Leffas, metal is smoke from Stannar, stone is smoke from Enur. As Pagel says, all this is 'very far' from van Helmont's 'gas' (p. 227). Paracelsus thought that the primary matter (*limbus*) was primordial water, over which the spirit of God (*yliaster*) moved as an Archeus. From this the four elements were first created, two compact (water and earth) and two immaterial (air and fire). From fire the ether is formed; from air the apparent void. The first form of corporeality is always a vapour (spiritus fumosus) which then gradually coagulates into a tangible body.[5] The cosmos is surrounded by a great air-like chaos called *yliados* which supports the heavens; the whole forms a cosmic egg.[6] Everything in the universe, including minerals, takes food and voids excrements.[7]

The primary man (*parens hominis*) is an emanation from God, and all spirits emanate from him; he is the limbus minor or last creature, who is Christ, an emanation from the limbus major and a subordinate person (an Arian heterodoxy). The limbus major is boundless light (the gnostic pleroma), and the seed (der Saame) of all creatures. The Saamen are of two kinds, one (the sperma) being the vehicle of the true Saame, which is generated by speculation and imagination, produced by the stars (*astri*). Paracelsus's 'seed' was 'a kind of vital sap, a quintessence of all parts of man, in contradistinction to "sperm", which in many cases serves to transmit it. It is everything that exists only potentially, not actually. The "sperm" is the tangible material component of semen, and does not include the spirit and essence, the active forces of the seed.'[8]

All individuation is opposed to creation. It is the main motive and

---

[1] 1958, 62.   [2] Pagel, 1958, 69.   [3] Pagel, 1958, 137.
[4] *Philosophiæ ad Athenienses Libri tres*; VII, ii, 239–52; tr. in *Philosophy Reformed & Improved in Four Profound Tractates . . . made English by H. Pinnell*, 12°, London, 1657; Pagel, 1958, 89.
[5] 32, 41, 42; VII, ii, 120, 239 f., 254; Kopp, (2), iii, 139; Rixner-Siber, 1829, i, 73 f.; Kiesewetter, (1), 1891, 51 f.; Spunda, 1925, 72.
[6] 3, 9, 43; VII, ii, 169, 255 f., 470; Rixner-Siber, i, 78 f.   [7] 26; VII, i, 812.
[8] 44; VII, i, 148; Sprengel, (2), iii, 454, 465; Jacobi, 1951, 332, 334.

constructive force in the world and is associated with the 'fall' of nature and of man. It appears in corruption and putrefaction and causes diseases, each an Ens or poison, in which an individual agent interferes with the harmoniously working organism and causes separation and deposition of impurities. The sum total of such disruptive processes Paracelsus called the Cagastrum, and because of it all created things are mortal.[1]

The body is born free from poison but receives it in food, part of which (the essence) serves for nutrition whilst the poison is separated by the Archeus, a directing force (vis) or spiritual being located in the stomach, and possessing a head and hands. The various parts of the body also have stomachs, producing secretions. The Archeus can become sick or incapacitated, when the separation is incomplete and illness results; he acts normally like an alchemist. All disease is curable and is not caused by a disturbance of the humours but by five 'entities (entia)':[2]

(1) *ens astrorum* or sidereal influence infecting the air, e.g. of realgaric stars; if there were no air, living beings would die asphyxiated;
(2) *ens veneni* or influence of poisons, which the Archeus fails to separate;
(3) *ens naturale* or influence existing in the individual (microcosm);
(4) *ens spirituale* or influence acting through the spirit (Geist) on the body;
(5) *ens deale*, the will of God producing disease as punishment or warning.[3]

The Archeus (ἀρχαῖος, origin ?), also called Iliaster (ὕλη + ἄστον ?) or Vulcan, is (like the φύσις of Hippokrates) an immaterial principle, a kind of world-soul which generates and rules everything, causes the development of plants and animals, and is an 'alchemist' of Nature which separates nutriment into useful and useless; it acts also in the form of emanations from the stars. By a 'vulcanic digestion' the human body is formed from the elements and chaos.[4] In man, Archeus is a principle residing in the stomach.[5] Each of the four elements has an Archeus, each divided into parts, and each part corresponds with a part of the human body. That emerging from the heart of the terrestrial Archeus (gold, emeralds, coral) fortifies the human heart, etc. Thus the action of drugs is an interaction of Archei and parts of Archei.[6]

The alchemist (Archeus) of an animal enables it to digest food which is unsuitable for other animals; an ostrich can digest iron. Digestion is the solution of food (sic esitatio nihil est aliud quam dissolutio corporum).[7] Just as the stomach digests food, converting part to the nourishment of the body and partly throwing out the residue from the body, so part of the air [in respiration] is digested and consumed and the other separated as a kind of excrement (cuius pars una digeritur ac consumitur, altera excernitur specie

---

[1] Pagel, 1958, 113.　　　　[2] Paracelsus had a liking for the number five; Thorndike, v, 627.
[3] 1; VII, i, 7 f.; Rixner-Siber, 1829, i, 148 f.; Strunz, 1903, 19; Liénard, 81; Stillman, 1920, 121; Sudhoff, (1), II, 1899, 415.
[4] 7, 11, 52; VII, i, 286, 528; ii, 525 f.; Lippmann, (6), 1933, 51; Richter, *A. Nat.*, 1913, vi, 294–304, thought *iliaster* was from Latin *ilex* [α + lex], 'gesetzlos'. It was a sort of 'animated star-matter'; Pagel, 1958, 88, 105 f., 112, thought 'Archeus is Vulcan operating inside objects', giving specificity by a kind of alchemy: Paracelsus said: 'for all the arts are present in man as well as in alchemy outside'; Koyré, 62.
[5] 14; VII, i, 378.　　　　[6] Pagel, 1958, 109.　　　　[7] 41, iii, 4; VII, ii, 252.

excrementi).[1] A man lived six months without food by having a fresh sod put on his stomach, replaced by a new one when it dried up. Cows live all summer in the Alps without drink, air supplying water, and a man could live without food if his feet were planted in the earth.[2] Francis Bacon[3] says a great man cultivated longevity by holding his head over a fresh sod in bed every morning, and Roger Bacon[4] had mentioned a woman in Norwich who lived twenty years without food, emitting no superfluity from the body, but he does not say how this was done.[5]

Paracelsus uses the name *clissus* for an occult generative power which in plants ascends from the roots into the seeds, causing the latter to produce a new organism, and then returning to the root.[6] His botany is largely astrological and based on the theory of 'signatures', which he says he learnt from peasants.[7] This doctrine, that plants having certain markings were cures for certain diseases, is derived partly from folklore and partly from the *Qabbalah* and late Neoplatonic authors such as Ficinus.[8]

The botanist Rembert Dodoens (Malines, 1518–Leyden, 1585) in his *De Stirpium Historia*, Antwerp, 1553,[9] spoke of the doctrine of signatures as recent and so variable and uncertain that it could not be accepted as a part of science. Croll (p. 175) wrote a special treatise on it. Paracelsus believed that plants could be revived from their ashes (*palingenesia*).[10]

William of Auvergne, bishop of Paris (1228–49), in his treatise on magic (Vol. I) said that men had tried to produce, and thought they succeeded in producing, human life in other ways than by the usual generative process.[11] Paracelsus spoke of the artificial production of a small human being (*homunculus*) by digesting sperm in a sealed cucurbit placed in putrefying horse-dung for forty days.[12] Rothscholtz[13] in a Treuhertzige Warnungs-Vermahnung, says the adepts of his time put tiny ivory models of bones in glasses[14] and said the homunculus had been there but had died through neglect. The idea of the homunculus is in Arnald of Villanova.[15] Paracelsus shared in the German belief in beings who live in all the four elements: nymphs, sylphs, salamanders, pygmies, etc.;[16] these took food and drink composed of their own element only and propagated their species but had no souls; they were the guardians of underground treasures which, if ever reached, were at once lost again. He calls them collectively Sagani. Only if irritated were they dangerous. These

[1] 23; VII, i, 707; based on Galen, from whom it was probably taken, Daremberg, 1870, i, 377; paraphrased by Boyle, *New Experiments ... touching the Spring of the Air*, 1660; in *Works*, 1744, i, 69.
[2] 27; VII, ii, 5.   [3] *Sylva Sylvarum*, 928.   [4] *Opus Minus*, ed. Brewer, 1859, 373.
[5] Alexis de Littre's *Ergo aer hominem nutrit*, Paris, 1689, I have not seen.
[6] 41, iv, 1; VII, 1658, ii, 277; Roch le Baillif, *Dictionariolum*, in VII, III, ii, appendix, 14.
[7] Rixner-Siber, 1829, i, 113.
[8] Franck, (1), 10; *id.*, (2), 57; Sigwart, *Kleine Schriften*, Freiberg i/B, 1889, i, 25; H. Leclerc, *Janus*, 1918, xxiii, 5–28; list of works on 'signatures' in Lippmann, (5), 79; see Croll, p. 175.
[9] Q. by Thorndike, vi, 294.
[10] 30, vi; VII, ii, 97; Kopp, (1), i, 111; ii, 243, incorrectly says this was first taught by Quercetanus, *c*. 1600.
[11] Thorndike, ii, 353   [12] 28, 30, 48 (de homunculis); VII, ii, 52, 86, 474.
[13] *Deutsches Theatrum Chemicum*, Nürnberg, 1728, i, 305.
[14] One is shown in Plate 12, Read, *The Alchemist in Life, Literature and Art*, 1947, 48.
[15] Lippmann, (6), 35.   [16] 49, 52; VII, ii, 388, 487, etc.; Rixner-Siber, 1829, i, 162.

spirits (Panes, Fauni, Fones Satyri Silvani, Fatui, Fatuæque vel Fautuæ vel enim Fanæ) were described by Martianus Capella of Carthage (5 cent.)[1] and Bernard Silvester of Tours (1150) (Silvani, Panes et Nerei)[2] and they are an inheritance from later Neoplatonism, if not from 'primitive Teutonic paganism'.[3] Paracelsus was sceptical as to the efficacy of the divining rod in searching for minerals.[4]

Living tissue has an innate healing force or balsam which Paracelsus called *mumia*, and the chief care of the surgeon should be to keep the wounds clean: 'if wounds are kept pure and clean they are healed by the operation of Nature herself.'[5] He recommended preparations of human flesh of a healthy body, containing mumia, as medicines,[6] and this attracted much attention:

Paracelsus, Of the Chymical Transmutation, Genealogy and Generation of Metals and Minerals, also of the Urim and Thummim of the Jews; . . . the Second Part of the Mumial Treatise, to which is added Experiments of that Famous Philosopher Raymond Lully, containing the Composition of both Elixirs; and the way of making the Philosopher's Stone . . . , tr. R. Turner, 8°, London, 1657.

Medicina Diastatica, or Sympatheticall Mumie; containing many mysterious and hidden secrets in Philosophy and Physick . . . Teaching the Magneticall cure of Diseases at Distance, etc. Abstracted from the Works of Dr. Theophra. Paracelsus; By the labour and industry of Andrea Tentzelius, Phil. and Med. Translated out of the Latin by Ferdinando Parkhurst, Gent. London: Printed by T. Newcomb for T. Heath, 24°, 1653.

German medicine in the time of Paracelsus was dominated by astrology. His disciples (who were mostly without education or science) were convinced of its truth and zealous in its propagation, and he himself says astronomy is one of the four important parts of medicine.[7] He thought that the planets in the universe (macrocosm) corresponded with 'planets' in the human body (microcosm), which have predetermined courses, so that the Sun corresponds with the heart, the Moon with the brain, Mercury with the lungs, Jupiter with the liver, Venus with the kidneys, Mars with the gall-bladder, etc.[8] Paracelsus says[9] the custom of assigning metals to planets was passing away in his time and was 'nothing but rubbish and confusion', yet he says that ulcers are formed by a corrosive 'realgar' (arsenic) from particular planets corresponding with parts of the body, and speaks of mercurial, sulphurous, arsenical

---

[1] *De Nuptiis philologiæ*, ii, §§ 154–67, ed. U. F. Kopp, 4°, Frankfurt, 1836, 207–23, and notes; Thorndike, i, 545–6.

[2] Bernard Silvester, *De mundi universitate*, II, vii, 92 f.; in *Bibliotheca Philosophorum Mediæ Ætatis*, ed. Barach and Wrobel, Innsbruck, 1876, i, 50.

[3] Thorndike, ii, 104, 141; the treatise *De nymphis, sylphis, pygmaeis et salamandris et de caeteris spiritibus* (VII, ii, 388), part of the *Philosophia magna*, is said by Sigerist, *Four Treatises of Paracelsus*, Baltimore, 1941, 215, to be spurious and of uncertain date, but Paracelsus got this part of his 'philosophy' from the same sources as Cornelius Agrippa, *De Occulta Philosophia*, 1533, bk. iii, ch. 16, p. 239 f., who has thirty 'et eiusmodi' of them.

[4] 30, ix; VII, ii, 112.

[5] 40, iv; 55, 56; VII, ii, 190; III, i, 90; III, ii, 7; Dictionariolum, end of III, ii, 16; Kiesewetter, 61; Stillman, 1920, 60.

[6] 49, iii (de carne et mumia); VII, ii, 504; Rixner-Siber, 1829, i, 155; Koyré mistook this for powder of dry mummies.

[7] 4; VII, i, 184; Moehsen, (1), 407 f., 419 f., 431 f.; Sprengel, (1), iii, 334.

[8] 1, iii, 6; 4, iii; VII, i, 19, 207; Rixner-Siber, 1829, i, 76, 164; Kiesewetter, (1), 1891, 15: cf. Van Helmont, *Archeus faber, Vita brevis*; in *Ortus Medicinæ*, 1648, 40, 738.

[9] 46, ii; VII, ii, 346; Thorndike, vii, 94, 97.

antimonial, saline, and bitter stars, causing various diseases by poisoning the air.[1]

Henning Scheunemann of Halberstadt regarded the plague as a mercurial disease and fever as a sulphurous disease, but later traced all diseases to ten roots, four mercurial, three sulphurous, and three saline, to which he added astral influences.[2] These ideas all go back to Arnald of Villanova, who said that every disease has its star, and its remedy has a *vis contraria* derived from its star, which does not act *tota species*. He had the homoeopathic view characteristic of Paracelsus,[3] Stephanus Rodericus Castrensis, of Portugal, first professor of medicine in the University of Pisa, wrote on the meteors of the microcosm.[4]

Jacques Fontaine of St. Maximin (Var) in Provence, professor of medicine at the new university of Aix, M.D. of Aix, councillor in medicine to Louis XIII, an opponent of astrology, attacked the idea that there are astral diseases, as the Hermetics and Paracelsists supposed, and thought that in giving medicines astrological rules must often give way to considerations of necessity.[5] In a *Detection of Paracelsan Magic* he attacks Paracelsus for following Pomponazzi, condemning others and promoting his reputation by professing to work marvels beyond nature and possible only by diabolical magic, concealing this by a screen of alchemy, astrology, etc.; also for using images, words, and characters. In his works, Fontaine often cites Libavius (who was at times too favourable towards alchemy) against Paracelsus.[6]

According to Paracelsus the stars have openings (*emunctoria*) through which they give birth to winds and meteors. Winds, rain, snow, heat, cold, frost, lightning, etc., are fruits of the stars. Lightning is formed in particular stars from the most combustible sulphur, the most fatty saltpetre (*sal nitrum*) and the most coagulated mercury, from which the Archeus makes the material of lightning (*materia fulguris*), which is poured out in the air as a cloud: interaction of the three principles in this produces lightning.[7] Rains of metals come from the corresponding planets and these metals are very different from those found in the earth; some stars draw up iron from the earth by magnetic force and let some of it fall again as meteorites.[8] Paracelsus (and many others, e.g. Croll and Van Helmont) believed that the gelatinous 'nostoc' (an alga) fell from the stars.[9] The various pulses in the body, and those which he believed existed in the universe, were under the control of the stars.[10]

The *Liber Azoth* ($= A + Z + \Omega + \Box$) is very mystical.[11] Nineteen treatises (XXX–XLVIII) in the Geneva edition[12] comprise the *Philosophia Magna*; they

---

[1] 1, i, 8; 45; 55, P. II, tract. ii, ch. 12; VII, i, 10 f.; III, i, 58; Stillman, 1920, 40 f., thought the idea was connected with observations of the effects of fumes from smelting furnaces.

[2] *Medicina Reformata seu Denarius Hermeticus philosophicus-medico- chymicus*, 8°, Frankfurt, 1617 (posthumous); Thorndike, vii, 174; Jöcher, iv, 260, says Scheunemann thought the principles of Paracelsus were revelations, but diverged from them in many cases.

[3] Pagel, 1958, 256; his insistence that Arnald's system of medicine was still based on Galen's 'humours' does not, in my opinion, negative Arnald's claims.

[4] *De meteoris microcosmi*, f°, Florence, 1621; Thorndike, vii, 124.

[5] *Discours de la puissance du ciel sur les corps inferieurs et principalement de l'influence contre les astrologues indiciaires* [i.e. judiciares] *avec Une dispute des elements contre les Paracelsistes*, 12°, Paris, 1581, BM 718. d. 27. (4.); Thorndike, v, 6, 44; vi, 188, 553.

[6] *Magiæ Paracelsicæ detecta authore D. I. Fontano . . . e Gallico Idiomate in Latinum conversa opere D. Andreae doctoris medici*; *Opera omnia*, Cologne, 1613, 313–25, 750–61; Thorndike, v, 644; vi, 188 f., 253.

[7] Rixner-Siber, 1829, i, 166 f.; 45; VII, ii, 304, 321 f., 332, 335, 339, 341.

[8] 43, 45; VII, ii, 265, 314, 320.

[9] Vallot, *J. de Phys.*, 1821, xcii, 216; Kopp, (4), 1886, ii, 274.

[10] 14; VII, i, 375; astrological medicine (Iatromathematics) was not a new thing in Paracelsus's time; see Sudhoff, *Iatromathematiker, vornehmlich im XV und XVI Jahrhundert, Abhl. zur Gesch. der Medizin*, Breslau, 1902, ii (not available); q. by Thorndike, iv, 135, 457.

[11] VII, ii, 675 f.; Pagel, 1958, 102.   [12] VII, ii, 373–480.

are followed by *De Occulta Philosophia*, five treatises of 'other' Philosophy, an *Astronomia magna*, works on astrology and divination, signatures, and *Archidoxis Magicæ* in seven books,[1] full of figures of magic seals, some like the old Abraxas gems (Vol. I). These works were all regarded as spurious by Sudhoff. Paracelsus used an alloy ('electrum') of the seven metals, for magic rings and beakers.[2] He believed in the curative effect of the magnet, the poles of which he called its stomach and back, and he applied the poles to various parts of the body to cure diseases due to the influence of Mars.[3]

Cornelius Agrippa[4] said 'the world is threefold, viz. elementary, sidereal and spiritual,' and natural magic comprises three branches, viz. physics or the knowledge of the nature of things in the universe, mathematics (including the *Qabbalah*), and theology (including magic). Paracelsus thought a fourth 'pillar' must be added to support the science of medicine, viz. alchemy, the other three of Agrippa he renamed philosophy, astronomy and virtue (*proprietas*).[5] He says 'nature yields nothing perfected, but man must perfect it. This perfecting is called alchemy. For the baker is an alchemist when he bakes bread, the vine-grower when he makes wine, the weaver when he makes cloth'; the food is first cooked by the fire and then the alchemist in the stomach digests it.[6] In defining alchemy as the art of extracting the 'stars' of metals, and saying that the 'star' in food is introduced into the body in nutrition,[7] he may have borrowed from the old astrology, in which στοιχεῖα meant the gods of the elements, then of the stars.[8] Paracelsus calls alchemy 'Spagyria' (disce ergo Alchimiam, quæ alias Spagyria dicitur).[9] The Paracelsic physicians are Archei of Spagyri, having arcana.[10] Alchemy is the art of separating what is useful from what is not by transmuting it into its ultimate matter and essence, without which no one can be a physician (sine quod nemo fieri medicus potest).[11] The new word *spagyric* was probably derived from σπαέιν separation, and ἀγείρειν combination.[12]

The importance of chemistry to medicine had long before been emphasised by Roger Bacon (Vol. I) and Arnald of Villanova (Vol. I), and Arnald had also anticipated Paracelsus in insisting that the quintessence of a medicine should be extracted and used as its active part.[13] There are also striking resemblances between the modes of life and the teachings of Rupescissa (Vol. I) and Paracelsus.[14] W. Ganzenmüller[15] who emphasised the dependence of Paracelsus on earlier alchemy and his belief in astrology and the relation of the microcosm to the macrocosm, assumed that he worked at practical

[1] VII, ii, 695–718.
[2] 54, vi (de compositione metallorum); VII, ii, 713 f.; Moehsen, (2), 138.
[3] 39, vi (de viribus magnetis); VII, ii, 175.   [4] *De Occulta Philosophia*, Cologne, 1532, 1 f.
[5] 4; VII, i, 181 f., 206 f.; Kopp, (2), iii, 135; Stillman, 1920, 33, 37, 43.
[6] 4; VII, i, 181 f., 206 (tertia medicinæ columna Alchimia); 8, xvi; VII, i, 324 (quod ad separationem attinet, scientia Alchimiæ est): 6; VII, i, 343 (alchimia est ars quæ docet astra separare a corporibus, ut astra illa deinceps astris et firmamento in dirigendo obsequantur).
[7] 22, ii (de caduco matricis); VII, i, 679.   [8] Diels, *Elementum*, Leipzig, 1899, 57.
[9] 1, i, 3; VII, i, 37.   [10] 1, i, 3; 4, pref.; VII, i, 37, 182 f.
[11] 7, ch. v; VII, i, 273; Jacobi, 1951, 215 f.
[12] Libavius, *Commentariorum Alchymiæ*, Pars I, Frankfurt, 1606, 77; Adam, *Vitæ*, 1620, 23 f.; Kopp, (1), ii, 160; (2), i, 63.
[13] Thorndike, v, 533, 541, 637; 657; vi, 219.   [14] Sherlock, 1948; Pagel, 1958, 263.
[15] *Angew. Chem.*, 1941, liv, 427; *Beitr.*, 1956, 300–14.

chemistry, but gives no discoveries of his in this field. His claims for Paracelsus are criticised by Pagel as extravagant.[1] The legends that Paracelsus busied himself in alchemical experiments and discovered the philosophers' stone are due to such credulous authors as Johann Conrad Creiling (1673–1750?).[2] His attitude towards alchemy is vacillating; sometimes he praises it and sometimes condemns it. In his wandering and disturbed life it is very improbable that he would have had any opportunity for practical work in chemistry. The remains of a laboratory in a house at Esslingen where he is said to have lived, were still shown in 1814[3] and Marx,[4] who thought that Paracelsus was more interested in chemistry than alchemy, quotes Praun[5] as reporting the finding in a house in Kempten of a tin box containing a red powder which may have belonged to Paracelsus, and was, no doubt, regarded as a powder of projection.

The chemical material in the writings of Paracelsus gives the impression that it was carelessly and inaccurately copied from books rather than a result of practical work.[6] The *Cœlum Philosophorum*, 'scientia et natura Alchimiæ, et quid de ea sentiendum sit',[7] containing alchemical recipes and symbols, is mostly regarded as spurious. A commentary on it was composed by Glauber.[8] The other treatises on alchemy printed in the works of Paracelsus[9] are probably spurious (as Huser supposed); a work published by his pupil Dorn[10] is compiled from genuine and spurious treatises. Many spurious alchemical works attributed to Paracelsus are contained in the *Aureum Vellus, oder guldin Schatz und Kunst-Kammer* (Rohrschach, 1598, and 1599).[11] Borrichius,[12] who condemned him as a charlatan, said he professed to be able to make gold (χρυσοποιήσεως peritum fuisse). Paracelsus has even been regarded as 'the founder of modern chemistry'.[13] He regarded himself as a reformer of alchemy as well as of medicine,[14] and he certainly directed attention to the utility of chemistry to medicine. The title of (58), *Theophrasti Paracelsi von Chemy und heilung der Franzosen*, found in the edition of Perna, Basel, 1577, is quite isolated and is perhaps a mistake of the publisher;[15] to describe it as the first use of 'Chemie' instead of 'Alchemie' by Paracelsus[16] is unjustified. It is not in Huser's edition.[17] Paracelsus, however, called himself an Iatrochemist, knowing both medicine and chemistry (Iatrochymista sum: vtrumque enim scio et Medicinam et Chemiã)[18] and he seems to have been the first writer of his period to use this name.

[1] 1958, 266 f.; Saunders, *Isis*, 1959, l, 274.
[2] *Die Edelgeborne Jungfer Alchymia*, Tübingen, 1730; Kiesewetter, (2), 1895, ii, 82 f., 85 f.
[3] J. J. Keller, *Geschichte der Stadt Esslingen*, 1814, 197; q. by Haeser, (1), 1881, ii, 71 f.
[4] 1843, 111.   [5] *Anleitung zu der Krebs-Cur ohne Schnitt*, Ulm, 1744, 21.
[6] Stillman, 1924, 317.   [7] VII, ii, 120–6.
[8] *Opus Minerale*, Part iii; *Works*, tr. Packe, 1689, i, 125.
[9] 31, 33, 37; VII, ii, 116, 126, 133; VIII, i, 19, 36; ii, 94; Manget, ii, 423.
[10] *Congeries Paracelsicæ Chemiæ de transmutationibus metallorum*, 8°, Frankfurt, 1581; VIII, i, 283.
[11] Contents in Bolton, (1), 1893, 954.   [12] (3), 1697, 30.
[13] K. L. Wolf, *Zeitschrift für die gesamte Naturwissenschaft*, 1935, i, 299.
[14] 55, iii, 1; VII, III, i, 66: illud quoque Augiae stabulum repurgandi pro virili nobis laborem sumpsimus.
[15] IV, vi, 13, 303.   [16] V, vii, 235.   [17] 1618, iii, 249.
[18] 55, bk. i, tr. 1, ch. 13 (also Chymia, Chymistæ); VII, III, i, 10.

Paracelsus's chemistry is mostly contained in the nine genuine books of *Archidoxis*[1] written in 1525–6 (or 1526–7) and first published in Cracow, 1569; in 1570 there were two editions published in Basel, two in Munich, and one each in Cologne and Strassburg.[2] It is said[3] that Paracelsus took his chemical prescriptions from earlier sources, and only later Paracelsists such as Croll gave them their modern form and utility; also that Paracelsus relied too exclusively on distillation, in which Brunschwig and others did better work. Sherlock thought much of Paracelsus's chemistry was derived from the Lullian school and Rupescissa, e.g. his recipe for making quintessences and potable metals[4] is from the latter. The 'sweetening' of metals was an older idea.[5] Too much has been made of Paracelsus's chemistry by 'interpreting' vague texts, and even Pagel[6] is too definite in saying that 'he attempted systematic chemical research incorporating metallurgy and pharmacology'; he is, however, correct in saying that the later Paracelsists like Croll 'are unthinkable without Paracelsus'. He created the stimulus to which they owed their existence.

Paracelsus says alchemy is not gold-making but the preparation of medicines (Nicht als die sagen, Alchimia mache Gold, mache Silber: Sie ist das fürnemmen, mach Arcana, und richte dieselbigen gegen den Kranckheiten). The physician must be an alchemist and see the sources of minerals (Also ist auch nohtt der Artzt sei ein Alchimist: will er nuhn derselbig seyn er muss die Mutter sehen auss der die Mineralia wachsen. . . . Wo nun die Mineralia ligen da seind die Künstler).[7] In turning attention away from the transmutation of metals and towards the applications of chemistry in medicine, Paracelsus performed a valuable and lasting service. He still believed in the possibility of transmutation.

Several of the recipes he gives for transmuting one metal into another are either misinterpretations of experiments, as when iron is converted into copper by means of blue vitriol, copper into lead by fusion with corrosive sublimate and arsenic, and lead into copper by heating with blue vitriol, or else mere imitations, e.g. of gold by brass or 'an excellent reddish electrum' formed by the cementation of copper with *tutia* (zinc oxide). A link with the old Byzantine-Greek sources is provided by his description of the preparation of imitation pearls (Vol. I).[8] He regarded the philosophers' stone as the same as the elixir and thought its action was transmitted through ten generations.[9] Paracelsus says[10] the 'spagyric' physicians (*Medica Spagyrica*) do not go about finely dressed, with gold rings on their fingers and white gloves, but toil night and day at the furnace, wear leather clothes and aprons, put their fingers

---

[1] VII, ii, 3–40; VIII, ii, 3–93; for early English tr. by Hester (incl. the perhaps spurious tenth book), see p. 126.

[2] Thorndike, v, 625.

[3] Multhauf, *Bull. Hist. Med.*, 1954, xxviii, 102–26; 1956, xxx, 329–46; *Isis*, 1954, xlv, 364 (Rupescissa).

[4] 27; VII, ii, 7, 10 f.   [5] Bracheschi, in Manget, i, 916.   [6] 1958, 278.

[7] 4, iii; VII, i, 206 f.; Rixner-Siber, 1829, i, 61, 82, 134; Franck, (1); 28; Strunz, (1), 1903, 22, 39; *id.*, (2), 1932 (alchemy and alchemical cosmogony).

[8] 30, vii; VII, ii, 100.

[9] 27, iii, v; VII, ii, 10 f., 18; Gmelin, (1), i, 223, 227, 229.

[10] 30, viii; VI, ii, 104.

among coals, soot and dirt, and busy themselves 'learning the steps of alchemy' (gradus scientiae Alchimiae), viz. distillation, resolution, putrefaction, extraction, calcination, reverberation, sublimation, fixation, separation, reduction, coagulation, tinction (tinctura) and the like.

The ladder of transmutation has seven steps: calcination, sublimation, solution, putrefaction, distillation, coagulation, and tincture, which must follow in the correct order.[1] In one place[2] Paracelsus said he had no experience of the philosophers' stone and had only read of it (auctor non sum, nec executor . . . ex auditu vel ex lectura); elsewhere[3] he speaks as if he possessed it, and his statements are full of contradictions.[4] There seems no doubt that he believed in it and his pupils believed that he had been in possession of it.[5] Paracelsus says:[6]

I publish and preach alchemy, which prepares secret remedies by which one cures diseases which are regarded as desperate; those who are ignorant of them cannot be called either chemists or physicians. . . . The ancient alchemists were so diligent and industrious in searching for and finding remedies that it does not seem to me to be impertinent to discover them. . . . They tried to transmute the viler metals, which I do not say is impossible to nature, although it is certain that this transmutation is enveloped in several difficulties. There is no one who doubts or does not know that iron can be transmuted into copper, and copper into lead. Those who have observed this wonderful transmutation have desired to transfer the art to medicine. Some alchemists threw away their tincture, when fowls ate it and, after losing their feathers, sprouted new and better ones, as I can testify myself.

The spagyric art and alchemy (Spagyrica et Alchimia) bring about changes of colour. Black is the fundamental colour and can produce other colours, since black matter on reverberation becomes white, yellow and finally red; the colours of the four elements are blue (water), green (earth), yellow (?; luteus; air) and red (fire).[7] The perfection of metals is compared with the development of shoots, buds, flowers and fruit on a tree; the alchemists will find there the secret.[8] The Archeus of the elements leaves his work incomplete; the *materia prima* is brought by him to the *materia media*; the *materia ultima* is the work of the Spagyrist or Alchemist, operating by fire, which separates the useless from the useful.[9] Paracelsus distinguished between natural and artificial alchemy; the most important work of the latter is the alteration and perfection of metals and the preparation of medicinal arcanas.[10] No physician can be useful without alchemy which, it is true, is often misapplied.[11] Alchemy is an art and Vulcan (the governor of fire) is the artist in it; he who is Vulcan has the power of the art, he who is not has no power (hæc Alchymia, hoc officium est Vulcani, pharmacopæum et elaborationem medicinæ agentis . . . id solum esse quod præparando per ignem impurum separat et purum elicit). Paracelsus describes the various degrees of heat used in chemical operations: dung baths,

---

[1] 30, vii; VII, ii, 97; Dorn, *Congeries Paracelsicæ*, 1581, 29.
[2] 27, v; VII, ii, 18; VIII, ii, 41.   [3] 30, ix; VII, ii, 113.   [4] Kopp, (1), 97; (2), iii, 134.
[5] Sennert, *De consenu ac dissensu Galenicorum et Peripateticorum cum Chymicis*, ch. iv; *Opera*, Lyon, 1656, i, 190 (Paracelsus aurum confecit).
[6] 55, bk. I, tract. i, ch. 13; bk. II, tract. i, ch. 5; VII, III, i, 10, 43.
[7] 50, ch. v; VII, ii, 497 f.; Strunz, Paracelsische Auffassungen über Farbenerscheinungen, *Acta Paracelsica*, 1932, v, 121.
[8] 33; VII, ii, 126.   [9] 4, iii; 45; VII, i, 206 f., 213; ii, 301.
[10] 7, v; 6; 55; VII, i, 273, 334; III, i, 155.   [11] 4, iii; 7, v; VII, i, 206 f., 274.

F

water bath (balneum Maris vel Mariae ut vocant: see Vol. I), a bath of iron filings, candles, the athanor, burning mirrors and lenses.[1] Paracelsus mentions 'liquor Alchahest' only once as a remedy for disease of the liver and says it is prepared thus: 'cheiri sumitur ac a sua nigredine in albedinem sublimatur. Hæc albedo cum vino vitæ bibitur'.[2] He says nothing of its great solvent properties, as later described by Van Helmont (p. 218).

A comparison of the stone formed in the bladder with the incrustation in vessels in which wine has stood is very old.[3] An important part of the pathology of Paracelsus deals with what he calls *tartar*, a name which he derives from Tartarus, 'enim Gehennam significat'. It is the principle of all diseases which are caused by thickening of humours, rigidity of solids, or deposition of earthy matter. He gives the name *duelech* to one of the fourteen kinds of stone deposited in the human body, and this is different from tartar. Very often tartar is formed from mucilage. Just as tartar deposits on the teeth, so it is deposited as an excrement in the internal organs when the Archeus acts too violently or irregularly, or too indolently, on the materials of food, and it can give rise to a number of diseases. This deposition Paracelsus compares with the separation of tartar (potassium hydrogen tartrate) in wine casks.

As remedies for diseases caused by tartar he used mineral waters and dilute sulphuric acid.[4] It must be noticed that Paracelsus did not restrict the name 'tartar' to solid deposits; in some respects it resembles Galen's 'black bile'.[5] The name tartar was used for deposits from wine (petra vini id est tartarum) in the 13 cent.[6] Paracelsus seems to have regarded tartar as formed in the body by the coagulation of the spirit of salt with an earthy principle, which usually exists *in prima materia* without being coagulated, the result being modified by an admixture of alum, vitriol, or common salt with the spirit of salt. He recommends a chemical examination of urine (which he does not describe, but mentions salt of urine) instead of a mere inspection. He called the sediment of urine *alcola*, distinguishing three kinds: *hypostasis* (from the stomach), *divulsio* (from the liver) and *sedimen* (from the kidneys), all modifications of tartar.[7]

The *De morbis ex tartaro oriundis* is based on lectures of 1527 and was published in Latin by Oporinus, who probably added some explanations.[8] The *Liber de morbis tartareis* contains essentially the same material; in it Paracelsus says the line of Ovid: 'Nescit nodosam Medicus curare Podagram', should be corrected to read: 'Nescit Tartaream Roades curare podagram', Roades meaning horse-doctors, and 'whoever wants a better verse can write it'.[9] Paracelsus thought the tartar of various organs is in a volatile state or 'chaos', or rises like 'distilled brandy'.[10]

[1] 30, vii; VII, ii, 99; Manget, ii, 426 f.   [2] 12, ii, 5; VII, i, 352.
[3] ψ-Aristotle, *Problemata*, x, 43; see Vol. I.
[4] 8, 9, 10, 11, 24; VII, i, 288, 313, 440, 515, 557, 741; an outline of the theory is given in Paracelsus's letter to Erasmus in 1526, VII, i, 485, facsim. in Strunz, (1), 46.
[5] Vol. I; Sprengel, (1), iii, 318, 326; (2), iii, 474; Pagel, 1958, 153.
[6] *Alphita*, ed. Mowat, Oxford, 1887, 143; Matthioli, *Commentarij in Dioscoridis*, Venice, 1570, 868: crustæ lapidosæ . . . officinorum vocabulo Tartarum vocatum.
[7] 25; VII, i, 797.   [8] Daremberg, 1870, i, 377.   [9] 8, xix; VII, i, 328.
[10] 1, iii (de origine morborum omnium ex tartaro); VII, i, 71 f., 75 (instar vini ardens, 'wie ein Brenterwein' in the German); Pagel, 1958, 155.

Paracelsus' theory of tartar was defended by Fabius Violet, Sieur de Coqueray, who also extols alchemy as one of the pillars of medicine (see p. 151). According to Guyton de Morveau,[1] Paracelsus regarded animal concretions as intermediate between tartar and stone, in which animal resin formed the first principle, and did not distinguish between urinary calculus (*duelech*) and arthritic or gouty concretions, except that the first were hardened by the spirit of urine and the latter contained more salt. Van Helmont[2] did not think the calculus contains any viscous matter or mucilage, had not hardened progressively, and is quite different from the chalky arthritic deposit which is produced only by hardening of the synovia and the slow acidification of this viscous substance.

Paracelsus recognised the effects of impure air in hospitals on diseases and describes how effluxes from the planets modify the air.[3] He says wood and fuel will not burn without air, which is the 'force of fire' (ignis vis summa est) and living beings are also suffocated without it.[4] Paracelsus often calls air 'chaos'[5] but he never uses the name gas or gas sylvestre introduced by Van Helmont (see p. 227). The nearest he got to this is his mention of 'impetuous spirits' produced from vitriol, tartar, alum, nitre, etc.: non minus quam spiritus vitrioli, tartari, aluminis, nitri, &c. si resolvitur, tumultose (ungestümer) sese exhibit.[6] The statement[7] that Paracelsus used the name *spiritus sylvestris* for the gas evolved in fermentation, effervescence, and combustion, may be based on this. Equally mistaken is the assertion that Paracelsus described the production of hydrogen from metals and acids,[8] based on a passage[9] which merely says: 'air cannot be shut in, as some falsely think, but in the moment of its separation raises itself and sometimes bursts forth like wind, and ascends sometimes with water, sometimes with earth, and at other times with fire (quia statim in momento separationis exaltat se, nec non ventus erumpit aliquando, cum aqua sursum ascendit, cum terra nonnunquam & alias cum igne).'

Air is formed from water and fire (aër quam aqua per ignem resoluta),[10] e.g. by boiling water.[11] The vague statement that 'air forms the body of tin and no other metal'[12] can hardly, as Hoefer[13] thought, refer to increase in weight on calcination. Paracelsus's theory of the elements is very confused and contradictory.[14]

Mazinus[15] had supposed that fire and air are not true elements, the first true elements being an ethereal fire and air, and air by virtue of its fatty moisture maintains the ethereal fire. Visible fire and water were created from ethereal fire and from air, respectively. Fire and water are active elements, air and earth passive. Mazinus criticised

---

[1] *Ency. Méthod., Chimie*, 1786–8, i, 407.   [2] *De lithiasi*, iii; *Ortus medicinæ*, 1652, 667.
[3] 57; 4°, Mülhausen, 1562, H iv; Arnald of Villanova had also had this idea, Thorndike, ii, 855.
[4] 20 (De apoplexia); 51, ii; VII, i, 602; ii, 503.
[5] 4, 5, 7, 8, 20, 23, 55; *De luis gallicæ*, i, 3; VII, i, 235, 270–1, 300, 496, 598, 707; iii 64, 80, 180.
[6] 1, i, 3; VII, i, 36; cf. Strunz, *J. B. Van Helmont*, 1907, 30; Stillman, 1924, 322–3.
[7] Bergman, *Essays*, Edinburgh, 1791, iii, 155; Gmelin, (1), i, 217; Lippmann, (1), ii, 360 f.; Stillman, 1920, 102 f.
[8] Hoefer, (2), ii, 16, q. Archidox. Luft erhebt sich und bricht herfür gleich wie ein Wind; corrected by Kopp, (2), iii, 241; Stillman, 1924, 357 f.; Dobbin, *Isis*, 1933, xix, 262.
[9] 27, ii; VII, ii, 7.   [10] Manget, ii, 426.   [11] 27, ii; VII, ii, 7.
[12] 27, iii; VII, ii, 8.   [13] (1), ii, 12.
[14] Hooykaas, *Janus*, 1935, xxxix, 175–87.
[15] *Pauli Mazini Aruerni De elemētorum natvra et eorvm sitv Paradoxa*, Paris, 1549 (BM 536. a. 2); *De Rerum Naturalium Generatione Paradoxa*, Paris, 1549.

the Aristotelian theories of qualities, mixture, and generation and corruption in a way reminiscent of Paracelsus' *Philosophia ad Atheniensis* and other works.[1]

Every thing has its 'complexion', depending on the complete formation of one of the four elements (fire, air, water, earth) in it, this one giving its essential complexion and the other three giving its accidental complexion. Since hot and cold, moist and dry, must imply the opposites, there are really only two complexions.[2]

Of great importance is the separation of the quintessence of a thing, which is obtained in great purity by art when the individual life of the thing is destroyed and it is freed from all incomplete elements. It contains the arcanum or curative force of the metal, salt, mineral, stone, or fresh plant. If a quintessence of a living heart could be obtained it would be the elixir of life.[3] The quintessences of gems are extracted, e.g. as a green solution formed by grinding emeralds with acids in a brass mortar (when copper is dissolved from the mortar), or by distilling with aqua fortis, etc.[4] An elixir of life[5] seems to have been only salt water, since the 'quintessence of gold' said to be mixed with it was no doubt purely imaginary. Paracelsus says:[6]

Besides the essences I have mentioned there exists another nature or essence of bodies which is called quintessence, or as the philosophers speak, the elementary accident (accidens Elementale) or as the old physicists had it, the specific form. It is called the fifth essence since the three first comprise four (quia in primis tribus quatuor Essentiæ delitescunt), and in consequence that which is here called the fifth is an elementary accident. . . . The fifth essence is the only one which preserves health . . . for all which drives out diseases is nothing but a kind of comfort (confortatio), as when an enemy is repulsed by force. . . . Every specific is a quintessence without any corruption in its body.

Paracelsus used the name *oportet* for a 'compulsory' cause of every disease; it is a factor inside man due to the multiplicity of his parts, and also the hostility of the external world.[7] *Relolleum* is an arcane virtue. The occult dispenser of nature, giving form and difference to species, is Ares. The three first essences are the hot and cold complexions and the *relolleum* (virtus ex complexione), the fourth essence being perhaps the degree which corresponds with one of four elements.[8]

'Nature can sometimes sin by appetitive virtue. Before Ares is entirely produced, the Archeus enters him with his Ilech [occult principle] adverse to the microcosm. . . . Whenever Archeus simulates nausea and hates his proper nature and work, the physician, his minister, cannot repress this abomination. Hence in preparing compositions it must be known that frequently Archeus wishes that his anatomy shall be composed of one thing and not of another, and this mode of composition is known by the spagiric degrees'.[9]

Paracelsus's views on the four elements are vacillating. He says there are

[1] Pagel, 1958, 305 f., who thinks he is one of the 'juniores' criticised by Fernel in his book *De Elementis*, in *Universa Medicina*, Utrecht, 1656, 60.
[2] 27, ii; VII, ii, 6; Rixner-Siber, 1829, i, 85.
[3] 27, iv; VII, ii, 10; VIII, ii, 22; *Archidoxis*, tr. J. H., London, 1663, 35 f.
[4] 27, 29, 41; VII, ii, 44, 79, 266, 285; Barchusen, *Pyrosophia*, 4°, Leyden, 1698, 256, says only rich Jews could afford such remedies.
[5] 27, viii; VII, ii, 31.   [6] 38, iii, 1–4; VII, ii, 150 f.
[7] 55, Pt. II, tract. ii, ch. 2; VII, iii, 52: oportet ist omnium morborum causa.
[8] 38, i, 4; VII, ii, 146; Daremberg, 1870, i, 617.   [9] 38, vii, 7; VII, ii, 162.

four elements and four complexions. The elements are earth, water, air, which is a chaos (aer sit chaos, non terra, non aqua, sed quiddam perspicuum, diaphanum, impalpabile, invisibile), and 'heaven' (coelum), which is a body, the generator of fire (matrix ex qua ignis gignitur et crescit). Heaven is not fire (nec debet id elementum ignis vocari, sed elementum cœli), since the Bible says God first created heaven and earth, and it is the first element, before earth.[1]

In each object one of the four elements is a 'predestined element' or 'quintessence' of the object. This idea is really an old one, going back to Aristotle and was a stock topic in the Middle Ages; Paracelsus perhaps derived it through Ramon Lull. The quintessence for him was not one of the material elements, but the kernel of an object and more intimate than the material composition.[2] Each of the four elements contains an Archeus, who completes its generation from seeds; the Archeus of the firmament forms rain, snow, hail, thunder, etc.; the Archeus of water forms from it salts, stones and metals; the Archeus of earth forms plants and trees. The spiritual force of the Archeus forms the arcanum of each thing, the rest being the dead matter of the elements.[3] Paracelsus recognised an intermediary between spirit and matter in each of the three kingdoms of Nature; in minerals it produces crystal forms and is called Stannar or Truphat; in vegetables it is Leffas, which unites with the life-force of the plant to form the primum ens; in animals and man it is Evestrum (or in man, the sidereal man), which is a dark principle used by evil spirits in occult phenomena.[4]

What would body be without spirit? Absolutely nothing. The spirit then and not the body contains concealed in itself the virtue and power. For death is in the body and the body is the subject of death, and one can seek nothing in the body but death. It can perish and suffer in many ways, the spirit in none. The spirit is always alive and it is the subject of life; it conserves the living body and when this perishes the spirit escapes and leaves the dead body and returns to the place whence it came, into the chaos, the air below and above the firmament. As bodies are various, so are spirits. There are spirits of the sky, of the infernal regions, of the earth, of metals, of minerals, of salts, of gems, of marcasites, arsenics, potable things, roots, liquors, fleshes, bloods, bones, etc. Know that spirit is the true life and balsam of all corporeal things. . . . The life of all men is nothing else than a kind of astral balsam, a balsamic impression, a celestial and invisible fire, an included air, a tingeing spirit of salt (inclusus aër, & tingens spiritus salis). I cannot name it more clearly, since many and different names can be proposed for it.[5]

Every natural thing has a life, which is a spirit which consumes the body and causes all transformations. The animal spirit is a heavenly fire or balsam, balsamic air, breath from the stars or a tingeing spirit of salt (tingens spiritus salis). The life of metals is sulphur, which makes them fat and fusible, that of sulphur is its combustibility, that of mercury is internal heat and external coldness, that of salt its corrosive force, that of gems and corals their colour,

---

[1] 45, i f.; VII, ii, 293 f.
[2] Pagel, 1958, 83, 98 f., 241, who points out that the doctrines in the *Archidoxis* (*c.* 1525–6) differ from those in the later works.
[3] 41, 45; VII, ii, 239 f., 293 ff.; Rixner-Siber, 1829, i, 82 f., 91 f., 94.
[4] 41, ii, 18; iii, 3; VII, ii, 249–51; Spunda, 1925, 74, says Evestrum is the Ethereal Body of the Theosophists, the Astral Body being Paracelsus' mumia.
[5] 30, iv; VII, ii, 91.

taken away by spirit of wine, that of pearls their lustre, that of magnet its attraction for iron, that of quartz and flint hardness, that of arsenic, orpiment
and realgar a mineral coagulated poison, that of animal excrements their unpleasant odour, that of aromatic things their pleasant odour, that of sweet
things their taste, that of resinous things their brilliant fat, etc. The life of
water is its fluidity, of fire its volatility (when the egress of flame is prevented,
the fire is extinguished); the life of fire is air, which makes fire burn more
vehemently, and there comes from all fires a kind of air which will extinguish a
candle and drive up a feather, as is seen daily, so that the flame of fire is
choked if it is enclosed so that it can neither receive air nor emit its own air;
the air lives by and of itself, and gives life to all other things. Earth has an invisible concealed life which gives it fertility.[1]

All things are generated from three principles, salt, sulphur, and mercury.[2]
Paracelsus thought that each substance contains different kinds of salt, sulphur
and mercury, 'and yet they are only three things'; there were even various
kinds of each metal, e.g. gold, each with different varieties of the three principles of that metal.[3] Apart from an imaginary 'sulphur embryonatum' of
metals, several sorts of sulphur are mentioned, also the bleaching of red roses
by the fumes of burning sulphur (sulphur dioxide).[4] The last is one of the
experiments of Joachim Fortius Ringelberg.[5] Paracelsus refers to sulphuric
acid *or* a solution of sulphur in oil as a wood preservative[6] and says that cotton
in a strong lixivium of lime and ashes is converted into silk — which would be
mercerising.[7]

The theory of the three principles (*tria prima*) salt, sulphur, and mercury,
was formerly attributed to the mythical 'Basil Valentine' (ch. V) and since
his writings were not printed till about 1600 Paracelsus was assumed to have
read them in manuscripts.[8] The priority of Paracelsus is now generally recognised.[9] Sulphur and mercury had been recognised long before by the alchemists (see Vol. I) and to them Paracelsus added salt.

The Provençal, Jacques Fontaine asserted that the three principles were not new:
salt had been named by the ancients and was only the earthy part of bodies, as mercury
was the watery and sulphur the aerial part, the new terminology being useless words.[10]

According to Rodwell[11] the three principles are '*principia* not *corpora*; they are
ἀνάλογα — representative bodies, types of classes, types of qualities; by them is expressed in other terms the fire, air, water, and earth of the ancients': fire=sulphur, air
and water=mercury, earth=salt; they express combustibility, volatility and fixity,
respectively.

[1] 30, iv; 41, iii, 4; VII, ii, 91 f., 252.   [2] 13; VII, i, 354; Rixner-Siber, 1829, i, 80 f.
[3] 46; VII, ii, 344.   [4] 40, vii–ix; VII, ii, 194 f.; VIII, ii, 231 f.; Manget, ii, 459.
[5] *Experimenta*, 1529; *Opera*, 1531, 606–15, q. by Thorndike, v, 147.
[6] 30, iii; VII, ii, 90.
[7] 30, vii; VII, ii, 101; Darmstaedter, *Janus*, 1933, xxxvii, 48 (56).
[8] Van Helmont, *Ortus Medicinæ*, 1652, 324 f.; Morhof, (1), 1747, ii, 250; Gmelin, (1), i, 206;
Kopp, (1), ii, 272; Rixner-Siber, 1829, i, 80, 201.
[9] Hallopeau, *Rev. gén. Sci.*, 1918, xxix, 246; Strunz, *J. B. Van Helmont*, 1907, 35; Stillman,
1920, 91, 106; *id.*, 1924, 319; J. C. Gregory, *Combustion from Heraclitos to Lavoisier*, 1934, 58;
Liénard, 67; Hooykaas, *Chem. Weekblad*, 1935, xxxii, 250, 422; *id.*, *Janus*, 1935, xxxix, 175–87;
Pagel, 1958, 82, 100.
[10] *Discours de la puissance du ciel . . . avec Une dispute des elements contre les Paracelsistes*,
Paris, 1581; Thorndike, v, 644; see Basil Valentine, ch. V.
[11] *Phil. Mag.*, 1868, xxxv, 6.

Paracelsus recognised the four Aristotelian elements (fire, air, water, earth) and their 'complexions' but thought they appeared (also in metals) in the form of the three principles: sulphur, the combustible principle, mercury, the principle of liquidity or fusibility and volatility, and salt, the principle of fixity and incombustibility. In the healthy body the three principles are present in the correct proportions; when one is in excess disease results. Sulphur is the basis of all oily, combustible materials; salt of all colours and alkalis, and mercury of all liquids. 'Whatever fumes and evaporates in the fire is mercury, whatever flames and is burnt is sulphur, and all ash is salt.'[1] Paracelsus did not, like Becher and Stahl (ch. XVII), assume a constant principle of combustibility, the same in all combustibles and metals.

It has been said[2] that the doctrine of the composition of salt, sulphur, and mercury from the four Aristotelian elements appears first in the later Paracelsists (except Oswald Croll). Paracelsus seems to have held the reverse view.[3] The three principles played a predominant part in his pathology.[4]

The death of metals occurs by separation of sulphurous fat (sulphureae pinguedinis) by calcination, reverberation, resolution, cementation and sublimation, as when iron is converted into *crocus*, copper into verdigris or burnt copper; the death of sulphur occurs by combustion of its combustible and fetid fatness, whereby it itself becomes fixed; the death of salts occurs by distillation of their watery and oily parts and extraction of spirit of salt (spiritus salis); the death of mercury occurs by sublimation with salt and vitriol, when it becomes dry and white as snow, or by calcination with aqua fortis to red precipitate; the death of vegetables and wood occurs by distillation or combustion.[5] Paracelsus refers to the separation of vegetable matter by destructive distillation (or wood by combustion) into phlegm, mercury (gaseous products?), oil, resin, 'sulphur' and 'salt' (ash or charcoal?), and says powerful remedies can be made by such separations, although the physicians are too lazy and ignorant to do this.[6] He calls the salt of plants balsam, the sulphur resin and the mercury *gotaronium*.[7]

'By calcination is separated watery moisture, fat, natural heat, odour, and whatever else is combustible.'[8] Wood on burning separates into salt (ash), sulphur and mercury; by putrefying these by digesting in a cucurbit in horse-dung and then burying the product in earth, the matter lives again and a small tree grows, called resuscitated wood, which is a great mystery.[9]

Paracelsus distinguished between the *calx* and ash (*cinis*) of a metal; the former is fixed and can be *reduced* to metal (*in suum metallum reduci potest*), whilst the latter is volatile and cannot be reduced to metal but becomes glass or scoria. Calcined mercury is reduced or restored simply by heating in a retort (resuscitatio vel restauratio mercurij calcinati fit per Retortam distillationes). He says mortification (*mortificatum*) is different from the death (*mortuum*) of a

---

[1] 1, i; 13; 30, vi; VII, i, 33 f., 354 f.; ii, 87 f.; Manget, ii, 462; Boerhaave, (4), 158 f.; Gmelin, (1), i, 216, 222; Kopp, (2), iii, 136; Strunz, (1), 17.
[2] Hooykaas, Die Elementenlehre der Iatrochemiker, *Janus*, 1937, xli, 1–28.
[3] Pagel, 1958, 129 f. [4] Pagel, 1958, 133 f.
[5] 30, v; VII, ii, 92 f., giving descriptions of several chemical processes.
[6] 2, i, 3; 30; VII, i, 34; ii, 87, 104. [7] 7, iii; VII, i, 270.
[8] 30, viii; VII, ii, 102. [9] 30, vi; VII, ii, 97.

metal; in the first process the metal can be revived from the product, but not in the second.[1] Metals when buried in the earth are converted first into rust but after a long time into stones; some ancient coins found, with inscriptions, had been turned completely into stone.[2]

The excretions are dissolved mercury escaping in perspiration, white sulphur from the nose, arsenic from the ears, sulphur dissolved in water from the eyes, dissolved salt in the urine, and sulphur in deliquescence as faeces.[3] The pathology of Paracelsus was largely based on the supposed effects of salt, sulphur, and mercury.[4] Apoplexy is caused by mercury in the body rising by distillation to the brain.[5] Fevers are formed in the body like saltpetre in the earth by a kind of putrefaction, a process which stops up the natural excretory canals and is called by Paracelsus *oppilatio* (stoppage).[6] All nitre is manure and when manure is collected together it heats. The nitrum formed by putrefaction in the body collects mostly in the blood and obstructs the veins. As an earthquake shakes the earth, so the nitrum shakes the body.[7]

Hermes says that mercury is spirit, sulphur is soul, and salt is body; metals are between spirit and body.[8] The theory may have had a religious, trinitarian, background.[9] The comparison of the three principles with body, soul, and spirit is found in the *Rosarium* (a work of uncertain date, see Vol. I).[10] The religious associations are found in the *Buch der heiligen Dreifaltigkeit* (MS. early 15 cent.); Ganzenmüller[11] thought Paracelsus introduced the third 'principle', salt, but this also is in the *Rosarium*;[12] he also thought that Paracelsus's three principles were 'dynamic' as contrasted with the 'static' or formal alchemical description, whereas this aspect is clearly laid down in Geber's *Summa*.[13] The alchemists also regarded sulphur and mercury as 'spiritual' as well as material, and as basic components of organic (microcosmic)substances.[14] The comparison of chemical with physiological processes, e.g. the creation of the philosophers' stone with the creation of man, is not peculiar to earlier alchemy as Ganzenmüller thought, since Paracelsus also uses it, and Sherlock[15] thought it was characteristic of him. Pagel thinks Paracelsus replaced the symbolical language of alchemy by a new language, shifted its emphasis to naturalistic and medical aspects, abandoned the idea of 'transmutation' in favour of 'separation', and elaborated traditional alchemy for the benefit of his system of pathology and medicine. Much of his material goes back to the Greek texts through Latin translations from Arabic (Vol. I).

Since diseases owe their origin (*ultima materia*) to something spiritual or living and not material, only those medicines can be effectual which are

---

[1] 30, vi; VII, ii, 95 f.; Hoefer, (1), ii, 13, says this is the first use of the word reduction (*reduziren* in German text; *resuscitatio et reductio* in Latin) in this sense.
[2] 32; VII, ii, 125.   [3] 1, 13, 26, 38; VII, i, 12, 355, 811; ii, 162.
[4] Sprengel, (1), iii, 316; Daremberg, 1870, i, 398 f.   [5] 3, ii; VII, i, 168.
[6] 14, ii; VII, i, 383.   [7] 11 (iv de tartaro nitreo); VII, i, 523–4.
[8] 30, vi; VII, ii, 87; Kayser, 342; J. Read, (1), 1936, 27, 297; Thomson, (1), 157, incorrectly gives spirit = sulphur, soul = mercury.
[9] 45; VII, ii, 295.   [10] Manget, ii, 94 (from the *Turba*, see Vol. I).   [11] 1956, 231 f.
[12] Manget, ii, 88, 94.   [13] Bk. i, chs. 13–15; Dantzig, 1682, 39–42.
[14] Ganzenmüller, 306.   [15] *Ambix*, 1948, iii, 33.

inimical to these spiritual organic beings which are the 'seeds' of the disease, and such remedies are *arcana*. This word is used in a double sense: (1) anything which cures, such as nature, blood-letting, medicines, and surgery, and (2) (and especially) remedies which act in virtue of their indwelling powers (*qualitates occultae*), which either destroy the seeds of diseases or awake the slumbering curative powers of nature. They act by an immaterial spiritual power allied to fire or seeds, and the recognition of the magic powers of remedies is the principal task of alchemy. This doctrine is cardinal in the system of Paracelsus.[1]

Paracelsus describes four *arcana*, the preparation of which is quite unintelligible: (1) *arcanum materiae primae*, (2) *arcanum lapidis philosophorum*, (3) *arcanum mercurii vitae*, (4) *arcanum tinctura*.[2] They have been supposed all to consist of mercuric oxide and chlorides. The *mercurius vitae* is vaguely said to be prepared by distilling 'essensificated mercury' with 'antimony' and 'coagulating' the product, so that Kopp[3] thought it might be antimonyl chloride formed by the reactions: $3HgCl_2 + 2Sb = 2SbCl_3 + 3Hg$; $SbCl_3 + H_2O = SbOCl + 2HCl$.[4] The sublimation of metals with sal ammoniac would give the double chlorides.[5] Gold can be sublimed in the form of a 'philosophical tree' by dissolving it in aqua regia, evaporating, and heating in a cucurbit; silver also can be sublimed in a way not described.[6] A list of drugs mentioned by Paracelsus is given by Marx.[7]

Paracelsus believed in experiment — perhaps some of his patients suffered from too much of it. Every experiment is like a weapon which must be used according to its peculiar power, as a spear to thrust, a club to strike. To use experiments requires an experienced man who is sure of his thrust and stroke.[8] Paracelsus used many preparations of metals (iron, lead, copper, antimony and mercury) in medicine, clearly recognising their poisonous properties.[9] He described the preparation of calomel or corrosive sublimate by subliming mercury with vitriol and salt; of red precipitate by distilling aqua fortis from mercury and heating till it becomes a beautiful red; and of cinnabar by subliming mercury with salt and sulphur, when it is formed 'like a bloodstone'. The red precipitate may be 'sweetened' and washed with rectified spirit of wine distilled from it, when it becomes diaphoretic precipitate; or it can be made as sweet as sugar (saccarum) or honey by solution of salt of tartar, when it is a principal arcanum for the French disease (morbus Gallicus).[10] It has been supposed that he also used turpeth mineral ($HgSO_4$, $2HgO$) and white precipitate ($HgClNH_2$).[11]

---

[1] 2, 4; VII, i, 50, 206, 226; Haeser, (1), i, 95.
[2] 27, v; VII, ii, 16; *Paracelsus his Archidoxis*, 1663, 60 f.; Sprengel, (1), iii, 324.   [3] (1), iv, 109.
[4] F. Dobler, Die chemische Arzneibereitung bei Theophrastus Paracelsus am Beispiel seiner Antimonpräparate, in *Pharmaceutica Acta Helvetiae*, 1957, xxxii, 181–93, 226–52. Many of Paracelsus's chemical preparations are found in the treatise (55).
[5] Manget, ii, 425.   [6] 30, ii; VII, ii, 88, before Boyle, p. 535.
[7] 1843, 185 f.   [8] 58, x; VII, III, i, 142.
[9] Neuburger-Pagel, 1903, ii, 34 f., 565 f.; 1905, iii, 403; Darmstaedter, 1931, xx, 18 f. (salt, sulphur, mercury theory), 45 f. (use of mercury and antimony preparations), 65 f. (pharmacology; quintessences, arcana, magisteria, specifica; mostly from *Archidoxis*.
[10] 30, v; VII, ii, 93.
[11] Strunz, (1), 1903, 20; Darmstaedter, *Acta Paracelsica*, Heft 1, 1930, 21 f.

Poisons are powerful remedies if deprived of their lethal properties by chemical treatment; a poison must be 'killed', 'sweetened', or 'fixed'. The old method of making alcoholic tinctures was insufficient and more drastic treatment is needed; e.g. arsenic must be fixed by fusing with saltpetre, pouring on a marble, and keeping in a damp place. The golden-yellow product (potassium arsenate) may be mixed with alcohol (vinum sublimatum). This is one of the few chemical experiments clearly described.[1] Paracelsus's medical theory is homœopathic — arsenical diseases are cured by arsenic, the stone is cured by quintessences of stones, vitriol (corrosive) cures ulcers, etc.[2]

Cyriacus Jacobus[3] said Paracelsus was able to cure the three gravest diseases, gout, leprosy, and epilepsy. Rheticus the astronomer (who proposed in 1574 to translate *Archidoxis* into Latin) reported that he cured a patient given up by doctors by means of three drops of an elixir, and Ramus praised him in 1568.[4] The use of mercurial remedies by Paracelsus cannot be claimed as a novelty. He may have got a hint of their use in venereal diseases from Jacob Berengarius (Carpus) (*c.* 1470–1530), who was professor at Bologna and then lived at Ferrara;[5] and John de Vigo (or Vico), physician to Pope Julius II, early in the 16 cent., described the preparation of mercuric oxide (*argentum vivum calcinatum quod apud alchemistum praecipitatum nuncupatur*) by dissolving mercury in aqua fortis in an alembic and calcining the nitrate so formed: he seems to have used the oxide internally.[6]

By the 'mortification' of metals Paracelsus understood the production of oxides and salts from them by treatment with acids, sublimation, etc.[7] He believed in the medical efficacy of potable gold and other metals.[8] Potable gold is described in older works, e.g. by Albini di Moncalieri in a 14-cent. Bologna MS.[9] Paracelsus praised the virtues of potable gold and oil of gold.[10] The use of potable gold as a medicine (condemned by Palissy),[11] which goes back long before Paracelsus, is connected with magic, astrology, religious (Indian) and mythical ideas; some recipes of an early work of Paracelsus would give colloidal gold.[12] Gold sometimes occurs in nature in much disguised (colloidal) forms, and the production of massive metal from these would suggest the idea of transmutation.[13] Sir Thomas Browne[14] said metallic gold is not absorbed in the body and has no medicinal virtue except perhaps by an effluvium. In his

---

[1] 40, ii, vii, ix (arsenic); VII, ii, 180, 197, 207.   [2] Pagel, 1958, 145 f.
[3] Pref. to *Alchimia Opuscula Complura*, 4°, Frankfurt, 1550; Ferguson, i, 19.
[4] Thorndike, v, 416–17, 642.   [5] Boerhaave, (4), i, 40.
[6] Sprengel, (1), iii, 72; (2), iii, 212; Sprengel says the first known certainly to have prescribed mercury for *internal* use was Matthioli (d. 1577), the commentator of Dioskourides, and the pills of Barbarossa or Cheireddin, an Algerian pirate, contained metallic mercury, his recipe being made known to François, king of France. Lessing, (2), (1839) 1937, 215, says Matthioli never used mercury as a specific but only as a purgative; he says Paracelsus learnt the use of mercury from Jacob Berengar.
[7] 30, v; Darmstaedter, *Janus*, 1933, xxxvii, 48.
[8] 12, i; 27, iv, vi; VII, i, 252; ii, 11 f., 20 f.   [9] Sudhoff, *A. Nat.*, 1913–15, v, 198–201.
[10] 19; VII, i, 587: aurum potabile, aut oleum auri, aut quintam essentiam auri ... quando rubes auro extrahitur.
[11] *Œuvres*, Paris, 1777, 363.
[12] Darmstaedter, *Chem. Ztg.*, 1924, xlviii, 653, 679; *Archeion*, 1924, v, 251; MGM, 1927, xxvi, 328; *Studien zur Geschichte der Medizin*, 1931, xx; *Janus*, 1933, xxxvii, 1, 48, 109.
[13] Traube, *Chem. Ztg.*, 1928, lii, 3.
[14] *Pseudodoxia Epidemica*, ii, 5; *Works*, ed. Sayle, 1927, i, 267.

short treatise on cements[1] Paracelsus gives recipes for powders for 'parting' gold (probably copied from a *Probierbuch*), and says this method of determining the purity of gold is more accurate than the use of test-needles and the touchstone (see Agricola, etc., ch. II). When a mixture of silver and gold is heated with aqua fortis (nitric acid) the gold remains as a black powder, and when a copper plate is put into the solution the silver falls to the bottom of the vessel like snow.[2]

Metals and minerals are formed and 'grow' in the bowels of the earth (*in visceribus terrae*), each in its given time, from water, and comprise: (1) metals, (2) gems, (3) salts, (4) mineral springs, (5) golden and silvery marcasites (containing many arcana and virtues), (6) common stones (including marble, jasper and alabaster), (7) sulphurous earths such as the yellow (amber) and black (jet) and *carabe* (Persian *kahrubā* = amber), (8) coral, eagle-stone, mussels, etc. (fossils), and 'sports of nature' (see Palissy, p. 75).[3] The colours of gems are due to metals, green emerald to copper, carbuncle to gold, ruby to iron, sapphire to silver, white sapphire to tin, yellow hyacinth to mercury, in each case corresponding with the appropriate planet.[4]

Paracelsus's account of the generation of metals, stones and minerals[5] is very like that of Arabic authors (e.g. al-Dimashqī).[6] They all correspond with particular planets, to which they owe their medicinal virtues. He thought, however, that salt also enters the composition of metals and criticised the old theory that they consist only of sulphur and mercury.[7] His views on geology are less accurate than Avicenna's (Vol. I); he says, e.g.,[8] that salt and sulphur cannot tolerate each other in the earth but struggle and cause the earth to enter into fermentation and eject a liquid which solidifies into sharp rocks (composed of salt, sulphur and mercury) on exposure to air. The nature of the metallic juice (*Guhr*) in the earth was explained by Boerhaave.[9]

There are seven metals (corresponding with the planets), male and female, if mercury is included, but mercury is not a true metal, so that it is better to differentiate between iron (female) and steel (male) to make up the number. Many undiscovered metals may exist.[10] Paracelsus describes arsenic as itself generating a peculiar metal (*sibi peculiare metallum generat*) and mixing easily with other metals, such as copper, with which it forms a white electrum. When melted with saltpetre it gives an *arsenicum fixum*, which on deliquescence gives a *liquor arsenici fixi* (potassium arsenate). Arsenic is the most poisonous of all things and is used only externally, with spirit of wine or burnt tartar. Paracelsus mentions realgar often, also yellow orpiment and white arsenic.[11] Antimony is a metal formed by the coagulation of mercury with sulphur and the

[1] 34, ix (De Cæmentis); VII, 128–33; Manget, ii, 446; Sudhoff, *A. Nat.*, 1909, i, 84–6.
[2] 30, viii; VII, ii, 103.
[3] 46, 47; VII, ii, 341 f., 352 f.; Rixner-Siber, 1829, i, 98, have 'Agat' in mistake for jet.
[4] 42, v, 3; VII, ii, 266.   [5] Rixner-Siber, 1829, i, 98 f., 108 f.
[6] *Manuel de la cosmographie du moyen âge*, tr. Mehren, Copenhagen, 1874, 61 f.; see Vol. I.
[7] 2, i; VII, i, 229.   [8] 43, iv (de lapidibus et gemmis); VII, ii, 283.
[9] In Gobet, 1779, i, 276; this name does not seem to be used by Paracelsus.
[10] 46; VII, ii, 346 f.
[11] 30, ix; VII, ii, 206 f.; Manget, ii, 461; Gmelin, (1), i, 214.

spirit of salt.[1] Cobalt (kobald, kobolt, kobelt) is a black metal of limited malleability.[2] Zinc (perhaps mentioned for the first time, as *zincken*)[3] 'not recognised in the writings of ancient philosophers nor usually considered as a metal', is a peculiar metal, fusible but not malleable, a metal and not a metal, a bastard copper (*spuria soboles de cupro*),[4] which occurs in Europe only in Carinthia.[5] Schroeter[6] says Paracelsus certainly knew of metallic zinc, which may have been known in Persia in Marco Polo's time (1275), but called by him 'pewter' (Vol. I). The name zincken, first used by Paracelsus for the metal, has been derived from O. H. Germ. zinco, white spot in the eye, but the same word also meant 'prong' (A.S. tind) and since it has been supposed that the metal deposits in this form from the vapour, this derivation is preferred.[7]

Bismuth (bisemutum, Wismat in the German text) is a bastard tin.[8] Bismuth was confused with antimony and tin as late as the 17 cent.:[9] it is called 'tin glasse' by Boyle, who also describes bismuth chloride (p. 537). Paracelsus also describes bismuth as a 'second antimony'.[10] Brass or *electrum* he calls *laton* and describes its preparation from copper and tutia or calamine (*thutia et calaminaris*).[11] Paracelsus was the first to use powdered tin for worms, although he says it should be calcined with sea-salt and bitumen and sometimes mixed with dragon's blood and colocynth.[12] He mentions gilding of iron[13] and copper amalgam.[14] When sheets of copper are ignited in a pot after smearing with honey and vinegar they give a black matter (CuO), but this becomes green on exposure to air.[15] Paracelsus describes the preparation of white lead, and says a fine and subtle product is obtained by the alchemical preparation, when sal ammoniac is dissolved in the vinegar used,[16] perhaps his careless description of the precipitation of lead chloride from lead acetate solution.

Mineral waters, hot and cold, having special tastes and odours, and medicinal properties, contain dissolved minerals. Some cannot dissolve salt or sugar, since they are already saturated. Other waters contain acids (*aqua acetosa*), salt, alum and vitriols; cupreous water in Hungary changes iron (*tingit ferrum*).[17] The heat of mineral waters comes from contact with sulphur or metallic calces,

[1] 41, v, 5; VII, ii, 286.
[2] 46; VII, ii, 349; Gmelin, (1), i, 214; *cobaltum* of various colours, including black, is mentioned by Agricola, *Bermannus* in *De Re Met.*, Basel, 1657, 701.
[3] Hommel, *Chem. Ztg.*, 1912, xxxvi, 905, 918; *Z. angew. Chem.*, 1919, xxxii, 74.
[4] 30, iv; 43, iii, 9; 46; VII, ii, 91, 282, 346, 349; Manget, ii, 462.
[5] *Brevis Carinthiæ Ducatus Descriptio*, Argentorati, 1575, 27: Habet metallum Zinken, quod excepta hac regione in tota Europa non invenitur; nam a cæteris omnibus metalli miris proprietatibus differt; q. by Stillman, 1924, 318–19.
[6] *Schweiz. Min. Petr. Mitt.*, 1942, xxi, 313.
[7] O. Schrader, *Real-Lexikon*, 1901, 540; in *Zinc and Spelter*, Oxford, 1950, 18–19, J. M. Dawkins thinks the shape was more probably that of the calamine ore. This etymology seems to be doubtful.
[8] 23, 4; 43, iii, 9; 46; VII, i, 170; ii, 282, 346; Gmelin, (1), i, 215.
[9] Rulandus, *Lexicon Alchemiæ*, 1612, 44; Eastlake, *Materials for a History of Oil Painting*, 1847, i, 537.
[10] 32; VII, ii, 122; VIII, i, 8.
[11] 30, vii, viii; VII, ii, 100, 103.
[12] 29, i, 5; VII, ii, 82.
[13] 30, iv; VII, ii, 190.
[14] 30, viii; VII, ii, 205; Manget, ii, 460; Gmelin, (1), i, 215.
[15] 30, v; VII, ii, 93.
[16] 30, v; VII, ii, 94.
[17] 31, vi; 43, iv, 2; VII, ii, 119, 278 f.; Rixner-Siber, 1829, i, 94, 105 f.

which behave towards water like quicklime.[1] Artificial mineral waters may be composed by dissolving the appropriate salts, stones or metals in water.[2]

In his book on diseases of miners[3] Paracelsus speaks vaguely of the ill effects of metallic, mercurial and arsenical vapours in the air or *chaos* which exists between earth and heaven, and also of three kinds of salts: salt, vitriol, and alum, each giving a spirit: sunt enim tria genera salium, sub quibus omnes species salium comprehenduntur, nempe sal, vitriolum et alumen. . . . Cum spiritus eorum sint tantum vapores. . . . Aër alumen sanat pruritum. Aër vitriolum sanat alopeciam; Aër salis communis scabiem. He distinguishes between soda (*sal nitrum*) and saltpetre (*sal petræ*) and says aqua fortis is made from saltpetre and vitriol or alum; he mentions its purification by silver, and the preparation of aqua regia by dissolving sal ammoniac in it.[4] He clearly distinguished alums as salts with an earthy admixture, from vitriols as salts with a metallic admixture.[5] He mentions the blackening of vitriol by galls or oakapples, an *aqua fortis* obtained from sulphur and a corrosive oil and a spirit from vitriol (these are probably sulphuric acid), also a 'sweetened' spirit of vitriol, copper vitriol as ane emetic, and a white vitriol (zinc sulphate).[6]

Paracelsus uses the name alcool for alcohol for a fine powder (alcool est rei cuiuslibet subtilissimum)[7] and for rectified spirit of wine.[8] Johnson[9] gives two definitions: 'alcohol, est Antimonium, sive stibium', and 'Alcohol, vini, quando omnis superfluitas vini a vino separatur, ita ut accensum ardeat, donec totum consumatur, nihilque fæcum, aut phlegmatis in fundo remaneat'; he also defines 'Alcool Paracelsi' as 'purior et mundior substantia ab impura separata', with an example of 'Alcool Antimonii'.

Paracelsus[10] prepared an *opodeldoch* containing spirit of wine, plant juices, and 'althoi a minera plumbis', which the dictionary[11] explains as 'sweet lead extracted with vinegar' (i.e. lead acetate); it was used as a lotion.[12] He describes several *magisteries*, a magistery being an extract prepared from a thing 'without separation or preparation of the elements, yet into which the powers and virtues of the thing are attracted and conserved by the addition of something else'. There are magisteries of metals, gems, pearls, corals, marcasites, amber, oils, plants, and blood. The magistery of wine is made by keeping it hermetically sealed in a dung-bath for four months, then freezing, taking out the

---

[1] Rixner-Siber, 1829, i, 106.   [2] 47; VII, ii, 353.
[3] *Von der Bergsucht*; *De morbis metallicis*; VII, i, 707 f., 719 f.
[4] 27, ii–iii; Manget, ii, 459; VII, ii, 7.
[5] 41, iv (De generibus salium); VII, ii, 279; Gmelin, (1), i, 213.
[6] Morhof, (1), P. II, lib. ii, p. 2, cap. 35 (1); 1747, ii, 417, says: vitriola nil aliud sunt, quam corpora metallica & salina mista temporato contubernio, non perpetuo aut radicali.
[7] 11, annotationes in tract. iii, ch. 5 (de usnea, grandine visicæ): alcool est dz subtileste eines jeglichen Dinges; VII, i, 537.
[8] 16, iii (alcohol vini, alcohol vini correcti), vii (alcool vini, alcool vini esstificati), viii (vinum essatum hic vocatur vinum sublimatum), scholia (tartarum . . . in alcool vini octo vicibus maceribis dein per alembicum destillabis, et per circulum octies, impurum abiicies; vinum essatum est quando vini extractio sumitur; alcool vini exiccati, id est, mundati à phlegmate, hoc est vinum ardens); VII, i, 498, 504–5, 547; alcohol vini, 28, x; VII, ii, 61; 11, annotationes in tract. iii, ch. 5 (de usnea), alcool vini, id est, vino ardenti; VII, i, 537; Richter, *A. Nat.*, 1913, iv, 448–9; Ruska, *Der Islam*, 1913, iv, 320; Lippmann, (3), i, 104–5.
[9] *Lexicon Chymicum*, 1652, 12–13.   [10] 28, x; VII, ii, 61.
[11] VII, III, ii, Dict., 13.
[12] 55, vi; VII, III, i, 95; he says, *ib.*, 108, it had been reprobated.

central part not frozen, and distilling.[1] This method of making strong alcohol is mentioned by Boyle.[2]

He speaks of distilling spirit of wine with 'colcotharis recentis', distilling in a phial a day and night and obtaining a phlegm, liquor, and oil, then distilling in a water bath and on a sand bath till oil passes over. The phlegm is given to infants, the oil in three grain doses to adults.[3] Also of distilling spirit of wine with vitriol (processus autem meus est, ut spiritus vini à vitriolo imbibatur, et postea distilletur).[4] This was probably ether, since he had just spoken of a 'sulphur embryonatum' in vitriol which is stupefactive, narcotic, and with an agreeable taste. Chickens will eat it, whereupon they sleep for a moderately long time and wake again without injury (Deinde, junctam sibi dulcidinem habet, ut etiam à gallinis edatur: à quo aliquandiu dormiunt; postea tamen citra noxam rursus evigilant).[5]

Turpentine was used to make amber varnish.[6] The odorous part of a plant, what Boerhaave later called the *spiritus rector* (ch. XX), Paracelsus called the *primum ens*.[7]

Opium, which he made better known in Europe, was used by the Arabs long before Paracelsus. A recipe for the 'laudanum or specific anodyne of Paracelsus', which is a compound tincture of opium, is given by Oswald Croll[8] and by LeFévre.[9] Thomson said:[10] 'There are two laudanums of Paracelsus; one was red oxide of mercury, the other consisted of the following substances: Chloride of antimony, 1 ounce; hepatic aloes, 1 ounce; rose-water, $\frac{1}{2}$ ounce; saffron, 3 ounces; ambergris, 2 drams. All these well mixed.' The recipes given by Paracelsus,[11] says La Wall,[12] leave it uncertain if Paracelsus's laudanum contained opium, and for more than a century after his time the name was given to solid preparations, only some containing opium (as in the first few eds. of the London *Pharmacopœia*). Thomas Sydenham (p. 450) first described an extract of opium and saffron in 1669, but perhaps borrowed it from London apothecaries. In Hoffmann's edition of Schroeder's *Pharmacopœia* (1687) a compound tincture of opium is called 'Ladanum Facile'. The name paregoric for tincture of opium does not seem to be used by Paracelsus; a remedy paregoricum is in Marcellus Empiricus (c. A.D. 400),[13] and paregoricus is used as an adjective by Theodorus Priscianus (4 cent. A.D.).[14] La Wall says paregoric, a tincture of opium and aromatics, was introduced by Le Mort, of Leyden (ch. XX), and its formula is given in the London *Pharmacopœia* of 1721.

Paracelsus mentions camphor, saying that it is 'cold' because it contains

---

[1] 27, vi; VII, ii, 20; *Paracelsus his Archidoxis*, 1663, 78 f.; Boerhaave, (4), i, 171.

[2] *Usefulness of Experimental Philosophy*, vi; *Works*, ed. Shaw, 1725, i, 144.

[3] 16, iii; VII, i, 498; the process is described in ψ-Lull, *Epistola de Accurtatione*, in Manget, i, 865.

[4] 40, viii; VII, ii, 203.

[5] 40, vii; VII, ii, 197; Leake, *Isis*, 1927, vii, 14 (22); Pagel, *Bull. Hist. Med.*, 1959, xxxiii, 480.

[6] 40, i (de Terpentina); VII, ii, 177 f., 181.   [7] 27, x; VII, ii, 38 (spurious ?).

[8] *Basilica Chymica*, 4°, Frankfurt, 1609, 173.

[9] *Traité de la Chymie*, 2 ed., Paris, 1674, ii, 59.   [10] (1), i, 147.

[11] 16, i; 8; 55; VII, i, 492, 540; iii, i, 31.   [12] 1927, 279, 420.   [13] *De Medicamentis*, 36.

[14] *Euporiston II (Logica)*, xxix, 86; ed. Rose, Teubner, 1894, 188; the word is derived from παρηγορια, alleviation (of pain).

'cherio' (one of his invented names).[1] T. Thomson[2] says camphor is not mentioned in Hartmann's *Praxis Chymiatrica* (Geneva, 1647), but it is mentioned by Van Helmont,[3] and Charas.[4] Paracelsus mentions rhubarb (rheubarb, rhabarb) as a purgative.[5]

A supposed recipe for making phosphorus from urine[6] is in a section on 'the separation of elements from watery substances'. Urine is distilled and the distillate and residue mixed; at the fourth distillation the water rises first, then the air and fire, but the earth remains at the bottom. 'Then take the air and the fire in a separate vessel, which put in a cold place, and there will be congealed certain icicles (stiriæ), which are the element of fire. This congelation will take place during the distillation but does so more easily in the cold.'[7]

Paracelsus had a vague idea that a supposed acid in the gastric juice, the 'hungry acid (acetum esurinum)', also exists in acidulous mineral waters and is formed artificially from vitriol:[8] Esurinum acetosum est Medicina, quæ suâ naturâ ventriculum adeo famelicum reddit, vt cibos etiam insolitos appetat. Quod autem appetit, id excoquit & digerit . . . acetosum Naturale acetosum fontale esse, vt sunt Acidulae. Acetosum artificiale est acetosum vitriolatum. Fabius Violet[9] mentions this, saying that if pathologically increased owing to irritation of the stomach by tartar it causes pain. Its action is that of a dissolving spirit and is not simply due to heat, for lemon juice which is cold as well as spirit of wine which is hot will digest pearls. Violet occupied a position intermediate between Paracelsus and Van Helmont, who mentioned the esurine acid in his *Supplementum de Spadanis Fontibus* and almost identified it with hydrochloric acid.[10] Paracelsus did recognise that acid (acetosa esrurina) can *assist* digestion, as an ostrich can digest metals, but he thought the principal agent in digestion is heat.

[1] 22, vi; 38, ii, 3; VII, i, 673; ii, 148.   [2] *Chemistry of Organic Bodies. Vegetables*, 1838, 487.
[3] *Ortus Medicinæ*, 1652, 369, 378, 678.   [4] *Pharmacopée Royale*, 1676, 704.
[5] 27, vii; VII, ii, 27.   [6] O. C. Ellis, *A History of Fire and Flame*, 1932, 24; no reference.
[7] 27, iii; VII, ii, 9.   [8] 8, xvi; VII, i, 323.
[9] *La Parfait et Entiere Cognoissance de Toutes les Maladies du Corps Humain, causees par Obstruction*, Paris, 1635, 142.
[10] *Ortus Medicinæ*, 1652, 550: sal . . . quod defectu nominis esurinum sive acetosum . . . acidum est; Pagel, 1958, 163.

CHAPTER IV

IATROCHEMISTS FOLLOWING PARACELSUS

The physicians who followed Paracelsus in the sixteenth and the first half of the seventeenth centuries were nearly all Germans or Swiss. Adam von Bodenstein (Karlstadt, 1528–Basel, 1577) son of the theologian, taught Paracelsus's system of medicine as professor in Basel, edited many of his writings, and wrote a dictionary of Paracelsan words.[1]

Michael Toxites (Bogner, or Schütz), born near Dillingen, studied in Italy, was a physician in Hagenau, and was made poet laureate in 1529 by the Emperor Charles V; he edited many works of Paracelsus, which he dedicated to the patron of alchemy the Kurfürst August I of Saxony.[2] Toxites also edited some works of Suchten (p. 156). He was attacked by Lucas Stengel (or Stenglen, or Stenglin), b. Augsburg 1523, d. 1587:[3]

Apologia adversus stibii spongiam non ita dudum a Micaele Toxita in lucem editam, Augsburg, 1565; 2 ed. Apologia adversus Stelvii spongiam non ita dudum a M. Toxite in lucem aeditam; in qua multa ... de viribus et facultatibus Stimmeos explicantur. Cui insuper est Quaestio: num idipsum ab aegris citra ullum incommodum per os assumi possit, Augsburg, 1569.

THURNEISSER

Leonhart Thurneisser zum Thurn (as he calls himself) was born the son of a goldsmith at Basel in 1531.[4] He worked at his father's trade but in consequence of having sold a gilded lead brick to some Jews, he left for England in 1548. Before this he had read the works of Paracelsus whilst gathering herbs for a physician of Basel. In 1549 he was in France and in 1552 he joined the troops of the Markgraf Albrecht of Brandenburg-Baireuth ('the German Alcibiades') and fought at Sievershausen in 1553, where he was taken prisoner by the Saxon army. On his release he worked as a miner, smelter, mechanic and goldsmith in Nürnburg, Strassburg, Constance, Tarenz in the Inn valley (1558), Scotland, the Tyrol (1565), Spain and Portugal; his supposed journeys in the East are probably fictitious. In 1571 he settled at Frankfurt on the Oder, where he published his book *Pison* (1572), in which he states that the waters of the Spree carry gold.[5] This attracted the attention of the Elector of Branden-

---

[1] *Onomasticum Paracelsicum*, 8°, Basel, 1577 (Sprengel gives 1574); *De lapide Philosophorum*, f°, Basel, 1581; *Isagoge in Arnaldi de Villa noua Rosarium chymicum* . . . *Epistola operi præfixa ad dominos Fuggeros* . . . , 8°, Basel, 1559 (BM 1033. f. 33); *Opera Omnia*, Basel, 1581; Brucker, 1766, IV, i, 672; Sprengel, (2), 1827, iii, 500.

[2] Kiesewetter, (1), 1891, 99; Brucker, 1766, IV, i, 674; Sprengel, (2), 1827, iii, 501.

[3] Jöcher, iv, 810; Thorndike, v, 642; vi, 743.

[4] Diergart, 1909, 307, from the register; 1530 is usually given, from Moehsen.

[5] *Ib.*, p. xlix.

burg, who made Thurneisser his physician. He cured the wife of the Elector, and in his laboratory in Berlin he made cosmetics, potable gold, tincture of rubies, amulets and talismans, which he sold at high prices. He taught boys chemistry for high fees, and practised astrology. His household now contained 200 persons and he became very wealthy. He had his own press in Berlin, where he published several books, often with fanciful titles in Hebrew and Greek, and containing words in these and other Oriental languages, of all of which he was ignorant.[1] He established or reorganised alum and saltpetre works and, in order to obtain apparatus, introduced improvements in glass factories. He so contributed to the development of chemical industry in Brandenburg and he attracted many clever artisans to Berlin. In this way he certainly laid the foundations of the chemical industry in Prussia.

From 1576 Thurneisser, then at the height of his prosperity, was severely criticised by eminent men and he was prosecuted by the magistrate at Rostock. He left Berlin about 1580 for Basel; his Berlin laboratory afterwards came into Kunckel's possession.[2] In 1584 Thurneisser arrived in poverty in Italy, became a Catholic, and practised alchemy in Rome, where he performed the trick of transmuting half an iron nail into gold for Cardinal Francisco de Medici.[3] In October 1644 Evelyn saw at Florence in the Ceimeliarcha or Repository 'an yron nayle, one halfe whereof being converted into gold by one Thornheuser, a German chymist, . . . looked upon as a greate rarity, but it plainly appeared to have been soldered together'.[4] The gold part was coloured like iron and on washing in the transmuting liquid the colour came off and the gold was revealed. In 1590 Thurneisser was in Switzerland, in 1591 back in Rome; finally he returned to Germany and died in poverty in a cloister at Cologne in 1595 or 1596, where he was buried, at his own request, near Albertus Magnus.[5]

Thurneisser was essentially a charlatan and a business man who, as Meyer said, stood near his master Paracelsus in 'Geist und Betriebsamkeit'. He had no real knowledge of medicine but was an unprincipled quack, selling all kinds of nostrums at immense prices. The titles of his books are intended to attract ignorant but wealthy readers, and since they mostly contain elaborate illustrations and passages in Hebrew, Syriac, Arabic, Ethiopian, and other Oriental characters, must have been very costly to produce. Some of his works are listed below,[6] the very long titles being abbreviated. (The weights he specifies are 1 Quint = 1 drachm (4·25 grams), 1 Lot = 4 Quinten.)

[1] Sudhoff, *A. Med.*, 1908, ii, 129.
[2] Kunckel, *Probierstein*; in *Fünf curiose Chymische Tractätlein*, Frankfurt and Leipzig, 1721, 397.
[3] Tachenius, *Hippocrates Chymicus*, c. 28, Paris, 1669, 240, who explains the fraud.
[4] *Diary*, ed. Bray, 1870, 81.
[5] Bugge, *Der Alchimist, die Geschichte Leonhard Thurneyssers, des Goldmachers von Berlin*, 1944 (304 pp., not seen); Diergart, 1909, 307 (Thurneyser); Ferguson, ii, 450; Gmelin, (1), i, 266; Haeser, 1881, ii, 110; Hoefer, (1), ii, 19; A. W. Hofmann, (1), 16; Kiesewetter, (1), 102; Kopp, (4), i, 107, 164; E. H. F. Meyer, 1857, iv, 434; Moehsen, (2), 1783, 55–198 (list of T.'s books, 188 f.); Petraeus, pref. to Basil Valentine, *Chymischer Schrifften*, Hamburg, 1740, i, e7 *v*; Speter, *Z. f. Bücherfreunde*, 1935, xxxix, 145 (T. MS.); Sprengel, (1), 1815, iii, 338; *id.*, (2), 1827, iii, 494; Thomson, (1), i, 168.
[6] See Moehsen, (2), 188 f.; Gmeling, (1), i, 271; Clifford, *Proc. Chem. Soc.*, 1906, xxii.

1. *ΜΕΓΑΛΗ ΧΥΜΙΑ*, Vel Magna Alchymia. Das ist ein Lehr vnd vnterweisung von den offenbaren vnd verborgenlichen Naturen / Arten vnd Eigenschafften / allerhandt wunderlicher Erdtgewechssen / als Ertzen / Metallen / Mineren / Erdsäfften / Schwefeln / Mercurien, Saltzen vnd Gesteinen . . . , f°, Berlin, Nicolaus Voltzen (or Volken), 1583, with portr. (aged 52), texts in Greek, Latin, Hebrew, Syriac, Arabic, Ethiopian, etc. (BM 726. m. 20; another ed., Köln, 1587 is mentioned). A German edition is described by Ferguson:

1A. Historia Vnnd Beschreibung Influentischer, Elementarische vnd Natürlicher Wirckungen, Aller fremden vnnd Heimischen Erdgewechsen, auch jrer Subtileteten, sampt warhafftiger vnd Künstlicher Conterfeitung derselbigen . . . , f°, Berlin, 1578, Gedruckt bei Michael Hentzsken.

2. Melitsath[1] *ΚΑ`Ι 'ΕΡΜΗΝΕ'ΙΑ* Das is ein Onomasticvm vnd Interpretatio . . . vber Etliche frembde vñ . . . vnbekante Nomina, Verba, Proverbia, Dicta, Sylben, Caracter, vnd sonst Reden. . . . Das Ander theil . . . , f°, Berlin, Nikolaus Voltzen (or Volken), 1583; words printed in Greek, Hebrew, Syriac, Ethiopian, etc.[2]

3. Archidoxa, darin der recht, war Motus, Lauff und Gang, auch heymlichkait, wirkung vnd krafft der Planeten, f°, and 4°, Münster, 1569 (BM 1032. c. 15); an ed. f°, Berlin, 1575, is mentioned.

4. Methodus brevis ac dilucidus, von ächter Extraktion der seelischen und spiritualischen Kräfte, 4°, Wittenberg, 1619 (BM 1033. h. 10); also attributed to Andreas Ellinger, professor at Jena, d. 1582.[3]

5. Historia sive Descriptio Plantarum omnium tam Domesticarum quam Exoticarum, f°, Berlin, 1578.

6. Pison. Das erst Theil. Von Kalten / Warmen, Minerischen vnd Metallischen Wassern / sampt der vergleichung der Plantarum vnd Erdgewechsen 10 Bücher, f°, Frankfurt an der Oder, J. Eichorn, 1572, ccccxx pp. + index (BM 717. l. 37).

7. Zehn Bücher Von kalten / Warmen / Mineralischen vnd Metallischen Wassern, Samt ihren Vergleichung mit den Plantis oder Erdgewächsen, f° in 6's, Strassburg, Zetzner, 1612 (pp. 324 and index; BM 717. b. 38. (2.); a copy advertised had a somewhat different title from the above and described the book as a second ed. of Pison . . . 1572).

8. Quinta Essentia. Das ist Die höchste subtilitet / krafft vnd wirckung / beyder der fürtrefflichzsten / vnd menschlichem geschlecht am nützlichsten Künsten (der Medicin vnd Alchemy) . . . , f° in 6's, Leipzig. Cvm Privilegio Caesareo, H. Steinman, 1574 (pref. dated 1570), pp. ccxii + 1 leaf, portrait (BM 717. b. 37); first publ., 4°, Münster, 1570 (BM 1032. c. 10), 178 ll.; another ed., f°, Berlin, 1575, is mentioned. Much of the work is in verse.

9. *Προκατάληψις* Oder Præoccupatio, Durch Zwölff verschiedenlicher Tractaten (gemachter Harrn Pro-ben), f°, Frankfurt an den Oder, 1571, pp. lxxxv + 1 leaf (BM 717. l. 37. (2.); another ed., f°, 1574 is mentioned).

10. *Βεβαίωσις ἀγωνισμου*. Das ist Confirmatio Concer-tationis (oder ein Bestettigung desszjenigen so Streitig / Häderig / oder Zenkisch ist / wie aufs vnuerstand die Neuwe vnd vor vnerhörte erfindung aller Nützlicheſtē vnd menschlichen geschlecht der Notturftigesten kunst dess Harnprobirens ein zeitlang gewest ist, f°, Berlin im Grauwen Closter, 1576 (blanks, 107 ll., port., figs., some moveable and superimposed).

The *Quinta Essentia* contains some repulsive pictures of the 'spirits' of mercury, sulphur, salt, etc.[4] and follows Paracelsus in the parallels salt = earth = body, sulphur = air = spirit, mercury = water = soul. Some other works are described by Ferguson.

Two unpublished manuscripts of Thurneisser's are in the Berlin Staatsbibliothek.[5]

The *Pison*[6] describes a crude method of water analysis by specific gravity

[1] In Hebrew.
[2] Latin, Greek, Phoenician, Hebrew, 'Egyptian', Syriac, Gallic, Dacian, Spanish, Phrygian, and Tuscan names of plants were given in the herbal of ψ-Apuleius (printed 1480); Thorndike, i, 597.
[3] Kiesewetter, 105.   [4] Reprod. in F. S. Taylor, *The Alchemists*, 1951.
[5] Möhsen, 198; Petraeus, 1740, i, e8 r; Speter, 1935.
[6] Bk. ii, ch. 6; 1572, pp. xxiiii, xxxi, xxxvii.

and by distillation and weighing the residue,[1] and vaguely proposes artificial mineral waters.[2] The προκατάληψις (1571) describes a process pretending to diagnose diseases by distilling urine, a tube on the receiver having a scale representing all parts of the body. The examination of urine was an old diagnostic process (it is mentioned by Pliny)[3] and innumerable books were written on it, but Thurneisser seems to have been the first to use the perfectly useless process of distillation. Such a process was described by Dorn in 1577 (see p. 159). This chemical uroscopy was condemned by James Hart, of Northampton, as 'great cry and little wooll':

> The Anatomie of Vrines. Containing the Conviction and condemnation of them. . . . Detecting and vnfolding the manifold falsehoods and abuses committed by the vulgar sort of Practitioners . . . wherein is contained plentie of profitable and delectable Histories concerning this subiect, 1625.

The *Magna Alchymia* is of a more practical character than the other works and contains descriptions of preparations of sulphur, salts[4] including sal urinæ,[5] mercury and its compounds,[6] and metals,[7] but includes a long section on astrology and horoscopes.[8] In it[9] there is mention of a 'herrliche Salz' from milk which may be milk sugar, but the text is so confused that nothing can be made of it:

> Denn wer weiss nicht was ich für ein herrlich [or herzlich?] Oell / Saltz vnd Mercurium nicht allein aus der Butter / sondern auch aus dem Kesz / so wol auch aus der Wodicken oder Buttermilch / ja das noch mehr ist / aus dem Kesewasser (welchem man glaubt alle Krafft entführt zu sein) gemacht vnd erst hernach ein viel edler Saltz / ein durchdringender öll / oder Sulphur vnd ein subtilern Mercurium aus dem vorigen bereitet.

It has also been said[10] that milk sugar is first definitely mentioned by Fabritio Bartoletti in 1619, but he then merely repeats what is said by Thurneisser.[11]

BARTOLETTI

Fabritio Bartoletti (Bologna 26 August 1588–Lendenaria 30 March 1630), doctor of philosophy and medicine, Bologna (1613), was professor at Bologna, Pisa (1620) and Mantua (1626). His *Encyclopædia* was edited by Theodore Bugeus, who says Bartoletti was so young that he would not have published it unless many friends had pressed him to do so. Bugeus mentions several other works by Bartoletti, including an *Antidotarium Chimico-Dogmaticum*, and says the *Encyclopædia* exposed Hermetic impostures on humours, temperaments, the three principia, the generation of metals, etc., and dealt with an *aqua benedicta* from the crocus of metals; salt and sweet oil of antimony; extracting a balsamic mercury from gold and silver; and an appendix on oils and waters, the gemmed liquors of the Duke of Tuscany, etc. The work criticises the salt-sulphur-mercury theory, the relation of parts of the body to the planets, and other Paracelsan dogmas, although it prescribes some chemical remedies.[12]

---

[1] Kopp, (1), ii, 54; G. Rath, *A. Med.*, 1957, xli, 1. [2] P. lx. [3] xxviii, 6 (19).
[4] 1583, pp. 38 f. [5] P. 49. [6] Pp. 80 f. [7] Pp. 132 f. [8] Pp. 96 f.
[9] 1583, p. 8. [10] Lippmann, (7), 1921, 2; *Isis*, 1936, xxv, 459.
[11] *Fabritii Bartoleti, Encyclopædia Hermetico-Dogmatica sive Orbis Doctrinarum Medicarum Physiologiæ, Hygiinæ Pathologiæ, Simioticæ, et Therapeuticæ*, 4°, Bologna, [1619], (BM 544. g. 3.), 42: sicut enim in *lacto* videre est, in quo *serosa* portio mercuriali liquori; *butyrosa sulphureæ*; *Caseosa* verò saline substantiæ respondet; 68, milk gives three parts, butter, serum (whey), and cheese.
[12] Thorndike, vii, 179.

Bartoletti's description of milk sugar is in another work, of 1633[1] describing the preparation of recrystallised milk sugar which he calls *manna seri* or *sal seri essentiale, seu nitrum*, and used instead of manna in medicine:

Manna seri hæc. Destilla leni balnei calore serum lactis, donec in fundo vasis butyracea fœx subsidiat, cui hærebit salina quædam substantia subalbida. Hanc curiosè segrega est enim sal seri essentiale; seu nitrum, cuius causa nitrosum dicitur serum huicque tota abstergêdis vis inest. Solue in aqua propria, & coagula. Opus repete, donec seri cremorem habeas saporè omninò mannam referentem. Operatur ad vnciam magis quàm manna vulgaris ad vncias tres.

SUCHTEN

Alexander von Suchten, of Dantzig, studied in Cracow, was canon at Frauenberg (1539), studied in Louvain and in Italy, and in 1549 was librarian to the Elector Otto Heinrich. He returned to Cracow in 1554, becoming physician to King Sigismund Augustus, but left for Germany in 1563.[2] His work on antimony appeared first in 1570:

Liber unus de Secretis Antimonii, das ist von der grossen Heimligkeit des Antimonii, ed. Toxites, Strassburg, 1570; Basel, 1575, Mümpelgart, 1598.
Antimonii Mysteria Gemina . . . Das ist: Von den grossen Geheimmüssen desz Antimonij, in zweene Tractat abgeteilet, Leipzig (Apels), 1604, and undated, Nürnberg.
Zween Tractat, Von Antimonio. Der Erste, von der grossen Heimligkeit des Antimonii . . . Der Ander, Clavis Alchemiæ, De Secretis Antimonii . . . Sampt einem Fragmento Dialogi de Hydropi, 8°, Mumpelgardt, 1604.
Alex von Suchten of the Secrets of Antimony in Two Treatises, tr. Cable, London, 1670; Chymische Schrifften Alle, so viel deren vorhanden, 8°, Frankfurt, 1680.

He described an experiment on 'transmutation' in which he got out as much gold as he put in. John de Suchten, whose work is in MS., is a different person.[3]

ERASTUS

Thomas Lieber, known as Erastus (Badenweiler nr. Basel, 1523–Basel, 1 January 1583), who studied theology and philosophy at Basel and medicine at Bologna and Padua, was professor of medicine in Heidelberg and later in Basel. In theology he opposed Calvin's use of excommunication and originated what was called after him Erastianism.[4] His attack on Paracelsus was launched in his *Disputations*, the attack on alchemy in the second part of which was composed mainly by 1566:

---

[1] *Methodvs in Dyspnoeam sev de Respirationibvs libvi IV*, 4°, Bologna, 1633 (BM 806. dd. 4. (1.), 561 pp. xv ll. index), bk. iv, p. 400, index, f. x r; the passage is quoted by Ettmuller, *Schröderi Dilucidati Zoologia*, art. 'Bos', in Ettmuller, *Opera Omnia*, 4°, Frankfurt, 1688, ii, 163, who incorrectly gives a reference to Bartoletti's *Encyclopædia*, p. 400, and says: præparat ex sero lactis remedium, quod vocat *manna s. nitrum seri lactis*; Spielmann, *Institutiones Chemiae*, Strassburg, 1766, 75; F. X. A. von Wasserberg, *Institutiones Chemicae. Regnum Animale. Sectio Prior: Ovum: Lac*, Vienna, 1773, 115, says the *manna* or *nitrum seri lactis* mentioned by Bartoletti was known earlier; in Wasserberg's time it was manufactured in Switzerland and sold in Paris. Whittier, *Isis*, 1944, xxxv, 31.
[2] Schmieder, 1832, 279 (9 works); Bolton, (1), 1893, 1048; Ferguson, ii, 416; W. Hubicke, *Endeavour*, 1958, xvii, 204.
[3] Thorndike, v, 640.   [4] Thorndike, v, 652–67; Pagel, *Paracelsus*, 1958, 311.

Disputationum de Medicina nova Philippi Paracelsi, 4 pts. Basel, 1572–3; pars prima is undated and is described on the t.p. as: qua quæ de remediis svperstitiosis & Magicis cvrationibvs ille prodidit, præcipue examinantur, 267 pp., portr. of Paracelsus at end; pars altera, 1572, 284 pp.: Disputationum de Nova Philippi Paracelsi Medicina Pars Altera: In qua Philosophiæ Paracelsicæ Principia & Elementa explorantur (attacking the three principles, salt, sulphur, and mercury); pars tertia, 1572, 258 pp.; pars quarta, 1573, 310 pp. another ed., Disputationum & Epistolarum Medicinalium, Zürich, 1595 (Davis and Orioli, Catalogue 158 (1958), no. 132, p. 41). The second part is followed, with separate pagination, by Explicatio Qvaestionis famosæ illivs, vtrvm ex Metallis Ignobilibvs Avrvm Verum & naturale arte conflare possit (123 pp.), which defends Aristotle against George Agricola, quotes Gilgil the Moor (p. 29) and other authorities, and says (p. 49) there are three kinds of books on chemistry. It is followed by an Epistola De Natvra, Materia, Ortv atqve Vsv Lapidis Sabvlosi, qvi in Palatinatv ad Rhenum reperitur, 1572 (sep. t.p., pp. 124–43; index).

His criticism of the three principles (salt, sulphur, and mercury) is detailed and important; he emphasised (nearly a century before Boyle) that no one has ever seen them produced as final products of the action of heat on bodies; this produces many heterogeneous substances which cannot possibly be constituents of the original bodies. The properties of a body are not due to principles but to the proportions of the four elements; sulphur is inflammable because of fine and warm air which it contains, and salt is related to earth by its solidity.[1] Paracelsus's quintessence is not the same as Aristotle's; he made it identical with a part of heaven or ether, whilst Aristotle only said there is something in the sperm which is similar to this, and how could it survive the processes which Paracelsus gives for its preparation?[2] Erastus denies that man is a microcosm[3] and condemns the use of metallic remedies; metals are not assimilable and there is no evidence that what refines metals can purify the body; Paracelsus's high-sounding panaceas are in the end nothing but mercury.[4] His reputed cures were failures and he did more harm than good.[5] It may be[6] that 'despite certain violences of expression and crudities of reasoning, the reaction of Erastus against . . . iatrochemistry . . . was generally wholesome', but his chemical knowledge was weak; he says that acids and salts do not alter contiguous bodies but act only by the sense of taste.[7] He erred in taking salt, sulphur, and mercury as the common substances, and his collection of alchemical deceptions and failures looked only on one side of the picture.[8] His Disputations also attack magic, necromancy, occult medicine, witchcraft, amulets and astrology, in what seems to us a very sensible way, although (as a theologian) Erastus did not doubt the powers of evil. He included 'natural magic,' which (as in Porta, see p. 16) was often experimental science.

Erastus also wrote[9] a reply to a question of Henricus Smetius (1537–1614), professor at Heidelberg, as to whether some drugs had occult virtues affecting particular parts of the body, and as to the powers of mercury and antimony. Erastus accepted occult virtues in a qualified form; he considered the use of

[1] Disputat., ii, 71 f.   [2] Ib., ii, 163 f., 183 f.; iii, 22 f., 51.
[3] Ib., iii, 60 f.   [4] Ib., iv, 160, 301.
[5] Ib., iv, 159, 253.   [6] Thorndike, v, 666.
[7] Disputat., ii, 216.   [8] Schmieder, 1832, 290.
[9] De occultis pharmacorum potestatibus . . . Accessit disputatio . . . de medicamentorum purgantium facultate, 4°, Basel, 1574 (BM 543. b. 6. (4.)).

antimony to be highly dangerous.[1] He wrote a work on potable gold[2] in which he opposed alchemy and calls Paracelsus 'an evil magician, atheist, and pig', and his followers 'either most ignorant or indubitably wicked'. He complained of the novelty of Paracelsus in adding salt to the old-established principles of metals, mercury and sulphur, and for making these three principles the components of all things, even men. Potable gold and all metals are unfit for internal use, and gold does not keep the body from corruption. Externally applied, the preparations of metals may be useful or even necessary. The new remedy, unicorn powder, ignored in antiquity, is of little use.

DUCLO

Gaston Duclo (Gaston Dulco Claveus, Gaston de Clave Le Doux, etc.), born c. 1530 in the Nivernois, an advocate at Nevers, answered the attack on Paracelsus by Erastus[3] and wrote alchemical works.[4] In the *Apologia*[5] he says that an ounce of pure gold heated in an earthen vessel in a glass furnace for two months did not lose the smallest portion of its weight (nec minimum de pondere decidisse conspexi), whilst silver lost $\frac{1}{12}$ part. Hoefer quotes from a MS. in the Bibliothèque de l'Arsenal on calcining lime with 'sel de fèces ou le nitre' to make an oil (calcium nitrate?), and calcining gold amalgam with flowers of sulphur, evaporating with 'vinegar of vitriol' (sulphuric acid?) and distilling with sal ammoniac and saltpetre, when the gold passes over (as chloride?). Duclo is reputed to have had the secret of transmutation.

DUBOIS

Jacques Dubois (Jacobus Sylvius) (Souvilly, nr. Amiens 1478 (or 1492)–Paris 13 January 1555), professor of medicine at the Collège Royal (now Collège de France) in Paris (1550) was (unlike Franciscus Sylvius, see p. 281, with whom he is sometimes confused) a Galenist, and compiled pharmaceutical works largely from Galen and classical authors.[6]

[1] Summary in Thorndike, v, 661–4.
[2] *Disputatio de Auro potabile, in qua accurate admodum disquiritur, num ex metallis, opera Chemiæ*, 2 pts., 8°, Basel, 1578 and 1580.
[3] *Apologia Chrysopoeiae & Argyropoeiae adversus Thomam Erastum*, 8°, Nevers, 1590 (224 pp., portr.); Geneva, 1598; Ursel, 1602.
[4] *De recta & vere ratione progignendi Lapidis Philosophici*, 8°, Nevers, 1592 (39 paragraphs); *De triplici præparatione argenti & auri*, 8°, Nevers, 1594; in *Philosophia Chymica tribus Tractatibus comprehensa*, sm. 8°, Cologne, 1612 (an ed. Neuchatel, 1596, is quoted) in two parts (151 and 94 pp.), on reverse of t.p. the treatises are given as: I. *Apologia*, etc. II. *De triplici præparatione auri & argenti.* . . . III. *De vera & recta ratione progignendi Lapidis Philosophici.* . . . At the beginning (unpaged) is *Bernardi G. Penoti à Portu S. Mariæ Aquitani Epistola*; French, *Traité Philosophique de la Triple Préparation de l'Or et de l'Argent*, 8°, Paris, 1695 (Duveen, 182); German, *Claveus Germanicus, das ist: ein köstliches Buchlein von dem Stein der Weisen*, Halle, 1617. The three works are printed in the *Theatrum Chemicum*, 1659, ii, 6; iv, 371, 388. The *De Recta et Ratione Progignendi* was published at Cologne, sm. 8°, 1592, 80 pp., dedicated to the Archbishop of Cologne. A book *Le Filet d'Ariadne, pour entrer avec sureté dans le labirinthe de la philosophie hermetique*, 12°, 1695 (176 pp.), has been (perhaps incorrectly) attributed to de Claves (BM 1033. l. 68, annotated). Gobet, 1779, i, 15–22; Hoefer, (1), ii, 118; Kopp, (4), i, 54; ii, 343; Ferguson, i, 227.
[5] *Theatrum Chemicum*, ii, 19.
[6] *Methodus medicamenta componendi quatuor libris distributa, ex simplicibus judicio summo delectis et arte certa*, Paris, 1541, and later eds., tr. André Caille as *La Pharmacopée, qui est la manière de bien choisier et préparer les simples et de bien faire les compositions*, Lyons, 1574, 1611;

GERARD DORN

Gerard Dorn, of whom nothing seems to be known except that he lived in Frankfurt in the 16 cent. and edited several works of Paracelsus,[1] published a large number of books:

1. Clavis totivs Philosophiæ Chymisticæ, 8°, Lyons, 1567 (302 pp.; BM 1035. a. 1); 24°, Frankfurt, 1583, 1594; in Theatrum Chemicum, 1659, i, 192; German, Schlüssel Der Chimistischen Philosophy, 8°, Strassburg, 1602 (414 pp. and index, BM 1034. g. 2).

2. Congeries Paracelsicæ Chemiæ de Transmutationibvs Metallorum ... accessit Genealogia Mineralium, atque Metallorum omnium, 8°, Frankfurt, 1581 (277 pp.); in Theatrum Chemicum, 1659, i, 326, 568.[2]

3. Chymisticum artificium naturæ, theoricum et practicum, 8°, Frankfurt, 1568–9 (eds. of 1583, 1594 are quoted).

4. Commentaria in Archidoxorum Libros X. D. Doctoris Theophrasti Paracelsi ... accessit Compendium Magnæ eiusdem autoris ... , 8°, Frankfurt, 1584.

5. De Naturæ Luce Physica ... Cui annexa est modesta quædam admonitio ad Thomam Erastum ... de retractandis calumnijs, & conuitijs in Paracelsum ... , 8°, Frankfurt, 1583.

6. Theophrastische Practica, das ist, ausserlesene Theophrastische Medicamenta, beneben eigentlicher Beschreibung derer Præparation, 8°, s.l., 1618.

7. Artificii Chymistici Physici, metaphisicique, Secunda Pars & Tertia ... Accessit etiam Tertiæ parti, de Præparationibus Metallicis in utrosque Lapidis Philosophorum, 12°, s.l. [Basel], 1570, and other eds.[3]

8. Aurora Thesavrvsqve Philosophorum, Theophrasti Paracelsi ... Accessit Monarchia Physica per Gerardvm Dornevm, in defensionem Paracelsicorum Principiorum, à suo Præceptore positorum. Præterea Anatomia uiua Paracelsi, ... Basel, 1577 (includes Dorn's Monarchia Triades in Unitate Soli Deo Sacra); tr. in Waite's *Writings of Paracelsus*, 1894, i, 18–71, who says it was first issued in 1575.

The *Aurora* deals with the chemical examination of urine by distillation and contains accounts of unsuccessful chemical processes, including one called 'a part with a part'.[4]

Dorn also wrote a commentary on the *Tabula Smaragdina* of Hermes.[5] In the preface to his edition of Paracelsus's *De Summis Naturis Mysteriis* (1584) he complained that the prevailing education was too pagan, literary, and scholastic; nothing but dregs of the arts remained, clothed in ornate language. Learning needed a reform like that of religion, and he had found a better philosophy and more Christian way of thinking in Paracelsus and those who followed nature than in scholastic Aristotelianism or classical humanism.[6] A mystic and spiritual 'philosophy of love', was needed and Dorn attempted a sketch of it.[7] In his *Chymisticum artificium* Dorn abandons the attempt at transmutation and concentrates on Paracelsan chemical remedies. He says

De medicamentorum simplicium praeparatione, delectu, mistionis modis, Paris, 1542 (1541 ?); *De delectu, compositione et duratione simplicium, de eorum adulterationibus cognoscendis et succedanea*, was printed in Valerius Cordus' *Dispensatorium*, Venice, 1556; *Opera Medica*, f°, Geneva, 1630; Schelenz, 1904, 410, 415, 417, 434 (Sylvius b. 1492); Jöcher, iv, 965 (b. 1478); Ashley Montagu, in Singer, (1), 1953, i, 376 (b. 1478); NBG, 1855, xiv, 854 (b. 1478).

[1] Gmelin, (1), i, 264; Sprengel, (2), iii, 502; Schmieder, 321; Lessing, 1838, 408; Hoefer, (1), ii, 22; Kopp, (4), i, 22; Ferguson, i, 220; Thorndike, v, 630.
[2] Parkes, *Chemical Essays*, 2 ed., 1823, i, 467, says this was first published in 1570.
[3] Duveen, 177–8.   [4] Pagel, *Paracelsus*, Basel, 1958, 191 f.
[5] Manget, i, 389.   [6] Thorndike, v, 631.
[7] *Clavis*, 1567, 199–242, 267; alchemical exposition, 243–50: the text has a colloquy between Soul, Body and Spirit. Thorndike, v, 631, who dates the book 1566, says Dorn frequently shows debt to the *Quinta Essentia* of Rupescissa (see Vol. I).

'metallic substances do not transmute metals but only colour them'.[1] Spirit of wine, the quintessence, by mere infusion extracts the spirits from all bodies, animal, vegetable, and mineral.[2] Virtues may be extracted from inanimate bodies but do not operate effectively in medicine unless purified and refined by chemical art, when they approach their first celestial influence, penetrate, and operate almost miraculously in all infirmities.[3] Dorn says two (fire and water) of the four elements are primary, a view which Pantheus attributed to Morienus and Albertus (Vol. I). The elements exist as such or in combination and natural bodies are resolved into them and the quintessence. He tried to reconcile the theory of the four elements with that of the three principles: salt = earth, sulphur = fire, mercury = water; air is omitted because pure air cannot be separated by alchemy (aer ille non est ars secretus ab elementis, sed permixtus). Matter is the whole elementary region.

The stars incline but do not necessitate, since they are far inferior to the minds of men.[4] Poisons are drawn from the body by applying the body (even dry) of the poisonous animal (such as a toad), which acts by a natural virtue or magnetic force familiar to chemists; the physical chemist (*chymista physicus*) is not content with experience alone but looks to the part of the sky concerned and compares it with the anatomy of man the microcosm by four methods: geomancy, hydromancy, pyromancy, and astrology.[5]

Dorn complained that opponents of chemical remedies called them corrosive and harmful, but he admits that potable gold cannot be properly made unless the gold is resolved into its first matter, mercury and sulphur.[6] The second part of the *Clavis* is practical, describing and illustrating furnaces and vessels and giving recipes for the distillation of medicinal water and oils, including oil of vitriol by distilling Hungarian or Roman vitriol,[7] spirit of wine, etc., and mentions Ulstadius. Dorn claims to be the first to describe the distillation of metals by fire and evaporation without vinegar, lye, or other acids; it is possible that he is speaking of zinc.[8] The general aim of chemistry is to investigate the latent forms of natural bodies by changing manifest into occult forms, by the corruption of species and the generation of a more general form (generatione generalioris formæ), and by the conversion of decomposed elements into compounds and of impure to pure. He illustrates this by a diagram of two cubes, with visible and invisible faces.[9]

Johann Pistorius (Nidda, Hesse 1544 or 1546–Freiburg 1608), doctor of theology and medicine, in succession a Lutheran, Calvinist, and Catholic anti-Lutheran, in a tract on the plague[10] recommended metallic and chemical remedies but did not neglect

---

[1] *Clavis*, 1567, 133–4.   [2] *Ib.*, 87–8.
[3] *Ib.*, 278; Thorndike sees in Dorn's ideas of the circulation of the elements, *Ib.*, 19–23: haec transmutationis circulatio, reminiscences of Perscrutator and Walter of Odington, but they occur in Aristotle (Vol. I).
[4] *Ib.*, 144; three chapters (7, 8, 9) of the *Clavis* are devoted to the number three and it is said God rejoices in an uneven number.
[5] *Ib.*, 267–8.   [6] *Ib.*, 36–7.   [7] *Ib.*, 147.
[8] *Ib.*, 89; bk. iii, ch. 7; *Theatrum Chemicum*, 1659, i, 217: de metallorum destillatione simplici.
[9] *Clavis*, 1567, 25.
[10] *De vera curandae pestis ratione*, Frankfurt, 1568, BM 1167. c. 30. (1.); Jöcher, iii, 1598; Thorndike, vi, 461.

the bezoar stone, bone from the heart of a stag, stone from the head of an asp, a stork chick calcined alive, a hundred and eighty scorpions, and a pure quintessence of a hundred and fifty unspecified simples. He also commenced to publish a collection of writers on the *Qabbalah*[1] and wrote on the microcosm.[2]

Bernard George Penotus (Port-Sainte-Marie, Guienne *c.* 1520–30 — Yverdun 1620), studied at Basel and was a follower of Paracelsus and an alchemist. He died in extreme poverty and said that if he wished to do an enemy the worst injury he would urge him to pursue alchemy. He wrote many pharmaceutical tracts, a *Theophrastisch Vade Mecum* (in German), Magdeburg, 1596, and collected some tracts by Paracelsus.[3] His alchemical works[4] are without interest but his pharmaceutical[5] contains some intelligible preparations.

RULAND

Martin Ruland (Freising, Bavaria, 1532–Prague, 3 February 1602), physician to the Pfalzgraf Philip Ludwig, was a follower of Paracelsus and used secret remedies, especially antimony compounds. Some works attributed to him are probably by his son Martin Ruland the Younger (Lauingen, 11 November 1569–Prague, 23 April 1611), physician to the Emperor Rudolph II:

1. *Lexicon Alchemiæ*, 4°, Frankfurt, 1612 (487 pp., 481–7 misnumbered, last page a reprint of signature):(; reissued 1661) giving the meanings of many words used by Paracelsus (the explanations often being as obscure as the originals).

2. Progymnasmata alchemiae, sine Problemata chymica, nonaginta & vna Quaestionibus dilucidata: cum lapidis philosophici vera conficiendi ratione, 8°, Frankfurt, 1607 (254 pp.) with appendix, Quaestionum Chemicarum, (136 pp.) and Lapidis Philosophici vera (164 pp. and sep. t.p. dated 1606).

3. Problematum medico-physicorum, 8°, Frankfurt, 1608, 2 pts. (189 pp. and index, 152 pp. and index; the first part is printed in Manget, ii, 172–83, as by Marsilio Ficini).

Some[6] attribute (1) and (2), also a *Thesaurus Rulandinum, sive Curationum empiricarum Centurias decem* (which Sprengel[7] dates 8°, Budissin, 1679) and other works, to Ruland the Elder; and two works on the golden tooth (see p. 247) and *Alexicacum Chymiatricum* to Martin Ruland the Younger. Kopp and Hoefer do not mention them. Thorndike[8] says (1) and (2) (the dedication of (2) is dated from Ratisbon or Regensburg, 10 May, 1606, by 'Martinus Rulandus') are by Martin Ruland the Younger. The dedication of the dictionary is dated Prague, 20 April, 1611. Both dedications suit only the younger Ruland. The imperial privilege for ten years for the dictionary is dated Prague, 2 September, 1607.

Definitely by the younger Ruland is:[9]

4. Propugnaculum Chymiatriæ: Das ist, Beautwortung vnd beschützung der Alchymistischen Artzneyen, etlicher Spuriogalenisten verleumbdungen vnd die vortrefflichen hochnutzbarlichen Chymiatriæ, vnchristlich vnd vnbillichem verdammen entgegen gesatzt, 4°, Leipzig, 1608.

He was attacked by the physician Johann von Oberndorffer, who claimed to

---

[1] *Artis cabalisticae scriptorum*, Tomus I, Basel, 1587.
[2] *Microcosmus*, Paris, 1607, Lyons, 1612, Toulouse, 1618.   [3] Ferguson, ii, 179.
[4] *Theatrum Chemicum*, 1659, ii, 81–109 (with table of metals, etc.), 129–38, 139–50; 1659, iv, 364–70; Hoefer, (1), ii, 24; Ferguson, ii, 179.
[5] *Tractatus Varii, de vera Præparatione et Usu Medicamentorum Chemicorum*, in *Theatrum Chemicum*, 1659, i, 592–682.
[6] Jöcher, iii, 2306; Gmelin, (1), i, 323; Ferguson, ii, 302.
[7] (2), 1827, iii, 513.   [8] vii, 159.   [9] Gmelin, (1), i, 571; Ferguson, ii, 304.

have used chemical remedies thirty years before, in a short book[1] to which Ruland replied.[2]

GOHORY

Jacques Gohory (or Gohorry) (d. Paris, 5 March, 1576) wrote under the name Leo Suavius on various subjects and translated many works into French.[3] He wrote a compendium of the philosophy and medicine of Paracelsus, citing a great number of authors (including Roger Bacon) from whom he said Paracelsus had borrowed:

Theophrasti Paracelsi Philosophiae et Medicinae vtrivsqve vniversae Compendium. Ex optimis quibusque eius libris: Cum scholijs in libros IIII. eiusdem De Vita Longa, Plenos mysteriorum, parabolarum, ænigmatum. Auctore Leone Suauio. Vite Paracelsi. Catalogus operum & librorum, 8°, Basel, 1568 (334 pp. xiv ll., BM 1032. b. 18. (2.); Thorndike, v, 636, mentions an ed. of Paris, n.d.)

The three Paracelsan elements, he says, were borrowed from the alchemists, especially Ioannes Valentianus. He recommends antimony (on which he says he wrote a treatise) and potable gold as medicines, and thought finer gold could be prepared artificially than that found in nature. He reproduces the superstitious and occult beliefs of Paracelsus. His criticism of Dorn's translations was answered by the latter,[4] who said the antimonial and mercurial remedies used by Gohory were even more Paracelsan than his own. Gohory published a defence of ancient medicine and philosophy:

Discours responsif à celui d'Alexandre de La Tourette sur les secrets de l'art chimique et confection de l'or potable, fait en la défense de la Philosophie et Médecine antique contre la nouvelle Paracelsique, 8°, Paris, 1575 (by 'L.S.S.').

La Tourette, who is said to have been Master of the Mint, had published on potable gold.[5] Gohory also published a book of verse combining romance and allegory with alchemy and astrology,[6] and a work on the ancient meaning of letters, numbers, and divine names 'from the Sibyl', also dealing with short-hand and mystic writing after the fashion of the Steganographia of Trithemius (Vol. I).[7] He wrote on tobacco and translated the book of Lemnius (p. 113) into French.[8]

Hoefer[9] says Gohory was prior of Marsilly, and his garden, the site of the

[1] Apologia Chymico-Medica Practica ... Adversus illiberales Martini Rulandi Person. Medici Calumnias ..., 4°, s.l. [Amberg], 1610 (88 pp.); Ferguson, ii, 149.
[2] Alexicacus Chymiatricvs: pvris pvtis, mendaciis, atqve Calumniis atrocissimis Ioannis Oberndorferi ... Oppositvs asserendæ veritatis & famæ integritatis suæ iure, 4°, Frankfurt, 1611 (111 pp.).
[3] Lacour, NBG, 1857, xxi, 83.
[4] Veneni Quod Leo (nescio qvis) Svavivs in Theophrasticos euomere conatur proprium in pectus eius, per Gerardvm Dorn Apologetica retorsio, 8°, Basel, 1568 (xviii ll. unpaged, BM 1032. b. 18. (3)).
[5] Discours des admirables Virtus de l'Or potable, tr. as De Auro Potabili, Lyons and Paris, 1575; Défense pour l'Alchimie, Paris, 1579; Lenglet du Fresnoy, iii, 312; Jöcher, iv, 1270.
[6] Livre De La Fontaine Perilleuse, Avec La Chambre D'Amours: autrement intitulé, le songe du verger, 8°, Paris, 1572 (Duveen, 262).
[7] Leo Suavius, De usu et mysteriis notarum liber in quo vetusta literarum et numerorum ac divinorum ex sibylla nominum ratio explicatur, Paris, 1550 (BM 1043. b. 24); Thorndike, vi, 475.
[8] Les occultes Merveilles et Secrets de Nature par Levin Lemre de Zirikzee en Hollande, 8°, Paris, 1567, Lyons, 1574.
[9] (1), ii, 102.

Jardin du Roi, was the scene of conferences about 1572 attended by Botal, Honoré Châtelain, Jean Champelier, Fernel, and Ambroise Paré. Adjoining was the garden of de la Brosse, the King's physician, with many rare plants, and in a laboratory near it chemical experiments were made, Duchesne and de Mayerne attending. On the return of Belon from his travels (p. 94) experiments were made on hatching eggs in stoves regulated by dampers (cf. Drebbel, p. 321).

Abraham Portaleone, a Spanish Jew, composed a book on potable gold prepared by chemical treatment of the metal.[1]

SEVERINUS

Peter Severinus (Rypen, Jutland, 1542 — Copenhagen, July, 1602), a Danish physician who practised in Flensburg and Copenhagen, Canon of Roskild, and for thirty years physician to the kings of Denmark, systematised Paracelsus's medicine.[2] Sprengel[3] and Barchusen[4] say Severinus taught that the four elements are divided into two spheres, an upper containing the heavens (or fire) and air, and a lower containing water and earth, but Bongars attributed this to Paracelsus.[5] Every material element contains all the insensible elements, so that there is a watery, airy, earthy, and fiery fire, etc. The forces of the elements are *astra*, which are two-fold, originating in the stars and causing material changes, or free after separation from body and rising to the empyrean of heaven. The *astra* of bodies are their seeds (*semina*); the visible seed of an animal is not the *semina* but only its vehicle and every part of the body is a spiritual testicle. Severinus accepted the macrocosm-microcosm idea and supposed that in the microcosm (man) there were rivers and seas, mountains and valleys, minerals and plants. His theories exceeded even those of Paracelsus in absurdity and hence he was (as Sprengel says) the most celebrated of his earlier followers and he is often quoted.

Severinus defended the universal medicine by two arguments. Just as there are poisons which kill all men, so there must be drugs which cure them all and all diseases. Antimony destroys all imperfect metals but not gold, hence there must be a medicine which destroys all impurities in the body but does not harm the heart, the source of life. Severinus reduced all diseases to four types: leprosy, gout, dropsy, and epilepsy. Gobet[6] quotes Severinus as saying:

Emittite calceos, montes accedite; valles, solitudines, littora maris, terræ profundos sinus inquirite; animalium discrimina, plantarum differentias, mineralium ordines, omnium proprietates noscendi modus, notate; rusticorum astronomiam et terrestrem

[1] *De Auro dialogi tres*, 4°, Venice, 1584; Hoefer, (1), ii, 126; Thorndike, v, 645.
[2] *Idea Medicinæ Philosophicæ Fundamenta Continens totius Doctrinæ Paracelsicæ Hippocraticæ & Galenicæ*, 4°, Basel, 1571 (BM 543. c. 4); probably read by F. Bacon: *Works of Francis Bacon*, ed. Spedding, i, 564; Lessing, 1838, 409; Thorndike, v, 627; vii, 312, 489; Ferguson, ii, 379; Severinus's letter to Paracelsus (who was dead before it was written) was printed in the works of the latter: *Epistola scripta Theophrasto Paracelso: In quâ ratio ordinis et nominum, adeòque totius Philosophiæ Adeptæ methodus compendiose et erudite ostenditur a Petro Severino Dano, Philosophiæ et Medicinæ Doctore*, sm. 8°, Basel (20 unnumb. pp.); in Paracelsus, *Opera*, 1658, i.
[3] (2), 1827, iii, 503–8.   [4] 1710, 442–9.   [5] Berne MS. q. by Thorndike, vii, 158.
[6] 1779, ii, 699 f.; Hoefer, (1), ii, 103, attributes it to Jean Ribit.

philosophiam diligenter ediscite; nec vos pudeat; tandem carbones emitte, fornaces construite, vigilate et coquite sine tædio; ita enim pervenientis ad corporum proprietatemque cognitionem, alias non.

Prepare yourselves to explore mountains, to visit valleys, deserts, the sea-shore, the bowels of the earth; note the characters of animals and plants, the orders of minerals; learn of agriculture and natural philosophy; do not blush to handle coals, to build furnaces; be diligent and work unceasingly, for it is only so that you will arrive at knowledge of the properties of things.

Paracelsan medicines had spread to the Low Countries by 1552, when they are mentioned by Peter Haschaert of Brussels.[1]

PHARMACOPŒIAS

The earlier pharmacopœias, such as the Florentine *Nuovo Receptario Composito* (1498), the Nürnberg *Dispensatorium* of Valerius Cordus (1546), the Augsburg *Enchiridion sive Dispensatorium* (1564), and the *Dispensarium Reipublicæ Coloniensis* (1565), are all orthodox. In 1589 the Royal College of Physicians in London (founded in 1518) appointed a committee to draw up a pharmacopœia which was to be obligatory for the whole of England. None of the members were graduates of Paris, the bulwark of medical conservatism; some had graduated in Nantes, Padua and Leyden, and then in Basel, the latter including Thomas Muffet (Moufet, or Moffat) (London, 1553–Wilton, Wiltshire, 25 June 1605), of Scottish descent, a physician in England. He is best known for his work on insects but also wrote on chemical medicines[2] and defended Paracelsus against the Galenists, although he also wrote a digest of Hippokrates. He was associated with a 'distiller' John Hester (d. 1593).[3]

The Annals of the College in 1589 contain a plan of the pharmacopœia, which included the old remedies but also 'extracta, sales, chemica, and metallica'; the work was not published and the matter was dropped until 1614, when it was revived at the main instance of Henry Atkins (1558–1635), M.D. of Nantes, and Turquet de Mayerne. In the meantime Du Chesne's *Pharmacopœa Dogmaticorum Restituta* (1601) and Croll's *Basilica Chymica* (1609) had appeared, both containing chemical remedies.

The Augsburg Pharmacopoeia (*Pharmacopœia Augustana*) in the 5 ed., 1597, appended a decree of the Augsburg Senate of 1582 admonishing apothecaries not to prepare or offer for sale 'substances which are known to be detrimental or poisonous, such as Labdanum minerale, the so-called antimony, also Turpethum minerale and other purging mercurials'; but in the edition of 1613 prepared by Minderer (see p. 171), who himself used chemical remedies, there is a decree of September, 1613, authorising the sale and use of 'spagyric' remedies when 'prepared according to directions and prescribed by

---

[1] Thorndike, v, 329, quoting Petrus Haschardus, *Clypeus astrologicus*, Louvain, 1552.
[2] *De Ivre et Præstantia Chymicorvm Medicamentorvm Dialogus Apologeticus*, 8°, Frankfurt, 1584 (dedicated to Severinus), containing also his *Epistolæ Chymicæ* (both works in *Theatrum Chemicum*, 1659, i, 64–108.
[3] Lee, DNB, 1894, xxxviii, 101.

very experienced physicians who know how to combine rationality and experiment'.[1]

The oldest German pharmacy is Ortloff von Bayrland's *Arzneibuch. Hie fahet an eyn büchlein von manigerley Artzeney*, Nürnberg, 1477, Mainz, 1485 and 1491, Augsburg, 1488. The book on plants is taken from Konrad von Megenberg (Vol. I) hence the author is often called Ortloff Meydenberger.[2] Otto Brunfels (1488–1534) composed a *Spiegel der Arznei*, Strassburg, 1532, and *Reformation der Apotheken*, Strassburg, 1536; he first describes the vapour from ant-hills as reddening vegetable colours (formic acid).[3] Leonhard Fuchs (1501–66) wrote *De Componendorum Miscendorumque Medicamentorum Ratione*, Basel, 1549, and Walther (Gualtherius) Hermann Ryff (Rivius) *Reformierte deutsche Apothek*, Frankfurt, 1563, Strassburg, 1573.[4] The first German pharmacopœia was edited by Valerius Cordus (1546; see p. 167). The so-called Augsburg Pharmacopœia[5] appeared in new editions until 1734.[6] Other early pharmacopœias[7] are those of Florence (1560), Antwerp (1560), Cologne (1565), Mantua (1559), Basel (1561), Bergamo (1580) and Salamanca (1588).

In 1618 an Act of Parliament authorised the Royal College of Physicians of London to 'survey and examine the stocks of apothecaries, druggists, distillers, and sellers of waters and oils and preparers of chemical medicines'. The London *Pharmacopœia* of 7 May 1618, prepared under the care of Atkins and Turquet de Mayerne, gave the formulas for chemical remedies (whereas Minderer's only referred to 'Andernacum, Osvaldum Crollium, Quercetanum et alios') and included three chemicals not in the Augsburg Pharmacopœia of 1614, viz. tartarus vitriolatus (potassium sulphate), mercurius vitæ (antimony oxychloride and oxide, $SbOCl$ and Sb_2O_3), and mercurius dulcis (calomel, Hg_2Cl_2). It was the first official formulary to give a preparation of calomel, by precipitating a solution of mercury in aqua fortis (a solution of mercurous nitrate) by pouring it into a solution of sal marinus (common salt) and then washing, a preparation deduced by Mayerne from an obscure description in Croll (see p. 176). The second edition (7 December 1618) gives the preparation by subliming a mixture of corrosive sublimate and mercury, which was generally used until the older process was revived by Scheele in 1777 (see Vol. III).[8]

---

[1] *A Facsimile of the First Edition of the Pharmacopœia Augustana* (Nürnburg, 1546), ed. F. Kremers, Madison, 1927; Sarton, *Isis*, 1928, x, 69 (facsimiles of t.ps. of Cologne, 1565, Lyons, 1556, Augsburg, 1564 and 1573); Kremers and Urdang, *A History of Pharmacy*, Philadelphia, 1940, (the 2 ed., 1951, has interesting material omitted), 78, 90, 105; Thorndike, viii, 82.

[2] Schelenz, 1904, 336.

[3] Schelenz, 397, 409.

[4] Schelenz, 1904, 408 f., giving only the 1573 ed.; for Ryff's *Destillierbuch*, Frankfurt, 1567, see p. 86.

[5] *Pharmacopœia seu Medicamentarium pro Reipublica Augustana. Author Adolphus Occo*, Augusta Vindelicorum, 1564.

[6] Schelenz, 416, who gives the title of the first ed. as *Enchiridion sive ut vulgo vocant dispensatorium . . . pro Reipubl. Augustburgensis Pharmacopœis*.

[7] La Wall, 1927, 231; Ferguson, ii, 188.

[8] *Pharmacopœia Londinensis of 1618*, facsim. reprint, New York, 1944; Urdang, *Chymia*, 1948, i, 93; *id., Archives*, 1954, xxxiii, 303.

VALERIUS CORDUS

The preparation of ether by distilling alcohol with concentrated sulphuric acid seems to have been known to Paracelsus (see p. 150).[1] The preparation is clearly described by Valerius Cordus (Simtshausen, Hesse, 18 February 1515–Rome, 25 September 1544), whose real name is said to have been Eberwein. He was educated at Erfurt where his father, Euricius Cordus (Simtshausen, 1486–Bremen, 24 December 1535), was professor of poetry who became M.D. at Ferrara in 1522 and later practised medicine. Valerius studied in Marburg and Wittenberg (where he later lectured on pharmacy). He travelled in Switzerland and Italy, but was taken ill and died near Rome at an early age. Since he was regarded as a heretic, his body would have been thrown into the Tiber had it not been rescued by two of his countrymen. His death was lamented in the lines: Ingenio superest Cordus: mens ipsa recepta est / Coelo; quod terrae est, maxima Roma tenet.[2] Cordus is best known as a botanist.[3] He also wrote on spermaceti.[4]

The recipe for ether is in Cordus' annotations on Dioskourides, published posthumously by Gesner in 1561.[5] After saying that there are two kinds of oil of vitriol, a sharp (*austerum*, i.e. common oil of vitriol) and sweet (*dulce*), and describing the preparation of the first, it gives the preparation of the 'sweet oil of vitriol' (*oleum vitrioli ducle*). Six ounces of thrice rectified spirit of wine (*vini ardentis acerrimi & ter sublimati*) are mixed with an equal weight of sharp oil of vitriol and the mixture allowed to stand for two months. It is then distilled. The distillate separates into a watery and an upper oily part (*aqueum humorem & oleosum ac pinguem*), the latter being the sweet oil of vitriol (*oleum vitrioli dulce verum*), presumably ether. The recipe is said[6] to have probably originated in the Leipzig pharmacy of Johann Ralla, where Cordus (a nephew of Ralla) studied, but it may have originated in Italy.

Hoffmann[7] quotes the preparation 'hujus Valerius Cordus, primus isque diligentissimus materiæ mineralium scrutator, ex quo desumsit Conradus Gesnerus processum, qui in *thesauro Evonymi de remediis secretis* L. II. Tiguri impresso anno 1552. hunc in modum enarratur.' Ferguson[8] says Gesner's book first appeared in Zürich in 1552, although that of Venice, 1554, is usually given as the first edition. This has no second book and does not, apparently, contain the recipe. Ferguson gives a Zürich edition in German, 1608, containing a second part, ascribed to Gesner, but I do not know if the recipe is in this. The dates of many of the books of Cordus are obscure.

[1] Sudhoff, *Isis*, 1928, x, 145; *A. Med.*, 1929, xxi, 121; Nierenstein, *Pharm. J.*, 1945, clv, 116; Darmstaedter, *J. prakt. Chem.*, 1929, cxx, 74 (Cordus recipe in full); *id.*, *Acta Paracelsica*, 1930, 29.
[2] Hoefer, NBG, 1855, xi, 804–7; Leake, *Isis*, 1925, vii, 14 (portr.); Talmadge, *ib.*, 394; R. Schmitz, *A. Med.*, 1958, xlii, 260.
[3] *Historiæ Stirpium libri IV*, in the edition of his works edited by Gesner, f°, Strasbourg, 1562, a fifth book being published in Strasbourg, f°, 1569 (a sixth book is in MS.).
[4] *De Halosantho seu Spermate Ceti vulgo dicto*, in Gesner's *De omni rerum fossilium genere*, Zürich, 1555, and also Zürich, 1566.
[5] *Annotationes in Pedacij Dioscoridis . . . De Medica Materia*, f°, Strasbourg, 1561, Appendix, f. 226 v–228 v. This part of the work (*De artificiosis extractionibus*) is said to have been composed in 1540.
[6] Schelenz, 1904, 396.
[7] *De vero oleo vitrioli dulci*; in *Opera*, Geneva, 1740, iv, 494; the passage is copied from Hoffmann in Thomson, (2), 1817, ii, 329; Kopp, (1), iv, 300.
[8] i, 315.

Cordus edited the first German pharmacopœia, first published at Nürnberg (undated) in 1546 or earlier, and a second edition soon after; the first dated edition is of 1548:

Pharmacorum omnium, quæ quidem in usu sunt, conficiendorum ratio. Vulgo vocant Dispensatorium Pharmacopolarum . . . Authore Valerio Cordo . . . f°, Norimbergæ, apud Joh. Petreium, 1548.

It was published in a large number of later editions in various places, including Lyons and Venice, till the end of the seventeenth century.[1] The ether recipe is not in the earlier editions but appears in that of Antwerp, 1580 (pp. 415–18).[2]

DU CHESNE

Joseph Du Chesne (Quercetanus) (L'Esture, Armagnac, Gascony, 1544 (or 1521)–Paris, 1609) graduated at Basel about 1573, went to Paris in 1593 and became physician-in-ordinary to King Henri IV.[3] He is said to have been arrogant. He certainly made many enemies, including Riolan and Aubert (whom he criticised).[4] He was a follower of Paracelsus. Sprengel says he taught that all diseases, like plants, spring from seeds, that all bodies are composed of three principles (as God is of three substances), the solid contained in saltpetre, the volatile salt of sulphur, and the volatile mercurial salt. The *sal generalis* can produce philosophical gold and draw potable gold from the three kingdoms of nature. He believed in the doctrine of signatures and thought that male and female plants were more suited to men and women, respectively. Sulphuric acid has a magnetic virtue and cures epilepsy. Antimony has many virtues, and the magistery of human skull (*magisterium cranii humani*) is an excellent medicine. In his dispute with Aubert, John Antony Fenot sided with the latter and asserted in his book[5] that gold has no medicinal virtue, that crabs' eyes are useless against intermittent fevers, and that the laudanum of Paracelsus is harmful rather than beneficial. Fenot also opposed alchemy.

Du Chesne wrote a large number of books; three were published together as:

Opera Medica: scilicet, ad Iacobi Avberti Vindonis de ortu & causis metallorum contra Chymicos explicationem, Brevis responsio. De Exqvisita Mineralivm Animalium & Vegetabilium medicamentorum Spagyrica praeparatione et vsu . . . Sclopetarivs, sive, de Cvrandis vulneribus . . . Antidotarium Spagyricum, . . . , sm. 8°, Leipzig, 1614 (viii ll., 175 pp., viii ll., the ed. quoted).

The Sclopetarius (on gun-shot wounds), and its supplement Antidotarium spagyricum were first published in Lyons, 8°, 1576 (BM), Frankfurt, 1602 (Duveen, 492); a

---

[1] Schelenz, 1904, 414; R. Schmitz, *A. Med.*, 1958, xlii, 260 (ed. of 1540 ?).
[2] Gildemeister and Hoffmann, 1928, i, 62, 202; Wiegleb, (1), 1792, 154.
[3] Gmelin, (1), i, 281; Thomson, (1), i, 170; Sprengel, (1), iii, 372; *id.*, (2), 1827, iii, 539; Hoefer, (1), ii, 24; Ferguson, (1), ii, 233 (very detailed).
[4] *Ad Jacobi Auberti Vendonis de ortu et causis metallorum contra chymicos explicationem* . . . *brevis responsio*, 8°, Lyons, 1575 (Duveen, 492); in *Opera Medica*, Leipzig, 1614, 1 f., and *Theatrum Chemicum*, 1659, ii, 150; (many references to Agricola).
[5] *Alexipharmacum, sive Antidotus Apologetica, ad virulantius Josephi cuiusdam Quercetani Armeniaci, euomitas in libellum Jacobi Auberti, de ortu & causis Metallorum contra Chymistas* . . . *In quo . . . omnia argumēta refelluntur, quibus Chymistæ probare conantur, aurum argentumq; arte fieri posse. . . .* , 8°, Basel, n.d. (1575); Ferguson, ii, 236; Sprengel, (2), 1827, iii, 543, says 1576.

French translation is: Traitte de la cure generale et particuliere des Arcbusades. Avec l'Antidotaire Spagirique pour preparer & composer les medicamens, sm. 8°, Lyon, 1586 (Quaritch, *Cat.* 724 (1954)); and an English translation is by J. Hester, *The Sclopetarie of J. Quercetanus*, 4°, London, 1596. Other editions are mentioned by Ferguson, ii, 233.

These treatises prescribe many mineral or new remedies, including turpeth mineral (turpeti mineralis, basic mercuric sulphate), a full recipe for the preparation of which is given,[1] sulphur of antimony (antimony sulphide) made by boiling stibnite with caustic alkali solution and then precipitating with vinegar,[2] a salt of urine (microcosmic salt, or urea) made by evaporating urine and crystallising from distilled vinegar,[3] etc., but other remedies are mummy (old specimens of which were no longer obtainable)[4] and human skull.[5] His recipes are clear and intelligible.

Hoefer thought Du Chesne was acquainted with nitrogen, since he speaks of a 'spirit' in saltpetre which is of the nature of air but extinguishes flame (in sale petrae spiritus quidam mercurialis, qui quidem est de natura aërea, & qui tamen flammam concipere haud possit, sed huic potius contrarius. Hic spiritus qualitate sua non est calidus sed potius frigidus, vt testatur eius aciditas).[6] He refers to the heat and red fumes produced on dissolving silver in aqua fortis.[7] Du Chesne's book on pharmacy[8] deals with waters, decoctions (including *seri lactis*, milk curdled with lemon, 1607, p. 151), wines, oxymels, syrups, purgatives, emetics (including antimony), clysters, conserves, antidotes (including theriac with 68 ingredients, and preparations of vipers) (pp. 443, 484), narcotics (including laudanum) (p. 556) and extracts. It contains many recipes. It perhaps describes the preparation of gluten from moistened flour-dough kneaded with the fingers (lib. i, c. 6, p. 26: si cum modico aquæ irroretur, digitisque subjugitur in tenacem, ceream, & prorsus glutinosam substantiam abeat); it tends to clog the bowels and was used to make biscuits: placentæ farinaceæ pistæ (fougasses vocant nostri).

The work was reprinted in the dispensatory of J. Renodaeus (Jean de Renou),[9] and it had a great influence.[10]

According to Kopp[11] 'Quercetanus is said to have used calomel, at least it

[1] *De med. spagyr.*; 1614, 82.   [2] *Sclopet*, 1614, 169.
[3] *Sclopet*, 1614, 162.   [4] *De med. spagyr.*; 1614, 99.   [5] *Ib.*, 1614, 103.
[6] *Liber De Priscorum Philosophorum veræ medicinæ materia præparationis modo, atque in curandis morbis præstantia*, sm. 8°, S. Gervasii, 1603; 8° Geneva, 1609, 20; also containing tracts on *De Simplicivm Signatvris Externis* (1603, p. 70 f.), *De Signatvris Rervm Internis* (*ib.*, p. 89 f.), and *De Dogmaticorvm Medicorvm* (*ib.*, pp. 131–212).
[7] *Ib.*, 1603, 102; *Pestis Alexicacus, Sive Luis Pestiferæ fuga*, 8°, Leipzig, 1609 (461 pp., index), 147 (. . . partim rutilantis, partim nigricantis specie . . . in omne latus diffundente); Also, p. 154, the 'serpent' or condensing tube: serpentinas (sic enim hæc vocantur instrumenta); and mercury amulets (p. 341).
[8] *Pharmacopoea Dogmaticorvm Restitvta*, Paris, Claudium Morellum, 4°, 1607, with good portrait of Du Chesne, aged 60, and engraved frontispiece by L. Gauetier (the same as that in Libavius's *Alchymia*, 1606); iv ll., 630 pp., viii ll. index; there is an *Editio vltima multis erratis repurgata*, 8°, Geneva, 1628.
[9] *Dispensatorium Galeno chymicum*, 4°, Hanau, 1631; French tr., *La Pharmacopée des Dogmatiques*, 8°, Paris, 1629 (vii ll., 509 pp., portr.). Also in French is Du Chesne's *Traicté familier de l'exacte Préparation Spagyrique des Médicamens, pris d'entre les Mineraux, Animaux & Vegetaux, avec une breve response au livret de Jacques Aubert, touchant la génération et les causes des métaux*, 8°, Paris, 1630 (152 pp., vii ll.). See note 4, p. 167.
[10] Urdang, *Archives*, 1954, xxxiii, 303.   [11] (1), 1847, iv, 192.

was called frequently in the 17 cent. *Panchymachogogum Quercetani* (also *Panchymachogogum minerale*)'; but Urdang[1] did not trace these names in Du Chesne's *Pharmacopoea Dogmaticorum Restituta* and other works. Urdang says a preparation by precipitating a solution of mercury in nitric acid by adding a solution of common salt was given by Renou[2] and is given in the *Pharmacopoeia Londinensis* of 1618, where it is due to Turquet de Mayerne (see p. 176). It is also in Beguin (1610, see Vol. III).

W. R. Whatton[3] said Turquet de Mayerne 'bk. ii, p. 20' first used the name calomel (calomelas, mercurius calomelanicus) for mercurous chloride, previously given many fanciful names: sublimatum dulce, aquila alba, aquila mitigata, draco mitigatus, manna metallorum, panchymogogum minerale, panchymogogus Quercetanus, etc. — he gives 27 names. Sennert called it mercurius dulcis. The derivation from καλός beautiful and μέλας black (since it forms a black powder with caustic alkali) was given by S. Blancard, *Lexicon Medicum Graeco-Latinum*, Amsterdam, 1679; Leyden, 1702, 113: 'quæ compositio nominum nihil significat'; R. James, 1745, ii, *s.v.* 'Calomelas', says this is 'mercury well pounded with sulphur and reduc'd to a black substance' (i.e. mercuric sulphide). Whatton suggests other derivations.

Du Chesne describes the preparation of spirit of wine (spiritus vini dicitur, aliud acetum distillatum & alcolisatum dicitur) and its rectification over salt of tartar (potassium carbonate) to produce spiritus vini circulationibus,[4] and mentions tincture of opium as 'laudanum' a name he derives from *laudano*, to be praised.[5]

Du Chesne is said by Gmelin to have first openly and clearly described resuscitation of a plant from its ashes.[6] He reported that a Pole showed him twelve hermetically sealed vessels containing ashes from which, in a gentle heat, flowering plants grew, which subsided on cooling. Ferguson[7] says 'he was one of the first to give an account of the notion of palingenesis' (the resuscitation of a plant from its ashes), but palingenesis is mentioned by Paracelsus (p. 131); it was denied by Van Helmont (p. 217). Daniel Coxe[8] thought vegetable salts resembled the shape of the plants from which they were obtained, ferns in one case and firs and pines in the other.

The resuscitation of plants (palingenesis) is also mentioned by Jacques Gaffarel (Mannes, Provence, 1601–Sigonce, 1681), who studied theology and Oriental languages at Valence, was doctor of canon law of Paris, and librarian to Cardinal Richelieu. He was associated with Leo Allatius in the Vatican library (1632), then lived in Venice with the French ambassador. He then travelled in Greece and the Asiatic coast. On his return to France he filled various ecclesiastical positions and died in a convent. He was very well read

---

[1] *Chymia*, 1948, i, 93.
[2] *Antidotarium Dogmaticorum Vetus*, Paris, 1608, lib. ii, pp. 140–1 (*pulvis mercurij praecipitatum*).
[3] *Ann. Phil.*, 1821, ii, 427.   [4] *De med. spagyr.*; 1614, 112.
[5] *Ad Jacobi Auberti . . .* , 1575; *Theatrum Chemicum*, 1659, ii, 152.
[6] Quercetanus, *Ad Veritatem Hermeticæ Medicinæ ex Hippocratis veterumque decretis ac Therapeusi . . . adversum cujusdam Anonymi phantasmata Responsio*, bk. i, ch. 23; 8°, Paris, 1604 (BM 1033. g. 9. (1.)), 292–301; 8°, Frankfurt, 1605 (BM 1034. b. 4. (1.)), 230–8; on this book see Thorndike, vii, 304. The 1604 ed. has viii ll., 312 pp., followed by *Tractatus Secundus*, 68 pp., iv ll. errata; the 1605 ed. has viii ll., 300 pp.
[7] ii, 237.
[8] *Phil. Trans.*, 1674, ix, 150–8, no. 107; J. Ozanam and M. Montucla, *Recreations in Mathematics and Natural Philosophy*, tr. C. Hutton, 1803, iv, 452–60.

170   IATROCHEMISTS FOLLOWING PARACELSUS

and had a good knowledge of the Jewish *Qabbalah* (on which he published a book in 1625) and other occult literature, and believed in astrology.[1] His interesting book[2] quotes many recent authors, including Paracelsus, Croll, and Du Chesne. It deals with 'lettered' natural stones (1632, pp. 73, 91), signatures of plants (p. 97) and animals (p. 104), and the zenexton of Paracelsus (p. 127), mentions the experiment of putting a frozen egg in water (p. 97) afterwards described by Boyle (p. 509), who quotes him on the revivification of plants from their ashes and the form of a plant assumed in the ice from a solution of its ashes (pp. 100–1; q. Du Chesne). Henry Power in a letter to Sir Thomas Browne in 1648[3] asks him to explain 'the re-individualling of an incinerated plant' which was only obscurely hinted in 'Quercitan and Angelus Salæ', but was 'a noble piece of chymistry'. Johann Ludwig Hannemann defended the chemical resuscitation of plants[4] and Becher[5] reported from Digby that crabs are regenerated from the ashes of burnt crabs 'proprio liquore perfusis'. Du Chesne's numerous writings attracted much attention.[6]

---

[1] NBG, 1857, xix, 146; Thorndike, vii, 304.
[2] *Cvriositez Inovyes svr la Scvlptvre Talismaniqve des Persans. Horoscope des Patriarches. Et Lectvre des Estoiles*, Roven, I. Bovllay, 1632 (sm. 8°, viii ll., 315 pp., 2 folding plates, BM 8630. aa. 17); 1 ed., 8°, Paris, 1629 (644 pp.; 2 copies in BN); Latin, Hamburg, 1676; tr. E. Chilmead, *Unheard of Curiosities Concerning the Talismanical Sculptures of the Persians . . .*, 8°, 1650, BM E. 1216. (1.). It was condemned in 1629 by the theological faculty in Paris and Gaffarel signed a vague retraction. His *Abdita Divinæ Cabalæ Mysteria contra Sophistarum logomachiam defensa*, 4°, Paris, 1625, is dedicated to Cardinal Richelieu.
[3] Sir Thomas Browne, *Letters*, ed. Keynes, 1946, 280; J. O. Halliwell [-Phillips], *A Collection of Letters*, 1841, 92.
[4] *Phœnix Botanicus*, Kiel (?), 1680 (?); BM 1033. h. 11. (19.).
[5] *Phys. Subterr.*, I, iii, 4; 1738, 76.
[6] Part of the *Pharmacopoea dogmaticorum* was printed (with some of Croll's *Basilica Chymica*) in A. Ziegler, *Pharmacopoea Spagyrica*, 4°, Tigurini, 1616 (141 pp., index), and a French translation of parts of Croll, Du Chesne, and Aubry, by Jollivet Castelot, *La Médecine Spagyrique*, Paris, 1912 (Du Chesne, 220 f.). Du Chesne's *Diaeticon Polyhistoricum*, 8°, Paris, 1606 (Ferguson, ii, 237), Leipzig, 1607, was tr. as *Le Pourtraict de la Santé*, 8°, Paris, 1606 (Duveen, 493). Other works attributed to Du Chesne are a poem on the constitution and properties of matter, *Le Grand Miroir Du Monde*, 4°, Lyons, 1584 (Ferguson, ii, 237), 1587 (Duveen, 492); *Recueil des plus Curieux et Rare Secrets touchant la Medecine Metallique et Minerale tirez des Manuscrits du feu Mr. Joseph du Chesne*, 8°, Paris, S. Piget, 1648 (iii ff., 370 pp., vii ff.; portrait); *The Practise of Chymicall, and Hermeticall Physicke, for the preservation of health. Written In Latin By Iosephus Quersitanus, Doctor of Physicke. And Translated into English, by Thomas Timme . . .* 2 parts in 1 vol., sm. 4°, London, Printed by Thomas Creede, 1605, CUL Dd.* 3. 43² (E); Timme says he has presented secrets 'as neither Quersitanus, Isacus Hollandus, nor any other Phylosopher, have before published in print to my knowledge, but have come to my hands in paper and parchment copies'); *Traicté Familier De L'Exacte Preparation Spagyrique des Medicamens, pris entre les Mineraux, Animaux & vegetaux. Avec Vne brève response au livret de Jacques Aubert, touchant la generation & les causes des metaux*, 8°, Paris, 1624 (Duveen, 493); *The True and Perfect Spagerike Preparation of Minerals, Animalles, and Vegitables*, tr. by I[ohn]. H[ester]., 8°, London, 1691; J. Schroeder, *Quercitanus Redivivus tribus tomis digesta*, 4°, Frankfurt, 1648 (CUL L. 4. 54) and 1679 (BM); *Ad Brevem Riolani excursum brevis Incursio*, 8°, Marburg, 1605; *Drey Medicinische Tractätlein*, 4°, Strassburg, 1631; *Le Richezze della Riformata Farmacopea*, tr. Giacomo Ferrari, 4°, Venice, 1677 and 1684; *Tetras gravissimorum . . . affectum*, Marburg, 1606; *Opera omnia*, Lyons, 1645. J. Du Chesne was sometimes styled Sieur de la Violette or Baron de Morence et d'Iserable (or Lyserable). Another Quercetanus was Nicolas Chesneau (Marseilles, 1601–c. 1675), who wrote a *Pharmacie Theorique*, 4°, 1660; 2 ed. 4°, 1670 (BM 546. i. 15), and *Observationum libri quinque*, 8°, Paris, 1672; 4°, Leyden, 1719.

MINDERER

Raymond Minderer (Augsburg; *c.* 1570–13 May 1621), M.D. Ingolstadt (1597), army doctor, physician in Augsburg and to the Emperors Mathias and Maximilian, wrote:[1]

1. De Pestilentia Liber Unus Veterum et Neotericorum observatione constans, 8°, Augsburg, 1608, 1619 (BM 1167. d. 1. 12.; 386 pp.), on the plague.
2. Aloedarivm Marocostinvm, 8°, Augsburg, 1616 (engr. t.p., pref., 232 pp., index); Aloedarivm Marcocostinvm. Cum annexis Compositionibvs aliqvot Magistratibvs Medicis Avtoris, qvas lux priùs nõ viderat, nunc publicæ salutis ergò in lucem datis, 12°, Augsburg, 1622 (pref., 308 pp., index) on aloes; Compositiones Medicæ Magistrales, sep. t.p., 53 pp., describing the preparation of tartarum saturnisatum (lead carbonate) by precipitating lead acetate solution with potassium carbonate (p. 51). The acetum ammoniacum (1616, 99) is a solution of gum ammoniac in vinegar, not ammonium acetate.
3. Threnodia Medica seu Planctus Medicinae lugentis, 8°, Augsburg, 1619, a medical dirge.
4. Medicina Militaris d. i. Gemeine Handstücklein zur Kriegsarznei, 12°, Augsburg, 1621 (BM 1170. a. 11; eds. of 1623, 1626, and Nürnberg, 1634, 1667, 1668, 1672 are mentioned); Pharmacopoliolum Campestris s. Itinerarium oder Feld- und Reiseapotheclein, ed. J. H. Cardilucius, 12°, Nürnberg, 1679 (BM 775. a. 10); Schelenz, 1904, 514, mentions English (1634, 1694) and Dutch (1694) trs.
5. De Calcantho sev Vitriolo. Eivs Qvalitate, Virtvte, ac Viribvs, nec non Medicinis ex eo parandis. Disqvisitio Iatrochymica. Frigida, ac Crvdis Qvorundam de Vitriolo sinistrè sententium opinionibus & sententijs opposita, 4°, Augsburg, 1617 (1 l., 113 + v pp.; BM 990. f. 1), on vitriol.

In (5) Minderen says that although he was:

born among chemical vapours and brought up amidst spagyric furnaces, I have as a physician always followed the Hippocratic and Galenical method ... if I ... occasionally employ metallic and mineral remedies, I do this that they may supplement vegetables pure and simple to which the new and graver or inveterate diseases will not yield. I do this that medicine may not despair.

He describes blue and green vitriol, colcothar, spirit of vitriol, oil of vitriol, and discourses on silver, vinegar, and mineral waters. He mentions that sulphuric acid reddens blue paper (p. 81).

Urdang[2] says Minderer in his edition of the Augsburg *Pharmacopœia* (1613) described sales artificiosi from plants, sal Saturni (lead acetate), sal vitrioli (ferrous sulphate), nitrum sulphure purgatum (a mixture of potassium nitrate and sulphate), flores sulphuris (sublimed sulphur), flores and vitrum antimonii (Sb_2O_3 with a little Sb_2S_3), crocus Martis (Fe_2O_3), antimonium diaphoreticum (antimony oxide and potassium antimonate), turpethum minerale (mercuric sulphate), lapis septicus (caustic potash) and lapis philosophorum (a melt of alum, vitriol, bole, white lead, camphor, and vinegar).

Minderer is always credited with the use of a solution of ammonium acetate made by dissolving sal volatile (ammonium carbonate) in distilled vinegar,[3] but the reference is never given. Tachenius[4] called it 'water of Minderus for hearing (aqua ad Auditum Mindereri)' and gives its preparation from vinegar

[1] Gmelin, i, 570; NBG, 1861, xxxv, 593.   [2] *Archives*, 1954, xxxiii, 303 (308).
[3] Gren, 1794, ii, 587; Gmelin, (1), i, 570; Sprengel, (2), 1827, iv, 288.
[4] *Hippocrates Chymicus*, Paris, 1669, 68.

and sal volatile. It was later called spiritus Mendereri, spiritus ophthal-micus Mindereri, and sal ammoniacum liquidum.[1] Gren suggested that solid acetate of ammonia might be obtained from glacial acetic acid and ammonia gas.

T. Redwood[2] said the genuine preparation made from ammonium carbonate and distilled vinegar was quite different from that made with ammonium hydroxide and concentrated acetic acid. Ammonium acetate is not described in any of the works of Minderer I have examined and no author who attributes it to him gives a correct reference. It does not seem to be mentioned in his edition of the Augsburg *Pharma-copœia*. There may be a *vague* reference to it in one of his works.[3]

TURQUET DE MAYERNE

Theodore Turquet de Mayerne (Mayerne, near Geneva, 28 September 1573–Chelsea, London, 1655) (the preface to Browne's edition of his works says b. 1572) studied at Heidelberg and at Montpellier (where he graduated M.D. in 1597) and practised in Paris, where he became physician to Henri IV in 1600, and in 1603 he opened courses of lectures for young surgeons and apothecaries. He used Galenical preparations and also chemical remedies (antimony, mercury, tin and iron compounds) and was a good chemist for his time.[4] In 1603 his enemies procured his unanimous condemnation by the Paris Medical Faculty [text in Sprengel, and Hoefer] 'propter temeritatem, im-pudentiam et veræ medicinæ ignorationem'. Physicians were not to meet him in consultation and it was recommended that he should be deprived of his office. He ceased to lecture (probably his main offence) but continued to practise unmolested.

There was a great quarrel lasting for a century (1566–1666) on the use of antimony in the Paris Faculty of Medicine[5] and it appears in Ben Jonson's play *Volpone* (1603, publ. 1607, dedicated to the universities of Oxford and Cambridge). De Mayerne replied[6] to an anonymous attack, saying that the use of chemical remedies does not contradict the teachings of Hippokrates and Galen. An attack on de Mayerne was made by Jean Riolan jr. (1577–1657) under the pseudonym Joannes Antarvetus,[7] who also replied to Israel Harvetus[8]

[1] Kopp, (1), iv, 341.
[2] *Pharm. J.*, 1864, v, 406 (408).
[3] *Consilium Medicum in Peste Anno 1667 ... publiciret*, unpaged appendix to *Pharmaco-polium Campestre*, 1679, f. Y f.
[4] Haag, *La France Protéstante*, 1861, vii, 350; Gmelin, (1), i, 503, 572 f.; Lessing, 1838, Beilag C; Sprengel, (1), 1815, iii, 376; Hoefer, (1), ii, 238; La Wall, 1927, 264; Moore, DNB, 1894, xxxvii, 150; NBG, xxiv, 544; Gibson, *Ann. Medical Hist.*, 1933, v, 315 (chemical expts. in Sloane MSS. 1990, 2041, 2052, 2222); S. Ayscough, *A Catalogue of the Manuscripts pre-served in the British Museum*, 1782, i, 489; J. O. Halliwell [-Phillips], *A Collection of Letters*, 1841, 46 (several vols. of medical MSS. in the 'Cambridge Public Library'); Urdang, *Archives*, 1954, xxxiii, 303; good portrait in De Mayerne's *Praxeos Mayerianæ*, f°, London, 1690.
[5] J. Lévy-Valensi, *La Médecine et les Médecins Français au XVIIᵉ Siècle*, Paris, 1933, 132 f.
[6] *Apologia. In qua videre est inviolatis Hippocratis & Galeni legibus, remedia Chymice pre-parata, tuto usurpari posse. Ad cuiusdam anonymi calumnias Responsio*, La Rochelle, 1603 (Duveen, 590).
[7] *Ad Famosam Turqueti Apologiam Responsio. Accessit Censura Scholae Parisiensis*, 12°, Paris, 1603.
[8] *Defensio Chymiæ adversus Apologiam & censuram Scholæ Medicorum Parisiensium & in easdem Guilelmi Baucyneti*, 8°, Paris, 1604.

by other tracts.[1] Riolan also attacked Libavius,[2] and Laurent Joubert (who had maintained that it was possible to live without food for 'plusieurs jours et années').

Jean Riolan was a vain, pompous, officious, quarrelsome and vindictive man who also attacked Van Helmont.[3] Unable to tolerate the conditions in Paris, de Mayerne left for England and became M.D. of Oxford in 1606. In 1611 he was called to London by James I as court physician, a post which he continued to hold under Charles I until the execution of that monarch. He was appointed physician to Charles II but in the same year he retired to Chelsea. He became Baron d'Aubonne in 1621 and was knighted in England in 1624. He left a large fortune and many of his manuscripts are in the British Museum.

Theophrastus Renaudot (Loudun, 1584–Paris 25 October 1653), M.D. Montpellier 1606, became a physician in Paris in 1612, but came into collision with the Medical Faculty under the professor, Guy Patin, which condemned him in 1643 for his use of antimony and was upheld by Parliament. His son Eusebius Renaudot (d. 1679) defended the use of antimony[4] and in 1653 the poet Colletet called it a 'precious elixir, divine magnesia'.[5]

The Medical College of Paris under the presidency of Riolan opposed all innovations, and Guy Patin opposed chemical remedies with great zeal. In his manuscript 'Martyrologium Antimonii' Patin collected cases in which the use of antimony had been injurious. But in 1666 the dispute relative to antimony (particularly tartar emetic) became so violent that the doctors of the faculty of Paris were, by order of Parliament, assembled under the Dean, Vignon, and after a long deliberation resolved by a majority of ninety-two votes that tartar emetic and other antimonials should not only be permitted but even recommended. At the instigation of Patin, François Blondel demanded that the resolution should be cancelled, but neither his efforts nor the writings of Guillemeau and Menjot against antimony had any effect. In England, the use of chemical remedies was generally favoured.[6]

De Mayerne was interested in the chemistry of pigments and assisted Vandyke, Petitot, and Rubens (who painted his portrait), and he invented a washable varnished memorandum tablet.[7] His works were collected and published by Joseph Browne.[8] The *Pharmacopœia*, first published in this work (1700), contains a description of the odorous and inflammable gas (hydrogen) evolved on dissolving steel filings in oil of vitriol diluted with water:

[1] *Ioannis Antarveti Medicinae Candidati Apologia, pro iudicio Scholae Parisiensis de Alchimia. Ad Harueti & Baucyneti recoctam crambem*, 12°, Paris, 1604; *Censura demonstrationum Harveti pro veritate Alchymiae. Per Io. Riolanum fil. Anatomiae & Pharm. Professorem Regium*, 12°, Paris, 1606, replying to Harvetus, *Demonstratio veritatis Chymicae*, 8°, Hannover, 1605; Duveen, 510; Ferguson, i, 366.

[2] *Ad Libavi Maniam, Joan. Rioliani Responsio pro Censura Scholæ Parisiensis contra Alchymiam lata*, 8°, Paris, 1606.

[3] *Curieuse Recherches sur les Escholes en Medecine De Paris, et de Montpelier ... Par vn Ancien Docteur en Medecine, de la Faculté de Paris*, 8°, Paris, 1651 (Duveen, 510); Sprengel, (2), iv, 80.

[4] *L'Antimoine justifié et l'Antimoine triomphant*, 4°, Paris, n.d. (1653), (396 pp.; BN 4°, Te[151]. 85); Lévy-Valensi, 133 f.; Thorndike, vii, 529.

[5] Lévy-Valensi, 150.   [6] Thomson, (1), i, 200.

[7] Eastlake, *Materials for a History of Oil Painting*, 1847, i, 575 (Sloane MS. 2052, written in 1620, partly by de Mayerne, with his signature; Sculptoria et quæ subalternum artium); Gibbs, *Chem. and Ind.*, 1938, lvii, 877 (Sloane MS. 1990).

[8] *Opera Medica Theo. Turquet. Mayernii in quibus continentur consilium, epistolæ, observationes, variæque medica mentorum formulæ, quæ in asum Annæ et H. Mariæ Angliæ reginorum præscripta fuere, una cum epistola præfatoria*, etc., *cura et studia Josephi Browne*, f°, London, 3 pts., 1700, 1703 (some copies dated 1701); portrait.

I have taken 8 oz. of iron filings and in a deep glass cup (*concha*) I have added successively 8 oz. of oil of vitriol and a little later an equal quantity of warm water. There
was produced an enormous agitation and a great ebullition and a meteorism of matter
easily quieted by stirring by a rod. There is also raised a most fetid sulphurous vapour
very noxious to the brain, which (as happened to me not without danger) if brought
near a candle takes fire, on account of which this operation should be made in the open
air or under a chimney.

Vitriolum Martis feci juxta preceptum Trogny. ℞. Limatures Chalybis ℥ i, olei
vitrioli ℥ iii vel plus; para in amplo vase ab igne remoto, & ista sensim misce, caveus
ab ingeni fumo, & horrendo foetore, qui elevatur ab impuro Martis sulphure . . . mox
affunde aquae fontanae tepidae . . . bulliat ad pelliculam . . . et in cellam repositionibus
christalliza.[1] . . . elevatur etiam vapor ⩲ fœtidissimus, cerebro valde noxius, qui, (ut
mihi aliquando non sine periculo contigit), si ad candelam appellat, flammam concipit,
proptereà haec operatio fiat sub dio vel Camino.[2]

There is little doubt that the work was printed from de Mayerne's papers, and
since he died in 1655 he must have observed the inflammability of hydrogen
before Boyle, who was, however, the first to publish a description of it in
1673 (p. 525).

Mayerne mentions the solubility of potassium acetate (*sal tartari dulcis*) in
alcohol,[3] the preparation of corrosive sublimate,[4] white precipitate of mercury
(*praecipitatum album*) for internal use,[5] the sublimation of benzoic acid,[6] and
the use of a mercurial wash.[7] He was the founder of the Distillers Company,
of which Thomas Cademan was the first Master.[8] It gives recipes for various
medicated spirits (liqueurs) and gives 'Usquebach' (whisky) as an Irish name.

In the preface of the 1618 London *Pharmacopœia* Mayerne says:

Although we revere the wisdom of the old masters and have arrayed their preparations, so to speak, in the first line of battle, nevertheless we have not in this book
rejected or disdained the auxiliary troops of the new chemistry, but have granted them
a place, a corner in the rear-guard, so as to have them at the disposal of dogmatic
medicine, that is, ready for service like auxiliaries.

Yet he did not add anything about the uses and attributes of the drugs, since:

From this quiver the itinerant drug peddlers and the quacks, being as ignorant as
they are unscrupulous, equip themselves for their medical practice, and seizing our
weapons are responsible for the death of the sick, to the detriment of the State. We . . .
write this book only for the learned . . . and for the welfare, not the information, of the
common people.

CROLL

Oswald Croll (Wetter, in Hesse, 1580–? 1609), who studied at Marburg,
Heidelberg, Strassburg and Geneva, and travelled in Italy, France, Germany,
Hungary, Poland and Bohemia, was the physician of Prince Christian of

---

[1] *Opera Medica*, 1700, ii, 5.
[2] *Opera Medica*, 1700, ii, 150; Meyerson, *Rev. Scient.*, 1888, xvi, 665; Jagnaux, i, 360, 386;
said Haller had stated that the *Pharmacopœia* appeared with de Mayerne's *Medicamentorum
formulæ* in 1640, but he adds: 'nous n'avons pas réussi à le retrouver jusqu'ici', and the first
publication, as Stillman, 1924, 357, says, was in 1700.
[3] *Opera*, ii, 3.   [4] *Ib.*, ii, 31.   [5] *Ib., id.*, ii, 38.   [6] *Ib.*, ii, 118.   [7] *Ib.*, ii, 210.
[8] *The Distiller of London. Compiled and set forth by the Special License of the King's Most
Excellent Majesty: For the sole vse of the Company of Distillers of London. And by them to be
duly Observed and Practiced*, London, 1698; the first preface is signed by Theodorau de Mayerne, Regiarum Majestatum Medicus Primum, and Thomas Cademan, Medicus Regemus.

Anhalt-Bernberg (to whom his book is dedicated), and afterwards councillor to the Emperor Rudolph II.[1]

His principal work is *Basilica Chymica* (1609), which probably was the main source from which a knowledge of Paracelsan medicines and teachings became known:

Oswaldi Crollii Veterani Hassi Basilica Chymica, Continens Philosophicam Propria laborum experientia confirmatum descriptionem & usum remediorum Chymicorum selectissimorum è Lumine Gratiæ & Naturæ desumptorum. In fine libri additus est eiusdem Autoris Tractatus nouus De Signaturis Rerum Internis. Francofvrti Apud Claudium Marnium & heredes Joannis Aubrii, 4°, 1609 (x ll. 283 pp. xiv ll. viii ll. 80 pp. viii ll. 24 pp.; ded. dated Prag 1608; engr. t.p. with portrs. of Hermes, Morienus, Geber, Lull, Roger Bacon, and Paracelsus). An undated ed., Frankfurt, Godefrid Tampachius (? 1609 or 1611), viii ll. 283 pp. xii ll. viii ll. 80 pp. viii ll. 20 pp. (Sotheran Cat. 800 (1926), no. 10528; Duveen 150) is sometimes misdated 1608 from the preface, e.g. by Gmelin, Kopp, and Ferguson; Brucker, 1766, IV, i, 675, says: 'Prima satis luculento charactere prodiit Francof., 1606. 4. qua nos vtimur.' It was republ. in 8° in Frankfurt in 1620, in Geneva in 1623, 1631, 1635, 1643 (revised by J. and G. E. Hartmann and J. Michaelis), and 1658, and Cologne in 1710 (Poggendorff, (1), i, 498, says there were eighteen editions to 1658; Sotheran Cat. 872 (1944), 50, correcting Ferguson, i, 185).

French tr. by J. Marcel de Boulene: La Royalle Chymie de Crollivs, 8°, Lyons, 1624, 1627 (engr. t.p. 223 pp. t.p. 210 pp. (last 2 misnumb. 537–8) xxvii ll. index, 119 pp. xiv ll. index), Paris, 1633, Rouen 1634.

English tr.: Bazilica Chymica et Praxis Chymiatricae, or Royal and Practical Chymistry in three treatises. . . . Translated, augmented and inlarged by John Hartman . . . englished by a lover of chymistry, sm. f°, London, 1670; containing a tr. of the Basilica Chymica, the Treatise of Signatures (dated 1669) and Hartmann's Praxis chymiatrica.

German tr. (by Hartmann ?): Basilica Chymica, oder Alchymistisch Königlich Kleynod, 4°, Frankfurt, [1629], iv ll., 248 pp., viii ll. index, 72 pp., iv ll., another ed., 1647, Chymisch Kleynod; with preface referring to the numerous vagrants and cheats in Germany who posed as alchemists (Sotheran Cat. 839 (1934) No. 383; Duveen, 150); re-issued in 1635 bound up with two tracts:

D.O.M.A. Hermetischer Wunderbaum . . . Auss dem grossen Hermetischen Lustgarten zusamengetragen und in sieben Büchlein abgetheilet. Durch Anonymum von Feldtaw . . . , 4°, Frankfurt, Anthoni Hummen, In Verlegung Johann Gottfried Schönwetters, 1635, 4 ll., with D.O.M.A. Crollius Redivivus. Das ist, Hermetischer Wunderbaum . . . , 4 ll. 66 pp. (Ferguson, i, 185; Duveen, 150 — his copy had 8 pp. tract by Feldtaw added, and last item only 8 pp. prelim. instead of Ferguson's 10). The vol. was issued in this form as a whole, sheets of the 1629 ed. being bound up with the two Feldtaw tracts of 1635. In Duveen's copy the name of Feldtaw is given in an old hand as Abraham von Franckenberg.

The book (1609) contains some complimentary verses (two by Elisabeth Johanna Weston, Angla), and a *Praefatio Admonitoria* which appeared separately in English in 1657: Philosophy Reformed and Improved, in Four Profound Tractates: The I., Discovering the Great and Deep Mysteries of Nature, by Osw. Crollius; the other III., Discovering the Wonderfull Mysteries of the Creation, by Paracelsus: . . . both made English by H. Pinnell, 2 vols. 8°, London, 1657 (portr. of Paracelsus); Marks, *Cat.* 27 (193–), No. 104.

After a long preface defending Paracelsan medicine, the book contains a collection of recipes as *Basilica Chymica* and a treatise on Signatures. Four of Croll's uninteresting letters of 1594 (mentioning the alchemist Kelly as Chyleo, nil boni mihi polliceor vereor) were printed by C. G. von Murr.[2] The

---

[1] Barchusen, 1710, 442 f.; James, 1745, i, pref.; Gmelin, (1), i, 290; Sprengel, (1), iii, 362; Kopp, (1), i, 112; Hoefer, (1), ii, 21; Ferguson, i, 185; Thorndike, v, 649.

[2] *Literarische Nachrichten zur Geschichte des sogenannten Goldmachens*, 8°, Leipzig, 1806, 39–43.

Basilica Chymica was partly translated (the Treatise on Signatures in full) by Jollivet Castelot.[1] All references below are to the first edition of 1609.

Croll was dominated by the theosophy of Paracelsus, of which he gives a summary in the preface;[2] he believed that Paracelsus possessed the elixir of life; his early death was a difficulty which Croll got over by the assumption that Paracelsus was poisoned — a ridiculous fable which was refuted by Libavius. Croll's treatise on signatures (*De signaturis internis rerum*) is also Paracelsan.

He says Paracelsus invented the theory of the microcosm (1609, p. 67), wrote in a magic style to conceal his arcana from vulgar alchemists (*ib.*, 77), spurious and adulterine Theophrasts being a most rascally set of men (sceleratissimum hominum genus) (p. 7). Paracelsus opposed sorcery and incantations by magic and supernatural procedure (*ib.*, 262–3). The Qabbalists had three worlds, (1) of the elements, (2) of intellects or angels, and (3) the archetypal, the last containing the ideas and dignities of God, the soul of the world having its seat in the sun (pp. 205–8). Croll accepts Paracelsus' theory of tartar, of which he recognised four kinds: in things growing in the earth, in the sea, in birds and quadrupeds, and in the air and firmament; tartar is in all food and drink and unless voided in excrement becomes the mother of all diseases (mater est omnium morborum). He also accepted the Archeus, which separates the pure and impure in the food (pp. 73–5). He complains of false and idle recipes crammed into medical books and extols his own remedies, acquired by long travels, prayer, experiment, and purchase from iatrochemists (Chymiatris), which he now reveals freely for the benefit of the sick poor and the public, not caring for the anger of many at his breaking the seal of Hermes and revealing such secret remedies (pp. 4–6). More perfect medicines were now known, since the harmony of the macrocosm and microcosm is better understood (p. 75). In his preface Croll quotes the Bible copiously, Paracelsus, Khunrath, Lull, Hermes Trismegistos, etc., and gives from Cornelius Agrippa a list of disputes between medical men, overlooking that between Fachs and Ryff in 1544–5.[3]

The many editions of a work by such a young man as Croll testify to the esteem in which it was rightly held, the practical part being mostly composed in a truly scientific spirit. He describes fulminating gold (*aurum volatile*) (p. 212), silver chloride precipitated and afterwards fused (*luna cornea*) (p. 218), used in alchemical cheating; and mercuric oxide (*arcanum corallinum Paracelsi seu mercurius sublimatus rubeus*) (p. 128). He seems to mention mercurous chloride when he says there are two other most secret ways of treating mercury for medicinal use; the first is the sublimation without addition to a 'very red cinnabar' (in Cinnabarim rubicundissimam — perhaps mercuric oxide), and the second a sublimation with the corrosive spirits of vitriol and salt to a completely insipid crystalline powder (pulvis Crystallinus planè insipidus), which is an excellent purgative — this is mercurous chloride (pp. 129–30).

In a British Museum copy of the second issue of the London *Pharmacopœia*, 7 December 1618, which belonged to Turquet de Mayerne, he has written opposite the description of the preparation of calomel by precipitation (see p. 169) 'Croilly in Basil. Chym. p. 130'. Croll here says:

In secundo modo mortificantur corrosivi spiritus Vitrioli & salis in mercurio sublimato, è quo miro & simplici artificio homogeneo fit pulvis crystallinus planè insipi-

[1] *La Médecine Spagyrique*, Paris, 1912, 35, 97.
[2] *Basilica Chymica*, 1609, pp. 1–110, summarised by Brucker, 1766, IV, i, 677–85.
[3] Thorndike, vi, 212.

dus: Unum è præstantıssımis Catharticis, per se vel cum aliis Catapotiis in uso medico radicaliter omnia noxia è corpore humano pellens. Hoc illis non videbitur mirũ, qui sciunt Mercurium esse Balsamum Naturæ, in quo est virtus Incarnativa & Regenerativa, mirabiliter renovãs & clarificans ab omnibus Impuritatibus.

In the second way may be killed the destructive spirit of vitriol and salt in mercury sublimate, by which wonderful and simple adequate artifice there results a crystalline completely tasteless powder. . . .[1]

Croll boasts of the medical virtues of a mercury preparation which he calls *turpetum minerale* (turpeth mineral) but kept its preparation secret. He points out its violent action, which he tried without success to moderate by long digestion (1609, pp. 122, 135–6, 227). It is basic mercuric sulphate and the preparation was given by Kunckel.[2] Croll describes *antimonium diaphoreticum* (antimonic acid) made from butter of antimony and nitric acid (p. 155), tin acetate (*sal Jovis*) (p. 225), potassium sulphate (*tartarus vitriolatus*; *specificum purgans Paracelsi*) (pp. 115, 143), and succinic acid (*sal succini*) (p. 191). His *sal margaritarum* and *sal corallorum* (pp. 162, 164), made by dissolving pearls and coral in distilled vinegar and evaporating, when a white salt deliquescing in moist air is formed (that from pearls curing sixteen diseases), are calcium acetate, first described by Croll.[3]

A panchymagogon contains twelve ingredients (1609, p. 137). Mumia is made from the corpse of a red-headed man twenty-four years old who has suffered a violent death, cut into bits, sprinkled with myrrh and aloes, soaked in alcohol, dried, and extracted with alcohol 'secundum artem'. The dry part is extracted with olive oil for a month, and the extract mixed with the tincture to form a theriac (p. 257). The zenexton of Paracelsus is stamped into trosichs by a stamp engraved with characters, and the substance is made from dried toads, arsenic, pearls, gems, musk, etc. (pp. 237–42).

HARTMANN

Johann Hartmann (Amberg, 15 January 1568–Marburg, 7 December 1631) was professor of mathematics (1592) and later (1609) of 'Chymiatria' (Iatrochemistry) in Marburg — the first professor of chemistry in Europe.[4] His inaugural oration printed in 1611[5] deals mostly with medical topics, but of the seven disputations following it five are chemical, and one by Rhenanus was republished by him in 1613 as *Solis e Puteo emergentis*. Hartmann wrote a dissertation on opium in which he criticised Libavius.[6] His *Praxis*

---

[1] My copy has written in an old hand in the margin '☿ dulcis' (i.e. calomel); Kopp, (1), 1847, iv, 192, said Croll obscurely (versteckt) described the preparation, and although Urdang, *Chymia*, 1948, i, 93; *Archives*, 1954, xxxiii, 303, claimed that Kopp was wrong and that Turquet de Mayerne first introduced calomel into official therapy, it seems to me that Kopp was correct.

[2] *Laboratorium Chymicum*, 1716, 236.   [3] Thomson, (2), 1807, iii, 63.

[4] Jöcher, ii, 1381; Ferguson, i, 366; Thorndike, viii, 116; Ganzenmüller, 1956, 314; W. in NBG, 1858, xxiii, 471; Gmelin, (1), i, 569.

[5] *Disputationes Chymico-medicæ pleræque sub præsidio Joh. Hartmanni, M.D. et Chymiatriæ in Academia Marpurgensi professoris ordinarii ab aliquot medicine candidatis et studiosis ibidem publicæ censuræ expositæ*, Marburg, 1611 (BN T³¹. 236); tr. *Choice Collection of Chymical Experiments*, 8°, 1682; Thorndike, viii, 116.

[6] *Tractatus Physico-Medicus de Opio . . . publice prælectus Marpurgi anno 1615*, ed. Pelshofer, 8°, Wittenberg, 1635 (175 pp.), q. by Ganzenmüller.

Chymiatrica is a collection of recipes, including antimonial and mercurial preparations:

Iohannis Hartmanni Medicinæ Doctoris et qvondam Chymiatriæ in Academia Marpurgensi Professoris . . . Praxis Chymiatrica Edita à Johanne Michaelis . . . & Georgio Euerhardo Hartmanno Authoris Filio, 4°, Leipzig, 1633 (BN 1033. l. 10); Huic postremæ editione adiecti sunt propter affinitatem materiæ, tres Tractatus noui. I. De Oleis variis Chymicè distillatis. II. Basilica Antimonij Hameri Poppij Thallini. III. Marci Cornachini D. M. Methodus, quæ omnes Humani Corporis affectiones ab humoribus copia, vel qualitate peccantibus, Chymicè & Galenicè curatur, 8°, Frankfurt, P. Chouët, 1647 (631 pp., 33 pp. index; Cornachini Methodus, pp. 112 and index 13 pp.; an inserted sheet (2 pp.) on Methodus in Puluerem) should be present; this is the edition I have used; other eds. mentioned are: 8°, Frankfurt, 1634; Geneva, 1635, 1649, 1659, 1682; 12°, Leyden, 1663; 4°, Frankfurt, 1671; 4°, Nürnberg, 1677; enlarged by Cardilucius, 4°, Nürnberg, 1679 (1082 pp.) and by Conrad Johrenius in his ed. of Hartmann's Opera Omnia Chymica (incl. some unpubl. MSS.), f°, Frankfurt, 1690 (with annotations on Croll); I have seen none of these.

Some of Hartmann's recipes are curious. To cure insanity, mania, melancholy, and madness induced by philtres, he recommends among other things blood drawn from behind the ears of an ass, emetics, holy water, powdered magnet, antimony, spirit of human brain, and a powder made in May to July of the livers of live green frogs (which cured Frederick IV of the Palatinate of epilepsy).[1]

MYNSICHT

Hadrian Mynsicht (Ottenstein, Brunswick, 1603–? October 1638) took the M.D. at Helmstädt under the name of Tribudenius; his real name is said to have been Sümenicht, which he first altered to Symnicht and then transposed to Mynsicht. He was physician to the Duke of Mecklenburg, etc., and Imperial Poet-Laureate 1631. He was a follower of Paracelsus.[2] He composed a *Medico-Chemical Treasure and Arsenal*:

Hadrianus à Mynsicht, Thesaurus et Armamentarium Medico-Chymicum, 4°; Hamburg, 1631; other eds. mentioned are Lübeck, 1638, 1646, 1662; 8°, Rouen, 1651; Frankfurt, 1658, 1675, 1701, 1707; Venice, 1696; Hanau, 1726; 8°, Geneva, 1726; Thorndike ('Armentarium') says Mercklin listed nine eds., incl. two at Lyon not mentioned by Ferguson but omitting Frankfurt, 1658; Thorndike noted an ed. Lyon, 1640, earlier than that of 1645 mentioned by Mercklin. German tr., Stuttgart, 1682; English (Thorndike says by the astrologer Partridge) tr.: Thesaurus et Armamentarium Medico-Chymicum, or a Treasury of Physick with the most secret way of preparing remedies against all diseases . . . faithfully rendered into English. 8°, London, J. M. for A. Churchill, 1682, (viii ll., 377 pp., xvii ll., portr.; Davis and Orioli, *Cat.* 82 (1938), no. 254.

He first gave the preparation of tartar emetic in crystals[3] by boiling cream of tartar (acidum tartarus) with powdered crocus metallorum absinthiacus, which a previous recipe says is formed by roasting 'crude antimony' (the sulphide) with salt of wormwood (potassium carbonate) and washing with water. The filtered solution crystallises in a cold place. The dose is 4 to 6 grains, and it cured nearly all diseases (which he lists). The recipe may[4] have been suggested by Marco Cornacchini, professor of medicine in Pisa, who

[1] *Praxis*, 1647, 55–74.   [2] Ferguson, ii, 122; Thorndike, viii, 84.
[3] *Thes. Armam.*, Rouen, 1651, 15; Geneva, 1726, 13.
[4] Thomson, (2), 1807, iii, 300; Thorndike, vii, 180.

had a powder composed of scammony, tartar, and 'antimonium'.[1] dedicated to Robert Dudley, Earl of Warwick.

Plot[2] says Robert Dudley, of Christ Church, Oxford, titular Duke of Northumberland, 'was the first *Inventor* of the *Pulvis Cornachinus*, being a mixture of *Diagridium*, *Tartar*, and *Diaphoretic Antimony*', with reference to Schroeder, *Pharm. Medico-Chym.*, l. ii, c. 77, but 'Marcus Cornachinus (from whom it has its name) wrote a whole treatise concerning it'.

Mynsicht in the preface to the Thesaurus says that God's grace and his own hard work had revealed to him many new compositions, not perhaps utterly unknown to Hippokrates, Galen, and Paracelsus, but required for new diseases and better adapted to the use of Germans, especially in the Baltic region and lower Saxony. They were also less nasty and violent than those usually prescribed. He begins with a 'mineral unicorn' (which seems to be ferric sulphate), a 'glorius and arcane medicine', previously 'because of the unworthy and ungrateful sons of the world hidden and involved in darkness, lest Spagyric gems would seem to be cast before swine'. His Christian affection and divine prompting induced him to publish it with other mysteries received from the light of nature or grace, his own experience, or the kindness of other Spagyrists. The later editions have an epilogue in which he complains of personal attacks, mentions Pharisees and dogs, and calls repeatedly on God. It is all very German. Mynsicht mentions potassium sulphate (1651, p. 11) as *arcanum duplicatum* or *sal duobus* or *nitrum vitriolatum* (p. 28), silver nitrate as *catharticum argentum* (p. 19), *turbith minerale* (p. 20) precipitated from corrosive sublimate with oil of tartar, calomel (*mercurius dulcis*) (p. 21) made by subliming 6 oz. of corrosive sublimate with 4 oz. of mercury, *magisterium jovis* (p. 25) precipitated by spirit of vitriol from a solution of *cinis stanni* in vinegar, and 'claret' as a medicated wine (p. 314 f.). At the end (pp. 469 f.) is a *Testamentum Hadrianeum de Aureo Philosophorum Lapide* in verse,[3] dedicated to Hermes Trismegistus.[4]

Mynsicht was defended against criticism by Carlo Musitano (Calabria, 5 January 1635–Naples, 1714), priest and physician in Naples, who wrote some iatrochemical works.[5]

---

[1] *Methodus qua omnes humani corporis affectiones ab humoribus copia vel qualitate peccantibus genitæ, tuto, cito, et iucunde chymice et Galenice curantur*, 4°, Florence, 1619 (pref. dated 1620); also repr. in Hartmann, *Praxis Chymiatricae*, Geneva, 1647, sep. pagin., 67 and inserted leaf.

[2] *Natural History of Oxfordshire*, 4°, Oxford, 1705, 305.

[3] In the 1726 ed. it has a separate t.p. and pagination, with alchemical symbols.

[4] Thorndike says it was also published separately, e.g. Venice, 1676, and that Mynsicht published *Aureum seculum redivivum* under the pseudonym Henricus Madathanus in *Musæum Hermeticum Reformatum* in 1635 (*sic*) and 1677, but Ferguson, ii, 61, is doubtful of the authorship and says it was published in German in 1621; the Latin appeared in the 1625 (not 1635) *Musæum Hermeticum*. Since Mynsicht would be aged only 18 in 1621 it seems unlikely that the work is his.

[5] *Pyrotechnia Sophica Rerum Naturalium*, 4°, Naples, 1683 (a catalogue of chemical preparations); *Trutina Medica*, 4°, Venice, 1688, Geneva, 1701, as *Opera Medici Chymico-Practica, seu Trutina Medico-Chymica*; *Mantissa ad Armamentarium Adriani a Mynsicht, accessit de lapide philosophorum*, 8°, Naples, 1697, Geneva, 1701; 4°, Geneva, 1709; *Pyretologia sive de febribus*, 4°, Geneva, 1701; Gmelin, (1), ii, 376, 416; P. in NBG, 1863, xxxvii, 24.

RHENANUS

Johann Rhenanus [Rheinland], b. Cassel, a pupil of Hartmann (his dates are, apparently, unknown), M.D., who worked for the Landgrave Moritz of Cassel, wrote several works[1] including:

Dissertatio Chymiotechnica, in qua Totius Operationis Chymiæ methodus practica clarè ob oculos ponitur, 4°, Marburg, 1610.

Solis e Puteo Emergentis: Sive Dissertationis Chymiotechnicæ Libri tres, 4°, Frankfurt, 1613–15–15, with engraved frontispiece, in three parts with sep. pagin. (80, 31, 24 pp.), the first part, illustrated, dealing with chemical apparatus and preparations, the second with the philosophers' stone, and the third is a 'Clavis & Manuductio in libros Theophrasti Paracelsi, vbi abstrusa explicantur, deficientia supplentur' (all in 24 pp.). This work was reprinted with others in Opera Chymiatrica, quae hactenus in Lucem prodierunt omnia, 8°, Frankfurt, 1635, 1641, 1668, 1676.

He edited the second part of the *Harmonia Imperscrutabilis Chymico-Philosophiæ*, Frankfurt, 1625, the first part being edited by Condeesyanus, Frankfurt, 1625.[2] Other works by or ascribed to Rhenanus are:

Urocriterium Chymiatricum, sive Ratio Chymiatrica Exacte Dijudicandi Urinas ..., 8°, Marburg, 1609, Frankfurt, 1614; Syntagmata Harmoniæ Chymico-Philosophicæ, 8°, Frankfurt, 1625 (probably the Harmonia); Binae Epistolae de Solutione Materiae, Frankfurt, 1635; and Antidotarium Pestilentiale, 4°, Frankfurt, 1613–14 (in German).

Johann Wolfgang Dienheim, professor of medicine at Freiburg im Breisgau, wrote a work on the universal medicine, the quintessence of the four elements, prepared from rain-water.[3]

MYLIUS

Johann Daniel Mylius from Wetterau in Hesse, of whom nothing else seems to be known, whilst still a 'candidate of medicine' prepared a number of works which were mostly printed by Lucas Jennis in Frankfurt.[4] He began by publishing the textbook of Duncan Burnet, 'Scot', which gives concise definitions of substances and operations and preparations, without mystification:

Iatrochymicvs, sive De Præparatione et Compositione Medicamentorvm Chymicorvm artificiosa Tractatus Duncani Bornetti Scoti: In quo methodice, perspicue ac breviter, quidquid ad Iatrochymica pertinet, Candidatis Medicinæ ac Philosophiæ interioris aperitur, 4°, Frankfurt, Jennis, 1616 (BM 1033. h. 40; 115 pp.; Ferguson, i, 133, gives a German tr., Tyrocinium Chymicum, das ist: Von Zubereitung vnd Composition der Chymischen Medicamenten ein ausführlicher vnnd trefflicher Tractat, 8°, Frankfurt, 1618.

In 1618 Mylius published his own treatise in three parts: Opvs Medico-Chymicvm: Continens tres Tractatus sive Basilicas: Qurom prior inscribitur Basilica Medica. Secundus Basilica Chymica. Tertius Basilica Philosophica, 4°, Frankfurt, Jennis, 1618, Index, 1630 (BM 1033. l. 4, 3); should have engraved title and Mylius's portr.; each part sep. pagin.; numerous plates of apparatus. The BM copy has a hand-drawn mystical sheet at the end. The title Basilica is borrowed from Croll, see p. 175.

In 1620 Mylius published an antidotary[5] in four books, on general pharmacy, on some exotic remedies omitted from the *Opus*, Galenical and chemical

---

[1] Ferguson, ii, 263; Thorndike, viii, 117.   [2] Thorndike, iii, 45.

[3] *Medicina Universalis*, 8°, Strassburg, 1610; German as *Taeda Trifida Chimica*, Nürnberg, 1674; Jöcher, ii, 116; Thorndike, vii, 161.

[4] Ferguson, ii, 120; Thorndike, vii, 177; viii, 82.

[5] *Antidotarium Medico-Chymicum Reformatum: Continens Quatuor Libros distinctos*, 4°, Frankfurt, Jennis, 1620, 1044 pp.; Ferguson, ii, 121; Gmelin, (1), i, 519, and Hoefer, (1), ii, 327,

precepts on preparing medicines, and resolving the forms and dividing the medicines of Galenists and chemists, thus making the most of two worlds.

In 1628 he published an 'anatomy of gold', with a sub-title borrowed from Beguin (see Vol. III).[1] and in 1628–9 a universal practical Galeno-Spagyric pharmacopoeia.[2] His most interesting work is his *Reformed Philosophy*[3] in two books, with two engraved title-pages to the first book, illustrations of apparatus, and sixty alchemical figures in blocks of four which were later used by Stolcius, also a 'candidate in medicine'.[4]

FABRE

Pierre Jean Fabre of Castelnaudary in Languedoc, who lived till 1650, M.D. Montpellier, physician in Montpellier and to Louis XIII, wrote a large number of little-esteemed works:[5]

Palladium Spagyricum, 8°, Toulouse, 1624 (6 ll., 394 pp., 9 ll., portr.), Strassburg, 1632; Alchimista Christianus, . . . Christianae mysteria, per analogias Chymicas & Figuras explicantur, 8°, Toulouse, 1632; Hercules pio-chymicus, 8°, Toulouse, 1634; L'abrégé des secrets chymiques, Paris, 1636; Annotationes in Currum Triumphalem Antimonii Fr. Basilii Valentini, Toulouse, 1646; Sapientia Universalis, Toulouse, 1648; Myrothecium Spagyricum sive Pharmacopoea Chymica Occultis Naturae Arcanis, ex Hermeticorum Medicorum scriniis depromptis abunde illustrata, 8°, Toulouse, 1628, 1645–6; and with Chirurgia Spagyrica (first publ. Toulouse, 1628) and Palladium Spagyricum, 8°, Strassburg, 1632; Propugnaculum Alchymiae adversus quosdam misochymicos, philosophos umbratile, naturae humanae larvas, qui se Philosophos profiteri audent, Toulouse, 1645; Sendschreiben an Herzog Friedrich von Holstein über die Dunkelheit der Alchymie, 4°, Nürnberg, 1690, also ed. by Horlacher as Die hellscheinende Sonne am alchymistischen Firmament des hochdeutschen Horizonts, Nürnberg, 1705, and as Res Alchymicorum obscuras extraordinariâ perspicuitate explanans, in Manget, i, 29; L'Abrégé des Secrets Chymiques. Ou l'on void [sic] la nature des animaux, végétaux, et minéraux entièrement découverte, sm. 8°, Paris, 1636; Opera Reliqua, 2 vols. 4°, Frankfurt, 1652, 3 vols. 1656; Universal Weissheit oder Anatomie des Menschen und der Metallen, 4°, Hamburg, 1713 (974 pp. and index); Gmelin, i, 507 (with other works, e.g. Auserlesene in zwey Theile verfasste Chymische Schrifften, Hamburg, 1713, 1730).

His description of the alkahest in the *Sendschreiben an Herzog Friedrich* as 'a pure mercurial metallic spirit closely united with its own natural body (est ergo Liquor iste mercurialis purus Spiritus metallicus corpore suo proprio et naturali conjunctus)'[6] is mentioned by Boerhaave.[7] That the 'salt' obtained from dew and rain[8] was ammonium nitrate is very doubtful.

Edward Bolnest, probably English although nothing is known of him, wrote in defence of chemical remedies:

mention a *Pharmacopœa nova de Mysteriis Medico-Chimicis*, Frankfurt, 1618, which seems to be the *Opus Medico-Chymicum*; Ferguson and Thorndike mention an ed. of Frankfurt, C. Schleichium, 4°, 1638.

[1] *Anatomia Auri sive Tyrocinium Medico-Chymicum*, 4°, Frankfurt (Jennis), 1628.
[2] *Pharmacopoeæ Spagyricæ sive Practicæ Vniuersalis Galeno-Chymicæ*, 2 vols. 8°, Frankfurt, 1628 (989 pp.) and 1629 (896 pp.), the second vol. including (sep. pagin.) Cornacchinus, *Methodus in Pulverem* (146 pp.); BM 1034. b. 8.
[3] *Philosophia Reformata*, 4°, Frankfurt, Jennis, 1622; pref. dated August 1620; BM 1033. i. 7.
[4] Stolcius, *Hortulus Hermeticus Flosculis Philosophorum*, 8°, Frankfurt, Jennis, 1627; first in German, in *Dyas Chymica Tripartita*, 4°, Frankfurt, Jennis, 1625; reprod. in Manget, ii, 895; Ferguson, ii, 410; J. Read, *Prelude to Chemistry*, 1939, 260.
[5] Schmieder, 386; Ferguson, i, 260; Duveen, 201–4; Thorndike, vii, 194.
[6] Manget, i, 303.   [7] *Elementa Chemiae*, Leyden, 1732, i, 867.   [8] Manget, i, 296

Medicina Instaurata, or: A Brief Account of the true Grounds and Principles of the Art of Physick, sm. 8°, London, 1665, with a preface by Marchmont Needham (BM 1035. a. 15). Aurora Chymica, or a Rational Way of preparing Animals, Vegetables, and Minerals for a Physical Use by which preparations they are made most efficacious, safe, pleasant medicines for the preservation and restoration of the Life of Man, 8°, London, 1672 (BM 1035. b. 10); Latin tr., Aurora Chymica. Sive Rationalis Methodus Præparandi Animalia, Vegetabilia, & Mineralia Ad usum Medicum, 8°, Hamburg, 1675; BM 1033. e. 16. (2.).

The *Aurora* describes the preparation of an *arcanum animale* and of quintessences of various things. The third part, on metals, is mostly on gold, mercury, and antimony.[1]

ANTHONY

Francis Anthony or Anthonie (London; 16 April 1550–1623), M.A. of Cambridge (1574), an unlicensed practitioner of medicine who got into trouble with the College of Physicians, wrote a book[2] on potable gold which was criticised by Matthew Gwynne[3] and Thomas Rawlin,[4] and Anthony replied.[5] John Cotta then wrote against him.[6] Anthony's potable gold was revived by Albert Otho Faber (Lübeck, 1641–London, 1678), who became physician to Charles II.[7] He had three kinds of potable gold which could be purchased from him, a gum-like, red as blood; a tincture of this in spirit of wine; and an ounce of tincture in sixteen ounces of another appropriate liquor; and it cured all diseases.[8]

WEIDENFELD

Johann Seger von Weidenfeld, of whom nothing is known, dedicated his work to Boyle, whom he admired for writing plainly and clearly and who received him graciously when he visited England. He wrote on spirit of wine (which he called Lullian), which he thought contained the whole secret of the art. His book is a collection of vegetable and mineral menstrua, divided into simplicia and composita, taken from earlier writers: he mentions that he could not find the alkahest in the writings of Paracelsus:

De Secretis Adeptorum, sive de Usu Spiritus Vini Lulliani Libri IV. Opus Practicum per Concordantias Philosophorum inter se discrepantium, tam ex antiquis, quam modernis Philosophiae adeptae Patribus mutuo conciliatis . . . , atque sic cavere sibi a vagabundis deceptoribus, imaginariis processibus & suarum pecuniarum dilapidatione, 4°, London, 1684 (602 pp.; BM 1035. a. 31); 8°, Leipzig, 1768 (548 pp., Catalogus Menstruorum, 12 pp.; Ferguson, ii, 538, mentions an English tr., London, 1685).

---

[1] Gmelin, (1), i, 510; ii, 230; Ferguson, i, 14; Thomas, in Singer, (1), 1953, ii, 56; Thorndike viii, 97.

[2] *Medicinæ Chymicæ et veri potabilis Auri assertio*, Cambridge, 1610.

[3] *Aurum non Aurum*, 1611.

[4] *Admonitio de Pseudochymicis, sen Alphabetarium Philosophicum in quo refutatur aurum potabile Antonij*, 8°, 1611.

[5] *The Apologie or Defence of a Verity heretofore published concerning a Medicine called Aurum Potabile*, 4°, 1616 (also in Latin); his two tracts were published in Latin in Hamburg, 8°, 1618; Payne, DNB, 1885, ii, 47; Ferguson, i, 36.

[6] *Cotta contra Antonium: or an Ant-Antony: or An Ant-Apology*, sm. 4°, Oxford, 1623.

[7] *Von dem Medicinalischen Auro Potabili*, 4°, zu bekommen zu Franckfurt, Amsterdam, und Dantzig, 1677; in English with a Latin title, *De Auro Potabili*, sm. 4°, London, 1677, and Latin, Frankfurt, 1678 (BM 1034. h. 24. 13.), dedicated to Charles II.

[8] Ferguson, i, 258; H. A. Sampson, *Isis*, 1943, xxxiv, 472–96; Thorndike, viii, 382.

CHAPTER V

BASIL VALENTINE

After 'Geber' (Vol. I) 'Basil Valentine' probably represents the literary forgery which has misled and perplexed chemists for the longest period. Both have been regarded as outstanding figures and if they had lived in the times formerly ascribed to them, their supposed works would have been important. As it is, much of the contents of these was well known from other sources when they actually appeared. In each case the later origin of the works is regarded as established but in neither case is the true author known.[1] All that is known about Basil Valentine is based on statements in works attributed to him. In these he represents himself as a German cleric, a brother of the Benedictine Order, originally of Alsace or 'High Germany above the Rhine', who made voyages to Belgium, Holland and England, a pilgrimage to St. James's (of Compostella, in Spain ?) and in his old age to Egypt.[2] A supposed reference to him by Guaineri of Pavia (d. after 1448)[3] as an unsuccessful alchemist who became a physician[4] is a mistake, since Guaineri does not name him but speaks only of 'quidam eremita alkimista magnus'[5] and praises alchemical medicines.

Basil Valentine is said to have been born in 1394.[6] The first mention of his period is said[7] to be that of J. M. Gudenus:[8]

[1] Berthelot, (3), 279 (mythical, 16 cent.); J. C. Brown, 1913, 194; Cadet, in Spielmann, *Instituts de Chymie*, Paris, 1770, ii, 435–7; Cadet-Gassicourt, in *Biographie Universelle*, Paris, 1811, iii, 483 (17-cent. eds. of works in Paris libraries); Dannemann, 1921, ii, 219 (16–17 cents.); Erhard, in Ersch-Gruber, 1822, Sect. I, Theil, viii, 40; Ferguson, i, 77; ii, 496; Gmelin, (1), i, 136–57; Hoefer, (1), i, 478–91; (2), i, 453–66; Kiesewetter, (2), 1895, ii, 52–68; Kopp, (1), i, 74; (2), iii, 110–28; (4), i, 29; Lasswitz, (1), i, 295–8; Lenglet du Fresnoy, i, 228, 469 (d. 1414); iii, 316; Lippmann, (2), i, 640; ii, 53; iii, 42; B. N. Petraeus, Neue Vorrede in Basil Valentine, *Chymische Schriften*, Hamburg, 1740, i–xciii (unpaged signs. a2–f8 *v*); Picton, 1889, 55; S. Pierce, *Science*, 1898, 169–76; Read, (1), 1936, 183–211, 308–11; H. W. Schaefer, *Die Alchemie*, Flensburg, 1887, 26 (not long before 1600); Schelenz, 1904, 479 (by Thölde); Schmieder, 1832, 197–209; Sprengel, (2), 1827, iii, 425–8; Stillman, 1924, 297, 372; Sudhoff, MGM, 1933, xii, 241; Thomson, (1), i, 44; W. G. Wedel, *Propempticon inaugurale Basilio Valentino*, Jena, 1704, printed in Petraeus's ed. of Basil Valentine, *Chymische Schriften*, Hamburg, 1740, preface, signs. g1–8.

[2] *B. Valentini Chymische Schriften*, ed. Petræus, Hamburg, 1740, 1, 67, 166, 304, 317–18, 328, 343, 420; T. Schaefer, *Über die Bedeutung der Alchemie*, Hamburg, 1885, 6, made him English, which is impossible.

[3] Jöcher, ii, 827; Thorndike, iv, 215.

[4] Gmelin, (1), i, 137; Sprengel, (1), iii, 267; *id.* in Ersch-Gruber, 1819, ii, 416.

[5] Guaineri, *Tractatus de Ægritudinibus*, Pavia, 1488 (BM IB 31340), f. d5 *r*; *id.*, *Opus præclarum ad praxim*, tract. ix, ch. 7, 8°, Lyons, 1525, f. xxviii *r*; Conring, *De Hermetica . . . Medicina*, 8°, Helmstädt, 1648, 385 (q. Guaineri); Kopp, (2), iii, 112.

[6] Boerhaave, (4), 1741, i, 35; Eloy, *Dictionnaire historique de la médecine ancienne et moderne*, 4 vols., 4°, Mons, 1778, i, 278; A. A. Barbier, *Biographie Universelle ou Dictionnaire historique*, Paris, 1833, 193.

[7] Kopp, (2), iii, 114.

[8] *Historia Erfordiensis*, bk. ii, ch. 21; 4°, Dudenstadii [Erfurt], 1675, 129; also in G. C. Joannis, *Rerum Moguntiacarum*, f°, Frankfurt, 1727, iii, 183; the index has the reference: Basilius Valentinus ordinis S. Benedicti in Monte S. Petri clarus.

eadem aetate [MCCCCXIII] Basilius Valentinus in Divi Petri Monasterio vixit, arte medicâ et naturalium indagine mirabilis. Insuper ijs accensetur, quos in augmentum Spei nominant aurum confecisse, sic alienâ dementiâ post saecula fallit, ideo minus culpabilis, quod non nisi decipi amantes facultatibus exuantur,

i.e. Basil Valentine lived about 1413[1] in the St. Peter's Benedictine monastery at Erfurt, was a searching investigator into the wonders of medicine and science, and of whom it was also said he was one of those who hoped to make gold but deceived himself. Gudenus does not give the source of his information. J. Ch. Motschmann[2] says no monk of that name appears in the provincial list at Erfurt or the general lists in the Vatican archives, but such lists do not seem to exist.

The statement that the Emperor Maximilian in 1515 could get no information about Basil Valentine, although he caused full enquiries to be made at Erfurt,[3] is probably fictitious.[4] Petraeus also suggests that Basil Valentine may have lived in the cloister at Walkenried (Cistercian, not Benedictine), not Erfurt, since Möllenbrock (d. 1675)[5] was told by the Abbot of St. Peter's, Erfurt, that Basil Valentine's name was not on the list of monks. Wedel says that about 1668 emblematic figures in the glass windows of a church at Erfurt were shown to the Kurfürst Johann Philipp, who was told that the figures were those used by Basil Valentine to represent the phases of the great art, but there was no trace of them when Wedel wrote in 1704.[6] Vincentius Placcius[7] quotes from a Dr. Waitz (or Weit) that about 1690 the portrait of Basil Valentine with allegorical figures was to be seen in good condition in the church at Walkenried, where the other portraits were largely destroyed.[8] To explain the absence of Basil Valentine's name, the Erfurt list was supposed to have been taken to Sweden in the Thirty Years War, or else he wrote under an assumed name to avoid the disapproval of the Church.[9]

Kopp[10] found no mention of 15–16 cent. manuscripts of works attributed to Basil Valentine in library catalogues, and Sudhoff[11] in 'thousands of manuscripts' came across nothing like the works attributed to Basil Valentine (and to Johann and Isaac Hollandus) before the time of Paracelsus. Kopp said the earliest was one in Munich (Fr. Basilius Valentinus ordinis S. Benedicti. *Fünf gehaime Bücher oder Theil von dem Stain der alten Weisen und andern verborgenen Geheimnissen der Natur*) described in the catalogue as 16–17 cent., which is really early 17 cent.,[12] and there are several 17 cent.[13] The

[1] Hence Lenglet du Fresnoy, i 469, says 'd. 1414' and Poggendorff, (1), i, 112 says 'b. 1413'.
[2] *Erfordia Litterata*, 6 pts. 8°, Erfurt, 1729–32, Samml. III, sect. ii, pp. 390–9.
[3] Morhof, *Epistola ad Langelottum*, Hamburg, 1673, 133; Petraeus, pref. to B.V. *Chymische Schriften*, 1740, fol. 3 r; Schmieder, 1832, 197 f.
[4] Kopp, (2), iii, 112.   [5] Jöcher, iii, 568.   [6] In Petraeus, B.V. *Chym. Schriften*, 1740, f. g5.
[7] *Theatrum Anonymorum et Pseudonymorum*, ed. J. A. Fabricius, 4°, Hamburg, 1708, *De Scriptoribus pseudonymis*, 112; Ferguson, ii, 261.
[8] Motschmann, *op. cit.*, 394 says it was removed in 1690.
[9] A. J. L. Jourdan, *Dictionnaire des sciences médicales: Biographie Médicale*, 7 vols. Paris (Pancoucke), 1820–25, ii, 15–22 (bibl.); Pouchet, *Histoire des sciences naturelles*, 1853, 392 f.: Motschmann says: ne in arte hac, monachis minus competenti et nunc sacris canonibus prohibita, sectatores nancisceretur.
[10] (2), iii, 113.   [11] Q. by Stillman, *Paracelsus*, 1920, 97.   [12] Kiesewetter, (2), 1895, ii, 54.
[13] Hoefer, (1), i, 479; Kopp, (2), iii, 113–14 (one of 1621 in Munich); a German MS. dated 1480 is mentioned by Gmelin, (1), i, 156, but his words leave it doubtful if it was attributed to B.V.

oldest is Basil Valentine, *Goldenes Los aller meiner geheimen Arzneien*, of 1582.[1]

Libavius does not mention Basil Valentine in his *Alchemia* (1597) but frequently quotes him (and Isaac Hollandus) in the commentaries to it and accepts him as genuine.[2] Libavius had attributed[3] the three principles salt, sulphur, and mercury, to Paracelsus, but Van Helmont[4] says Paracelsus was more than a century later than Basil Valentine and borrowed from the latter without mentioning his name. He called the soul of a metal the sulphur or tincture, the body the salt, and the spirit the mercury, which Paracelsus then transferred into the principles of all bodies, suppressing the real author's name and taking the doctrine for his own, since the doctrine of Basil Valentine was not commonly known. Wiegleb[5] thought Paracelsus in his travels collected manuscripts of Basil Valentine.

Becher[6] quotes Basil Valentine 'Monachus Benedictinus', but Stahl doubted his early date,[7] as did Morhof,[8] who thought the published works attributed to him were incomplete. Francis Bacon[9] mentions Basil Valentine among the alchemical authors with a pretended zeal for religion but yet impostors.

Basil Valentine mentions America[10] and speaks of 'die neue Kranckheit der Kriegs-Leute in dieser Zeit',[11] or 'Franzosen',[12] a name used in this sense only from about 1493.[13] He also[14] mentions metal printer's type, not used before the 15 cent.,[15] and tobacco,[16] introduced into Europe by Nicot in 1560. A minor tract[17] refers to a process begun 'in the city of Strasburg . . . the 19. of October, Anno 1605'.

In order to explain why nothing was known until about 1600 of writings supposed to go back to the 14 cent., the manuscript works were said to have been first disclosed when the church at Erfurt was damaged by lightning, when they came to light under a marble tablet on the high altar.[18] Some powder of projection was found with them.[19] As time went on and the works had a good sale, more marble tablets were lifted. The name Basil Valentine is apparently fictitious: Boerhaave[20] said it is composed partly from Greek ($\beta\alpha\sigma\iota\lambda\epsilon\acute{\upsilon}\varsigma$, king)

---

[1] German. Museum, Nürnberg, 961 u; A. Jegel, *A. Med.*, 1933, xxvi, 1 (12).

[2] *Syntagma Alchymiæ Arcanorum*, 1611, Part I, often, usually mentioning Thölde as editor; *ib.*, 1613, Part II, 67: Basilii Valentini Monachi de Antimonio libri si extarunt ante plus quam 200 annos sunt illi ipsi ex quib. Paracelsus potissima sua medicamenta hausit; *id., Pro defensione Syntagmatis Chymici*, 1615, 30, 72.

[3] *Epistolica*, Frankfurt, 1595, i, 187 f.

[4] *Ortus medicinæ*, Amsterdam, 1652, 324.   [5] (3), 1777, pref. 4.

[6] *Physica Subterranea*, Suppl. I, vi; 1738, 323, 341, 344; Suppl. II, 365.

[7] *Von dem Sulphure*, Halle, 1718, 48: Basilius Valentinus kan sein wahres Alter nicht erweisen.

[8] *Epistola ad Langelottum*, Hamburg, 1673, 133; *id.*, (1), P. II, lib. ii, pt. 1, ch. 1; 1747, i, 84.

[9] *Works*, ed. Spedding, 1857–9, iii, 747; v, 523.

[10] *Schriften*, 1740, i, 190.   [11] *Ib.*, i, 393, 400.   [12] *Ib.*, i, 80, and often; see index.

[13] Sennert, *De Chymicorum cum Aristotelicis et Galenicis Consensu ac Dissensu*, 1619, c. xi; *Opera*, Lyons, 1656, i, 224 (qui vixit circa initia morbi Gallici, excitati in Europa circa annum 1493); Lessing, 1838, 358; Kiesewetter, (2), ii, 55; S. J. von Romocki, *Geschichte der Explosivstoffe*, Berlin, 1895, i, 221 (arrived in Germany from Italy *c.* 1480).

[14] *Schriften*, 1740, i, 442.   [15] Hoefer, (2), i, 454.

[16] *Ib.*, ii, 912: Nicotiana . . . Tabacum.   [17] *Last Will and Testament*, 1671, 362.

[18] Title page of the *Grossen Stein der Uralten* (1651) attributed to Basil Valentine; Kopp, (2) iii, 114; in Borrichius, (3), 1697, 30, it is a pillar which was split.

[19] Jöcher, iv, 1406.   [20] (2), 1732, i, 18; (4), 1741, i, 35.

and partly Latin (*valens*, mighty). Toll[1] explained it as: Basilius regalis proles Regali; Valentinus a valendo seu potentia, qua cuncta penetrat.

Jöcher[2] said it had been suggested (wrongly he thought) that Basil Valentine was a fictitious person, J. C. Adelung (Spantekow, Pomerania, 1732 or 1734–Dresden, September 1806)[3] that he was later than Paracelsus. Sprengel[4] thought the *Triumph-Wagen* attributed to Basil Valentine was not later than the 16 cent. (ein Product wenigstens der sechzehnten Jahrhunderts ist). Hoefer[5] said everything points to there never having been a Benedictine monk called Basil Valentine about 1413, and that the pseudonymous author lived at the end of the 15 cent. or perhaps even later. Kopp[6] at first thought the works dated from the second half of the 14 cent., since they were already famous early in the 16 cent., but he later changed his opinion, as will be seen below. Vincentius Placcius[7] suggested that the works of Basil Valentine were written by Thölde, the supposed 'editor' (arbitrari vero se, quendam hoc nomine latitare voluisse ex familia Johann. Thoeldeni Hessi, cujus *Haligraphia* Germanica, sive Beschreibung aller Saltz-Mineralien, Erfurti 1612 in 8 edita Chymiae notitiam non proletariam arguit), and Westrumb[8] was of this opinion.

Nothing appears to be known about Johann Thölde except that he was a councillor (Rathskämmer) and salt boiler (Pfannenherr) of Frankenhausen in Thuringia.[9] Kopp,[10] who says that Hoefer[11] had pointed out that Thölde's *Haligraphia* is practically identical with the *Letztes Testament* attributed to Basil Valentine, at first thought that Thölde edited works of Basil Valentine, would hardly have ascribed such important new chemical material to a mythical person, and seems to have been an honest man. Later, however, Kopp[12] concluded that the works are not of the fifteenth but of the end of the sixteenth or the beginning of the seventeenth century and are 'deliberate forgeries', 'Basil Valentine' being fictitious. Schorlemmer[13] concluded that the works attributed to Basil Valentine were written by Thölde, who published them under a high-sounding fictitious name so that they would have a better sale. The mixture of mystical and practical in the books would appeal to a certain type of reader.

Thölde had published a medical work in 1599,[14] and in 1603 and again in 1612 published a *Haligraphia*, with a dedication to the Dean of Marburg

[1] *Sapientia insaniens sive promissa Chemiæ*, Amsterdam, 1689, q. by Petraeus, *B.V. Schriften*, 1741, pref. f. 3 r; Wedel, *ib.*, f. 91 f. See also Leibniz, 'Oedipus Chymicus aenigmatis Graeci & Germanici', in *Miscellanea Berolinensia*, Berlin, 1710, i, 17 (nomen fictum puto . . . *Basilius* Regem, id est Aurum indicat, *Valentinus* Sanitatem); Latz, *Die Alchemie*, Bonn, 1869, 276, 521; Kiesewetter, (2), 1895, ii, 58.
[2] 1751, iv, 1406.
[3] *Geschichte der menschlichen Narrheit, oder Lebensbeschreibungen berühmter Schwarz-künstler, Goldmacher, Teufelsbanner, Zeichen- und Liniendeuter, Schwärmer, Wahrsager, und anderer philosophischer Unholden*, 8 pts., sm. 8°, Leipzig, 1785–6–7–7–7–8–9–99 (anonymous), 1789, vii, 327; q. by Pagel, *Paracelsus*, Basel, 1958, 277.
[4] (2), iii, 425–8.   [5] (2), 1842, i, 453.   [6] (1), 1843, i, 74 f.
[7] *Theatrum . . .*, 1708, De scriptoribus pseudonymis, 111.
[8] *Kleine physikalisch-chemische Abhandlungen*, Leipzig, 1786, I, ii, 11.
[9] Jöcher, iv, 1138.   [10] (2), 1875, iii, 118.   [11] (1), 1866, i, 481.
[12] (4), 1886, i, 29–33.
[13] Roscoe and Schorlemmer, *Treatise on Chemistry*, 1905, i, 9; 1923, ii, 998.
[14] *Bericht der abschewlichen Kranckheit*, 4°, Erfurt, 1599 (BN Te 891).

Cathedral dated Franckenhausen, 1 January 1603 (words italicised in the titles below are in red):

Haligraphia, Das ist / *Gründliche vnd eigendliche* Beschreibung aller Saltz Mineralien. *Darin von dass Saltzes erster Materia / Vrsprung / Geschlecht / Vnter*-schied / Eigenschafft / wie man auch die Saltzwasser probiren / Die Saltz sol durch vielerley Art künstlich zu gute sieden / durchs Fewer vnd ohne Fewer erreichern / vnd verbessern möge / klerlich gehandelt wird, *Beneben einer Historischen Beschrei*-bung aller Saltzwercke jhrer Vmbsten-de vnd Gelegenheit. *Auch wie man aus allen Metallen vnd* vornembsten Mineralien / dessgleichen aus Thieren / Kreu-tern vnd Gewürtzen jhre Saltz aussiehen / vnd zu Mensch-licher Gesundheit brauchen sol. Menniglich / sonderlich aber denen / so mit Saltzwerck vmb-gehen / am Tag geben / Durch *Johan Thölden* / *HESSVM.* Cvm privilegio. *In Verlegung Jacob Apels* / Buchhendl. Im M. DC. III Jahr. Gedruckt zu Eissleben durch Jacobum Gaubisch. In Vorlegung Jacob Apels Buchhendlers. Anno Christi M. DC. III. (sm. 8°, pp. [48] 316 [1, 1 blank] Register [11, 1 blank]; the BM has two copies, 1033. a. 1; 8632. b. 25, one bound up in old (contemporary) covers with Basil Valentine's *Von der grossen Stein der Vhralten* (1602). Caillet, *Manuel Bibliographique*, 1912, iii, 602 says it was published in Leipzig and gives, incorrectly, 317 pp.; Ferguson, ii, 445, has 361 pp.

Haliographia Das ist: *Gründliche vnnd eigendliche Be*-schreibung aller Saltzmineralien Darinn von des *Saltzes erster Materia / Vrsprung / Geschlecht, / vn*-terschied / Eigenschafft / Wie man auch die Saltzwasser probiren / die Saltzsole durch vielerley art künstlich zu gute sieden / durchs Fewer vnd ohne Fewer erreichern / vnd verbessern möge / klärlich gehandelt wird / *Beneben einer Historischen Beschreibung* aller Saltzwercke / ihrer Vmbstände vnd gelegenheit / *Auch wie man aus allen Metallen vnd* vornembsten Mineralien / dessgleichen aus Thieren / Kräutern vnd Gewürtzen jhre Saltz aussziehen / vnd zu Menschlicher gesundheit brauchen soll. *Männiglich, / sonderlich aber denen / so mit* Saltzwerck vmbgehen / an tag geben / Durch *Johann*: *Thölden* / *Hessum.* Cum Privilegio. In verlegung Jacob Apels / Buchhändl. Im M. DC. XII. Jahr. [Leipzig], sm. 8°, 336 pp. [15, 1 blank], 2 woodcuts; the text is the same as that of the 1603 edition but the pagination and typography are quite different. The copy in the Manchester University Library was Prof. Schorlemmer's, a duplicate from the Stadt-Bibliothek, Leipzig.

The work was published in Latin as by Basil Valentine and without any mention of Thölde:

Haliographia. De Praeparatione, vsu, ac Virtutibus omnium Salium, Mineralium, Animalium, & Vegetabilium, ex Manuscriptis, & Originalibus Fratris Basilii Valentini Ordinis S. Benedicti Collecta: Bononiae, apud Andream Salmincium, 1644, sm. square 8°, 102 pp., engr. t.p., BM 726. b. 1. (2.); BN Te[131]. 160 and 163; mentioned by Hoefer, who (in spite of Kopp's remark, see p. 186) does not attribute it to Thölde but says it is practically identical with 'Basil Valentine's' *Letztes Testament* (VII, p. 192).

In his preface[1] Thölde says he collected his book from good printed and manuscript sources, theological, medical and philosophical, old and new, as well as verbal accounts of many learned and truthful people who had collected secrets in their travels:

dieses Buch von mir zusammen gebracht aus vornemer alter vnd newer Scribentē anzeige / derer eins teils Theologi, eines theils Medici vnd Philosophi gewesen / in gedruckten vnnd geschriebenen Büchern hinderlassen / auch aus vieler hochgelehrter / wahrafftiger Leute bericht / welche durch weiters vielfeltiges reysen hin vnd wieder viel gesehen / vnd in aller hand Künsten / Secreten vnd Heimligkeiten erfahren.

The first three parts deal with salts, the testing of brine and salt-boiling (including the use of pit coal) and descriptions of several salt works. *Sal Elebrot* (Alembroth) is a salt like a mixture of saltpetre and alum found on Mount Olympus in Cyprus.[2] The second chapter of the first part, on salts, alums,

---

[1] *Haliographia*, 1612, 41.   [2] *Ib.*, 1612, 69.

vitriols, etc., is like parts of the third book of the *Letztes Testament*.[1] The fourth part of Thölde's book, after a short introduction[2] is (as Hoefer says) practically the same as substantial portions of the fourth part of the *Letztes Testament*, but arranged in a different order:

Letztes Test. (1740) pp.	*Thölde* (1612) pp.
780–816	201–218 (much contracted)
871–895	219–256
943–950	256–267
919–942	267–300
902–919	301–325
895–901	325–333.

The description with picture of a hydrometer (Probirspindel) in the work[3] is the oldest in a post-classical author. In the introductory verses by J. Tanckius Basil is mentioned:

> Sic tu Mater es autorum, quos, Tholde, sophorũ
> Eruis tenebris, dasq́; videre diem.
> Per te Basilius lucem squallore remoto
> Cernit, Basilii mater os alma tui.[4]
>
> Non condus sis, Basilii monumẽta recondens
> Sed promus, pateat Basilijq́; penu.
> Quo magne Basili à doctis nunc scripta legũtur
> Tanto maior erit gloria Tholde tua.[5]

Kircner[6] says: 'In Basilium Valentinum Theophrasticæ disciplinæ auctorum eruditissimum editum à doctissimo viro Iohanne Thôldio', which Fritz thinks[7] is perhaps the first reference to Paracelsus's supposed plagiarism (welcher den Paracelsus des Plagiats bezichtigt). Fritz thinks Thölde published manuscripts which came into his hands with an eye to the improvement of medicine, but as a layman he attributed them to a fictitious author, and he was not a forger. Sudhoff[8] had a copy of the *Triumph Wagen Antimonii* (1604) which had been autographed by Thölde as its author (doctissimo viro domino M. Georgio Dorbergero dedit Author 21 Julij [1604]); he says Thölde did not edit any more works of 'Basil Valentine' afterwards (but see below). A copy of the 1624 edition bound in vellum with the arms of the owner in 1636 has a note that the author was 'Thölden'.[9]

Lindroth[10] thinks the real author was Joachim Tancke (Tancius) (Perleberg, 9 December 1537–Leipzig, 27 November 1609), professor of anatomy and surgery in Leipzig, who wrote an *Alchimistisch Waitzenbäumlein* (1605), contributed verses to Thölde's *Haligraphia* (p. 187) and a preface to the *Triumph*

[1] *B.V. Schriften*, 1740, 773 f.; Thölde, 1612, 54 f.: Von vieherley Geschlecht vnd vunterschied der Saltz-Mineralien.
[2] 1612, 200: Wie man aus allen Metallen und vornembsten Mineralien, auch Animalien vñ Vegetabilien, ihre Salia extrahirn vnnd bereiten soll.
[3] 1612, 76 and another form, 78.   [4] 1612, 22.   [5] 1612, 28.
[6] In the introductory matter of Thölde's edition of *Von dem grossen Stein der Vhralten*, Zerbst, 1602, A2 r.   [7] *Z. angew. Chem.*, 1925, xxxviii, 325.
[8] *Janus*, 1921, xxv, 120; *Philobiblon* (Vienna), 1933, vi, 163–70; *Isis*, 1938, xxviii, 583; Speter, *ib.*, 1939, xxx, 125 (127).
[9] Read, 1936 (1939), (1), 185.   [10] *Lychnos*, 1940, v, 325.

Wagen Antimonii (1604), and published some works attributed to Basil Valentine in his *Promptuarium Alchemiæ*, 1614.[1]

Tancke also wrote a brief manual of chemical instruction[2] and an alchemical work on the generation of metals.[3] In the first he discusses the preparation of the philosophers' stone by the *via universalis* drawn from true and natural principles, which is easy as compared with the difficult *via particularis*, which often fails. The first proceeds either by the dry way or wet way. The work is obscurely alchemical and cites ancient authors, Paracelsus, and Marcellus Palingenius (i.e. Pier Angelo Manzolli, whose *Zodiacus Vitæ* was printed at Basel in 1537). Tancke also wrote a preface to a collection of medical prescriptions, attributed to Fidejustus Reinneccerus.[4]

A similarity between parts of the works of Basil Valentine and those of Paracelsus has long been remarked.[5] Ferguson[6] and Hommel[7] pointed out that the earlier part of the *Triumph Wagen Antimonii* of 'Basil Valentine' is full of diatribes against physicians in the manner of Paracelsus and suggested that the work was based on a work of Alexander von Suchten,[8] an edition of which was put out by Thölde,[9] but as Neumann[10] pointed out, only glass of antimony, calcined antimony[11] and the regulus made with iron (showing the star: 'signat Stern')[12] are described by Suchten, whose account is full of vague references to a 'mercury of antimony', and the works of 'Basil Valentine' contain much more information.

Morhof[13] said Nicolas Solea had put out a book *vom Ursprung der Metallen* under the name of Basil Valentine (qui sub Bas. Valentini nomine prodiit). Stahl[14] noticed that the first part (chs. 1–49) of the *Letztes Testament* attributed to 'Basil Valentine' was the same as the *Bergwercks-Schatz* or *Büchlein von dem Bergwergk* of Nicolas Soleas or Solea (Zerbst, 1600); the second part in the edition of the *Letztes Testament* published by Dietzel (Strassburg, 1645) is not in the earlier edition by Elias Montanus nor in manuscripts in Stahl's possession. The author is much later than the supposed 'Basil Valentine' (ungleich neuer als der angegebene Basilius Valentinus). Soleas cites Agricola (ch. 39) but his name is carefully left out in the work attributed to 'Basil

[1] Ferguson, i, 78; ii, 426.
[2] *Succincta & brevis Artis Chemiæ Instructio* (in German), 8°, Leipzig, 1605 (106 pp.); BM 1033. f. 10. (1.).
[3] *Metallurgia, das ist: Von der Generation und Geburt der Metallen . . . von einem Philosopho Hermetico beschrieben, und publiciret, durch Joachimum Tanckium D.* in *Chymisch-Unterirdischer Sonnen-Glantz*, Frankfurt and Leipzig, 1728; Ferguson, ii, 428; Thorndike, viii, 105.
[4] *Thesaurus Chymicus Experimentorum centissimorum Collectorum*, Leipzig, 1609; Thorndike, vii, 160.
[5] Sprengel, (1), iii, 267; Dezeimeris, *Dictionnaire historique de la médecine ancienne et moderne*, 4 vols., Paris, 1828–39, i, 301; Guhrauer, *Joachim Jungius und sein Zeitalter*, Stuttgart and Tübingen, 1850, 55; Kiesewetter, (2), 1895, ii, 61; Sudhoff, *Bibliographia Paracelsica*, 1894, 71; *id.*, in Diergart, 1909, 254; Strunz, *Paracelsus*, 1903, 30.
[6] ii, 417, quoting the *Beytrag zur Geschichte der höhern Chemie*, 1785.
[7] *Z. angew. Chem.*, 1919, xxxii, 73.
[8] *De Secretis Antimonii*, Basel, 1575; Suchten, *Chymische Schrifften*, Hamburg, 1680, 229, 268.
[9] *Antimonii Mysteria Gemina d.i. Von den grossen Geheimnussen dess Antimonij*, Leipzig (Apel), 1604 (BM 7510. a. 37); Gera, 1613 (in Lynge's *Katalog 74* (Copenhagen, 1937), no. 546; Schmieder, 279; Waite, *The Secret Tradition in Alchemy*, 1926, 261.
[10] *Z. angew. Chem.*, 1919, xxxii, 184.   [11] *Chym. Schrifften*, 1680, 237.   [12] *Ib.*, 270.
[13] (1), II, ii, 29 (4); 1747, 403; Jöcher, iv, 662.
[14] *Billig Bedencken, Erinnerung und Erklärung über J. J. Bechers Natur-Kündigung der Metallen*, Frankfurt and Leipzig, 1723, 13 f., 16; cf. *id.*, *Von den Saltzen*, Halle, 1723, 306.

Valentine'. Fritz[1] also thinks the work of Nicolas Soleas is the source of the first part of the *Letztes Testament*; the author is perhaps the clerical alchemist Nicolaus Solia of Altenstein in Thuringia who is mentioned in 1566.[2] Petræus[3] commented on the resemblance of the *Letztes Testament* to the book published in 1600 as by N. Soleas and edited by Elias Montanus, who says in the preface that the original MS. was in a hand very like that of Paracelsus,[4] and in 1618 as by Montanus.[5] Another work attributed to Nicolaus Solea[6] is very short and does not correspond with any work of 'Basil Valentine'.

The name 'Theophrastus' (i.e. Paracelsus), which occurs frequently in the work of Elias Montanus, is always omitted in the *Letztes Testament*, and although the numbers and (with occasional slight modifications) titles of the chapters are the same in both, the later chapters have been curtailed in quite an arbitrary way in the *Letztes Testament*, as Petraeus noticed. An edition (Jena, 1626) of the *Letztes Testament* published by Claromontanus, who is perhaps Elias Montanus, contains only parts I and II; all five parts were first published by C. Dietzel (Strasbourg, 1651). All mentions of Paracelsus have been omitted and the text is contracted, but in the Hamburg edition of 1677 (see below) errors in the text have been corrected and the text amplified.

Works

The works attributed to 'Basil Valentine', the oldest all 'edited' by Thölde, are very numerous.[7] Two or more were often printed together and the contents vary in different editions. Many were published in alchemical collections[8] and the bibliography is difficult. Some have very long titles and several title-pages; many have only alchemical interest. The following summary will suffice for our purposes.

I. Ein kurtz Summarischer Tractat, Fratris Basilij Valentini Benedicter Ordens, Von dem grossen Stein der Vralten, daran so viel tausent Meister anfangs der Welt hero gemacht haben . . . durch den Druck ans Liecht bracht. Durch Iohannem Thölden Hessum. Gedruckt zu Eisleben, durch Bartholomæum Hornigk. Anno M.D.IC (1599), sm. 8°, unpaged (Ferguson, ii, 428); 8°, Zerbst, 1602 (BM 8632. b. 25); Leipzig 1602 Stein der Uralten . . . De Microcosmo Von der grossen Heimlichkeit der Welt. Von (Duveen, 46) and 1612 (Sotheran *Cat.* 839 (1934), no. 288); Tractat von dem Grossen der Wissenschafft und verborgenen Geheimnüssen der sieben Planeten, publ. J. Thölden, 8°, *s.l.*, Barthel Voight, 1626 (BN R 53124; contains the second part of the Geheime Bücher oder letztes Testament); 8°, Strasbourg, 1651 (see VII) and 1711 (Schmieder, 205).

[1] *Z. angew. Chem.*, 1925, xxxviii, 325.
[2] A. Rhamm, *Die betrüglichen Goldmacher am Hofe Herzogs Julius von Braunschweig*, Wolfenbüttel, 1883, 4; q. by Fritz.
[3] *B.V. Chym. Schriften*, 1740, pref. f 6 *v*; Klinckcowstroem, MGM, 1926, xxv, 25.
[4] *Ein Büchlein von der Bergwergk . . . Itz durch Eliam Montanum . . . Erstlich an Tag geben*, 4°, Zerbst, 1600, q. by Fritz.
[5] *Bergwerckschatz; Das ist, Ausführlichen vnd vollkommener Bericht Von Bergwercken*, 4°, Frankfurt, 1618; BM 1033. i. 6, having words on opposite pages joined in ink by a previous owner in a most intricate way.
[6] *Philosophische Grund-Sätz von Verbesserung der Metallen*, in *Drey curieuse . . . Chymische Schrifften*, 8°, Leipzig, 1723, beginning: 'Die Wurtzel der Metallen ist ein höchst flüchtigen Geist, aus der Kraft des Feuers'.
[7] Lists in Gmelin, (1), i, 152 f.; Schmieder, 203 f.; Lenglet du Fresnoy, 1742, iii, 316 f.; Ferguson, i, 77 f.; Sotheran *Cat.* 300, items 10105 f.; and Sudhoff, *Acta Paracelsica*, 1930, Heft i, Nachweise 142–7.
[8] See Ferguson, i, 79 f.

1602 ed. includes *Tractat de Microcosmo, oder der kleinen Welt des Menschen, Von der grossen Heimligkeit der Welt*, and *Von der Wissenschaft und verborgenen geheimnisen der sieben Planeten*; the Vier Tractätlein von dem grossen Stäin der uralten weysen Maister und Artzneyen menschlicher Gesundheyt, q. by Hoefer, is part of [Condeesyanus], Dyas Chymica tripartica das ist sechs herrliche teutsche philosophische Tractätlein, 4°, Frankfurt, Luca Jennis, 1625 (BM 1034. h. 21; BN R 8696); the *Stein der Uhralten* and the *Zwölff Schlüssel* are in the third part of the *Aurei Velleris oder Der Güldin Schatz und Kunstkammer*, Tractatus III, *s.l.*, deliberately antedated 1600 (Read, (1), 1936, 300). This is quite a different work from the *Aureum Vellus Oder Guldin Schatz vnd Kunstkañer*, Rorschach, 1598 (and later eds.) which does not contain the treatises. The *Von dem grossen Stein* ends with alchemical poems, some quoted by Kopp, (4), ii, 13. It includes twelve 'keys' (*Zwölff Schlüssel*) with allegorical illustrations, one representing the purification of gold by fusion with antimony (no. 1).

Latin in Maier, *Tripus Aureus*, Frankfurt, 1618 and 1749 (pp. 377–432), and Manget, ii, 409–23; English with sep. t.p. dated 1670 with *Letztes Testament*, 1671 (see below), and in *The Hermetic Museum*, ed. Waite, 1893, i, 315–57; French, Les douze Clefs de Philosophie du Frere Basile Valentin, Paris, J. et C. Perier, sm. 8°, 1624 (BM 1135. e. 24) and Paris, Pierre Moët, 1659 (BM 1034. e. 18) and 1660 (BN R 53113–4; 53116–7), with dedic. to Sir Kenelm Digby; these eds. contain also the *Azoth* (see VIII*b*) and the *Traicté de la nature de l'oeuf des Philosophes* of Bernard Trevisan. Repr. in Richebourg's *Bibliothèque des Philosophes Chimiques*, 1741, iii, 1 f., and with 'explanations' by F. Canseliet, Paris, 1956 (*Ambix*, 1957, vi, 55).

In the preface to the 1603 ed. of the *Von der natürlichen und Übernatürlichen Dingen* (see below), Thölde complains that the *Zwölf Schlüssel* (1599), printed at his expense, had been issued in a pirated edition, according to Fritz, Frankfurt and Leipzig, 1601.

II. Von dem natürlichen vnnd vbernatürlichen Dingen. Auch von der ersten Tinctur, Wurtzel vnd Geiste der Metallen vnd Mineralien, wie dieselbe entpfangen, ausgekochet, geboren, verendert vnd vermehret werden. Trewlich eröffnet durch Fratrem Basilium Valentinum, Benedicter Ordens. Vnnd nunmehr aus seiner eigenen Handschrifft in druck publiceret durch Johan Thölden Hessum. 8°, Leipzig, Apels, 1603 (dedication dated 1602) (BM 8630. a. 47) and 1611 (BM 1033. a. 5); 8°, Leipzig, Voigt, 1624 (BM 1033. c. 8).

Latin: Tractatus Chymico-Philosophicus de Rebus Naturalibus & Supernaturalibus Metallorum & Mineralium, sm. 8°, Frankfurt, Seyler, 1676 (BM 1033. f. 38), 64 pp.; 1679 (Ferguson, i, 79).

English: Of Natural & Supernatural Things, tr. Daniel Cable, 8°, London, Moses Pitt, 1671 (BM 8905. a. 9); the title page says with works by Roger Bacon, Isaac of Holland, and Alexander Van Suchten's Of the Secrets of Antimony, but the last is not in the BM copy. Bolton's copy, (1), 1893, 1063, dated 1670, contained it; Duveen, 48, gives Friar Roger Bacon, of the Medicine or Tincture of Antimony, p. 152; Mr. John Isaac of Holland, his Work of Saturn, p. 182; Alex. Van Suchten, of the Secrets of Antimony, sept. t.p. dated 1670, and pagination.

III. De Occulta Philosophia oder von der heimlichen Wundergeburt der sieben Planeten / vnd Metallen / Fratris Basilii Valentini, Benedictiner Ordens / neben einer Taffel der gantzen Philosophischen Weisheit. Itzo ganz new ausgegangen . . . durch Johan Thölden Hessum, 16° (8°?), Leipzig, Jac. Apel, 1603 (Sotheran *Cat.* 832 (1932), No. 5010); 1611 (Ferguson, i, 79) and 1613 (BM 1033. h. 10 (2)).

French: Revelation des Mysteres des Teintvres Essencieles (Essentielles in 1668 ed.) des Sept Metavx. & (et de in 1668) de leurs Vertus Medicinales. Composée en Allemand par F. Basile Valentin, Religieux de l'Ordre de Saint Benoist. Et traduite par le Sieur I. Israel, Medecin, Allemand, sm. f°, Paris, Chez Iacqves de Senlecqve . . . ou . . . Chez Iean Henavlt (Chez le veufve I. de Senlecque, 1668), 1646 (engr. t.p., incl. in v ll., 64 pp., i l. engr. symbols); 4°, 1668 (Duveen, 47), who has also 4°, 1645.

IV. Triumph Wagen Antimonii Fratris Basilii Valentini, Benedicter Ordens. . . . Zu gut publiciret und an Tag geben, Durch Johann Thölden Hessum, Mit einer Vorrede Doctoris Joachimi Tanckij, Prof. in Univ. Leipzig, 8°, Leipzig, Apels, 1604, (264 pp., with 7 tracts by Roger Bacon, Isaac Hollandus, etc., making in all 694 pp. (BM 1033. a. 3) (it contains the first publication of the work *Uralter Ritter-Krieg*, Ferguson, ii, 485); repr. 18°, Leipzig, 1611 (Sotheran *Cat.* 839 (1934), no. 285) and 8°, Leipzig (Voigt), 1624 (BM 1033. a. 6); many other eds. are given, e.g. Leipzig,

1646, 1676, 1684; Nürnberg, 8°, 1676, 1724 (BM 1232. a. 26), 1733, 1752; Frankfurt, 8°, 1770.

Latin: Currus triumphalis Antimonii . . . e Germanico in Latinum versum, by Peter John Fabre of Montpellier, 8°, Toulouse, 1646 (BM 1033. a. 8. (1.), pp. xxvi, 398); with Roger Bacon, De oleo Stibii (p. 116), and Basil Valentine, Conclusiones (p. 294).

Theodori Kerckringii Doctoris Medici Commentarivs In Cvrrvm Trivumphalem Antimonii Basilii Valentini, à se latinitate donatum, 12°, Amsterdam, 1671, 1685 (both eds., engr. t.p., 10 ll., 342 pp., 9 ll. index; 5 figs. in text, pp. 179, 210, 221, 280, 291); Gmelin, (1), ii, 24, says the commentary was publ. in 1665, but gives no reference.

English: The Triumphant Chariot of Antimony; being a Conscientious Discovery of the many Reall Transcendent Excellencies included in that Minerall, written by Basil Valentine A Benedictine Monke. Faithfully Englished and pnblished (sic) for the Common Good By I. H. Oxon. Printed for Thomas Bruster, 16°, London, 1660 (175 pp. Chemical Society Library; Bolton, (1), i, 1063, gives 1661; a very free translation differing from that of 1678; I. H. is perhaps the astrologer and rosicrucian John Heydon, imprisoned in the King's Bench Prison, Waite, The *Brotherhood of the Rosy Cross*, 1924, 388; Sotheran *Cat.* 806 (1927), No. 14000, but the British Museum Catalogue gives John Harding).

Basil Valentine His Triumphant Chariot of Antimony, with Annotations of Theodore Kerckringius. M.D. With The True Book of the Learned Synesius, a Greek Abbot taken out of the Emperour's Library, concerning the Philosopher's Stone, 8°, London, D. Newman, 1678 (Duveen, 49; the translation of Basil Valentine, but not Synesios, is by Richard Russell: see his translation of Geber, London, 1678, preface);

The Triumphal Chariot of Antimony by Basilius Valentinus with the commentary of Theodore Kerckringius . . . Being the Latin Version published at Amsterdam in the year 1685 translated into English, with a Biographical Preface. London, James Elliott and Co., 1893 (Pp. xxxiii, 284: tr. by A. E. Waite, whose (signed) preface is rather inaccurate); extracts from the earlier editions and illustrations are given by T. L. Davis, *J. Chem. Education*, 1930, vii, 1141; P. S. Wellby, *J. Alchemical Society*, 1914, ii, 91 (only 3 vols. were issued); Schmidt, *Z. angew. Chem.*, 1930, xliii, 964; W. H. Haberling, Der Triumphwagen des Antimons; Therap. Berichte Bayer, Leverkusen, 1927 (not seen).

V. De Microcosmo oder der kleinen Welt des Menschen Leibes, ed. Thölde, 8°, Zerbst, 1602; tr. Angelus, De Microcosmo: deque magno mundi mysterio et medicina hominis, liber geminus, 2 ed., sm. 8°, Marburg, 1609 (BM 1033. f. 15. (1.)); BN R53122–3, 2 pts. 1608–9, sec. pt. with title Aphorismi Basiliani, sive Canones hermetici de spiritu, anima et corpore majoris et minoris mundi, conscripta ab Hermophilo Philochemico, 1608.

VI. Offenbarung der verborgenen Handgriffe auff das Universal gerichtet . . . C. Drebbel Tractatus von Natur der Elementen, etc., 4°, Erffurt, 1624 (BM 1033. f. 15. (4.); contains also Conclusiones oder Schlussreden, in VII, 1651); Dutch, Openbaringhe der verborgener Handgrepen Frat. B. Valentini, 16°, Rotterdam, 1632 (BM 8632. b. 8).

VII. *Letztes Testament.*

Letztes Testament und Offenbahrung der himmlischen und virdischen Geheimnüss . . . zuvor nie in Druck ausgegeben, publiciret durch Georgium Claromontanum, 8°, Jena, H. Eyring and J. Perferts Erben, 1626, 271 pp. (BN R 53119; Schmieder, 206, says it is in Latin, Basilii Testamentum ultimum, and that the German name of Claromontanus was Hellberger), this publication contains only two parts; the same two parts publ. by Dietzel:Letztes Testament, 8°, Strassburg, Caspar Dietzel, 1645 (BM 1033. a. 7; BN R 53120–1, 2 pts.); again by Dietzel including 5 parts: Letztes Testament / Fr. Basilii Valentini Benedictiner Ordens. Darinnen die Geheime Bücher vom Grossen Stein der Vralten Weisen vnd andern verborgenen Geheimnüssen der Natur. Aus dem Original, so zu Erffurt in dem hohen Altar, unter einem Marmorsteinen Täfflein gefunden, nachgeschrieben . . . , 8°, Strassburg, In verlägung Caspari Dietzels, 1651; dedication by Caspar Dietzel dated 12 September 1645, viii ll., 114 pp.; Sec. t.p., Ander Theil / Geheimer Bücher oder Testament . . . , 1651, pp. [115] 116–160; third t.p., Letzten Testaments Dritte Buch oder Theil, 1651, pp. [161] 162–210; fourth t.p., Vierdter Theil Letzten Testaments . . . oder Hand-Griffe, 1651, pp. [211] 212–49, unnumb. pp. a–q, 1 p. Register; fifth t.p., Letzten Testaments

Fünffter Theil, pp. [251] 252–64; sixth t.p., Conclusiones Oder Schluss-Reden . . . vnd Tractaten: Vom Schwefel / Vitriol vnd Magneten . . . , ii ll., unnumb. ll. aa–tt, pp. 265–72, i blank; seventh t.p., Von dem grossen Stein der Uhralten . . . Neben angehängten Tractätlein, iv ll., 1–64 (with Zwölff Schlüssel); t.p. [65], Kurtzer Anhang Vnd klare Repetition oder Widerholung . . . Neben einem Bericht von Quecksilber . . . vnd dem Weins, [65] 66–100; t.p., [101] De Microcosmo, Oder Von der Kleinen Welt dess Menschlichen Leibes, 102–115; Von der grossen Heimlichkeit der Welt, 116–144; Von der Meisterschaft der Sieben Planeten, 144–56 (in verse), ii ll. Register. In the dedication Dietzel says others had copied the works from the 'original' found under the marble tablet for gain (von etlichen Geldsüchtigẽ vmb ein zimlich stück Geldts nachgeschrieben verkaufft worden); this ed. was reprinted by Georg Andreas Dolhopffen and Johann Eberhard Zetzner, 8°, Strassburg, 1667 (156 pp. and Register; BM 1033. a. 10); parts in Johann Hiskia Cardilucius, Magnalia Medico-Chymica, Oder Die höchste Artzney =und Feurkunstige Geheimnisse, 2 vols. Nürnburg, 1676–80. Vol. I contains: Wunderartzney (3 books), pp. 1–296; Introitus Apertus, pp. 297–399; Errata to Cardilucio's ed. of Ercker's Probirbüch, pp. 400 f.; Index; Appendix Introitus Aperti, pp. 1–32. Vol. II contains: Verwandlung der Metallen, pp. 1–56; Handleitung zum himmlichen Rubin, pp. 57–97; Brunn der Chemischen Philosophy, pp. 98–123; Enarratio Methodica, pp. 124–330; Experimenta, pp. 331–41; Vade Mecum Agricola Rhomaeo, pp. 342–78; Ripley's works, pp. 379–710; Fünfter Theil Letzen Testament B. Valent., pp. 711–97; Dritter Theil Letzen Testament B. Valent. etwas anders zu lesen weder in den gedruckten Exemplarien befunden wird, und zwar folgender Gestalt . . . hierauf folget im Manuscript folgende Text = Ordnung, pp. 798–818.

English: Basilius Valentinus, Friar of the Order of St. Benedict. His Last Will and Testament, 8°, London, 1657 (5 pts. anon. translator, BM 8905. aa. 12); Basilius Valentinus, Monk of the Order of St. Bennet: His Last Will and Testament, 12°, London, printed by W. B. for T. Davis, 1658 (separate parts dated 1656; Chem. Soc. Library); The Last Will and Testament of Basil Valentine, Monke of the Order of St. Bennet. Which being alone, He hid under a Table of Marble, behind the High-Altar of the Cathedral Church, in the Imperial City of Erford: leaving it there to be found by him, whom Gods Providence should make worthy of it. To which is added Two Treatises The First declaring his Manual Operations. The Second shewing things Natural and Supernatural. Never before Published in English, 8°, London. Printed by S.G. and B.G. for Edward Brewster, 1671 (tr., with preface, by J[ohn] W[ebster]. This has several works with sep. t.ps. all dated 1670 but continuous pagination; pts 1–2, xii ll., 131 pp.; pt. 3, p. 132; pt. 4, p. 177, pt. 5 (and last), p. 368; Treatise Concerning the Microcosme or the little World, which is Man's body, p. 382; Two Treatises, The first p. 415, the second p. 464, ends in all copies seen (also Duveen, 49) p. 534 'Finis'. The Manual Operations (Handgriffe) is part of the Letztes Testament.

The *Vier Tractätlein* quoted by Hoefer form part of a work by H. Condeesyanus:

Dyas Chymice tripartita, das ist sechs Heerliche Teutsche Philosophische Tractat-lein, Frankfurt, 1625 (BM 1034. h. 21. (1–3.), containing Vier Tractätlein . . . B. Valentini . . . nemblich . . . (1) Handgriffe über die Bereitung des Grossen Steins. (2) Handgriffe, wie er seine Artzneyen gemacht hat. (3) Schluss-réden vom Sulphure, Vitriole, und Magnetstoff. (4) Supplementum oder Zugabe.

VIII. Dubious works attributed in whole or in part to 'Basil Valentine'[1] are:

(*a*) Tractatus Chymicus de Quinta-Essentia, Das ist: Chymisches Werk von dem Fünfften Wesen welches bishero niemals gedruckt . . . wie auch einem andern raren MSto eben dieses Auctoris . . . von Sincero Aletophilo,[2] 12°, Erfurt, 1738 (Sotheran Cat. 806 (1927), no. 13998).

(*b*) Symbolum Basilii Valentini, in Aureliae Occultae Philosophorum partes Duo. Georgio Beato Interprete (*Theatrum Chemicum*, 1659, iv, 498–508 (6 figs.); Manget, 1702, ii, 213–15); German: Occulta Philosophia von den verborgenen Philosophischen Geheimnussen der heimlichen Goldblumen . . . , 4°, Frankfurt, J. Bringer, 1613 (BM 1033. h. 6. (3.); Ferguson, ii, 151). The title of the complete work (*Theatrum Chemi-cum*, iv, 457) is: Ænigma Philosophorum sive Symbolum Saturni, per Parabolas Azoth dilucide ostendens; Latin: Azoth sive Avreliae Occultae Philosophorum, materiam primam, tr. by M. Georgius Beatus, Frankfurt, 1613 (BM 1033. h. 6); French: Azoth,

---

[1] Schmieder, 1832, 208; Ferguson, i, 77.   [2] Christian Friedrich Sattler ?.

ou le moyen de faire l'Or caché des philosophes . . . Reueu, corrigé & augmenté par
Mr. l'Agneau, Medecin, 8°, Paris, Pierre Moët, 1659, 196 pp.; 1624 (BM) (with
the Traicté de La Nature de l'Oeuf of Bernard Trevisan); also in Richebourg, Bibliothèque des Philosophes Chimiques, 1740, iii, 84; repr. by Moët, Paris, 1660, with the
Doux Clefs de Philosophie (see I above).

(c) Chymischer Kern und Auszug der allerfürtreflichsten Schriften Basilii Valentini, 8°, Berlin, 1658.

(d) Basilius Valentinus Redivivus, seu Astrum Rutilans Alchymicum, L. G. de
Knör, 8°, Leipzig, 1716.

(f) Redivivus Fr. Basilius Valentinus, 8°, J. G. Weitbrett, Calwer Amts, 1723 (BM
1232. a. 26. (2.)).

IX. Collected editions:

Chymische Schriften, alle, so viel derer verhanden, anitzo zum Ersten mahl zusammen gedruckt, aus vielen so wol geschrieben als gedruckten Exemplaren vermehret und
verbessert, und in zwei Theile verfasset, 8°, Hamburg, Johann Nauman und Georg
Wolff, 1677 (Chemical Society, BM 1033. a. 11, with cancel of t.p., imperfect, inserted;
pp. 440, Register); 2 ed., same title but 'zum Andern mahe zusammen
gedruckt', Hamburg, Gottfried Liebezeits, 1694 (Chemical Society); 3 ed., same title
but 'zum Dritten mahl zusammen gedruckt', Hamburg, 1700 (Sotheran *Cat.* 832
(1932), no. 5002); 4 ed., same title but 'anjetzo zum Vierdten mahl zusammen
Gedruckt', Hamburg, 1717 (Ehrenfeld, in Diergart, 1909, 68); 5 ed., Chymische
Schriften, aus einigen MSten aufs fleissigste verbessert,[1] mit vielen Tractaten, auch
etlichen Figuren vermehret, und nebst einem völlständigen Register in drey Theile
verfasset: samt einer neuen Vorrede, von Beurtheilung der Alchymistischen Schriften
und dem Leben des Basilii, begleitet von Bened. Nic. Petraeo, Med. D., Fünfte
Edition. Hamburg, bey Gottfried Richter, 1740, 3 vols., 8°, usually bound in two; continuous pagination; 6 ed., Leipzig, 1769 (Chemical Society), is merely a reprint of the
5 ed.; four pages of a fictitious 'life' of the author at the end in the earlier editions are
omitted in the 5 and 6 eds.; the 3 ed. was, apparently, issued again at Hamburg, 2 vols.,
1775 (Marks, *Cat.* 35, No. 122; same title as 1700 edit.); The ed. quoted below is that
of 1740; the pagination is continuous and the titles of the treatises are fixed by the
pages quoted.

Vol. I: 46 + 8 + 24 ll. preliminary.
         1. Von der grossen Stein der Uhralten Weisen: 1–65.
         2. Anhang (Wiederholung) to (1): 66–102.
         3. De Microcosmo oder von der kleinen Welt des Menschlichen Leibes:
            103–18.
         4. Von der grossen Heimlichkeit der Welt und ihrer Artzney: 119–62.
         5. De occulta philosophia oder von der heimlichen Wunder-Gebuhrt der
            sieben Planeten und Metallen: 163–204.
         6. Von der näturlichen und übernaturlichen Dingen: 205–86.
         7. Triumph-Wagen des Antimonii: 287–464. interest begins only p. 364 f.
Vol. II: 8. Die fünff letzte Bücher Basilii betitulieret: sein letztes Testament: 467–
            778 (in 5 books, incl. 9–11 below).
         9. Handgriffe: 779–825.
        10. Offenbahrung seiner verborgenen Handgriffe: 826–56.
        11. V Thiels noch nie gedruckt Wunder Artzney: 857–956.
        12. Conclusiones oder Beschluss-Reden: 957–82.
        13. Zugabe oder Supplementum: 982–92.
Vol. III. 14. Eschenreuters Tractätlein: 993–1048 (full of symbols).
        15. Clavis oder Schlüssel: 1049–56 (contains explanations of symbols in
            14).
        16. Hand-Griffe . . . ex Dyade Chym. H. Condes.: 1057–96.
        17. Schrifften so er mit eigner Hand geschrieben . . . von Particular Lunae
            und Mercurii: 1097–1133.
            Inhalt: xv ll. unpaged (contains full titles of treatises and contents).
            Register: lxiv ll. unpaged.

---

[1] Cadet, in Spielmann, 1770, ii, 436, says it is an identical reprint of the 4 ed. except for a
few words on the t.p.

The only Latin collected edition is: Basilii Valentini Scripta Chymica, 8°, Hamburg, 1700 (Schmieder, 204).

A summary of the chemical facts in the works is given by Wiegleb[1] and by Gmelin;[2] many quotations from them are given by Kopp[3] and by Roscoe and Schorlemmer.[4] The references in the text below are to the 1740 edition of the *Chymische Schriften* (IX above). Since the importance formerly attached to these writings on account of their supposed early date has now receded, a brief summary will be sufficient. The language is an Upper Saxony dialect, the style is a mixture of pious mysticism, intolerable verbosity, and sharp invective very reminiscent of Paracelsus, or of the pseudo-Lull (see Vol. I) at his worst.[5] The first part of the *Triumphal Chariot of Antimony*, for example, is almost unreadable but the later part (p. 364 f.) contains some interesting observations. In the rational parts, the works of 'Basil Valentine' are much clearer and more orderly than those of Paracelsus and show a more scholarly style. Also, after saying that his two medicines, *phalia* for internal and *asa* for external use, were revealed to him by God and no common doctor has any real knowledge, he goes on to recommend 'diligent reading' — but perhaps he means only of his own books (pp. 119 f., 129), whilst Paracelsus disdained books. 'Basil Valentine' in the *Triumphal Chariot* had no better opinion of the orthodox physicians than had Paracelsus (pp. 339–43):

'O you wretched wordly-wise little smart-Alicks, blown up with your seeming knowledge, walking over bottomless mountains in the clouds but not knowing where you will come to rest . . . you infamous men, madder than bacchanalian fools, who will neither learn nor soil your hands with coals, judge not lest ye be judged . . . you titular doctors, you poor wretched people, who write long scrolls of recipes; you, apothecaries, who fill pots as big as those used to boil enough meat to feed a hundred men, . . . you miserable stinking bag of maggots, you poor earthworm, why do you look so intently on the shell and neglect the kernel? . . . But I will put an end to this discourse, lest my tears, which I can hardly restrain, should blot this my writing.'

The author speaks, like Paracelsus, of the spirits inhabiting fire, air, water, and earth (p. 305). He explains that the macrocosm like the microcosm was created by God from nothing, first as a primal matter (materia) which then took on forms: such form and matter is earth and water, which were separated in the creation and everything else, including animals and plants, and air and fire (daraus alle andere Thiere und Gewächse ihren Anfang haben, und durch die andern zwey nachfolgende ihr Leben gewürcket, als durch Luft und Feuer). Life came from the form or matter through motion (Bewegung), which took its first origin in air and its completion by warmth and heat, which is a sulphurous hot spirit (pp. 103–5). 'Basil Valentine', although thus adopting the traditional four elements, laid much more stress on the three principles, salt, sulphur and mercury, of Paracelsus; he was formerly believed to be the inventor of these (see p. 185). All natural things are animal, vegetable and mineral, and minerals contain a mercurial spirit, cold and moist, a sulphurous spirit, warm and dry, and a white salt (p. 201 f.).

[1] (2), 1790, I, i, 100.   [2] (1), i, 136 f.
[3] (1), see index; (2), iii, 123.   [4] *Treatise on Chemistry, passim.*
[5] Gmelin, (1), i, 138; Kopp, (1), i, 76; ii, 236.

His views on the generation of metals (p. 163 f.)[1] are mystical and unintelligible, but some of his diagrams are said to have special occult meanings.[2] He is thoroughly acquainted with chemical apparatus and preparations. He mentions tubulated stoneware retorts (pp. 781, 830) and a copper still with a glass receiver in a tub provided with a tap for running off the warm water (p. 847). He complains that the spirit lamp is too expensive for heating, and the horse-dung bath is condemned as likely to spoil the material (p. 75), although he himself specifies its use (pp. 405, 434).

The author shows an excellent knowledge of mining and metallurgy, including the metals then not very familiar, such as bismuth (Wismuth) or marcasite, which is called a bastard tin (pp. 347, 516, 525, 553, 585, 693, 968), and zinc (p. 347), and minerals such as mispickel (Miss-puckel) (pp. 525, 684 f.), and cobalt (Kobolt) (p. 662) in a curious passage mentioning seven hills of metals, as in the *Book of Enoch*.[3] He also mentions salt mines in Halle (p. 492), alum works in Hungary, Bohemia and Saxony (pp. 491, 778), salt-petre works in Saxony, Thuringia and Hesse (p. 881), vitriol works in South Tyrol, Hungary and the Harz (Goslar) (pp. 491 f., 511, 881), copper mines in the Orient, Hungary, Bohemia, Silesia, Thuringia, Hesse, etc. (p. 673), cement copper in Schmölnitz, Hungary (p. 556), red mountain sulphur (realgar ?) in Tyrol, Tarnowitz and Engadine (p. 694), and metallurgical processes used in Norway, Sweden, and England (pp. 522, 566). The explosive fire damp of mines (böse Wetter) and the choke damp producing asphyxiation (pp. 546, 589 f.)[4] are mentioned. The author thought fire damp was fire concealed in stones (darinn denn solch Feuer innen verborgen ist, so wischt es heraus, und zündet immer fort). The choke damp (stickender Dampf) was heavy like the gas (Dunst) from fermenting wine and extinguished a taper (leidet er kein Licht). Mine gas (böse Wetter) is different from common air since it bears some heavier and poisonous material (sie führet immer etwas mit sich, das da dicker und dem Menschen schädlicher ist). Flame is emitted from the rocks to destroy the dampf. Fish die from suffocation and not from cold when they are frozen in and under ice (p. 415).

The aeolipile (spirone oder Selb-Gebläse) is a metal sphere with a small hole, containing water, and put on a fire with the hole towards the coals. The escaping steam blows the fire better than a bellows (p. 611).[5] The author then describes a hollow ball with a small hole, filled with gunpowder, the hole being closed with cotton soaked in saltpetre, pitch and sulphur. This is put in a shaft or gallery of a mine and kindled, when it drives out the bad air (Dampf) not only by its smoke (Rauch) but also by its impact (Stoss); thrown into water, this contrivance kills fish (p. 614).[6] He describes the purification of gold by

[1] Kopp, (1), i, 77; iii, 99.
[2] E.g., in *Theatrum Chemicum*, 1659, iv, 497, explained by R. Bernoulli, Seelische Entwicklung der Alchemie, in *Eranos Jahrbuch*, Zürich, 1936, 231 f.
[3] Tr. Charles, 1893, 141.
[4] Roseve and Schorlemmer, *Treatise on Chemistry*, 1920, i, 781.
[5] The aeolipile was known to Vitruvius, *Architectura*, i, 6: vim spiritus flantis . . . ex aeolipilis aereis licet ad spicere.
[6] Romocki, *Geschichte der Explosivstoffe*, Berlin, 1895, i, 222; the oldest account of the use of explosives in mines; blasting of rocks by gunpowder was used about 1620 and very common about 1700, in Germany.

fusion with metallic antimony or stibnite (pp. 78, 693, 718, 828; the purification of gold with stibnite is described in the German *Hausbuch* of *c.* 1480; see Vol. I), the reduction of gold to a powder (which he calls a calx) by heating gold amalgam (p. 781), the powder being soluble in 'vinegar' to a purple solution (pp. 828, 833). He speaks of volatilising gold by distillation of its solution in aqua regia (p. 722). Gold dissolves in spirit of salt mixed with saltpetre (p. 783). Gold and silver are separated by nitric acid (Scheidewasser). He obtained an amalgam of gold by adding mercury to a solution of gold chloride ('vitriol of gold') (p. 785): thue wohl purgirten ☿ dreymal so schwer darzu, als der Crystallen gewesen, schwencks eine gute Weile wohl um, so erscheinen viel Farben, und fällt ein Amalgama zu Grund, und das Wasser wird gantz lauter. His 'philosopher's stone' contained gold and it converted 30,000 parts of silver or base metal into gold (p. 985) (spurious ?). Fulminating gold was made by dissolving gold-leaf in a mixture of aqua fortis and sal ammoniac and precipitating with salt of tartar (potassium carbonate), when there was effervescence. The explosive property was removed by vinegar or heating with flowers of sulphur (p. 790 f.): trockne den Gold-Kalck in der Luft, da keine Sonne hin scheinet, und ja nicht über dem Feuer, dann so bald dieses Pulver eine sehr geringe Hitze oder Wärme empfindet, zündet sich solches an, und tuht mercklichen grossen Schaden, dann so würde es flüchtig davon gehen, mit grosser Gewalt und Macht, das ihm kein Mensch würde steuren können.

The silver of Markirchen in Lorraine is the purest (p. 518); that of Sweden contains copper (p. 522), that of Hungary, gold (p. 512). Silver can be purified by antimony (p. 719) and tartar (p. 96). By the action of spirit of salt on silver a 'potable silver' (luna potabilis) is obtained (pp. 72, 797).

The precipitation of copper from solution (e.g. from Hungarian mines) by iron was regarded as a transmutation (transmutirt Martem wahrhafting in Venerem) (pp. 397, 556). The precipitation of one metal by another is classed with all kinds of other precipitations: du solt wissen, wie der Vitriol den ☿ niederschlägt wie das Queck-Silber selbst und das Sal Tartari das ☉, item ♀ und gemein Saltz schlagen das ☽ nieder, ♂ die ♀, eine Lauge von Büchen-Aschen den Vitriol, Essig den gemeinen Schwefel, Eisen, Wein-Stein und Salpeter das Antimonium, und also dieser Sachen vielmehr (for the symbols, see table) (p. 817: the passage is in Thölde's *Haligraphia*, 1612, 92). The author speaks of glass coloured green with copper (p. 509), of silver in Mansfeld and Swedish copper and gold in Hungarian silver (pp. 512, 522). Hungarian iron is brittle because it contains copper (p. 515). Copper acetate (vitriol veneris) was prepared by dissolving verdigris in vinegar and crystallising; on distillation it gave an 'oil' which dissolved iron when water was added (pp. 800, 834 f., 966).

Litharge, red lead, white lead, sugar of lead (pp. 98, 806) — which on distillation gave a red oil (p. 972), and lead chloride, obtained from lead, vinegar and sal ammoniac (p. 806), were well known, and the description of the preparation of sugar of lead (the acetate) is very clear (p. 98): 'Note that pure distilled vinegar poured on calcined (zersthörten) lead and warmed in the water-bath entirely loses its acid and becomes sweet as sugar. If then two or three parts of the vinegar be distilled off and the rest put in a cellar, you will find a beautiful white stone, transparent as crystal.' Glazing of pots with galena is mentioned (p. 686): der Glantz ♄ giebt ohne Vermischung eine sehr schöne und grüne Vergläsung den Hafnern. Tin is brittle when it contains impurities such as iron (p. 688).

Basil Valentine's account of antimony and its compounds is detailed. He describes the preparation of metallic antimony from stibnite, tartar and salt; if iron is added the metal exhibits a star: aus ihm wird aus Weinstein und Saltz ein König gemacht, so man dem Spiess-Glass im Schmeltzen etwas vom Stahl-Eisen zugiebt, giebt es durch einen Handgriff einen wunderbaren Stern, so die Weisen vor mir den Philosophischen Signat-Stern, geheissen haben (pp. 79, 402, 408, 427, 436). The metal is also obtained by fusing equal weights of Hungarian stibnite with tartar and half the weight of saltpetre in a wind furnace (p. 402). The metal is similar to lead but is the true regulus of stibnite (das Bley im Spiess-Glass nicht anders ist denn sein eigener Regulus) (p. 440). Antimony compounds described are glass of antimony from roasted stibnite (pp. 362, 367, 820, 876, etc.); calcined antimony (p. 364); the yellow oxide from stibnite and nitric acid (p. 384); red and white flowers of antimony (a mixture of oxide and sulphide) (pp. 79, 386), and the product of detonating stibnite or metallic antimony with saltpetre (potassium antimonate) (pp. 398, 853).

From the end of the 16 cent. a preparation made by deflagrating stibnite with nitre and fusing was called *antimonium diaphoreticum non ablutum* or later 'Fondant de Rotrou' (a physician of St. Cyr, end of 17 cent.). On washing this with water a residue of *antimonium diaphoreticum ablutum* was left, and on acidifying the solution a precipitate of *cerussa antimonii, magisterium antimonii*, or *materia perlata Kerckringii* (see p. 192). By fusing the first product of deflagration seven times a 'powder of Chevalleray' was obtained. These impure antimonates and antimonic acid were much later investigated by Berzelius and by Fremy.

'Liver (Leber) of antimony' was made by fusing stibnite and raw tartar and washing the product with water (p. 394); the golden sulphide (Sb_2S_5) of antimony was precipitated by adding vinegar to a decoction of stibnite in alkaline lye (so fällt der Schwefel nieder ganz roth) (p. 432). By heating metallic mercury with stibnite, cinnabar (HgS) sublimed into the neck of the retort (p. 1075). (According to Thomson[1] the first to prove that stibnite is a compound of metallic antimony and sulphur was the Dresden chemist E. P. Meuder.)[2] Butter of antimony ($SbCl_3$) is made by distilling stibnite with corrosive sublimate ($HgCl_2$), or with salt and clay, or distilling a solution of stibnite in spirit of salt, when acid first passes over and is followed by the antimony chloride, like thin butter or olive oil (wanns starck durch Anhalten des Feuers fortgetrieben wird, so kömmt eine Materia, wie eine dünne Butter, oder grünlich Baum-Oel) (pp. 393, 396, 404, 419, 421, 432, 888, 1075).

Basil Valentine made extensive use of antimony preparations in medicine, although he recognised that they were very poisonous (so ist das Antimonium

[1] *Ann. Phil.*, 1814, iv, 95.
[2] *Analysis antimonii physico-chymico-rationalis*, Dresden and Leipzig, 1738 (in German); Gmelin, (1), ii, 585.

ein lauter Gifft, und nicht ein geringes, kleines und niedriges Gifft, sondern ein sehr hohes vornehmes Gifft) so that the common people and doctors were afraid of them (p. 350). He made use of emetic antimonial wine and anti-monial tinctures or solutions in vinegar, etc. (pp. 367, 370 f., 427, 435, etc.) which are purging and emetic. He mentions hard antimonial lead and alloys, which can be used for type-metal, seals, amulets, mirrors, bells and gongs (p. 442 f.): als zu den Schrifften, so in den Druckereyen gebrauchet werden.

Mercury was purified by distilling with quicklime (p. 818), and dissolved in aqua fortis to make mercurous nitrate (p. 974): vitriolum mercurii wird leicht-lich gemacht aus einem Aqua fort von Salpeter und Alaun ana destillirt, so er darinn solvirt wird, so scheust er einen Vitriol gantz weiss.[1] Mercury is dis-solved in hot oil of vitriol to form a sulphate which on heating gave a sublimate of oxide (p. 411); sublimed with salt and vitriol it forms corrosive sublimate (p. 838), from a solution of which mercury is precipitated by spiritus vitrioli (containing sulphur dioxide) (p. 816): tröpple etliche Tropffen Spiritus Vitrioli in . . . der schlägts alsobald nieder. Red precipitate (mercuric oxide) is made by dissolving mercury in nitric acid (spiritus salis nitri) and oil of vitriol, evaporating, and repeating three times, then heating more strongly (so findestu den Præcipitat in der allerhöchsten Röthe) (p. 810).

Basil Valentine had a good knowledge of arsenic and its compounds. Hütten-Rauch (furnace smoke), i.e. the oxide driven off in smelting ores, is 'a poisonous volatile bird' but a good medicine. Arsenic is white, yellow (orpi-ment), and red (realgar), and gives metallic arsenic (arsenicum), which is like mercury and antimony (gleichwie ein Banckhard in der Freundschaft zu-gewandt), but useless for the transmutation of metals. It can be sublimed by itself without addition and also with addition in various ways. When it is sub-limed with salt and iron it is as transparent as crystal (in seiner Farbe ist es weiss, gelb und roth . . . es wird sublimirt für sich ohne Zusatz, und auch mit Zusatz vielerley Manier. Allein so es durch Saltz und den Martem auffge-trieben wird, ist es durchsichtig wie ein Crystall anzusehen) (pp. 91 f., 147, 322 f., 494, 693). By fusing white arsenic with saltpetre a deliquescent salt (potassium arsenate) is obtained (p. 896).

Metallic salts are called vitriols and all metals can give them (pp. 740, 784): aus allen Metallen als ♄, ♃, ♂, ♀, ☽ und ☉ selbsten Vitriol-Crystallen wieder können gemacht werden. Green vitriol was obtained by dissolving iron filings in oil of vitriol (which occurs only if water is added — there is no mention of the inflammable gas evolved) (pp. 799, 835). White vitriol (zinc sulphate) was made at Goslar from mine water (p. 556): man sehe die ▽ zu Goslar an, wie einen schönen reinen weissen und rothen Vitriol . . . findet. There are many references to vitriols (index, $2\frac{1}{2}$ pages) and mention of the varieties of alum and alum mines (pp. 491, 778, 885). Manganese dixoide (Braun-Stein) is used for making glass (p. 679): zum andern den Braun-Stein, daraus man Glass und Essen-Farbe machet.

'Basil Valentine' was very familiar with the three mineral acids, which are frequently mentioned and clear recipes for their preparation are given. Spirit

---

[1] 'Saltz' instead of 'Alaun' by mistake in the 1740 ed.

of salt (hydrochloric acid, also called *aqua caustica* and sometimes 'vinegar', Essig) was made by distilling common salt with green vitriol (p. 396): nimm guten Vitriol und Sal commune, in gleicher Viele oder Quantität, und distillir per latus ein Wasser davon.

Nitric acid (aquafort; spiritus salis nitri; spiritus salis petræ; Scheidewasser) was made by distilling saltpetre with alum and green vitriol, or a mixture of 1 part of saltpetre with 3 of powdered pots, with $\frac{1}{2}$ part of water put in the receiver (pp. 783, 794, 796, 900, 1076). The author describes the neutralisation with salt of tartar but does not appear to know that saltpetre is formed. When iron is dissolved in nitric acid (in einem starcken Wasser auflöset oder solvirt) and oil of tartar (potassium carbonate solution) added, great heat is evolved because the contrary natures strike from one another as gunpowder does (die wieder wärtige Naturen stassen Feuer von sich aus, wie Büchsen-Pulver thut). The doctor in long robes can give no explanation of this, since he does not know and must help himself by silence (p. 341).

Aqua regia (aqua regis) was made by distilling saltpetre, sal ammoniac (equal parts) with powdered flint ($\frac{1}{2}$ part) in a tubulated earthen retort and condensing in a luted well-cooled receiver (p. 830); or by mixing aqua fortis with spirit of salt or sal ammoniac (pp. 29, 720, 790).

The descriptions of sulphuric acid are especially complete. Oil of vitriol both white (mercurius philosophorum) and red (sulphur philosophorum) was made by distilling green vitriol previously calcined in a muffle and stirred with an iron hook till it was reddish-brown, in a coated glass retort (pp. 84, 765, 836). The red kind was probably the fuming acid. A third distillate (?), called 'philosophical salt', was perhaps sulphur trioxide. Sulphuric acid was made by burning sulphur under a glass bell (the old method), or better a mixture of sulphur, stibnite and saltpetre was burnt in an alembic, which gave a product (ein Wund-Oel) of the same colour as the acid made by the bell (per Campanam) but more of it and stronger (p. 429):

es wird genommen Antimonium, Schwefel, Saltpeter, gleich viel nach dem Gewichte, verpuffs unter einer Glocken, wie das Oleum Sulphuris oder das Schwefel-Oel, wie solches per Campanam gemacht wird; welcher Brauch dann bey den Alten vor langer Zeit hero bekannt gewesen; doch mercke, das es am besten ist, und der rechte Weg, dass du anstatt der Glocken einen Helm brauchest überzuhängen, daran ein Vorlage geleget, so bekömmt man mehr Oel denn sonsten, ist an der Farbe wie ein ander Oel aus dem gemeinen Schwefel, ist aber . . . einer mächtigern Stärcke und Tugend.[1]

'Basil Valentine's' knowledge of alkalis was behind that of acids, since he thought the alkali in different plant ashes differed in virtue, e.g. that from vine ash was better than that from burnt tartar (pp. 902 f., 870), but he knew that the alkali of the kali plant (largely soda) differs from that of wood ashes (p. 916). He calls native soda sal anatron (p. 778) and is familiar with borax (borras; Venedischen Borras) (pp. 367, 778, 893). He appears to have known that caustic (but not mild) alkali is soluble in alcohol, although the passage is very

---

[1] Wiegleb, (2), 1790, I, i, 100, says the preparation of sulphuric acid from sulphur was first described by Robert St. Clair, *The Abyssinian Philosophy Confuted, or telluris theoria neither sacred nor agreeable to reason*, London, 1697, but it was known long before this time.

obscure (p. 91):[1] Der lebendige Kalck wird gestärcket, feuriger und hitziger gemacht, durch den reinen unverfälschten Wein-Geist, welcher öffters von neuen darauf gegossen und wieder abgezogen wird, darnach das weisse Saltz vom Tartaro darunter getrieben . . . so bekomst du einen sehr höllischen Geist.

He explained the process of caustification of an alkali as due to the transfer of a matter of fire from the quicklime to the alkali (p. 71): das Sal des Wein-steins per se figirt auch hefftig, sonderlich wann die Hitze aus dem lebendigen Kalcke darzu einverleibet wird, dann sie haben beyde zu figiren einen wunderbarlichen Grad.

Solid carbonate of ammonia is made by distilling sal ammoniac (Saltz von Armenia) with very concentrated potassium carbonate solution (oleum tartari), when it separates in crystals (so legt sich alsbald der Spiritus Salis Urinæ im Helm an Crystallisch) (p. 991).[2] Ammonium polysulphide was obtained as a blood-red oil by heating a mixture of stibnite, quicklime, sal ammoniac and common sulphur (pp. 81, 422; cf. Boyle, p. 542). Sal armoniac or Salmiak (ammonium chloride) is often mentioned (pp. 95, 774, 778, 783, 885, and often). Metals (e.g. iron) sublimed with it in the form of 'flowers' (double chlorides) (pp. 95, 778, 975): dieses Saltz greifft an die Metallen sehr begierig, führet andre Geister zu ihnen ein . . . und führet sie mit über sich. Micro-cosmic salt (sal urinæ), or perhaps urea, was obtained by evaporation and crystallisation of urine (p. 923).

Saltpetre contains two elements, fire and air, in excess of the other two, water and earth, also a subtle spirit (ein subtiler Geist steckt in mir). Its greatest enemy is common sulphur, and yet its best friend since it is purified by it.[3] It is very cooling yet its spirit is more heating than anything (mein Geist aber viel hitziger denn einig Ding) (p. 93). By burning sulphur with fused saltpetre 'saltpeter salt' (Saltpeter-Salz), i.e. potassium sulphate, was obtained (p. 881). Flowers of sulphur (Schwefel Flores per se) were obtained by sub-limation and milk of sulphur by precipitation, grey sulphur, and an 'oil', i.e. plastic sulphur (p. 89) (der Schwefel durch ein sehr hoch Instrument mit ziemlichen Feuer über sich getrieben wird, darnach durch lange Zeit sich in loco humido in ein Oel oder Liquorem verwandelt), were known, as well as liver of sulphur (pp. 878, 970), and the solution (balsam) of sulphur in turpen-tine or oil of juniper or linseed oil (pp. 88, 402, 970).

'Basil Valentine' mentions the different coloured varieties of fluorspar, like gems (man findet feine grüne, blaue, weisse, braune Flüsse, wie die Flores Metallorum gewesen seynd . . . sie möchten für Edelsteine vertuschet werden aber sie sind zu weich . . . und sind diese Flüsse ein Mittel zwischen den Steinen und Marcasiten) (p. 605). Calcium chloride was obtained by strongly heating quicklime with common salt or sal ammoniac (pp. 795, 885: also in Isaac Hollandus, p. 207).

A French manuscript,[4] *Macrocosme, ou Traité des Minéraux*, refers to preparations of antimony, a solution of sulphur in aqua fortis (sulphuric acid), transparent sublimed

[1] Kopp, (1), iv, 10.   [2] Wiegleb, (1), 1792, 215: flüchtiges Alkali.
[3] For the method, see Partington, (5), 315.
[4] Bibl. de l'Arsenal, Français 163, f. 47, described by Hoefer, (1), i, 482-5.

arsenic (As_2O_3?), and a soliloquy of saltpetre saying: un subtil esprit est en moy; je sers d'accident nécessaire dans la corrosion des métaux . . . quand la fin de ma vie arrive, je ne puis subsister seul; mes embrasements sont accompagné d'une flamme gaillarde.

Fermentation consists of a number of processes which are clearly described, including the use of hops (Hopffen) as a 'vegetable salt and preservative'; on adding yeast an 'internal inflammation' occurs in the liquid, causing a 'separation' of the turbid from the clear, the impure from the pure. The spirit produced in the fermentation can be separated from the beer (or wine) by distillation: (abermals eine neue Scheidung angestellt werden, durch eine vegetabilische Sublimation, als dass der Spiritus des Weins oder des Biers abgesondert, und durch die Destillation in einen andern Tranck, als in Vinum ardens, bereitet wird). 'Basil Valentine' had seen malt made in Belgium and England in his younger days (pp. 317–19). Ardent spirit is made by distilling beer as well as wine (pp. 319, 847, 869).

Although wine goes into vinegar on putrefaction, the spirit of wine separated by distillation does not pass into vinegar. On distillation of wine the spirit passes over first, but on the distillation of vinegar the watery part (die Wasserkeit) comes over first and the spirit (spiritus, i.e. acetic acid) last (So geht die Wasserkeit am ersten, und der Spiritus am letzten; the boiling-point of acetic acid is higher than that of water) (p. 315). Spirit of wine should burn away without leaving any water when kindled in a dish (pp. 846, 869). It may be concentrated by freezing out water as well as by distillation (Etliche haben den rectificirten Brandt-Wein in der grossen Kälte frieren lassen, vermeynende, die Phlegma werde zu Eyss, und der Spiritus bleibe resolviret und offen) (p. 100; the method is described by Paracelsus, see p. 150). When alcohol (aqua vitæ) burns the sulphur and mercury separate and the sulphur burns (so scheidet sich der Mercurius und der Sulphur Vegetabilis von einander, der Schwefel brennt gantz hitzig, dann es ist ein lauter Feuer, so fleugt der zarter Mercurius hinweg in der Lufft, und gehet wiederum in sein Chaos) (p. 101). By repeated rectification, spirit of wine, the fiery spirit and the true fire and soul of wine (der feurige Geist des Weins ist das rechte Feuer und Seele des Weins) is made stronger and by distillation over salt of tartar its 'vegetable mercury' is separated and the 'true secret spirit' (which would be almost absolute alcohol) obtained (pp. 756 f., 847, 982, 1090).[1]

The rather obscure description of the 'Bereitung des feurigen Wein-Geistes', in which alcohol is imperfectly burnt in a copper apparatus and the volatile products condensed in a cooled receiver, is probably the first mention of aldehyde (p. 847).[2] The preparation of ethyl chloride is clearly described, from 1 part of very concentrated spirit of salt and $\frac{1}{2}$ part highly rectified spirit of wine, distilled three times, each time adding more alcohol, then keeping in a flask for a fortnight or more till it becomes sweet (bis es alles gantz süss worden . . . so ist der Spiritus Salis et Vini bereitet) (p. 786). It is possible that

[1] The correct reading 'sublimirten Tartari' is in the unnumbered *Offenbahrung der verborgenen Handgriffe*, p. 'p', after p. 249 in the collection VII, Strassburg, 1650.

[2] Speter, *Chemische Apparatur*, 1933, xx, 83, q. *Offenbahrung der verborgenen Handgriffe*, Erfurt, 1624, 23.

'Basil Valentine' may have obtained ether, since he says that on heating in a sealed glass for a month 2 parts of highly rectified spirit of wine and 1 of oil of vitriol (then probably distilling): 'the sharpness of the oil of vitriol is removed by the spirit of wine and the two together become a wonderful medicine' (p. 867). Alcohol and nitric acid on mixing inflame (als so man Spiritum Vini in Scheide-Wasser geust, so geschiehet eine grosse Entzündung), but they can be united by distillation 'according to the proper philosophical procedure' (p. 340).

By adding salt of tartar to vinegar there is effervescence, and by evaporation (to fusion ?, perhaps only a concentrated solution) a thick oil (potassium acetate) is obtained (pp. 341, 898).

The preparation of solid potassium acetate (terra foliata secretissima) was described by Philipp Müller (Herzberg, 11 February 1585–Leipzig, 26 March 1659), professor of mathematics and physics in Leipzig.[1] Müller dissolved calcined tartar (potassium carbonate) in vinegar, evaporated to dryness, dissolved in water, filtered, and again evaporated, repeating the process till the terra foliata secretissima was perfectly white (candidissima). He describes a solution of potassium arsenate as butter of arsenic (butyrum arsenici).[2]

Müller's book deals with instruments (with figures), on the material of the philosophers' stone, mercury, sun and moon (gold and silver), the 'work' in seven stages, particular transmutations, rarer preparations (from mercury, sulphur, vitriol, tartar and arsenic), making extracts, distilled waters, balsams, essences, and philosophic salts from vegetable simples, and the extraction of essences and tinctures from stones. It gives amulets and superstitious remedies. Müller also wrote on astrology (criticising Ostwald Croll) and botany.[3] He was criticised as 'rancid butter' by Billich,[4] who also criticised Deguin.[5]

ISAAC AND JOHN ISAAC HOLLANDUS

Of the person or persons called Hollandus very little is known. By those who consider them two persons, Isaac is regarded as the father and John Isaac as the son, or sometimes as uncle and nephew.[6] Attempts to apportion the works between the two persons are incompatible with the titles as printed.[7] Boerhaave,[8] who had a 'very large folio' of their works in manuscript, speaks

---

[1] *Miracula Chymica et Misteria Medica. Libris quinque enucleta* (sic) ... *Studio & Opera Philippi Mulleri Friburg-Brisgoi, Philosoph. & Med. D.*, 12°, Leipzig, 1611, 189 pp. (BM 1036. a. 12; the CUL copy, U*. 8. 164 (b), is without t.p., the catalogue describes it as of Wittenberg; the preface is dated Freiburg in Breisgau, 4 August, 1610; Ferguson, ii, 115, gives the first ed. as 1610, but Sotheran *Cat.* 852 (1938), no. 1524, says 1611 is the first); 12°, Rouen, 1651 (CUL K. 12. 69³; 191 pp.); the recipe is on p. 66 in both eds. Other eds. mentioned are Wittenberg, 12°, 1614, 1616, 1623 (*Miracula & Mysteria Chymico-Medica Libris quinq; ... enucleata ... Editio quarta*, with Beguin, *Tyrocinium Chymicum* and Sendivogius, *Novum Lumen Chymicum* — which Poggendorff, ii, 221, lists as works of Müller), 1656; Amsterdam, 1656, 1659, 1668; Geneva, 1660; 18°, Paris, 1644 (Sotheran *Cat.* 907 (1954), no. 288); Thorndike, vii, 163.

[2] *Mirac.*, 1611 or 1651, 70.   [3] *De Plantis in genere*, Leipzig, 1607.
[4] *Observationum ac Paradoxorum Chymiatricorum Libri Duo*, 4°, Leyden, 1631, 105; Thorndike, vii, 165.
[5] Billich, *De Tribus Chymicorum Principiis et Quinta Essentia*, 8°, Bremen, 1621, 31; Thorndike, viii, 113.
[6] Manget, *Bibliotheca Scriptorum Medicorum*, Geneva, 1731, I, ii, 745: De Isaacô Hollande & Johanne ejus Patre & Filius; Schmieder, 1832, 210; Kopp, (1), i, 73 (Isaac the father and John Isaac the son); *id.*, (2), iii, 109; *id.*, (4), i, 97, 348 f. (relation reversed).
[7] Ferguson, i, 414.   [8] (3), 1727, 20; (4), 1741, 34.

of John and Isaac as father and son or two brothers, whether English (Holland is a common English name) or Dutch it is not easy to say; he had one manuscript of their works in English and one in Dutch interpolated with English. He praised them highly. A Dutch MS. of the works of Isaac of Holland, with notes by Boerhaave, is in the British Museum.[1] Boerhaave and Van der Aa[2] assumed they were natives of Stolkwijk in Krimpenaarwaard.

The dates assigned to the Hollands are very various. They have been put in the thirteenth,[3] fourteenth,[4] and fifteenth[5] centuries. Van der Aa put Isaac the elder early in the 15 cent. and John Isaac about 1440. Van Helmont (d. 1644) spoke of 'Isaac Hollandus and other moderns'.[6]

Neri, who wrote in 1612,[7] says he received a process for making imitation gems 'from Isaac Hollandus during my sojourn in Flanders' and such imitation gems and 'amausa' are mentioned by Hollandus[8] as coloured with metallic oxides. Stahl[9] expressed doubts as to the early date of Hollandus. Bergman[10] says Isaac lived in the beginning of the seventeenth century. The accusation that Paracelsus plagiarised from the works of Hollandus seems to have originated with Penot.[11] Sala[12] names Isaac Hollandus with Arnald of Villanova, Raymund Lully and Paracelsus as one of 'the four most celebrated hermetic philosophers of Europe'.

Boerhaave said: 'they describe all the operations to the most minute circumstances . . . , write excellently of distillation, fermentation, putrefaction and their effects, and seem to have understood at least as much of these matters as any of the moderns.' Van Helmont, however, thought that their preparation of vitriol was wide of the mark (non miserit sagittas ad verum scopum).

Ben Jonson (who served in the army in Flanders, returning to London about 1592) in his play *The Alchemist* (acted in 1610, published in 1612) speaks of: 'the spirit of dead Holland, living Isaac / you'ld swear were in him',[13] which is taken to mean that the son [John] Isaac was living in 1610. Van der Aa quotes

---

[1] J. H. Hampe, *An Experimental System of Metallurgy*, f°, London, 1777, 26.

[2] A. J. Van der Aa, *Biographisch Woordenboek der Nederlanden*, Haarlem, 1860, ix, 33; bibl.; M. Wagenaar, *Isaac Hollandus. De Alchimist van Stolkwijk*, Zeist, c. 1937–8, 348 pp., I have not seen.

[3] Boerhaave, (3), 20 (doubtful); Thomson, (1), i, 43 (says their works are clearer than those of other alchemists of that time); S. Brown, 1858, i, 167.

[4] Borrichius, (3), 1697, 29; Kopp, (1), i, 48, 72; ii, 157, 164, 179; iii, 244, 336; iv, 19, 50; *id.*, (2), iii, 108; *id.*, (4), i, 97.

[5] Boerhaave, (4), i, 34 (dates them 1420); Lenglet du Fresnoy, 1742, i, 231; Spielmann, *Institutiones Chemiæ*, 1766, unpaged Syllabus Auctorum; Schmieder, 1832, 210 (dates them 1425); O. Zachar, *Janus*, 1912, xvii, 335–56; Jorissen, *Chem. Weekbl.*, 1917, xiv, 304, 897; 1918, xv, 1343; *id.*, *Chem. Ztg.*, 1919, xliii, 105.

[6] *Ortus Medicinæ*, 1652, 708; Lippmann, (3), i, 233, among other errors says that Van Helmont did not mention Hollandus.

[7] In Kunckel, *Ars Vitraria Experimentalis*, 4°, Frankfurt and Leipzig, 1679, 125; *Art de la Verrerie, de Neri, Merret et Kunckel*, 4°, Paris, 1752, 195.

[8] *Theatrum Chemicum*, 1659, iii, 472 f.

[9] *Beweiss von den Saltzen*, Halle, 1723, 344, 389.

[10] *Opuscula*, Leipzig, 1787, iv, 112; *Essays*, Edinburgh, 1791, iii, 123 ('seventh' in mistake for 'seventeenth').

[11] See p. 205; Libavius, *Syntagmatis Arcanorum Chymicorum*, Frankfurt, 1613, ii, 103; *Appendix necessarius Arcanorum Chymicorum*, Frankfurt, 1615, 54; Boerhaave, (4), i, 34; Sprengel, (1), 1815, iii, 270.

[12] *Chrysologia*, 1623; *Opera*, 1647, 238.

[13] Act i, scene 1; facsimile reprint, N. Douglas, London, 1927; Lippmann, and Schelenz, misread 'spirit' as 'spirits'.

Kamm to the effect that Isaac was still living in Antwerp in 1601. Goossen van Vreeswyck (1675) said the real name should be Johannes Isaaci Hollandus, 'John son of Isaac'[1] The first mention of 'Isaac the Philosopher' is in the Leyden MS. Voss Chym. No. 3, begun in May, 1567, of which there is a Czech translation made in 1585 by Bawor Rodovsky also in Leyden.[2] A *Liber de minerali lapide et vera metamorphosi metallorum, germanice descriptus*, 1572, of Johann Isaac Hollandus is in the Copenhagen Royal Library.[3]

According to Sudhoff[4] the *Libello de Opere vegetabili et opere animali* of Jo. Isaac Holland, with a fragment *Ex Theoriis* of the same, were first published in 1582 by B. G. Penot (formerly a pupil but later an enemy of Paracelsus)[5] along with a work attributed to Paracelsus, *Centumquindecim curationes experimentaque* (8°, Lyon, 1582) which mentions 'J.I.H.' and his *Opus Vegetabile et Animale* on the title-page and twice in the text, but Sudhoff says it is spurious. It is mentioned by F. Sweertius.[6] There is an English translation.[7] Ganzenmüller[8] found an extract from the *Opus Minerale* in a MS. *Kuntsbuch* compiled in 1562–74 by Beringer von Kotzau, so that the assumed first mention in 1582 of the Hollands[9] is too late.

The references to Hessian glass;[10] striking clocks;[11] 'best sugar of the island of Madeira [Madeva], very white and hard, 10 or 12 lb., more or less',[12] indicate a late date but may be interpolations. Hoefer[13] suggested that the works were by a single author who also compiled the works attributed to Basil Valentine (peut-être sont-ils tous du même auteur).

Works

I. Magistri Joannis Isaaci Hollandi . . . Opera Mineralia, sive de Lapide Philosophico, omnia, duobus libris comprehensa. Nunquam antehac edita, ac nunc primùm ex optimis manu-scriptis Teutonicis exemplaribus fidelissimè in Latinum sermonem translata, à P.M.G., sm. 8°, Middelburg, Richardus Schilders, 1600 (viii ll., 431 pp. (1 blank); BM 8907. a. 26; Ferguson, i, 412).

---

[1] W. P. Jorissen, Isaac de Hollander en Jan Isaacz. de Hollander, *Chemisch Weekblad*, 1917, xiv, 304, 897; *Chem. Ztg.*, 1919, xliii, 105; J. D. Moerman, Uit alchemistische geschriften Isaak en Johan Isaac Hollandus; *Chem. Weekblad*, 1932, xxix, 702.

[2] O. Zachar, *Chem. Weekblad*, 1913, x, 41, with a summary of contents of works of Hollandus; Jorissen, *opp. cit.*

[3] Holgen, *Chem. Ztg.*, 1917, xli, 643, calls it a book; Jorissen, *ib.*, 1919, xliii, 105, says it is manuscript, one of six with dates 1567–72.

[4] *Bibliographia Paracelsica*, Berlin, 1894, 328; *id.*, no. 103, Nachweis zur Paracelsus Lit., in *Acta Paracelsica*, 1930, Heft 1.

[5] Ferguson, ii, 179.

[6] *Athenæ Belgicæ sive Nomenclator infer. Germaniæ Scriptorum*, f°, Antwerp, 1628, 441, 496 (Joannes Isaacvs Batavus. Abdita quaedam de opere vegetabili & animali, 1582, 8; the statement, Jorissen, *Chem. Weekblad*, 1917, xiv, 900, that Sweertius put the author in the sixteenth century is incorrect, since he knows nothing of the date.

[7] *Certaine Secrets of Isacke Hollandus concerning the Vegetall and Animall worke*, printed with Paracelsus's *A hundred and foureteene Experiments and Cures of the famous Physitian . . . Paracelsus . . .*, sm. 4°, London, 1596, pp. 28–54 (first ed. *s.l.e.a.* [1584]); Ferguson, i, 413; ii, 180.

[8] *Glastechnische Berichte*, 1936, xvi, 321; *id., Beitr.*, 1956, 61.

[9] Kiesewetter, (2), 1895, ii, 61; Lippmann, *Chem. Ztg.*, 1916, xl, 605; 1919, xliii, 286, 301; (3), i, 228; Schelenz, *Z. angew. Chem.*, 1917, xxx, I, 195; Diergart, *Chem. Ztg.*, 1919, xliii, 201.

[10] *Opus veget.*, 1667, 232.

[11] *Ib.*, 259: 'nach dem Klockenschlage'; yet striking clocks go back to the early 14 cent.; Sarton, iii, 717.

[12] *Opus veget.*, 1659, 82; not in the other eds.

[13] (1), i, 478.

II. Johannis Isaaci Hollandi de tribus ordinibus Elixiris & Lapidis Theoria, in Bernard Penotus, De Denario Medico, Berne, 1608 (pp. 163–203 (BM 1152. a. 25).

III. D. Magistri Joannis Isaaci Hollandi Opera Mineralia et Vegetabilia, sive de lapide Philosophico, quae reperire potuimus omnia. Nunquam ante hac edita . . . , 8°, Arnheim, apud Joannem Jansonium, 1616 (BM 1033. d. 6; a reprint of I with the dedication to G. Eberhard omitted and a final tract, De Lapide Vegetabili ex Vini (with woodcuts) added; vii ll., 429 pp., 88 pp.; Gmelin, (1), i, 128, and Hoefer, (1), i, 478, dated it 1617).

IV. Opus Saturni M. Johannis Isaaci Hollandi, with the Triumph-Wagen Antimonii of 'Basil Valentine', 8°, Leipzig, 1604, 1624, 1646, 1684; (Gmelin, (1), i, 126, gives Nürnberg, 1676, and Hoefer, (1), i, 678, Nürnberg, 1670; Schmieder says Saturni mean 'of the black' not 'of lead').

English in Basil Valentine, Of Natural and Supernatural Things . . . wherunto is added, Frier Roger Bacon, of the Medicine or Tincture of Antimony; Mr. John Isaac Holland, his Work of Saturn, and [with separate title and pagination] Alex. van Suchten, of the Secrets of Antimony; in two Treatises . . . To which is added B. Valentine's Salt of Antimony . . . translated out of High Dutch by Daniel Cable, 12°, London, 1671–[70].

V. Des hocherleuchteten . . . Johannis Isaci Hollandi Opus Vegetabile. Worin er den treuhertzigen Filiis doctrinae, getreuwarhafften massen umbständlichen unterricht gibt . . . Auss Niederländischen Manuscriptis nach genauer collation mit fleiss verhochdeutschet herausgegebes Vom Sohn Sendivogii, genant J.F.H.S. [J. Harprecht or J. F. Hautnorthon], 8°, Amsterdam, H. Bektio, 1659 (BM 1033. d. 24; Frankfurt, 1667 (?), Ferguson, i, 413; Duveen, 300, is wrong in saying that Ferguson refers to a Latin ed. of 1659).

VI. Das Dritte Theil Des Mineral-Wercks Johannis Isaci Hollandi, Darinn die Figuren seiner geheimen Oefen und eticher andern Gefässen und Instrumenten enthalten . . . , 8°, Frankfurt, 1665; also (pp. 157 f.) Das Büchlein Cabala Isaci Hollandi (BM 1034. b. 15. (1); Duveen, 301, dates it 1666, 'first edition').

VII. Dess weit und breit berühmten Johannis Isaci Hollandi Geheimer und biss dato verborgen gehaltener trefflicher Tractat, von ihm genannt: Die Hand der Philosophen, mit ihren verborgenen Zeichen. Wie auch desselben Opvs Satvrni mit Annotationibvs. Item: Opera Vegetabilia . . . angehenckt worden Ein zwar kleiner, aber überass herrlicher Tractat so von Michael Sendivogii Diener herkomt . . . , 8°, Frankfurt (T. M. Götz), 1667 (MDCLXIVI). The preface to the Opus vegetabile purports to be from a manuscript written by Hollandus himself (p. 170).

VIII. Isaaci Hollandi Tractatus de Lapide Philosophico Oder vom Stein der Weisen, Frankfurt (Götz), 1669; Götz's dedication to Helvetius is dated 20 August, 1669.

IX. Isaaci Hollandi sonst auch Flandri genannt. Curieuse und rare Chymische Operationes . . . aus einem alten Autographo MSCto des Autoris heraus gegeben von R.H.C., Leipzig and Gardeleben, 8°, 1714 (Ferguson, i, 412).

X. Sammlung unterschiedlicher bewährter Chymischer Schriften, namentlich: Joh. Isaaci Hollandi Hand der Philosophen, Opus Saturni, Opera Vegetabilia, Opus Minerale, Cabala, de Lapide Philosophico . . . , 8°, 16 plates, Vienna, 1746 (Chemical Society), 1773 (xvi, 762 pp.; BM 1033. l. 19); Ferguson, i, 413, giving contents and saying first printed in Frankfurt, 1667, presumably VII; a 'newly discovered' part iii of the Opus Mineralis is added.

XI. Isaaci Hollandi Fragmentum de lapide Philosophorum (in Theatrum Chemicum, 1659, ii, 126–9; quite different from VIII).

XII. Fragmenta (in Tractatus aliquot chemici singulares, Ludwig Combach, 12°, Geismariæ, 1647, 33 f.; Ferguson, i, 172).

XIII. Operum mineralium Joannis Isaaci Hollandi sive de lapide philosophico (in Theatrum Chemicum, 1659, iii, 304–515, in 2 books).

XIV. Tractatus Johannis Isaaci Hollandi de Urina quomodo per spiritum ejus omnes Tincturae sint extrahendae. (In Theatrum Chemicum, 1661, vi, 566–8.)

XV. Tractatus Isaaci Hollandi de Salibus & Oleis Metallorum. (Appendix to Stahl, Fundamenta Chymiae, Nürnberg, 1723, 237–55; Schmieder, 1832, 214, says this treatise appeared in 1604, 12°, without place of publication, and a German tr. in 1677, 8°, Budissin, with three other works. There is a German tr. in Alchymia Vera, s.l.e.a. [1608 ?], unpaginated, but p. 142.) Stahl, who often quotes Isaac Holland in his works says[1] that the digestions often lasting a lifetime mentioned by Holland as necessary for maturation, are probably an experimental truth. He regarded the treatise as containing all Holland's innumerable and dispersed treatises in a condensed form.[2]

XVI. Three Exact Pieces of Leonard Phioravant . . . Together with a Book of Excellent Experiments and Secrets . . . Paracelsus his One hundred and fourteen Experiments; With certain Excellent Works of B.G. à Portu Aquitano. Also Isaac Hollandus his Secrets containing his Vegetall and Animall Work. With Quercetanus his Spagyrick Antidotary for Gun-Shot, tr. by J.H., 4°, London, 1652 (2 t.p.'s. The work A Fragment out of the Theoricks of John Isacacus Hollands begins on p. 27 of the last tract; title incorrect in Ferguson, i, 417).

Other works are listed by Borel,[3] Petraeus,[4] Juncker,[5] and Lenglet du Fresnoy.[6] A treatise on amausa (coloured glass pastes) mentioned by Boerhaave[7] and Fourcroy[8] is one of the parts of I.

Lenglet du Fresnoy (who quotes the titles of most of the other works inaccurately) and Kopp,[9] probably from him, refer to a: Libellus rarissimus, dictus secreta revelatio veræ operationis manualis, pro universali opere & Lapide sapientum, sicut filio suo M. Johanni Isaaco Hollando, è Flandria, paterno animo fidelissimo manu tradidit. It may be VII.

Most of the works are in a canting alchemical style and almost unreadable. The *De triplici ordine Elixiris* explains that there are animal, vegetable and mineral forms of the philosophers' stone, and also a compound stone. When the *materia prima* is found, the preparation of the stone is 'a work for women and child's play' (opus mulierum et ludus puerorum).[10] The transmutation of lead, mercury, or silver into gold by projection of the elixir, and the wonderful medicinal virtues of the philosophers' stone, are asserted in detail.[11]

The three principles are mercury, sulphur and salt.[12] A *sal ammoniacum fixum* might be calcium chloride, obtained by heating sal ammoniac with lime, but no details of its preparation are given.[13] The athanor furnace is called the 'Stupha of the philosophers'.[14] The 'Cologne quart' is mentioned,[15] the mark as the unit of weight and the Ave Maria as the unit of time,[16] and the sun in mid-March as a specification of temperature.[17]

Some of the alchemical recipes are clearly described and would give white alloys, as was found by trial.[18] It is said[19] that the ancient chemists did not use the mineral acids (*aquas fortes*) and made little progress; each metal contains in its interior the principle of the tincture of gold or silver and when the elixir is projected on the metal this principle comes to the surface and colours the metal yellow or white. The plant *Chelidonia* converts mercury into gold.[20]

The *Tractatus de urina*[21] refers to the preparation of a salt by evaporating

[1] *Beweiss von den Saltzen*, Halle, 1723, 344. [2] *Ib.*, 390.
[3] *Bibliotheca Chimica*, Paris, 1654, 126 f., reproduced by Gmelin, (1), i, 129.
[4] In pref. to Basil Valentine's *Chymische Schriften*, Hamburg, 1740, i, fol. e 3 r.
[5] *Conspectus Chemiae*, Halle, 1730, i, 18. [6] iii, 191 f.
[7] (1), 1724, i, 152; (4), 1741, i, 179.
[8] *Ency. Méthod.*, Chimie, 1797, iii, 744; Ganzenmüller thinks the name is from Lat. musiva + Arabic article al.
[9] (4), ii, 348, 350.
[10] In Penot, *Denarium Medicum*, 8°, Berne, 1608; Gmelin, (1), i, 129; Kopp, (1), ii, 221, 226.
[11] *Opus Saturni*; VIII, 124 f., 155, 156. [12] *Opus Vegetabile*, 1667, 195.
[13] Bergman, *Opuscula*, Leipzig, 1787, iv, 135. [14] *Hand der Philosophen*, Frankfurt, 1667, 77.
[15] *Theatrum Chemicum*, 1659, iii, 392: *Opus mineralium*, bk. i, ch. 122.
[16] *Ib.*, 449 f.; bk. ii, ch. 45. [17] *Ib.*, 461; bk. ii, ch. 65.
[18] J. C. Brown, *History of Chemistry*, 1913, 179.
[19] *Fragmentum de lapide philosophorum*, *Theatrum Chemicum*, 1659, ii, 126–9.
[20] *Opus Vegetabile*, 1667, 292 f., 315.
[21] *Theatrum Chemicum*, 1661, vi, 566; *Hand der Philosophen*; X, 1746, 86.

urine, calcining the black residue and purifying by crystallisation from water. This may have been a sodium phosphate. It refers to a solution of common salt, sal ammoniac and quicklime in urine, to distilled vinegar, and to spirit of wine. The *Opus mineralia* (bk. i, ch. 72) mentions a salt extracted from the residue (*caput mortuum*) of the distillation of aqua fortis from nitre and green vitriol, crystallised from water.[1] This would be potassium sulphate, which was sold as a secret remedy to the Duke of Holstein-Gottorp in 1673 for 500 Reichthalers by his physician Georg Bassius; hence it was called *panacea holsatica*, *arcanum duplicatum*, or *arcanum Holsteiniense*.[2] It mentions a *spiritus sylvestris* made by distilling white arsenic, salt, and alum, or *spiritus sylvestres ventosi* made by distilling aqua regia and likely to burst the receiver.[3]

KERCKRING

The translator and commentator of 'Basil Valentine' (p. 192), Theodor Kerckring, was, according to Haeser,[4] born in Hamburg in 1640, according to Poggendorff[5] in Amsterdam (date not given) of a Lübeck family; he died in Hamburg, 2 November 1693. He was a pupil of Sylvius de le Boë, was a physician in Amsterdam, Resident of the Grand Duke of Tuscany in Hamburg, F.R.S. 1677, an opponent of Iatrophysics (and also of microscopy), and is known for his anatomical works.[6] Kerckring is said to have invented a method of preserving dead bodies by covering them with varnish, and Kopp[7] says he prepared antimonic acid from potassium antimonate and acid, whence it was known as *materia perlata Kerckringii*:[8] it was, however, previously described by Libavius (1597).[9]

[1] *Theatrum Chemicum*, iii, 353.
[2] Schelhamer, *De Nitro*, Amsterdam, 1709, 190; Gmelin, (1), i, 670 (calls him Bussius); Kopp, (1), iv, 19.
[3] *Theatrum Chemicum*, 1659, iii, 371, 392; probably from Van Helmont.
[4] (1), 1881, ii, 304.   [5] (1), i, 1246.
[6] Roth-Scholtz, *Deutsches Theatrum Chemicum*, 1728, i, pref. 19; Jöcher, ii, 2069; *Phil. Trans.*, 1671, vi, 2162, no. 71 (review of book); Kerckring, *ib.*, 1672, vii, 4018, no. 81.
[7] (1), iv, 108.
[8] *Commentarius in Currum triumphalem Antimonii Basilii Valentini*, 1671, 224.
[9] *Alchymia*, lib. II, tract. ii, 41; 1606, 168: antimonium diaphoreticum.

CHAPTER VI

VAN HELMONT

Thomson[1] says a main service of Paracelsus was 'the high rank to which he raised chemistry, by making a knowledge of it indispensable to all medical men; and by insisting that the great importance of chemistry did not consist in the formation of gold, but in the preparation of medicines . . . for after his time the art of chemistry was cultivated by medical men in general — it became a necessary part of their education, and began to be taught in colleges and medical schools . . . and a great number of new medicines . . . soon issued from the laboratories of the chemical physicians.' He goes on to say[2] that after Paracelsus, Libavius and Angelus Sala 'carefully separated chemistry from the fanatical opinions of the followers of Paracelsus and the Rosicrucians', but it 'underwent a new revolution at this period, which shook the Spagirical system to its foundation; substituted other principles, and gave to medicine an aspect entirely new. This revolution was in great measure due to the labours of Van Helmont,' whose merits were infinitely greater than those of Paracelsus; 'his erudition was great, his understanding excellent, and his industry indefati gable'. His preference for chemical medicines and the uses to which he applied chemical theory 'had a natural tendency to raise chemistry to a higher rank in the eyes of medical men than it had yet reached'.[3] Although some more recent writers have criticised Van Helmont on many grounds, and with some justification, the general opinion of him is favourable.[4]

[1] (1), i, 166. [2] *Ib.*, 179. [3] *Ib.*, 192–3.
[4] J. C. Barchusen, *Historia Medicinæ*, 8°, Amsterdam, 1710, 461–85; Boerhaave, (3), 1727, 30; C. Broeckx, (1), *Essai sur l'histoire de la médicine Belge avant le XIXᵉ siècle*, Antwerp (also Brussels and Mons ?), 1837; (2), *id.*, *Documents pour servir à l'histoire de la bibliographie médicale Belge*, Antwerp, 1858; (3) *id.*, *Interrogations du docteur J. B. van Helmont sur le magnétisme animal*, Antwerp, 1856; J. C. Brown, 1913 (1920), 198; Brucker, 1743, IV, i, 709; P. A. Cap, Notice biographique sur J. B. van Helmont, *Journal de Pharmacie*, Antwerp, 1852, viii, 265, 319; Chevreul, *J. des Savants*, 1850, 71–9 (74), 136–53; Cuvelier, *Koninklijke Vlaamsche Academie voor Taal-en Letterkunde. Verslagen en Mededeelingen*, Ledeberg-Gent, 1930, 101; Daremberg, 1870, i, 465–539; Delacre, (1), 1920, 73–85; (2), *id.*, Le rôle de Van Helmont dans l'histoire des sciences, *Rev. gén. des sciences*, 1924, xxxv, 703; J. E. Dezeimeris, *Dictionnaire historique et critique de la médecine ancienne et moderne*, 4 vols., Paris, 1828–39; 1836, iii, 99; N. F. J. Eloy, *Dictionnaire historique de la médecine ancienne et moderne*, 2 vols., Liége, 1755, ii, 20; 4 vols., Mons, 1778, ii, 478; Florkin, *Bull. Acad. Roy. Méd. Belg.*, 1945, x, 355–69; J. F. Foppens, *Bibliotheca Belgica*, 4°, Brussels, 1739, i, 570–2; Foster, 1901, 128 f.; Gmelin, (1), 1797, i, 524–55; Haeser, (1), 1881, ii, 344; F. M. Van Helmont, in J. B. Van Helmont, *Ortus Medicinæ*, 1652, 14 f., 834; *id.*, BM Sloane MS. 617, ff.142–51; Kiesewetter, (1), 1891, 182; Van Klooster, *J. Chem. Educ.*, 1947, xxiv, 319 (portrait by Lely of H. in Nat. Portrait Gallery, London); Lasswitz, (1), i, 343; L-t, in NBG, 1858, xxiii, 853 (bibl.); J. A. Mandon, J. B. van Helmont, sa Biographie, Histoire critique de ses oeuvres, etc., *Mémoires des concours et des savants étrangers publ. par l'Académie Royale de Médecine de Belgique*, Brussels, 1866, vi, 553–739; Melsens, Note historique sur J. B. van Helmont à propos de la definition et de la théorie de la flamme, *Mém. couronnés et autres mémoires publ. par l'Acad. Roy.*, 8°, Brussels, 1875, xxiv, 1 f. (omits to mention Aristotle and Albertus Magnus); G. A. Mercklein, *Lindenius*

Joan Baptista Van Helmont (Brussels, January 1579–30 December 1644)[1] was descended from a noble and ancient family: his mother was Marie de Stassert, and he belonged to the family of Mérode through his wife. Van Helmont's father died in 1580 and he was the youngest of five children. He studied arts at Louvain until 1594 but took no degree, since he considered academic honours a mere vanity. He then went to the Jesuit school in Louvain, recently formed in spite of the prohibition of the King, the Pope, and the university, where he studied the *Qabbalah* and heard the lectures of Martin Del Rio (Antwerp, 1551–Louvain, 1608) on the topics of his famous book on magic, *Disquisitionum Magicarum* (Louvain, 1599).[2] Still dissatisfied, Van Helmont turned to the mystics Johann Tauler (1290–1361) and Thomas à Kempis (1379–1471), both of whom wrote on the *Imitation of Christ*. He then took up medicine (against the wish of his mother), reading the works of Hippokrates (whom he usually praises), Galen (of whom he speaks with con-

renovatus, sive J. A. van der Linden de scriptis medicis libri duo . . . continuati . . . et purgati, 4°, Nürnberg, 1686, 528; Metzger, *Annales Guébhard-Séverine*, 1936, xii, 140; P. Nève de Mévergnies, Jean Baptiste van Helmont, Philosophe par le Feu, in *Bibl. Fac. Phil. et Lett. Univ. Liége*, Fasc. LXIX, Liége, 1935 (prejudiced, and superficial on the scientific aspects, but bibliographically useful); R. O. Moon, *Proc. Roy. Soc. Med.* (*Sect. Hist. Med.*), 1931, xxv, 23; W. Pagel, (*a*) *Jo. Bapt. van Helmont. Einführung in die philosophische Medizin des Barock*, Berlin, 1930; (*b*) Helmont, Leibnitz, Stahl, *A. Med.*, 1931, xxiv, 19–59; (*c*) *Bull. Soc. Hist. Med.* (Baltimore), Suppl., 1944, no. 2; (*d*) *Isis*, 1942, xxxiii, 621; (*e*) *Nature*, 1944, cliii, 675; (*f*) *Brit. Med. J.*, 1945, I, 59; (*g*) *Isis*, 1946, xxxvi, 277; (*h*) *Osiris*, 1948, viii, 346; (*i*) in Singer, (1), 1953, i, 489; (*j*) *J. Hist. of Med. and Allied Sciences*, 1958, xiii, no. 2; J. R. Partington, *Ann. Sci.*, 1936, i, 359; Prescott, *A. Nat.*, 1929, xii, 70–92; H. S. and M. L. Redgrove, *J. B. Van Helmont*, 1922; Rodwell, *Chem. News*, 1864, x, 195; W. Rommelaere, Études sur J. B. van Helmont, *Mémoires des concours et des savants étrangers publ. par l' Académie Royale de Médecine de Belgique*, Brussels, 1866, vi, 281–541; Sprengel, (1), 1815, v, 22; *id.*, (2), 1827, iv, 292–317; F. Strunz, (1), *J. B. van Helmont*, Leipzig and Vienna, 1907; (2), *id.*, *Die Vergangenheit der Naturforschung*, Jena, 1913, 143 f.; (3), *id.*, *Chem Ztg.*, 1909, xxxiii, 1195, 1209; Süssenguth, *Pharm. Ztg.*, 1937, lxxxii, 859; W. G. Tennemann, 1814, ix, 222; Thorndike, 1958, vii, 218–40; A. J. J. Van de Velde, Helmontiana, I–III: *Koninklijke Vlaamsche Academie voor Taal-en Letterkunde. Verslagen en Mededeelingen*, Ledeberg-Gent, 1929, 453, 716; IV, *ib.*, 1932, 109–22; V, *ib.*, 1936, 339–87; Venel, *Ency. Méthod. Chimie*, 1796, iii, 296; H. de Waele, *J. B. Van Helmont*, Brussels, n.d., 82 pp. (see Pagel, *Isis*, 1948, xxxviii, 248); P. Walden, Von Iatrochemie zur organischen Chemie, *Z. angew. Chem.*, 1927, xl, 1; H. Weiss, *Isis*, 1942, xxxiii, 624; Wiegleb, (1), 1792, 200; Wooton, *Chronicles of Pharmacy*, 2 vols., London, 1910, i, 258 (Portrait of H. as young man, in Bibliothèque Nationale). Publications which I have not seen include: Bibliography of essays on the life and works of H. in *Gazette médicale de Paris*, 1868, 457; J. M. Caillau, *Mémoir sur Jean Baptiste van Helmont et ses écrits*, Bordeaux, 1819; P. d'Elmotte, *Essai philosophique et critique sur la vie et les ouvrages de J. B. van Helmont*, Brussels, 1821 (72 pp.); Fraenkel, *Vita et opiniones Helmontii*, Leipzig, 1837; V. Goethals, *Notice sur J. B. van Helmont*, Brussels, 1840 (49 pp.); F. Giesecke, *Die Mystik Joh. Bapt. van Helmont*, Dissert. Erlangen, 1908; J. J. Loos, *Biographie des Joh. Bapt. van Helmont*, Heidelberg, 1807; Masson, *Essai sur la Vie et les Ouvrages de Van Helmont*, Brussels, 1857; Spiess, *J. B. Van Helmont's System der Medicin*, Frankfurt, 1840.

The numbered references to the separate treatises of Van Helmont given in the footnotes are from the list on p. 215, and the page references to V*b* are to the second edition of his collected writings, *Ortus Medicinæ*, 1652, described on p. 213.

[1] Van Helmont himself says he was born in 1577; 2, V*b*, 14; the entry of baptism in the registers of St. Gudula, Brussels, is on 12 January 1579; this was first supposed by Van de Velde, 1929, 453, 716, to be Old Style and the New Style date 1580, but Cuvelier, 1930, 101, pointed out that the reformed calendar was introduced in 1575, and the date of birth would be late in 1578 or early in 1579, and Van de Velde, 1932, 109, then took early in 1579; a statue of Van Helmont was unveiled on 15 July 1889, on the Place Nouveaux Marché aux Grains in Brussels; var. authors in *Bull. Acad. Roy. Médec.*, Brussels, 1889, iii, 343; a plaque was put in 1889 on No. 72, Rue de Louvain, Vilvorde, supposed to be his house; he died in Brussels, not Vilvorde, where he lived only in the period 1609–16; Mévergnies, 110, 114 (titles), 118–20.

[2] V*b*, 1652, 476; on Del Rio, see Mévergnies, 115, who says the 'Turma Hispanica' mentioned by Van Helmont was a squadron of Spanish Cavalry, probably of the Duke of Alba.

tempt), Avicenna, and a great number of later authors, from whom, he says, he 'noted all that seemed certain and incontrovertible, but was dismayed on reading my notes to find that the pains I had bestowed and the years I had spent were altogether fruitless'. He gave to students books worth 200 crowns, but wished he had burnt them.[1] He had visions, in one of which he saw his own soul in the form of a resplendent crystal,[2] and he regarded all science and wisdom as a gift of God.[3]

He took the degree of M.D. at Louvain in 1609 after ten years of study and travel, in which he visited the Alps, Switzerland, Italy, Spain, France and England (London, 1604–5).[4] D'Elmotte says he was admitted to the Rosicrucian order in Bavaria, but gives no authority.[5] Among other lucrative offers, he refused one from the Elector of Bavaria and one from the Emperor Rudolph II at Vienna made because he was supposed to be an adept.[6] In 1609 he married Margaret Van Ranst, and he says: 'God has given me a pious and noble wife; I retired with her to Vilvorde and there for seven years I dedicated myself to pyrotechny [i.e. Chemistry] and

FIG. 7. J. B. VAN HELMONT (1579–1644).

to the relief of the poor.'[7] Boerhaave[8] says he was told that Helmont was 'wholly taken up in chemical operations, night and day, was scarce known in his neighbourhood, did not apply himself to practice, nor scarce ever stirr'd out of doors'. This may have been during his house-arrest by the Inquisition. The Netherlands was under Spanish rule and in 1567 the Duke of Alba was sent there with an army, instituting a reign of terror. The Spanish Inquisition was flourishing in Van Helmont's time and he came under its notice in the following way.

In 1608 Rudolph Göckel (Goclenius) the younger (Wittenberg, 1572–Marburg, 2 March 1621), who had studied in Marburg, M.D. 1601, and became professor of medicine (1607) and also mathematics (1612) there, wrote many books on Paracelsan medicine, his best known on the magnetic cure of wounds.[9] A Belgian Jesuit, Jean Roberti (1569–1651) attacked this.[10] Van Helmont rashly intervened in the quarrel and in his first published work[11] he

---

[1] 2, 6, 75, 78; V*b*, 14, 34, 834, 837.   [2] 37, 66; V*b*, 214, 565.   [3] 1; V*b*, 8.
[4] 1, 20, 53, 75; V*b*, 11, 103, 408, 667.   [5] Rommelaere, 1866, 301.
[6] 79; V*b*, 501; Mévergnies, 78 f.   [7] 78; V*b*, 835.   [8] (3), 31 f.
[9] *Tractatus novus de magnetica vulnerum curatione, citra ullum et dolorem, et remedii applicationem*, Marburg, 1608, Frankfurt, 1613, 1621. He also edited a *Trinum Magicum* under the name Longinus Cæsar or Cæsar Longinus in 1609 and (with different contents) in 1614; Thorndike, vi, 600, 602 (fails to notice that R.G. M.D. is Rudolph Goclenius, M.D.); vii, 283; Ferguson, *Bibliographical Notes on Histories of Inventions and Books of Secrets*, Part VI, Glasgow, 1890, 7.
[10] *Dissertatio theologica de Superstitione . . . Inseritur magici libelli de magnetica vulnerum curatione authore D. Rodolpho Goclenio . . . brevis anatome*, Trier, 1615.
[11] *De Magnetica Vulnerum Naturalis et Legitima Curatione*, Paris, 1621; V*b*, 593.

criticised both Goclenius and Roberti. The book was very similar to others by Catholics and permission for publication was given. Owing to intervention by the Jesuits, the *imprimatur* was withdrawn, but the book appeared without Van Helmont's consent (it has been said that he was encouraged by Jesuits to publish it and fell into the trap).

Roberti published a reply.[1] Van Helmont received the attention of the Spanish Inquisition, which considered his case for thirteen years. He was a good Catholic and offered to have the book burned if condemned, but it seems as if severe punishment in any event was decided. In 1634 he was sent to a Franciscan prison in Brussels, but after the intervention of powerful friends (including, it is said, Marie de Medici) he was released after a few weeks and confined to his own house, which he was not allowed to leave without a dispensation of the Archbishop of Malines. When the plague broke out, his family refused to leave without him and as a result two of his sons died. He appears to have been left alone after 1636 or 1638. Some of his papers were confiscated and were unknown until they were published.[2] The chief objection seems to have been to the suggestion that the relics of saints acted by some magnetic or corporeal property, although Van Helmont added that they had also been given a divine virtue,[3] which might normally have satisfied the Catholic authorities. He was formally acquitted two years after his death.

Foppens gives a decretal from the Archbishop of Malines of 30 October 1646, saying that although it had been found that the book contained much that was detestable, yet Van Helmont was not a heretic (Nos eum non habere pro hæretico, sed pie existimare quod vixerit et obierit Catholicus et Sanctus Romanæ Ecclesiæ obediens filius).

Pomponazzi (1462–1525), whose work on the soul (*De Immortalitate Animæ*, 1516) was publicly burned at Venice, said in his *De Incantationibus* (posthumously published by Gratarolo, Basel, 1556) that cures by relics were due to faith or imagination, and that dogs' bones would have been just as effective as saints'. This impious opinion was rebutted by Thomas Fienus (*De Viribus Imaginationis Tractatus*, Louvain, 1608), who said Pomponazzi's book had been prohibited by the Holy See. Pomponazzi thought there might be healing virtues in the bones themselves or in exhalations from them.[4]

Van Helmont said that Copernicus had taught that the earth is moved in a circle, but as this did not agree with the decree of the Church 'I have withdrawn the name of moving from the earth (ideo nomen motus à terra sustuli)'.[5] He was a good Catholic and his main ideal was the unification of knowledge of God and nature.[6] He received the sacrament on his death-bed. Shortly before his death he gave his papers, which he had thought of burning, to his son Francis Mercurius, charging him to publish them all, 'even the crude and incorrect'. The result was the work, containing parts previously published separately, entitled *Ortus Medicinæ*, or the 'Origins of Medicine', dedicated

---

[1] *Curationis Magneticæ, et Unguenti Armarii Magica Impostura . . . demonstrata a J. Roberti . . . Responsio ad . . . Disputationem J. B. ab H[elmont] contra eundem Roberti . . . conscriptum,* 8°, Luxemburg, 1621 (BM 1033. e. 26).

[2] Broeckx, (2), (3); Rommelaire, 1866; Mévergnies, 122 f., 140 f., who went through the papers again, could not explain the 'manœuvres'.

[3] 71, § 48; Vb, 602.

[4] Ueberweg, 1924, iii, 28; Cassirer, Kristeller, and Randall, *The Renaissance Philosophy of Man*, Chicago, 1948, 257–381; Thorndike, v, 106.

[5] 17; Vb, 75.   [6] Haeser, (1), 1881, ii, 348.

to Jehova (Verbo ineffabili), the first edition of which appeared in 1648 and the last in 1707. Of the works of Van Helmont, only four were published up to the year of his death (1644):

I. De Magnetica Vulnerum Naturalis et Legitima Curatione, Paris, 1621; English tr. in VA.

II. Supplementum de Spadanis Fontibus, 8°, Liége, 1624; BM 1171. a. 3. (1.); Hoefer and Ferguson mention a Cologne ed.).

III. Febrium Doctrina Inaudita, 12°, Antwerp, 1642; BM 1168. a. 28. (3.); French tr. by Bauda, 8°, Paris, 1653.

IV. Opuscula Medica Inaudita, 8°, Cologne, 1644 (dedication dated Brussels, October 1643) (BM 545. c. 7), 8°, Amsterdam, 1648 (BM 542. h. 9) and with sep. t.ps. and signs. in V, 1648; containing III and three new tracts:

(a) Doctrina Inaudita, de Causis, Modis fiendi, Contentis, Radice, et Resolutione Lithiasis.
(b) Tumulus Pestis.
(c) Scholarum Humoristarum Passiva Deceptio atque Ignorantia (a supplement to III).

V. (a) Ortvs Medicinæ. Id est, Initia Physicæ Inavdita. Progressus medicinæ novus, in Morborum Ultionem, ad Vitam Longam. Avthore Ioanne Baptista Van Helmont, Toparchâ in Merode, Royenborch, Oorschot, Pellines, &c. Edente Authoris Filio, Francisco Mercvrio Van Helmont, Cum ejus Præfatione ex Belgico translatâ, sm. 4°, Amsterdam, Elzevir, 1648, xviii ll. (portrs.), 800 pp., tracts III–IV with sep. t.ps., iv ll. 110 pp., ii ll. (i blank). 116 pp., 88 pp.; no index.

(a') 2 ed., hf.t. Ioan. Baptista Van Helmont Ortvs et Progressvs Medicinæ Inavdita, . . . , t.p. red and black, as in (a) but cont. Nostra autem hæc editio, emendatius multò, & auctius cum indice, rerum, & verborum locupletissimo, prodit. Ad Clarissimum, & Excellentissimum Virum Antonivm Serrati Medicum, & Philosophum, Ciuem Venetum, Venice, Apud Iuntas, & Ioan. Iacobum Hertz, f°, 1651, xxvii ll. (incl. index), 700 pp. (no portrs.), the index was compiled by Tachenius; (b) 3 ed. (usually called 2 ed.), t.p. as (a) but addit. Editio nova, cumque locupletiori Rerum & Verborum Indice, pro illa Venetiis nuper excusa, multam partem adauctior reddita & exornatior, sm. 4°, Amsterdam, Elzevir, 1652, xvi ll., 894 pp., index (with note to reader: Ecce tibi, amice Lector, quid boni nuntii allatum (vulgari diverbio) ex America), this is the best ed.; (c) Editio Qvarta. In qua præter quædam Auth. Fragmenta adiecti fuerunt Indices, f°, Lyons, Joannis Baptistæ Deuenet, 1655, hf.t. Ioannis Baptistæ Helmont Opera, engr. t.p., x ll., 487 pp., sep. t.p. Opvscvla Medica Inavdita, 192 pp., xxix ll. index; (d) reprint of (c), f°, Lyons, Ioann. Ant. Huguctan & Guillielmi Barbier, 1667; (e) Opera Omnia. Additis his de novo Tractatibus Aliquot posthumis ejusdem Authoris, maximè curiosis pariter ac perutilissimis, antehac non in lucem editis . . . , 4°, Francofurti, Sumptibus Johannis Justi Erythropili. Typis Johannis Philippe Andreæ, 1682, engr. t.p., t.p., xviii ll., 765 pp., xxxvi ll. index, t.p. Opuscula Medica Inaudita, vii ll., 275 pp., xxi ll. index; (f) Opera Omnia, Novissima hac Editione ab innumeris mendis repurgata, et Indice Rerum ac Verborum Locupletiori Instructa, Una cum Introductione atque Clavi Michaelis Bernhardi Valentini, Hæreditarii in Dirshrot. . . . Ex Bibliopolio Hafniensi Hieronymi Christiani Paulli, 4°, Frankfurt, Typis M. Andreæ, 1707, xxviii ll. (incl. t.p., second engr. t.p., Clavis ad Obscuriorum sensum referandum), 765 pp., xxxvi ll. index, t.p. Opuscula Medica Inaudita, vii ll., 275 pp., xxi ll. index; BM 542. d. 12.

Michael Bernhard Valentini (Giessen; 26 November 1657–1729), who graduated at Giessen in 1680, travelled in Holland, England, and France, and was professor of medicine in Giessen (1687), F.R.S. 1715.

(e) and (f) contain a Tractatus Novus Posthumus, communicatus ab Authoris Filio, Francisco Mercurio van Helmont; De Virtvte Magna Verborvm ac Rervm, not in the other eds.[1] The above, so far as I know, are the only Latin editions, those of Leyden,

---

[1] Boerhaave, (4), 1741, 45 (T. L. Davis, *J. Chem. Educ.*, 1928, v, 678), who calls Van Helmont 'the greatest and most experienced of all the chemists that have yet appeared', says the Venice and German editions contain 'morsels not in the fashion of the author'.

f°, 1653, and Ulm, 12°, 1680, given by Ferguson and by Haeser, being probably non-existent. Van Helmont's handwriting was difficult to read[1] and the printed works probably contain errors. In spite of the claim in (g) that the text was 'purged of innumerable errors', the text in all editions seems to me to be the same.

Translations

(A) *Partial English:* (a) Three Treatises, Of the Magnetic Cure of Wounds [pp. 1–93]; The Nativity of Tartar in Wine [pp. 111–19]; and The Image of God in Man [pp. 121–47]. A Ternary of Paradoxes. Translated, Illustrated, and Ampliated by Walter Charleton, sm. 4°, London, 1650 (dedicated to Viscount Brouncker).

(b) Deliramenti catarrhi: or the Incongruities, Impossibilities, and Absurdities couched under the Vulgar Opinion of Defluxions . . . The Translator and Paraphrast Dr. Charleton, 4°, London, 1650.

(B) *Complete English:* (a) Oriatrike Or, Physick Refined. The Common Errors therein Refuted, And the whole Art Reformed & Rectified: Being A New Rise and Progress of Phylosophy and Medicine, for the Destruction of Diseases and Prolongation of Life. Written By that most Learned, Famous, Profound, and Acute Phylosopher, and Chymical Physitian, John Baptista Van Helmont . . . And now faithfully rendred into English . . . By J[ohn]. C[handler]. of M[erton]. H[all]. Oxon. [now Hertford College], la. 4°, London, Printed for Lodowick Loyd, 1662, engr. xxii ll., 1161 pp. (sep. t.p. 815, vii ll., t.p., pp. 827–1161), xi ll. index and verses.

(b) Reissued with new t.p. and prelim. matter as Van Helmont's Works, containing his most excellent Philosophy, Physick, Chirurgery, Anatomy; wherein the philosophy of the schools is examined, the errours therein refuted, and the whole art reformed . . . done into English by J. C., f°, 1664 (the BM copy has R. Southey's autograph, Keswick, 7 September, 1835). This English tr. is in places unintelligible.

(C) *Partial French* by Jean le Conte: Les Oevvres de Iean Baptiste Van Helmont, traittant des Principes de Medecine et Physique, pour la guérison assurée des Maladies, 4°, Lyon, Iean Antoine Hvgvetan and Guillavme Barbier, 1670, and 1671, iv ll., 396 pp. (with Preface, pp. 1–38, giving a summary of the contents).

(D) *German,* by Knorr von Rosenroth with the assistance of F. M. Van Helmont:[2] hf.t. Johannis Baptistæ von Helmont / etc. Schrifften, v Erklärung des Kupffer-Tituls, f.p. engr. (the vision descr. at beginning of Tumulus Pestis) by J. J. de Sandrart, t.p. red and black, Aufgang der Artzney-Kunst / Das ist: Noch nie erhörte Grund-Lehren von der Natur / zu einer neuen Beförderung der Artzney-Sachen . . . Anitzo auf Beyrahten dessen Herrn Sohnes / H. Francisci Mercurii Freyherrn von Helmont / In die Hochteutsche Sprache übersetzt / in seine rechte Ordnung gebracht / mit Beyfügung dessen / was in der Ersten auf Niederländisch gedruckten Edition / genannt Die Morgen Röthe / Mehr / oder auch anders / als in der Lateinischen / durchgehends / wie auch mit einem ehemals ausgelassenen Tractat von der grossen Krafft der Worte und Dinge / aus dem geschriebenen vermehret . . . , f°, Sultzbach, J. A. Endters Sel. Söhne / Gedruckt bey J. Holst, 1683, full p. portr. by J. A. Baener, in all xvii ll., 1270 pp., xxx ll. index; contains text from the Dageraed (see VI) in parallel columns; the name of Knorr von Rosenroth (who translated the Qabbalah) does not appear.

VI. Dageraed aft Nieuwe Opkomst der Geneeskonst, in verborgen grondt-regelen der Natuere. Nooyt in't licht gesien, en van den Autheur selve in't Nederduyts beschreven, T'Amsterdam, By Jan Jacob Schipper, 4°, 1659, 391 pp. (BM 544. f. 6); Dageraad, ofte Nieuwe Opkomst der Geneeskonst, in verborgen grond-regulen der Nature . . . Noit in't licht gesien, en van der Autheur zelve in't Nederduits beschreven, Tot Rotterdam By J. Næranus, 4°, 1660, ix ll., 404 pp. (BM Ac 3791 b; CUL 300. 3. c. 90. 31); facsim. repr. of 1660 ed. published by the Flemish Academy of Medicine (Koninklijke Vlaamsche Academie voor Geneeskunde), Antwerp, 1944.[3] Although VI

---

[1] Specimens in *Correspondance de Mersenne*, 1936, ii, 498 (signature), 536.

[2] Rixner and Siber, 27, say the tr. is literal but obscure.

[3] Rixner and Siber, 1827, vii, 25, say the MS. was given by Van Helmont to his daughter, from whom it was obtained by a friend who had it printed as 'Dagereat ef the nieuwe Opkonst der Genees-Konst in verborgen Grond-Regulen der Nature. Leiden, 1615. 4to', and this date is mentioned by Dezeimeris (1836, iii, 101; the only work of Van Helmont mentioned in the *Catalogue des Livres* of his library, Paris, 1852, is the French tr. C), Broeckx ((1), 1837, 85) and Rommelaere (1866, 307, 327), but there is little doubt that it is non-existent — no one

is sometimes called a Dutch tr. of V, it is quite a different work. Rommelaere says the text is clearer than the Latin in V but less detailed. VI contains some fundamental ideas which are expanded in V, including the criticism of Galenical medicine and the ideas of *gas* and *blas* but not the important treatise Complexionum atque mixtionum elementalium, etc.

VII. Fundamenta Medicinæ . . . sub annum Conceptum . . . contracta de causis ac principiis morborum constitutivis . . . , 12°, Ulm, 1680 (BM 774. a. 27).

Of the 118 treatises contained in V the following are referred to by number in the footnotes:

1. Promissa Authoris.
2. Studia Authoris.
3. Venatio scientiarum.
4. Causæ et initia naturalium.
5. Archeus faber.
6. Logica inutilis.
7. Physica Aristotelis et Galeni ignara.
8. Elementa.
9. Terra.
10. Aqua.
11. Aër.
12. Progymnasma meteori.
13. Gas aquæ.
14. Blas meteoron.
15. Vacuum naturæ.
16. Meteoron anomalum.
17. Terræ tremor.
18. Complexionum atque mistionum elementalium figmentum.
19. Imago fermenti imprægnat massam semine.
20. Astra necessitant.
21. Formarum ortus.
22. Magnum oportet.
23. Natura contrariorum nescia.
24. Blas humanum.
25. Endemica.
26. Spiritus vitæ.
27. Calor efficienter.
28. Triplex scholarum digestio.
29. Sextuplex digestio alimenti humani.
30. Pylorus rector.
31. Tartari historia.
32. Tartari vini historia.
33. Inventis tartari in morbis temeraria.
34. Alimenta tartari insontia causæ.
35. Tartarus non in potu.
36. Custos errans.
37. Imago mentis.
38. Demens idea.
39. Sedes animæ.
40. A sedo animæ ad morbos.
41. Jus duum viratus.
42. Ignota actio regiminis.
43. Duumviratus.
44. Asthma et Tussis.
45. Volupe viventium morbus antiquitus putatus.
46. Pleura furens.
47. Tria prima chymicorum principia.
48. De flatibus.
49. Catarrhi deliramenta.
50. Pharmacopolium et dispensatorium modernum.
51. Potestas medicaminum.
52. Ignotus hospes morbus.
53. Ignotus hydrops.
54. Puerilis Humanistarum vindicata.
55. Respondet Author.
56. De morbis Archealibus.
57. Morborum phalanx et divisio.
58. In verbis, herbis, et lapidibus est magna virtus.
59. Butler.
60. De inspiratis.
61. Vita longa.
62. Thesis.
63. Demonstratur thesis.
64. Quædam imperfectoria.
65. Supplementum de Spadanis fontibus.
66. Imago Dei.
67. Humidum radicale.
68. Aura vitalis.
69. Vita.
70. Vita æterna.
71. De magnetica vulnerum curatione.
72. In Sole tabernaculum.
73. Aracana Paracelsi.
74. Arbor vitæ.
75. De lithiasi.
76. De febribus.
77. Scholarum Humoristarum passiva deceptio et ignorantia.
78. Tumulus pestis.
79. Præfatio.
80. Mortis occasiones.
81. Progreditur ad morbum cognitionem.
82. Ortus imaginis morbosas.

An unknown contemporary says Van Helmont was pious, learned and famous. He was called usually to patients who were abandoned by other

claims to have seen a copy; Delacre, (2), 1924; Van de Velde, 1929, 453, 715, 857; Boerhaave, (2), 1732, ii, 527, quotes *Aurora medicinae Belgice edita* but gives no date.

physicians as incurable, and they were never long in his hands, since on the second or third day they were either dead or cured.[1] Van Helmont's contributions to medicine are said[2] to include: (i) the discovery of acid digestion in the stomach, (ii) the appreciation of the significance of bile for digestion in the intestine, (iii) a description of the rhythmic movement of muscular viscera such as the pylorus, (iv) the recognition of the role of acid in inflammation and production of pus, (v) the association of the kidney with dropsy and œdema, (vi) a denial of the existence of innate heat and radical humour, cooled by respiration and the pulse, (vii) the recognition of the effect of silica dust in causing disease, and occupational diseases, (viii) a description of the great variety of causes of bronchial asthma, including frustration and repression, (ix) the introduction of aetiological therapy and new chemical remedies, (x) one of the first attempts at disease classification, (xi) the refutation of putrefaction and decay of humours as causes of disease and fever. To these I would add (xii) his rejection of bleeding (in use even in the nineteenth century) as curative, and (xiii) his condemnation of strong purgatives.

Florkin, who is critical, says: 'In all impartiality, it can be said that Van Helmont was a great physician (un grand médecin), one of the fathers of medicine, and that he exercised a considerable and lasting influence on the development of medicine.' His therapeutic method aimed at discovering the cause of the disease, and treating this and not the symptoms; in this he was in advance of his time and even of much later times. The contemporary physicians thought that asthma resulted from the descent of catarrhal matters from the head to the lungs, and applied remedies to the head. Van Helmont recognised its cause as a *pulmonis vitium* and prescribed metallic remedies for dry asthma and tonics for humid asthma, aiming at treating the mucous membranes. Rolleston[3] reported that Osler considered that in 'magnetic sympathy' Van Helmont 'clearly expressed the doctrine of immunity and the cure of diseases by immune sera', and Moon[4] thought that 'fanciful explanations in medicine, as in other things, are often stimulating and fertilizing and are perhaps better than none at all'. Daremberg,[5] who otherwise criticised him severely, says that 'In spite of his resemblances to Paracelsus, Van Helmont is greatly superior to him, as a man, as a physician, as a chemist, as a physiologist, and lastly as an anatomist. He really loved science and the sick'.

In an early work published by Broeckx,[6] also in the treatise I (in which he also expresses admiration of Gilbert),[7] and in fifteen letters (1630–1) to Mersenne[8] which deal with subjects contained in the *Ortus*, theology, and a cannon invented by Van Helmont, he shows a strong influence of Paracelsus and an admiration of his reform of medicine, but in his later works[9] he criticised him acutely but sympathetically; in others he condemns the excesses of Paracelsus in his usual outspoken way.[10] He used some of Paracelsus's obscure names, such

---

[1] Rixner-Siber, vii, 243.   [2] Pagel, (*h*), 1948.
[3] *Bull. Hist. Med.*, 1940, viii, 403–16.   [4] 1931, 28.   [5] 1870, i, 472.
[6] *Eisagoge in artem medicam a Paracelso restitutam.*   [7] V*b*, 597, 603.
[8] Gobet, *Essays de Iean Rey*, 1777, 115; *Correspondance de Mersenne*, ed. Tannery and de Waarde, 3 vols., 1932–46; 1936, ii, 496, 530, 582; 1946, iii, 10–155, 164, 180.
[9] 33, 78, V*b*, 190, 826 f.   [10] See, e.g., V*b*, 140, 141, 187, 189, 712; de Mévergnies, 96 f.

as *Relolleum* for 'an efficient quality not proceeding from the ferments or seeds
of things (qualitas efficiens, non procedens e fermentis et seminibus rerum)'[1]
and he reproduced some of Paracelsus's ideas about fauns, satyrs, sylphs,
gnomes, etc.[2] Attempts to prove the great dependence of Van Helmont on
Paracelsus have gone too far, and are too vaguely expressed.[3] Van Helmont
knew something of the *Qabbalah*; he mentions the Rabbinical *mors binsica*[4]
but he rejected as impious the idea of the microcosm which is central in the
Qabbalah; man is the image of God, not of the universe.[5]

Van Helmont was not free from the superstition and credulity of his time,
any more than Boyle for his later time (see p. 499). He believed in spontaneous generation; he asserts that full-grown mice, capable of generation with
natural mice, are produced in three weeks from wheat in a glass stopped with
dirty linen from which a ferment was exhaled and was changed by the odour
of the grain; and that scorpions are formed from the herb basil crushed in a
cavity between two bricks (as he had seen himself); but he also gives some good
observations in natural history which seemed to support the theory,[6] which
was accepted as late as last century. He criticised the doctrine of signatures, as
when Quercetanus thought the ice formed on freezing weak lye from the ashes
of nettles was in the form of nettles.[7] He used sympathetic remedies and the
usual 'Dreckapotheke' of his time, prescribing disgusting remedies even for
his own illnesses.[8] He used an amulet called Zenexton (a name due to Paracelsus),[9] made from worms in the eyes of toads, as a remedy for plague.[10] He
asserts from his own observations that many were cured by taking oil into
which a stone had been dipped by an Irishman, Butler, imprisoned at Vilvorde.[11] He tells a tall story of a church tower at Leyden struck by lightning in
1554 (before he was born) and disappearing entirely into the ground, where it
was afterwards found entire by digging.[12]

Van Helmont's description of himself as 'Philosopher by Fire (*Philosophus
per ignem*)' appears on the title-page of the *Opuscula Medica Inaudita* and at
the head of the preface of *De Lithiasi* and *Tumulus Pestis*, published in his
lifetime. He praised God for having called him to the Art of Fire from the
dregs of other professions:[13]

Laudo benignum mihi Deum, qui me in Pyrotechniam vocavit, extra aliarum pro-
fessionum fæcem. Siquidem Chymia principia habet non logismis parta: sed quæ per

---

[1] 23, § 25 f.; V*b*, 131 f.   [2] 63, § 98; V*b*, 543.
[3] Pagel, (*a*), 41: views of Helmont can be found in Paracelsus 'in höchst sublimierter Form
und als Niederschlag intuitiver Ganzheitsschau'; *id.*, (*b*), Helmont's complex 'Faust-like'
personality (a phrase used by Haeser, (1), 1881, ii, 348) was influenced by the *Qabbalah* and
Campanella; later, (*g*), Pagel said that Van Helmont, although influenced by Paracelsus, was
more scientific, and the great change in philosophic outlook between the two was emphasised
by Delacre, (2).
[4] 3, 71; V*b*, 24, 616.   [5] 76; V*b*, 748.
[6] 19, §§ 9–14; 63, § 90 f.; V*b*, 92, 542 f.; Mévergnies, 74 f.
[7] 50, § 13; V*b*, 368; cf. Boyle, p. 509.
[8] E.g., 46, § 35; V*b*, 322: sumsi cervi genitale carptum . . . mox bibi drachmam cruoris
hircini.
[9] *De Peste*, ii, 3; V*b*, i, 411: Zenexton de collo suppendatur.
[10] 78; V*b*, 879; de Mévergnies, 205.
[11] 59; V*b*, 466; on Butler, who was captured by Arab pirates on his travels and was taught
alchemy by an alchemist whom he served as a slave, see Lenglet du Fresnoy, 1742, i, 398.
[12] 16; V*b*, 74.   [13] 50, § 32; V*b*, 371.

naturam sunt cognita, & per ignem conspicua: præparatque Intellectum ad penetrandum occulta naturæ ponitque investigationem in natura ulteriorem, quàm aliæ scientiæ omnes simul, & penetrat usque ad ultimas profunditates veritatis realis.

The common doctors sneered at chemistry as a smoke-selling, delusive or false art (Scientiam Chymicam velut fumi vendulam atque illusoriam sive falsam).[1] The art of fire (Pyrotechnia) was not known to Galen but was concealed among the adepts (inter symmistas occultabatur) under a Pythagorean oath of silence, for Galen never saw even the distillation of roses (rhodostagma).[2] It was engraved originally on stelæ and became known to Pythagoras, who revealed it only to a few pupils.[3] There are traces of Hermetism in the *Ortus*.[4] Van Helmont says he sat in contemplation before an athanor until he received illumination,[5] which is typical of Hermetics. God had sent Paracelsus in the past age to propose the more profound preparations of medicines; He had revealed to Van Helmont knowledge of the nature of diseases; wherefore he expected shortly another to come, whose scholar he was not worthy to be.[6] His references to the artist Elias[7] show his belief in Hermetic messianism; Elias was not only exempt from some results of original sin, but also possessed the fruit of the tree of life, a means revealed to him 'to pass from the power to the act of immortality'.

Van Helmont believed in alchemy and the philosophers' stone. He gives a very circumstantial account of the transmutation of nearly 2000 times its weight of mercury into gold by means of a quarter of a grain of the philosophers' stone given him by a stranger whom he saw only once. This was a heavy red powder glittering like powdered glass and smelling of saffron: it was enclosed in wax and projected on the mercury heated to the melting point of lead, when the metal grew thick and on raising the fire melted into pure gold.[8] Van Helmont believed that Paracelsus possessed the philosophers' stone,[9] but he did not believe, with Paracelsus, that it was also the elixir of life. He claimed that he possessed the Alkahest or universal solvent, and that with it he had converted vegetables and even oak charcoal into water.[10] He calls it 'ignis aqua', first being of salts, lily, first metal, diaphoretic mercury, and horizontal gold, and any of these will cure all diseases.[11] Schmieder[12] gives a derivation of the name alkahest from al + $\kappa\alpha\nu\sigma\tau\dot{\eta}s$, i.e., a Greco-Arabic word. J. le Pelletier,[13]

[1] 76, xv, 1; V*b*, 777.   [2] 33, § 7; 75, pref.; V*b*, 191, 645.
[3] IV, pref.; V*b*, 645; the glossary (*Clavis*) of Valentini's ed. V*g*, f. F, says: 'Adepti sunt Philosophi per ignem, qui laborem Sophiæ Universalem, h.e., Transmutationem Metallorum promovent', with a reference to Helmont's *Magnum Oportet*; V*b*, 128: Idcirco qui student adeptis contendunt laborem Sophiæ promovere per objecta visus, & quidem per lumen lunæ, which does not bear this interpretation; De Mévergnies, 43, thought the meaning was alchemical, and Van Helmont believed himself in possession of a marvellous secret, which he could use with certainty; 'all the obscurities, all that is bizarre and naïve in the *Ortus* result from this', *ib.*, 5, 36 f., 62 f., 68, 90 (overdone).
[4] Collected by Mévergnies, 62–89, 187 f., 193 f., 205 f., who thought that if the Hermetic passages are suppressed, the whole work becomes unintelligible, and the name 'Mercurius' given to his son (who did not interpolate the passages) reflects the Hermetism of the father.
[5] 3; V*b*, 23.   [6] 33, § 10; 50, § 15; 52, § 95; 75, vii, § 25; V*b*, 191, 369, 406, 701.
[7] Collected by Mévergnies, 202 f., 223.   [8] 63, 70, 74; V*b*, 534, 590, 630.
[9] 73; V*b*, 626: lapidis illius chrysopoei verus compos.
[10] 18, § 29; 42, § 11, 74; V*b*, 88, 265, 635.   [11] 51, 55; V*b*, 384, 419.   [12] 1832, 86.
[13] *L'Alkaest ou le dissolvant universel de Van Helmont. Revelé dans plusieurs Traitez qui en découvrent le Secret*, 12°, Rouen, 1704; cf. O. Tachenius, *Epistola de famoso liquore Alkahest*,

after a long dissertation on the nature of the alkahest, and extracts from Ripley, Philalethes and Starkey, leaves the matter where he found it. Since the alkahest would dissolve any vessel in which it was put, Kunckel[1] said it was fabulous and its name could be derived from the German, 'alles Lügen est' (it is all lies). Boerhaave[2] collected all the passages on the alkahest in Van Helmont, but none 'will enable us to form any solid or satisfactory judgment about this surprising menstruum'; Francis Mercurius Van Helmont had told him 'that his father often boasted of more than he could perform'. Tornetta[3] thought it was a solution of caustic soda, but in some cases it may have been nitric acid, which dissolves charcoal on boiling.

Van Helmont, who rejects the 'fables' of Paracelsus, thought 300 years an absolute maximum duration of life, 120 years being a reasonable ideal.[4] The tree of life is the cedar of Lebanon, and he saw one on the summit of Lebanon which had been growing there since before the Flood (subter diluvium integras permanisse). He prepared an elixir by dissolving cedar wood in the alkahest and distilling off an oil, a few drops of which in wine will cure diseases in a few hours.[5]

Van Helmont distinguished four 'forms' of things: (1) the *essential form*, belonging to things almost without manifestation of life, as stone, metal, salt, sulphur, earths, dry bone, barren vegetables, etc.; (2) the *vital form* of those which seem to contain a vital beginning and are capable of nourishment and growth, viz. vegetables; (3) the *substantial form* in truly motive and sensitive things; (4) the *formal substance*, the only substantial one, as angels and human minds.[6] He quotes Aristotle and gives specimens of scholastic logic,[7] but he thought that young men in their three or seven years of study in the universities should be taught, not the pagan philosophy of Aristotle, but mathematics, geography, political economy, natural history and mineralogy, and especially *practical* chemistry:

to know and separate the first principles of bodies . . . their fixedness, volatility, separation, life, death, transformations, alteration, weakness, corruption, transplanting, solution, coagulation, resolution and new operations . . . not by naked discourse but by handicraft demonstration of the fire . . . by distilling, moistening, drying, calcining, resolving, as Nature works.

If any one shows him zinc ore, and the preparation of cadmia (zinc oxide) and the production of brass from it and copper, he teaches, shows, and gives knowledge of that not known before, whereas logic never taught such things and cannot teach anything which is not known before the argument:[8]

dum quis mihi ostendit lapidem calaminarem, Cadmiæ præparationem, contentum, Cupri, miscellam, & Aurichalci usus, quæ antea nesciebam, is docet, demonstrat, datque scientiam ejus, quod ante ignorabatur. Similia vero nunquam docuit Logica.

He saw a naked natural philosophy everywhere and did not apply figures or the moving forces of mathematics to nature, shunned analogies and metaphors

4°, Venice, 1655; id., *Echo ad Vindicias Chirosophi in qua, de liquore Alcaeist, Paracelsi et Helmonti, Veterum vestigia perquiruntur*, 4°, Venice, 1656; Kopp, (1), ii, 241.
  [1] *Laboratorium Chymicum*, 1716, 506.   [2] (2), 1732, i, 848–68; (3), 1727, i, 362.
  [3] *Amer. Chem. Abstr.*, 1943, xxxvii, 3644   [4] 61; V*b*, 512.
  [5] 74; V*b*, 633; Mévergnies, 193 f., 199 f.   [6] 21, § 67; V*b*, 117.
  [7] 7, 6, 11; V*b*, 34, 37, 52, etc.; Mévergnies, 148 f., 166, 171 f.   [8] 6; V*b*, 36.

as much as possible, and referred all natural necessities to the seeds, derived from the ferments.[1]

Plants are produced from a primordial juice called *Leffas*, metals and minerals are generated in the earth from a whitish-green paste (saponis liquidi) called *Bur*, seen oozing from cracks in rocks in mines and then turning white, yellow, or deeper green.[2] Van Helmont had in his museum the tusk of an elephant (mammoth) several feet long, found twelve feet below the surface at Hingsen on the Scheldt.[3] His account of the origin of springs, which he thought came from the sea, is not satisfactory.[4]

Daremberg[5] thinks Van Helmont may have got some details of chemical operations from the *Magia Naturalis* (1589) and *De Distillatione* (1608) of Porta, he also had available Libavius's *Alchemia* (1597). Boyle,[6] who often quotes him, thought Van Helmont was 'an author more considerable for his experiments than many learned men are pleas'd to think him'. An important feature of Van Helmont's work is its quantitative character; he made extensive use of the balance and such other measuring instruments as were available to him. An air thermoscope described and shown in a figure consists of two glass bulbs separated by a U-shaped tube with a long and a short leg and containing sulphuric acid coloured with roses. The upper bulb is closed and contains air, the lower bulb communicates with the atmosphere by a small hole. The instrument was used to measure the temperature of the body.[7] Van Helmont gives a scale of temperatures with fifteen 'fixed points' instead of the usual four of the alchemists: the greatest cold, melting ice (aqua nondum glaciata), well water, gentle lukewarm, lukewarm, human body temperature, feverish temperature, May sun, distillatory, boiling (water), subliming sulphur, melting pyrites, dark red heat, bright red heat, reverberatory with bellows. Touch is an uncertain guide near body temperature.[8]

In an experiment ice was put in a large glass bottle and the neck hermetically sealed. The bottle and ice were weighed and the ice allowed to melt, when the water was found to be nearly an eighth part heavier than the ice (propemodum octava sui parte, aqua, post resolutam glaciem, erit ponderosior seipsa glacie), and this again could be recovered, repeatedly, with its original weight. He perhaps meant changes in specific gravity.[9] Van Helmont measured the specific gravity of various specimens of urine by weighing in a vessel with a short neck ending in a fine point — a specific gravity bottle — and noticed that the weight is a few grains lighter when the liquid is lukewarm. He gives a number of figures for the weights.[10] He criticised the examination of urine by distillation, used by Thurneisser (see p. 155), as deceit and nonsense.[11] He determined the specific gravities of metals as in the ratios: tin 1, iron $1\frac{7}{12}$, copper $1\frac{2}{9}$, silver

[1] 19, § 7; Vb, 91.　　　　　[2] 10, 22; 8, § 13; Vb, 43, 47, 127.
[3] 9; Vb, 46; Hoefer, (3), 1872, 325, says he 'peut être consideré comme l'un des fondateurs de la paléontologie'.
[4] 10, 65; Vb, 46, 545.　　　[5] (1), 1870, i, 527.　　　[6] *Sceptical Chymist*, 1680, 112.
[7] 11, § 12; 67; Vb, 52, 574; Davy, *Elements of Chemical Philosophy*, 1812, 76.
[8] 27, § 35; Vb, 165; he anticipated Hooke in using the temperatures of melting ice and boiling water as fixed points.
[9] 13, § 35; Vb, 63; Patterson, *Ann. Sci.*, 1936, i, 462.
[10] 77, iv. 31; Vb, 819.　　　[11] 75, iii, 20; Vb, 671.

1¾, lead 1⅝, mercury 1⅞, gold 2⅔.[1] He describes an early observation of phosphorescence, probably of fluorspar:[2]

Scias lumen, esse revera ens extra lucem. Nam penes me asservo silicem, quem si ad aerem, Sole existente supra horizontem exposuero, ad spatium trium vel quatuor saltem pausarum (nec etiam refert, sive dies serenus, sive obnubilus fuerit) ac inde ad obscurum locum detulero, servat conceptum Solis lumen, ad aliquod simile fortassis spatium. Idque fit, quoties reperitur praefata illuminatio.

He described the fluorescence of an infusion of lignum nephriticum.[3]

Van Helmont expressed clearly the law of indestructibility of matter, and emphasised that metals when dissolved in acids are not destroyed but can be recovered again by suitable means. He also realised that when one metal precipitates another from a solution of a salt, there is no transmutation as Paracelsus thought.[4] He says Paracelsus taught that 'although a metal is destroyed ten thousand times, it will always rise again more perfect by its destruction'.[5] The fume of mercury is always mercury, however it is masked.[6] Silver dissolved in aqua fortis (chrysulca) is not destroyed but is concealed in the clear liquid as salt is contained in a solution in water, and can be recovered unchanged (permanet tamen in pristina sui essentia).[7] When gold is distilled seven times with sal ammoniac, antimony, and mercury sublimate it is converted into a red oil, but this is easily reduced again into its former weight and body (in pristinum auri pondus et corpus):[8]

Nam utcunque ista metalla, per quædam mineralia sibi adjuncta, nunc specie olei, salis, vel sulfuris, per retortam pellantur, horumque larvam mentiantur: ablatis tamen ejusmodi adjunctis, semper idem manet aurum, idemque qui ante Mercurius, redeuntque in pristina corpora.[9]

When pearls are dissolved in distilled vinegar or lemon juice, and a solution of salt of tartar added, the concealed powder of the pearls is precipitated.[10] Dissolved copper is precipitated by iron, which takes its place (putatus est ferrum in æs mutare, delusionem scilicet viri metallarii vix agnoscentes; eo quod ferri absumit locum æris succedentes atomi explerent), and copper similarly precipitates silver.[11]

Pierre Borel[12] and Kircher[13] also denied a transmutation of iron into copper.

Nothing is made of nothing, therefore weight is made of another body of equal weight in which there is a transmutation as it were of the matter (ut

---

[1] Correspondance de Mersenne, 1946, iii, 57. [2] 22, § 35; Vb, 126.
[3] 77, iv, 5; Vb, 816; Partington, Ann. Sci., 1955, xi, 1.
[4] Delacre, (2), 1924; this seems to have been realised before by Thomas Norton of Bristol, c. 1470; The Ordinal of Alchemy, in Ashmole, Theatrum Chemicum Britannicum, 1652, 20.
[5] 47, § 59; Vb, 331 — 'in vexatione præfata', i.e. the vague statement 'destructio bonum perficit' in Paracelsus's (perhaps spurious) preface to the Coelum philosophorum sive liber vexationum, Opera, Geneva, 1658, ii, 120.
[6] 44; Vb, 293. [7] 9, § 14; 12, § 17; 42, § 11; Vb, 45, 57, 265, 765.
[8] 12, § 6; 75, iv, § 9; viii, § 10; Vb, 55, 678, 706; VI, 1659, 86; Boyle, Sceptical Chymist, 1661, 40.
[9] 75, viii, 10; Vb, 705–6. [10] 76, viii, 10; Vb, 765.
[11] 65, paradoxum tertium, § 14; paradoxum quintum, § 11; Vb, 550, 554.
[12] Historiarvm, et Observationvm Medicophysicarum, Centuriæ IV, 8°, Paris, 1656; Cent. III, obs. lxxv, p. 255: ferrum autem paulatim corroditur & attrahit cupro in Vitriolo latens . . . nulle fuerit facta transmutatio.
[13] Mundus Subterraneus, f°, Amsterdam, 1668, i, 319, 321; 1665, ii, 185.

materiae sit transmutatio).[1] When mercury is boiled with oil of vitriol it forms a white precipitate like snow (præcipitatus albus nivis instar), which on washing with water turns yellow, and on revivification gives the same weight of mercury.[2]

Van Helmont describes the preparation of blue vitriol (a) by concentrating mine water, (b) by lixiviating roasted pyrites exposed to air, (c) by throwing sulphur on melted copper and putting the mass (cuprous sulphide) in rain water, and (d) by boiling copper plates with oil of vitriol, when a black mass is obtained which is dissolved to a blue solution in water. Contrary to the statements of Isaac Hollandus, George Agricola and 'other moderns' (Paracelsus, see p. 149), copper vitriol yields little or no acid on distillation, but when common (iron) vitriol is distilled by a strong fire in a coated glass retort it yields a very acid oil (oleum acidissimum) of vitriol[3] — a clear distinction between copper and iron vitriols, not made by Paracelsus. This acid on mixing with water generates great heat and breaks the container.[4]

The Elements

Van Helmont's criticism of prevailing views on the elements is contained especially in the treatise *Complexionum atque mixtionum elementalium figmentum* (the fiction of elementary complexions and mixtures)[5] in which he rejects both the four elements and the three principles (salt, sulphur, and mercury), introduces the theory that water is the primary element, and explains his new views on gas.[6] He rejected the 'heathen' theory of a primary matter taught by Aristotle.[7] He thought Paracelsus had borrowed the three principles from 'Basil Valentine' (see p. 185), who called them salt, sulphur, and mercury, but he says that Hermes Trismegistos taught that metals consist of body and soul held together by spirit.[8] The three principles said to be separated from a body are really made by fire (non tamen id fit per separationem . . . sed quatenus per transmutationem ab igne factam).[9] Mercury is a simple body actually existing (viz. the metal) and is not a constituent of things.[10] Metals combine only among themselves without losing their lustre.[11]

Van Helmont asserts that the true elements are air and water (duo dixi primitiva elementa, aërem et aquam); water, with heaven and earth, was formed on the first day in the account of Creation in Genesis.[12] Air or the sky served to separate the water above from that below the firmament, and air has two properties, cold and dryness (Cœlum ergo, sive aër, est constituans separator aquarum, duraturus, quamdiu ipsemet mundus. Cujus ergo duas obtinuit insignes potestates. Excelsum nempe frigus, eique proportionatam siccitatam proprium est quippe aëri semper aquas ab aquis separare).[13]

Neither of the two primary elements (air and water) is convertible into the

[1] 12, § 18; V*b*, 57.   [2] 75, iv, § 13; 76, xv, § 20; V*b*, 679, 779.
[3] 65, paradox. iii, § 12 f.; 75, viii, § 11 f.; V*b*, 550 f., 706.
[4] 75, viii, § 20; V*b*, 707.
[5] Summary, Partington, 1936, 369.   [6] See also 8; 12, § 27; V*b*, 42 f., 58.
[7] 4; V*b*, 26.   [8] 47, §§ 3–13, 67; V*b*, 324, 332.
[9] 19, § 7; 47, § 47; V*b*, 91, 323, 329; anticipating Boyle.   [10] 75, iii, 17; V*b*, 671.
[11] 14; V*b*, 630.   [12] 8, 18; V*b*, 43, 85.   [13] 13, §§ 4, 13; V*b*, 60.

other,[1] and an element cannot be reduced to a simpler state.[2] Van Helmont proceeds to show that the other two so-called elements, fire and earth, do not deserve the title, since fire is not a form of matter at all and earth can be formed from water, as he thought he proved by experiment. It is curious that he says that air is neither light nor heavy, because it is without weight (est sine pondere) and cannot be weighed or compared with the weight of water.[3] He did not believe that tin increases in weight on calcination.[4]

Earth is not an element but is formed from water. For if sand is fused with excess of alkali it forms a glass. If this glass is exposed to the air it liquefies to water (resolvi in aquam) and if sufficient aqua fortis is added to saturate the alkali (quantum *saturando* alcali sufficit) the sand [really the silica of the sand] settles out again of the same weight as was used to make the glass.[5] To prove that 'all vegetables proceed out of the element of water only' Van Helmont made the famous 'tree experiment':[6]

I took an earthen vessel, in which I put 200 pounds of Earth that had been dried in a Furnace, which I moystened with Rain-water, and I implanted therein the Trunk or Stem of a Willow Tree, weighing five pounds; and at length, five years being finished, the Tree sprung from thence did weigh 169 pounds, and about three ounces: But I moystened the Earthen Vessel with Rain-water, or distilled water (always when there was need) and it was large, and implanted into the Earth, and least the dust that flew about should be co-mingled with the Earth, I covered the lip or mouth of the Vessel, with an Iron plate covered with Tin (lamina ferrea, stanno obducta) and easily passable with many holes. I computed not the weight of the leaves that fell off in the four Automnes. At length, I again dried the Earth of the Vessel, and there were found the same 200 pounds, wanting about two ounces. Therefore 164 pounds of Wood, Barks, and Roots, arose out of water onely.

The conclusion is mainly correct, since the tree is largely water (about 50 per cent of fresh willow wood is free water), but Van Helmont did not know the part played by the carbon dioxide in the air, although he was the first to recognise its existence and give it a special name, 'gas sylvestre.'

If 16 oz. of the best tartar is distilled it gives 1 oz. of water and at most $2\frac{1}{2}$ oz. of salt: hence nearly 13 is oil. Hence, by distillation an acid salt is changed into oil which did not previously exist in it. And if the oil is joined to alkali it makes soap (smegma), which when distilled gives mostly water. Thus, there is not a mere separation of dissimilar things but a transmuting of the concrete body by the fire (see p. 222):[7]

Quin enim clarius hac mechanica, ut eluescet, ignem esse confectorum primorum: adeoque nec esse in se prima, neque præexistere talia in concreto, qualia separantur indè per ignem? Si quidem non est nuda separatio dissimilium: sed transmutatio concreti per ignem, juxta activitatem, quàm heterogenea inter se peragunt.

Fire, which is clearly distinguished from light,[8] is not an element, cannot form a material constituent of bodies (nec materialiter corporibus commiscetur), and is 'a positive death of things, a singular creature, second to no other',

---

[1] 18, § 1; V*b*, 85.   [2] 12, § 5; V*b*, 55.   [3] 76, xvii, § 13; V*b*, 787.
[4] *Correspondance de Mersenne*, 1946, iii, 181; Mersenne was then corresponding with Jean Rey; see p. 636.
[5] 9, § 16; 75, iii, 28; V*b*, 46, 672.
[6] 18, § 30; V*b*, 88; transl. in text is from VB, 109.   [7] 47, § 68; V*b*, 332.
[8] 21, § 22; V*b*, 108.

which can pierce glass.[1] Air cannot be condensed to water (aërem et aquam esse corpora impermutabilia), as is proved by the experiment with the air-gun (in canna ferrea . . . instar sclopeti), in which compressed air remains elastic and can propel a ball through a board.[2]

In his earliest work[3] Van Helmont used the three principles, salt, sulphur, and mercury, which he later rejected.[4] Still, 'to meet the weakness of our understanding (ut intelligendi imbecillitate nostræ)',[5] it can be said that water contains the three principles.

> Then we must suppose the elements of water to be a fluid mercury and an insipid salt, both absolutely simple, surrounding a uniform, homogeneous, simple and in-separable sulphur. On heating water, the salt, which cannot tolerate heat, rises to a cooler region, taking the proportionate amount of mercury. The sulphur must follow, and the three form vapour. In the very cold higher regions of the atmosphere the mercury is frozen solid and can no longer dissolve the salt. The sulphur is driven out-wards by the cold, is divided and surrounds the mercury and salt. As it is equal in amount to each of these, they also divide. All three form fine particles of gas in which the sulphur is now outside as a solid crust. In vapour the arrangement of the three elements is the same as in water, and hence it can recondense to water; but as in gas the sulphur is outside it cannot form water unless it is driven by the impulse of *Blas* (or the motion proceeding from the stars) into a lukewarm lower region, when the dry outer skin of sulphur breaks, the mercury redissolves the salt, and the sulphur (now become liquid) passes inside the particle, which is now vapour and can recondense into water. In the upper regions of the sky the thick layers of gas show their blue colour.[6]

Although Prescott accused Van Helmont of plagiarising Nicolaus of Cusa (1401–64)[7] in the tree experiment, Pagel[8] does not think he did so intention-ally. Paracelsus speaks of water as the 'matrix of all creatures', e.g. stones, tartar, vitriol, alum, etc., also metals, plants, and animals, but he seems to have thought that the things dissolved in the water, such as salts and earth, take part in the production.[9]

As further proofs of his thesis, Van Helmont says that spirit of wine, care-fully dephlegmated (dehydrated) with salt of tartar gives only water on com-bustion, and that fish are nourished and their fatty matter produced from the water in which they swim. He establishes links between materials to prove that they are formed from water; for example, since wood was shown to be formed from water in the tree experiment, all the products obtained from wood, such as charcoal and ash, must also consist of water. If gold is to be formed from water, this will involve a compression to one-sixteenth the volume, which is quite possible to Nature, although water has no pores.[10] Grain by fermentation is converted into beer, which still leaves a solid residue on evaporation. But beer can undergo a further fermentation, becoming sour and consuming its dregs, and finally it returns of its own accord into water.[11] In some examples he gives of converting bodies into water he neutralises acids

---

[1] 9, § 1; 12, § 30; 21, § 32; Vb, 44, 59, 111 (ignis mors artificialis).
[2] 11, § 3; 65, ii, 10 f.; Vb, 50, 548.   [3] I, § 153; Vb, 616.   [4] E.g. 4; Vb, 26 f.
[5] 13, § 8; Vb, 60; cf. 47, § 54; Vb, 330: quod autem quandoque elemento aquæ sua tria tri-buerim, id analogicê locutum est.
[6] 13, §§ 8, 16, 21; Vb, 60–2; Brucker.
[7] *Idiotæ, dialogus IIII*; *Opera*, Basel, 1565, 172–80; *The Idiot in four books*, 12°, 1650; text in Partington, 1936, 376–7.
[8] b, 42.   [9] Pagel, *Paracelsus*, 1958, 96 f.   [10] 12, 18; Vb, 57–8, 86.
[11] 19, § 2; Vb, 91; vinegar, in fact, loses its acidity by attack of organisms.

with chalk and distils off water.[1] When oil is burnt the flame consumes the fatness and this flies to the clouds, where it is condensed by cold to water (ignis nempe, cremans pinguedinem, in aërem, totum ad nubes evolat, ibique in aquam, frigore loci, quandaque concrescit).[2]

Van Helmont was familiar with the preparation of sulphuric acid, both by the distillation of green vitriol and by burning sulphur under a glass bell. He describes the preparation of nitric acid by distilling equal parts of saltpetre (salis petræ), vitriol, and alum, first dried and then mixed together, [3] and apparently knew that it converted sulphur into sulphuric acid (salispetræ spiritus elevat sulfur humidum et embryonatum vitrioli).[4] He mentions aqua regia, made from nitric acid and sal ammoniac, and the gas (chlorine and nitrosyl chloride) evolved from it.[5] He describes the distillation of spirit of sea salt (spiritus salis marini), i.e. hydrochloric acid, from salt calcined, liquefied between slices of radish, dried again, and then distilled in a reverberatory with dry potter's clay.[6]

Quicklime contains a two-fold alkaline salt, one lixivial (alkaline) and the other acid as may be perceived by the taste (in calce vive est duplex sal alcalisatum. Unde quidem lixiviale, et alterum acidum): by the action of water these salts become hot, as when acid spirit of vitriol is poured upon salt of tartar.[7] Fixed alkali is not present (as such) in plants but is produced by combustion (alkali fixum in vegetabilibus non præexstitisse: fixari vero cremando),[8] and quantitative experiments to prove this are described.[9] 'Weedaschen' (crude potassium carbonate) brought in casks from Scandinavia, are mostly made from pine but some from oak, and called *Cineres clavellati*, and from them a salt called 'Potaschen' is made. Alkali salt is also made by burning tartar of wine, 16 oz. giving hardly $2\frac{1}{2}$ oz. of alkali salt, so that the remaining $13\frac{1}{2}$ oz. of volatile matter perish in the calcination (ergo 13 cum dimidia unciae volatiles, calcinando perire). But if the tartar is distilled and the distillate [containing acetic acid] cohobated with the coal remaining, $4\frac{1}{3}$ oz. of salt are obtained. For, alkali of tartar not only fixes aqua vitæ but also distilled vinegar, so that the volatile salt of a thing is fixed by its own fixed alkali or salt, all which things he learnt by experiment (hæc quidem me docuit mechanica).[10]

Alkali neutralises all acidity (quatenus alkali quodvis omnem aciditatem, quam attingit, perimit).[11] Van Helmont uses the name *sal salsum* for a neutral salt.[12] When strong spirit of vitriol is poured on salt of tartar, heat is produced, and when sugar of lead is calcined the residue takes fire when exposed to the air (he thought because the alkali in it took up moisture).[13]

The volatile red oil formed by repeatedly distilling sulphur may have been ammonium sulphide if ammonia was used.[14] Sulphur is dissolved by boiling milk of lime to a yellow liquid but on adding vinegar the original sulphur is precipitated white like milk (lac ejus), with an unpleasant odour; common flowers of sulphur (sulphur flores venales) are made from copper ores and

[1] 18, § 37; Vb, 89.   [2] 18, § 12; Vb, 86.   [3] 18, §§ 33, 37; Vb, 89.
[4] 51, § 65; Vb, 387.   [5] 18, § 37; Vb, 89; etc.   [6] 59, 75, vii, § 28; Vb, 475, 702.
[7] 76, ix; Vb, 768.   [8] 47; Vb, 329.   [9] 24, § 38 f.; Vb, 150 f.
[10] 24, § 39 f.; Vb, 150 f.   [11] 24, § 53; Vb, 153.   [12] 29, § 27; Vb, 170.
[13] 76, ix; Vb, 768: pyrophoric lead.   [14] 64; Vb, 458; Patterson, *Ann. Sci.*, 1937, ii, 243.

pyrites; native sulphur is called 'sulphur vivum'.[1] What Van Helmont calls 'Paracelsus's ludum'[2] was some mineral, perhaps boracite or magnesium borate, found near Antwerp.[3] It is mentioned by Boyle.[4]

Potable gold and silver, and solutions of corals and pearls in acids, are useless medicines, as they are not digested.[5] Van Helmont describes the blue solution of precipitated silver chloride (apparently containing a little copper) in the spirit (ammonia) distilled from urine:

ick stelde hem op kalck van silver gemaeckt door't scheydt-waeter, en met zeesout nedergeslaegen, en seer nauw afgesoet, door veel warme waeteren, en ten lesten gedrooght. Ick sagh den voorschreven pis-geest met kleynder lauwheyt hemelsblaeuw worden.[6]

Van Helmont, following Paracelsus, rejected the old Galenical pharmacopoeia and used many mineral remedies.[7] These were sold by his old servants, who left him on marriage.[8] He gives a list of the *arcana* of Paracelsus,[9] including antimony and mercury compounds (*tinctura lili, corallatum Paracelsi, mercurius vitæ, arcanum corallinum, mercurius praecipitatus, mercurius diaphoreticus, corallatum dulci mercurii diaphoretici, praecipitatus diaphoreticus solis horizontis, liquor alkahest*), the *præcipitatus* probably including red oxide of mercury, and Turpeth minerale (basic sulphate), which he used in venereal cases, gout, fevers, dropsy, and many other diseases.[10] Mercury is dissolved by aqua fortis with heat and effervescence to give a clear liquor, whilst with spirit of vitriol (sulphuric acid) it gives a solid white as snow (in una quippe actione, Mercurius fit invisibilis, qui in altera, nivis instar albescit): this was mercurous or mercuric sulphate. Aqua regia dissolves gold but not silver, this being a particular quality of the acid and not of the metals.[11]

Arsenic, orpiment, or arsenical things, however fixed and dulcified, should never be taken inwardly, whatever others may say.[12] Arsenic gives a salt fixed in the fire [potassium arsenate] when fused with saltpetre (sal-petræ et arsenicum, ambo volatilia, per colliquationem fixantur).[13] The three colours of the rainbow [red, yellow and blue] are those of the three sulphurs in burnt minerals (trium sulfurum in mineralibus concremati).[14] What Van Helmont calls *Aroph*[15] has been identified with ferric ammonium chloride. He prescribed burnt sponge (containing iodine) for goître.[16] Wine is strengthened by freezing out water, as whalers in Greenland discovered.[17] The common people distil spirit (aqua vitæ) from beer, mead, fruits, grains, etc., as well as from wine.[18] The sweet spirit of vitriol, with the smell, vapour, and fury of opium, which is very hot and causes sleep,[19] was probably ether, which was known to Paracelsus (p. 150). White or loaf sugar (saccharum Tabarzet, sive albissimum) was 'adulterated' by boiling with milk of lime (ubi nomen puritatis fecit

[1] 36, §§ 39–40; V*b*, 211.   [2] 75; V*b*, 672, 699, 706.
[3] C. A. Becker, *Das Geheimmittel des Paracelsus gegen den Stein*, Mühlhausen, 1842; Haeser, (1), 1881, ii, 362.
[4] *Works*, 1744, ii, 74.   [5] 50, § 54; V*b*, 375.   [6] VI, 1659, 242; not in V.
[7] 50, 65; V*b*, 366 f., 556.   [8] 54, § 4; V*b*, 418.   [9] 73; V*b*, 624.
[10] V*b*, 134, 151, 248, 315, 384, 416 f., 455, 498, 624 f.   [11] 42; V*b*, 265.
[12] 50, § 52; V*b*, 375.   [13] 18, § 10; V*b*, 86.   [14] 16; V*b*, 72.
[15] 65, paradox. numero crit., § 53; V*b*, 560.   [16] 35, § 15; V*b*, 205.
[17] 32, § 3 f.; V*b*, 188; Paracelsus knew this, see p. 149.   [18] 68, 74; V*b*, 576, 633.
[19] 43, § 9; V*b*, 275.

imposturam . . . saccharum Tabarzet, sive albissimum . . . sed quia carius, sæpiusque cum lixivio calcis vivæ bullieret).[1] The 'sweet oil' obtained from olive oil by digestion with Paracelsus's *sal circulatum* may have been glycerol.[2]

Gas

To the moist and watery and the dry and oily vapours of Aristotle there is a third, smoke, added by Chemistry (viz. a sublimate) and Van Helmont says he added a fourth, gas. A sublimate (of sulphur, arsenic, camphor, pyrites, zinc, sal ammoniac, etc.), gives the same substance as at first, but a solid body by virtue of a ferment may become a windy blast or wild gas[3] (dum scilicet corpus solidum, vi fermenti, disponitur in flatum, sive Gas sylvestre).

I call this spirit, hitherto unknown, by the new name of gas, which can neither be retained in vessels nor reduced to a visible form, unless the seed is first extinguished.

Hunc spiritum, incognitum hactenus, novo nomine Gas voco, qui nec vasis cogi, nec in corpus visibile reduci, nisi extincto prius semine, potest.[4]

He gave the name *gas sylvestre* to the wild spirit (*sylvestris*, of the wood; sylva or silva, a wood or forest), the untameable gas which breaks vessels and escapes into the air (vasis incoercibile, foras in aërem prorumpit). If nitric acid is poured on sal ammoniac in a glass vessel which is closed by cement or by melting the glass, a gas is produced which bursts the vessel: 'the vessel is filled with plentiful exhalation (yet an invisible one) and however it may be feigned to be stronger than iron, yet it straightway dangerously leapeth asunder into broken pieces.'[5] This explains the effects of gunpowder (historiam enim gas exprimit proxime pulvis tormentarius).[6]

Van Helmont derived the name gas from the Greek chaos (non longe a chao veterum secretum).[7]

Derivations of the name 'gas' from the German words Gäscht (froth), gasesen or gesen (to ferment or foam), and Geist (spirit) are all incorrect.[8] Paracelsus sometimes calls the element air a 'chaos' (see p. 139) and this perhaps suggested its generalisation as 'gas' by Van Helmont,[9] but as far as I know Paracelsus never used the name gas sylvestre.

Van Helmont[10] speaks of *gas ventosum* (air), *gas pingue, gas siccum, gas foliginosum sive endimicum, gas sylvestre* (sive incoërcibile, quod in corpus cogi non potest visibile), *gas sulphureum, gas uvæ, gas vini, gas musti, gas flammeum*, etc., all unknown to the Galenical school, some of which are really the same, so that he reckons five or six gases: Nescivit inquam Schola Galenica hactenus differentiam inter Gas ventosum (quod mere aër est, id est, ventus, per siderum Blas commotus) Gas pingue, Gas siccum, quod sublimatum dicitur, Gas fuliginosum, sive endimicum, & Gas sylvestre, sive incoërcibile, quod in

[1] 50, § 57; V*b*, 376.　　[2] 68; V*b*, 576; Boyle, *Sceptical Chymist*, Oxford, 1680, 213.
[3] 44, § 54; V*b*, 295.　　[4] 18, § 14; V*b*, 86; for the last part of the definition, see p. 232.
[5] 18, § 37; V*b*, 89; VB, 96; cf. 48, § 62; V*b*, 343; VB, 426; VI, 1659, 90, 216 f., uses 'wind' in describing the experiment, but the name 'gas' occurs in other places.
[6] 18, § 24; V*b*, 87.
[7] 12, § 28; V*b*, 59; VI, 1659, 92: gas, dat ist einen Griexschen water-chaos.
[8] Juncker, *Conspectus Chemiae*, Halle, 1730, i, 365; Lippmann, (1), ii, 360; Kirkby, *Chem. and Ind.*, 1923, xlii, 325; Darmstaedter, *Chem. Ztg.*, 1929, liii, 565; Speter, *ib.*, 701.
[9] Strunz, 1907, 30; Stillman, 1924, 322–3.　　[10] 48; V*b*, 335 f.

corpus cogi non potest visibile.[1] No flatus is air (which is not contained in concrete bodies) but is a wild gas, formed each by its own ferment.[2] Some bodies contain this spirit and sometimes totally, and so they are resolved into it; not that it was actually contained in that form in them, when nothing could have retained it, and all the parts would be dissipated, but it was contained as a concrete spirit, as if fixed or coagulated, to be set free again by fermentation as in wine, must, bread, mead, etc., or by addition as in sal ammoniac:[3]

Corpora verò continent hunc spiritum, & quandoque tota, in ejusmodi spiritum obscedunt, non quidem quod actu in ipsis sit, (siquidem detineri non posset, imo totum concretum simul evolaret) sed est spiritus concretus, & corporis more coagulatus, excitaturque acquisito fermento, ut in vino, omphacio, pane, hydromelite, &c. Vel additamento peregrino, ut quandoque de sale dicam armeniaco, vel tandem per aliquam dispositionem alteritivam.

Gas is also driven out by fire from its fixed state in bodies, as from sour apples (pomum austerum torrendo, plurimos flatus excitat).[4]

Van Helmont's book on the Spa water (II) criticised a work by Henri de Heer (Henricus ab Heers), born at Tongres and town physician at Liége.[5] A different person was Martin Heer (Lauban, 10 November 1643–Görlitz, 1707), a supporter of Van Helmont (see p. 234).

Van Helmont gives the theories of the origin of springs; he says they are not formed from condensed air, which he proved experimentally is not convertible into water (see p. 224), but wrongly supposed (on the authority of Jesus Sirach, the author of *Ecclesiasticus*) that they come from the sea. Mineral waters had been supposed from the time of Hippokrates (see Vol. I) to contain alum, soda, lead, copper, vitriol, bitumen, etc., but Van Helmont says he found in them only water and iron vitriol (really ferrous bicarbonate), and Spa water is formed from a vein of iron ore dissolved by a hungry salt (sal esurinum). He later[6] found that Spa water evolves gas in bubbles and deposits an ochry sediment (bullas atque silvestre Gas excitant, ac tandem se vase affigunt). This is an advance on previous descriptions of the examination of mineral waters,[7] especially in the use of qualitative tests, which preceded Boyle's account (p. 533).

Van Helmont says more than once that he was the 'inventor' of gas (halitum illum Gas vocavi), of which Paracelsus was ignorant (ignoravit . . . quidditatem Gas, meum scil. inventum; Gas et Blas nova quidem sunt nomina à me introducta eo quod illorum cognitio verteribus fuerit ignota).[8] He distinguished gases from condensable vapours, from air, and from one another:[9] Sat mihi interim sciri, quod Gas, vapore, fuligine et stillatis oleositatibus, longe sit subtilius, quamquam multiotes aëre adhuc densius. Gas is an incondensable spirit (Gas est spiritus non coaguabilis).[10] Elsewhere he says that gas is com-

---

[1] 48, § 4; V*b*, 336.   [2] 48, § 34; V*b*, 339.   [3] 18, § 14; V*b*, 86.   [4] 48, § 67; V*b*, 343.
[5] *Spadacrene, hoc est Fons Spadanus*, 8°, Liége, 1614 (CUL copy, t.p. missing), 1622; 12°, Leyden, 1645, 1685; *Les Fontaines de Spa, decrit premiérement en Latin soubs le titre de Spadacrene, maintenant traduict en frãçoys avec les additions par Henri de Heer*, 8°, Liége, 1616, 1630; two 'dernière' eds., 1646 (by I. de Beaurieu), 1654; *Spadacrene ou dissertation physique sur les eaux de Spa. Nouvelle édit.*, by W. Chrouet, 8°, Hague, 1739.
[6] 75, iv; V*b*, 677–8.   [7] G. Rath, *A. Med.*, 1957, xli, 1.   [8] 12, § 27; 13, § 1; V*b*, 58–9.
[9] 12, § 29; V*b*, 59.   [10] 75, pref. (Explicatio aliquot verborum artis); IV (*a*).

posed of invisible atoms which can come together by *intense* cold and condense
to minute liquid drops (atomi Gas, ob nimiam exiguitatem invisibiles, . . .
frigoris excessum, in minimas rursus guttulas concidant).[1] He uses the 'new
name *Blas*' to designate the principle of movement of the stars (Blas motivum
stellarum est virtus pulsiva, ratione itineris, per loca et secundum aspectus),
which pours its influences on the earth.[2] He thought the stars cause events by
their blas but do not affect man, nor do they presage the course of mortal
life.[3] It may well be that 'Van Helmont was at heart more pleased with his Blas
than with his Gas',[4] but this does not minimise the importance of the second.[5]
Van Helmont says wind is air moved by the blas of the stars, running through
the *peroledes* of the air (see p. 233), and also causes the tides. Besides this
cosmic *blas meteoron* there is a *blas humanum* presiding over and determining
the functions of the human body. The *blas motivum* regulates movements and
is dual, according as the movements are voluntary or involuntary; there is a
blas alterativum presiding over metabolic changes, and a *blas ventris*, *blas
pyloris*, etc., in the human body.[6] Jungken[7] still used a *blas lunare* in explaining the causticity of ammonia (spiritus urinæ): in hunc urinosum simul igneum spiritum realiter Lunare aliquod Blas . . . imprimere haud possent.

Blas dropped out of use but gas was used by several authors such as Becher[8]
long before its revival by Macquer,[9] but it was avoided by English chemists
such as Boyle, Hales, Black, Cavendish, and Priestley, who used the confusing
name 'air'.

The common opinion[10] that Van Helmont made no distinction between
different gases is hardly justified. He sometimes used 'gas sylvestre' as a
general name for gas, sometimes for one particular gas (as one of a group), and
he realised clearly that there were gases with different properties. He speaks of
gas in a number of treatises[11] and distinguished the following varieties of it:

(i) The poisonous gas, extinguishing a candle flame, which collects in
mines and in the Grotto del Cane (in crypta Canis), i.e. carbon dioxide (70, 78,
90, 126, 863).

(ii) The *gas carbonum* formed by burning charcoal and other combustibles
(86, 88, 90, 111, 329 f., 490, 868), which is usually carbon dioxide but sometimes carbon monoxide, since Helmont says he was himself once nearly
poisoned at the age of 65 by the fumes of burning charcoal, and he gives the
symptoms of carbon monoxide poisoning (242, 720).

[1] 13, § 22; 14, § 11; V*b*, 62, 66.   [2] 14, 24; V*b*, 65, 143.
[3] 20; V*b*, 95 f.; on the tides, see 14, § 6; V*b*, 68.   [4] Foster, 1901, 142.
[5] Brucker, 1743, 721, said: qualia sunt Gas et Blas ejus, quibus tamen inventionibus mire
gaudet, licet nec perspicuitatem gignant, nec solidi quid dicant, nec distinctam notionem
faciant.
[6] 24, 30, 48; V*b*, 143 f., 181, 335.
[7] *Chymia Experimentalis*, 4°, Frankfurt, 1702, 90, 93–6.
[8] *Physica Subterranea*, 1669; 1738, 132–92; Lippmann, (1), ii, 361, 365.
[9] *Dictionnaire de Chymie*, Paris, 1766, i, 550; 1778, ii, 240.
[10] Thomson, (1), i, 185; Kopp, (2), iii, 155; Delacre, (2); but not Hoefer, (1), ii, 140.
[11] The page references in the text are to V*b*, the treatises corresponding being (as numbered
in the list on p. 215): 13, p. 60; 15, p. 70; 17, p. 78; 18, pp. 86–90; 19, pp. 91–4; 21, p. 111;
22, p. 126; 24, pp. 146–51; 25, p. 155; 41, p. 242; 46, p. 323; 48, pp. 336–43; 49, p. 349; 53,
p. 416; 60, p. 490; 65, p. 550; 72, p. 621; 75, ch. iv, p. 677; 75, ch. ix, p. 720; 76, ch. ix,
p. 768; 78, pp. 863–88.

(iii) The gas forming in cellars, especially from fermenting wine (carbon dioxide). Grapes can be dried to raisins if the skin remains whole, but if the skin is broken they ferment and evolve gas sylvestre, which makes them appear to boil; this gas is contained in wines which have been closed up in casks before the fermentation is ended, and makes them effervescent (vina furiosa reddit). Since the fresh grape on distillation is reduced by art to elementary water, but gives rise to gas in presence of a ferment, it follows that gas itself is water (87, 89–90, 126, 343, 490).

(iv) The gas formed by effervescence of sulphuric acid on salt of tartar (768) or distilled vinegar on calcium carbonate (carbon dioxide) (343): acetum stillatitium dum lapides cancrorum solvit eructatur spiritus sylvester (crabs' eyes or crab stones, mainly calcium carbonate, are formed in the stomach of the crayfish and some other crustaceans and were used, finely powdered, as an absorbent and antacid, the name being later given to a similar powder from any source).[1] If, as seems likely, the sal armoniac in the following experiment[2] was carbonate of ammonia the gas would be carbon dioxide, otherwise (see vi) it would be chlorine and nitrosyl chloride:

Let there be a Glasse-bottle, spatious, thick and strong; infuse in it four ounces of *Aqua Fortis* . . . cast into that water, one ounce of the Powder of *Sal Armoniac*, and straightway let the neck of the Glasse be shut by melting it, which is called *Hermes Seal*: As soon as the voluntary action shall begin, and the Vessel is filled with a plentiful exhalation (yet an invisible one) and however it may be feigned to be stronger than Iron, yet it straightway dangerously leapeth asunder into broken pieces.

(v) A poisonous gas formed when aqua fortis (*chrysulca*) acts on metals such as silver, which becomes red in air (343, 490): chrysulca argentum, eructatur spiritus sylvestre. The *Explicatio aliquot verborum artis*, preceding the preface in the 1648 edition of *De Lithiasi*, has: gas, qualis è fermentante vino; itemque ruber ille, qui chrysulca operante, eructatur, etc. This was nitric oxide, which Juncker[3] still called 'gas sylvestre'.

(vi) The gas evolved in the cold from aqua fortis and sal ammoniac (343), a mixture of chlorine and nitrosyl chloride.

(vii) The gas evolved in bubbles from Spa water (677; see p. 228), carbon dioxide.

(viii) The gas evolved in eructations (*gas sylvestre*; *gas ventosum*), i.e. carbon dioxide, which extinguishes a candle flame, and is sharply distinguished from inflammable intestinal gas (94, 341, 349).

(ix) *Gas pingue*, or gas of dung, which is inflammable, is evolved in putrefaction, and is contained in the gas from the large intestine, which he, as did Albertus Magnus (Vol. I), knew was inflammable (341): ructus sive flatus originalis in stomacho . . . extinguant flammam candelae. Stercoreus autem flatus, qui in ultimis formatur intestinis, atque per anum erumpit, transmissus per flammam candelae, transvolando accenditur, ac flammam diversicolorem, iridis instar exprimit (hydrogen or methane with fetid impurities).

[1] Lemery, *Traité universel des drogues simples*, Paris, 1798, 141: oculus cancri, pierre d'ecrevisse.
[2] 17, § 14; V*b*, 78; tr. from VB, 96.
[3] *Conspectus Chemiae*, Halle, 1730, i, 569.

(x) A gas different from (ix) which inflates the tympanum (in gas gangrene?).

(xi) A *gas pingue, siccum, fuliginosum, endimicum*, combustible, formed on dry distillation of organic matter (336), a mixture of hydrogen, methane and carbon monoxide.

(xii) A sulphurous gas (*gas sulfuris, sal acidum*) i.e. sulphur dioxide, from burning sulphur, which is a material all fatty and combustible (totum sit pingue et φλογιστόν): this gas formed in a vessel filled with air extinguishes a candle flame; it can be condensed in a bell-jar into a juice (per campanam in succum cogitur).[1] Yellow sulphur when ignited wholly flies away, hence it was called inflammable (totum avolat, semel accensum, idcirce φλογιστόν nominatum).[2] The word φλογιστόν is given in both places; it also occurs in VI, 1659, 378: Dit is't het welck wy levende swavel noemen, en φλογιστόν uyt den swavel-plaets getrocken.

(xiii) A gas sylvestre from melted saltpetre and charcoal: sal petræ liquescit candenti igne . . . adjuncto carbone, utrumque statim consumitur, & in Gas flammeum evolat (343, also carbon dioxide); Van Helmont missed the oxygen gas from the fused nitre, saying (87) that when strongly heated this gives a little acid water and leaves salt of tartar (really potassium oxide).

(xiv) Gunpowder when inflamed evolves gas which bursts vessels, yet the charcoal, sulphur and saltpetre separately heated do not explode: the explosion of the mixture is due to a mutual antipathy by which they try to destroy one another by conversion into gas: ergo illa apposita se mutuo in gas convertunt, per destructionem (87).

(xv) An ethereal and vital gas (gas aethereum ac vitale), a kind of vital spirit of a gaseous nature (Spiritum vitæ nostræ materialem de natura gas esse), which is the reason why other gases act so swiftly and powerfully on the body; this is a preservative balsam, formed in the blood in the heart and not inspired from the outer air. From the arterial blood no dregs or filth are expelled, smoky vapours being wanting where there is no adustion; but venous blood in wasting itself by the guidance of heat produces a gas, as water does a vapour, and this gas is subsequently of necessity expelled (89, 146, 149, 155 f.). In respiration, the air mingles in the cavity of the lungs (in toro pulmonis & thoracis) with the venous blood which would otherwise coagulate; it mixes with the sulphur of the blood and exhales together with watery vapour as an unperceivable gas (per gas insensibile transpiratum) (151).

Van Helmont thought the inspired air is not in the lungs (which do not move) but in the cavity of the chest outside them (ductus inspiratusque aër, trans pulmonem, in thoracem pergat).[3] Senguerd[4] tried to prove this by enclosing a lung in a receiver and pumping out the air, when the lung swelled because the air between it and the glass was removed — a result which Sprengel says is really against Van Helmont's hypothesis.

Van Helmont criticised Galen (unjustly according to Adams)[5] for teaching that the object of respiration is refrigeration: its purpose is to maintain animal

[1] 65, § 18; V*b*, 550.   [2] 78, xvii; V*b*, 888.   [3] 49, § 45 F; V*b*, 355.
[4] *Inquisitiones Experimentales, quibus aëris atmosphaerici natura traditur*, 4°, Leyden, 1690; Sprengel, (2), iv, 143.
[5] *Paulus Ægineta*, 1844, i, 214.

heat by a ferment in the left ventricle of the heart changing the arterial blood into a vital spirit, human life being a formal flame (vita humana est lux formalis).[1] The friction together of saline and sulphureous particles in the blood, caused by the beating of the heart, produces heat and a 'formal light' in the blood (sanguis arterialis sit partim salsus, partrinque pinguis atque sulfureus, tum demum, quod deberet esse pulsum concussio . . . in spiritu volatili lumen concipit, propagaturque formale sive vitale lumen).[2]

Flame

Flame is only burning smoke (non est nisi accensa fuligo).[3] A flame perishes at once in a closed vessel and charcoal may be heated continuously in a closed vessel without wasting. Yet if 62 lb. of oak charcoal contain 1 lb. of ashes, the remaining 61 lb. are wild spirit (*spiritus sylvester*) which cannot escape from the shut vessel. 'I call this spirit, hitherto unknown, by the new name of gas, which can neither be retained in vessels nor reduced to a visible form, unless the seed is first extinguished' (see p. 227). The last part of the definition he explains by saying that the gas of flame is not yet water (the fundamental element) because, 'although the fire has consumed the seminal forces of the burning body, yet some primitive fermentive differentiations of the body remain' (tamen permanent primæ fermentales aliquot concreti notæ), which being at last consumed in the air and extinguished, the gas returns to the element of water (quibus tandem in aëre consumtis & enectis, redit istud Gas in elementum aquae).[4] Flame is burning smoke and smoke is gas (1. Imprimis indubium sit, quia flamma sit fumus accensus. 2. Quod fumus sit corpus Gas).[5]

Van Helmont[6] describes an experiment of burning a candle in air in a cupping glass over water, when the water rises and the flame goes out. He concluded that: 'There is in the air something that is less than a body, which fills up the vacuities in the air and is wholly annihilated by fire.' The contraction is due to the pressing together of the empty spaces in the air by the smoke from the burning candle, the air having been 'created to be a receptacle of exhalations'. The air in mines, saturated with exhalations from minerals, extinguishes a flame. (Calor ergo, per se aërem dilatat ut patet per machinam, ambientis gradus dimetientem: sed ignis ob suas fuligines comprimet. Adeoque sequitur fortius agere fuligines, per compressionem, quàm calorem in dilatando. . . . Aër ergo creatus est, ut sit receptaculum exhalatuum; quare etiam vacuum in poris habeat, est necesse). The water rises by suction and this is caused by the consuming of part of the air (flamma immediatè non elevat aquam, sed suctus, consumta aliqua parte in aëre). The experiment proves that a vacuum, which Aristotle thought impossible, is something quite ordinary (vacuum in Natura ordinarium in aëre; nunc igitur de vacuo, Aristotelis

---

[1] 24; V*b*, 147.   [2] 72; V*b*, 621; see Willis, p. 307.
[3] This definition was not given first by Van Helmont (as Roscoe and Schorlemmer, *Treatise*, 1920, i, 821, say); Kopp, (2), iii, 84, attributes it to Albertus Magnus (see Vol. I), but it is in Aristotle: *De cœlo*, iii, 4; *De gen. et corr.*, ii, 4; *Meteor.*, iv, 9 (also using the word φλογιστά); see Vol. I, and Partington, *Nature*, 1935, cxxxv, 916.
[4] 21, § 31; V*b*, 111.   [5] 15, § 7; V*b*, 68.   [6] 15; V*b*, 67 f.

impossibili, naturæ requisitum ordinarium).[1] If a sulphured torch or candle is suspended by a wire in a bottle tightly corked and containing a little water, and then after the flame has gone out the bottle is uncorked under water, this will enter the bottle, a suction being caused through a consuming of some part of the air.[2]

The vacuities of the air are usually filled by *magnale*, which is not light but a special form (forma quædam assistens aëri); on heating the air, the matter is really condensed, but the *magnale* in the pores is extended.[3] The air, no less than the earth, has its strata or foundations which the adepts call *peroledes* (habet ergo aër suos, non minus quam terra, fundos, quos Adepti Peroledos. Invisibile itaque Gas, variis aëris Stratis pospitatur vocant).[4] A flame is extinguished in a vessel in which sulphur is burnt because of the gas sylvestre, also present in vaults and mines, and poisonous.[5] In some ways Van Helmont's *magnale* plays the part of oxygen:[6] flamma perit, quod vocant defectu aeris. Ego vero demonstravi, id contingere, defectu novi Magnalis (misprinted Magnetis); he had defined it in 1624:[7] inter corpus, et non corpus, medium ambigens, externorum soli sui natalitii astrorum . . . et non aëris.

On the Stone

Of all Helmont's works, that on urinary calculi (*De Lithiasi*) in nine chapters is said by Boerhaave[8] to be 'incomparable, and the best', and it also contains the greatest number of chemical experiments, which must have occupied him for a long period of time. Van Helmont in other works[9] criticises Paracelsus's theory of tartar, gives a fairly accurate description of the formation of tartar (which differs from the lees) in wine casks, recognising vaguely that it has something to do with the alcohol content, and says that tartar, which is a salt and not a stone, is not contained in food and does not cause the disease of the stone. The tartar of wine is more soluble in a solution of salt of tartar (potassium carbonate) than in water: 6 oz. of salt of tartar will dissolve 7 oz. of crude tartar. It is less soluble in wine than in water.

In his *De Lithiasi* Van Helmont says the urinary calculus or stone, called *Duelech* by Paracelsus, is not tartar, since it does not dissolve in boiling water. Although urine is clear when voided, even if it has been retained for several hours, it soon deposits a sandy sediment or crust when allowed to stand in a vessel. By mixing spirit of urine (ammonium carbonate solution) with spirit of wine he observed that the two form a white precipitate (ambo simul in offam albam coagulata sunt), afterwards called *offa Helmontii*.[10] As Boerhaave[11] said, this experiment has been made by Raymund Lully.[12]

Van Helmont discusses a number of ways in which solid concretions and coagulations are formed in nature and concludes that they are all different

---

[1] 15, §§ 6, 18; V*b*, 68, 70; cf. 78, § xiii, V*b*, 865.   [2] 15, § 8; V*b*, 68.
[3] 13, §§ 6–7; V*b*, 68.   [4] 13, § 23; V*b*, 62.   [5] 22, § 59; V*b*, 126.
[6] 80; V*b*, 591.   [7] II; V*b*, 548.   [8] (4), 1741, i, 45.
[9] 31, 32, 33, 34, 35; V*b*, 186 f., 188 f., 190 f., 194 f., 202 f.
[10] 75, iii; V*b*, 668; in VI, 1659, 242: ick goot dit leste waeter, dat over den helm was gekomen, in een fleschen met den besten brande-wijn, di op eenen oogenblick in een schoon wit vluchtigh sont worde verkeert, niet min, als den geest des wijns, oft der pisse.
[11] (2), 1732, ii, 372.   [12] *Experimenta*, in Manget, i, 829.

from the formation of *duelech*. This is deposited from urine in the bladder by the concurrence of three things: (i) the spirit of urine (spiritus urinæ), (ii) spirit of wine (aqua vitæ), and (iii) a corrupting ferment from the kidneys.[1] This conclusion is faulty, since spirit of wine does not occur in the body, and the spirit of urine which Van Helmont used, containing ammonium carbonate, does not occur in fresh urine. Van Helmont isolated from urine two fixed salts, one of them common salt, which he asserted was that taken with food, and another, which is volatile in fire and has a different crystalline form (probably urea).[2] As cures he used common salt and arcanum philosophorum (perhaps ferric ammonium chloride). Van Helmont invented a leather tube catheter[3] and tried injections into the bladder, but found them too irritating.

For the volatile ammonium salt (ammonium carbonate) Van Helmont uses the names *spiritus urinæ*, *sal volatile* (also ammonium chloride in soot), *spiritus lotii*, etc.[4] A spirit can be distilled from blood which cannot be distinguished by smell or taste from spirit of urine, but cures epilepsy, which spirit of urine does not.[5] By distilling a calculus (*duelech*) Van Helmont obtained a fetid spirit of urine, yellow crystals, and an oil like that from dried urine, and a black unsavoury earth remained.[6]

Archeus

Van Helmont's theory of the Archeus, a modification of Paracelsus's (p. 130), is a peculiar form of vitalism.[7] Van Helmont 'proved' by an experiment (which he was never able to repeat) that the seat of the Archeus is in the stomach. He took aconite (*Napellus*) and felt himself thinking in the stomach, not in the head.[8] He recognised the following scale of spiritual controllers:

mens   (= soul or spirit; from God; eternal)
|
anima sensitiva   (= mortal; psychic life of the body)
|
archeus influus   (= inner architect; controller)
|
archei insiti   (= vital centres in organism) = Blas locales.

The mortal sensitive soul coexists in man (in his present state) with the immortal mind (*mens*), the soul being as it were the husk or shell of the mind, and the latter works through it, so that at the bidding of the mind the soul makes use of the Archeus, whether it itself will or not. Before the Fall of Adam, man had only the immortal mind which acted directly on the Archeus, discharging all the functions of life, and man was immortal, the shadows of the brute beast not blurring his intellect. At the Fall, God

---

[1] 75, iii, v f.; V*b*, 669, 683 f.; Rommelaere, 448, says spirit of urine is uric acid.
[2] 29, § 58; 75, iii, 19; V*b*, 177, 671.   [3] 75, vii, 34; V*b*, 703.
[4] 18, § 37; 75, iii; V*b*, 89, 669 f., 675.   [5] 68; V*b*, 577; cf. Boyle, p. 548.
[6] 75, v, 9; V*b*, 684.
[7] 5, 52, 81, 56, 57, 62; V*b*, 33–4, 393, 405, 428, 441, 452, 520; Martin Heer, *Introductio in Archivum Archei vitale et fermentali viri magnifici Johannis Baptistæ van Helmont, Philosophi per ignem*, 4°, Laubæ, 1703 (365 pp.; BN R 7636); Sprengel, (1), 1815, v, 22; (2), 1827, iv, 297; Rixner-Siber, vii, 125; A. Lemoine, *Le vitalisme et animisme de Stahl*, Paris, 1864; Strunz, *Paracelsus*, 1903, 18; Mévergnies, 179 f.; Heer, 56, pointed out that the Archeus appears in the writings of 'Basil Valentine'.
[8] 38; V*b*, 222.

introduced into man the sensitive soul and with it death, the immortal mind retiring into the sensitive soul and becoming as it were its kernel.[1]

The vital spirit (spiritus vitalis), breath of life or ether (aether) is illuminated by a pure living light (lumine pure vitali), not fiery, inflaming or visible but a formal intelligible light of the nature of the sensitive soul (animæ sensitivæ) and incapable of observation and description, which rises to the brain.[2]

The combination of matter (*materia*) and force (*causa efficiens*, Archeus, fermentum) in the body gives life, which exists in gradations from the *vita minima prima* through the *media* to the *ultima*. The *vita* of external bodies such as nutriment remains, even in the conflict with the organism, and the relation is the *magnum oportet*. On death, the Archeus returns to the matrix of Nature, to the ferments, to begin a new life. The Archeus influus is not the soul but its organ, and it resides in the duumvirate of the stomach and spleen, ruling the archei insiti by its indwelling actio regiminis, which acts on the ferments of the solid and especially the fluid parts, impressing on them its idea seals (ideae sigillares) to form the archei insiti. The archei are ether-like or are Blas, with the varieties Blas motivum, sensitivum, alterativum, etc. The blood is formed from nutriments by five kinds of concoctions brought about by ferments; its living principle is the plasma (*latex*) from which all the bodily parts are formed. Animal heat is not the cause but an effect of life, and there is no 'vital spirit'.

The animal soul arose from sin in the fall of man; it controls the Archeus, depriving the *mens* of complete mastery, and in this way disease originated. There is no essential difference between normal and pathological processes, disease being a positive and substantial phenomenon (ens reale subsistens in corpore), the causes irritating the Archeus influus and causing diseased ideas (passiones, perturbationes, exarthroses), impressed on the Archei insiti as ideae sigillares, which cause changes in the ferments and alterations of the juices (excitaverit Archeum, ad indignitationem, furorem, metum, &c. . . . sigillaturque in Archeo; eoque vestita, mox morbus in scenam intrat).[3]

Van Helmont's idea of the Archeus was taken up by Johannes Dolæus, of French extraction (Geismar 1638–Cassel 1707), who called it *Gasteranax* (king of the stomach), *Cardimelech* (king of the heart), or *Microcosmetor*, and attributed diseases to the vagaries of these 'kings (nostrum Regentum)', who produced toxic bodies in the blood.[4]

Ferments

Van Helmont says the name of ferment (*fermentum*) was unknown before except for the leaven used for making bread, whereas there is no change or transmutation brought about by the sleeping affinity of matter except by the work of the ferment (nulla in rebus fiat vicissitudo, aut transmutatio, per somniatum appetitum hyles: sed duntaxat solius fermenti opera).

The two chief beginnings of bodies (prima initia) are water and ferment or seminal origin (fermentum sive initium seminale); the ferment is an indwelling

[1] 62, 63, 69; V*b*, 515, 521, 585.   [2] 26, §§ 10, 21; V*b*, 158 f.   [3] 52, 82; V*b*, 400, 441.
[4] Dolaeus, *Encyclopædia Medicinæ Theoretico-Practicæ*, 4°, Frankfurt, 1684, pref. 26, 74, 86, 163, 369, 722, etc.; Sprengel, (1), 1815, v, 110; Jöcher, 1750, ii, 167, (says b. 1651, and his *Opera omnia* publ. Frankfurt, 1703).

formative energy, 'hardly 1/8200 part of a body', which disposes (disponit) the material of water so that a seed is produced and life (vita), and the mass develops into a stone, metal, plant or animal.[1] The horns of stags contain some woody matter since, like leaves, they fall off every year.[2]

The idea of a minute quantity of indwelling energy Van Helmont attributes to Sendivogius (juxta Chymicorum Cosmopolitam).[3] By the action of the Archeus, as the efficient cause, matter too develops from within to certain forms: 'the seed is a substance in which the Archeus is already contained, a spiritual gas containing in it a ferment, the image of the thing, and moreover a dispositive knowledge of things to be done . . . one thing is not changed into another without a ferment and a seed.' The ferment pre-exists in the seed, which is developed by it, and this contains also a second ferment of the seed, the product of the first. The ferment exhales an odour, which attracts the generating spirit of the Archeus. This spirit (aura vitalis) creates bodies after its own Idea: it disappears only at the instant of death to produce a new creation of the body, which then enters for the second time into fermentation. Seed is not indispensable for generation: animals produced when the Archeus acts on a suitable ferment are as perfect as those produced from eggs.[4]

Probably Van Helmont borrowed the Stoic theory of seminal reasons (rationes seminales) from St. Augustine, who taught that God deposited in matter a hidden treasure of active forces or seminal principles (rationes seminales), which, by successive germination in the matrix of matter, as occasion presented (acceptis opportunitatibus), produced each a different species of corporeal being.[5]

The central Archeus, according to Van Helmont, operated through local archei on the matter of the different organs by chemical processes. He recognised the existence of specific ferments and archei in the stomach, the liver, and other parts of the body, which bring about digestions and other physiological changes (in aliis locis continuò aliis fermentis).[6] His ideas on ferments, although naturally rather crude and undeveloped, were in the right direction and in many ways resemble the modern theory of enzymes.[7] Becher's ideas on fermentation[8] are similar, and Stahl[9] begins his account of fermentation by mentioning Van Helmont.

The acid of the gastric juice is necessary for digestion, but an excess of acid causes discomfort and illness, since it cannot be neutralised into salt by the alkali of the gall in the duodenum, as it normally is (aciditatem sui in salem commutat).[10] The pylorus, opening and closing under the influence of the Archeus, regulates the transfer of chyme (cremor) from the stomach to the duodenum.[11] Van Helmont compared the interactions of various juices in the organs with chemical reactions between liquids outside the body.

[1] 4, 18, 19, 81; Vb, 29 f., 86 f., 90 f., 428 f.   [2] 78, i; Vb, 649.
[3] 18; Vb, 86; Sendivogius, *Novum Lumen Chemicum*, in Albineus, *Bibliotheca Chemica Contracta*, 8°, Geneva, 1653, 1 f.
[4] 4, 5, 19, 22; Vb, 30, 33, 91, 120.
[5] Vol. I; Prescott, 1929; De Wulf, *History of Medieval Philosophy*, 1909, 93.
[6] 19, § 23; 29, 68; Vb, 93, 167, 577.
[7] Foster, 1901, 135; W. M. Bayliss, *Principles of General Physiology*, 1915, 307.
[8] *Physica Subterranea*, 1738, 132–92: he often uses the names *gas* and *spiritus sylvestris*.
[9] *Fundamenta Chymiae*, Pars II, 1746, 124.
[10] 29, § 56; Vb, 176.   [11] 30; Vb, 180.

Florkin[1] says: 'His great merit is to have proved the acidity of the gastric juice and to have recognised that digestion begins in the stomach and ends by assimilation at the level of the tissues; also in having seen that the process in its entirety is a chemical change.'

Van Helmont showed by experiment that salt can pass with water through a bladder and he thought the digested food (chyle) can pass through the walls of the intestines into the veins.[2] He did not know the existence of the lacteals, discovered by Aselli of Cremona in 1622 but first published in 1627.[3]

Van Helmont distinguished six fermentations of food in passing through the body.[4] The stomach and spleen, acting under the direction of the Archeus, constitute a Duumvirate and cannot act separately.[5] The ferment comes from the spleen, and the spleen and stomach produce an acid liquor (which Van Helmont said he had tasted in the saliva of birds) which is not the ferment but carries out the first digestion. If an acid only were necessary in digestion, vinegar would digest bread. The mass then passes through the pylorus, the regulating functions of which were most important,[6] into the duodenum, where it is neutralised by the gall (fel) of the gall bladder (he did not know of the pancreatic juice), a vital balsam different from the excrementitious biliary principle in the mass of the blood, and this is the second digestion. The third digestion takes place in the mesentery and continues in the liver, to which the gall-bladder sends the prepared fluid. The residue of the food, after the absorption of the nutritious chyle by the veins (when it becomes blood) passes along the intestine, where it meets a stercoraceous ferment which converts it into fæces.

The fourth digestion occurs in the heart, where the red blood becomes more yellow by the addition of vital spirit; the fifth digestion consists in the conversion of arterial blood into vital spirit (spiritus vitalis), a ferment always present in the left ventricle of the heart, some of it passing through the septum by minute pores too small to allow blood itself to pass. This spirit converts crude into vitalised blood. Van Helmont had no idea of the general circulation of the blood.

The sixth digestion consists in the elaboration of the nutritive principle from the blood in each separate member by a separate ferment. There are, thus, six digestions, not three as the schools taught. The number seven was chosen by Nature for a state of repose.[7]

Foster[8] says that Van Helmont's statement that 'the sixth digestion takes place in the kitchens of the several members, for there are as many stomachs as there are nutritive members', i.e. the tissue and not the blood primarily determines assimilation, anticipated conclusions not reached till long after. But Gerard Dorn[9] said that Paracelsus had taught that each member of the body has its own stomach in which its nutriment is cooked and the superfluous separated from the necessary. John Rogers[10] thought five digestions were sufficient: chylosis, chymosis, haematosis, pneumatosis, and spermatosis.

[1] Op. cit., 364.　　　[2] 29, § 48; Vb, 174.　　　[3] NBU, iii, 429.
[4] 51, § 57; Vb, 385.　　　[5] 42, 43; Vb, 273.　　　[6] 30; Vb, 180.
[7] 26, §§ 12–14; 28, 29; Vb, 158, 165 f.; Pagel, (a), 1930, 115.
[8] 1901, 140–1.　　　[9] Clavis totivs philosophiæ chymisticæ, 1567, 149.
[10] Analecta inauguralia de quinque humorum concoctionibus, 8°, London, 1664, q. by Sprengel, (1), 1815, v, 77.

Van Helmont's theory of ferment is summarised, in a series of 77 paragraphs giving his opinions, by Brucker:[1] 'VI. Materia ex qua, aqua est, initium autem per quod, fermentum seminale dispositiuum, unde mox producitur semen in materia. VII. Materia acquisito semine, fit eo ipso vita, sive materia illius entis media, discurrens in rei utriusque periodum, sive materiam ultimam. VIII. Est autem fermentum, ens creatum, formale quod neque substantia, neque accidens, sed neutrum, per modum lucis, ignis, magnalis formarum etc. conditum a mundi principio in locis suae monarchiae, ut semina praeparet, excitet et praecedat. IX. Haec fermenta dona et radices sunt a creatore domino stabilitatae in seculorum consummationem propagatione sufficientes, atque durabiles, quae ex aqua semina sibi propria excitent atque faciant.'

Van Helmont's theory of the connexion between fermentation and digestion was soon replaced by other less accurate views; in the article on 'Fermentation' in the French *Encyclopédie*[2] it is ridiculed and those who adopted it are called 'fermentateurs'. The article often mentions Van Helmont and Sylvius; the former 'voulut transporter dans tous les organes ... les fermens des laboratoires ... des levains particuliers qui changent les fluides qui y abonde' — which is, in fact, the modern biochemical theory.

In the article 'Grotte'[3] no notice is taken of gas sylvestre and the dogs suffocated in the Grotto del Cane were supposed to be poisoned by mineral vapours (respirent au lieu d'air, des vapeurs minérales, suffoquantes ... imprégnée de certaines particules ... qu'elles doivent être pour la plûpart vitrioliques). Evelyn,[4] who saw one exhibition with dogs, ascribed the effects to 'hot and dry vapours which ascend out of the earth' and on the top of the cave 'are converted into chrystalline drops' by cold, so that a torch near the bottom 'being extinguished, and lifted a little distance, was suddenly relighted'.

Physiology and Pathology

Van Helmont felt himself called to destroy the whole of ancient physiology and to make anew the doctrines of the schools: 'last of all, I will treat of the root of life, wherof none hath treated':[5] opus fuit, totam antiquorum Physiologiam destruere, atque innovare Scholarum Physices documenta. Postremo de vitæ radice (de quo nemo) agam. He was an expert anatomist, recognising (unlike Paracelsus) the great importance both of normal and pathological anatomy. Unlike Paracelsus also, he was fully acquainted with new scientific advances. Harvey's discovery of the circulation of the blood (1628) came too late for him to take account of it. Valentini[6] puts him alongside Francis Bacon and Descartes (nec multum absimile) as an innovator. Van Helmont's harsh but deserved criticism of the conventional medicine of his time made him many enemies and prejudiced the general acceptance of his views.

Diseases are caused by the irritated Archeus in the stomach sending acid ferments or juices to the various parts of the body.[7] Diseases are classified into two large groups: (i) those of the Archeus influus (morbi archeales), due to its inborn idea morbosa, producing the morbi silentes (epilepsy, etc.), the typical diseases (torturæ noctis), and those due to unequal division of forces (robur inaequale); and (ii) those due to the Archei insiti, caused by external influences, viz.: (*a*) recepta and (*b*) retenta. The recepta are of four kinds: (α) injecta a sagis, due to magic and fascination, natural but unknown causes; (β) concepta, due to poisons formed by the activities of the soul (rabies, etc.) and caused by sin (hysteria, etc.); (γ) inspirata, taken in by respiration; and (δ) suscepta, due to wounds. The retenta are either assumta (due to incompletely

[1] 1743, IV, i, 715; from Van Helmont, 19; V*b*, 90 f.   [2] 1756, vi, 517–26 (523).
[3] *Ib.*, 1757, vii, 967–9.   [4] *Diary*, 7 Feb. 1645; ed. Bray, 1870, 128.
[5] 1; V*b*, 6.   [6] V (*g*), Introductio, sign. A1.   [7] 40, 76, ix; V*b*, 234, 767.

assimilated food, poisons, etc.), or innata, due to disease of the Archei insiti.[1]

Van Helmont[2] rejected the doctrine that fevers are due to putrefaction; they are due to a 'thorn (calcar, spina)' or irritation, to foreign mixtures in the latex sanguinis, irritation of the Archei insiti by retenta, errors of the Archeus influus. Uræmia is due to a scoria or stercus liquidum, normally excreted by the urine but now absorbed and sent to the præcordial veins. The Archeus tries to shake off the excrementa and this causes shivering. If this is unsuccessful, the Archeus forms the Blas alterativum, causing turbid urine and fetid perspiration. The cures must aim at calming the Archeus by arcana, wine and diaphoretica (particularly *Præcipitatus diaphoreticus Paracelsi*, perhaps calomel).

Catarrh[3] is not due to vapours rising from the stomach to the brain but to a separation caused by ferments; the olefactory nerves and larynx are then 'erring guardians' (custodes errantes), mucus being normally formed to protect the respiratory organs but in catarrh an abnormal amount to protect them.

Van Helmont's work on the plague, 'The Plague Grave' (*Tumulus Pestis*), which is outstanding in several respects, epitomises the whole of his reform of medicine, and criticises Paracelsus severely. It proposes the theory that a pestilential poisonous gas (spiritus sylvestris, veneno tinctus) coming from patients, or corpses, or marshes or crude gas of the earth, which receives a ferment in the body, stirs up the Archeus who produces an image of death, which is the plague. In the sixth digestion (see p. 237) there is produced filth which can be called tartar of the blood, producing a poisonous ferment which affects the Archeus, and the image of death combining with the poison of tartar produces the plague.[4] Gout is due to a congenital or acquired diseased state of the Archeus, a sigillum podagræ, causing acid in the latex and deposition of limy matter (calx, creta podagrae) in the joints; it is treated with arcanum corallinum (mercuric oxide ?).[5]

Medicines do not act because of similarity or opposition to the disease but owing to divinely given forces (virtutes, sapores), which act like light falling on an illuminated object (solo velut radio, vel aspectu sui).[6] They produce healing ideas in the Archeus and do not act directly on the 'seeds' of diseases, as Paracelsus taught. Blood letting was condemned as weakening; the Galenical idea that purgatives acted by a vis selectiva, expelling particular humours, was rejected, since they produce the same effects on the healthy body; plasters and vesicants[7] cause loss of inoffensive serum. Van Helmont combated scholastic medicine but he retained its teleology; he explained 'life' by a 'vital force', personified as the Archeus; he was, Haeser thought, 'led astray by the blinding brilliance of the new Chemistry', and his ideas fell into disrepute in the development of the philosophies of Bacon and Descartes.[8] Sprengel[9] says few

[1] 56, 57; V*b*, 437, 452 (the table, p. 452, does not agree with the description on pp. 492 f., and the table is differently bracketed in V*a*, p. 566; it was rearranged in VD, p. 977, by Rixner and Siber, p. 225, and by Pagel, (*a*), 1930.
[2] 76; V*b*, 737 f.   [3] 49; V*b*, 345.
[4] 78, viii, xii–xiii; V*b*, 826, 856 f.; Pagel, *Paracelsus*, 1958, 185 f.
[5] 45; V*b*, 312.   [6] 58, 77; V*b*, 790, 459   [7] 1; 76, v, 24; vii, 6; V*b*, 7, 758, 763.
[8] Haeser, (1), 1881, ii, 360–2; Multhauf, *Isis*, 1954, xlv, 359.   [9] (2), 1827, iv, 316.

adopted Van Helmont's teachings in their entirety, practically only the Salzburg physician Franz Oswald Grembs,[1] who still tried to combine them with Galen's. Charleton accepted some of Helmont's ideas and translated some of his writings (see p. 214); Johann Jacob Wepfer (Schaffhausen; 23 December 1620–28 January 1695)[2] supported the theory of the Archeus, which presided over the nervous system and in plants was the Architect, although he rejected the theory of ferments. Schelhamer[3] tried to disprove the theory of the Archeus.

Jean Le Conte, of whom nothing seems to be known, in his 'Hermetic Key'[4] attempted to obtain the fire of copper (Venus) extolled by Van Helmont:[5] ignis Veneris est sulfur cupri volatile, in forma olei viridis, melle dulcius. Joachim Polemann, also otherwise unknown, wrote a 'New Light of Medicine',[6] experimented by heating red copper ore with sal ammoniac (obtaining green cupric chloride) and treating the distillate with spirit of wine and spirit of volatile alkali (ammonia). The result was disappointing, a damnable and pernicious vomitive. Metallic sulphurs need stronger solvents than mineral sulphurs, since they are firmly and compactly combined with their mercury. What he used in making Fire of Venus operated only on sulphurs of solar character and not on mercury.

Other Continental works referring to Van Helmont collected by Thorndike[7] include Gaspar Schott,[8] Luigi Conti,[9] Marten Schoock,[10] Martin Kerger,[11] George Stirk or Starkey (born in Bermuda, graduated Harvard 1646, then went to England),[12] J. F. Helvetius,[13] Albert Otho Faber,[14] Friedrich Hoffmann senr.,[15] Jean-Baptiste Du

---

[1] *Arbor integra et ruinosa hominis*, 4°, Munich, 1657.

[2] *Cicutæ Aqvaticæ Historia et Noxæ. Commentario illustrata*, 4°, Basel, 1679 (336 pp.), 73–80, 151.

[3] *Natura sibi et Medicis vindicata sive de Natura liber . . . Denique artis medicæ existentia ac certitudo . . . demonstratur . . .* , 4°, Kiel, 1697; BM 784. l. 9. (1.).

[4] *Clavis Hermetica, seu metallorum mineraliumque legitima solutio, cui Ignis Veneris aliaque non spernenda remedia absque ambagius candide elucidata*, Lyons, 1680 (19 pp.; BM 1033. e. 17. (4.)).

[5] 75, viii, 5; Vb, 705.

[6] *Novum Lumen Medicum, in welchem die vortreffliche Lehre des hochbegabten Philosophi Helmontii, von dem hohem Geheimnüs des Sulphuris Philosophorum . . . gründlich erkläret wird*, 8°, Frankfurt, 1647 (?); 12°, Amsterdam, 1659 (BM 1033. c. 25), 1699 (Ferguson, ii, 210); English tr., *Novum Lumen Medicum; wherein the excellent and most necessary Doctrine of the highly-gifted Philosopher Helmont concerning the Great Mystery of the Phoolosopher's* (sic) *Sulphur is fundamentally cleared*, sm. 8° (Ferguson, BM Cat. has 12°), London, 1662 (BM 1035. b. 36).

[7] vii, 230–40.

[8] *Thavmatvrgvs Physicvs, Sive Magiæ Universalis Naturæ et Artis*, 4°, Pars IV, Würzburg, 1659, 530–1.

[9] *Ludovicus de Comitibus, Clara disceptatio . . . De duobus Artis, & Naturæ miraculis: hoc est de liquore Alkhaest; necnon Lapide Philosophico*, 4°, Venice, 1661; BM 1033. h. 11. (11.); Ferguson, i, 173; Manget, 1702, i , 764.

[10] *De Fermento et Fermentatione Liber*, 12°, Groningen, 1662, 404 (BM 784. a. 21).

[11] *De Fermentatione Liber Physico-Medicus Omnia experimentis firmata*, 4°, Wittenberg, 1663, 15, 46, 62, 222 (BM 784. m. 15).

[12] *Liquor Alchahest*, 8°, London, 1675; Ferguson, ii, 401; Thorndike, vii, 233.

[13] *Vitulus Aureus . . .* , 16°, Amsterdam, 1667, 7, 21 (BM 1148. a. 5).

[14] *De Auro Potabili Medicinale* (in English), sm. 4°, [London], 1677 (BM 1034. h. 24. (2.)); German, *Von dem medicinalischen Auro Potabili*, 4°, Frankfurt, 1677 (BN R. 7014, 4° Te[131]. 132); Latin (and appendix), *De Auro Potabili Medicinali*, 4°, Frankfurt, 1678, BM 1034. h. 24. (3.).

[15] *Opus de Methodo Medendi . . . Dogmaticis, Paracelsiscis, Helmontianis, Harveianis principiis et propriis observationibus illustratum*, 4°, Leipzig, 1668 (BM 775. i. 15).

Hamel,[1] Rolfinck,[2] Sebastian Wirdig,[3] P. Ammann,[4] Pantaleon (i.e. Franz Gassmann),[5] David von der Beck,[6] E. H. von Henckel,[7] J. W. Wolff,[8] G. A. Mercklein,[9] L. C. F. Garmann,[10] G. Stolle,[11] and Bartholomaeus de Moor.[12]

CHARLETON

There was much interest in Van Helmont's works in England. There was a complete translation of the *Ortus Medicinæ* (p. 214) and parts were translated by Walter Charleton (Shepton Mallet, 2 February 1620–London, 24 April 1707), M.D. Oxon. 1642, physician to Charles I and (honorary) to Charles II in exile, an original F.R.S. (elected 1663), president of the College of Physicians.[13] He also wrote (under the inspiration of Van Helmont's *De Lithiasi*) *Spiritus Gorgonicus, vi sua saxipara exutus; sive de causis, signis, & sanatione litheasews, diatriba*, 8°, Leyden, 1650.

His best-known book is the *Physiologia Epicuro-Gassendo-Charletoniana: or, a Fabrick of Science Natural, Upon the Hypothesis of Atoms* (f°, London, 1654, see p. 467). In this, with a reference to Van Helmont,[14] he gives the experiment of burning a sulphured wax taper in a corked bottle (p. 233), together with Van Helmont's explanation that air, which is 'a pure, simple and Homogeneous substance ... was created to be the "Ἀτμουδοχεῖον, or common Receptary of Exhalations: and for the satisfaction of this End, it doth of necessity contain a Vacuum Deseminatum', adding that Lord Brouncker thought the pores were not empty but filled with ether.

Charleton was a copious author; some of his other works are: *The Darkness of Atheism dispelled by the Light of Nature, a Physico-Theologicall Treatise*, 4°, London, 1652; *Oeconomia Animalis novis in medicina hypothesibus superstructa & mechanicè explicata*, 12°, London, 1659, 1666, 1669; 'editio secunda', *Exercitationes Physico-Anatomicae de Oeconomia Animali novis in Medicina Hypothesibus superstructura et mechanice explicata*, 12°, Amsterdam, 1659, Leyden, 1678, Hague, 1681; *Exercitationes Pathologicæ, in quibus morborum pene omnium natura, generatione et causæ ... inquirunt*, 4°, London, 1661.

Disputes arose between the 'Chymical Physitians' or 'Helmontians' such as

---

[1] *De corporum affectionibus cum manifestis, tum occultis*, 12°, Paris, 1670 (BN R. 13536).
[2] *De Vegetabilibus*, etc., 4°, Jena, 1670 (BM 452. c. 11).
[3] *Nova Medicina Spirituum ...*, 12°, Hamburg, 1673 (BM 784. a. 25).
[4] *Brevis ad Materiam Medicam ... Manuductio*, in his *Supellex Botanica*, 8°, Leipzig, 1675 (BM 972. a. 11. (1.)).
[5] *Tumulus Hermetis apertus*, 8°, Nürnberg, 1676 (BM 1034. f. 27. (1.)); *Bifolium Metallicum*, 8°, Nürnberg, 1676, BM 1034. f. 27. (2.).
[6] *Experimenta et Meditationes circa Naturalium Rerum Principia*, 8°, Hamburg, 1674 (BM 1136. d. 6.).
[7] *De Philtris*, 8°, Frankfurt, 1690, BM 441. a. 22. (4.).
[8] *Curiosus Amuletorum Scrutator*, 4°, Leipzig and Jena, 1690 (BM).
[9] *Sylloge Physico-Medicinalium Casuum ...*, 4°, Nürnberg, 1698 (BM 1165. h. 12).
[10] *De Miraculis Mortuorum*, 4°, Leipzig, 1670 (BM 1038. l. 23); *ib.*, quibus præmissa dissertatio de cadavere et miraculis in genere, 4°, 2 pts., ed. L. J. H. Garmann, Dresden and Leipzig, 1709 (BM 1038. b. 24).
[11] *Anleitung zur Historie der medicinische Gelahrheit*, 4°, Jena, 1731 (BM 550. b. 27.).
[12] *Oratio de Hypothesibus medicis*, 4°, Amsterdam, 1706 BM 1185. i. 15. (42.).
[13] Moore, DNB, 1887, x, 116; Rolleston, *Bull. Hist. Med.*, 1940, viii, 403–16 (portrs.); Pagel, in Singer, (1), i, 497 (portr.); Thorndike, vii, 459.
[14] *Ib.*, 27–30; Lord Brouncker in his annotated copy, CUL Adv. a. 27. 7, opposite the statement that corking the vial prevents 'the eruption of the most subtle Atom', wrote 'Is that possible? Will not an atom of fire or heat pass anything?'

William Goddard, Edward Bolnest and George Starkey, on the one side, and the Galenical School, one of the latter, James Thompson, coming to its defence.[1] John Webster[2] said that, 'now an Helmontian seems to overtop a common Chymist, Paracelsian, and Galenist', he wonders that no one has collected 'those Pearly drops of Mineral learning, wherewith here and there he hath watered his polite and pithy sheets'. Sylvester Rattray[3] rejected the Archeus but retained the ferments. William Bacon published an anonymous 'key';[4] his authorship is disclosed by Mackaile[5] who says he believed, with Helmont, 'that Water is the sole material Principle of Generation, because Moses writeth, Genes. 1. 2. The Spirit of God moved upon the face of the Waters', but Mackaile 'humbly proposed' another theory.

F. M. VAN HELMONT

Francis Mercurius Van Helmont (Vilvorde, 20 October 1614–Cöln a.d. Spree, nr. Berlin, 1699) studied and practised medicine but apparently not at a university, and for a time led an irregular life among gipsies. He was a friend of the Qabbalist Knorr von Rosenroth and of Leibniz (who shows the influence of Neoplatonism, Paracelsus, and J. B. Van Helmont). He had the idea that the letters of the Hebrew alphabet, the primitive language, represent the positions of the organs of speech and he published a work on the education of deaf-mutes.[6] His *Opuscula Philosophica*, (Amsterdam, 1690) is mostly theological. An alchemical work[7] is said to be by F. M. Van Helmont or Limojon de Saint-Disdier[8] and a small historical work[9] is attributed to him.

F. M. Van Helmont describes some chemical experiments and facts in his writings, e.g. the formation of ferrous sulphide when a bar of red-hot iron is rubbed with sulphur,[10] steel with a soft iron core for armour-plate;[11] brass from copper and metallic zinc;[12] the increase in weight of lead on oxidation (100 parts of lead give 110 parts of minium),[13] volcanic sal ammoniac,[14] and the pre-

---

[1] *Helmont Disguised: or the Vulgar Errours of Impiricall and Unskilfull Practisers of Physick Confuted*, 8° (16°), London, 1657; Thomas, in Singer, (1), 1953, ii, 56.

[2] *Metallographia*, 1671, 34.

[3] *Aditus Novus ad occultas sympathiæ et antipathiæ causas inveniendas: per principia philosophiæ naturalis, ex fermentorum artificiosa anatomia hausta perfaectus*, 8°, Glasgow, 1658 (135 pp., BM 7410. de. 32).

[4] *A Key to Helmont. Or, A Short Introduction to the better understanding of the Theory and Method Of the most Profound Chymical Physicians*, 4°, London, 1682, 34 pp. (BM 1034. h. 35).

[5] *The Diversitie of Salts and Spirits Maintained*, v. sm. 4°, Aberdeen ,1683, 5.

[6] *Alphabeti vere naturalis Hebraici brevissima Delineatio quae simul methodum . . . quam surdi nati sunt sic informari possunt*, Sulzbach, 1657, 36 plates); L.L. in NBG, 1858, xxiii, 864; Haeser, (1), 1881, ii, 479; Kiesewetter, (1), 220; Van de Velde, 1929, 864; M. J. Nicholson, *The Conway Letters*, 1930, 84 f., 309 f.; Foppens, *Bibliotheca Belgica*, 1739, i, 570, says he died in Switzerland, 'Acatholicus'. Some writings of F. M. Van Helmont are in BM Sloane MS. 3984, ff. 151–2 (chymical opinions) and BM MS. Sloane 530 (alchemical enquiries), both tr. by Dr. A. Foote.

[7] *Aphorismes chimiques . . . mis en ordre par les soins et le travail de l'Hermite de Fauxbourg. Nouvellement traduit du Latin en François*, par M.S.D.R., 12°, Paris, 1692.

[8] Sarton, *Isis*, 1924, vi, 63; Ferguson, i, 379.

[9] *Seder Olam, sive Ordo Seculorum Historica*, s.l. (Leyden ?), 1693; Engl. tr., London, 1694.

[10] *The Paradoxal Discourses of F. M. Van Helmont, concerning the Macrocosm and Microcosm, or the Greater and Lesser World, and their Union, set down in writing by J.B. and now published*, London, 1685, Pt. I, 79.

[11] *Ib.*, 85.   [12] *Ib.*, 94.   [13] *Ib.*, 108.   [14] *Ib.*, 114.

paration of phosphorus[1] from evaporated urine distilled with 3 parts of sand. The last probably describes experiments made with Leibniz on the basis of information about Brand (p. 372).

Ferguson says he was more brilliant than his father, and seemed able to learn whatever he wished, but lacked his persistence and perseverence. It is only in circles outside chemistry that he is of any interest. He refers to an essay by Broeckx.[2]

[1] *Ib.*, Pt. II, 99.   [2] *Le Baron François Mercure van Helmont*, Antwerp, 1870, 28 pp.

CHAPTER VII

LIBAVIUS

Andreas Libavius (Libau or Liebau: the family is still living at Halle)[1] (Halle, *c.* 1540–Coburg, 25 July 1616) was born at Halle, in Saxony, about 1540 (Ferguson) or 1560 (Hoefer), the exact date being unknown. The family, which came from the Harz, was in poor but respectable circumstances, the father, Johann, being a linen weaver.[2] After a period of study in philosophy, history and medicine at Jena, Libavius graduated M.D. at that university, became a teacher at Ilmenau (1581) and Coburg (1586) and in 1586–91 was professor of history and poetry at Jena. From 1591 to 1607 he was town-physician (Stadtphysikus) in Rothenburg on the Tauber in Bavaria, and in 1592 became inspector of schools and of the Gymnasium in that town. He very naturally quarrelled with the Rector of the Gymnasium, and from 1607 (Dreyhaupt says from 1605, Hoefer 1606) until his death in 1616, Libavius was the first Director of the Gymnasium Casimirianum at Coburg, which was founded in 1605. In all his positions he took a keen interest in chemistry and besides several school books and works on philosophy, etc., he managed to compose a large literature on his favourite subject. As a physician, Libavius used chemical remedies, including potable gold, so following Paracelsus. He could not have been the 'Dr. Andreas' mentioned by Paracelsus, since the latter died in 1541.[3] He realised that such remedies should be used very carefully, criticised the extravagance of Paracelsus and his disciples, and exposed many high-priced 'elixirs' as merely common materials.

He says that certain devotees of chemistry differ little from magicians and, like impious Paracelsus (ut ille impius Paracelsus), construct from the motion of the stars and from the constellations magic mirrors, gems, globes, and many similar devices for exploring the future and predicting the occurrence of disease (morborumque momenta).[4] He says 'Paracelsus, as in many other matters he is stupid and uncertain, so also here writes like a madman', and he enlarges on 'the stolidity of Paracelsus'.[5]

Libavius nevertheless defended chemical remedies against the prohibition

---

[1] E. O. von Lippmann, letter to the author.

[2] J. C. von Dreyhaupt, *Pagus Neletici et Nudzici oder ausführliche diplomatisch-historische Beschreibung des . . . Saal-kreises*, f°, Halle, 1755, ii, 658; Mercklin, *Lindenius renovatus*, Nürnberg, 1686, 47; Venel, art. Chimie, *Encyclopédie Méthodique, Chimie*, 1796, iii, 295; Gmelin, (1), i, 345 f., 557 (list of polemical writings); Kopp, (1), i, 113, ii, 11; (2), iii, 145 (with an opening sentence of 164 words); Hoefer, (1), ii, 26; Ferguson, ii, 34; Ferchl and Süssenguth, (2), 1939, 68; Thorndike, vi, 238.

[3] Rixner and Siber, 1829, i, 25; Paracelsus, *Opera*, Geneva, 1658, iii, 159; Libavius, *Defensio et Declaratio Perspicua Alchymiæ*, Urselli, 1604, 154–5: præceptorem meum D. Theophrastum, quæ ei Basileæ contingerint; præceptor meus carus, beatæ memoriæ, Philippus Theophrastus, Paracelsus vocatus.

[4] VA, 2, ch. 1; 1606, 181; see the list of Libavius's works on pp. 246 f.

[5] IV, 1597; VB, 6, 1606, 166, 179 (De Iudicio aquarum).

of the medical faculty of Paris. Although a believer in transmutation, he warned against its many frauds, and he also criticised the Rosicrucians:

Wolmeinendes Bedencken / Von der Fama, vnd Confession der Brüderschafft dess Rosen Creutzes . . . ; sm. 8°, Frankfurt, 1616 (BM 1032. b. 23; 294 pp.); Analysis Confessionis Fraternitatis De Rosea Cruce, in Appendix Necessaria Syntagmatis Arcanorum Chymicorum, f°, Frankfurt, 1615.

FIG. 8. ANDREAS LIBAVIUS, 1540?–1616.
(By courtesy of the National Museum Library, Vienna)

In his writings Libavius generally has the outlook of the university professor rather than that of the practical alchemist or fanatical doctor; his language is moderate and his attitude independent. As a professor of poetry and an excellent classical scholar, he was able to write in a clear and elegant Latin style, including verse.[1] In some of his publications he uses the name Basilius de Varna. He read very widely and quotes a large number of authors.[2] His

---

[1] E.g. *Ad Marcum Amlingum Andreæ Libavii ode amica strenæ nomine missa*, 4°, Coburg, 1589 (BM 11409. dd. 9/3).
[2] List of 186 in VA, 1606, 69–70.

main fault is credulity and uncritical use of alchemical works; his later and his long replies to his critics are tedious. He tried to extract sense from alchemical authorities, a task which frequently proved too severe even for his painstaking efforts.

One of the earliest works of Libavius is a collection of letters on chemical subjects, published in 1595; one (No. 79. Pt. II) is dated 1591 and several 1594:

I. Rervm Chymicarvm Epistolica Forma ad Philosophos et Medicos qvosdam in Germania excellentes descriptarum. . . . Avtore Andrea Libavio Med. D. Poeta & Physica Rotemburgo tuberano. . . . Excudibat Ionnes Saurius, impensis Petri Kopffii, 8°, Frankfurt, Parts I (36 letters; 300 pp.) and II (100 letters: 615 pp.), 1595; III (63 letters, viii ll. 448 pp.), 1599 (BM 1032. a. 22; Speter, *Chem. Ztg.*, 1932, lvi, 1021). Libavius has the confusion of *u* and *v* common in Latin of the period; initial *u* or *v* is given as *v*, and medial *u* or *v* as *u*, except in capital letters, when it is *V*. He also often uses a mark for *m* or *n* over the last vowel, e.g. *ũ* for *um*, and *&* for *et*.

The first volume contains philosophical discussions, criticisms of Paracelsus, the definition of chemistry, the explanations of obscure chemical terms (I, p. 162), a commentary on the *Tabula smaragdina* (I, p. 144), the philosopher's egg, etc.; volume two deals with chemical operations (putrefaction, digestion, maceration, solution, coagulation, distillation, sublimation, descension, calcination, etc.), with the examination of metals by fire (cineritium), antimony and mineral acids, mercury, etc., with quotations from old authors, including Classical, Geber (King of Spain and grandson of Mahomet) (II, p. 125), and modern writers such as Rubeus and Porta. One letter, on fulmination, is addressed to Martin Rulandus (II, p. 428). The third volume deals with the theory and practice of alchemy (III, p. 10), the definition 'Chymiæ est mineralium elaboratio' (III, p. 34), realgar (risa galla) (III, p. 59), various dyes and colours (III, pp. 75–98), potable gold (III, p. 154), potable silver, etc. (III, p. 161), the fixation of mercury (III, p. 233), 'increasing' gold and silver (III, p. 261: ego in Alchymia non fraudum gratia), a defence of chemists (III, p. 286), chemical symbols (III, p. 345: very complicated), lac virginis (basic lead acetate) (III, p. 368), magisteries of odours (III, p. 399), the nature of tastes (III, p. 413), a 'sweet oil' (ether) by distilling alcohol and sulphuric acid (III, p. 422), and the magistery of sound (III, p. 425).

A letter of Libavius is included in his *Alchemia* (1597) and there are 52 letters from him, mostly to Sigismund Schnitzer of Bamberg, in a collection published by Johann Hornung (a physician of Nürnberg):

Cista Medica Quâ in Epistolæ Clarissimorum Germaniæ Medicorum, familiares, & in Re Medica, tàm quoad Hermetica & Chymica quàm etiam Galenica principia, lectu jucundæ & utiles, cum diu recondis Experimentis asservantur . . . , 4°, Noribergæ Sumptibus Simonis Halbmayri, engr. t.p., xi ll., 516 pp., pref. dated January, 1626 (BM 1169. g. 4; CUL K. 16. 52). They deal with alchemical and medical subjects and date from 1599 to 1616.

In a collection of essays on 'Singularities' in four parts:

II. Singvlarivm, Part I, 375 pp., 1599; Part II, 524 pp., 1599; Part III, 1155 pp. and index, 1601; Part IV, 704 pp. and index, 1601; 8°, Frankfurt (BM 957. h. 22, complete).

Libavius discusses a range of subjects with considerable learning: the nature and transmutation of metals, amber (i, 208 f., 'salt' on distillation, 227), fossil teeth, the magistery of Paracelsus, the flight of witches, 'de gestatione Cacodæmonum', poisons, manna and honey (ii, 79 f.), mumia, asphalt, bitumen, naphtha, petroleum, coal, turf and belemnites (iii, 1–1115). The chapters on amber (iii, 406, 587 f., 644 f.)[1] include general, medicinal, and chemical information, e.g. the preparation of varnishes. The work also discusses the antipathy between parents and children, spermaceti, astrology and comets, the golden tooth,[2] somnambulism, the vegetable lamb of Scythia and other zoophytes,[3] silkworms, the intellect of beasts, mineral waters, frogs and toads (with a section of an oval toad-stone filling more than a page; iv, 424), and other matters. The essays probably reproduce Libavius's lectures and may have been used as a school manual: they are of considerable interest in the history of science. Libavius's declamation on the comet of 1604 was published with a work by Gisbertus Voetius on prognostications of comets.[4]

The most important work of Libavius, at the same time the first systematic text-book of chemistry, is his *Alchemia* (1597):

III. D.O.M.A. / Alchemia / Andreae Li- / bavii Med. D. Poet. / Physici Rotembvrg. / operâ / e dispersis passim optimorvm avto- / rum, veterum & recentium exemplis potissimum, tum etiam præ- / ceptis quibusdam operosè collecta, adhibitisq; ratione & ex / perientia, quanta potuit esse, methodo accura- / tâ explicata, & / In integrum corpus redacta. / Accesserunt / Tractatus nonnulli Physici Chymici, item methodicè ab eodem autore explicati, / quorum titulus versa pagella exhibet. / Sunt etiam in Chymicis eiusdem D. Libavii epistolis, iam antè im- / pressis, multa, huic operi lucem allatura. / Cum gratia & Priuilegio Cæsareo speciali ad decennium. / Francofvrti / Excudebat Iohannes Saurius, impensis Petri Kopffij, / *M.D.XCVII*. 4°, Pp. un-numb. xviii, 424; index xix, un-numb.; 1 blank; Device and Colophon.

On *verso* of t.p.: Tractatvs Physici Chymici [*sic*] Alchemiæ adiecti. I. Epitome metallica, qua metallorum natura declaratur, ad opus Chymicum scitu necessaria [pp. 1–48]. II. Dialogus de Mercurio philosophorum [pp. 49–82]. III. De *AZOTHO* & aqua permanente [pp. 83–96][5] IIII. De lapide philosophorum [pp. 97–162]. V. Ars probandi duobus libris comprehensa [pp. 163–274]. VI. Tractatus de iudicio aquarum mineralium tres libri [pp. 275–392].

This commentary has a sep. t.p. and pagination (given above):

IV. D.O.M.A. Commentationvm Metallicarvm Libri Qvatvor de Natvra Metallorvm, Mercvrio Philosophorvm, Azotho, et Lapide sev tinctura physicorum conficienda. è Rervm Natvra, Experientia, et Avtorum praestantium fide Studio & labore

---

[1] Eastlake, *Materials for a History of Oil Painting*, 1847, 288 f.
[2] Cf. Liebig, *Letters on Chemistry*, 1851, 527, and Rolfinck, p. 314.
[3] On the 'vegetable lamb' see H. Lee, *The Vegetable Lamb of Tartary. A Curious Fable of the Cotton Plant*, 1887 (112 pp.); Lippmann, (6), 1933, 46 f. The myth of the barnacle goose, which appears in Alexander Neckam (Vol. I), is dealt with by Libavius in his *De Vniversitate, et Originibvs*, 1610 (see 251); E. Heron-Allen, *Barnacles in Nature and Myth*, Oxford Univ. Press, 1928 (180 pp.; he did not know who Libavius was); Lippmann, (6), 36 f.; F. Moll, *A. Nat.*, 1928, xi, 123–49 (Teredo navalis); it appears in Arabic works (al-Qazwīnī, d. A.D. 1283); Ruska, *A. Nat.*, 1929–30, xii, 413–14.
[4] Libavius, *Declematio de cometa anni 1604*, 4°, Amsterdam, 1665; Voetius, *Exercitatio de prognosticis cometarum*, 4°, Amsterdam, 1665 (BM 532. e. 16. (3.)).
[5] The alchemists' name azoth for mercury is probably the Spanish azogue, based on the Spanish pronunciation azzōq of the Arabic name al zāwūq of the metal; Darmstaedter, *Alchemie des Gebers*, 1922, 166. In the later period it had various meanings, sometimes the nature of an acid, but mainly something containing potentially the metallic nature, or a substance used in the artificial preparation of noble metals; Kopp, (4), i, 30.

A. Libavii ... depromti & expositi, more veteris philosophiæ cum perspicuitate euidente, 4°, Frankfurt, 1597; iv ll., 2nd t.p. with motto verso, pp. 3–392; with sep. t.ps., p. 163 Ars probandi mineralia; p. 275 De Ivdicio Aqvarvm Mineralivm (lib. iii, p. 374, De Aqva Nili is a letter Ad præstantem virum D.Ph. Scherbium).

IV was certainly issued separately. The British Museum, which has no copy of III (1597) has it (BM 726. c. 1) and it is not found in some copies of III in contemporary bindings (Young copy, Ferguson, ii, 31, and my copy). III and IV, like other books printed at the time in Frankfurt, are on poor paper, now usually browned. III is much rarer than the first eds. of Newton's *Principia* or Boyle's *Sceptical Chymist*.

The commentary includes the six treatises named under III, which for purposes of reference are numbered as follows:

i. Epitome metallica, qua metallorum natura declaratur, ad opus Chymicum necessaria (alt. title: De Natura Metallorum, et cognatorum mineralium).
ii. Dialogus de Mercurio Philosophorum.
iii. De Azotho et aqua permanente (alt. title: De Azoth Philosophorum, et aqua permanente).
iv. De Lapide Philosophorum.
v. Ars probandi duobus libris comprehensa (De Sceuasia artis probatoriæ; De Docimasia artis probatoriæ).
vi. Tractatus de iudicio aquarum mineralium in tres libros distributus (Pars I, Pars II, Pars III De Aqua Nili).

Treatises ii to iv extend the favourable attitude towards alchemy in III and assume that metals are composed of mercury and sulphur, v deals with analyses of ores in the dry way, fluxes, etc., vi is an early treatise on chemical analysis.[1] iii contains mystical figures.

In the catalogue of his own works, Libavius[2] gives as editions of his Alchymia 'cum prima parte Commentationum, 1597, ibid. Alchymia in folio cum Commentarii 1 et 2 parte 1606', and[3] he also mentions 'Alchemia mea anno 1597 latine edita'. The spelling 'Alchemia' in 1597 is changed to 'Alchymia' in 1606, and in a discussion of the name in 1611[4] he derives it from χυμός (chymos). In the 1597 ed., ch. 26 in Bk. II, tract. i, is mis-numbered 27 and the remaining chapters are numbered one too high; otherwise the division and contents are identical. Many authors[5] date the first edition 1595 but this is, apparently, incorrect. The second edition of the *Alchemia* was published in 1606, and is the one quoted by most authors:

V. D.O.M.A. / Alchymia / Andreæ / Libavii, Recogni- / ta, Emendata, et / aucta, tum dogmatibus & / experimentis nonnullis; / Tvm Commentario / Medico Physico Chymico: / Qvi exornatvs est va- / riis Instrumentorum Chymicorum picturis; / partim aliunde translatis, partim / planè nouis: / In gratiam eorum, / Qvi Arcanorvm Natvr- alivm / cupidi, ea absq; inuolucris elementarium & / ænigmaticarum sordium, intueri / gaudent. / Præmissa Defensione Artis: / opposita censuræ Parisianæ: / Cum gratia & Priuilegio Cæsareo speciali ad decennium. / Francofvrti, / Excudebat Joannes

---

[1] G. Chesneau, *Revue Scient.*, 1905, iii, 321, 357.
[2] VII, 1613, pref.   [3] X, 1604, 246.   [4] VI, 1611, 1.
[5] Lenglet du Fresnoy, iii, 203; Gmelin, (1), i, 348; Kopp, (1), i, 115; ii, 11, and throughout the 4 vols.; *id.*, (2), iii, 146; Hoefer, (1), ii, 27, 30 (no date in 1 ed. (2), 1843, ii, 29); Roscoe and Schorlemmer, *Treatise*, 1905, i, 10; Hiortdahl, *Skrifter Vidensk. Selsk. Christiania, mat. naturv. Kl.*, 1905, No. vii, 68; Lippmann, (1), ii, 442 (correct date in (2), i, 598, 641); Stillman, 1924, 364.

Saurius, impensis Petri Kopffii. / Anno c Iↄ. Iↄ. VI, (1606), f°, engr. border to t.p., x ll., 196 pp., vi ll. index (BM 535. k. 5).

The two parts of the commentary have separate t.ps.

VA. D.O.M.A. Commentariorvm Alchymiæ Andreæ Libavii Med. D. Pars Prima, Sex libris declarata: Continens Explicationem Operationvm Chymicarvm Priore Artis Libro comprehensarvm, adiectis Fornacvm et aliorvm vasorvm figvris, partim ex impressis antehac autoribus, partim aliunde acceptis, & ex latibulis officinarum productis. Præmissa est Defensio Alchemiæ et refutatio obiectionum ex Censura scholæ Parisiensis, quæ licet videri nolit hanc Alchemiam, sed Quercetani damnasse, nimis tamen frigidè de arte sentit . . . Alchymiae hîc caussa agitur, non Quercetani, v ll., 402 pp.

VB. D.O.M.A. Commentariorvm Alchemiæ Andreæ Libavii Med. Doct. Pars Secunda, Continens Tractatvs Qvosdam singulares ad illustrationem eorum potissimum, quæ libro Alchemiæ secundo habentur difficiliora laboriosioraq́;, quæq́; plurium simul artium adminiculo indigent, & veluti ex multis constituta, peculiarium scientiarum dignitatem & nomen merentur, pp. 192, v ll. index and errata. This a reprint of IV.

VA has along prefatory letter to Jacob Boncarsi, 'in Germania legato ordinaris', of the King of France, mostly about Quercetanus, a lengthy refutation of the attack by John Riolan and the Paris school on Libavius's book IX and X, and then six treatises:

  1. Commentariorvm in Librvm Primvm Alchymiæ Partis I. Lib. I. De Sceuastica Artis (pp. 71–179), dealing with chemical apparatus and operations with numerous interesting illustrations.[1]
  2. Commentarii Chymici Partis I. Liber Secvndvs De Pyrotechnia [& Affinibus] (pp. 180–243), in which not only the degrees of fire but also the old Aristotelian doctrines of the four elements are expounded, with quotations from Classical authors and their commentators.
  3. Commentariorvm Alchymiæ Liber Tertivs. De Distractionibus, dealing with chemical operations (fusion, liquation, powdering, granulation, filtration, separation of liquids, calcination — including that in a stream of air in a tube, etc., etc.).
  4. Commentariorvm Chymicorvm Liber Qvartvs. De Extractionibus (including sublimation and distillation).
  5. Commentariorvm Alchymiæ. Liber Qvintvs. De Compositionibus.
  6. Commentariorvm Alchymiæ. Liber Sextvs. De Enchiria exaltationum.

In (1), pp. 92 f., Libavius gives his ideas of the plan, a description and illustrations of a large chemical laboratory or 'house' (Domus chymici), which includes bathrooms, museum, wine cellars (cella vinaria, cujus spiracula meridionalia maxima ex parte debent esse clausa), covered walks and gardens, as well as the professional rooms.

A further commentary appeared in three folio parts (of which the last two are largely polemical on alchemical and medical topics) in 1611–15, which are here numbered separately as:

VI. D.O.M.A. Syntagmua selectorvm vndiqvaqve et perspicve traditorvm Alchymiæ Arcanorum. Pro III. Parte Commentariorum Chymiæ hactenus desideratorum, Insertis passim Scholiis, & commentationibus ipsis, ad penitissima huius Philosophiæ & Medicinæ ducentibus. Conscriptvm, et in IIX. libros digestum. . . . Francofvrti Excudebat Nicolaus Hoffmannus, Impensis Petri Kopffii. Anno M.D.CXI, pp. xii, 480, index viii; engr. border to title; dedic. dated April 1611.

VII. D.O.M.A. Syntagmatis Arcanorvm Chymicorvm, ex Optimis Avtoribvs Scriptis, impressis, experientaque artifice collectorum, Tomvs Secvndvs. In qvem congesta svnt partim noua, eaq́; penitiora Spagyrorum secreta, partim prioris tomi nonnulla explicatius tradita, & inter ea etiam ænigmatica Quercitani, aliorumque Hermeticorum non pauca studiosè inuestigata, declarata & iudicata . . . Francofurti Excudibat Nicolaus Hoffmannus, Jmpensis Petri Kopffii. Anno M.D.CXIII. pp. xii,

---

[1] Schelenz, in Diergart, 1909 ,162.

453, index xv, engraved border to title, sep. un-numb. leaf with woodcut between pp. 306–7; dedic. dated April 1613.

VIII. D.O.M.A. Appendex necessaria Syntagmatis Arcanorum Chymicorum Andreæ Libavii Professoris Pvbl. et Medici Chymici practici. ... In Qva Præter Arcanorvm Nonnvllorum expositionem & illustrationem, quorundam item Medicorum Hermeticorum & mysticorum descriptionem continentur defensiones geminæ Primum ... ab Henningo Schevnemano ... Postea à Nicolao Guiberto ... Accesservnt I. Iudicium breue de Dea Hippocratis, seu Hygeia argentea (argentipara) Henningi Schevnemani . . . ; II. Schema medicinæ Hippocraticæ & Hermeticæ simul ... ; III. Examen Philosophiæ magicæ Crollii; IV. Censura Philosophiæ vitalis Ioannis Hartmanni ... ; V. Admonitio de regulis Nouæ Rotæ, seu harmonicæ Sphæræ Fratrvm De Sociietate Roseæ Crvcis ... , M.DC.XV. Francofvrti Excudebat Nicolaus Hoffmannus. Impensis Petri Kopfij, pp. xii, 279, x, Colophon; followed by (both printed by Kopff): D.O.M.A. Examen Philosophiae novæ, quæ Veteri Abrogandæ opponitvr ... , pp. 306, xii; D.O.M.A. Analysis Confessionis Fraternitatis De Rosea Crvce, pp. 28, Finis; with sep. t.p.'s both dated 1615.

Another ed. of VI with same pagin. but without engr. title appeared in 1615 and another in 1655 (BM 535. k. 6; pp. viii, 480, vii). Gmelin, (1), i, 348, gives VI–VIII, 1631. An ed. of at least VI–VII appeared at Frankfurt in 1595, and is mentd. by Lenglet du Fresnoy, iii, 203. An *Alchymia Pharmaceutica* sometimes quoted is merely part of VII.

In VIII (p. 8) Libavius gives an account of blood transfusion:

magister artis habeat tubulos argenteos inter se [a strong man and the patient] congruentes. Aperiat arteriam robusti, & tubulum inserat, muniatque: mox & ægroti arteriam findat, & tubulum fœmineum infigit. Iam duos tubalos sibi mutuo applicet, & ex sano sanguis arterialis, calens, & spirituosus saliet in ægrotum, vnaque vitæ fontem afferet, omnemque languorem pellet.

This was probably quoted from Magnus Pegel, professor in Rostock.[1] Libavius in this reply to Henning Scheunemann, a physician of Bamberg and a Rosicrucian, gives an account of Scheunemann's opinions. He divided the internal nature of man into seven degrees, from the seven modifications it undergoes: combustion, sublimation, dissolution, putrefaction, distillation, coagulation, and tincture, and also gives an account of ten modifications which the three principles can undergo. As Thomson[2] said, 'Libavius had the patience to analyze and expose all these gallimatias.'

One of the few works of Libavius in German is his book on practical chemistry:

IX. Alchymistische Practic: Das ist, von künstlicher Zubereytung der vornembsten chymischen Medicinen: In zweyen Tractätlein klärlich entdecket: Deren das Erste, von destillirten Wassern, Öhlen, Saltzen, Extracten, quintis essentiis, aquis vitae ... von einem vnbekandten Artisten aufs eigner Erfahrung, bester form, auffs fleissigst vnd trewlichst beschrieben: Das Ander, vom Lapide Philosophorum: Wie derselbe künstlich soll gemacht werden: ohn figürliche vnd Parabolische reden, eigentlich vnnd deutlich also gelehret ... corrigieret, vnnd erkläret durch Andream Libavium ... Getruckt zu Franckfort am Mayn, bey Johann Saurn, in Verlegung Petri Kopffen. M.DC. III, 4°, pp. 293, iii. Translated by L. Doldius as:

X. Praxis Alchymiæ, hoc est, doctrina de artificiosa Præparatione praecipvorum medicamentorvm chymicorum: duobus libris explicata: quorum primus de destillatione aquarum et oleorum: de salium & extractorum ... ab auctore anonymo, propria

---

[1] *Thesaurus rerum selectarum, magnarum, dignarum, utilium pro generis humani saluti oblatus*, s.l., 4°, 1604, q. by Haeser, (1), 1881, ii, 417, who refers to P. Scheel, *Die Transfusion des Blutes und Einspritzung der Arzneien in die Adern*, 2 vols., Copenhagen, 1802, and part II (by Dieffenbach) in Rust, *Handwörterbuch der Chirurgie*, Berlin, 1838; the experiment of transfusion from an artery to an artery could not be carried out. Haeser suggests that Libavius had also a second work by Pegel available.

[2] (1), i, 176.

experientia conscriptus est: Alter de lapide philosophorvm agit: in quo vt recte is comparandus sit, remotis omnibus figuris & parabolis dilucide docetur... Opera Andreæ Libavii... ex Germanico idiomate in Latinam traductus. Annexus est libellus J. Bessoni de absoluta ratione extrahendi olea et aquas a medicamentis simplicibus, 8°, Frankfurt, 1604 (BM 1032. a. 16), reprinted 1605 and 1607 (Sotheran *Cat.* 845 (1935), Suppl., No. 86; Gmelin, (1), i, 347).

Bk. I, pts. 1 and 2, pp. 1–244; pt. 1 deals with distillation of waters, quintessences and oils of vegetables, of spirit of wine with a long alembic (p. 44), of an aqua vitae made for the Emperor Frederick III (p. 53), oils of human skull (p. 146), of amber (p. 179), etc., and has crude illustrations; the apparatus is repeatedly specified as of Waldenburg glass; Libavius's commentary (Declaratio), pp. 245–503; pt. 2 (De Mineralium Apparatu) deals with the sublimation of sulphur, antimony, sal ammoniac ('called by some sal Armeniacus since it is found native in Armenia') (p. 331), arsenic, mercury (corrosive sublimate), etc.; Bk. II, Ars hermetica, pp. 504–680, contains extracts from the unknown work (which he thought was by a Belgian) and Libavius's commentary, and is purely alchemical; Libavius says (p. 507) that the revelation of the secret of the philosophers' stone would be punished by instant death; also (p. 636) that Paracelsus still lived in his grave in Salzburg. An Anonymi Praxeos Alchimiæ Liber cum Andreæ Libavii Additionibus is printed in Manget, ii, 700–13.

XI. Variarvm Controversiarvm... Libri dvo Schediastici..., 8°, Frankfurt, 1600 (BM 775. b. 8; 728 pp., p. heading: Schediasmata Philos.).

XII. Neoparacelsica. In Qvibvs Vetus medicina Defenditvr aduersus τερετίσματα. Tum Georgii Amvvald... liber de Panacea... Tum Johannis Gramani, olim Theologi, nunc Pseudochymici..., 8°, Frankfurt, 1594, xii ll. 783 pp. (errata 783 *v.*) (BM 1032. a. 21).[1]

XIII. Nouus de Medicina Vetervm tam Hippocratica, quam Hermetica Tractatus. In cvivs priore parte Dogmata plæraq; inter vtriusque Professores recentes controuersa, aduersus vltimum per Iosephum Michelium Paracelsitarum conatum discutiuntur; In posteriore Vniversale Alchymistarum, autoribus Lvllis & Arnoldo, quam liquidissimè exponitur.... 8°, Frankfurt, 1599, viii ll., 240 pp. (sep. t.p. 241 Medicinæ Hermeticæ Artificibus Catholicæ ad Hominis Sanitatem), 242 blank, 243–567. The commentary on Lully's *Clavis* is contained in pp. 253 (misnumb. 153)–440, and on Arnold of Villanova's *Rosarium* in pp. 456–567 (BM 1032. a. 15.).

XIV. Dialectica Philippo Ramæa, ex Descriptionibvs et Commentariis Philippi Melanchthonis & Petri Rami... Addita est Rhetorica... Melanchthonianis Oratoriæ præceptis aucta, 8°, Frankfurt, 1609, viii ll., 667 pp.; on logical matters (BM 1133. b. 35).

XV. Schediasmata Medica et Philosophica Ad Henningvm Rennemanum Philosophum M. apud Erfurdenses. Pro Galenicæ Medicinæ, & Peripateticæ familiæ scholarumq; Germaniæ dignitate edita, 8°, Frankfurt, 1596, pp. [1–13] 14–728, italic type (BM 1170. b. 6; Gmelin, (1), i, 347, dates 1598).

XVI. Tractatvs dvo Physici; prior de impostoria vvlnervm per vngventvm armarium sanatione Paracelsis vsitata commendataque. Posterior de Crventatione Cadavervm in ivsta caede factorum praesente..., 8°, Frankfurt, 1594 (BM 780. a. 29; deals with magnetic cure of wounds and the bleeding of corpses formerly used as an important legal method, rejecting the first and accepting the second as a fact).

XVII. D.O.M.A. Alchimia Trivmphans de Inivstamin se Collegii Galenici spvrii in Academia Parisiensi Censvra; et Ioannes Riolani maniographia, falsa convicta. Opus Hermeticvm, vere didacticum... solida explicans Chymiatriæ Hippocraticæ fundamenta: De Qvinta Essentia, Magno Perfectoqvo Lapidis Magisterio, principiis, extractis, oleis, aquis, salibus, elixyribus, &c diligenter elaboratvm, 8°, Frankfurt off. Io. Saurii Impens. P. Kopfii, 1607, 926 pp. (BM 1032. a. 18; a defence of alchemy).

XVIII. D.O.M.A. De Vniversitate, et Originibvs Rervm Conditarvm Contemplatio Singvlaris, Theologica, et Philosophica; Ivxta Historiam Hexaëmeri Mosaici in

---

[1] Amwald (Georgius an und von Wald) practised in Augsburg and sold a *terra sigillata* or *Panacea anwaldina*, which Libavius showed was merely cinnabar, having none of the pretended virtues and not worth the high price charged for it. Am Wald published: *Georg Am Wald, Bericht vnd Erklerung... wie vnd was Gestalt des new von jm erfunden Terra Sigillata vnd Universal Artzeney... zugebrauchen*, 4°, St. Gallen, 1581 (12 ll.); *Kurtzer Bericht, wie, was gestalt vnd warvmb das Panacea am Waldina... an Tag gegeben...*, 4°, Frankfurt a.M., 1591, 1592, and other eds.; Ferguson, ii, 526.

Genesin propositam instituta. Et in VII. Libros distributa, 4°, Frankfurt, 1610, vi ll.
742 pp. vi ll. (BM 1009. b. 16; deals with six days of Creation; pillars of Seth (p. 32);
aqua sicca =mercury (p. 216) transmutation of plants (p. 268); rejects the divining rod
(p. 350, de Virgula divina theses, mentioning Agricola); rejects astrology (pp. 361, 401);
accepts the barnacle goose (p. 533).

XIX. D.O.M.A. Tractatus Medicus Physicus vnnd Historia / Dess fürtrefflichen
Casimirianischen Sawer Brunnen / . . ., sm. 8°, Coburg, 1610, 126 unnumb. ll., in
German (BM 1168. d. 19; Medical properties and chemical examination of the mineral
water).

XX. Qvæstionvm Physicarvm, Controversarvm inter Peripateticos & Rameos,
Tractatvs . . . Iacobvs Martinvs Scotvs Dunkeldiensis . . . cvm Præfatione Guilielmi
Tempelii, Cantabrigæ . . . Exercendi ingenii & naturalium exactius noscendorum
gratia disputatæ ab Andrea Libavio Halensi, 8°, Frankfurt, 1591 (MD LXXXXI),
xvii ll. 362 pp., colophon (verso blank), blank leaf, ii ll. corrections (BM 519. c. 20: (2)).

This is directed against two Ramists, James Martin, a Scot, of Oxford, and
Temple of Cambridge; too much time was spent on method and science and
learning had declined, although the Ramian method (Pierre de la Ramée,
Ramus, 1515–72, precursor of Descartes and opponent of Aristotelianism) had
its merits. Ramus had praised Paracelsus in 1568 as 'the German Asclepiades'
and Ramism had certain affinities with Paracelsism.[1]

XXI. Antigramania secvnda Svpplemento Absvrditatvm et Convitiorvm in Galeni
Artem . . ., 8°, Frankfurt, 1595, iii ll. 127 pp. (BM 1032. a. 21).

XXII. D.O.M.A. Defensio et Declaratio Perspicua Alchymiæ Transmvtatoriæ
opposita Nicolai Gviperti . . . expugnationi virili: Et Gastonis Clavei . . . Apologiæ
contra Erastum malè sartæ & prauæ, 8°, Vrsellis, 1604 (dedic. dated 1603), xii ll.
694 pp. xii ll. BM 1032. a. 17.

A logical defence of alchemy of some interest: the 'transmutation' of plants (p. 88);
the Tabula Smaragdina known to Albertus Magnus (p. 177); Avicenna's Alchemy
genuine (p. 186); the conversion of iron into copper a real transmutation (pp. 216–82);
argyrogonia and chrysogonia, vim argentificam & aurificam dicit inesse seminibus suis
(p. 553); de vi aurifica & argentifica (p. 553); de mixtione (p. 587). A reply to Nicolas
Guibert (see p. 268).

An *Opera omnia medico-chimica* said to have been published in several folio
volumes[2] seems to consist of the separate works described above, and has no
independent existence.

In the preface to his *Alchemia* (1597) Libavius says many would prefer to
know his own experiments, not those of others, which are already described in
many books, but he says:

I will not, however, teach my art, but the chemical art, already proved by others. It
is enough if the exposition and didactic method are mine. The reader must know that I
have some study in Chemistry (etiam me aliquid studij in Chymicis posuisse) and do
not understand less of the matter than the cooks, courtesans, barbers, domestic
servants, salve merchants, actors (agyrtis), etc., with whose help many practise
Chemistry. If necessary, I will show you how well-water can be distilled, not to mention the conversion of wine into vinegar. I have added also much from my own store
although I have not always added my name, and much not found elsewhere.

He claims to teach the whole art, not a part, and to have put its principles into
a methodical shape for the first time (nondum tamen hactenus in methodicam
formam redactam). The classification of the material is very elaborate and

---

[1] Ueberweg, (2), 1874, ii, 12; Stones, *Isis*, 1928, x, 449; Thorndike, v, 642.
[2] Seven vols., Frankfurt, 1606, according to Mercklin, *Lindenius renovatus*, 1686, 47; 1613
and 1615 (no number of volumes or details given) according to Kopp, (2), iii, 146.

perhaps too pedantic, and the standard of the book seems to have been thought too high; it was not translated into any modern language and went through very few editions. Its title was also perhaps a drawback. Boyle does not seem to have read it; he quotes Libavius only once, from Sennert, as giving only 'a negative description' of the mercurial principle.[1] Libavius, while recognising some important services of Paracelsus, refused to follow him in blind admiration (non est noua mea sententia, qui Paracelsicus nec esse, nec vocari volo), and to admit that he was the originator of Chemistry (Chymia non est inuentum Paracelsi). The work quotes a large number of authors (a list is given at the beginning), from mediæval alchemists such as Geber, Albertus Magnus, and Arnald of Villanova, to contemporaries such as Cardan, Porta, Conrad Gesner, Paracelsus, and Agricola, but not Basil Valentine or Isaac Hollandus, who were, therefore, almost certainly unknown then; one authority, Diodorus Euchyon (Euchion)[2] was Kaspar Wolf (1525–1601), Gesner's successor at Zürich.

Libavius's *Alchemia* is an excellent practical text-book in the sense that the author shows a full mastery of his sources and a clear, concise and sensible style, entirely different from the rambling, bombastic, and obscure verbosity of Paracelsus or the alchemical authors. A scheme of the divisions of the work follows the preface. Alchemy is defined as the art of extracting perfect magisteries and pure essences from mixed bodies (Alchemia est ars perficiendi magisteria, & essentias puras à mistis separato corpore, extrahendi); it is valuable in medicine, in metallurgy and in daily life (ornamenta vitæ conferat plurima).

It is divided into *Encheria* (from ἐγχείρησις) or methods of operation, and *Chymia* or the description of substances and their properties. Encheria is divided into *Elaboratio*, the ordinary chemical operations (solution, fusion, precipitation, distillation, etc.) and *Exaltatio*, the production of higher activity in a substance, further divided into *Maturatio* and *Gradatio*, each of these being further subdivided, e.g. the first into digestion and circulation, and fermentation and projection. There is a brief description of vessels and furnaces, with only one simple illustration of a sublimation vessel with three bulbs. The description of apparatus was much enlarged in the richly illustrated commentary VA, (1), which also gives a list of symbols.[3]

Libavius distinguishes four degrees of heat: (1) that which does not cause pain to the hand, (2) that which causes pain but not injury to the hand, (3) the temperature of hot sand or iron filings, and (4) the highest temperature attainable in a furnace.[4] In the Commentary,[5] he describes the sealing of the neck of a flask by heating with a charcoal fire and drawing out with tongs; an illustration of this is given by J. French.[6]

The first tract of the second book deals with 'magisteries'. A magistery is

[1] *Sceptical Chymist*, part iv; *Works*, 1744, i, 341.
[2] *De Polychimia Libri Qvatvor*, s.l., 1567; Duveen, 626; Gmelin, (1), i, 314, adds Amsterdam, 1604, Frankfurt, 1609.
[3] VA, (1), c. 6; 1606, 85–8.
[4] De pyronomia, in III, i, 14; 1606, 11; de pyrotechnia et affinibus, in VA; 1606, 207.
[5] VA, 1, ch. 35; 1606, 178.   [6] *Art of Distillation*, 1653, 8.

defined as a chemical species extracted from a compound body with separation of the unessential impurities (ex toto citra extractionem, impuritatibus
duntaxat externis ablatis, elaborata exaltaque); but it may be a quality as well
as a substance (est aliud qualitatis, aliud substantiae), and the quality may be
either occult or manifest, the former including magnetic attractions, and the
latter such things as crystalline form, lustre, weight, colour, smell, taste and
sound (the cry of tin), all of which are altered in chemical changes, including
transmutation of metals. In this section he gives a number of recipes and
chemical preparations, including (chapt. 19: De magisteriis substantiae, ubi
primum de metallorum transformatione) transmutations of silver into gold
(specialis conversio) and of various metals into silver and gold, and the statement: magisterium substantiae fit vel genesi vel catalysi, the latter word being
taken (chapt. 39: De magisteriis catalyseos) to mean decomposition (cum
totum in partes integrales dissolvitur, ex quibus compositum erat: and catalysis sit dupliciter. Aut enim repurgatio sit substantiæ, aut separatio).[1] This use
in the original sense (κατά down, λύσις loosing) of 'breaking down, decomposing', is found in Evelyn[2] who on 15 March 1655 spoke of 'this sad catalysis and declension of piety to which we are reduced', and in a letter to Sir
Thomas Browne in 1658[3] of 'so generall a catalysis of integrity'.

Libavius then deals with alloys, imitation of gems in coloured glasses,
solders, lutes, extraction of metals from ores, and juices of plants. Then comes
a description of the 'elements of substances', including the three principles of
Paracelsus: this section is more in the old alchemical style and lacks the precision, scepticism and clarity of Helmont and Boyle. Metals are still regarded
as composed of mercury and sulphur, etc., but there is a distinction between
elements (chapt. 48: De elementis substantiæ), which are substances separable
by chemical operations from bodies, such as metals (elementa artis naturæ
elementis sunt analoga, et operationibus artis è misto educuntur), and *principles* (chapt. 50: De Magisterio principiorum), which are mercury, sulphur
and salt according to Paracelsus.[4] Libavius had mentioned the atomic theory
with disfavour[5] and he makes no use of it.

The second tract of book II deals with extracts and tinctures and is mostly
composed of recipes; 'mysteries' are essences of interior nature, divided into
quintessences and arcana on Paracelsan grounds, although there are numbers
of useful recipes for oils, spirits, acids, distilled waters, alkalis, salts, 'flowers',
etc. The short third tract deals with compound bodies (de speciebus chymicis
compositis), but in the pharmaceutical sense of compound medicines. A
clyssus is here[6] defined as: species composita ex eiusdem rei speciebus variis
seorsim elaboratis, i.e. a combination of different kinds of the same substance,
e.g. a solution of salt of tartar in wine. This definition[7] was later replaced by

---

[1] III, Bk. II, tract. i, chs. 19, 39, 42; 1597, pp. 130, 204, 217; 1606, pp. 62, 96, 102; Lippmann, (7), 1921, 22; (3), 1953, ii, 183.
[2] *Diary and Correspondence*, ed. Bray, 4 vols., 1852, iii, 67; *Memoirs*, ed. Bray, 1870, 593.
[3] Sir Thomas Browne *Letters*, ed. Keynes, 1946, 301.
[4] Cf. VII, 1613, ii, 101.   [5] I, ii, 5; 1595, 35.
[6] Also in I, 1595, i, 285.
[7] Also used by Ruland, 1612, 157, and Boerhaave, (3), 1727, i, 190.

one meaning the volatile product collected in a receiver from a deflagration reaction, e.g. of charcoal with nitre.[1]

In his description of metals, Libavius largely follows Agricola, Ercker, and Caesalpinus. He gives a good description of fluxes.[2] Libavius gives a graphic description of the precipitation of silver chloride from a silver solution by a solution of salt, like wormy cheese (argentum descendit instar vermiculorum casei minutorum): he calls it 'calx of silver' (calx argenti; calx lunæ).[3] Silver is contained in most commercial lead.[4] Various recipes are given for coloured glasses, including a red or purple gold glass (Topasius conflatur ex croco Martis, minio et massa, additis auri foliis. . . . Hyacinthus fit ex utraque Martis et terrea Solis, etc.). The ruby was thought to owe its colour to gold and the red (colloidal) solutions of gold in liquors and oils (ex tinctura auri rubea in liquorem seu oleum soluta) are mentioned.[5] Libavius believed in the virtues of potable gold and silver[6] and the use of chemical remedies, especially potable gold, was defended by Giovanni Bratti, 'Ivstinopolitani'.[7] Gold is purified by triple fusion with stibnite (antimonium) and pouring into a conical mould. In 'quartation' the silver may be extracted from the alloy with three parts of silver by aqua regia, leaving the gold (quartatione purgatur, si tribus argenti partibus confusum solvitur aqua regia quicquid in eo est alienum, solo auro resistente).[8]

Libavius believed that iron was really turned into copper by vitriol water.[9] What Libavius calls *vitriolum Veneris* includes verdigris or the basic chloride (lamelli cupri . . . oblinuntur aqua salis, vel liquore salis nitri, vel aceto destillato suspenduntur ad aërem).[10] Lime water containing sal ammoniac becomes blue in contact with brass: aqua calcis, in qua sal ammonius solutus sit, eodem [caeruleo] colore tingitur super orichalco;[11] si aquam calcis cum sale ammonio ponas per noctem in pelui orichalcea, cærulea euadit.[12]

Lead nitrate (calx plumbi dulcis) was made by dissolving lead in aqua fortis in a flask cooled by water and crystallising (fit per aquam fortem comminuto plumbo affusam vase in aqua frigida locato. Fit instar crystallorum).[13] This is said to be the first mention of it.[14] Libavius describes the preparation of 'quintessence of lead or sugar of lead (quinta Saturni essentia, quam & Saccharum vocant)' by dissolving litharge in distilled vinegar and crystallising, and its

---

[1] Rolfink, *Chimia in artis formam redacta*, Jena, 1662, 173; Barner, *Chymia philosophica*, Nürnberg, 1689, 298; Spielmann, *Institutiones Chemiae*, Strassburg, 1766, 262; Baumé, *Chymie expérimentale et raisonné*, Paris, 1773, i, 421.

[2] Also in I, 1595, ii, 250: additamenta calcium δυαλύτων sunt plumbago, vitrum, arsenicum, lithargyros, borax, etc.

[3] III, Bk. II, tract. i, c. 5; 1606, 47.   [4] IV, (i), i, c. 7; VB, 1606, 18.

[5] III, bk. II, tract. i, c. 34; V, 1606, 88; cf. IV, bk. i, c. 4; VB, 1606, 13.

[6] VI, 1611, 60 f., 83 f.

[7] *Discorso della Vecchia et nvova medicina, Nel quale si ragiona delle cose ritrouate à nostri secoli, & particolarmente dell' Oro Artificiale*, 4°, Venice, 1592, 42 f. (BM 1033. h. 28).

[8] III, Bk. II, tract. i, c. 40; V, 1606, 99–100 (aqua fortis is meant).

[9] IV, i; VB, 1606, 20 f.; VI, 1611, 280–1: sic ex chalcantho æs conflatur, quod chalcanthum prius nihil aliud erat quam liquor; *ib.*, 297: certum est per vitriolum veneris ferrum in æs cyprium transmutari.

[10] III, Bk. II, tract. ii, c. 39; V, 1606, 179.

[11] IV, vi, P. II, c. 19; VB, 1606, 158.

[12] III, Bk. II, tract. ii, c. 9; V, 1606, 133.

[13] III, Bk. II, tract. i, c. 25; V, 1606, 71.   [14] Kopp, (1), iv, 136.

distillation in an alembic (giving acetone);[1] or as 'cerussa' (really white lead) by dissolving lead filings in strongest vinegar to a milky liquid and evaporating (scobs Saturni soluitur in acri aceto in lacteum liquorem, qui abstracta humiditate relinquit cerussam).[2] *Lac virginis* made by extracting litharge with strong vinegar and precipitating with salt water (præcipitantur aqua et sale injectis) or solution of alum,[3] would be a suspension of lead chloride or sulphate (not distinguished). White lead is blackened by fumes of sulphur (cerussata facies caveant sibi à fumo sulphuris, quo denigrantur).[4]

Libavius[5] mentions the 8 or 10 per cent increase in weight when lead is calcined, which Cæsalpinus[6] had explained as due to condensation of smoke, whilst Modestin Fachs[7] had noticed this increase without explaining its origin.[8] Libavius classes several metallic oxides as ashes (*cineres*)[9] as well as calces[10] but he distinguished the operations of calcination and cinefaction.[11] He explained calcination and vitrification as loss of humidity (metalla, præsertim imperfecta, calcinantur reverberanturque fortiter, donec fusionem vitrariam accipiant, humiditate nimirum tenaci ut plurimum absumpta)[12] — a theory expressed in Geber (Vol. I). Libavius calls all kinds of burnt materials (talc, tartar, alum, glass, pumice, etc.) 'calces'.[13]

Tin sulphate (vitriolum Jovis) was made by dissolving tin dross (recremento stanni excocti vetera) in dilute vitriol (?) (Solvuntur aquis acribus et vitriolum aquæ dulci pulchrum committunt),[14] and stannous nitrate by dissolving tin in aqua fortis, when a white residue is also left (Vitriolum stanni: solve lamellas in aqua forti, vel irriga aqua forti, et fac quasi cerussam. Quam elue aqua et cola. Colatum fine coagulare in lapillos in vitro).[15] Libavius mentioned only briefly in 1603 the preparation of anhydrous stannic chloride by distilling corrosive sublimate (mercuric chloride) with tin amalgam.[16] The process was described in more detail in 1611,[17] and in 1613[18] as follows:

Sp[iritus]. Sublimati. Fit alius ex sublimato. Eliquate stanni libræ immisce argenti vivi calefacti quadrantem, diligenterque subige bacillo ligneo, aut stylo osseo, ut fiat amalgama. Hoc extende, et explana super lapidea tabula cui in cella dispositae insperge parem quantitatem argenti vivi septies sublimati, et in subtilem pulverem redacti. Solvatur ibi per deliquium. Solutionem, quae jam dulcis evasit, coagula, iterum solve. Tandem destilla, et rectificata oleum per destillationem confectum, à quo separabis spiritum coelestem, quanquam totum nihil aliud fit, quam spiritus aethereae subtilitatis, qui cum vini spiritu circulari potest.

[1] III, Bk. II, tract. ii, c. 4; V, 1606, 123; from Guinther of Andernach, *De Medicina Veteri et Nova*, 1571 (BM 773. m. 20).
[2] III, Bk. II, tract. i, c. 25; V, 1606, 71.   [3] VI, 1611, 352, 474.
[4] III, Bk. II, tract. i, c. 15; V, 1606, 60.   [5] VI, 1611, 225.
[6] *De metallicis*, bk. iii, ch. 7; Rome, 1596. 184 [180].
[7] *Probir Büchlein*, Leipzig, 1595, pref
[8] Libavius, *op. cit.*; Walden, *Mass, Zahl und Gewicht in der Chemie der Vergangenheit*, Stuttgart, 1931, 56; McKie, *The Essays of Jean Rey*, 1951, pp. xxviii–xxix, who quotes from an ed. of VI, 1595, p. 225, notes that the book by Fachs q. in it appeared in 1595, and thinks Libavius used 'an untraced edition, possibly of 1567 or 1568'; see p. 66; 'Fachsius Zygostata' (i.e. assay-master) is in the list of authors in III, f. b4.
[9] III, Bk. II, tract. i, c. 26; V, 1606, 74.   [10] *Ib.*, c. 25; V, 1606, 70 f.
[11] III, Bk. I, chs. 26–8; V, 1606, 20.
[12] III, Bk. II, tract. i, c. 23; V,1606, 68.
[13] *Ib.*, c. 25; V, 1606, 70 f.   [14] VI, viii, 44; 1611, 474.
[15] III, Bk. II, tract. ii, c. 39; V, 1606, 179. [16] IX; X, 1604, 142.
[17] VI, 1611, 119.   [18] VIA, 1613, 190.

That is, an amalgam of 1 part of tin and 4 parts of mercury is spread on a flat stone in a cellar and is sprinkled with corrosive sublimate, when it liquefies. The solution running off forms a paste and is again liquefied. Finally it is distilled and a rectified oil is made, from which a heavenly spirit separates which as a subtle ethereal spirit can be rectified like spirit of wine. The fuming stannic chloride was later called *spiritus fumans Libavii* or *fumigatorium perpetuum joviale*[1] and the discovery attributed either to Libavius or to Andreas Cassius (d. 1673, see p. 371), who also described the distillation of tin amalgam and corrosive sublimate with production of a fuming liquid.[2] Hoefer[3] had remarked that Libavius makes no claim to the discovery. The preparation was described by Arnald of Villanova (see Vol. I), and in an anonymous *Das Buch der heyligen Dryvaltigkeit*, a parchment MS. in the Germanische Museum, Nürnberg, written in 1414–18, dedicated to Frederick I of Brandenburg and probably used by his son Johann, which also mentions the preparation of mineral acids, the purification of nitric acid by silver (precipitating silver chloride) before Agricola, and the precipitation of silver chloride, before Libavius.[4]

The name *mercurius* for *argentum vivum* is not favoured by Libavius (tribuamus enim ei hoc nomen per catachresin populare).[5] Mercury is described in alchemical style among the things resembling metals (de his quæ Metallis sunt affinia) along with bismuth (marcasita stannea), antimony, sulphur, arsenic, vitriol (chalcanthum) and cinnabar, as a 'liquid mineral': liquor mineralis, ex aqua metallica viscida, terraque sulphurea exacte contemperatus, spirituosus, frigidus, humidus, albus in manifesto, calidus, siccus, citrinus, rubeus in occulto.[6] Although Proust says Libavius mentions the solidification of mercury by cold, the statement obviously refers to silver amalgam (vidi argentum vivum administratione argenti solidi primum æquabiliter instar aquæ fluxisse; at postea in massam coagulasse, quam resolvit denuo calor).[7] Mercury is purified from lead by expressing through leather, distillation and washing with acid brine (lotionem ex acida muria).[8]

The red oxide (hydrargyrus præcipitatus), obtained by simple heating of mercury (in air) or of the nitrate, is easily reconverted [by heat] into the metal (facili opera ad vivum revocabilis).[9] Cinnabar was prepared by heating and subliming mercury and sulphur: cinabaris factitia est magisterium compositum ex hydrargyro et sulphure una commistis, et sublimatione in massam sanguineam unitis. It is decomposed by heating with calcined tartar into its two principles: segregatur in sua principia, seu membra, ex quibus fuit

---

[1] Juncker, *Conspectus Chemiae*, Halle, 1730, i, 427, 498; J. C. P. Erxleben, *Anfangsgründe der Chemie. Mit neuen Zusätzen vermehrt von J. C. Wiegleb*, Göttingen, 1784, 456; Gren, *Handbuch der gesammten Chemie*, Halle, 1795, iii, 568.
[2] Orschall, *Sol sine Veste*, 12°, Augspurg, 1684; tr. in Kunckel, *Art de la Verrerie*, 4°, Paris, 1752, 499.
[3] (1), ii, 27.
[4] Peters, *Mitteilungen aus dem germanischen Nationalmuseum*, Nürnberg, 1893, 98 (104); *id.*, *Chemiker Zeitung*, 1908, xxxii, 754; Ganzenmüller, 1956, 231.
[5] VI, Bk. ii, c. 23; 1611, 89. [6] IV, (i), c. 11; VB, 1606, 21.
[7] I, 1595, ii, 45; Proust, *J. de Phys.*, 1815, lxxxi, 321.
[8] III, Bk. II, tract. i, c. 32; V, 1606, 86.
[9] III, Bk. II, tract. i, c. 6; V, 1606, 49; cf. I, 1595, ii, 263.

constituta.[1] Libavius was well acquainted with calomel, which he sometimes calls *aquila alba* (the 'white eagle'), although he also uses this name for sal ammoniac;[2] also with corrosive sublimate (*mercurius sublimatus*) made by subliming mercury with salt and vitriol,[3] and its reduction to mercury in various ways.[4] He explains the derivation of the name amalgam, through Arabic, from the Greek μάλαγμα.[5] Libavius mentions the fanciful names of corrosive sublimate: metallina sapientum, mercurius essentificatus, Luna Philosophorum, crystallus artis, Aquila alba, Astrum mercurii, Leo viridis, Draco, serpens, Basilicus, Bufo, et aliis pene infinitis nominibus.[6] He gives a large number of processes for its sublimation, including that used in Venice[7] and mentions its use as a cosmetic. In one process (from Geber) a mixture of specified amounts of mercury, calcined alum, red vitriol, common salt, and saltpetre, is sublimed. The addition of vinegar, prescribed by Bulcasis and Alexius, is not approved, and arsenic, also specified, should be avoided. Every author thought he knew the best process (omnino quisque in hac re sibi videtur optimus esse artifex). A solution of mercury in aqua fortis stains the skin red.[8]

Turpeth (or turbith) mineral is the old name for basic mercuric sulphate obtained by the action of water on mercuric sulphate. Libavius, who describes the preparation of this and other metallic turpeths, explains that turpeth is from an Arabic word meaning the skin or root of a plant (seu corticem herbæ ferulaceæ seu radicem signat), and defines a turpeth as a specific fixed precipitate (turpethum est coagulum specificum fixum), but his statements lack precision.[9] Libavius says *climia* is a kind of cadmia[10] also called Galmia,[11] and it has a volatile spirit (volatiles habet spiritus) producing pompholyx[12] on combustion. He gives a description (with historical notes) of the preparation of brass (orichalcum) from copper and calamine and says calamine (zelamina, calamina, lapis calaminaris or terra calaminaaris) is the same as cadmia.[13] He classed a number of ores and also zinc and bismuth as marcasites.[14] He calls zinc calaem (following Linschoten), which is *qalam*, the Indian name for tin,[15]

[1] III, Bk II, tract. i, cs. 32, 43; V, 1606, 85, 104.   [2] VB, 1606, 15, 31; VII, 1613, 232.
[3] III, Bk. II, tract. i, c. 33; V, 1606, 86.   [4] III, Bk. II, tract. i, c. 43; V, 1606, 104.
[5] I, 1595, ii, 398; VA, bk. iii, c. 12; 1606, 262: corruptum vocabulum esse ex Græco μάλαγμα non dubitant; the name has also been derived from al +μίγμα (Zosimos, in Berthelot, (2), ii, 197. 15, for tin amalgam).
[6] VI, 1611, 333.   [7] VI, 1611, 335 f., 339 f.   [8] IV, (vi), De judie., ii, 21; VB, 1606, 159.
[9] III, Bk. II, tract. ii, c. 41; V, 1606, 185 f.; VI, 1611, 244–7.
[10] III, Bk. II, tract. i, c. 25; V, 1606, 73.
[11] VA, 1606, 126.   [12] VB, 1606, 126.   [13] VI, 1611, 325.
[14] III, Bk. II, tract. i, c. 25; V, 1606, 72 (vocabulo marcasitarum varij lapides minerales designantur . . . cadmia, cobaltum, bismuthum erudum, . . . Zinckum album & rubeum de natura cupri); VI, 1611, 91 (in Carinthia, & Comitatu Tyrolensi effoditur alia species, alba vel rubea, quam Metallici nuncupant Zinccum, q. Mathesius, see p. 63), 114 (nomine marcasitharum comprehendi mineralia plura . . . vti est antimonium cum suo regulo, Bismuthum, cadmia argentaria, calaëmum, Zincum, Gelfum &c.; ch. heading includes cadmiæ Indicæ), 214 (aliquando Calaëmum seu plumbum Indicum confundere cum cinereo nostrate, quod marcasitham vocant . . . bismuthum), 297 (calaëmum Indicum seu stannum), 308 (calaëmum Indicum), 318 (calaëm Malabaricum; marcasitha . . . æream nominant Zinckum); VII, 1613, 181 (marcasitharum quarum variæ sunt species; vt stibium, bismuthum, cobaltum, Zinckum, Lechum, Gelfum, stannum Malabaricum, & alia etiam; also in X, 1604, 512); VIII, 1615, 183 (est in India metallum ex genere stanni, Calaëm vocant).
[15] Oppert, in Diergart, 1909, 137.

also used for zinc. Libavius[1] says the Dutch had (1596) captured a Portuguese ship off Malacca with a cargo of 'Indian tin', which was taken to Holland and he obtained a specimen from his friend Dr. Leonhard Doldius of Nürnberg. He describes a number of its properties, e.g. its combustibility, the fact that its solution in aqua fortis is not precipitated by water (distinguishing it from bismuth), that it is not easily amalgamated, etc. He says it was not known how the Indians extracted the metal, which his experiments led him to think was a mixture of silver, cadmia, mercury, and arsenic (sulphur arsenicale). He says it might be a peculiar metal (possit pro peculiari metallo) but imperfect, between silver and tin, but it was more probably a mixture. On heating strongly in a crucible with bellows it inflamed and formed pompholyx or tutia, of which it is the mercurial metallic part (nihil est aliud quam pars metalli mercurialis). With nitre it deflagrated brilliantly and persistently (flagrat luculentius, & pertinacius); it is the spirit of pompholyx (quaedam pars est plane spirituosa). He noticed that the product of combustion (zinc oxide) was yellow when hot but became white on cooling (mirum est favillam istam in igne totam esse auream, sed extra ignem plane niveam), and nevertheless converts copper into brass (nihilominus æs in aurichalcum mutare).

Libavius was familiar with white vitriol (zinc sulphate) made at Goslar, used as a collyrium, related to alum, verdigris and chrysocolla, and likewise called Zinck:[2] chalcanthum ... album vitriolum est oculorum affectibus quibusdam utile ... cognatum est cum alumine ... cognata est ei aerugo, chrysocolla, quae est quasi putrefacta ærugo, item Zinckum dictum. Libavius exchanged a number of letters on zinc with Sigismund Schnitzer of Bamberg. Schnitzer in a letter of 26 July 1611 said: Gelfum & Zinckum Cancellarius noster Tyrolensis ex Carinthia & Tyrolensi Comitatu.[3] On 14 September 1611, Libavius told Schnitzer that the mineral called zinc in Carinthia and the Tyrol was the same as the calaëm of Malabar:

Marchasithæ argentiferæ & auriferæ genera esse Zincum & Helsum; hoc Ungaricum, illud Carinthiacum & Tyrolense, arbitrantúrq; nostras & Bohemorum fodinas illis non carere, nisi quod nomina à barbaris imposita sint alia. Itáque sunt, qui Zinckum vocant Cadmiam Argentarium, cujusmodi est Calaëmum malabaricum. Verùm temerè quid affirmarè nolim, cupidus saltem videre id, quod Carni & Tyrolenses Zinckum vocant, sive idem sit, sive diversum.

Since he was eager to see if the two were the same or different, he asked Schnitzer to send him some of the Carinthian and Tyrolian metal.[4] In a postscript to a letter of 18 October 1614, he says: noli oblivisci Zincki ex Carinthia,

[1] IV, 1597, (i), c. 8; VB, 1606, 18–20: De stanno Indico calaem dicto; he quotes Linschoten, 'Lib. 2. orient. nauig. c. 17. In 3.part.nauig, or. cap. 27. stannũ & plumbum veniũt de. Pera & Gustean in littore Malacensi apud Cudam.' The reference is to the Latin ed. of Linschoten (see p. 109), *Indiæ Orientalis*, Secunda Pars, ed. Teucrides Annæus Lonicerus, la. 4°, Frankfurt, 1599, c. 19 (not 17), p. 47: a Queda regno in Euroanstrum secus litus ad. 40. mill. Pera ciuitas cõsurgit, vbi Calaen (*sic*) metalli genus in copia est, stanno non absimile; Tertia Pars, tr. by Bilibaldo Strobæo Silesio, 1601, ch. 27, p. 102: stannum & plumbum à Pera & Gustean, iuxta littora Malaccæ; the chapter is on the merchandise in Bantam, the capital of Java, where there were many Chinese and some Portuguese; nothing more is said on these metals. Libavius continues: Quadam arbitrati sunt esse æs album quod contra finum vocant. Sed non est.
[2] IV, (i), c. 11; VB, 1606, 23.
[3] J. Hornung, *Cista Medica*, 4°, Nürnberg, 1626, 161, Epist. liii.
[4] *Ib.*, 85, Epist. xxxiv.

ubi Paracelsus scribit tantùm nasci. Perquàm enim velim ejus specimen,[1] and Schnitzer, also in a postscript, says: Zincum à D. Mosero ad me missum iri, spero, promisit cum aliis.[2] Apparently Schnitzer did not get his specimen from Moser, since on 9 June 1616 Libavius wrote to Schnitzer: Rogo mihi ab eo aliquam particulam impetres, ut possim videre quæres fit nostrate zinckum, quæ Indicum, quæ Carinthiacum.[3] A month later Libavius was dead.

Libavius mentions bismuth as plumbum cinereum and describes its liquation, but confused it with antimony (stibium adjectis ferri lamellis, saepius funditur per salem petræ in regulum plumbeum, quem aliqui vocant marcasitam,[4] et videtur parum differre à plumbo cinereo duro, quod bismuthum nominant).[5] In another place he correctly describes the liquation of plumbum cinereum seu bismuthum without mentioning the later fusion with saltpetre (which is really used to purify antimony)[6] but in a later commentary[7] he says it did not differ from antimony, or was intermediate in species between lead and antimony (nihil differt ejus regulus à regulo stibii; medium inter plumbi genera et antimonium). He says a solution of it in aqua fortis (bismuth nitrate) at once gives a milky precipitate with water (solutio bismuthi statim in lac crassum abeat).[8] He mentions the play of colours of the metal when melted (nigrum cæruleum, viride, purpureum, ad miraculum vsque).[9] He thought bismuth was one of the things called marcasite,[10] and antimony was another.

Libavius did not clearly distinguish native antimony sulphide (stibnite) from manganese dioxide (pyrolusite; coniungimus Marcasitham & Magnesiam, quam stibij speciem alij faciunt).[10] He says (from the alchemical standpoint) that antimony is composed of impure sulphur and arsenic and much earthy mercury (Antimonium . . . constans ex sulphure & arsenico turbido, & hydrargyro magis terreo). There were three kinds: black, used to purify gold and containing much red tincture, white (album vel plumbeum, quod vocant magnesiam, estq; regulus ex illo eductus aut potius bismuthum), and yellow (luteum vel subcroceum).[11] These were the sulphide, the metal, and the impure oxide. Glass of antimony (vitrum antimonii) can be made in various ways, e.g. fusion with saltpetre, when a black product is obtained, the powder of which is red.[12] Antimony compounds are purgatives and also emetics and sudorifics (exhibebat ad vomendum, cacandum, sudandum).[13]

Antimonium (stibnite) is 'calcined' with aqua fortis (calcinantur prompte per aquam fortem: sed caue tibi à fumo, & vase amplo vtere), or by mixing with saltpetre, throwing into a heated crucible, and washing the product with water until white or yellowish (donec in calcem albam abieret, vel subcitrinam).[14] This product (antimonic acid) is also called *antimonium diaphoreticum* when the product of deflagration of stibnite and saltpetre (potassium antimonate) is washed with spirit of vitriol (dilute sulphuric acid) and vinegar.[15]

[1] *Ib.*, 158, Epist. xlix. [2] *Ib.*, 158; Epist. l. [3] *Ib.*, Epist. lxxviii.
[4] Cf. Albertus Magnus, Vol. I. [5] III, Bk. II, tract. i, c. 21; V, 1606, 67.
[6] III, Bk. II, tract. i, c. 39; V, 1606, 99. [7] IV, (i), c. 11; VIB, 1606, 22.
[8] IV, (i), c. 8; VIB, 1606, 19. [9] VI, Bk. vi, c. 4, 1611, 214.
[10] VI, Bk. ii, c. 24; 1611, 91. [11] IV, (i), c. 11; VB, 1606, 22.
[12] III, Bk. II, tract. i, c. 23; V, 1606, 68; VII, 1613 (Alchymia Pharmaceutica, c. 17), 168.
[13] VII, 1613 (Alchymia Pharmaceutica, c. 17), 168.
[14] III, Bk. II, tract. i, c. 25; V, 1606, 72. [15] III, Bk. II, tract. ii, c. 41; V, 1606, 168.

Butter of antimony is made according to Zapata and Ellenberger by distilling mercury sublimate ground with stibnite or metallic antimony (stella
antimonii), respectively, when it comes over as a thick oil (oleum crassum,
quod lateribus receptaculi adhæret instar butyri).[1] Metallic arsenic, of a
silvery appearance, is made by subliming realgar or orpiment (reagalli auripigmenti seu arsenici citrini) with fresh white quicklime and white tartar.
White arsenic (arsenicum sublimatum album) is used as a remedy for cancer
(according to Paracelsus) and made into pastilles with milk and flour, or
sprinkled over bacon, for killing mice (adhibetur ad necandos mures, sive quis
pastillos cum farina et lacte facere velit, sive lardo inspergere, etc.).[2]

Arsenic (i.e. the mineral sulphide) is nearly the same as sulphur, containing
fatty sulphur, a little mercury, and spirit of salt (arsenicum est succus mineralis pinguis, inflammabilis, vicinus sulphuri, virulentior tamen, ob salem
conjunctum, constans pinguedine sulphurea, hydrargyro pauco et spiritu
salis).[3] What Libavius calls butter of arsenic (*butyrum arsenici*) is potassium
arsenate made by fusing white arsenic with twice its weight of saltpetre: ut
instar butyri in lebete resideat; refrigeratum albescat.[4] Rosagallum, risa Galli,
or Reuschgäl, is a mixture of orpiment (As_2S_3)and sandarach (As_2S_2) made by
fusing arsenic and orpiment.[5] Werner called it 'Rauschgelb'.[6] The yellow residue after melting out bismuth from its ore is made in a reverberatory furnace
into blue glaze or glass; it is called Zafhhara (Zaffre), a name which Libavius
thought was derived from the German safran, crocus: recrementa ... croceoq;
colore placentia tinctoribus pictoribusq; inserviunt, alicubi etiam reverberii
furno exercitata in Lazurium figulorum vitrariorumq; & similium trans-
mutantur, titulo Zapharæ (fors ex Germanorum safran, quo crocum indi-
getant) prostans.[7] It was used in painting pottery blue: Zaffara cruda tingit
fictilia subnigro: igne percocta in caeruleum praestantissimum mutatur;[8] est
enim magnesia plumbi cinerei, seu bismuthi, de qua Erkerus scribit, grana seu
reliquias excocti bismuthi praebere colorem blavium seu caeruleum in magna
copia, qui sit Zephera ... Germanorum figuli appellant Zepherfarb.[9] Cobalt
pyrites is like galena in appearance (galena, aut pyrites cobalti instar).[10]

The production of steel from iron was regarded as due to assumption of
sulphur and compared with the precipitation of copper from solution by iron:
ferrum mutatur in aciem fluorum mineralium & extinctionis adjumento, &
cuprum, auxilio chalcanthi. Notum est ex ferro fieri stomoma, & cuprum per
augmentum vitriolati sulphuris. Si jam hoc cuprum spolietur; mercurius et
sulphur evadent sicciora, redibitque natura ferri.[11] The preparation of green
vitriol by dissolving iron in dilute spirit of vitriol, and crystallising, is described
from Turquet de Mayerne.[12]

[1] VI, Bk. iii, *c.* 14; Bk. vi, *c.* 19; 1611, 120, 246.   [2] VI, Bk. vii, *c.* 26; 1611, 331.
[3] IV, (i), *c.* 11; VB, 1606, 22.   [4] III, Bk. II, tract. ii, *c.* 41; V, 1606, 189.
[5] III, Bk. II, tract. i, c. 35; V, 1606, 91.   [6] Zippe, 1857, 218.
[7] VA, (1), *c.* 16; V, 1606, 127.
[8] VI, Bk. vi, *c.* 4; 1611, 215; ref. to Cardan, Mathesius, and Cæsalpinus.
[9] VI, Bk. vii, *c.* 21; 1611, 315.   [10] III, Bk. II, tract. i, c. 39; V, 1606, 98.
[11] IV, (i), *cc.* 9–10; VB, 1606, 20–1; VI, Bk. vii, *c.* 4; 1611, 280–1.
[12] VI, Bk. viii, *c.* 41; 1611, 473–4; Turquet de Mayerne, *Pharmacopoia*, in *Opera Medica*, ed.
Brown, London, 1700, ii, 5; see p. 173.

Alum is purified from vitriol by adding urine (ammoniacal?).[1] Fluor mineralis[2] is fluorspar. Libavius mentions soda, also called clavellated ash (cinis clavellatus quem aliqui sodam appelant) or mountain ashe (cinis montani) or in German wood-ashes (Weyde Aschen), as made from the soda plant (herba alkali), and gives an account from Bulcasis (Abu'l-Qāsim; see Vol. I) of its manufacture in the Levant (alkali Saracenorum), Tripoli and Syria, by burning the plant in pits, lixiviating the ash, decanting, and evaporating in pots. The product went to Venice. It was also made in France. The crude alkali was purified by ignition, solution, filtration, and evaporation.[3] Alkali was also extracted from (extrahitur ex) various plants by burning, best in a closed vessel so that the volatile essences could not escape.[4] Lobelius[5] described the soda plant of Narbonne and Aquitaine as *Kali, Blanchette,* and *Salicornia.* Libavius says the caput mortuum (sodium sulphate) from the preparation of aqua fortis was sometimes called *alkitram,* although this was also a name for wood vinegar or *cedria.*[6] Libavius several times refers to borax, but he confuses several materials and mixtures under that name, such as chrysocolla, mixtures of alum and saltpetre, or starch and resins, or tartar and common salt, etc.[7] What he calls Venetian borax is made from milk, honey, crocus, saltpetre, and alkaline lye, boiled and evaporated.[8] He does not seem to know true borax.

A long description of making saltpetre (*halonitrum*) is condensed from Ercker.[9] Libavius describes the deflagration of fused saltpetre by alcohol: [sal petræ] in vase terreo non pingui super prunis sinitur paulatim liquefieri; spuma tollitur ligneo cochleari; vbi totus fusus est, iniicitur parum spiritus vini, vt deflagret.[10] *Sal prunellæ mineralis* was made by throwing sulphur on fused saltpetre.[11]

Salt of tartar (potassium carbonate) was prepared by deflagrating tartar and saltpetre; on exposure it deliquesced to an oil (liquor) of tartar:[12]

Tartari libra, salis nitri selibra, puluerata in olla vel testa vitrata super prunis locentur, donec incipiant crepare. Semoueantur et agitentur versenturque crebro, donec satis albeant. Iniice in vesicam bubulam, suspende in aqua calente, donec incipiant mollescere. Immitte in sacculum, & super vitro in cella pone, liquor effluit, qui sane compositus est.

The use of a bladder and treatment with spirit of wine, given in other recipes, are unnecessary.

Sulphur is a coagulated oil, the principle of fatty things, and containing air and fire as its elements (oleum ist . . . radicalis pinguedinis forma . . . facile pro

---

[1] III, Bk. II, tract. i, *c.* 45; tract. ii, *c.* 38; V, 1606, 105, 175; VI, Bk. viii, *c.* 40, 1611, 470.
[2] III, Bk. II, tract. i, *c.* 38; V, 1606, 95.
[3] III, Bk. II, tract. i, *c.* 28; V, 1606, 74; VI, Bk. v, *c.* 19; Bk. viii, *c.* 38; 1611, 195, 459; VII (Alchymia Pharmaceutica, *c.* 30), 1613, 198.
[4] III, Bk. II, tract. ii, *c.* 37; V, 1606, 172.
[5] P. Pena and Mathiae de Lobel, *Nova Stirpivm Adversaria,* Antwerp (Plantin), 4°, 1576, 169.
[6] III, Bk. II, tract. ii, *c.* 37 (sal alkitram); V, 1606, 175; VI, Bk. viii, *c.* 39, 1611, 467 (alkitram; Alchitran apud Mesuen).
[7] Compositiones boracis; III, Bk. II, tract. i, *c.* 38; V, 1606, 95.
[8] III, Bk. II, tract. ii, *c.* 38; V, 1606, 178.
[9] VI, Bk. viii, *c.* 40; 1611, 468; see p. 106.
[10] III, Bk. II, tract. i, *c.* 41, V, 1606, 101.
[11] VI, Bk. vii, *c.* 32; 1611, 349.
[12] III, Bk. II, tract. i, *c.* 28; V, 1606, 79.

elemento aëris et igni se gerunt. Ex eo fit sulphur per coagulationem).[1]
Flowers of sulphur (flore sulphuris) is made by sublimation: colloca in arena,
lentoque igni humidos euoca spiritus. His dissipatis, clausoque foramine per
conum mobilem, ignem auge, et siccos spiritus sublima quoad satis.[2]
Libavius mentions the red solution of sulphur in warm spirit of turpentine,[3] on
cooling which crystals (prismatic sulphur) can be obtained (imo & alias oleo
solutum sulphur . . . per colum traiectum, postquam refriait, in lapillos abit
magna ex parte — the section is entitled 'crystalli sulphuris').[4] He gives a
description and figure of a furnace used for subliming flowers of sulphur from
pyrites in Thuringia.[5] Liver of sulphur was made in the wet way by boiling
sulphur with potash solution, filtering and evaporating to a red mass: Sulphur
vivum miscetur cum pari aqua salis tartari. Coquuntur donec coloretur aqua.
Filtratur, coagulatur in sanguineam massam.[6]

Libavius[7] describes the preparation of spirit of sulphur or acid oil of sulphur
(spiritus sulphuris, oleum sulphuris acidum) by burning sulphur in (moist)
air under a glass bell:

(b) Campana vitrea lutata, vel alembicus vastus rostratus, à filo ferreo suspenditur,
aut etiam collocatur super ferreo collari ambituvi, in quo sit ostiolum & limbus. Subtus
accommodatur paropsis lata, siquidem campana vsurpatur: sin alembicus, receptaculum admovetur rostro. Imponitur concha in strata ferrea lamella. In hanc sulphur
collocatum incenditur per ferrum ignitum, operaque datur vt fumus ascendat recta; id
quod facilius assequere, si in summo sit angustum spiraculum. Si absumta est pars,
sufficitur noua, & spiritus coagulatus defluit . . . Si sulphur purum est, spiritus
decurrit albus: sin impurum, à flamma vitiatur & nigrescit. Potest tamen corrigi
destillando.

The method is from Baptista Porta (see p. 23) but Libavius claims to have
obtained a purer product by distillation. A marginal note says 1 lb. of spirit
was obtained from 5 lb. of sulphur.

In another preparation, from Wecker, sulphur is burnt in a cucurbit with an
alembic, the spout of which passes into a receiver half full of spirit of wine
(impletum spiritu vini ad dimidium). The product is then distilled in a retort
'per gradus' until all the spirit passes off (omnes spiritus exierint).

Oil of vitriol (spiritus vitrioli rubeus) is made by distilling previously calcined green vitriol in a retort of earthenware, well luted to a capacious cooled
receiver, by a reverberatory fire (Nordhausen oil of vitriol).[8] Alum contains the
same acid as vitriol:

alumen sequitur vitriolum, in quo tamen aluminis non virtus tantum est, sed & corpus.
Itaque & ex pyrite communi interdum excoquuntur et spiritus aluminosi segregantur,
dum fit oleum vitrioli. . . . Tertium locum sibi vendicat sulphur, cujus spiritus per
campanam factus parum distat ab oleo acido chalcanthi.[9]

[1] III, Bk. II, tract. ii, c. 10; V, 1606, 133.   [2] III, Bk. II, tract. ii, c. 40; V, 1606, 183.
[3] III, Bk. II, tract. ii, c. 13; V, 1606, 140.
[4] VII (Alchymia Pharmaceutica, c. 22), 1613, 181.
[5] VI, Bk. vi, c. 24; 1611, 260.   [6] III, Bk. II, tract. ii, c. 9; V, 1606, 132.
[7] (a) I, 1595, ii, 103; (b) III, Bk. II, tract. ii, c. 26; V, 1606, 159; (c) VI, Bk. viii, cc. 19, 27
(and figs.), 1611, 413, 436–8.
[8] III, Bk. II, tract. ii, 26; V, 1606, 158; from 'Euonymus, Cordus, Dornæus, &c.'.
[9] IV, (vi), Pt. ii, c. 36; VB, 1606, 164; Kopp, (1), iii, 305, says this is the first statement of the
fact.

LIBAVIUS

What Libavius calls *acida muria*[1] is only a mixture of salt brine (*muria*) and vinegar. Mineral acids are called 'vinegars (aceti minerali)'.[2] Spirit of salt (spiritus salis) is prepared by distilling bricks which had been heated and quenched in brine: In sale soluto per raphanum extingue candentes lateres, quos, vbi sat sunt poti, destilla: destillatum quidam nominant oleum salis viridis. Nonnulli tamen igni eliquant salem, & in eo restinguunt lateres. Salem qui foris accreuit, abstrahunt, lateres destillant.[3]

Aqua fortis was distilled from saltpetre and alum or vitriol or a mixture of the two: fortis communis fit ex alumine & halinitro, vel etiam addito illis vitriolo, vel vitriolo & halinitro, although all kinds of other useless things could be added. It was purified by adding silver and letting the precipitate (of silver chloride) settle: tandem purificamus injecta parte argenti, et soluta, quae crassa ad fundum.[4]

Libavius describes a sal ammoniac (sal ammoniacus), both native from Libya and artificial from boiling urine, common salt and rock salt dissolved in water, evaporated to dryness, and mixed with sharp lixivium and soda.[5] This would not give ammonium chloride but an alkaline common salt. In another place he describes the sublimation of sal ammoniac from urine, common salt and soot, as well as other materials.[6] A blood-red liquid (ammonium polysulphide) is obtained by distilling calcium sulphide (from quicklime and melted sulphur) with calcined flints and sal ammoniac.[7] Libavius obtained ammonium sulphate by mixing ammonia with oil of vitriol: Compendiosior ratio est per spiritum urinæ. Hic enim affusus oleo vitrioli, id figit in crystallos vel etiam pulverem, instar alcali.[8]

Libavius must be regarded as one of the founders of qualitative analysis, although he made little progress in this subject. In his treatise on mineral waters[9] he says the water must be tested near the source, so that the *spiritus* (gas) shall not have escaped. The water is first gently warmed in a retort luted to a strongly cooled receiver, when the spirit passes over (segregatio spirituum). Then follows the separation of the water from the solids (aquositatis segregatio et contentorum) by evaporation on an ash bath to a syrupy consistency, when the salts (alum, vitriol, common salt, nitre, etc.) are allowed to crystallise on straws or threads, the mother liquor being further evaporated. A simple test (experimentum per pannum) for dissolved minerals (derived from the soil and rocks) is to soak a linen cloth in the water, dry it, examine it for spots, and weigh it.[10] The black colour produced by infusion of galls, etc.,[11] is also produced by vitriol contained in certain waters, such as Schwalbach: aqua vinei fontis Langensbalbensis ... nigra evasit tanquam atramentum sutorium.

---

[1] I, 1595, i, 285.   [2] VI, Bk. viii, *c.* 28; 1611, 439.
[3] III, Bk. II, tract. ii, *c.* 26; V, 1606, 159; the use of sea salt fermented with radish juice is from Paracelsus, *Archidoxa*, x, 3; *Opera*, 1658, ii, 38; see Boerhaave, (4), 1741, i, 41.
[4] III, Bk. II, tract. ii, *c.* 26; V, 1606, 160.   [5] III, Bk. II, tract. ii, *c.* 38; V, 1606, 177.
[6] VI, viii, 39; 1611, 464.   [7] VI, viii, 19; 1611, 412.
[8] III, Bk. II, tract. ii, *c.* 38; V, 1606, 177.
[9] *De judicio aquarum mineralium*, 1597, pars ii, c. 1 f.; VIB, 1606, 153 f.; mentioning the work of Andrea Bacci, *De Thermis*, f°, Venice, 1571; G. Rath, *A. Med.*, 1957, xli, 1, thought the *Pison* of Thurneisser was used, see p. 154.
[10] *Ib.*, *c.* 4, VI B, 1606, 154.   [11] I, 1595, ii, 537.

Indicio est, illas aquas multo corporali chalcantho constare, id quod arguitur quoque flore puniceo. Sed et ferri minera indicatur. Nam hujus quoque, ut et æris vitriolo, nigrantur aquæ.[1] He seems to have had a vague idea of the presence of a volatile acid (carbonic acid) in acidulous mineral waters: sapor acidus, vnde acidulæ dictæ modo ex putredine est, cum aquæ quiescentes dilutæq; succis plantarum vel aliarum rerum commodarum putrefieri incipiunt & acescunt. Libavius deals with the tastes, colours, odours, etc., of mineral waters, as well as chemical tests. Another work on the mineral waters of Coburg by Libavius[2] mentions the apparent transmutation of iron into copper by the vitriolic waters of Goslar as disproving those who denied the transmutation of metals:[3] damit die jenigen Augenscheinlich widerlegt werden / so die Transmutation der Metallen leugnen. It describes the evaporation of the water on a steel blade or brass plate for examination of the residue,[4] and the possible presence of arsenic and 'cobold' in the water.[5] Part iv of his *Singularium* (Frankfurt, 1601) deals at great length with the mineral waters of Rothenburg, with chemical tests, and their medicinal uses both internally and as baths.

Libavius recognised the existence in mines of gases both inflammable (flammæ incidant) and extinguishing flames,[6] and the second kind occurred in acidulous waters.

Libavius makes no distinction between inorganic and organic substances, describing the various materials according to their superficial properties ('oils' of mineral, vegetable and animal origin) or modes of preparation (the 'quintessence' of vegetables, spirit of wine, is classed with 'quintessences' of minerals, arsenic, etc.). He considered that the constituents of organic substances are the same as those of mineral bodies: salt, sulphur and mercury, ex quibus fiunt spiritus, liquoresque, olea, aquæ essentiales.[7] Fermentation is exaltation by admixture with a ferment: fermentatio est rei in substantia, per admistionem fermenti, quod virtute per spiritum distributa totam penetrat massam & in suam naturam immutat, exaltatio. The fermentible substance must be liquid or at least easily divisible (fluxilis aut saltem diuisibilis per minima) and of the same nature as the ferment, which acts by its internal heat (agit quidem fermentum præsidio caloris interni).[8] It is motion by the ferment in some moveable subject (motum à fermento in aliquo subiecto mobili); a motion of mixture not perfection (motus ad mistionem, non ad perfectionem) but otherwise the same as digestion. Putrefaction is distinguished from fermentation only by the nature of the products.[9]

Spirit of wine (aqua ardens) is distilled from various fermented products.[10]

---

[1] *Ib.*, c. 16, p. 157.
[2] *D.O.M.A. Tractatus Medicus Physicus vnnd Historia Dess fürtrefflichen Casimirianischen Sawer-Brunnen / vnter Liebenstein / nicht fern von Schmalkalden gelegen . . .* , sm. 8°, Coburgk, MDCX (1610); unpaged, sign. A1–Q6bv; BM 1168. d. 19.
[3] Fol. C vii *v.*   [4] Fol. G iiii *r.*   [5] Fols. D v *r*, E ii *r.*
[6] IV, (vi), c. 18; VIB, 1606, 147; VII, Bk. viii, c. 41, 1611, 472: in cuniculis halitus grauitas suffocat, & vt Galenus indicat, lumina extinguit; Germani Schwaden vocant, qualis & circa acidulas nonnullas in cryptis inuenitur; Kopp, (1), iii, 178.
[7] IVA, (1), i, c. 1; 1606, 73.   [8] III, Bk. I, c. 59; V, 1606, 35.
[9] IVA, Bk. vi (De exaltationibus); 1606, 371, 374 f.
[10] III, Bk. II, tract. ii, c. 32; V, 1606, 167.

K

Libavius[1] calls vinum ardens the alcohol obtained both from the residues of must or poor wine as well as from grain by fermentation with yeast:

appellant vinum ardens quod ex fecibus musti postquam deferbuit, & in vinum transiit exugitur; vel ex cereuisiæ fecula aut polenta additis fecibus, aut fermento destillatur. . . . Lobelius non fastidit essentiam vini, quæ spiritus vini appellatur; repudiat autem aquam vitæ, quam ex vini fecibus, aut zytho conficiunt.

It is possible that the manufacture of whisky from grain was practised in Ireland in the 12 cent., perhaps by a process imported from the Continent.[2] The distillation of a medicinal 'water' (half a pint from 12 pints of beer and two handsfull of salt) from beer in a still with a delivery tube cooled by water is described by John Wenod, physician in Prague, in 1420.[3]

Libavius uses the name *vini alcool* for the 'quintessence of wine' (quinta essentia vini), obtained by rectification of strong wine. He gives nine tests for its strength, including burning without residue in a tin, burning linen (cum lintes comburitur), and when a drop of oil is injected on the surface it sinks

Spirit of wine is distilled seven times to give 'purest ether' (donec aetheris purissimi instar pelluceat). Spirit can also be obtained from beer or other drinks (quiuis succi potabiles). He describes the processes of various authors, and the dehydration with salt of tartar, i.e. potassium carbonate (quando vini spiritus rectificatur per suam salem, seu potius exasperatur, nominant vini alcool, vel vinum alcalisatum; alii pro sale fecum accipiunt salem tartari). Oil of wine (oleum vini) obtained by digesting strong wine in a pelican for 30 to 60 days and then distilling with a gentle heat would also be alcohol, since he says elsewhere the spirit is oily (oleiformis; spir. vini est spir. oleosior ex vino).[4]

Oil of vitriol when refluxed with spirit of wine (circulando et abstrahendo) is converted into a sweet oil (dulce oleum);[5] this would be ether.

Radical vinegar (acetum radicatum) is the distillate from the *caput mortuum* of vinegar,[6] i.e. the last part of the distillate, richer in acetic acid. Sugar of lead (saccharum plumbi, cerussa attenuata dulcis) is prepared by dissolving litharge (calx Saturni) in vinegar and crystallising the salt (coagula solutiones in saccharum; coagula acetum in salem), and by distilling it in strong heat a quintessence (acetone) is obtained (eliciunt essentiam quintam),[7] first a colourless spirit like alcohol, then a red liquor called fixed oil of lead: primo exit alborum spirituum forma spiritus ille ardens; Postea liquor sanguineus, qui dicitur oleum Saturni fixum.[8] Various distilled oils (olea stillatitia) or aromatic oils (olea aromatica), of cinnamon, cloves, cumin, various flowers, resins, etc., are mentioned, also oil of turpentine, and the fœtid oil from

[1] VI, Bk. viii, c. 9; 1611, 380 f.
[2] T. Fairley, *Analyst*, 1905, xxx, 293–306; Underwood, *Trans. Inst. Chem. Eng.*, 1935, xiii, 34 (41).
[3] Sudhoff, *A. Nat.*, 1914, v, 282–8.
[4] III, Bk. II, tract. ii, cc. 5, 15, 26, 32; V, 1606, 125, 142, 157, 167; VI, Bk. viii, c. 25, 1611, 429 (rectified with calcined tartar).
[5] VI, Bk. viii, c. 21; 1611, 419.
[6] III, Bk. II, tract. i, c. 7 (qui dum acetum destillatur, vltimo exit, quod vocant acetum radicatum); tract. ii, c. 26 qui abstracto phlegmate in fundo restat); VI, Bk. viii, c. 28; 1611, 439.
[7] III, Bk. II, tract. i, c. 28; tract. ii, c. 4; V, 1606, 78, 123.
[8] VI, Bk. vii, c. 36; 1611, 360.

bones.[1] Oil of turpentine was regarded as very similar to spirit of wine: sicut loco spiritus vini usurpatur sæpe aqua ardens quater destillata, ita et hic aqua vel oleum terebinthi.[2]

Oil of camphor (oleum caphurae) was obtained by dissolving camphor in boiling aqua fortis.[3] By distilling gum benzoin (laser vel benzoin) with a gentle heat, water, oil and finally a gum or manna (ultimo exit instar mannæ, gummi) are obtained:[4] this would contain benzoic acid. Libavius also speaks of flowers of amber (flos succini) like salt crystals (sal crystalli instar) obtained by distilling amber:[5] this would be succinic acid, already mentioned by Agricola.[6]

Sugar candy (saccharum crystallinum quod candi appellant) was obtained by clarifying Madeira sugar with white of egg:[7]

Sacchari de Medera libras viginti tusas solue aqua q.s. in caldario. Sine parum ebullire, ne lentescat aut rubescat saccharum, mora ad ignem. Fiat consistentia syrupi spissi. Funde in labrum figulinum quadratus intus vitratum, & diuersis tabulatis distinctum, ita vt ab amplo in angustum desinant. Foris istis impone bacillos abiegnos vel pineos à se tres digitos distantes. Saccharum affusum accrescit more crystalli. . . . Saccharum necesse est prius depuratum esse oui candido, vel filtris.

In a process used first in Venice the sugar was clarified by milk of lime and white of egg successively, the scum taken off, and some butter added in the final boiling if the liquid tends to boil over:[8]

Ars Venetorum, qua sacharum prius finiunt, seu puritate finali elaborant . . . Fit lixiuium ex sola calce viua purissimum. Hoc soluitur sacharum impurum in cortina, coquitur, despumatur ita vt portio albuminum in spumam concussiorum iniicatur, & spuma sordidata tollatur, iterumque alia portio itidem polluta ciicitur . . . Colatui per setaceum traiectorium. Coquitur ad coagulationem. Si eueniat, vt exundet sacharum, butyri momento iniecto statim compescitur, & sidit feruor . . . postea bis, terve aqua pura dissoluitur, filtratur, coagulaturque denuo. Si crystallos requiris; solue sacharum finissimum aqua pura pauca . . . ouorum albo rectificata, & cola; postea coque ad regulam. . . . Vtuntur sacharo isto non tantum ad delicias, & condituras aromatum.

An oil was obtained by distilling sugar, together with an acid like vinegar (oleum rubini . . . & phlegma acidum aceti instar).[9] Cream of tartar is tartar purified by crystallisation (tartarum purgatum seu cremor tartari).[10]

---

[1] III, Bk. II, tract. ii, cc. 12–13; V, 1606, 133 f.
[2] Ib., c. 36; V, 1606, 157.
[3] III, Bk. II, tract. ii, c. 24; V, 1606, 155; Arabic kāfūr, Sanskrit kapūra, white; camphor is converted into camphoric acid only by long boiling with nitric acid, so that Hoefer's suggestion, (1), ii, 29, that this was obtained is unlikely.
[4] III, Bk. II, tract. ii, c. 13; V, 1606, 138.
[5] III, Bk. II, tract. ii, cc. 13, 40; V, 1606, 139, 185; VI, 1611, 411 (ultimo sal ascendit).
[6] De natura fossilium, 1546, c. iv; 1657, 599.
[7] III, Bk. II, tract. ii, c. 38; V, 1606, 178.
[8] VI, Bk. vii, c. 32, 1611, 349: describuntur à Lobelio in aduersariis, pag. 20; the reference is to Lobel, Planturvm seu Stirpivm Historia, 4°, Antwerp, 1576, with appendix with sep. t.p.: Nova Stirpivm Adversaria . . . Auctoribus Petro Pena et Matthia de Lobel . . . , 4°, Antwerp, 1576 (Additis Gvillielmi Rondeletii aliquot Remediorum formulis, antehac in lucem editis), pp. 20–22; Lobel says the process with milk of lime was used in Antwerp and London, where pottery (figlina) coolers were used, in Venice copper (ænea). He mentions the draining: mucronem in foraminulum immittût, vt faciliùs effluat crassamentum pinguis, & sordidius, quod Syrupum vulgo vocant, Gallis Melasse. Sugar candy: quo Veneti Candum saccharum efficiunt; violet sugar (ment. by Libavius) is made only in Venice. The Stirpium adversaria nova was first publ. separately in London, 1570.
[9] VI, Bk. viii, c. 19; 1611, 411.   [10] VI, Bk. vii, c. 32; 1611, 350.

GUIBERT

Libavius's most redoubtable opponent was Nicolas Guibert, a Lorraine physician (St. Nicolas, Lorraine, *c.* 1547–Vaucouleurs, *c.* 1620), who had travelled in France, Italy, Germany and Spain, and was at one time alchemist to the Cardinal of Augsburg. He later became a fierce opponent of alchemy and of Paracelsus and died in poverty.[1]

I. De Interitv Alchymiæ Metallorvm Transmvtatoriæ tractatus aliquot. Adiuncta est eiusdem Apologia in Sophistam Libauium, Alchymiæ refutatæ furentem calumniatorem, 8°, Toul, 1614.

    (*a*) In Sophistam Libauium, Alchymiæ refutatæ furentem calumniatorem Apologia (88 pp.).

    (*b*) Alchymica Metallorvm Transmvtatoria, Armis Sacris Impvgnata et Expugnata (141 pp.).

II. Alchymiâ Ratione et Experientiâ ita demvm viriliter impvgnata & expvgnata, una cum suis fallaciis et deliramentis, quibus homines imbobinarat, ut numquam in posterum se erigere valeat, sm. 8°, Strassburg (Zetzner), 1603, 104 pp., together with his De Balsamo eivsqve Lachrymæ quod Opobalsamvm dicitur, Natura, Viribus & Facultatibus admirandis 18 pp. (on balsam).

III. Assertio de Murrhinis, sive de iis quæ Murrhino nomine exprimuntur, sm. 8°, Frankfurt, 1597; on murrhine vessels, see Vol. I.

In II, *Alchymiâ*, Guibert gives accounts of various supposed transmutations and denies the validity of alchemy: omnia sunt ridicula commenta, ad examen veritatis serio revocata; omnia sunt falsissima. He says he spent forty years in chemical reading and experiments and came to the conclusion that metals are species and as such cannot be transmuted: 'From privation to possession (*habitus*) there is no regress, and generation is not circular.' Iron is not transmutable into copper, analogies such as changes of grubs to butterflies, hatching eggs by heat, and variations in plants, are rejected, and alchemical books are not by their reputed authors: the *Tabula Smaragdina* is not by Hermes and the alchemical works of Avicenna, Albertus Magnus, and Thomas Aquinas are spurious. Arnald of Villanova and Lull (whom he dates 1254) did write on alchemy but were quacks deluded by demons. Roger Bacon is called impious, stupid, and superstitious; Paracelsus is a limb of Satan and the world's worst liar; Agrippa, Ficino, and Fernel come in for censure. The impostor Bragadino confessed to fraud in 1591, and Angelus Siculus, who feigned transmutation by sleight of hand before Pope Gregory XIII died in great poverty in Naples.

Guibert also criticised a theory of a spirit of metals proposed by Francesco Giorgio (Franciscus Georgius) of Venice, a Franciscan Qabbalist, author of a 'Harmony of the Universe',[2] saying that it was delirious but more against transmutation than for it, since Georgio said this spirit could be separated from metals with great difficulty, if at all.

Benito Pereyra (Benedictus Pererius) (1535–1601), a Jesuit of Valencia, was

---

[1] L. in NBG, 1858, xxii, 517; Gobet, 1779, ii, 465; Wiegleb, (1), 205; Hoefer, (1), ii, 121; Thorndike, vi, 244.

[2] *De harmonia mundi totius cantica*, Venice, 1525 (BM 526. m. 5); Thorndike, vi, 450–1; Brucker, 1744, iv, 374–86, analysed the work of Giorgio, which was not without influence.

not favourable towards alchemy. He quoted authorities for and against trans-mutation, including Arabic and mediaeval scholastic authors, Cardan, Lacinius, and Antonius Mirandulanus, and decided that there is no philosophical argument against it; animals are produced by incubators, and drugs and other things are made artificially. Yet the alchemists fail to succeed and this leads to poverty, counterfeiting, and harmful medicines.[1]

Other works criticising Libavius were:

J. S. Martinus, De Prima Simplicium et Concretorum Corporum, 8°, Cambridge, 1584 (BM 536. d. 16. (3)).

Joseph Michelius, Apologia Chymica adversvs invectivus Andreæ Libavii Calumnias. . . . Middelburg, 1597 (xii ll. 364 pp., errata 364 v) (BM 1035. b. 16).

Ortvini Gratius, Polemica de Neoparacelsis. D. Andreæ Libavij, vt Medicorum Galenicorum, Galenicentissimi, ita Chymicorum quoque Chymicissimi. Das ist / Von Galenischen vnd Paracelsischen gvverris. Kappen lauffen mitvnder, 2 ed., s.l., 1595 (20 unnumb. ll., BM 8905. aaa. 27).

Petrus Palmarius (Pierre Le Paulmier) (Paris; 1568–15 January 1610), M.D. of Paris and physician in the Hôtel-Dieu, attacked Paracelsus and Libavius and ostensibly supported the old medicine and pharmacy of the Paris school, but he prescribed potable gold and antimony:

P. Palmarius, Doctor Paris-Galenico-chymic. Lapis Philosophicvs Dogmaticorvm. Quo paracelsista Libauius restituitur, Scholæ Medicæ Parisiensis iudicium de Chymi-cis declaratur. Censura in adulteria & fraudes Parachymicorum deffenditur, asserto veræ Alchemiæ honore, sm. 8°, Paris, 1609 (xvi ll. 160 pp. vi ll. appendix); Ferguson, ii, 163 (who says it was first issued in 1608, also a Historia Læprosæ Mulieris Persanatæ, which is contained as an appendix in the 1609 ed.); Thorndike, vi, 251 (BM 1033. e. 43).

He was condemned by the Medical Faculty of Paris and replied in a short tract:

Laurus Palmaria fugans ventaneum fulmen cyclopum aliquot falso Scholæ Parisiensis nomine evulgatum in librum Petri Palmarij, 8°, Paris, 1609, BM 1180. b. 1. (5.).

Jacques Fontaine,[2] who also attacked astrology but believed in demons, sided with Libavius (although he disapproved of his favourable attitude towards alchemy) in his criticisms of Paracelsan physicians.[3]

Another supporter of Libavius was Bernard Georges Penot (Penotus) (Porte-Ste.-Marie, Guienne, 1520–30—The Hague, 1620), who studied at Basel, worked at alchemy, and died in extreme poverty; he is said to have remarked that if he had an enemy whom he wished to injure he would induce him to pursue alchemy. He wrote:

Tractatus Varii, de vera praeparatione et usu medicamentorum chymicorum, 8°, Frankfurt, 1594 (containing also tracts by Paracelsus, Lull, etc.); Apologia . . . De Physici Lapidis materia . . . de multiplici igne lapidis, 8°, Frankfurt, 1600; Theophrastisch Vade Mecum. Das ist: Etliche sehr nützliche Tractat, von der . . . bereittung vnd rechtem Gebrauch der Chymischen Medicamenten, 4°, Magdeburg, 1596; De Denario Medico (dedicated to Libavius), 8°, Berne, 1608 (containing works by Arnald of Villanova, John Isaac Holland, etc.); Penotus Παλιμοσιο: Or the Alchymists Enchiridion.

[1] Pererius, De communibus omnium rerum naturalium principiis, Rome, 1562, Cologne, 1595; Thorndike, vi, 411.

[2] Discours de la puissance du ciel sur les corps inferieurs . . . avec Une dispute des elements contre les Paracelsistes, 12°, Paris, 1581, BM 718. d. 27. (4.).

[3] Thorndike, vi, 188, 253.

In Two Parts, sm. 8°, London, 1692 (attacking Guibert and dealing with the red and white elixirs, etc.); several works by Penot are printed in the Theatrum Chemicum; Ferguson, ii, 179; Duveen, 464.

Lorenz Hofman, of Halle (1582–1630), wrote[1] on the use and abuse of chemical medicines.

John Henry Alsted (Ballersbach, Nassau, 1588–Weissemburg, Transylvania, 1638), professor of theology in the Protestant university of Herborn (Nassau), a prolific writer and hence nicknamed Sedulitas, composed four books of Physical Harmony (one on chemical physics) and an encyclopædia:

Physica Harmonica quatuor libellis methodice proponens: I Physicam Mosaicam, II Physicam Hebraeorum, III Physicam Peripateticam, IV Physicam Chemicam, 12°, Alstedii Herbornæ Nassoviorum, 1616; Cursus philosophici Encyclopedia libri xxvii, 4°, Herborn, 1620; enlarged as Encyclopedia septem tomis distincta, f°, Herborn, 1630, BM 742. g. 21; Scientiarum omnium Encyclopedia I–IV, Lyons, 1649; Thorndike, vi, 433.

in which he accepts the possibility of transmutation, and attributes great virtues to gold (which holds the first place in the mineral kingdom, as the sun among the planets) and gems, which set in rings, in suspension, taken in drink, or resolved into their quintessence. In a letter of 1618 he described four pillars of physical science like those of Paracelsus (p. 134); the first was true chemistry, whose principle and the mother of all sublunary things was that kind of water which contains in itself fire; the second was the astrological concord of superiors and inferiors; the third was experience by the hand and fire; and the fourth was physionomy. He warns against the impostors who 'macerate and lacerate salt, vitriol, gold, vulgar mercury, and the like'. He believed in barnacle geese and plants with leaves of pure gold, as well as astrology, and gives examples of the arcane virtues of stones, marvellous waters, fires and candles, tricks with mirrors, and automata moved by the spirit of the world in them.

[1] *De vero usu & fero abusu Medicamentorum Chymicorum Commentatio*, 4°, Halle, 1611, 139 pp. and index.

CHAPTER VIII

THE DEVELOPMENT OF IATROCHEMISTRY

Sennert

Daniel Sennert (Breslau, 25 November 1572–Wittenberg, 21 July 1637) M.A. 1597, M.D. 1601, then professor of medicine at Wittenberg from 1602, followed Paracelsus in the theory of salt, sulphur and mercury as the constituents of bodies and the use of chemical remedies but avoided some of his excesses.

Sprengel calls Sennert 'a man who combined an uncommon learning of the ancients with little taste and judgment, but on the contrary, and for that reason, all the more credulity (ein Mann, der mit ungemeiner Belesenheit in den Alten wenig Geschmack und Urteil, dagegen desto mehr Leichtgläubigkeit verband)'. He refers to Sennert's belief in transmutation, the doctrine of signatures in plants, palingenesis, pacts with the Devil, witchcraft, astrology, the world soul, etc. — all delusions of Paracelsus. Sennert, however, opposed magic, the use of characters, and the idea of wise-men, the 'gabalia' of the *Qabbalah*.[1]

In medicine he was eclectic, taking much from Galen as well as something from Paracelsus, including the three principles.[2] He retained many Aristotelian ideas. He thought the properties of bodies did not arise solely from their elements, which furnished only the matter, but were impressed by a more spiritual principle (*Natura quinta*). The particles of which, he assumed, bodies are composed are not hard indivisible atoms but divisible, like those of Asklepiades of Prusa (Vol. I), and he probably did not assume a vacuum between them.[3]

Works by Sennert of interest to us are:

I. Epitome Naturalis Scientiae, Wittenberg, 1618, and later eds. (from that of 1633, inclusive, interpolated; Lasswitz, (1), i, 438–9); Editio Vltima, Amsterdam, 12°, 1651, including (with sep. t.p.) Auctarium Epitomes Physicæ, based on cap. xi of II (this is the only ed. I have seen; an editio ultima, Oxford, 1664, is mentioned); Operum, 1656, i, 1 f.; this work is said by Lasswitz, (1), ii, 250, to be really by Joachim Jungius (Hamburg, 1635), but Wolf and Ramsauer, 357, says the 1635 ed., Auctarium Epitome Physicæ D. Sennerti, a viro quodam docto, is really by Sennert.

---

[1] Brucker, 1766, IV, i, 503 (inter Germanos in naturali philosophia desipere coepit); Gmelin, (1), i, 596; Sprengel, (1), v, 17; *id.*, (2), iv, 284; Kopp, (2), iii, 160; *id.*, (4), i, 48; Lasswitz, (2), 1879, iii, 408–34 (cf. *ib.*, 1884, viii, 46); *id.*, (1), 1890, i, 436 f.; Stones, *Isis*, 1928, x, 454; Frost, *F. Bacon und die Naturphilosophie*, Munich, 1927, 348; K. L. Wolf and R. Ramsauer, *Zeitschrift für die gesamte Naturwissenschaft*, 1935, i, 129, 357; Mahnke, *ib.*, 1936–7, ii, 61 (copious quotations); Thorndike, vii, 203; Ramsauer, *Die Atomistik des Daniel Sennert*, Brunswick, 1935 (?, 123 pp.) I have not seen.

[2] Pagel, *Paracelsus*, Basel, 1958, 333–43, 383 f.   [3] Lasswitz, *opp. cit.*

II. De Chymicorum Cum Aristotelicis et Galenicis Consensu ac Dissensu, Liber I,
8°, Wittenberg, 1619 (pref. dated 1 Jan., 1619, pp. xxxii, 709, xxi index, ii
errata); 2 ed., 4°, Wittenberg, 1629 (434 pp., index; in this and later eds. the I is
omitted after *Liber*); 3 ed., 4°, Frankfurt, 1655, with Appendix, De Constitutione
Chymiæ, pp. 385–434, and index (Thorndike gives an ed. Paris, 1633); Operum,
Lyons, 1656, i, 180–284, with title De Consensu & Dissensu Galenicorum &
Peripateticorum cum Chymicis. Although an ed. of Venice, 1541, is mentioned,
those of 1629 and 1656 are described on the t.p.'s as 'second' and 'third' eds. Tr.
as: Chymistry made easie and useful. Or, the agreement and disagreement of the
Chymists and Galenists, by N. Culpeper and Abdiah Cole (166 pp.), as part of
The Physitians Library, 8°, London, 1622 (BM 7580. a. (2.); Sennertus, Culpeper, and Cole, Thirteen Books of Natural Philosophy . . . , 1660 (Ferguson,
ii, 371).[1]

III. Hypomnemata Physica, 8°, Frankfurt, 1636; Operum, Lyons, 1656, i, 102 f.; five
parts: (i) De rerum naturalium principiis, (ii) De occultis qualitatibus, (iii) De
atomis et mistione, (iv) De generatione viventium, (v) De spontanea viventium
generatione. It is quoted below by part and chapter.

IV. Institutionum Medicinæ Libri quinque, 4°, Wittenberg, 1611, 1620 (neither in
BM or BN), 1628 (BM 544. f. 3), 1667; in Operum, 1654, ii, 307–696 (plate of
chemical apparatus, 646; bk. V, pt. iii, sect. 2, ch. 1 is 'De natura Chymiæ); tr.
The Institution or Fundamentals of the whole art both of Physick and Chirurgery . . . also the grounds of Chymistry and the way of making all sorts of Salves
and preparing of medicines, made English by N.D.B.P., 8° London, 1656 (viii ll.,
492 pp., iii ll.; Davis and Orioli Cat. no. 82 (1938), 283).

V. Medicamenta officinalia cum Galenica tum Chymica, f°, Wittenberg, 1670
(quoted by Gmelin, i, 597).

VI. Practicæ Medicinæ, 6 vols. 4°, Wittenberg, 1635–52.

VII. Operum (or Opera) Omnia, (*a*) 3 vols. f°, Paris, 1641; (*b*) 3 vols. f°, Lyons, 1650;
(*c*) 4 vols. f°, Lyons, 1654–6 (the ed. mostly quoted; the two Lyons eds. are
differently paginated).

Sennert's views on atoms and corpuscles are based on the chemical phenomena of sublimation, solution (including metals in acids), petrifaction, etc.,[2]
rather than philosophical speculations. It is more than likely that his 'physical
atomism', with its emphasis on 'corpuscles' rather than hard indivisible
atoms, was derived from a study of medical authors, to whom it was known
from the account of the theory of Asklepiades of Prusa in the work of Cœlius
Aurelianus (Vol. I), which was included in the reading of the medical student;
the doctrines of the 'Methodic School' were well known to Leonhard Fuchs
(1501–66), professor of medicine in Ingolstadt and Tübingen.[3] Of newer
authors Sennert quotes Fracastoro (d. 1553), François Aguillon (the French
Jesuit, 1566–1617), Titelmann (d. 1550 or 1553) and Pererius; it is doubtful if
he was influenced by Bruno, Bacon's *Novum Organum* (1620) appeared after
Sennert's first work dealing with the corpuscular theory, and his sources were
medical rather than philosophical.[4] Sennert's views are contained in I (1618)
but fully only in the later editions (analysis in Lasswitz).

[1] On Nicholas Culpeper (1616–54), see S. Peel, *Nineteenth Century*, 1898, xliii, 755–63; Mabel
Tyrrell, *The Secrets of Nicholas Culpeper*, 1945; on the occultist John Heydon (1629–after
1667) who was associated with Culpeper, see Waite, *The Real History of the Rosicrucians*,
1887, 315–86; *id.*, *The Brotherhood of the Rosy Cross*, 1924, 388. Heydon invented a Rosicrucian New Atlantis in which chemical experiments had a place. Martinus, *Commentatiun-
cula in libri qui inscribitur de chymicorum cum Aristotlicis et Galenicis consensu ac dissensu*,
Frankfurt, 1621, I have not been able to trace.
[2] II, chs. viii, xii; VII *c*, i, 198, 225.
[3] *Institutionum Medicinæ, ad Hippocratis, Galeni, aliorumque veterum scripta recte intelli-
genda mire utiles Libri quinque*, 8°, Basel, 1567 (pref. dated June 1565); Lasswitz, (1), i, 452.
[4] Lasswitz, (1), i, 403, 452–4.

Wolf and Ramsauer, and Mahnke, regarded Sennert as the true representative of 'German' science as typified by Kepler and Paracelsus, and continued by Van Helmont, Digby, and Flud, a 'Platonic' type based on 'creative realism' rather than the 'Demokritan' mechanistic type exemplified by Gassendi and continued by Galileo and Boyle. They think he was acquainted

FIG. 9. DANIEL SENNERT, 1572–1637.

with the writings of Basso (p. 387). He gives the atoms properties or qualities in addition to the mechanical ones of pure atomism.[1] They are 'units of formation' or of 'action (ἐνεργεία)', formative forces, archei, or monads (as understood by Leibniz),[2] 'organic individuals' in animal bodies, in the Aristotelian sense, and not simply chemical molecules. In II, Sennert speaks of the formative spirits of metals (*spiritus aurificus* of gold, etc.).[3] Sennert did not reject the mechanical view altogether, but limited its application.

[1] Gadamer, *Z. gesamte Naturwiss.*, 1935, i, 81.
[2] Hildebrand, *Z. gesamte Naturwiss.*, 1935, i, 1, 242; 1936–7, ii, 169.
[3] VIIc, 1656, i, 208.

Thorndike says the atomic theory occupies only a small part of a single chapter of II, and in later works occupies relatively little space. In his introduction to the subject[1] Sennert says: 'To use the words of Scaliger in Exercise 101[2] . . . if I am forced to speak, I confess that I am now won over by the opinion of Scaliger, who defines mistion as "the motion of very small bodies to mutual contact in order to achieve union (Mistio est motus corporum minimorum ad mutuum contactum, ut fiat unio)." ' Scaliger is repeatedly cited and Thorndike thinks German claims for Sennert as 'the new founder of the corpuscular theory' are exaggerated, and 'his belief that the heavens were a simple body, his faith in occult qualities and in the existence of spiritual qualities . . . were all quite inconsistent with the developed mechanistic corpuscular theory, which accounted for everything in nature by such corpuscles alone'. Ramsauer and other recent German writers (of whom Thorndike was, apparently, ignorant), however, emphasise that Sennert's importance rests on the fact that he did not take over a purely *mechanical* corpuscular theory from such as Gassendi, as Boyle did, and the matter is not quite so simple; Sennert also deals with the atomic theory in works other than the one quoted by Thorndike.

His atomic theory is more fully explained in III;[3] according to Lasswitz[4] this is 'the revival of physical atomism', and the 'first explanation of chemical processes by unchangeable elementary particles; and in addition the conception of chemical matter (Stoff) as permanent in all combinations and transformations'. It was followed by Otto von Guericke (see p. 515).

The atomic theory was explained in the text-book of his pupil Johannes Sperling (1603–58), from 1634 professor of medicine and physics in Wittenberg:

Institutiones Physicæ, Bk. v, *c.* 2 (de Atomis); 8°, Lübeck, 1647 (colophon dated 1646, 1309 pp., index), 787 f.; 3 ed., 8°, Wittenberg, 1653 (1333 pp., index), 812 f.; Bk. v, *c.* 5 is on Qualitatibus Principiorum Chymicorum, 1647, 847; see Lasswitz, (1), ii, 261, q. 6 ed., 1572, 714 f.

In considering natural things, subject to generation and corruption, Sennert says one must necessarily suppose simple bodies of a particular kind, from which compound bodies are constituted and into which they are resolved. These simple bodies are physical, not mathematical, minima (minima naturae, atomi, atoma corpuscula, σώματα ἀδιαίρετα, *corpora indivisibilia*) not perceivable by the senses, the smallest indivisible particles and the origin of all natural bodies. There are atoms of the four elements (fire, air, water and earth) and atoms of the second order (*prima mixta*, our molecules) derived from compound bodies by solution and formed by mistion:[5]

sunt secundo alterius, præter elementares, generis atomi, (quas siquis prima mixta appellare velit, suo sensu utatur), in quæ, ut similaria, alia corpora composita resolvuntur.

All fermentations, separations and coctions, natural and artificial, depend only on the separation of bodies into their smallest parts and the intimate reunion of these.

Although at first[6] he thought that the four elements were transformable

[1] II, ch. xii; VIIc, 1656, i, 230 a.
[2] Scaliger, *Exotericarvm Exercitationvm*, Paris, 1557, Exerc. CI, 1[16], f. 143 v.
[3] VIIc, i, 115 f. (interpolated).   [4] (1), i, 436 f., 441.
[5] II, iii, 1; VIIc, i, 115 f., 118; crit. in Brucker, IV, i, 503.   [6] I, iii; VIIc, i, 34.

secundum partes if not *secundum totum*, Sennert later[1] concluded that exhalations and vapours consist of myriads of atoms, which recombine when rain or snow are formed, since water on evaporation is not changed into air but into its proper vapour, as spirit of wine, etc., also give their own vapours:

Neque enim hic quis sibi persuadeat, dum ex aqua, spiritu vini, vaporem, ex pice, sulphure, lignis accensis, fumum ascendere vidit, esse mutationem horum corporum in aërem; sed aqua, spiritus vini, ut et alia corpora, in minimas atomos resolvuntur, quae ubi coëunt, in aquam, spiritum vini, vel aliud corpus rursus abeunt; id quod Chymicorum Alembici, et vasa recipientia docent.

The small size of the atoms is clear from many experiments. The vapour of spirit of wine penetrates four thicknesses of writing paper; in distillation a large volume of vapour containing myriads of atoms yields hardly a small drop of liquid; when gold and silver are melted together, the atoms blend together so that the different metals cannot be detected in the alloy, yet each can be again obtained from it by the action of aqua fortis in its original state. The smallness of some insects (*acari*) is also evidence for the minute sizes of atoms, since living plants and animals are composed of atoms. The essential forms of species remain unchanged in their smallest parts, the atoms.

In the alloy of gold and silver, each retains its own form, gold remains gold and silver remains silver; on treating the alloy with aqua fortis the silver dissolves and the gold remains as a powder. The silver may also be precipitated as a fine powder from the solution. Mercury may be sublimed or dissolved or made to suffer other changes by a variation of the atoms into which it is resolved when it is mixed with others, yet it always retains its essential form and can readily be separated from the bodies with which it is mixed and recovered in its pristine form of running mercury.[2]

In the dedication to the 1619 edition of II to the Archbishop of Magdeburg, Sennert speaks of the changes in medicine in Germany during the last thirty years, owing to the replacement of the old medicines of Galen and Avicenna by the chemical remedies introduced by Paracelsus the Swiss, and he gives some examples of Paracelsus's superstitions and absurdities. In the book, Sennert did not deny the existence of salt, sulphur, and mercury. Sulphur can be traced in plants and metals. It is a constituent of all combustibles and is the actual component $\phi\lambda o\gamma\iota\sigma\tau\acute{o}v$, which confers inflammability.[3] Salt also is present in most natural objects and is the cause of crystallisability and also of hardness, behaving as a solidifying spirit.[4] The position of mercury is not clear, and its existence is not beyond doubt.[5] Besides Paracelsus, Sennert quotes Isaac of Holland, Basil Valentine, Libavius, Quercetanus, and other chemical authors. He says the three 'principles' should be regarded rather as material constituents of bodies and not be exalted in rank above the four elements of ancient philosophy, of which, indeed, the three principles are utlimately composed.[6]

Sennert says Paracelsus's basic error in medicine is his rejection of the four

[1] II, iii, 1; VII*c*, i, 118.   [2] II, iii, 1; VII*c*, i, 118–19.
[3] II, 1619, ch. xi, 264 f., 273, 281 ($\phi\lambda o\gamma$), 295, 297, 311 f.
[4] II, 1619, ch. xi, 299 f.   [5] II, 1619, ch. xi, 313 f.   [6] II, 1619, ch. xi, 269, 281, 315.

humours of Galen. His *ens deale, ens astrorum, ens mentale* (Pagoycum), and *ens veneni* are to be rejected,[1] also his doctrine of signatures and planetary influences.[2] Sennert thought the good parts of chemical medicine could be adopted without rejecting the whole of Galenical medicine,[3] and he retained the Aristotelian doctrine of the four elements,[4] as well as adopting the atomic theory. He felt sure the transmutation of metals had been so solidly proved by experiment that it was a waste of time to argue about it (metalla autem transmutari toties hodie experientiâ comprobatum est, vt disputando de eo frustra tempus teratur), although the art is difficult and frauds have been practised.[5]

In his early work[6] Sennert referred briefly to the doctrine of signatures 'of the chemists', but he later[7] dealt with it in detail and generally favourably, disagreeing with Libavius, who thought the resemblances only fortuitous.

In his chapter on poisons[8] Sennert deals with mineral poisons, quicklime, gypsum, vitriol, aqua fortis, antimony, magnet, diamond (he doubts if it is broken by goat's blood), lapis lazuli, arsenic, orpiment, sandaracha, realgar, copper scales, burnt copper, verdigris, brass and filings of bells, iron, iron rust, lead, white lead, minium, litharge, mercury, corrosive sublimate, red precipitate, and cinnabar; as well as plant (including nux vomica) and animal poisons (including bull's blood), in all cases giving the symptoms and antidotes.

FREITAG

Sennert was attacked by John Freitag (Nieder-Wesel, 30 October 1581–Groningen, 8 February 1641), who studied in Helmstädt and was at first professor of medicine there and physician to the bishop of Osnabrück. On religious grounds he left to become professor of medicine in Groningen in 1631:[9] in his enormous book[10] he quotes freely in Hebrew and other languages and denounces Sennert as a heretic, since he had said that form and the animal soul are independent of matter, which was created from nothing. Sennert, who no doubt felt rather out of his depth, consulted eight theological faculties and issued a reply to Freitag.[11]

SALA

Angelus (*sic*) Sala (Vicenza, 1576 ?–Güstrow, 2 October 1637) left Italy with his father, as Calvinists, about 1602, was at The Hague (1612–17), then became physician to the Count of Oldenburg (1617–20), was then in Hamburg (1620–5) and then physician to the Dukes of Mecklenburg-Güstrow (1625–36). He died by suicide after a painful illness. He probably learnt

---

[1] II, chs. xv, xvi, 1619, 428 f., 471 f.; Pagel, *Paracelsus*, 1958, 341.
[2] II, ch. xviii, 1619, 589, 604.   [3] II, ch. xviii, 1619, 678 f.
[4] II, chs. viii, xii, 1619, 153 f., 318 f.   [5] II, ch. ii, 1619, 20, 27 f.
[6] IV, bk. V, pt. i, sect. 1, ch. 22; VIIc, ii, 566, with ref. to II, ch. 18.
[7] II, ch. 18; VIIc, i, 258–60.   [8] VI, Bk. vi, pars 5–6; VIIc, iv, 1030 f.
[9] Jöcher, ii, 741; Thorndike, viii, 508.
[10] *Novæ Sectæ Sennerto-Paracelsicæ, Recens in Philosophiam & Medicinam introductæ* ... *Detectio & solida refutatio* ..., Amsterdam, 1636, 2 ed. 1637 (1356 pp., 1 errata).
[11] *De origine et natura animarum in brutis sententiæ Cl. Theologorum in aliquot Germaniæ academiis*, 8°, Wittenberg, 1638; VIIc, i, 285–306.

chemistry in Venice from about 1593. Most of his works were composed from 1610 to 1630.[1] Since he did not know Latin, Sala's writings were translated into that language by others. His separate works are very numerous[2] and some were published in several editions; the following list is not intended to be complete (items marked with an asterisk were not seen in the form quoted):

1.* Tractatus duo de variis tum chymicorum tum Galenistarum erroribus in præparatione medicinali commissis, 12°, Hannover, 1608; printed as appendix with sep. t.p. dated 1649 and sep. sign. and pagin., in my ed. of (18), with a preface by S. Schröder dated 1648.

2. Anatomi Vitrioli, in duos tractatus divisa; in quibus vera ratio vitrioli in diversas substantias resolvendi . . . traditur. Accedit arcanorum complurium ex substantiis istis deductorum ex Italica in Latinam . . . J.P.C.P., 12°, Aureliæ Allobrogam [Geneva], 1609 (BM 778. a. 6. (1.)); 1613 (BM 1035. a. 5. (1.)).

3. Emetologia ov Enarration du naturel et vsages des Vomitaires, sm. 8°, Delphis [Delft], 1613 (BM 547. a. 19).

4. Septem Planetarum Terrestrium Spagirica recensio, . . . Authore Angelo Sala . . . 12°, Amsterdam, 1614 (98 pp.; BM 1035. a. 5. (2.)).

5. Ternarius bezoarticorum, ou trois souverains médicaments bézoardiques (in French), 4°, Leyden, 1616 (BM 546. d. 20. (1.); this is different from the Latin no. 8).

6. Anatomia Antimonii; id est Dissectio tam dogmatica quam Hermetica antimonii; usum, proprietatem, et vires ejus declarans, 8°, Leyden, 1617 (BM 1034. b. 5. (2.)).

7. Opiologia ov Traicté concérnant . . . l'Opium: . . . , La Haye, 1614 (68 pp.); Opiologia. Or, A Treatise concerning the Nature . . . of Opium . . . by Angelvs Sala, translated and 'something inlarged' by Tho. Bretnor, sm. 8°, London, 1618 (81 pp.).

8. Ternarius bezoardicorum et hemetologia seu triumphus vomitoriorum, cum exegesi chymiatrica Andreae Tentzelli, 12° or 8°, Erfurt, 1618 (BM 1035. a. 8).[3]

9. Aphorismorum Chymiatricorum Synopsis Universa Chymiatriæ intima fundamenta, . . . sm. 8°, Bremen, 1620.

10.* Descriptio brevis Antidoti Pretiosi: Quâ antiquissimae ejus virtutes, ususq; multiplex variis in morbis, & humani corporis affectibus, 8°, Marburg, 1620 (Duveen, 525) incl. poems by Hartmann, Billich, and Raphael Eglinus Iconius.

11. Chrysologia, seu Examen Auri Chymicum In quo demonstratur, auro nec inesse substantiam aliquam potabilem: nec illud arte spagyrica transmutari posse in substantiam aquosam, oleosam vel salinam; & quid propriè intelligatur per aurum potabile. Adjecti sunt in fine ejusdem Aphorismi Chymiatrici recogniti, 2 pts., 8°, Hamburg, 1622 (BM 1034. c. 7. (2.)).

12. Essentiarvm Vegetabilium Anatome. Darinnen von den fürtrefflichsten Nutzarbeiten der Vegetabilischen Essenzen in der Artzney . . . , sm. 8°, Rostock, 1630 (259 pp.), * 1635 (Gilhofer and Ranschburg Cat. 257 (1936), no. 301).

13.* De Auro Potabili, novo paucisque adhuc cognito: Cui quidam alii ex Basilii Valentini, Iosephi Quercetani, Portæ, & aliorum scriptis exerpti, cum commentariolis . . . , 8°, Strassburg, 1631.[4]

14. Tartarologia. Das ist: Von der Natur vnd Eigenschaft des Weinsteins . . . , sm. 8°, Rostock, 1632 (111 pp.), * 1636 (Gilhofer and Ranschburg).

15.* Hydrelæologia, darinnen, wie man allerley Wasser, Oliteten, vnd brennende Spiritus . . . distillieren vnd rectificieren soll. . . . Neben e. Unterricht wie Aquaviten zubereiten, 8°, Rostock, 1633 (Gilhofer and Ranschburg).

16. Spagyrische Schatzkammer, von Erbrechmachender, Purgirenden, Harntreibenden u.a. Medicamenten, 8°, Rostock, 1637 (BM 1034. c. 10).

17.* Saccharalogia, 8°, Rostock, 1637 (German and Latin).

[1] Jöcher, iv, 41; Gmelin, (1), 586; Sprengel, (1), v, 14; Thomson, (1), i, 178; Kopp, (1), i, 115; id., (4), i, 48; Hoefer, (1), ii, 208; NBG, 1864, xliii, 162; Ferguson, ii, 314; R. Capobus, *Angelus Sala, Leibarzt des Herzogs Johann Albrecht II von Mecklenburg-Güstrow. Seine wissenschaftliche Bedeutung als Chemiker im XVII Jahrhundert*, Berlin, 1933 (67 pp.; portr.; correcting many errors); von Buchka, *A. Nat.*, 1913, vi, 20; A. Blanck, *Die Mecklinburgischen Aerzte von den ältesten Zeiten bis zur Gegenwart*, Schwerin, 1874; Thorndike, vii, 167.
[2] List in Capobus, 53–67.   [3] On Tentzel's work, see Ferguson, ii, 432.
[4] For some other works on potable gold, see Thorndike, vii, 195.

18. Angeli Salæ Vicentini Chymiatri Candidissimi et Archiatri Megapolitani, Opera Medico-Chymica qvæ extant omnia. Frustulatim hactenus, diversisque linguis excusa, nunc in unum collecta latinoque idiomate edita, 4°, Frankfurt, Joannis Beyeri, 1647 (often mispaged); 4°, Rouen, 1650; *4°, Frankfurt, 1682 (with additional works); Collectanea Chimica Curiosa, 4°, Frankfurt, 1693 (viii, 927, xxv pp.; Bolton, (1), 796); see (19).

19. Myrothecium Spagyricum, with Appendix, printed in (18) and in Collectanea Chimica Curiosa quæ veram continent rerum naturalium anatomiam sive analysin, J. D. Thom. A., 4°, Frankfurt, 1693 (BM 1033. k. 18. (1.)); q. without date by Ferguson.

20. Compositio et Formula Antidoti pretiosi, aliorumque nonnullorum medicamentorum Angeli Salæ, with preface by Ludwig Combach dated January, 1649, appended to my ed. of (18).

21. Descriptio brevis Antidoti Pretiosi, in (18).

22. Processus de Auro Potabili, novo, paucisque adhuc cognito, in (18).

In the following references the number of the separate work in this list is given first, followed by the page reference to the reprint in (18), 1647.

Sala (following Paracelsus) defined the Spagyric Art as that part of chemistry which has for its subject the natural bodies, vegetable, animal, and mineral, and such operations as tend to the end of rendering them useful in medicine: Ars spagyrica sit illa Chymiæ pars, quae pro subjecto habet corpora naturalia Vegetabilium videlicet, Animalium, ac Mineralium: in quibus quicquid operatur, id ad utilem in Medicina finem tendit.[1] Its principal operations are separation, subtilisation, and sublimation.

Sala, like Sennert, followed Paracelsus (chymiatrorum facile principe),[2] in adopting his theory of tartar[3] and his use of remedies from antimony (including glass of antimony)[4] and mercury,[5] e.g. calomel (not named, made by subliming mercury with corrosive sublimate),[6] in both cases with proper precautions,[7] yet he rejected some of the ideas of the Iatrochemists, e.g. the universal remedy (res absurdissima est),[8] the use of potable gold,[9] etc.

In his treatise on antimony he quotes ancient and modern authors for its virtues and uses, points out that it is poisonous and must be used with caution, questions the existence in it of gold, silver, and copper, or the separation of mercury, liquor, oil or tincture from it. He describes the preparation of metallic antimony (regulus antimonii), crocus, and flowers of antimony, and an antimonial remedy which purges by perspiration and insensible transpiration, which is a white powder (cerusa antimonii) made by deflagrating the metal with nitre and washing (i.e. antimonic acid).[10]

Sala describes the preparation of crystalline silver nitrate (magisterium argenti, crystalli Dianæ, cathartica lunari) by dissolving silver in aqua fortis and evaporating, and says it turns black in sunlight (si lapidem lunarem pulveratum ad solem exponas instar atramenti nigerrimus evadit).[11] Fulminating gold (Ceraunochryson, uti vocant Solis, sclopetantem, fulminantem), which was the only preparation of gold he used medicinally, is not formed

---

[1] 11; 18, 215.   [2] 11; 18, 215.   [3] 14; 18, 120 f.
[4] 6; 18, 291 f., 330.
[5] 4; 18, 203 f.   [6] 8; 18, 504.   [7] 6, 8; 18, 301 f., 330, 503 f.
[8] 21; 18, 478, 489.   [9] 11, 22; 18, 222, 268; Capobus, 29 f.
[10] 6; 18, 352.   [11] 4; 18, 194–200.

unless sal ammoniac, not spirit of salt, is added to the aqua fortis to make the aqua regia for dissolving gold. Its explosive force is destroyed (vim sclopetandi amittet) by mixing with sulphur and burning off the sulphur.[1]

Sala's criticism of potable gold is partly directed against Francis Anthony, an English quack (and a friend of Michael Maier) who had published a *Panacea aurea* (Hamburg, 1598?, 1618) dedicated to King James I.[2] Sala, however, gives preparations of it of his own; his work is largely a commentary on Croll but quotes Basil Valentine and other authors. Anthony's book was 'refuted' by Matthew Gwinne (c. 1558–1627), first professor of physics at Gresham College, in 1611, and Anthony replied in 1616.[3]

Sala emphasised that copper precipitated by iron is present before in the solution.[4] He thought, however, that the iron 'attracted' the copper from the solution and that the sulphuric acid previously united with the copper remained as such: et nihil aliud ampliùs superest quàm Aqua, & Spiritus acidus Sulphuris;[5] the true explanation, that the iron went into solution and changed place with the copper was given by Jungius (p. 420) and Van Helmont (p. 221). Sala combated the ideas of the transmutation of metals and the universal medicine.[6]

Sulphuric acid (spiritus vitrioli) is the same whether got from iron or copper vitriol by distillation, or by burning sulphur; it is a very useful remedy but must not be used with saltpetre, from which it liberates the poisonous nitric acid.[7] Sala describes the preparation of sal ammoniac from spirit of salt and ammonia: duabus partibus est compactum, sale volatili . . . et sale communi . . . Si partem salis volatilis cum debita spiritus salis communis quantitate ad artis praescriptum misceas, sal inde Armoniacum . . . conficens.[8] Salt of tartar potassium carbonate (K_2CO_3) is an antidote to corrosive sublimate, which it precipitates.[9]

What Sala calls 'acid of tartar (acidum tartari)' is really cream of tartar:[10] the *tartari acidum chalybeatum*, obtained by boiling cream of tartar with green vitriol, is potassium ferrous tartrate.[11] The 'tartar' crystallised from the juice of sorrel clarified with white of egg[12] is salt of sorrel, acid potassium oxalate, KHC_2O_4. The salts obtained from plants by burning, and the oils produced from vegetable and animal matters by distillation, have not the same virtues as the original material.[13]

Sala classified bodies into vegetable, animal, and mineral; they are all composed of the three Elements, sulphur, mercury, and salt,[14] sulphur being the principle of combustibility — a fatty principle, the same in essence in all bodies but differing in kinds; on combustion, 'the fire goes to its chaos'.[15] Water cannot be converted into air or into earth: quod aliquot chimicos eo praesumptionis induxit, ut aquam puram in lapidem substantiam, & vice versa,

[1] 21; 18, 266; 20 (unpaged), iii: qui non fulminat igne, ut facit commune.
[2] Ferguson, i, 36; Sala, 21; 17, 271, 288.   [3] Thorndike, vii, 170.
[4] 2; 18, 398 f.   [5] 2; 18, 401; correcting Kopp, (1), i, 116.
[6] 4, 2, 15, 16; 18, 183, 398 f., 787 f.   [7] 2, 8; 18, 405 f., 543.
[8] 9; 18, 246.   [9] 4; 18, 204.   [10] 14; 18, 129.   [11] 14; 18, 131.
[12] 14; 18, 138; Boerhaave, (2), 1732, ii, 36.   [13] 14, 9; 18, 144, 254.
[14] 9, i, 10–11; 18, 1647, 241.
[15] 15, ii, 1; 11, i, 2; 18, 65–6, 217–18; Capobus, 31.

hanc in illam, transmutari posse ... errore.[1] He does not mention Van Helmont (whose works were not fully published in his lifetime), Sennert, or Agricola.

Sala defines fermentation as an internal motion of the particles of bodies brought about by internal heat in the presence of moisture, which groups them in new arrangements, partly by separation and partly by reduction into a new kind of more noble mixt.[2] Metals and minerals cannot be fermented, and the supposed extraction of mercury from metals is impossible.[3] Spirit of wine may be distilled from beer, fermented grain, fermented fruits and fruit juices, and fermented sugar (saccharum): Sala does not mention the gas evolved.[4] Bernburg beer (containing 1 part of spirit in 6 parts) and Normandy cider (zithus in Normandia) were, in his day, as strong and intoxicating as Spanish wine. Alcohol is the best solvent for the odoriferous constituents of plants, whilst water dissolves the bitter principles.[5]

In his treatise on sugar[6] Sala (following Libavius, p. 267) describes its purification by white of egg and milk of lime (which he says is not injurious, but Helmont, p. 226, says it is), and mentions the acid (which dissolves coral pearls, etc.) obtained by its distillation (aqua acerrimæ & penetrantis qualitatis particeps ... coralia, margaritas, caneros, lapidem pumicem, in subtilissimos atomos resolvendi vim obtineat).[7] By its fermentation with yeast and distillation a 'phlogistic spirit' is formed (quomodo ex saccharo spiritus phlogisticos eliciatur).[8]

BILLICH

Peter Lauremberg (Rostock; 26 August 1585–13 May 1639), translator of Drebbel's works into Latin, and professor of philosophy, medicine, physics and mathematics, and poetry in Rostock, published a criticism of Sala[9] which called forth from Anthor Gunther Billich, son-in-law of Sala and private physician (Leibmedicus) to the Count of Oldenburg,[10] a reply with a vituperative title.[11] A hand was then taken in defence of Lauremberg by Arnolde Schröder.[12] Billich had previously defended Sala in a pamphlet.[13] Billich, a good chemist who is quoted by Boyle,[14] wrote on fermentation and the vanity

[1] 15; 18, 54.   [2] 15; 18, 95 f.   [3] 6; 18, 308.   [4] 15; 18, 97 f., 165 f.
[5] 15; 18, 102.   [6] 17; 18, 150–79.   [7] 17; 18, 162.   [8] 17; 18, 164.
[9] *Synopsin Aphorismorum Chymiatricorum Angeli Salæ Vicentini, Notæ et Animadversiones*, sm. 4°, *s.l.*, 1624 (27 pp., t.p. gives Laurenberg; Thorndike, viii, 7.
[10] He was born in Friesland but his dates are unknown; Gmelin, (1), i, 595; Ferguson, i, 107; Thorndike, vii, 169, 191.
[11] *Adsertionum Chimicarvm Sylloge ... opposita clangoso latratui & venenatis morsibus Petri Lawrembergii, Canis Scholastici rabiosi scabiosi &*, 1624 (40 pp.); *Petri Laurembergii deliria Chymica*, 1625.
[12] *Defensio Animadversionum et Notarum ... Petri Laurembergii, In Aphorismos Chymiatricos Angeli Salæ, Opposita Responsioni Anton. Gunther Billich*, sm. 4°, Frankfurt, 1624 (159 pp.); *Bonum factum. Flabellum, quo fumus chymicus & cinis contumeliarum ... et medico ac philosopho celeberrimo Petro Laurembergio afflare conatus est Anton. Gunther Billich, ex infami ac perfidioso milite nuper transformatus in stercoreum et pediculosum empyricum ...*, 1625; Kopp, (4), ii, 334; Ferguson, ii, 342, gives a different title; Capobus, 47 f.
[13] *Ad Aminadversiones quas Anonymus quidam in Angeli Salæ Aphorismos Chymiatricos conscripsit responsio*, 8°, Leyden, 1622; Thorndike, vii, 169.
[14] *Sceptical Chymist*, 1680, 319.

of the Spagirists[1] claiming[2] to prove, against Beguin (see Vol. III), that the *tri prima* (salt, sulphur, mercury) really consist of the four elements (fire, air, water, earth), and quoting the experiment on burning wood mentioned by Boyle (p. 505). Billich had written against the three principles in an earlier work,[3] and he also wrote a work on chemical paradoxes[4] in which he also rejected the *tria prima* and said potable gold was imaginary, but Algarotti's powder (*mercurium vitae*; really antimony oxychloride) had won a fortune of some thousand gold pieces and an immortal name. In his *Thessalus* (1643) Billich was much less favourable to chemical remedies, and he devotes a good deal of space in his books to rather pedantic criticism of Beguin and Quercetanus.[5]

Henry Lavater, professor of medicine in Zürich and director of the Caroline College (d. 1623) wrote a defence of Galenical medicine against Sala.[6] Lavater also compiled an epitome of natural philosophy from Aristotle[7] and wrote a disputation on the motion of the earth.

SYLVIUS DE LE BOË

François Dubois, Franciscus de le Boë (or Deleboe), Latinised as Sylvius (Hanau, 1614–Leyden, 14 November 1672),[8] not to be confused with the Paris professor of medicine and miser Jacob Sylvius (1478–1555),[9] is said to have been descended from a noble French Protestant family of Crèvecoeur which had gone from Cambrai to Germany. He was educated at Sedan, Leyden, and Basel (where he graduated in 1637), and practised medicine with success at Hanau, Leyden and (from 1641) at Amsterdam. In 1658 he became professor of medicine at Leyden, where he died in 1672. His lectures were famous and he had great numbers of students, including French, German, Italian, Russian and English. He taught Harvey's theory of the circulation of the blood in spite of opposition, and made many dissections. He was essentially a teacher as distinguished from an original investigator, and he took many of his ideas from Paracelsus, Descartes, and Van Helmont. Sylvius himself says his ideas were taught in his lectures from 1641, whilst Helmont's writings appeared

---

[1] *Thessalus In Chymicis Redivivus Id est, De Vanitate Medicinæ Chymicæ, Hermeticæ, seu Spagiricæ Dissertatio. Ejusdem Anatomica Fermentationis Platonicæ. Accesservnt De eadem Hermanni Conringii Exercitationes & Danielis Sennerti Epistola*, 8°, Frankfurt, 1643 (pp. xvi, 318; BM 1033. d. 13); Conring, *De Sangvinis generatione, et motv natvrali. Accedunt ejusdem, et Antonii Gvntheri Billichii de fermentatione libri duo*, Leyden and Amsterdam, 8°, 1646; Billich's *Anatome Fermentationis Platonicæ* occupies pp. 463–546, commenting on a passage in Plato's *Timaios*.

[2] *Ib.*, 1643, 143.

[3] *D.O.M.A. De Tribus Chymicorum Principiis, et Quincta Essentia Exercitatio*, 8°, Bremen, 1621, pp. viii, 69.

[4] *Observationum ac Paradoxorum chymiatricorum Libri Duo: Quorum Unus medicamentorum Chymicorum praeparationum: Alter eorundem usum succincte perspicueque explicat*, 4°, Leyden, 1631.

[5] Thorndike, viii, 113.

[6] *Defensio Medicorvm Galenicorum Adversvs Calumnias Angeli Salæ operarii Chymici*, 8°, Hanover, 1610, 1640 (95 pp.); BM 7509. b. (2.); The Lavater family, descended from the Protestant theologian Ludwig Lavater (1527–86), included the famous physiognomist Johann Kaspar Lavater (1741–1801).

[7] *Epitome Philosophiæ Naturalis, ex Aristotelis*, 8°, Zürich, 1621 (BM 519. a. 25).

[8] Some accounts give 1623–16 December 1672.

[9] *Opera Medica*, f°, Geneva, 1630.

complete first in 1648.[1] Gmelin, however, points out that Helmont's teachings were well known in the Low Countries before they were printed, and some of Sylvius's resemble them very closely in points of detail. Sylvius discarded their mysticism, over-simplified them, rejected the archei and ferments, and founded a school, having an immense reputation among his pupils, who followed him uncritically. He represents the culmination of Iatrochemistry

FIG. 10. F. SYLVIUS DE LE BOË (1614–72).

(although he is sometimes mistakenly called its founder), but as compared with Helmont he is superficial, and he was satisfied with very inadequate explanations. He probably made chemical experiments but was mostly a theorist.[2]

A. Disputationum Medicarum Decas primarias Corporis Humani Functiones Naturales Nec non Febrium Naturam, ex Anatomicis, Practicis & Chymicis Experimentis deductas complectens, 12°, Amsterdam, 1663, Jena, 1674 (presented as dissertations in 1659–61):

   (a) De Alimentorum Fermentatione in Ventriculo, (b) De Chyli â Fæcibus alvinis

---

[1] Preface to *Disputationum Medicarum Decas*, Amsterdam, 1663, § 40; *Opera Medica*, f°, Geneva, 1698, fol. †† 4 r°.

[2] Barchusen, 1710, 497; Gmelin, (1), i, 677–730; Sprengel, (1), v, 59–69; *id.*, (2), iv, 336–48; Thomson, (1), i, 193; Kopp, (1), i, 134; NBG, 1865, xliv, 729; Hoefer, (1), ii, 214; Daremberg, 1870, i, 540–71 ('d'un monotonie désespérante'); Haeser, (1), 1881, ii, 363; Foster, 1901, 147; Süssenguth, *Pharm. Ztg.*, 1937, lxxxii, 859; E. D. Baumann, *François De le Boe Sylvius*, Leyden, 1949 (242 pp., q. in *Archives*, 1950, xxix, 999); the funeral oration by Prof. L. Schacht, on 29 December 1672, in the Theological Auditorium at Leyden, *Oratio funebris in obitum Fr. de le Boe Sylvii*, 4°, Leyden, 1673, is printed in the *Opera*, Geneva, 1698, pp. 738–47; the epitaph, p. 747 *v*, is dated Leyden, 1665.

Secretione, (c) De Chyli Mutatione in Sanguinem, (d) De Spirituum Animalium in Cerebro etc., (e) De Lienis et Glandularum Usu, (f) De Bilis ac Hepatis Usu, (g) De Respiratione, Usuque Pulmonem, (h) De Vasis Lymphaticis, et Lymphâ, (i) De Febribus Prima, (j) De Febribus Altera.

These are all quite short (33 pp. in *Opera*, 1698).

B. Praxeos Medicæ idea nova, 12°, Leyden, 1671; 23, 980 pp., 122 index (unpaged), with Index Materiæ Medicæ by Martin Carcëus de Karczagh-Uiszallasa, sep. t.p., 96 pp. (unpaged); this part comprises only Book I; Books II and III were published as an appendix by Schrader, 12°, Amsterdam, 1674.

C. Methodus Medendi, publ. posthumously in the *Opera*, 1679.

D. Opera Medica, 2 vols. 8°, Paris, 1671, containing Institutiones Medicæ and De Chemia which are spurious and were disowned by Sylvius.

E. Opera Medica, Tam hactenus inedita, . . . cum duplici Indice . . . , ed. Justus Schrader, 4°, Amsterdam, 1679.

F. Opera medica . . . Accessit . . . hactenus ineditum Collegivm Nosocomicvm . . . Cum duplici Indice . . . , f° (in 6's), Geneva (Coloniæ Allobrogvm), S. de Tournes, 1681 (fine portrait).

G. Opera medica . . . editio nova, Cui accedunt Casus Medicinales . . . , ed. J. Merian, 4°, Utrecht and Amsterdam, 1695 (with very fine portrait).

H. Opera medica, ed. J. Merian, f° (in 6's), Geneva, de Tournes, 1698 (the ed. used): (xll., 747 pp., epitaph, xx ll. index, 67 pp. (poor portrait); other eds. quoted which I have not seen are Geneva, 1680, 1731; Utrecht, 1691; Venice, f°, 1696, 1707 (Art Ancien *Cat.* Zürich, 21 (1938), No. 813), 1708, 1736; Paris, 1771.

I. Casus Medicinales, sive Historiæ Ægrotorum . . . curam An. 1659. 60. & 61 in Nosocomio Leydensi . . . J. Meiran volante calamo excepit; in H, Appendix, sep. pag.; followed by Remedia Sylviana and Remedia Extraordinaria.

J. De Affectus Epidemii Anno 1669 Leidensem Civitatem depopulantia . . . 1670 . . . causis naturalibus; in H, 701–8.

K. Collegium Nosocomicum a D. D. Sylvio habitum; in H, 709–37.

L. De Medicamentis Chymicis Theses; in H, 694.

Sylvius was too busy to do much research; his pupil Stensen (Steno) said: 'he expounds, in the shape of views and speculations, matters concerning which he has not yet arrived at a clear and definite result, and thus stimulates others to inquiry, supplying them at the same time with problems to begin with.'[1] In discussing the secretion of urine, for example, Sylvius said: 'Although I cannot as yet fully follow out the process, nevertheless I hope to arrive at it by the process of precipitation.'[2] Foster says Sylvius persuaded the curators of the University of Leyden to build him a 'Laboratorium, as they call it', which would be the first university chemical laboratory.

Sylvius's one-sided attachment to chemical theories in medicine (Iatrochemistry) came in for some severe criticism from Boerhaave;[3] Sprengel[4] says that Sylvius, with his exaggeration of the importance of fermentation in the human body, 'had degraded the physician to the rank of a brewer or distiller', and speaks of the 'terrifying results' of his medical method. Sylvius's chemical theories were criticised by Boyle.[5] Sylvius himself[6] emphasised the hypothetical nature of many parts of his medical system.

The leading idea of the Iatrochemical School was that the functions of the

---

[1] Foster, 1901, 149.   [2] B, i, 3; H, 1698, 240.
[3] De Chemia suos errores expurgante, Leyden oration of 1718, in (2), 1732, ii, *Opuscula omnia*, 36 f., 41, with an excellent brief summary of Sylvius's theories.
[4] (1), v, 64.
[5] Reflections upon the Hypothesis of Alcali and Acidum, 1675; in *Works*, ed. Birch, 1744, iii, 603.
[6] *Disputat. Medic.*, pref.

living organism were mainly determined by chemical activities ('effervescences'), particularly the acidic or alkaline character of certain, often imaginary, constituents — a precursor of the modern pH cult; he generally neglected
the solid parts of the body and considered only the liquids, in which, he
supposed, an excess of one of these constituents gave rise to a disturbance in
the chemical processes taking place in the body, and that a removal of the
excess or the supplementing of the defect could effect a cure of the disease — a
survival of the old humoral pathology (Vol. I). Sylvius's main idea was that
disease is caused by 'acridity' (a name which he introduced into medicine)
produced by an acid or alkali, which could be removed by neutralisation by a
substance of the opposite class.

It must not be overlooked that such assumptions led to important chemical
discoveries, and the interest in chemistry on the part of educated men raised its
status from alchemy, a belief in which, however, still persisted. Whewell[1]
thought that 'the mutual relation of acids to alkalies was . . . the first distinct
form in which the notion of chemical attraction or affinity appeared', and J. E.
Marsh[2] that it was in this idea and its development 'that chemistry first became a science'.

Sylvius replaced the triumvirate of organs of Van Helmont (p. 237) by a
'triumvirate of humours': saliva (the importance of which he exaggerated),
pancreatic juice, and bile, which he thought played the principal parts in
digestion.[3] In his theory of digestion, Sylvius rejected the Archeus of Van
Helmont and explained everything on chemical principles as due to fermentation, caused by a ferment in the saliva, which he thought was the most
important juice and was neutral in reaction.[4] His pupil Régnier de Graaf had
collected pancreatic juice from dogs, and, from its taste only, concluded that
it was feebly acid (actually it is feebly alkaline):

offendimus namque ipsum quandoque acidum gratissimum, aliquando penè insipidum, nonnunquam austerum, sæpius salsum, sæpissime vero acidosalsum; Pack's
translation: 'we sometimes have found it most gratefully acid, sometimes almost insipid, sometimes auster, often times salt, but most often acidly salt'.[5]

By the 'effervescence' of this with the alkaline bile, formed from the blood by a
ferment, and with the saliva, an acid chyle is produced from the food, which
is carried to the heart; by mixing with the alkaline bile it produces blood and
animal heat (ignis vitalis). Part of the bile passes into the blood, making it
more fluid and giving to it a colouring matter and bitter taste.[6] Another part
acts chemically in decomposing the food in the intestines and is rejected with
the faeces.[7] De Graaf found that, actually, pancreatic juice and bile do not
effervesce when mixed, but he explained that for this a special heat of the
warm viscera in the body is required. Bile, according to Sylvius, contains

[1] 1857, iii, 98.   [2] 1929, 35 ff.   [3] B; I, ch. xi, § 3.
[4] C; Bk. I, c. v, § 18 f.; c. xvi, § 6; B; Bk. I, cc. vii, x; etc.; Gmelin, (1), i, 684 f.; Foster, 154 f.
[5] Régnier de Graaf, Tractatus Anatomico-medicus de Succi Pancreatici Natura & Usu,
Leyden, 1663; in Opera omnia, 8°, Leyden, 1677, 491 f.; 540; reprinted in Manget, Bibliotheca
Anatomica, 2 vols., f°, Geneva, 1685, i, 177 f., 187; English tr. by C. Pack, De Succo Pancreatico: Or, A Physical and Anatomical Treatise of the Nature and Office of the Pancreatick
Juice; . . . sm. 8°, London, 1676 (151 pp.), 35; Sylvius, B; I, c. xi, § 4.
[6] C; Bk. I, c. vi, §§ 8 and 16; Bk. II, c. xxviii, §§ 5, 9, 10.   [7] B; Bk. I, c. i, § 3; c. xi, § 7.

much parched alkaline lixivial salt (sal lixiviosum retorridum), a little volatile spirit, and a temperate oil, and it is the only one of the three humours to be alkaline. Pancreatic juice contains an acid and a volatile spirit.[1] Chyle contains a lixivial salt, a volatile spirit of the nutriment, a little acid spirit, and water.[2]

Jean Conrad Peyer (Schaffhausen; 1653–1712) who studied in Basel and Paris, says[3] that in 1673 he discovered glands in the intestine ('Peyer's patches') the secretion from which must play a part in digestion. The efficacy of the pancreatic juice becomes exhausted as the food descends to the lower part of the intestine, where the new glands are more abundant. (It is now known that these glands do not secrete anything concerned with digestion.)

The importance of the pancreatic juice was denied by John Conrad Brunner (Dieffenhofen, 1653–Mannheim, 1727),[4] who showed that dogs lived without the pancreas, but 'made water very frequently'.[5]

Although Sylvius[6] refers to diabetes it probably does not mean true diabetes.[7] Foster[8] says: 'With Brunner's and Peyer's discovery, the short-lived glory of the pancreatic juice, raised up for it by Sylvius and De Graaf, passed away. The minds of physiologists went back to the older view that the stomach was the chief seat of digestion, and that bile either served in some way as an aid to gastric digestion, or was merely an excrement.'

Effervescence with acid was regarded as a characteristic property of an alkali: in qua [effervescentia] semper observatur concurrere spiritus acidus et sal lixiviosum, corpusve lixivioso sale præditum.[9]

Although acid and alkali usually produce heat on mixing, Sylvius observed a 'cold effervescence' when oil of vitriol reacts with volatile alkali (ammonium carbonate): observamus Spiritum Vitrioli Sali Volatili cuivis, non tamen Oleoso, affusum, Effervescentiam excitare cum notabili Algore ac Frigore copulatam.[10] The heat evolved in slaking lime is due to the liberation of fire absorbed during the burning of the limestone: à conclusio quidem prius calci ex calcinatione igne, est per accedentem aquam à compedibus iterum liberato producantur.[11] This is an old idea; it is in St. Augustine (Vol. I). The theory was adopted by Lemery:[12] la chaux est une pierre de laquelle le feu a desseiché toute l'humidité et a introduit en sa place une grande quantité de corps ignées; and Homberg:[13] la chaux vive contient des particules du feu, qui sont fort agissantes. They regarded fire as material and corpuscular.

Sylvius supposed that the acrimony of acids as well as alkalis is derived from fire: ubi observandum est salem lixivium et spiritum acidum insignem ab igne suam obtinere acrimoniam.[14] He also mentions the heat evolved on mixing oil of vitriol with turpentine[15] and the heat and effervescence produced when oil of vitriol diluted with water is poured on iron filings.[16] He believed

[1] B; Bk. I, c. x, §§ 9–10; A, (f), §§ 39–40. [2] A, (b), § 26.
[3] Exercitatio anatomico-medica de glandulis intestinorum, earumque usu & affectionibus, 8°, Amsterdam, 1681; NBG, 1862, xxxix, 776, says this was first publ. in 8°, Schaffhausen, 1677.
[4] Experimenta nova circa pancreas, Amsterdam, 8°, 1683.
[5] Foster, 163: this was glycosuria produced by lack of insulin, which is formed by islet cells in the pancreas.
[6] B; Appendix, V, § 339; H, 1698, 555. [7] Daremberg, i, 549.
[8] 1901, 164. [9] A, (b), § 13. [10] B; I, c. xiv, § 18. [11] A, (a), § 2.
[12] Cours de Chymie, Part I, ch. xi: 1690, 317. [13] A d S, 1700 (1703), h 48.
[14] A, (h), § 47. [15] B; Appendix, tract. V, § 400. [16] B; Appendix, tract. V, § 425.

that volatile alkali (ammonia) occurred in plants as well as in animals.[1] He speaks of a 'volatile salt' as abounding in sharp and aromatic plants: in universum omnes Acriores & Aromaticas Volatili Sale abundare.[2] He paid much attention to the sounds produced on pouring various kinds of liquids into a vessel, and to the sounds produced by the movement of liquids in the body as a means of diagnosis.[3]

Sylvius was not always consistent in assigning acid or alkaline reaction to juices: at first[4] he said lymph contained an alkali but elsewhere[5] that it contained an acid spirit. Actually, he rarely troubled to ascertain the reactions by chemical tests. He says that urine is frequently acid, as is found by the taste:[6] patet ex Vrinæ istius Sapore acido et acri; qualem sæpius me jubente gustarunt (fresh urine has an acid reaction). His theory led him to suppose that some alleged remedies, such as jasper and emerald, must contain fixed or volatile alkali, although they show no signs of these:[7] quos omnes sale abundare norunt chymici.

Fermentation is promoted by plenty of water, a mild heat and ample free air.[8] Although Foster says Sylvius identified fermentation with effervescence, he really sharply distinguished them: effervescentia ex spiritûs acidi et salis lixiviosi . . . toto cœlo differt a fermentatione; fermentation is a decomposition (vinculi dissolutionem), effervescence is caused by combination (conjunctio).[9] He distinguishes different kinds of fermentation,[10] and also speaks of unnatural effervescence as causing disease.[11]

Sylvius regarded combustion and respiration as similar processes.[12] A smoky or flaming fire requires more air than a charcoal fire, and a breathing animal more than a transpiring animal: plus in respirationibus animalibus . . . minus in transpirantibus. More or less air is required for a strong or weak fire, and in respiration when the vital fire is strong or weak. The state of the air, whether clear, cold and dry, or foggy, hot and moist, has an influence on fires and also on the vital fire of the heart. Finally, the fire of a furnace burns more vigorously when air has free access above and below the fuel, and dies out when the air is cut off, and the same is seen in breathing. He gives a reasonably good account of the mechanism of respiration, including the motion of the diaphragm. He imagined that the inspired air *cools* the blood.[13]

By what power, or in what manner and way the inspired air so alters the blood is not equally clear. I, for my part, think that it is brought about by reason of there being dispersed in the air nitrous and subacid particles able to condense the rarefied and boiling blood and so gently to restrain its ebullition;

Quâ vi autem, quove modo et ratione Sanguinem in utrumque hunc finem alteret Inspiratus Aër, non æquè patet. Ego id fieri puto, quatenus *in Aerè dispersæ sunt partes Nitrosæ atque Subacidæ*, Sanguinem æstuantem, rarefactumque condensare, atque ipsius æstum quoque blandè compescere potentes.[14]

---

[1] B; Appendix, tract. II, § 574.
[2] B; Bk. II, c. 36; H, 349: Foster, 1901, 148, says he 'was the first to prove the presence of volatile alkalis in plants'.
[3] B; Appendix, tract. V, c. 375; C; I, vi, 9; vii, 7; viii, 2; ix, 5; x, 4; xi, 3; xii, 2.
[4] A, (e), § 40.   [5] A, (h), § 42, etc.   [6] C; II, c. xxiv, § 32.   [7] B; II, c. xx, § 142.
[8] A, (a), (1659), § 14 f.   [9] A, (a), Corollaria, § 1; Kopp, (1), iv, 290.
[10] B; II, c. vii.   [11] B; Appendix, tract. viii, §§ 102, 115.   [12] A, (g), (1660), §§ 52-7, 69-78.
[13] B; I, c. xxli, § 1; c. xxv, § 4; c. xxvi, § 3; Foster, 161, 186.   [14] A, (g), § 69.

I distinguish, however, between the subacid and the nitrous parts of the air, since the subacid and acid parts are for the most part simple but the nitrous on the contrary are compound, composed of acids if you like, though not with any you please, but also joined to oily and lixivious salts, as is clearly proved by the artificial chemical analysis and synthesis of nitre;

Distinguo autem inter partes Aëris Subacidas & Nitrosas; cùm Subacidæ, Acidæque sint magis simplices, Nitrosæ verò magis compositæ, ex Acidis puta, non quibusvis, sed simul Oleosis, cum Sale lixivio junctis, quod artificiosa, Chymica nempe Nitri Analysis & Synthesis manifestum facit.[1]

The heat is generated in the heart from the acid chyle and the alkaline blood (see above) and the vapours emitted in this effervescence are expelled with the expired air.[2] The red colour of arterial blood is caused by the inspired air, acting in the left ventricle of the heart:[3] the different colours of the blood in the two ventricles are recognised, and the circulation of the blood is fully accepted.[4] The dark colour of menstrual blood is due to an excess of acid.[5] In the mammary glands, however, an acid converts blood into milk (since acids change red colours to white), yet milk may be curdled, even in the breast, by an acid or alum.[6] In the spleen the blood is more than perfected (plusquam perficitur) by a ferment or tincture.[7] Sylvius thought that arterial blood had a higher temperature than venous blood, which was soon afterwards disproved by Baglivi,[8] and that this was due to *calor innatus* provided by the heart. This innate heat is not used up, since a burning candle can kindle many other candles without itself being extinguished. Sylvius, however, rejected the idea that animal heat in the heart is like an actual flame, such as that of a candle.[9] He supposed that the heat of the blood comes from the collision of the igneous particles in the acid spirit of the lymph and the alkaline (lixivial) salt of the bile, mixing in the heart: putamus insuper multas partes Igneas tum in acido Lymphæ Spiritu tum in amaro Bilis sale lixivioso semper abundantes in conflictu . . . accendendo calorem . . . causare.[10]

The animal spirits separated from the blood rise to the brain and are similar to spirit of wine, coagulating (like this) with volatile salt (ammonium carbonate: Van Helmont's experiment, p. 233):[11] spiritum vini rectificatissimum . . . quamvis non cogatur, coaguleturve à frigore, cogitamen ac coagulari à volatili sale urinæ, spiritu salis armoniaci & alio forsan . . . idem fieri posse in corpore humano spiritibus animalibus ab eodem sale volatili aut aliâ re simili.

Diseases are caused by an excess of a corrosive chemical principle (acrimonia) in the humours, e.g. gout by an acid passing into the blood and the lymph;[12] most diseases are caused by corrosive acids, but malignant fevers by excess of alkali, and plague by volatile salt (sal volatile; ammonia) present in the blood, giving it an abnormal fluidity opposing its coagulation; this is proved by injecting a solution of the volatile salt into the veins, when the symptoms of plague are produced, and hence an acid is used as a remedy.[13]

---

[1] B; I, *c.* xxi, §§ 3–4.　　　　[2] A, (*g*), § 57; B; *Appendix*, tract. IX, §§ 117, 119.
[3] B; I, *c.* xxv.　　　[4] A, (*c*), § 15.　　　[5] B; III, *c.* iii, §§ 405, 439.
[6] B; III, *c.* x, § 44–59.　　[7] A, (*e*), § 16.　　　[8] Haeser, (1), ii, 369.
[9] A, (*j*), §§ 15–17.　　[10] A, (*g*), § 56.　　　[11] A, (*d*), § 29; C; I, *c.* xii, §§ 4, 29.
[12] B; *Appendix*, tract. VIII ,§§ 70–1.　　　[13] B; *Appendix*, tract. II, §§ 55 f., 90 f.

This experiment is typical of a large mass of modern biochemical research. Many diseases of the stomach are caused by an acid principle from food (cibi acidum) and are cured by alkalis or other substances capable of combining with acids.[1] Sylvius made considerable use of acid and alkaline remedies; he kept himself free from plague by taking vinegar every morning,[2] and nitric acid was a valuable remedy.[3] He also used more violent mineral remedies.[4] such as silver nitrate (crystallis lunae);[5] zinc sulphate (vitriolum album, quod Germanis vocatur Chalizstein, vel Augenstein) as an emetic;[6] corrosive sublimate, prescribed in quarter grain doses but not more,[7] and calomel (sublimatum dulce), made by subliming corrosive sublimate with mercury, when the mercury tempers the acid spirit in the corrosive sublimate. The function of the acid is to make the mercury more soluble. Sylvius valued calomel highly.[8] He admitted that the efficacy of mercury salts made with acids is due to the metal and not the acid: mercurium putà cum variis Acido præcipititatum, aut sublimatum . . . dicendo, curam istam non tàm pendere ab acido quàm à mercurio . . . nisi acidum sit valdè in ipso temperamentum.[9]

Antimony preparations used were: (1) pills (globuli) of the metal (regulus) used as a purgative, recovered from the stool and used again after washing; (2) butter of antimony (butyrum antimonii), made by distilling a mixture of stibnite (antimony sulphide) and corrosive sublimate; (3) mercurius vitæ (powder of Algaroth), obtained by precipitating butter of antimony with water or oil of tartar (potassium carbonate), i.e. antimony oxychloride, free from mercury; (4) glass of antimony (vitrum antimonii), prepared in various ways; (5) stibnite (antimonium crudum); (6) crocus metallorum (a mixture of antimony oxide and sulphide).[10] Sylvius mentions that a lye boiled with sulphur or stibnite effervesces with vinegar or sour wine (hydrogen sulphide gas: no mention of odour):[11] in antimonii cum salis tartari lixivio soluti ad aceti affusionem effervescentiâ idem contingit.

Precipitation of one metal from solution by another was explained as due to the varying affinities for the acid: sic metalla spiritu acido, aquâ forti puta, corrosa, quoties aliud metallum, corpusve prædicto spiritui magis affine additur solutione, toties à spiritu corrodente derelicta sensim subsident dum illa immisso unitur corpori.[12] Sylvius believed the transmutation of metals to be possible:[13] quod si metalla quævis magnâ licet quantitate fusa (dummodo secretioris ac sublimioris Artis Chimicæ antistitibus adhibenda fides) ad philosophici lapidis excellentioris etiam paucissimi admistionem, mox itidem in lapidem tingentem sive tincturam similem transeant.

Sylvius had crude ideas about the composition of the atmosphere.[14] He says it contains nitric acid (acidum nitrosum) and volatile alkali (ammonia). The first is brought by the north wind from the north, where it is expelled into the

[1] B; Bk. I, c. ii, § 5 f.   [2] B; Appendix II, § 489.   [3] B; I, c. xiv, § 34.
[4] B; Appendix, VI, § 169.   [5] C; Bk. II, c. x, § 83.   [6] Ib., § 27.
[7] Ib., § 45; c. v, § 22.   [8] B; Appendix, III, §§ 81, 266 f.; VII, § 260.
[9] B; Appendix, III, §§ 81–2.
[10] B; Appendix, II, § 553 f., § 600 f.; III, § 297; VI, § 169; VII, § 261 f.; C; II, c. x, § 30 f.; L, § 12; Gmelin, (1), i, 716 f.; Haeser, (1), ii, 372.
[11] A, (g), § 55; B; Appendix, tract. V, § 425.   [12] A, (b), § 12 (1659).
[13] A, (f), § 37 (1660).   [14] J, §§ 34, 40 f., 53 f.; B, Appendix, tract. X, § 73 f.

air from subterranean fires; the second is brought by the south wind. When the two mix, cold is produced, as when sal ammoniac dissolves in water; greater cold is produced when the north wind carries common salt, and very intense cold when it brings volatile alkaline salt:

frigus blandum tribuo acido nitroso . . . frigus acrius . . . acido puriori vel muriatico sale juncto . . . frigus glacians deduco à spiritus acido cum sale volatili puriore unito, et sali Armeniaco planè consimili; postquam non semel observavi, hunc aqua recèns solutum etiam æstate media circa vitreum vas miscellam istam continens, allicere ac gelare aëris ambientis humiditatem aqueam.[1]

The air contains all kinds of exhalations from water, minerals, and plants, which affect men and animals:

magis probabile mihi videtur, aliquid ex terra et aqua in aërem ubique attoli . . . id probant 1. vapores visibiliter ex quavis aquâ elevati. 2. Halitum similiter ex terra assurgentes, ac imprimis è locis ubi metallorum et mineralium aliorum fodinæ sunt frequentes, sulphuris præsertim;[2]
    ab aquis assurgunt et aëri communicantur vapores multifarii, puri et impuri, et forsan aliquid salis marini. A terræ visceribus attolluntur et aëri admiscentur halitus, exhalationesque multifarii, sulphurei, acidi, salsi, arsenicales, et similes plures;[3]
    idem omninò statuendum de vaporibus ex aquis, exhalationibusque ex terræ superficie, plantarumque partibus maximè volatilibus assurgentibus, ac per aërem dispersis, atque pro sui abundantia et diversitate animalibus et homini præsertim mutationem aliquam afferentibus.[4]

That air contains many flying parts: aqueous, igneous, earthy, oily, spirituous, saline, and acid, is shown by chemical experiments.[5] Sprengel[6] thought that 'Sylvius had clearer ideas on gases than Van Helmont; he called them *halitus* and described their chemical differences as well as the influence they exert in certain maladies.' It cannot be said, however, that his ideas were very precise. His theory of the composition of the atmosphere is practically identical with Boyle's (p. 528).

Sylvius thought that sulphur is a compound of an oil (i.e. combustible part) and an acid spirit.[7]

Sylvius's iatrochemical ideas were supported by his pupils and many physicians, but were opposed by Hermann Conring, Bohn,[8] Boyle, Borelli, Baglivi, Pitcairne, and Sydenham. Sprengel[9] says the opponents of Iatrochemistry were, in general, poorly educated men imbued with prejudice, who put forward no real objections to it. It was opposed in France under the lead of Jean Riolan, dean of the Paris faculty; in Spain; and by only a few Germans. In England, under the influence of a good knowledge of anatomy and a taste for research, it flourished. Charleton had adopted some ideas of Helmont's, and Willis, a contemporary of Sylvius, defended the chemical sect. Boyle, although criticising Sylvius,[10] was generally favourably disposed

[1] J, §§ 56–8.   [2] B; *Appendix*, tract. X, §§ 100–3.   [3] *Ib.*, §§ 112–13.
[4] *Ib.*, § 132.   [5] B; I, *c.* xxi, § 4.   [6] (1), V, 63.
    [7] B; II, *c.* xxiii, § 237: sulphur enim omne oleo imprimis constare et acido spiritu; *Appendix*, tract. V, § 335: sic acidus in sulphure latens spiritus sub corpore insipido, aerimoniam suam manifestat, quamprimùm accenditur, et à parte oleosâ recedit acida.
    [8] *Circulus anatomico-physiologicus, seu oeconomia corporis animalis*, 4°, Leipzig, 1686.
    [9] (1), v, 69–130 (Propagation du Système chémiatrique); *id.*, (2), iv, 349–418.
    [10] *Reflections upon the Hypothesis of Alcali and Acidum*, in *Origin of Forms and Qualities*, 1666; *Works*, 1744, iii, 603.

towards the application of chemistry to medicine. Boyle did not hesitate to explain the supposed efficacy of amulets by effluvia from them.[1] Iatrochemistry was in favour in Denmark under Borrichius and Thomas Bartholinus. Only a few in Holland (e.g. Bernard Swalwe) opposed it. Wolferd Senguerd particularly,[2] tried to explain all the bodily functions, including generation, by fermentation and chemical processes.

Hermann Conring, of Helmstädt,[3] opposed the introduction of chemistry into medicine and denied the presence of the three principles in the body, whilst Olaus Borrichius, of Copenhagen,[4] defended chemical remedies, but admitted that antimony when injudiciously administered is a strong poison.[5]

COLBATCH

John Colbatch[6] thought the causes of many diseases were alkaline, not acid, and that acid and not alkaline remedies should be used. He says experience had proved that scurvy among sailors is relieved by eating apples, oranges, and lemons, and in general his remedies are sensible.

VIEUSSENS

Raymund de Vieussens (Vieussens nr. Montpellier, 1641–Montpellier, 1716) was from 1671 physician in the hospital of St Éloi, where after 1693 he carried out research in chemistry.[7] He published a famous book on neurology (*Nevrologia Universalis*, f°, Lyons, 1685) and the following works of interest to us:

I. Tractatus duo. Primus. De remotis et proximis mixti principiis in ordine ad corpus humanum spectatis. Secundus. De natura differentiis, subjectis, conditionibus, et causis fermentationis . . . , 8°, Leyden, 1687 (altered to 1688 in copy BM 548. i. 30); 4°, Lyons, 1688.

II. Deux dissertations . . . La première touchant l'extraction du sel acide du sang. La seconde sur la proportion de quantité de ses principes sensibles, 8°, Montpellier, 1698 (BM 1169. c. 20).

III. Epistola de Sanguinis Humani, cum sale fixo, spiritum acidum suggerente, tum volatile, in certa proportione sanguinis phlegma, spiritum subrufum ac oleum fœtidum ingrediente, 4°, Leipzig, 1698 (BM 780. g. 4. (3.)).

In his tract on fermentation[8] he says: 'Fermentation is the adventitious and expansive movement of the heterogeneous parts and of insensible fermenting

[1] *Works*, 1744, iv, 310.

[2] *Philosophia Naturalis*, 4°, Leyden, 1681; Thorndike, vii, 690; viii, 36, 228.

[3] *De Hermetica Ægyptiorum vetere et Paracelsicorum Nova Medicina*, Helmstädt, 4°, 1648; id., *De Hermetica Medicina*, 4°, Helmstädt, 1669.

[4] *De Ortu et Progressu Chemiae*, 4°, Copenhagen, 1668; *Hermetis Ægyptiorum, et Chemicorum Sapientia*, 4°, Copenhagen, 1674.

[5] Sprengel, (2), iv, 362.

[6] *A Physico-Medical Essay concerning Acid and Alkali*, 8°, London, 1696; *The Doctrine of Acids in the Cure of Diseases further asserted*, 8°, London, 1698; *A Collection of Tracts Chirurgical and Medical*, 8°, London, 1704; Thorndike, viii, 446.

[7] Sprengel, (1), v, 97; Hoefer, (1), ii, 240; he is not mentioned by Kopp; Gmelin, (1), ii, 242, 273, 753 (mineral water of Balarue); P.L. in NBG, 1866, xlvi, 137; he was F.R.S. in 1688; Foster, 150 f.

[8] I, Lyons, 1688, 314.

bodies excited without sensible cause, which, when it is vehement or of long duration, brings about an essential change or a conspicuous alteration in the fermenting bodies.' He distinguished six types of fermentation: latent (in dough beginning to ferment), sensible (water on quicklime or spirits of vitriol mixed with oil of tartar), vehement (spirits of vitriol poured on oil of tartar or water on quicklime), moderate (either without noise or only a buzzing — *fremitus*; must or wort, treacle, etc., fermenting), hot (vinegar mixed with quicklime, 'which is indeed accompanied with fire and flame and therefore heat'), and cold (coral dissolving in vinegar). 'Fermentation' is here confused with a mere escape of gas (effervescence) due to chemical action, and the idea is a retrograde step from Van Helmont's (pp. 227, 235).

In his treatises on blood (II, III) Vieussens claimed to have discovered an acid in the residue of 4 oz. from 50 lb. of evaporated blood, the priority of this discovery being claimed by Pierre Chirac (1650–1732) of Montpellier.[1] Vieussens also discovered a ferment in saliva.[2] Vieussens supposed that he had discovered very minute neurolymphatic vessels at the ends of the arteries of the heart muscle, connecting with the veins and 'flesh vessels'. The motion of the heart was caused by the action of the 'saline sulphur' of the blood and the 'nitrous vital spirits' carried by the nerves to the heart.[3]

HECQUET

Vieussens was opposed by Philippe Hecquet (Abbeville, 11 February 1661–Paris, 11 April 1737), who had graduated M.D. at Rheims in 1684 but on going to Paris had to attend all the courses as a student before graduating M.D. in 1694; he then taught materia medica in Paris. He was a very religious man and in 1727 retired to a Carmelite monastery. As an iatromathematician (see p. 442) he considered the vibrations of the fibres as the main cause of organic action, the trituration of the body fluids by the mechanical constriction of the solid parts leading to their attenuation. His numerous works, mostly polemical, diminished the credit of iatrochemistry in France.[4]

TACHENIUS

Otto Tachenius (Tachen) (Herford, Westphalia ?–still living in Venice, 1699), said to be the son of a miller and a former abbess, was apprenticed to a pharmacist David Welman at Lemgo, then to a physician Rötger Timpler, but was dismissed for theft. After acting as assistant to pharmacists at Kiel, Danzig (1640) and Königsberg (1641), where he met Helwig Dieterich (with whom he later quarrelled), he went to Italy in 1644, took the M.D. at Padua in

[1] Éloge by Fontenelle, AdS, 1732, h 120–30; Hoefer, (1), ii, 241.
[2] *Supplementum Anatomicum*, 1710, 113, q. by Haeser, (1), 1881, ii, 301, 321, who also quotes a *Traité Nouveau des Liqueurs du Corps humain*, Toulouse, 1715.
[3] *Novum Vasorum Corporis Humani Systema*, 8°, Amsterdam, 1705.
[4] Sprengel, (1), v, 99–101; Saucerotte, in NBG, 1858, xxiii, 711–14, q. Hecquet, *De la Digestion des Aliments et des Maladies de l'Estomac, suivant le système de la trituration ou du broyement sans l'aide du levain ou de la fermentation*, 12°, Paris, 1712; 2 ed., 2 vols. 12°, 1729.

1652, and settled in Venice, where he sold a secret remedy distilled from vipers, called *sal viperinum*. He was something of a charlatan.[1]

After Tachenius had accused the Danish physician Helwig Dieterich of publishing in a garbled form a letter on the alkahest which he had entrusted to him for seeing through the press, Dieterich published an attack on Tachenius containing documents proving that he had been dishonourably discharged by more than one employer.[2]

The most important publications by Tachenius are:

I. Hippocrates Chimicus, Per ignem et aquam Methodo inaudita Novissimi Salis Viperini antiquissima fundamenta ostendens, 12°, Venice, 1666; Hippocrates Chimicus qui Novissimi Viperini Salis Antiquissima ostendit, 12°, Brunswick, 1668 (BM 1037. a. 13). Hippocrates Chymicvs, Omnibus à mendis vindicatus. In qvo novissimi Viperini Salis Antiquissima Fundamenta simul & Acidi Alcaliqve Natvra fusè ac dilucidè explicantur, 12°, Paris, 1669 (xviii ll., 259 pp., ii ll.); 12°, Venice, 1678, 1697; Ferguson gives eds. of Leyden, 1671, and Paris, 1673 and 1674; tr. by J. W.: Otto Tachenius His Hippocrates Chymicus, which Discovers the Ancient Foundations of the late Viperine Salt. And his Clavis thereunto . . . Licensed Aug. 30, 1676. Roger L'Estrange, 4°, London, 1677 and 1690 (BM 7509. 6).

II. Antiquissimæ Hippocraticæ Medicinæ Clavis Manuali experientia in Naturæ fontibus elaborata, 12°, Brunswick, 1668 (not seen); Venice, 1669, 1697; eds. of Frankfurt, 1669, 1673; Leyden, Lyons, and Paris, 1671, are quoted.

III. Tractatus De Morborum Principe, In quo Plerorumque gravium ac sonticorum, præter naturam affectuum, dilucida enodatio, & Hermetica, id est, vera & solida eorundem curatio proponitur; Opus tanto Achille dignum . . . , sm. 8°, Osnabrück, 1679 (210 pp.); Hippocrates Chimicus. Secundæ Partis. Tractatus de Morborum Principe, in the edition of Hippocrates Chimicus, Venice, 1678, pp. 279–464 (with sep. half-title, and approbation dated 3 November 1677; Ferguson was unaware of its existence).

I is largely a reply to Zwelfer, who is called in it 'Reformer' (Reformator). Zwelfer had attacked Tachenius in his edition of the *Pharmacopoeia Augustana* (1657), and he later published a verbose criticism of I (see p. 296). Tachenius claimed that his viperine salt was his own invention, quoting a letter of Severinus from Naples of 15 May 1650.[3] II is even more polemical than I; in one place it says: 'The Martigenous Hornets provoke and challenge the Eagle. Take notice, Brethren of the woful Combate.'[4]

Tachenius introduced into Italy the acid-alkali theory of Sylvius; he professed to find it in the writings of Hippokrates and Galen, in which, he said, fire = acid and water = alkali:[5] aqua . . . quam nos nunc et in posterum cum aliis philosophis pro majori lumine Alcali nominabimus; . . . ignem ostendi acidum. He enthusiastically extended this theory to cover all natural phenomena:[6] adeoque Naturae primus labor nil aliud est quam pinsere sal et deinde alcali, etc. It was criticised by Bertrand,[7] a Marseilles physician. Tachenius

---

[1] Barchusen, 1710, 497; Jöcher, iv, 980; Gmelin, (1), i, 730; Sprengel, (1), v, 83; Hoefer, (1), ii, 217; Ferguson, ii, 424, 597; Thorndike, viii, 357.

[2] Dieterich, *Vindiciæ adversus Ottonem Tackenium*, 4°, Hamburg, 1655 (BM 1033. k. 14).

[3] I, ch. 12; 1669, 76–8.

[4] II, ch. viii; Engl. tr., 1677, 68.

[5] III, chs. iii and vi.   [6] III, chs. ii–v.

[7] *Réflexions nouvelles sur l'acide et sur l'alcalie: où après avoir demontré que ces deux sels ne peuvent être les principes des mixtes on fait voir le véritable usage que l'on peut faire dans la physique et dans la médecine*, 12°, Lyons, 1683.

says that fire and water by their congress produce the salt of nature (sal naturæ), the universal ferment and radical humidity.[1]

Tachenius says that rotten wood yields no alkali, all of it having exhaled in the process of putrefaction. He thought that the amount and quality of alkali obtained from plants depended on whether a strong or weak fire was used, the strong fire giving less alkali.[2] In spite of this, he believed that the alkali is generated from the plant by fire (nullum vegetabile habere fixum sal, cuius-cunque sit generis, nisi comburatur actuali igne), and that each plant gave a different kind of alkali, some, e.g. from wormwood, which must be fresh, better for medicinal purposes than others: the best were obtained by slow burning without flame. Corrosive sublimate (mercuric chloride) solution gave with the different kinds of fixed alkali precipitates of various colours, shades of yellow and red, and iron vitriol (ferrous sulphate) precipitates from green to red. (These are really due to the varying proportions of alkali carbonate and bicarbonate.) Volatile alkali (Balsamum samechi; ammonium carbonate) gave a white precipitate with corrosive sublimate.[3] The supposed varying kinds of alkali made by burning without flame were later called salia Tacheniana.[4] An alkali from Spain, sal kali, used for making glass[5] would be soda. Boyle found no difference between alkali made from tartar and from various plants (p. 539) and Kunckel (p. 376) showed that the *salia Tacheniana* were all the same. About 1700 the old names (e.g. *cineres clavellati*) were given up and *alcali fixum* was generally adopted.

Tachenius had a very clear idea of the composition of salts: 'all salts can be divided into two parts, into alkali and acid (omnia salsa in duas dividuntur partes in alcali nimirum et acidum).'[6] From this definition he was able to conclude that soap is a salt, the acid part coming from the oil:[7] oleum vel pingue-dinem alcali contrarium acidum enim occultum continet. Litharge contains alkali, since it acts on the occult acid of oil and forms a neutral coagulum (lead soap);[8] it is, in fact, a basic oxide. Silica (silex) is an acid which is absorbed by the alkali in making glass:[9] alcali inquam pars absorbet acidum illud quod silex pro calce continet . . . altera pars alcali coit cum silice saturaturque de eo . . . evadunt ambo in pellucidam massam, aiuntque artifices vitrum esse coctum. Acids differ in strength, strong acids displacing weak acids from their salts: tunc deserit proprium acidum, et combibit potens illud;[10] quiquid dissolvitur in acido extra familiam suam, vel innato potentiori, statim supprimitur eius debile acidum.[11]

Alkalis also differ in strength. When sal ammoniac is distilled with salt of tartar 'the fixed alkali apprehends and catches the acid spirit of salt [hydro-chloric acid] of the sal ammoniac and the volatile alkali willingly leaves her acid companion and is forced to fly away by heat':[12] videbis statim alcali ex viperis per collum ascendere, eò quod fixum alcali tartari, apprehendit solem

---

[1] III, ch. iv.   [2] I, ch. xxi.   [3] I, chs. vii, xvi.   [4] Boerhaave, (2), ii, 42.   [5] I, ch. iii.
[6] I, ch. ii; 1669, 11; J. E. Marsh, 1929, 44, says Tachenius's 'generalisation is altogether too comprehensive'.
[7] I, ch. iv.   [8] I, ch. xxv.
[9] I, ch. v; cf. Nordenskiöld, *Scheele, Nachgelassene Briefe*, Stockholm, 1892, 74.
[10] I, ch. xv.   [11] II, ch. viii.   [12] I, ch. xi; 1669, 67.

acidum; tunc alcali viperinum acidum socium lubens derelinquit, cum cogitur à calore in fugam abire. Fac idem cum sale armoniaco vulgari.

In his description of the manufacture of soap at Venice (the first account of soap-making, copied by Boerhaave),[1] Tachenius gives a graphic example of the great corrosive power of the caustic lye: he was told that a workman accidentally fell into a vat of the boiling liquid, and nothing was found except the linen shirt and the harder bones: consumpsit enim in momento bulliens hoc lixivium ebrium hominem cum laneis vestibus ut nil ejus repertum fuerit præter lineum indusium, et duriora ossa, ut accepi à fide digno hujus artis professore.[2] Common salt is not coagulated with fat or tallow into soap, since its acid and alkali are separated only with difficulty.

The use of common salt in causing soap to separate is said[3] to be mentioned first in BM MS. Sloane 1990, perhaps by Sir Theodore de Vaux (a friend of Turquet de Mayerne).

Tachenius showed that artificial sal ammoniac is obtained from the acid spirit of salt and the volatile alkali (alcali animalium): all volatile alkalis are really the same, and the purest (alcali urinæ purum) is obtained by decomposing sal ammoniac with salt of tartar (potassium carbonate).[4] Similarly, sal marinus regeneratus (potassium chloride) — which he confused with common salt — is obtained from salt of tartar and spirit of salt; saltpetre from salt of tartar and spirit of nitre; and vitriolated tartar (*tartarus vitriolatus*) can be obtained by adding salt of tartar to vitriolic acid or by precipitating a solution of green vitriol with salt of tartar, filtering and evaporating ($FeSO_4 + K_2CO_3 + H_2O = Fe(OH)_2 + K_2SO_4 + CO_2$): the salt made in this way was afterwards called *tartarus vitriolatus Tachenianus*.[5] What he calls *tartarus regeneratus*, made from vinegar and salt of tartar,[5] is potassium acetate, and he points out that the 'water of Minderus (*aqua Mindereri*)' is made by neutralising vinegar with ammonia:[6] it is a solution of ammonium acetate.

The common salt taken with food can be recovered from urine by calcination, solution and crystallisation.[7] Vitriol taken as medicine is not excreted in the urine, which gives no black colour with galls, but it is rendered insoluble and must therefore be excreted by the intestines (necessariò in intestinis permanere debeat), colouring the fæces black.[8] This is an example of the use of qualitative tests in the wet way. Tachenius points out that distilled water gives no precipitate with a solution of silver, whilst river and well waters give a white precipitate like that given by a solution of common salt.[9] He showed that an infusion of galls produces colour reactions not only with iron but also with other metals such as copper, silver, tin, lead and mercury, but copper vitriol does not give a black colour with galls. The sympathetic ink from galls and iron vitriol is decolorised by acids but restored by alkalis: rursus imbue car-

---

[1] (2), ii, 257.
[2] I, ch. iv; Marsh, 1929, 44, says this 'story has gone the round of chemical factories ever since'.
[3] F. W. Gibbs, *Chem. and Ind.*, 1938, lvii, 877; Partington, *History of Greek Fire and Gunpowder*, Cambridge, 1960, 306.
[4] I, ch. xi.   [5] I, ch. x.
[6] I, ch. xi; see p. 171.   [7] I, ch. xv.   [8] I, ch. xvi.   [9] I, ch. xix; 1669, 145.

tam cum alcali fixo, quod iterum absumit acidum, et iterum apparebit scriptura.[1]

Tachenius called the principle in galls their 'alkali'; it was really tannin or gallic acid. He also speaks of 'perfecting' this by smearing the galls with oil and heating till they became black, when he must have obtained pyrogallic acid.[2]

The rose water distilled in Venice owed its anthelmintic properties to copper (from the stills), which can be precipitated with volatile alkali, the precipitate on fusion with borax giving copper: fundum autem viridem liqua cum borrace et redit in cuprum.[3] A gold salt solution mixed with infusion of galls is strongly coloured and if the liquid is spread on paper, the latter is gilded on drying:[4] post exsiccationem lucet ut vernix. Silver dissolves in aqua fortis because it is pleased with it, but when copper is added the acid is more delighted with it than with silver, deserts the silver and dissolves the copper, which is in turn precipitated by iron:[5]

aqua fortis . . . amat cuprum et ferrum . . . argentum dissolvit, illoque delectatur . . . in hanc solutionem injeceris cuprum nimirum, quo ratione symboli plus delectatur quam argento, statim deserit argentum, et rursus dissolvit cuprum . . . si injeceris ferrum, quod est facilioris solutionis vel concoctionis cupro, aqua statim negligit cuprum, ferrumque solvit.

Fulminating gold (*ceraunocryson*: κεραυνός, thunderbolt, χρυσός, gold)[6] gives a purple colour to glass when fused with it:[7]

aurum fulminans . . . una cum cocto, perfecto, purissimque vitro (cujus pars alcali est contritum, licet celeri fusione transeat in corpus opacum (quod amauson sive vulgo smaltum vocant) purpurei coloris.

Tachenius was well acquainted with the tricks of the alchemists and explains how the supposed conversion of half an iron nail into gold by Thurneisser (p. 153) could be effected by soldering gold to coppered iron:[8] he believed, however, that metals grow in the earth, as in the iron mines of Elba (Vol. I).[9] He gives[10] a detailed description of the manufacture of corrosive sublimate (sublimatum corrosivum) in Venice. A mixture of 280 lb. of mercury (the contents of one leather bottle from the mines in Idria), 20 lb. mercury sublimate, 200 lb. each of common salt and saltpetre, 50 lb. of the caput mortuum of a previous sublimation and 400 lb. of vitriol heated until red, is ground under a vertical millstone. The mixture is filled into 16 large glass vessels, three-quarters full, and sublimed in an ash bath in four furnaces. First a strong smell of aqua fortis comes off, then in the fifth day the sublimate appears in the form of a cake, the total weight being 380 lb. He thought there was no change in weight when mercury is converted into red precipitate (mercuric oxide) by dissolving in aqua fortis, evaporating to dryness, and heating the residue (mercuric nitrate): sic in vasis fundo hærebit pulvis rubeus præcipitatus splendens, nilque acquisiuit ponderis. There was also no increase when mercury was converted into oxide by heating in a flask with a flat bottom and

[1] I, ch. xvii.   [2] Nierenstein, *The Natural Organic Tannins*, 1934, 104.
[3] I, ch. xix.   [4] I, ch. xi.   [5] II, ch. viii; 1697, 139–40.
[6] II, ch. ii.   [7] III, ch. vi; 1697, 331.
[8] I, ch. xxvi; 1697, 256.   [9] II, ch. ii.   [10] I, ch. xxiii; 1697, 227.

narrow neck, nor when mercury was converted into cinnabar (mercuric sulphide).[1] These results are contrasted with the large increase in weight in forming corrosive sublimate.

Tachenius gives an account of how he was once nearly poisoned by breathing the vapour of arsenic (arsenious oxide) in a sublimation; the vapour had a sweet and agreeable smell (inspiravi auram palato, adeò suavem, dulcem, ac gratam).[2]

When lead is converted into minium by roasting, it increases in weight by one-tenth. This is due to absorption of acid from the flame of the wood (an acid is formed on distilling wood) and not from the air, and on reduction the acid is expelled and the original weight of lead is obtained: hoc autem corpus, quod plumbum auxit ex flamma est acidi saporis;[3] debile acidum in plumbo supprimit, fixatur in alcali, eique dominatur, atque pondus dat.[4]

By distilling verdigris, Tachenius obtained concentrated acetic acid, and the residue contains copper: sic et ærugo (quatenus ex maturo cupro et aceto) ... exinde nil nisi acetum distillare posse, eo quod remanens caput mortuum post distillationem in purum cuprum per fusionis ignem reducitur.[5] He proved by experiments, some quantitative, that this acid is the same as common vinegar, but stronger, and he thought it was Van Helmont's alkahest.[6] The stomach contains an acid juice, which forms a salt with the alkali of food in the process of digestion.[7]

ZWELFER

Tachenius was opposed by Johann Zwelfer (Zwelffer, or Zwölfer) (b. Pfalz 1618, d. 1668), at first an apothecary, then a physician in Vienna. He published a revision of the Augsburg *Pharmacopœia* (1652) and other pharmaceutical works:

   I. Pharmacopoeia Augustana et eius mantissa cum animadversionibus, f°, Vienna, 1652; Pharmacopoeia Augustana reformata ... cum animadversionibus, 8°, Gouda, 1653 (BM 777. b. 2, pref. dated Vienna, 1 May 1652); Thorndike, viii, 94, says it was also published at Rotterdam, 1653, Nürnberg 1657 and 1675, and 4°, Dordrecht 1672; Animadversiones in Pharmacopoeiam Augustanam, 4°, Nürnburg, 1667 (with Appendix, sep. pagin., describing, p. 52, the preparation of spiritus Veneris (glacial acetic acid) by distilling copper acetate; dedication dated 1656).
  II. Pharmacopeia Regia sive Dispensatorium Novum locupletatum et absolutum cum annexa Mantissa Spagyrica et gemino discursu apologetico contra Ott. Tachenium et Franc. Vernis, f°, 1668.
 III. Discursus Apologeticus ... adversus Hippocratem Chymicum Ottonis Tackenii (sic): Ejusǿ; adulterini Salis Viperini novissimi Fundamenta, ut ait, antiquissima. Cui & accessere eiusdem Justissimæ Vindiciæ contra Franciscum Verny ...

---

[1] I, ch. xxiv; 1697, 231–2.   [2] I, ch. xxiii; 1697, 224.   [3] I, ch. xxvi.
[4] II, ch. viii; the same theory is given by J. H. Jungken, *Chymia Experimentalis*, 4°, Frankfurt, 1702, 312, 698.
[5] I, ch. xvii.
[6] I, ch. x: alcahest nil aliud esse quam acetum distillatum ex ærugine; Tachenius, *Epistola de famoso liquore Alcahest*, 4°, Venice, 1652 (?), and (with *Helv. Dieterici Vindiciæ adversus O. Tackenium*), 4°, Hamburg, 1655; q. by Ferguson; *Echo ad Vindicias Chirosophi de liquore Alcæist*, 4°, Venice, 1656 (Thorndike, viii, 358, notes that Zedler dated this 1652 and Hoefer, 1655; he had not seen it).
[7] I, ch. cxiii.

Annexo etiam Apologemate Epistolico Anonymi, f°, Nürnberg, 1675, pref. dated
1667; Ferguson, ii, 571; it is said by Thorndike, viii, 95, to have been published
as an appendix to II; I have seen it as an appendix (sep. t.p. and pagin.) to I, Dordrecht, 1672.

Zwelfer said Tachenius confused lyes and alkalis with the salts of minerals and
animals, calling them all alkali. François Verney of Montpellier had criticised
Zwelfer's compound acid syrup of Mesuë and his confection of alkermes.
Zwelfer was not opposed to chemical remedies; he used successfully a solar
diaphoretic antimony (apparently tartar emetic), and three kinds of mercury
precipitate (yellowish, solar, and per se), mercury sublimate, turpethum
minerale, and turpethum minerale rubrum. Zwelfer also criticised Tachenius's
method of fixing the volatile salt of vipers, and he complained that most
oriental bezoars were spurious, the only genuine one being from a single species
of wild goat found only in one corner of the East Indies (see p. 97).

Italian followers of the theories of Tachenius were Joseph Pompeius Sacco;[1]
Alexander Pascoli,[2] who said oil and salt were the fire of the ancients and that quicklime
contains an acid because it boils when sprinkled with water; Michel Angelo Andriolli;[3]
Jean Baptist Volpi (or Volpini),[4] who said that acids were a general cause of diseases;
and Bernardino Ramazzini (Carpi, 5 November 1633–Padua, 5 November 1714), professor of medicine at Modena (1682) and Padua (1700) and the author of a famous book
on occupational diseases,[5] who[6] first used alkalis as remedies and then, since they gave
no results, prescribed acids. Domenico Sanguinetti[7] and Joseph del Papa (physician to
the Grand Duke of Tuscany)[8] were practically the only Italian physicians of the time
to oppose the chemical theory and prefer Iatrophysics (see 442); Bellini (see 450)
and others tried to combine the two.

In France, Iatrochemistry was not taught officially in Paris or Montpellier but Jean
Pierre Fabre adopted Van Helmont's views.[9] Charles Barbeyrac adopted the views of
Sylvius and Descartes and took account of the shapes of the atoms of salts.[10] François
Calmette, in Montpellier, prepared a mercurial remedy by dissolving mercury in nitric
acid and precipitating with ammonia,[11] and other supporters were Jean Bonnet, Jacques
Mossard, Nicolas de Blégny (who founded an iatrochemical academy in Paris), Jean
Pascal[12] and Jacques Minot, who seems to have first described the 'buffy coat' on blood
extracted in fever.[13] Dominic Beddevole, in Geneva (d. c. 1692), distinguished five
degrees of fermentation: boiling, elevation, sparkling, effervescence, and exhalation; he
supposed that blood contains phlegm, volatile sulphur, volatile alkali, fixed alkali,
and a small quantity of acid disengaged by the fixed alkali, and the nervous fluid is
composed of sulphur and volatile alkali.[14] Jean Viridet, of Geneva, claimed to have
found an acid in saliva and pancreatic juice, and an alkali in gastric juice and bile.[15]

[1] Nova methodus febres curandi, 8°, Geneva, 1685, 3 f.; q. by Sprengel, (1), v, 86.
[2] De homine, 4°, Rome, 1728; Sprengel, (1), v, 87.
[3] Enchiridion (sic) practicum medicum, 4°, Venice, 1700; Sprengel, (1), v, 87–8.
[4] Spasmologia, 4°, Asti, 1710; Gmelin, (1), ii, 415; Sprengel, (1), v, 88.
[5] De morbis artificium, Venice, 1701; French tr. by Fourcroy, Paris, 1777, new ed. 1822.
[6] Opera omnia, 4°, London, 1716; Geneva, 1717; 2 vols. 4°, Naples, 1739; NBG, 1862, xli,
524; Sprengel, (1), v, 88.
[7] Dissertationes iatrophysicæ, 4°, Naples, 1699; Sprengel, (1), v, 89.
[8] De præcipuis humoribus, 8°, Leyden, 1736; Sprengel, (1), v, 89.
[9] Sapientia universalis, Opera, 4°, Frankfurt, 1656; Sprengel, (1), v, 90.
[10] Dissertations sur les maladies, 8°, Amsterdam, 1731, 280; Sprengel, (1), v, 91.
[11] Riverius renovatus, 12°, Lyons, 1714 (written in 1677), 167; Sprengel, (1), v, 91; Samuel
Hahnemann later used this preparation, as 'soluble mercury'.
[12] La nouvelle découverte, et les admirables effets des fermens dans le corps humain, 12°, Paris,
1681.
[13] De la nature et des causes des fièvres, 12°, Paris, 1710 (written in 1684); Sprengel, (1), v,
93–4.
[14] Essais d'anatomie, 12°, Leyden, 1686; Paris, 1722 (written in 1685); Sprengel, (1), v, 95.
[15] De primâ coctione et ventriculi fermento, 8°, Geneva, 1691; Sprengel, (1), v, 96.

ETTMULLER

Michael Ettmuller (or Ettmüller) (Leipzig; 26 May 1644–9 March 1683; the dates of birth 1646 and death 1668 are incorrect) studied in Leipzig, Italy, France, Holland, and England (where he is said to have been influenced by Boyle), and became professor of botany (1681) and medicine in Leipzig, where he also lectured on chemistry; he is sometimes said to have died as a result of a chemical experiment.[1] Ettmuller was a famous teacher and wrote books on chemistry and medicine:

I. Medicina Hippocraticis Chimica, 4°, Leipzig, 1670, Leyden, 1671, quoting Van Helmont, Tachenius, Boyle, etc.; printed in III, 1685, Appendix, 337–62.
II. (a) Chimia Rationalis ac Experimentalis Curiosa, Secundùm principia recentiorum adornata . . . edita . . . Joh. Christophori Ausfeldi, 4°, Leyden, 1684 (iv ll., 159 pp., no index), pref. dated Haarburg, March, 1684, symbols in text; (b) French tr. Nouvelle Chymie Raisonné, 12°, Lyon, T. Amaubry, 1693 (xii ll., 443 pp., xxx ll.). Some contemporary notices say this posthumous work was disowned by Ettmuller's widow and heirs as by an un-named 'gold-digger' and it is probably compiled from lecture notes; Thorndike, viii, 154.
III. Opera omnia theoretica et practica . . . Secundum Principia & experimenta chymica et anatomica . . . accedit Chirurgia medica . . . , 4°, Lyons, 1685 (pp. 428, 436, 212, 362; this ed. is incomplete).
IV. Opera Pharmaceutico-Chymica . . . i. Schröderus Dilucidatus seu Commentariu in Joh. Schröderi Pharmacopœiam Medico-Chymicam. ii. Commentarius in Danielis Ludovici Dissert. De Pharmacia Moderno Seculo applicanda. iii. Pyrotechnia Rationalis seu Collegium Chymicum Experimentale; sm. 4°, Lyons, 1686 (pp. 251, 104, index, 276, 230). iv. Dissertationes Academicæ pp. 320. These works are contained in V and VII).
V. Opera omnia: Nempe Institutiones Medicinæ . . . Chymia Rationalis; cum Collegio Causali et variis curiosisque Dissertationibus, cum Praefatione D. Georgii Franci, la 4°, Frankfurt a/M, 1688 (pp. 718, 628, 270, Index). Also la 4°, London, 1688 (identical).
VI. Operum Medicorum Theoretico-Practicorum . . . Cum Indicibus locupletissimis, studio et cura Johannis Casp. Westphali, . . . la 4°, Frankfurt a/M and Amsterdam, I, 1696 (with title Opera Medica Theoretico-Practica); II, i and ii, 1697 (pp. 1333, 980, 981 to 1940, Index). Other editions of the Opera Omnia quoted are: 4°, London, 1683; Frankfurt, 1708 (ed. by his son Ernst); ed. Cyrillus (prof. at Naples), 4 vols. f°., 1728, 1736.
VII. Opera Omnia in Compendium Redacta, 8°, London, 1701 (pp. 184, 194, 104); 8°, Amsterdam, 1702 (pp. 493); containing Institutionum Medicarum; Collegium Chymicum, seu Pyrotechnia Rationalis; Commentarius in Joh. Schroederi Pharmacopeiam Medico-Chymicam; Collegium Practicum (5 books); another ed., 4°, Venice, 1704 (Sotheran *Cat.* 917 (1957), no. 34). In this edition of the Collegium Chymicum the text is difficult to read since it is full of symbols. It appears to be an abbreviation of II and the two are different works. The text of II*b* is somewhat different from the Latin text of the Collegium, although the preface says it was made from 'la Pyrotechnie Raisonnée'.

II is mainly phramaceutical. It cites a large number of authors (Thorndike says 70 and some of the names are misprinted) and is critical, some processes being said to be better than others; it frequently refers to works evidently intended to be read by students. Ettmuller speaks as if he had himself tried many of the processes he describes. He opposed the acid-alkali theory of

[1] Jöcher, ii, 417; *Phil. Trans.* abridged, 1809, iii, 209; Sprengel, (1), v, 111; Thomson, (1), i, 207; Hoefer, (1), ii, 291; NBG, 1856, xvi, 638; Haeser, (1), ii, 379; Ferguson, i, 251; Thorndike, viii, 153–63.

Sylvius and frequently quotes Boyle. He calls a neutral salt *sel sali*, and divides acids into mineral, vegetable and animal (in soap).[1] He says that if a whole man were calcined he would give hardly a drachm of fixed alkali.[2] He prepared a golden spirit of sulphur (ammonium sulphide) by distilling sal ammoniac, sulphur and quicklime.[3] He says alum is formed on dissolving *terra sigillata* (clay) in sulphuric acid and is composed of acid of sulphur and a stony or earthy body.[4] He distinguished effervescence from fermentation.[5] In making sulphuric acid 'by the bell' (p. 263) most of the sulphur is lost as 'the incoërcible gas of Van Helmont'.[6] A large number of preparations of antimony are described,[7] with some confusion (the same process is said in different places to give different products) and errors. The description is a collection from various sources. The presence of sulphur in common antimony (stibnite, Sb_2S_3) is shown by its inflammability, its sulphurous smell (on burning), its detonation with nitre and tartar, the tinctures which it forms with alkalis, which attract sulphur strongly from minerals (a mass like liver of sulphur would be formed), and the sulphureous smell of butter of antimony (antimony trichloride), which distils like butter when antimony is distilled with corrosive sublimate (he describes this in detail). The sulphur is separated by distilling the powder with spirit of vitriol (sulphuric acid), when the sulphur distils and collects on the neck of the retort; or by dissolving in aqua regia and adding water, when sulphur (really antimony oxychloride) precipitates. The mercurial or metallic part, or regulus (metallic antimony), which Basil Valentine said could be changed into lead, is also called 'leprous Sol (gold)', 'the wolf' (lupus, since it devours all metals except gold), or Proteus. The regulus is made by detonating stibnite with equal parts of nitre and tartar, or by fusing stibnite with iron or tin. The antimony (sulphide) is calcined either in a crucible or by a burning glass. Liver of antimony, made by detonating stibnite with nitre and tartar, is decomposed by water giving a dark yellow saffron or crocus of metals (metals, because antimony is regarded as the father of all metals). The fixed alkalis 'absorb or collect' the sulphur of the stibnite, which quits the mercurial part, which forms the regulus. If the scoriæ (alkaline sulphantimonates) formed in the preparation of the metal are dissolved in water and vinegar added, orange 'golden sulphur of antimony' is precipitated. If spirit of vitriol is used instead of vinegar a horrible smell (sulphuretted hydrogen) is produced, but the 'sulphur' precipitated is still more diaphoretic. The true antihecticum of Potier (see p. 335) is made by calcining an alloy of four parts of metallic antimony and five of tin with three parts of nitre, Potier's own recipe being useless.

Bezoar mineral (antimonic acid) is made by treating butter of antimony with spirit of nitre (nitric acid), separating the acid by distillation, and burning spirit of wine off the residue. Tincture of antimony (*lilium antimonii* of Hartmann) is made by subliming red flowers of antimony with sal ammoniac. The flowers are also made by subliming stibnite with sal ammoniac and the

---

[1] II*b*, 416.   [2] *Ib.*, 13.
[3] *Ib.*, 26; cf. Boyle, p. 542.   [4] *Ib.*, 87.
[5] *Ib.*, 118 f.   [6] *Ib.*, 171.   [7] *Ib.*, 174–237.

Paracelsans called them 'cheiri' or yellow (from the yellow wallflower, Cheiranthus cheiri).

Ettmuller says 1 lb. of iron on calcination increases in weight to 1 lb. 2 oz. because of the absorption of acids from the charcoal fire.[1] Steel is only hard iron; it is made by heating iron plates with charcoal and horns, when the fixed alkali of the charcoal and the volatile alkali of the horn neutralise the acid of the iron which reduces its hardness.[2]

Among non-entities (non entibus)[3] is the homunculus of Paracelsus, but the transmutation of metals 'non est non ens', and is supported by such natural phenomena as the conversion of wood into stone in petrifaction.

The elixir proprietatis (elixir de propriété) was made by dissolving aloes, myrrh and saffron in a solution of salt of tartar (potassium carbonate) and evaporating, then extracting with spirit of wine; the best kind contained terra foliata tartari (potassium acetate).[4]

By distilling alcohol with nitric acid crystals of (oxalic) acid are formed.[5] Ants give out a sour smell when crushed and on distillation produce an acid spirit which corrodes iron. It is, however, tempered by a urinous spirit (ammonia), which is set free on the putrefaction of ants or by distilling them with quicklime and a little hot water to excite effervescence.[6]

Formic acid was obtained from ants by Samuel Fisher who described it in a letter of January 1670 to John Ray;[7] its lead and iron salts were prepared, and the lead salt when distilled gave the acid again, whilst that made with vinegar (lead acetate) does not, but gives an inflammable oil and water.

S. B. Manitius published a dissertation on the chemical analysis of ants.[8] He distilled cleaned ants in a retort and obtained a 'urinous spirit' which he says united with ammonia, salt of tartar, and spirit of earthworms, so that Ettmuller and others had classed it with acid spirits. Manitius thought it was more urinous (ammoniacal) than acid, because it unites more easily with urinous things than with acid and does not boil with quicklime (as had been said) nor extract rust from iron until after two days. He did once observe it to effervesce with salt of tartar, so that sometimes it may have acid constituents. Manitius treats of the medicinal uses of ants and how to get rid of them by fumigation, etc. He mentions a spirit of ants prepared in the Danish royal apothecary shop and one from the nymphs of ants, and quotes Schröder, Jungken, Kuhnrad (Khunrath) and Hoffmann.

BOHN

Johann Bohn (Leipzig; 1640–19 December 1718) studied in various universities, visited Le Févre in London, and graduated M.D. in Leipzig in 1665. He was appointed professor of anatomy (1668) and therapeutics (1691) in

[1] IIb, 292.   [2] Ib., 287.   [3] IIa, 157; IIb, 441.
[4] IIb, 428; Boerhaave, (2), ii, 277 f., gives recipes for several kinds.
[5] Ib., 54.   [6] Ib., 413.
[7] Wray, Phil. Trans., 1671, v, 2063, No. 68; abridged ed., 1809, i, 554; Partington, Chem. and Ind., 1933, lii, 765.
[8] Chymica formicarum analysis, Wittenberg, 1689, BM 1033. h. 20. (12.), unnumb. pp.; Thorndike, viii, 398.

Leipzig, becoming dean of the medical faculty in 1700. He survived all but two of his seventeen children. Bohn was very highly esteemed.[1]

Bohn's writings of interest to us are:

1. De aëris in sublunaria influxu, Leipzig, 1675, 1678, 1681.
2. Dissertationes chymico-physicæ, chymiæ finem, instrumenta & operationes frequentiores explicantes . . . Quibus accessit ejusdem tractatus olim editus, de aeris in sublunaria influxu, sm. 4°, Leipzig, 1685, 1696 (Gmelin gives also 1690); the book is unpaged.
3. Circulus anatomico-physiologicus, seu Oeconomia corporis animalis, 4°, Leipzig, 1686, 1697 (BM 549. e. 18). Daremberg says the ideas on muscular motion in this are practically the same as Mayow's.
4. Circulus anatomico-physica . . . Accesserunt dissertationes physiologicae, 4°, Leipzig, 1710 (BM 784. k. 3; portr.; summary in Sprengel).
5. De alcali et acidi insufficientia pro principiorum, seu elementorum corporum naturalium munere gerendo, Leipzig, 1681.
6. Experimenta ac dubia nonnulla chymica, auri et argenti solutionem spectantia, in Acta Eruditorum, Leipzig, 1683, 409.

Bohn's dictated chemical lectures at Leipzig from 1679 were not published, although Stahl[2] says they were better than Rolfinck's. The British Museum has a large collection of works connected with Bohn (dissertations, etc.).

In (4) Bohn attacks the Iatrochemical theories of Sylvius de le Boë, which were then very popular. He did not admit the immediate passage of air in mass into the blood, denied that digestion is a fermentation, said there is no acid in the stomach, that bile does not effervesce with acids and hence contains no free alkali, that pancreatic juice does not effervesce with alkalis and contains no acid, that bile is secreted in the liver, that there is no nervous fluid, and that animal spirits are ethereal particles from the atmosphere which mix with the blood in the lungs and are then separated in the brain (Mayow's theory).[3]

In (2) Bohn discusses the possible porosity of glass, mentioning Boyle and Cherubin,[4] mentions the crystallisation of alkaline salt (K_2CO_3, perhaps as $KHCO_3$) by slow evaporation of the solution,[5] and the formation of cubic nitre ($NaNO_3$) from a solution of common salt in boiling nitric acid:[6]

Inter alios aquam regiam parandi modus hic pluribus innotescit, ut spiritus nitri â sale communi cohobetur . . . ; quippe sal in fundo retortæ remanens, si crystallisetur, figuram quidem salis cubicam præ se fert, quantum tamen est, Nitrum evasit, quod ejus inflammabilitas, sapor ac spiritus inde elicitus credere jubent.[7]

Bohn quotes Mayow without naming him,[8] mentions that oil of vitriol does not dissolve iron, nor aqua fortis silver and lead unless water is added,[9] and says metals were more easily corroded by the air in London, where coal was burnt, than in Paris (â Carbonum fossilium concrematorum exhalationibus salino-sulphureis adulterata).[10] The colour of red flowers bleached by sulphur gas (Gas seu fumus sulphuris) is restored by dilute oil of vitriol.[11] Silver is

---

[1] Gmelin, (1), ii, 140; Sprengel, (1), v, 115; Daremberg, 1870, ii, 695; Ferguson, i, 113.
[2] Zufällige Gedencken . . . von dem Sulphure, Halle, 1718, 15.
[3] (4), 308.   [4] Diss. xiii.   [5] Diss. xiii, § 27.
[6] (6), and Diss. ii, § 7.
[7] See also Diss. vi, § 15; this had previously been observed by Boyle, Origin of Forms and Qualities, 1666; Works, ed. Birch, 1744, ii, 509.
[8] Diss. iv, § 20: ex aëre spiritum seu salem igneum, quem Nitro aëreum appellant.
[9] Diss. ii, § 24; vi, § 8, mentioning Boyle.   [10] Diss. xii, § 3.   [11] Diss. xiv, § 25.

precipitated from solution in aqua fortis by copper, copper by iron, and iron by bismuth.[1] Not all these observations are original.

HOFFMANN

Johann Moritz Hoffmann (Altdorf, 6 October 1653–Anspach, 31 October 1727), professor of medicine at Altdorf, Leibmedicus to the Markgraf of Anspach, president of the Leopoldina Academy, established a teaching laboratory at Altdorf, the foundation stone being laid in 1685:

Laboratorium novum chemicum apertum medicinae cultoribus cum amica ad orationem inauguralem invitatione denunciat, 4°, Altdorf, 1683 (8 unnumb. ll., BN 4° Te⁶, 454); repr. in Acta Laboratorii chemici Altdorfini. Chemiae fundamenta, operationes praecipuas et tentamina curiosa . . . ; Auctarium Notas, Observationes et Experimenta ad Actorum Sect. I declarationem ulteriorem necessaria una cum Programmate invitatorio ad inaugurationem Laboratorii Chymici Altdorfini promisso, et Monumento ad Memoriam posteritatis publice erecto, sm. 4°, Nürnberg and Altdorf, 1719 (iv, 288, 54, xiv pp., portr.).[2]

Hoffmann's publications (including many on medicine and botany) in the *Miscellanea sive Ephemeridum Medico-Physicarum Academiæ Naturæ Curiosorum* (Nürnberg) are of little interest.[3]

HANNEMANN

Johann Ludwig Hannemann (Amsterdam, 25 October 1640–Kiel, 24 October 1724) who first studied theology, then medicine, was a member of the Academia Naturæ Curiosorum and practised as a physician in various German towns, becoming professor of physics in Kiel in 1675. He wrote a large number of theological and alchemical tracts and books.[4] He upheld a belief in the universal spirit or world soul,[5] defended astrology[6] and the chemical resuscitation of plants,[7] saying that every atom has the virtue of reviving the entire compound. A long book on the Hermetic-Paracelsic-Trismegistic Egg[8] in which he solves 108 questions proposed to him by Morhof (which are other-

---

[1] Diss. xv, § 26.

[2] Gmelin, ii, 133; F. Henrich, *Z. angew. Chem.*, 1926, xxxix, 92–8; summary in Gerding, 1869, 94–7; Poggendorff, (1), i, 1122; Bolton, 1893, 538; Kopp, (1), ii, 19, dates Fürstenwald, Brandenburg, 1621–Altdorf, 1698, but this would be his father, Moritz Hoffmann, who, Henrich says, was responsible for the erection of the laboratory; Gmelin, (1), ii, 223, 257, 435, quotes Hoffmann's *Disputationes anatomico-physiologicae ad J. von Horwe microsomum*, 4°, Altdorf, 1685; Διατυπωσις *praxeos chymiatricæ Hartmanni*, f°, Leipzig, 1725, and says he was president of the Academia Naturæ Curiosorum (p. 317).

[3] Liquor et sal volatile melissæ, 1688, Dec. II, An VII, 463; De salis lixivi sive alcalisatica, citra acidi associati beneficium, eveniente et perdurante crystallisatione, 1691, Dec. II, An X, 359; De liquore pro vitriolo martis parando collecta, â frigore non coaguabili, 1697–8, Dec. III, An V, 194; De lixivio salis melissæ, *ib.*, 195; De terra foliata tartari botriode, *ib.*, 196 (potassium acetate crystals).

[4] Jöcher, ii, 1352–3; Gmelin, (1), ii, 219; Ferguson, i, 363, who says his library is in Kiel University Library.

[5] *Spiritus Universalis Mundo restitutus*, 12°, Hamburg, 1670, BM 8630. ccc. 12.

[6] *Verthädigung der Astrologia*, 4°, Hamburg, 1699, BM 718. g. 8. (11.).

[7] *Phoenix Botanicus*, Kiel (?), 1680 (?); BM 1033. h. 11. (19.).

[8] *Ovum Hermetico-Paracelsico-Trismegistum . . . de Auro . . . In quo et 108 Quæstiones Chemicæ ab . . . Morhofio propositæ . . . solvuntur*, 8°, Frankfurt, 1694 (440, 28 pp., pref. dated Jan.–Feb., 1692; BN R 38169); Thorndike, viii, 401.

wise unknown), deals with natural, artificial, and potable gold, and adds an appendix (28 pp.) on the philosophers' stone. Gmelin mentions his papers on the supposed extraction of mercury from bloodstone and the analysis of ivory (1683–4).

JUNGKEN

Johann Helfrich Jungken (also spelled Junken, Juncken, and Jüngken) (Caldern, Hesse, 19 December 1648–Frankfurt, 5 January 1726), M.D. Heidelberg 1671, then physician to various notabilities and Physicus Ordinarius in Frankfurt, wrote an experimental chemistry:[1]

Chymia Experimentalis Curiosa, ex Principiis Mathematicis demonstrata . . . , 8°, Frankfurt, 1681 (BM 1034. e. 20, pp. 898, engr. title and plate of apparatus); Chymia Experimentalis Medicus praesenti seculo accommodandus, per veram philosophiam Spagiricam rerum naturalium veris fundamentis exornandus . . . , 8°, Frankfurt, 1682 (BM 1034. e. 21, 841 pp.); Chymia Experimentalis, Sive, Naturalis Philosophia Mechanica . . . , 4°, Frankfurt, 1701 and 1702 (iv ll. incl. engr. title, 830 pp., iv ll. index, i l. errata).

and a pharmaceutical dictionary:

Corpus Pharmaceutico-Chymico-Medicum, sive Concordantia Pharmaceuticorum Compositorum Discordans; Modernis Medicinæ Practicis dicata . . . , 4°, Frankfurt, 1697 (1698 ?), 2 pts., 744, 712 pp. (also 1711); Lexicon Chymico-Pharmaceuticum, in Duas Partes distinctum, Editio Tertia, 8°, Nürnberg, 1729, 275, 535 pp.; I have not seen any of these.

After a short introduction on the three active principles (salt, sulphur and mercury) and the two passive (water and earth), apparatus and operations, the book on chemistry deals with the three kingdoms: animal (including the analysis of human blood, its oily volatile salt being supposed to be the basis of Burggrav's lamp of life and death[2], and phosphorus); vegetable (abbreviated in the 1702 edition; including wine, alcohol, vinegar, tartar, and opium); and the longest section on the mineral kingdom. The treatment resembles that in the second volume of Boerhaave's later *Elementa Chemiae* (1732) but includes numerous recipes. There is a rather long section on mercury preparations. Amber, coral, and pearls are classed as minerals. Jungken quotes many authorities, including Van Helmont, Boyle, and Glauber, and his text is straightforward and non-mystical. There is a short section on artificial gems. An author quoted is George Thomson (born *c.* 1625), who served in the Civil Wars under Prince Maurice (brother of Prince Rupert) graduated M.D. at Leyden in 1648, and died about 1679 or later,[3] who was a follower of Van Helmont. Jungken thought tin could be converted into silver by scorifying with arsenic, as Sigismund Van of Vogtland found, who in 1464 built a splendid hospital, and his epitaph could still be seen.[4] The second part of the book consists of recipes classified under diseases, and the 1702 edition ends with a Commentary on the Principles of Things of Nature which, although

[1] Hoefer, (1), ii, 275; Ferguson, i, 444, 830; Thorndike, viii, 390.
[2] J. E. Burggrav, *Biolychnium, seu Lampas vitæ & mortis*, 8°, Leyden, 1610; 12°, Frankfurt, 1630.
[3] Ferguson, ii, 448, with a list of his works, many with Greek titles.
[4] Jungken, 1702, 316.

wandering into philosophy, religion, astrology, and spontaneous generation, is on the whole reasonably positive and intelligible.

WILLIS

Thomas Willis (Great Bedwyn, Wiltshire, 29 January 1621–London, 11 November 1675) was educated in Christ Church, Oxford, and in 1642 joined the other students in bearing arms in the Royalist cause when the city was garrisoned. He graduated M.A. in 1642 and M.B. in 1646 and practised in Oxford. In 1660, on the restoration of the monarchy, he became Sedleian professor of natural philosophy in Oxford, taking in the same year the degree of doctor of physic. He was one of the founders of the Royal Society. In 1666 he moved to London as physician in ordinary to the King. On his death he was buried at great expense in Westminster Abbey.

Willis was an independent thinker, although influenced by de le Boë Sylvius, whose theory of diseases he largely adopted. Thomson says his views are closer to those of Paracelsus than to those of Van Helmont, but he was, like Sylvius, influenced by Descartes. He was one of the first to recognise an active principle of combustion in the air, to represent combustion and respiration as similar phenomena (with an explanation of the source of animal heat), and to put forward a reasonable theory of fermentation.[1]

Willis's most important work was on the anatomy of the brain.[2] In his dissections he was assisted by Richard Lower, whose assistance he fully acknowledges in the preface.[3] At a time when the Royal Society prided itself on plain speaking, Willis's rhetorical style was found too ornate; he says, e.g.[4]

> The corporeal soul common to man and the higher animals, while it extends over the whole organic body and vivifies, actuates, and irradiates every part, both tissues and humours, yet seems more eminently to subsist in two of these, and to hold them as its imperial seats, as it were. These subjects of the soul are on the one hand the vital fluid, the blood, circulated in a perpetual round in the heart, arteries, and veins, and on the other the animal fluid or nervous juice, streaming gently through the brain and its appendices. Both these provinces the soul inhabits and adorns with its presence, but since the soul cannot be in both provinces at the same time, it is as it were divided; it actuates each province by its appropriate half. One of its halves, since it is as we have shown of the nature of fire, glides into the blood after the fashion of a burning flame, while the other half seems diffused through the animal fluid after the manner of light, like the rays of light emanating from that flame; rays which, taken up by the brain and the nerves as by dioptric glasses and manifoldly reflected or refracted, form various figures according to the working of the animal faculties.

He goes on to compare the movement of the animal spirits with a distillation process, not by a heat like a common flame but, by a wise dispensation of the

---

[1] Barchusen, 1710, 503–18; Gmelin, (1), i, 675; Sprengel, (1), iv, 183, 249; v, 73, 434; Thomson, (1), i, 201; (3), 106; Kopp, (1), i, 141; iii, 135, 194; iv, 263, 283, 301; (2), iii, 183; Haeser, (1), ii, 288, 329, 382; Anon., NBG, 1866, xlvi, 755; Moore, DNB, 1900, lxii, 25; Foster, 1901, 269–87; Meyer-Steineg and Sudhof, 1922, 318; Gunther, (1), 1926, iii, 59, 96; Rolleston, *Medical Life*, 1934, xli, 177–91; Thorndike, viii, 524.

[2] *Cerebri Anatome: cui accessit Nervorvm Descriptio Et Usus*, 4°, London, 1664, with plates by Sir Christopher Wren; *Opera*, Venice, 1720, 109 f.

[3] 1664, a2 *v*; Anthony à Wood, *Athenæ Oxoniensis*, 2 ed., Oxford, 1721, ii, 857, says maliciously that his crony Lower 'helped, or rather instructed' Willis.

[4] *De Anima Brutorum*, ch. iv; *Opera*, 1720, ii, 20; tr. in Foster, 1901, 272.

Creator, by such a tepid heat as that of a water bath: atque naturæ usibus à Creatore destinatis inserviens, cum blando et amico tepore instar ignis clausi balneo Mariæ ... tanquam lucis radii à flamma dimissi in cerebrum, ac cerebellum velut distillantur.

The works of Willis of interest to us are:

I. Diatribæ duæ Medico-philosophicæ, quarum prior agit De Fermentatione sive De Motu intestino particularum in quovis corpore. Altera De Febribus. His accessit Dissertatio Epistolica De Urinis, 8°, London, 1659 (pp. 239 + 52); 2 ed., London, 1660; 3 ed., London, 1662, The Hague, 1662; 4 ed., London, 1677; *Opera*, 1720, i, 1–27; Fulton, Bibliography of Lower and Mayow, Oxford, 1935, 13, says the first ed. was published late in 1658. A criticism by Edmund de Meara: Examen Diatribæ Thomæ Willisii, ... de Febribus, sm. 8°, London, 1665, was answered by Richard Lower: Diatribæ Thomæ Willisii ... De Febribus Vindicatio adversus Edmundum de Meara, sm. 8°, London, 1665; 12°, Amsterdam, 1666; dedicated to Robert Boyle. In the *Opera* the first tract has the title: De Fermentatione, sive De Motu Corporum in Naturalium Inorganico. In what follows the two tracts are denoted by: De Fermentatione I*a* and De Febribus I*b*.

II. Pathologiæ Cerebri et Nervosi generis specimen. In quo agitur de Morbis Convulsivis et de Scorbuto, 4°, Oxford, 1667; 12°, Amsterdam, 1668, 1670. The two parts are denoted by II*a* and II*b*.

III. Affectionum quæ dicuntur Hystericæ & Hypocondriacæ Pathologia spasmodica vindicata ... Cui accesserunt Exercitationes Medico-Physicæ Duæ I De Sanguinis Accensione II De Motu Musculari, sm. 4°, London, 1670. The first part is a reply to Nathaniel Highmore. In what follows the two appendices I and II are denoted by III*a* and III*b*. Although Highmore criticised Willis, he also belonged to the Iatrochemical school: Sprengel, (1), v, 76.

IV. Pharmaceutice rationalis. Sive Diatribe de Medicamentorvm Operationibus in humano Corpore, 2 pts. large paper, 4°, Oxford, 1674–5, with engr. t.p. of Sheldonian Theatre; small paper, 4°, Oxford, 1675; *Opera*, 1720, ii, 142.

V. Opera Omnia, 2 vols. 4°, [Lyons, 1676], Geneva [1676], 1680; 4°, Amsterdam, ed. G. Blasius, 1682 (6 pts., portr.); 2 vols. f°, Venice, 1720 (portr.; the ed. used); tr. by Samuel Pordage (1633–91 ?), the poet:[1] Pharmaceutice Rationalis: or, an Exercitation of the Operations of Medicines in Humane Bodies ... In Two Parts ... As Also A Treatise of the Scurvy, ... , 4°, London, 1679;

The Remaining Medical Works of ... Dr. Thomas Willis. With large Alphabetical Tables ... and an Index for Explaining all the hard and unusual Words ... for the benefit of the meer English Reader, and meanest capacity ... The First Part, though last published, 4°, London, 1681 (portr., 18 copperplates);

Dr. Willis's Practice of Physick, Being the Whole Works ... containing these Eleven Several Treatises, viz. I. Of Fermentation. II. Of Feavers. III. Of Urines. IV. Of the Accension of the Blood. V. Of Musculary Motion. VI. Of the Anatomy of the Brain. VII. Of the Description and Use of the Nerves. VIII. Of Convulsive Diseases. IX. Pharmaceutice Rationalis the First and Second Part. X. Of the Scurvy. XI. Two Discourses concerning the Soul of Brutes; each with sep. pag., f°, London, 1684 (with 40 copper plates);

Another tr. by Eugenius φιλίατρος (medical works only): The London Practice of Physick: Or the whole part of Physick Contained in the Works of Dr. Willis, 8°, London, 1685.

Willis adopted some ideas from Paracelsus; he recognised five elements or principles, three active: spirit (replacing mercury), sulphur, and salt; and two passive, water and earth.[2] Although Venel[3] said Willis first added the two 'passive principles' to the *tria prima*, and his statement has been copied by

---

[1] Aitken, DNB, 1896, xlvi, 151.
[2] I*a*, chs. 1 (De principiis rerum naturalium), 2 (Chymicorum principiarum descriptio); V, 1720, i, 1 f.
[3] Diderot and D'Alembert, *Encyclopédie*, art. *Chymie*, 1753, iii, 434.

practically everybody writing on the subject, the *five* principles were proposed by Basso in 1621.[1]

Willis gave to spirit (=mercury) the property of volatilising the constituent parts of bodies, salt is the basis of fixity, sulphur produces colours, odours, and heat, and unites spirit and salt. Spirits are a most subtle ethereal substance and particles of diviner aura which the parent of nature had established in this sublunar world as instruments of the life and soul, movement and sense of every thing. They determine the form and figure of everything. By their presence they maintain the bonds of mixtures and loose these on their departure (mixtionis vincula præsentia sua conservant, discessu pro libitu referant). They restrain the disagreement of sulphur and salt. The perfect state of every thing is attained by abundance and exaltation (in copia et exaltatione) of spirits, decline consists in their defect and destitution. Spirits are few in minerals, more in vegetables, and most in animals. Convulsions and epilepsy are due to the impetuous motion and 'explosion' of animal spirits.[2]

In his theory of combustion[3] Willis (who mentions Boyle) assumed that sulphureous particles thrown off by the burning body united with nitrous particles which abound in the air to produce all sublunary fire and particularly flame:

ut flamma accendatur, maneatque accensa, libero, et indiscontinuo aëris accessu opus est; idque non solum ut effluvia vaporosa flammæ suffocationem minantia foras convehantur, et perpetim decedant; attamen longe potius, ut *pabulum nitrosum* propter cujusvis rei incendium necessario requisitum ab aëre suppeditetur. Enimvero omnis *ignis* sublunaris, ac potissimum *flamma*, omnino conflatur a *particulis sulphureis* e corpore combustibili confertim erumpentibus, atque *nitrosis*, quæ ubique in aëre scatent, iis in occursum datis.

He mentions the brilliant combustion of sulphur in nitre fused in a crucible and Boyle's experiments on the extinction of a candle in an exhausted receiver (see p. 524).

He supposed that limestone on burning takes up igneous particles and becomes harder; these particles are driven out by the water used to slake the quicklime.[4] An acid ferment in the stomach forms chyle with the sulphur of food, and this chyle effervesces in the heart, the salt and sulphur taking fire together and producing the vital flame, which penetrates the whole, and passes to the brain, just as when spirit of wine is distilled in an alembic with a sponge in the mouth of the vessel, which transmits the more subtle parts.[5] The blood is a fermentible liquor, comparable with the must of wine.[6]

Willis attached the greatest importance to fermentation. 'Every disease acts its tragedy by the power of some ferment (quilibet morbus virtute fermenti cujusdam suas excitat tragœdias).'[7] He assumed that the particles of the ferment are in violent motion, that they transfer this internal (intestine) motion

[1] Sebastian Basso, *Philosophia Naturalis adversus Aristotelem Libri XII*, 8°, Geneva, 1621, 31, 36: spirit, oil, salt, earth, and phlegm (spirit =mercury, oil =sulphur); see p. 387.
[2] II, chs. i, iv; V, i, 209, 219.
[3] III*a*, 1670, 47 f., 54; V, 1720, i, 304 f., 306; cf. I*a*, ch. x (De natura ignis), V, 1720, i, 19 f.
[4] I*a*, ch. x; V, 1720, i, 23.   [5] I*a*, ch. v; V, 1720, i, 7–8.
[6] *Ib.*, chs. xiv–xv; V, 1720, i, 70, 74.   [7] I*a*, ch. v; V, 1720, i, 9.

from the ferment to the body fermented, the particles of which are set in motion, and the elements are so redistributed that new bodies are formed:[1]

Fermentatio est motus intestinus particularum, seu principiorum cujusvis corporis, cum tendentia ad perfectionem ejusdem corporis, vel propter mutationem in aliud. . . . Plures sunt modi, quibus fermentatio, aut promovetur, aut fistitur. Primus, et præcipuus erit, fermenti cujusdam corpori fermentando adjectio; cujus particulæ, cum prius sint in vigore, et motu positæ, alias in massa fermentanda otiosas, et torpidas exsuscitant, et in motum vindicant.

He denied that liquids become hot by fermentation.[2] Willis's theory of fermentation as due to the transmission of molecular motion was criticised by Barner[3] but was adopted by Stahl[4] and Boerhaave.[5]

Willis[6] explained the formation of ether from alcohol by supposing that the sulphuric acid took a spirituous part from the alcohol and set free the oil (oleum) or sulphur of the spirit of wine (vini pars sulphurea pura, putaque est, separata et per se manens, dum pars spirituosa sali acido connubit). He also considered succinic acid (sal succini) sublimed from amber as sulphureous (multum sulphuris in se continet).[7] This 'sulphur of wine' (ether) when mixed with Canary wine, sugar, and elder flowers formed a yellow 'syrupus diasulphuris' used for coughs.[8] Willis's 'tincture of sulphur' (ether) is mentioned by Harris (see p. 311) and Vigani.[9]

According to Lippman[10] Willis was the first to describe clearly the very sweet taste of diabetic urine, although he did not attribute it to sugar.[11]

Although La Wall[12] says Avicenna was 'the first to note the sweet taste of the urine of diabetic patients', Lippmann says it is not mentioned by Arabic physicians (Rasis, Avicenna, etc.), although it is in the Indian Suśruta (Vol. I), perhaps as a late interpolation. Sarton[13] includes diabetes mellitus among diseases given in the Suśruta, but his reference[14] to the 'first description of diabetes' in Aretaios (c. A.D. 120–200) is said by Lippmann[15] to confuse it with polyuria.

The part of the soul present in the blood is of the nature of an actual flame, and the part present in the brain is of the nature of light (see Descartes, p. 440). The heat and light of the blood are due to the friction of saline and sulphureous particles in the blood caused by the beating of the heart,[16] a theory previously given by Van Helmont.[17] The heat of the blood is due to combustion by nitrous particles present in the air, since nitre supports combustion. Willis gives a description of the various colours of the blood, the purple changing to scarlet, 'almost flame-like', by admixture of nitrous particles, as is proved by the scarlet colour formed in parts most freely exposed to air:

ad flammam excitandam plurimæ aeris nitrosæ particulæ circumcirca consistæ simul accendi debent . . . secundum flammæ sustinendæ requisitum est constans pabuli sulphurei . . . tertio. Ut flamma accensa aliquandiu permaneat, jugi eventilatione opus est, nempe ut effluvia ejus fuliginosa continenter avolent . . . ignis vitalis pabulum

[1] Ia, chs. iii, vi; V, 1720, i, 5, 9.
[2] IIIa; IV, Pars ii; V, 1720, i, 306; ii, 242 f.
[3] Chymia Philosophica, 1689, 315.
[4] Fundamenta Chymiae, Nürnberg, 1723, 31.
[5] (2), ii, 166.
[6] IV, 1675; V, 1720, ii, 183.
[7] Ib., 183.
[8] III, Part II (posthumous), Sect. i, ch. 6; V, 1720, ii, 258.
[9] Medulla Chymiæ, 8°, London, 1683, 7.
[10] (1), 1906, i, 329.
[11] Willis, III, sect. V, ch. 3; V, 1720, ii, 184.
[12] 1927, 107.
[13] (1), i, 77.
[14] Ib., 307.
[15] Isis, 1928, xi, 161.
[16] IIIa; V, 1720, i, 304–10; Foster, 272–4.
[17] In sole tabernaculum; Ortus Medicinæ, 1652, 621.

nitrosum illico accipiens . . . ac per totam massam sanguineam effervescentia excitata, quamdam quasi flammam accendit . . . quod autem spectat ad colorem sanguinis inter circulandum ab atro-purpureo in coccinum . . . dico, hujus causam immediatam esse aeris nitrosi cum sanguine admixtionem. Quod certe constat, quia mutatio in coccineum ibidem loci incipit, ubi sanguis aeris accessu maxime potitur . . . prout Doctissimus D.D. Lowerus observavit.

The objection that the flame of blood is not visible is not serious: red-hot iron, fireflies, ignes fatui, and phosphorescent wood do not show in daylight what they do at night; some warm-blooded people taking off their under-clothing on going to bed near a candle emit a delicate flame on the lower parts of the body, and the fur of warm-blooded animals when rubbed emits sparks in the dark. An ingenious man with an active brain told Willis that after an extra good bout of wine (à pleniori vini potu) he was able to read print clearly on a very dark night.[1]

Willis's theory that 'blood is aflame' was also held by Jacob Holst,[2] but it was criticised by Mayow,[3] who compared it with a salamander, adding that 'fires of this kind, and new lights, no less in Anatomy than in . . . Religion seem to me vain and fanatical.'

Willis supposed that muscular motion is due to animal spirits in the nerves, coming from the brain, but suggested that the immediate cause was sulphureous and nitrous particles in the blood:[4]

potentiam, sive virtutem, qua musculus movetur, a Cerebro proficisci, per nervos convehi, ac à fibris carneis contractis . . . Sin verò inquiratur: cujus naturæ, scilicet, an spirituo-salinæ (prout opinari fas sit) aut cujusnam alterius indolis sint spiritus animales à Cerebro in musculos derivati? Et deinde utrum latex alter iis immediatius à sanguine suggestus sulphureus, aut nitrosus existat? Super his, quia sensui non constat, nihil temere, aut positive pronunciamus.

Willis disproved a theory held in his time that the force of explosion of fulminating gold ($\chi\rho\upsilon\sigma\sigma\kappa\epsilon\rho\acute{\alpha}\nu\nu\iota\sigma\varsigma$) struck downwards only. He put some fulminating gold in a silver spoon and laid a coin over it. On explosion, the coin was thrown upward (usque ad cameræ tectum), thus showing that the explosion acted in all directions (ejus vis in orbem diffunditur). If exploded in a covered vessel, it left a purple powder of gold: si enim in vase cooperto hic pulvere fulminet, quicquid auri est, sub forma pulvisculi purpurei post detonationem remanet, et colligi potest.[5]

Sprengel gives as the medical theory of Willis that every humour in which salt, sulphur, and spirit predominate in a certain manner may be converted into a ferment. All diseases proceed from a morbid state or action of this ferment, 'and a physician may be compared to a wine-merchant.' Fever is the result of a violent and preternatural effervescence of the blood and other humours, produced either by external causes or by internal ferments, into which the chyle is converted when it mixes with the blood. The effervescence of the vital spirits produces quotidian fevers, that of salt and sulphur the continued fever, malignant fevers result from external ferments of a malignant nature. Smallpox is due to the seeds of fermentation set in activity by an external principle of contagion. Spasms and convulsions are produced by an explosion of salt and sulphur with the animal spirits. Hypochondria and hysteria are due to a

[1] IIIa; V, 1720, i, 309.
[2] Thom. Bartholinus, De flammula cordis epistola; cum Jacobi Holsti ejusdem argumenti dissertatione, Copenhagen, 1667; Sprengel, (1), v, 81.
[3] Tractatus Quinque, Oxford, 1674, 152, 157.
[4] IIIb; V, 1720, i, 314.   [5] IIIa, ch. x; V, i, 22.

morbid putrefaction of the blood in the spleen, or to a bad fermentescible principle loaded with salt and sulphur, which unites with, and deranges, the vital spirits. Scurvy is due to an alteration of the blood like that producing vapid or stale wine. Gout is a coagulation of the nutritive juices altered by acidified animal spirits, in the same way as sulphuric acid produces a coagulum with potash. The action of medicines is explained by the effects they produce on the nourishing principles. Sudorifics are cordials because they augment the sulphur of the blood; cordials purify the animal spirits and fix the too volatile blood.

Willis gives the methods of preparation (from earlier chemical authors) of sulphuric acid (spiritus vitrioli) by distilling Hungarian vitriol in a coated retort (retorta loricata)[1] and of nitric, hydrochloric, and succinic (sal succini) acids;[2] of ammonia solution (spiritus salis armoniaci) by distilling sal ammoniac with potassium carbonate solution, spirits by distilling soot, bones, hartshorn, and blood (containing ammonia), and 'flowers of sal ammoniac' (a mixture of ferric and ammonium chlorides made by distilling sal ammoniac with iron filings);[3] mercury compounds such as calomel and corrosive sublimate,[4] mercuric oxide by heating mercuric nitrate (mercurius præcipitatus commune), this being made by dissolving mercury in nitric acid and evaporating, or (mercurius præcipitatus per se) by heating mercury in a flask with a narrow neck, turbith mineral, and 'Hercules of Bovius',[5] a solution of mercuric and gold chlorides described by Thomas Bovius (d. 1609), an Italian physician who claimed to have a familiar spirit, Zephyriel, and potable gold and extract of hellebore with occult virtues.[6] Willis also described the preparation of several antimony compounds: butter of antimony by distilling antimony sulphide and corrosive sublimate, and antimony oxychloride, obtained by the action of water on it, called 'mercurius vitæ' although it contains no mercury (nihil mercurium in se continere); also glass, flowers, crocus, and sulphur of antimony,[7] bezoar mineral (antimonic acid) and diaphoretic antimony (antimony oxide).[8] Willis used six 'preparations of steel (chalybis præparationes)': iron filings, iron calcined with sulphur, iron filings treated with vinegar (when there is effervescence), iron rust, green vitriol made by dissolving iron in sulphuric acid and crystallising, and crocus made by calcining iron filings or scoria or plates in a reverberatory furnace; also something he calls 'our preparation of steel', with which artificial chalybeate waters can be prepared from common water.[9]

Although he calls his pharmacopœia 'rational' he still prescribed human skull,[10] powdered dried toads,[11] pearls, coral, bezoar, and theriac,[12] and waters of snails and earthworms.[13] In the first edition of I (1659) Willis first mentions a powder curing fever which comes from India; in an appendix to the

---

[1] II*a*, ch. iii; V, 1720, i, 218.   [2] IV, Sect. iv, ch. 2; V, 1720, ii, 183.
[3] IV, Sect. v, ch. 2; V, 1720, ii, 195.
[4] IV, Sect. iii, ch. 2; V, 1720, ii, 171.   [5] IV, Sect. ii, ch. 2; V, 1720, ii, 160–1.
[6] Jöcher, i, 1295; Gmelin, (1), i, 302, with list of works, incl. *Flagello contra gli Medici communi detti rationale*, 4°, Venice, 1583, and later eds.
[7] IV, Sect. II, ch. 2; V, 1720, ii, 158–9.   [8] IV, Sect. V, ch. 2; V, 1720, ii, 194.
[9] II*a*, ch. xii; IV, part ii, Sect. III, ch. 7; V, i, 258, ii, 332.
[10] II*a*, ch. i; II*b*, ch. ix; V, 1720, i, 218, 283; and often elsewhere.
[11] IV, Sect. V, ch. ii; V, 1720, ii, 192.
[12] *Cerebri Anatome*, ch. iv; IV, Sect. V, ch. ii; V, 1720, i, 122; ii, 192; and often elsewhere.
[13] II*a*, ch. xii; II*b*, ch. ix; IV, Sect. VI, ch. iii; V, 1720, i, 261, 283; ii, 209; and elsewhere.

second edition (also 1659) he says it was much used in quartan fevers and could restrain the fermentation of the fever, but was not a certain cure. In the third edition (1662) he says there was no theory to explain its action.[1] This was Peruvian bark, which was imported from Antwerp; its use was popularised by John Tabor senr.[2]

Plot,[3] who gives a summary of Willis's medical theories, says he enriched the pharmacopœia with his diasulphuric syrup, preparation of steel, and a spirit of ammonia and amber (spiritus salis armoniaci succinatus).

Walter Harris[4] spoke of Willis's preparation of steel as a 'masterpiece', but 'hitherto a great secret and sold at a great price'. He used iron filings, crude tartar (better than cream of tartar) and water, but says white wine can be used. He says it is the same as Lemery's crocus Martis, but it seems to be more like Lemery's tincture of Mars with Tartar.[5] George Wilson[6] says the preparation of steel without acids is made by drying at a gentle heat a paste of equal parts of iron filings and cream of tartar with white wine.

Willis gives several striking examples of the effect of volatility in the operations of chemical affinities. He says sal ammoniac is composed of volatile and marine salts. When it is distilled with a solution of salt of tartar (potassium carbonate) 'the bond is broken, the marine salt (hydrochloric acid) cohering with the fixed salt of tartar, whilst the volatile part (ammonia) is dismissed from the complex and can easily fly upwards:

hoc vinculum solvitur, vidclicet, quando hoc sal compositus cum Sale Tartari in aqua dissolutus intimè miscetur, particulæ salis marini salino fixis Tartari cohærent; proindeque volatiles earum complexibus dismissæ, & ad, avolandum paratæ facillimè ascendunt.[7]

A different person was Timothy Willis, Fellow of St. John's College, Oxford, and one of the founders of the Royal Society, who wrote on chemistry and on the transmutation of metals, which he thought was possible.[8]

A book on fermentation 'based on perpetual experiments'[9] by Martin Kerger consists mainly of quotations from Willis, Boyle, Helmont, Sennert, 'Basil Valentine', Digby, etc. Kerger claimed to have cured all kinds of fevers by a *medicamentum præcipitans*.

Gottfried Hennicke or Hennig (Hennickius), d. after 1727 and before 1743, physician to the Count of Erbach, in a treatise on panaceas,[10] dealt with cinnabar, mercury sublimate, antimony, and butter and cinnabar of antimony, al-

---

[1] *Ib.*, ch. vi; V, 1720, i, 44.   [2] Sprengel, (2), 1827, iv, 523, 529, 534.
[3] *Natural History of Oxfordshire*, 2 ed., f°, Oxford, 1705, 308.
[4] *Pharmacologia Anti-Empirica*, 8°, London, 1683, 149–55 (BM 547. c. 9).
[5] Lemery, *Course of Chymistry*, tr. W. Harris, 1686, 147.
[6] *A Compleat Course of Chymistry*, 1721, 41.
[7] IV, v, 2; Oxford, 1674, i, 211; V, 1720, ii, 195; see Mayow, p. 606.
[8] *Propositiones Tentationum: Sive Propaedeumata De Vitis et Fæcunditate Compositorum naturalium: Quæ sunt elementa Chymica*, 8°, London, J. Legatt, 1615 (iv ll. 40 pp., BM 1033. d. 5); reprinted 1616 with alternative title *Elementa Chymica; The Search of Causes. Containing a Theosophysicall inuestigation of the possibilitie of transmutatorie Alchimie*, 8°, London, 1616 (BM 1036. a. 13. (2.)); Thorndike, vii, 171.
[9] *De Fermentatione Liber physico-medicus . . . omnia perpetuis experimentis firmata*, 4°, Wittenberg, 1663; Thorndike, viii, 211.
[10] *De Panaceis. Tractatio Medico-Chymica curiosis Experimentis ac Ratiociniis illustrata*, Frankfurt, 1689, 106 pp. (BM 1034. l. 24. (2.); Thorndike, viii, 400.

though he also recommended vegetable and animal panaceas. He translated George Thomson's *Direct Method of Curing Chymically* (1675) as *Acum Chymice Curandi Methodus* (12°, Frankfurt and Marburg, 1686).[1]

Nathaniel Highmore (Fordingbridge, Hampshire, 6 February 1613– Sherburne, 21 March 1685), M.D. Oxford 1642,[2] had a controversy with Willis on the cause of hysteria (p. 305).[3] He wrote on generation[4] and on animal spirits as atoms or minute fiery particles, attenuated and exalted by heat and fermentation in the heart, transmitted with the blood through the arteries to the brain, where they were separated and stored for very rapid transmission through the nerves to all parts of the body.[5]

HARRIS

Walter Harris (Gloucester, 1647–London, 1725),[6] son of a shoemaker, entered Oxford in 1666, becoming M.B. in 1670. He became a Catholic and went to Douai, then Paris, where he became M.D. in 1676. In 1677 he returned to practise in London. As a result of the Popish Plot invented by Titus Oates in 1678, Harris apostasised again and returned to Protestantism. In 1688 he became physician to William III and had a great reputation.

In his small book on diseases of children he attributed all infantile diseases to acidity and prescribed some form of alkali. His use of calcium salts in convulsions was good.[7] He described the preparation of black mercuric sulphide (Æthiops mineralis, Æ. mercurialis) by triturating 4 pts. of mercury with 3 pts. of flowers of sulphur, and it was called after him Æthiops Harisii.[8]

In his very readable book on pharmacy[9] Harris opposed belief in transmutation and the use of chemical remedies such as potable gold, and thought the virtues of mercury, antimony, vitriol, steel (except Dr. Willis's 'masterpiece'), Jesuits' bark, and opium were exaggerated. Some mercurial preparations were poisons. He also criticised the contemporary surgeons. He favoured complicated remedies such as the Theriac Andromache or Venice treacle (with over 60 ingredients) and Mithradate, but says these were little used in France. In the preface to his translation of Lemery, *A Course of Chymistry*, 1686, Harris

[1] Ferguson, ii, 448.   [2] Moore, DNB, 1891, xxvi, 378.
[3] Highmore, *De Hysterica & Hypochondriaca Passione, responsio epistolaris ad Doctorem Willis*, 4°, London, 1670.
[4] *The History of Generation . . . as well in Plants as Animals*, 8°, London, 1651; BM E. 1369. (3.); incl. a discussion of the weapon ointment, Thorndike, viii, 417.
[5] *Exercitationes duæ; quarum prior de Passione Hysterica; altera de Affectione Hypochondriaca*, 12°, Oxford, 1660; 3 ed., 12°, Jena, 1677; NBG, 1858, xxiv, 658: 'qui rappellent et qui ont peut-être suggéré les molécules organiques de Buffon.'
[6] NBG, 1858, xxiii, 451; Morton, in Singer, (1), ii, 532 (dates 1647–1732); Thorndike, viii, 99; *id., Speculum*, 1953, xxviii, 692.
[7] *De Morbis Acutis Infantum*, 8°, London, 1689, 2 ed. 1705; tr. J. Martyn, *A Treatise of the Acute Diseases of Infants*, 8°, 1742; Gmelin, (1), ii, 241, gives eds. 4°, Geneva, 1696, 1698; 8°, Amsterdam, 1715, 1736; German tr., 12°, Leipzig, 1691; French tr. by de Vaux, 8°, Paris, 1710, 12°, 1738, 1754.
[8] *De Morb. Acut.*, 1689, 136.
[9] *Pharmacologia Anti-Empirica: Or A Rational Discourse of Remedies Both Chymical and Galenical*, sm. 8°, 1683; xvi ll. (i approbation by Coll. Phys.), 332 pp., vi ll.; on Paracelsus, 15–24; Helmont, 24–7 (his 'head was heated too much'); potable gold, 38; transmutation, 49; Willis's prep. of steel, 149–53; Jesuits' bark, 164; Gmelin, (1), ii, 249, gives an ed. 1684; Thorndike, viii, 99; *id., Speculum*, 1953, xxviii, 692.

says 'He is perhaps the first who has taken such particular notice, what an augmentation of weight is added to many Preparations by the concurrence and incorporation of the substance of Fire into their composition', as in the calcination of lead and antimony.

BRENDEL

Zacharias Brendel (Jena; 1592–13 June 1638), professor of medicine at Jena, wrote a small textbook, *Chimia in Artis formam redacta*:

Chimia in Artis formam redacta, 12°, Jena, 1630 (218 pp., BM 1036. a. 2. (1.)), and later eds.: Jena, 1641 (BM 1034. f. 2); Amsterdam, 1659, 1668; Leyden, 1671 (BM 1036. a. 26. (1.), all the latter revised by Rolfinck).

Gmelin, (1), i, 344, 604; Ferugson, i, 124; Thorndike, viii, 119, gives the full title of the 1630 ed. as: Chymia in artis formam redacta et publicis praelectionibus philatris in Academia Ienensi communicata, ubi, praeter methodum addiscendi ἐγχειρήσεις ('ἐγχειορήσεις in Thorndike) chymicas facilimam (*sic*) et plurimorum medicamentorum correctionem, varii discursus chymici reperiuntur, quorum agmen claudit disquisitio accurata de famosissima praeparatione auri potabilis, nunc certis de caussis publici iuris facta; the shorter title of the 1641 ed. (175 pp.) is given by Ferguson; the still shorter one of the 1671 ed. is Chimia in artis formam redacta Cum discursu de auro potabili (167 pp.).

The basis of the arrangement is the use of the four degrees of fire in various operations (mentioning Duncan Burnet's book, see p. 180), viz. the vapour or water bath, ash bath, flame (used in subliming sulphur, etc.), and the blast furnace (used in distilling spirit of vitriol in an earthen retort). The distillation of wine and vinegar is done on a water bath (balneum Maris & Mariæ). After the preparation of various remedies, the book ends on the blessed water of Ruland or the true use of glass of antimony, and on potable gold, on which many previous writers have babbled but on which the most eminent chemist Basil Valentine alone approached the truth.

ROLFINCK

Werner Rolfinck (Hamburg, 15 November 1599–Jena, 6 May 1673), M.D. Padua 1625, first professor of chemistry (from 1641) in Jena, where he established a laboratory and gave practical instruction. He also taught anatomy, surgery, and botany.[1] He revised Brendel's text-book and wrote one himself with the same title:

Chimia in Artis formam redacta, Sex Libris comprehensa, 4°, Jena, 1661 (BM 1034. h. 5. (2.)), Geneva, 1661, Jena, 1662, Geneva, 1671 (BM 1034. h. 4); Berlin, 1674, with Elsholtz, Distillatoria Curiosa (BM 1034. c. 16. (1.)), Jena, 1679, Frankfurt, 1686 (all 443 pp. and index); Resp. ad Chimiam in Artis formam redactam illustrandam breves notæ, 4°, Jena, 1669 (BM 1034. h. 5. (1.)).

It deals mostly with pharmaceutical chemistry. There is a short preface and a list of the respondents. The first part (prolegomena) is on chemistry in

---

[1] Kopp, (4), i, 230; Ferguson, ii, 283; Chemnitius, *Die Chemie in Jena von Rolfinck bis Knorr* (1629–1921), Jena, 1929 (192 pp., 11, 17, portr.); *id.*, *Naturforschung und Naturlehre im alten Hamburg. Erinnerungsblätter zu Ehren der 90. Versamml. Ges. Deutscher Naturforscher und Ärzte in Hamburg*, Staats- und Universität Bibliothek, Hamburg, 1928, 19 (portr.); Thorndike, viii, 133.

general, the second on means by which chemistry gained its end (manipulative operations), the third on artificial works (τεχνουργήματα) or effects of operations (mostly on spirits and oils), the fourth on soft essences, or tinctures, elixirs, extracts, mixtures, balsams, elæosaccharia, gelatins and alcohol; the fifth on solids (salts, magisteries, fecula, flowers, sublimates, precipitates, calces, stones, fixation, croci, reguli, amber, stars, and amulets), and the sixth on non-entia (or non-existent chemical effects and works).

Alchemical and chemical symbols are used instead of names; Greek words and quotations are frequent, and even words in Arabic appear, and the book would be hard reading as compared with the French text-books. There are long branched tables summarising text.

A magistery is defined (with Beguin) as a mixed body so prepared without extraction that all its parts are kept homogeneous but a nobler degree of substance or quality is attained by removing exterior impurities.[1] The sixth book[2] entitled: 'De effectis seu operibus imaginariis, & non entibus chimicis', was also published separately.[3] It quotes the warning of Bernard Penotus (see p. 161) against alchemy:

Caveat sibi ab hac opum deprædatrice arte, cui salus sua cordi. Qui alicui malè vult, cum autem aperto marte aggredi non audet, saltem autor ipsi sit, ut huic studia se tradat.

Some chemical non-entities (the resuscitation of a plant from its ashes, the extraction of mercury from blood or dung, the homunculus of Paracelsus, potable gold, transmutation, and the extraction of essences and tinctures from metals, stones, pearls and coral) had been listed in a work published anonymously in 1645:

Non-Entia Chymica sive Catalogus eorum operum operationemque Chymicarum, quæ, cum nou sint in rerum natura, nec esse possint . . . , 12°, Frankfurt, 1645, 35 pp. (BM 1036. a. 3. (1.)); ed. with pref. by G. W. Wedel, 12°, Frankfurt, 1670; Berlin, 1674, with Elsholtz, Distillatoria Curiosa; Ferguson, ii, 489; Thorndike, vii, 196.

which Ferguson attributed to Michael Kirsten (1620–78) and Thorndike to George Kirsten (1613–60), professor of medicine at Stettin, who wrote an attack on a commentary of Johann Agricola on Johann Poppe:

Kirsten, Adversaria, et Animadversiones, in Johannis Agricolæ . . . Commentaria in Poppium . . . Darinnen der falsche, und betriegliche gebrauch der Chymischen Artzneyen . . . wiederleget wird, 4°, Stettin, 1648; Ferguson, i, 471; for Poppe, ib., ii, 213.

Rolfinck listed as chemical non-entities the astral quintessences of Paracelsus, the resuscitation of a plant from its ashes or from salts, extracting running mercury from vegetables, the homunculus of Paracelsus, the generation of gold in the human body, the mercury, salt, and sulphur of metals, the universal medicine, and the transmutation of metals into gold and silver, or of

---

[1] 1662, 319.   [2] 1662, 419–38.
[3] Non Ens Chimicum, mercurius metallorum et mineralium, 4°, Jena, 1670, BM 1185. f. 20. (1).

one imperfect metal into another. He mentions the famous gold tooth grown by a boy of seven in Silesia in 1593 as a fake, covered with gold leaf.

This tooth had a large literature, beginning with Jakob Horst of Helmstädt[1] and Martin Ruland junr.[2] Duncan Liddel of Aberdeen, who was then teaching at Helmstädt, exposed the credulity of his colleague Horst[3], and Tylkowski in 1674 showed by an examination of the tooth itself that it was bone covered with gold leaf.[4]

Rolfinck, a physician and anatomist, held two public dissections in 1629 which caused a great uproar in Germany;[5] it is said that he procured the cadavers of executed criminals and dissection became known as 'rolfincking'.

Rolfinck[6] discussed the origin of the name 'chimia', suggesting a derivation as χυμεία or χυμία from χέω, although Zosimos wrote χημεία, as well as other authors quoted by Rolfinck. His derivation of the name alcohol from the Arabic qāhālā[7] is quite wrong, although he suspected the true derivation,[8] which was given by Wedel (p. 316). Rolfinck published other works on chemical subjects, all at Jena,[9] and a book on botany[10] in which he dilates on barnacle geese, the vegetable lamb of Tartary, talking trees, etc., but thought the doctrine of signatures had its limitations, and palingenesis was untrue.

Dissertations presented under Rudolph Wilhelm Krause (Rudolphus Guilelmus Crausius) (Naumburg, 22 October 1642– Jena?, 26 December 1718), professor of medicine and chemistry in Jena (1671), included many on chemical, alchemical, and 'magical' subjects,[11] e.g. on the universal medicine (1679), the principles and transmutation of metals (1686) and signatures in plants (1697), and one denying fermentation in the blood (1682).

CLAUDER

Rolfinck's (and Kircher's) criticisms of alchemy were answered by Rolfinck's pupil Gabriel Clauder (Altenburg, 18 October 1633–? 9 January (or 10 October) 1691), physician to several Saxon princes. In his *Dissertatio de Tinctura Universali* (Altenburg, 1678; see p. 331) he collected historical evidence and did not rely only on his own experience.[12] Clauder shows some knowledge of recent experiments on air (perhaps Mayow's, since Clauder mentions Harvey), speaking of a volatile salt of air which cannot be perfectly

[1] *De auro dente maxillari pueri Silesii*, 8° and 12°, Leipzig, 1595.
[2] *Nova et in omni memoria omnino inaudita historia de aureo dente*, 4°, Frankfurt, 1595.
[3] *Tractatus de Dente Aureo*, 12°, Hamburg, 1628.
[4] Sprengel, (2), 1827, iii, 403; Thorndike, viii, 371.
[5] Meyer-Steineg and Sudhof, 1922, 336.
[6] *Chimia in artis formam redacta*, 1662, 19.
[7] *Ib.*, 279; Richter, *A. Nat.*, 1913, iv, 429 (450); Ruska, *Islam*, 1913, iv, 320.
[8] Vox est πολύσημος non unam habet significationem. A chimicis nunc ad subtilissimum pulverem, eumque pollinis farinae tenuissimae instar ad sensum tactus quasi inpalpabilem, nunc ad tenuem et observatu difficilem essentiam in humore denotandum, vel spiritum tenuissimum reiteratis destillationibus omni phlegmate spoliatum adhibetur.
[9] *De objecto chimiæ et de metallis perfectis sole et luna*, 1637; De metallis imperfectis et mollibus, 1638; Dissertationes chymicæ sex: de tartaro, sulphure, margaritis, perfectis metallis duobus auro et argento, antimonio, et imperfectis metallis duobus ferro et cupro, 4°, 1660 (BM 990. a. 4), repr. with sep. t.ps., 1679; Scrutinium chimicum vitrioli, 1666; De minera martis, 1668.
[10] De Vegetabilibus Plantis Suffructibus Fructibus Arboribus in genere, 4°, Jena, 1670; Thorndike, viii, 70.
[11] BM Cat., Crausius, R.G.   [12] Gmelin, ii, 31, 220; Ferguson, i, 161; Thorndike, viii, 385.

united to fixed salt of earth except by fermentation (nitrification). The spirit of the universe is extracted from rich soil at dawn by exposing it to sunlight concentrated by a burning glass, and straining the liquor condensed through a linen cloth. Air is the chief constituent of the matter of the universal tincture, the food of life is hidden in it, and many residues (caput mortua chymica) regain their pristine quality by exposure to it.

WEDEL

Georg Wolfgang Wedel (Golzen (or Glossen), Niederlausitz, 13 November 1645–Jena, 7 September 1721), Rolfinck's pupil, was professor of medicine at Jena (1673) and a believer in alchemy.[1] He reprinted the *Tabula Smaragdina* of Hermes (Vol. I)[2] and wrote a commentary on it.[3] He regarded Moses as an alchemist[4] and attempted a solution to a chemical riddle.[5] This is contained in lines 141–5 of the Greek text in book i of the *Sibylline Oracles* (*c.* A.D. 300) (see Vol. I),[6] which were quoted by the Greek alchemists Olympiodoros[7] (5 cent.) and Stephanos (7 cent.).[8] The favourite solution is ἀρσενικόν, which Cardan[9] says was proposed by Aymer de Ranconet (Périgueux, 1498–Paris, 1559); it is also given by Gohory (1568), Borrichius,[10] Kircher,[11] Reyher,[12] Morhof,[13] Leibniz,[14] and Hans Gram.[15]

Wedel proposed as the solution κα-σι-τε-ρος tin (by omitting α σ); K. A Kortum proposed ἀμ-πε-λῖ-τις, pitch or mineral coal.[16]

Another enigma, beginning: D.M. Aelia Laelia Crispis, nec vir nec mulier nec androgyna . . . , said to have been first published by M. L. Michael Angelus, *Super . . . ænigma Eliæ Leliæ Crispis*, 4°, Venice, 1548 (a work unknown to me), was said to have been cut on a block of white and red marble which existed at Bologna; *Theatrum Chemicum*, 1659, iv, 805; Nicolaus Barnaud wrote an alchemical commentary on it, *ib.*, 1659, iii, 744–54; Ferguson, i, 6; Jung, *Ambix*, 1946, ii, 182, who quotes a publication of it by Malvasius, Bologna, 1683, thinks it goes back to an epigram of Agathias Scholasticus, *c.* A.D. 582.

[1] Chemnitius, *op. cit.*, 13, 48, portr.
[2] *Introdvctio in Alchymiam*, 4°, Jena, 1705, and 1706, 59–60.
[3] *Exercitatio in tabulam Hermetis smaragdinam, adversus Kircherum*, 4°, Jena, 1704.
[4] *Centvria Exercitationvm medico-philologicarvm Sacrarvm et Profanarvm*, Decades I–X, 4°, Jena, 1686–1701; Decas IX, 1699, 15.
[5] *Ib.*, Decas IX, 1699, 48.
[6] *Oracula Sibyllina*, ed. J. H. Friedlieb, with German tr., Leipzig, 1852, 14–15; ed. C. Alexandre, with Latin tr., Paris, 1869, 32–3, 345 (θεος σωτηρ suggested); ed. J. Geffcken, *Griechischen-christllichen Schriftsteller des ersten drei Jahrhundert*, 1902, 12–13 (heretical); Kopp, (2), i, 506–18, based on Fabricius, *Bibliotheca Græca*, Hamburg, 1724, xii, 764 f.
[7] In Fabricius, 1724, xii, 764 (= λιθάργυρον); Berthelot, (2), ii, 71. 9.
[8] Ideler, *Physici et Medici Græci Minores*, Berlin, 1842, ii, 225 (gives no solution).
[9] *De Rerum Varietate*, 8°, Basel, 1557, bk. x, ch. 51, p. 714.
[10] *De Ortu et Progressu Chemiæ*, Copenhagen, 1668, 98, 100.
[11] *Mundus Subterraneus*, Amsterdam, 1665, ii, 274.
[12] *Dissertatio de nummis quibusdam ex chymico metallo factis*, Kiel, 1692, ch. 3; Kopp, (2), i, 516.
[13] *Polyhistor*, Lübeck, 1695 (1747, i, 104).
[14] *Miscell. Berolin.*, 1710, i, 16 (Oedipus Chymicus aenigmatis Græci & Germanii).
[15] Om Sybillæ mørke Tale, eller ni Bogstavers ørd, in *Skrifter, som udi Det Kiøbenhavnska Selskab af Lærdoms og Videnskabernes Elskere*, Copenhagen, 1746, ii, 23; Latin tr., *Scriptorum à Societate Hafniensi Bonis Artibus Promovendis Dedita . . . nunc autem in Latinum Sermonem Conversum Interprete*, Copenhagen, 1746, ii, 21.
[16] Kopp, (1), 1844, ii, 226; (2), ii, 506; (4), ii, 293.

Wedel was an extremely copious author[1] and only a few of his works of chemical interest can be mentioned:

I. Tabulæ chimicæ XV in Synopsi universam Chimiam exhibentes, 4°, Jena, 1692.
II. Compendivm Chimiæ theoreticæ et practicæ methodo analytica propositæ, 4°, Jena, 1715 (v ll., 208 pp., iv ll.).
III. Specimen Experimenti Chimici Novi, De Sale Volatili Plantarum, quo demonstratur, Posse ex plantis modo peculiari parari Sal volatile verum & genuinam, 12°, Frankfurt, 1672 (Duveen, 613); Jena, 1682 (2 pts., pp. 96, 96, index) treating of woad (pt. ii, p. 46) and using the word φλογιστὸν (pt. ii, p. 70).
    The second part of the 1682 ed. was published separately as: Experimentum Chimicum Novum De Sale Volatile Plantarum quo latius exponuntur, specimene ipso exhibita, 12°, Jena, 1675 (Duveen, 614). A different work is:
IV. Schediasma de Sale Volatili Oleoso, 4°, Jena, 1711 (52 pp.); by 'volatile salt' Wedel understood what is usually called 'essential oil'.
V. Physiologia Medica, Jena, 1680, 2 ed. 1694 (dedication dated 1 September, 1679) (BM 549. d. 27).
VI. Physiologia Reformata, 4°, Jena, 1688.
VII. Pharmacia Acroamatica, 4°, Jena, J. Bielckius, 1686 (BM 546. e. 9).

In V he retained the three principles, salt, sulphur, and mercury, but thought the new hypotheses of acid and alkali, acid and sulphur, and acid and volatile were insufficient. Scheunemann and others had obscured chemistry by speculation, others had over-stressed transmutation. In VI he did not accept the current theory (he does not name Mayow) that in respiration nitro-aerial particles or spirit pass from air into the blood. VII contains descriptions of operations, such as solution (p. 28), crystallisation (p. 44), effervescence (p. 73), fermentation (p. 87), and distillation (p. 96). It mentions phlogeston (φλογιστὸν) several times, e.g. (p. 32) as 'sulphureum φλογιστὸν duplex est . . . spirituosum . . . et oleosum', and 'spiritus φλογιστοὶ vegetabilium'. The discussion of calcination (pp. 128 f.) mentions the increase in weight of antimony observed by Le Fèvre (p. 140) and of lead observed by Tachenius (p. 141). Wedel accepts the theory that it is due to absorption of igneous corpuscles. There are descriptions of instruments and preparations, including elixirs (p. 302) and magisteries (p. 379). The book deals with chemistry as much as pharmacy. He (p. 16) criticised Rolfinck's derivation (see p. 314) of the name alcohol from an Arabic word qāhāla, saying correctly that it came from an Arabic word kuhl for a fine powder used as an eye-paint, and hence derivatively for a subtle spirit:

kahhala stibio, tanquam collyrio, antimoniato subtilissimo pulvere et alia præceperunt subtilisari ut alcohol, i.e. ut antimonium pro collyrio tali . . . Nicolai Flor in l. 3 in cap. de curatione ægritudimun oculorum[2] . . . cohel, vel chofel, vel alchofol, et significat pulverem debere subtilissimum esse sicut atomi, qui apparent in sphæra solis, intelligitur proprie loquendo per alcohol pulvis subtilissimus. Adæquate verò alcohol etiam prædicatur de subtilitate liquidorum nominatim spirituum, unde spiritus vini alcoholisatus audit, quid adeò subtilis est.

Wedel also published in *Miscellanea Curiosa Medico-Physica Academiæ Naturæ Curiosorum* (the dates are those on the t.p. as the year of communication, the dates of publication are later) on: Specimen experimenti chimici novi, de sale volatili plantarum (1673–4, Appendix x, pp. 190, 223), de

---

[1] Jöcher, iv, 1841–5, has a long list of his writings.   [2] See Jöcher, iii, 910.

principiis rerum in genere (1675–6, 331; 1682, 30), de principiis chemicis (1675–6, 333), de spiritu vitrioli regenerato (1675–6, 158), mutatio naturalis et artificialis ferri in cuprum (1675–6, 155) de sulphure matrici lucis (1678–9, 368), de Misy Dioscoridis (geminum est minera vitrioli) (1682, 380), and de mercurio saturni (1682, 382). In the last he reported that mercury had collected in a lead ink-pot in use for fifteen years, and assumed that the ink had drawn it out of the lead. In his de spiritu vitrioli regeneratio he reported that all the acid cannot be driven from green vitriol by heating; on exposure of the residue to moist air it continued to give acid on heating, the residual acid distilling with the absorbed moisture. In his paper on the artificial change of iron into copper (1675–6), he relied on the production of copper by the 'cementation process' in Hungary, in which plates of iron were placed in a solution of blue vitriol formed as drainings from copper mines, and in 1664 he had written to Hungary at the command of his prince to obtain information about the process. Newton was also interested in the process (see p. 470).

The Academia Germanicæ Naturæ Curiosorum was a reorganisation of a Collegium Naturæ Curiosorum founded in 1652 (before the Royal Society or the Académie des Sciences). From 1670 it published in Nürnberg *Miscellanea* or *Ephemerides*, the first ten years (*Decuriæ*) in seven volumes, a second *Decuria* being published in 1683–92 (vol. i was reprinted in 1684), and an index to both Decuriæ in 1695. The Emperor Leopold I became its patron in 1677, and in 1687 it became the Academia Cæsarea Leopoldina.[1] It continues to publish the *Nova Acta Academiæ Cæsareæ Leopoldina-Carolinæ Germanicæ Naturæ Curiosorum* (Halle). Its earlier members took the names of famous Classical or Arabian philosophers. The interest in the earlier volumes was largely medical, with emphasis on 'monsters',[2] as in the earlier volumes of the *Philosophical Transactions* of the Royal Society.[3]

Ernst Heinrich Wedel (Gotha, 1 August 1671–Jena, 13 April 1709), second son of G. W. Wedel, was a physician and professor extraordinarius in Jena. The third son, Johann Adolph Wedel (Jena; 17 August 1675–23 February 1747) was professor of theoretical medicine (1717) and later of practical medicine and chemistry in Jena; he published dissertations: de fermentis chymicis, de camphora, de sulphureo flammam non concipiente, and de magnesia alba compendiose paranda.[4]

TEICHMEYER

Hermann Friedrich Teichmeyer (Minden, 30 April 1685–Jena, 5 February 1744), professor of experimental physics (1717), lecturer in chemistry (1720–1743), and professor of botany, surgery, and anatomy (1727) in Jena, published books[5] and a number of dissertations (all published in Jena): de arcano tartari vel sale essentiali vini (1730, giving an improved preparation of potassium acetate), de sale de Seignetta (1742; German tr. by Burghardt, Breslau,

[1] Gmelin, (1), ii, 213.   [2] Thorndike, viii, 232–48.

[3] Thorndike, viii, 252–61: 'whether legs and arms still continue to stand out of the ground on Good Friday', the 'confirmation' by Dr. Stubbes that lice dropped off sailors as they crossed a certain latitude, and returned when they recrossed it on the voyage home, etc.

[4] Chemnitius, *op. cit.*, 15.

[5] *Elementa Philosophiæ Naturalis Experimentalis*, 4°, Jena, 1717, and *Institutiones Chemiæ Dogmaticæ et Experimentalis, in usum Auditorii sui*, 4°, Jena, 1729, 2 ed. 1752; Gmelin (1), ii, 362, 683, 697, 736; Poggendorff, (1), ii, 1075; Kopp, (1), iv, 156, 178; Chemnitius, 17, 80 (portr.).

1749), de spiritibus acidis (1720), de anodynis quibusdam spiritibus mineralibus (1731), de tincturis (1734), de corporum solutione (1717), de affectione ex musto fermentante (1729), and de antimonio ejusque regulis (1733).

Teichmeyer claimed to have described cobalt sympathetic ink in his lectures before 1731, i.e. before Hellot's description of it in 1737 (Vol. III).[1] Beckmann[2] pointed out that Pott in his dissertation on bismuth[3] had said it had already been published in 1705 by an author who, he believed, was a woman, whose works were signed only with the initials D.J.W. Wiegleb[4] says the author was D.[Dr.?] Jacob Waitz, in *Schlüssel zu dem Cabinet der geheimen Schatzkammer der Natur*, etc., 1705, and (as he could not see this first edition) he gives a reference to the second.[5] Ferguson[6] says the work (he gives both editions) is by Dorothea Juliana Walchin, but adds: 'Of the author, whether male or female, I have found no notice.'

KÖNIG

Emanuel König (Basel; 1 November 1658–30 July 1731), who travelled in France and Italy and was professor of physics and (1731) of theoretical medicine in Basel, presented as his dissertation for the Basel doctorate a work on the animal kingdom,[7] short but meaty, showing wide reading of books and publications of learned societies. He was a member of the Academia Naturæ Curiosorum, taking the name of Avicenna. He published treatises on the vegetable[8] and the mineral kingdoms[9] of similar character (see p. 713). The *Regnum Minerale* contains a good deal of chemical information and makes free use of symbols, an explanatory plate of which is given; it quotes Agricola. The works on animals and minerals refer frequently and favourably to Mayow (see p. 616). Appended to the *Regnum Vegetabile* is a pharmacopœia.[10]

The *Regnum Vegetabile* has chapters on medicine and astrology, signatures, magnetism, transplanting diseases, and incantations.[11] The *Regnum Animale* has chapters on the sensitive soul (3, 9), the secretion of spirits (7), the rational soul (12), the spirits as causes of actions (14), humours (15), respiration (20), the nervous juice (22), and the secretion and distribution of spirits (23). It frequently mentions Mayow (pref. 4v, 19, 25, 31, 47, 68, 72, 75, 85, 98). The *Regnum Minerale* deals with metals and mentions Willis's preparation of iron (p. 37, see p. 310).

Johann Jacob Wepfer (Schaffhausen; 23 December 1620–28 January 1695), who belonged to a gifted Basel family, became a doctor there in 1647, then (1675) physician

---

[1] Teichmeyer, *Commercium Litterarium ad rei medicæ et scientiæ ... Norimbergense*, Nürnberg, 1737, xii, 91 (BM 431. c. 4–11).
[2] (1), 1846, i, 109.
[3] Pott, *Dissertations Chymiques*, Paris, 1759, iii, 328.   [4] (2), 1790, I, i, 127.
    Frankfurt and Leipzig, 1722, 186, 188, 190.   [6] ii, 523, 525.
[7] *Regnum Animale*, 4°, Basel (Coloniæ Munationæ), 1682, 1708.
[8] *Regnum Vegetabile*, 4°, Basel, 1688, 1696, 1708.
[9] *Regnum Minerale*, 4°, Basel, 1686 (193 pp.), 1708.
[10] *Pharmaciæ Ludovicianæ* (sep. t.p., 166 pp.).
[11] Thorndike, vii, 266; viii, 43, 79, 426; L. in NBG, 1859, xxviii, 7.

to the Duke of Würtemburg, later to the Margrave of Baden and to the Kürfürst of Pfalz and was the author of several medical and botanical works. He obtained ammonia by distilling putrefied wine yeast.[1]

Matthias Tiling (Tilingius), professor of medicine at Rinteln and physician to the Landgrave of Hesse-Cassel, wrote on botany, medicine, and fermentation,[2] and a large Iatrochemical work[3] containing a brief introduction to chemistry and dealing with universal medicines or panaceas (including the philosophers' stone and potable gold), but mostly with remedies such as spirits of human brain and after-birth, goose-dung, and salt of toads and frogs. Tiling also wrote on mineral cinnabar,[4] and rhubarb.[5]

CRAMER

Caspar Cramer (Bautzen, Lausitz, 1648–Erfurt, 8 August 1682), professor of medicine in Erfurt, believed in alchemy.[6] His lectures, showing an acquaintance with many authors, were published in 1688:

Collegium Chymicum . . . Studiosæ Juventuti olim propositum. Jam verò Quinque Dissertationibus editum . . . a Justo Vesti . . . Cuius etiam accessit Observationum Medicarum rariorum decas prima, 4°, Frankfurt and Leipzig (printed in Erfurt), pref. dated Nov. 1688, 144 pp.; the BM Catalogue dates it 1688; Demachy, in Pott, Dissertations Chymiques, Paris, 1759, iv, 455, dates it 1689; Thorndike, viii, 165 (1688).

by Justus Vesti (Hildesheim, 1651–2—Erfurt, 27 May 1715), who wrote an immense number of medical and pharmaceutical works.[7]

Cramer's book deals with fermentation, chemical and spagirical principles and chemical operations (distillation, digestion, sublimation, calcination, liquefaction, solution, and precipitation). He says metals increase in weight on calcination by taking up fire (ex $\triangle$e ingrediuntur qvam ingressa sunt) (p. 73) and rejects the alkahest (p. 106).

Cramer thought fermentation is due to the inflow of an ethereal spirit related to primitive light, which concurs with implanted spirit of the same essence but already combined with matter, which some call nature, Archeus, or star. From their concurrence, universal ferments are formed in water or air, from which all particular ones depend and a basic salt of nature is produced. But specific forms are implanted by light from the stars. Air is only a rarefied form of water. Of the three principles, mercury is Cramer's spirit, salt is his earth, but not common earth; sulphur is not accepted as a comparable principle. Fire is dispersed light and when light is collected by a burning-glass it forms fire. The fiery ferment can invade all three kingdoms but in vegetables there is another kind, vinous fermentation, and in animals putrefactive fermentation. The acid in vegetables is fixed by the ethereal spirit into oil, and

[1] Jöcher, iv, 1892; Gmelin, (1), ii, 133, 215; Wepfer, *Cicutæ Aqvaticæ Historia et Noxæ Commentario illustrata*, 4°, Basel, 1679, 73 f. (on ferments), 151 (Archeus), 289 f. (arsenic).
[2] *Disquisitio physico-medica de fermentatione, sive de motu intestine particularum in quovis corpore . . .* , 12°, Bremen, 1674 (BM 1035. a. 20.).
[3] *Prodromus Praxeos Chimiatricæ . . . mysteriorum . . . secretissimorum*, 8°, Rinteln, 1674 (BM 1034. b. 16; 1004 pp.); Gmelin, (1), ii, 209, 220, 246, 257; Thorndike, viii, 373.
[4] *Cinnabaris Mineralis sive Minii naturalis scrutinium*, 8°, Frankfurt, 1681 (BM 957. m. 32).
[5] *Rhabarbalogia seu Curiosa Rharbari disquisitio . . .* , 4°, Frankfurt, 1679.
[6] *Dissertatio de transmutatione metallorum* resp. J. C. Calckhoff, 4°, Erfurt, 1675.
[7] Jöcher, iv, 1556; Gmelin, (1), ii, 354, q. *De præstantia medicamentorum simplicium et Galenicorum præ Chymicis*, 4°, Erfurt, 1713.

attenuated into ardent spirit. If there is no acid the ether is lost and putridity results, any oil remaining becoming alkali. Tachenius's views of acid and alkali are contested.

Friedrich Hoffmann (or Hofmann) senr., M.D., d. 1675, was physician to the Administrator of Magdeburg and a physician in Halle. He wrote several medical works[1] and edited and annotated the Pharmacopœia of the Frankfurt physician Johann Christian Schröder (Salzuffeln, Westphalia, 1600–Frankfurt a/M, 30 January 1664).[2] Hoffmann also wrote a 'key' to Schröder's work.[3]

Thomas Reinesius (Gotha, 13 December 1587–Leipzig, 13 or 14 February 1667), who studied in Wittenberg, Jena, Frankfurt a.O., and Padua, graduated at Basel, practised medicine there and in Nürnberg (1615), Hof (1616), Reuss (Gera) near Altenburg (1618), and Altenburg from 1628, where he was Physikus, Saxon Leibmedicus, and finally Burgomaster. For some reason he resigned in 1661 and went to Leipzig, where he had no post, devoting himself to study. He was the most learned man in Germany, receiving a pension from Louis XIV of France; his knowledge of languages and antiquities was profound. He made a study of the Greek chemical authors (Vol. I). His small work on chemistry:

Chemiatria, Hoc est, Medicina nobili et necessaria sui parte, Chemia, instrvcta et exornata, 4°, Geræ Ruthenicæ [Reuss], 1624 (96 pp., printed on very bad paper); 4°, Jena, 1678 (Chimiatria . . . Chimia . . . ; 56 pp.).

mentions Libavius, Dorn, Sala, Croll, etc. (p. 45), but Paracelsus only in passing (p. 89 f.). The book is a plea for the use of chemical remedies but is of little chemical interest.[4]

[1] Opus de Methodo Medendi . . . Dogmatibus Paracelsicis Helmontianis principiis et propriis Observationibus illustratum, 4°, Leipzig, 1668; others in Jöcher, ii, 1655; Dissertationum Physico-Medicarum Selectiorum decas, 8°, Leyden, 1713 (pp. 416 and part X pp. a 46; Jöcher calls it Disputationes . . . and dates it 1708).
[2] Pharmacopoea Medico-Chymica, 4°, Ulm, 1641, 1644, 1649, 1655; revised, 1662, 1667, 1669, 1681, 1685 (ed. Horst and Witzel), 1705 (Poggendorff gives Cologne, 1687, 1746, 1748; Thorndike, Frankfurt 1669, 1679; Leyden 1672 (ed. Horst and Wizel (sic)); German tr. by Johann Ulrich Müller of Nürnberg: D. Johann Schröders vollstandige und nutz-reicher Apothecke oder: Artzney-Schatz. Nebst D. Friedrich Hoffmanns darüber verfassten herrlichen Anmerckungen, Zweyten Edition. Franckfurt und Leipzig, Bey Johann Hoffmanns und Engelbert Streckseel, 1709, 4°, pp. 1324, 120, index. Also ed. Koschwitz, of Stolp, Frankfurt and Leipzig, 1718, etc.; see Schelenz, 1904, 210, 495; Poggendorff, (1), ii, 843 (neither mentioning the 1709 ed., the only one I have seen); Thorndike, viii, 88–92. It has chapters entitled 'De colligendi tempore secundum constitutionem' and 'De colligendi tempore secundum influentias particulares', with diagrams, dealing with pharmaceutical astrology, a knowledge of which was necessary at the time, and associates green colour with the moon.
[3] Clavis Pharmacevtica Schroederiana, seu Animadversiones cum Annotationibus in Pharmacopoeiam Schröderianam, Baconianis, Cartesianis, & Helmontianis Principiis illustratae & Johannis Michaelis & aliorum . . . concinnatae . . . cum Thesauro Pharmaceutico . . . , 4°, Halle, 1675, 1681, 1687; Gmelin, i, 666.
[4] Morhof, (1), 1732, i, 101, 284, 753, 771, 794, 919, 925; ii, 184, 253, 419; Jöcher, iii, 1989; Kopp, (2), ii, 245; Ferguson, ii, 250.

CHAPTER IX

INVENTORS AND THEORISTS

DREBBEL

Cornelius Jacobszoon Drebbel (Alkmaar, 1572–London, 1633), born in Holland of a good family, came to England in 1604–5 and was received by James I, who gave him lodgings in Eltham Palace. In 1610 the Emperor Rudolph II entreated James I to allow Drebbel to go to Prague; after the Emperor's death in 1612 Drebbel returned to England in 1613, but he went back to Prague and was appointed tutor to the son of the Emperor Ferdinand II. When Prague was captured by the Elector Frederick V in 1620, Drebbel lost all his possessions and was imprisoned, but he was freed on the intercession of James I and returned to England. He was sent out to La Rochelle with the Duke of Buckingham for military service. Before his death he seems to have been in poor circumstances and from 1629 to 1633 he kept an alehouse below London Bridge.[1]

Drebbel was a fertile inventor. Although considered by some as a mere charlatan, he was highly thought of by Boyle and others, but mostly by repute. Besides a machine for perpetual motion (on which he wrote to King James I)[2] and all kinds of other inventions mentioned by Monconys, he is credited with an incubator, microscope, telescope, pump, clock, and thermometer, but he probably only introduced these into England. He also invented machines for producing rain, lightning, thunder and extreme cold — the last experiment being performed before the King in Westminster Hall, when the audience was hastily driven from the building. He invented a submarine (submerged tank) which he navigated from Westminster to Greenwich.

The idea of the submarine is an old one; Alexander Neckam (1157–1217)[3] attributes its invention, as a glass vessel, to Alexander the Great and Roger Bacon (1214–92) also tells of Alexander descending to learn the secrets of the deep,[4] but these seem to have been diving bells rather than moving vessels.

[1] *Jovrnal des Voyages de Monsievr de Monconys*, Lyons, 1666, Pt. II, 33, 40–1; Pepys, *Diary* (14 March 1661, 11 November 1663), ed. Braybrook, 1848, i, 334; ii, 241; Jöcher, ii, 212 (says d. 1634); Hoefer, (1), ii, 128; Dawson Turner, *Descriptive Index of the contents of five Manuscript Volumes illustrative of the History of Great Britain*, Great Yarmouth (privately printed), 1851, 155 (letter to King James I, n.d., proposals for working a silver mine); Cust, DNB, 1888, xvi, 13; F. M. Jaeger, *Cornelis Drebbel en zijne Tijdgenooten*, Groningen, 1922 (138 pp., portr., list of works); Gerrit Tierie, *Cornelius Drebbel (1572–1633)*, Amsterdam, 1932 (124 pp.); *Chem. Age*, 1932, xxvii, 602; Van Deventer, *Chem. Weekbl.*, 1924, xxi, 405; Romocki, *Geschichte der Explosivstoffe*, Berlin, 1895, i, 364–76; Gibbs, *Ann. Sci.*, 1948, vi, 32 (anticipated by Jaeger, 1922, 85, 135 f.); Thorndike, vii, 492; an Oxford MS. q. by Jaeger, 1922, 107, says Drebbel's real name was Drummel.

[2] Thomas Tymme, *A Dialogve Philosophicall*, London, 1612, 60, and figure; 'Cornelius Dezaleel'.

[3] *De naturis rerum*, ii, 21.

[4] *Epistola de secretis operibus*, c. 4; Brewer, *R. Bacon Opera Inedita*, 1859, 533, on the authority of Ethicus; Thorndike, ii, 263, 654.

Boyle in 1661 reported that he was told 'that Drebbel conceived, that it is not the whole body of the air, but a certain quintessence (as Chymists speak) or spirituous part of it, that makes it fit for respiration; which being spent, the remaining grosser body, or carcase, if I may so call it, of the air, is unable to cherish the vital flame residing in the heart . . . he would, by unstopping a vessel full of this liquor [a chemical of his invention], speedily restore to the troubled air such a proportion of vital parts, as would make it again, for a good while, fit for respiration.'[1] This was probably a concentrated solution of caustic alkali to remove carbon dioxide, if the story is true. Thorndike calls Drebbel 'the most pretentious, secretive and magical figure in the scientific and technical world of the early seventeenth century'; he says Drebbel could not write either in English or Latin and composed his letter to James I and his brief tracts in Dutch.

1. Ein kurzer Tractat von der Natur Der Elementen und wie sie den Windt, Regen, Blitz vnd Donner vervrsachen, vnd vvar sie nutzen. durch Cornelium Drebbel in Niederlandisch geschrieben, unnd allen der Natur-liebhaben zu nutz in Hochteutsch getreulich vber gesetzt. Gedruckt zu Leyden in Holland, Bey Henrichen van Haestens im jahr Christ 1608 (BM 1033. c. 2. (3.); sm. 8°, 15 ll. unpaged; portr.); a Dutch ed. of 1604, with portr., mentioned by Burckhardt[2] as actually seen by him, was not traced by Jaeger, *op. cit.*, 5, or Tierie, and is doubtful.

2. Een Kort Tractaet van de Natvere der Elementen, ende hoe sy veroorsaecken, den vvint, reghen, Blixem, Donder, ende Waernomme dienstlich zijn. Gedaen door Cornelis Drebbel, sm. 8°, Haerlem, 1621 (64 pp. portr. on t.p., BM 1136. c. 3. (1.)).

3. With the same title as (2) pp. 57–109 of: Openbaringhe der verborgener Handtgrepen Frat. Basilij Valentini . . . Daer by gebroecht is een Tractaet vande Natuere der vier Elementen Door Cornelis Drebbel, sm. 8°, Rotterdam, 1632, BM 1136. c. 3. (1.).

4. Cornelii Drebbel . . . de Quinta Essentia Tractatus, editus cura Joach. Morsii. Accedit ejusdem Epistola ad . . . Britanniae Monarchum Jacobum de Perpetui Mobilis inventione, 8°, Hamburg (?), 1621, BM 1033. d. 16. (8.); printed from a MS. brought from England by the theologian Joachim Morsius (Hamburg, 3 January 1593–?, after 1643), who travelled all over Europe, M.A. Oxford (where he studied chemistry).[3]

5. No. (4) reprinted with Latin tr. of (1) and letter to James I as: Tractatus duo: prior de Natura Elementorum . . . posterior de Quinta Essentia . . . ed J. Morsii. Accedit Epistola . . . de Perpetui Mobilis Inventione, 8°, Hamburg, 1621 (BM 1033. d. 16. (7.)); tr. J. E. Burggraf, 8°, Frankfurt, 1628 (BM 1033. d. 16. (6.)); Lyon, 1628 (BM 1036. a. 1. (3.)).[4]

6. Tractatus von Natur der Elementen (with works of Basil Valentine), Erfurt, Verlag J. Birckner, 1624, 71 (BM 1033. f. 41; 8630. bbb. 2).

7. Ein kurtzer Tractat von der Natur der Elementen / vnd wie sie den Wind / Regen / Blitz vnnd Donner vervrsachen / &c. Durch Cornelium Drebbel in Nider Teutsch geschrieben / vnd allen . . . in Hoch Teutsch . . . vbergesetzt durch Johann Ernst Burggraffen, Frankfurt, Caspar Rötell, 16°, 1628 (not seen).

8. Grondige Oplossinge van de Natuur en Eygenschappen der Elementen, en hoe sy veroorzaaken Donder, Blixem, Hitte, Koude, Wind, Regen, Hagel, Sneeuw, &c. En waar toe sy dienstig zyn. Als mede en klare Beschryving van de Quinta Essentia, noyt voor desen gedrukt. Noch een Dedicatie van't Primum Mobile, 18°, Amsterdam, Jan Graaf, 1709 (not seen). Thorndike mentions 'a late edition of the three tracts at Rotterdam in 1702'.

9. Tractat . . . von Natur und Eigenschaften der Elementen. Nebst einer Anhang

---

[1] Boyle, *New Experiments . . . touching the Spring of the Air*, 1661; *Works*, ed. Birch, 1744, i, 69; *Usefulness of Experimental Natural Philosophy, ib.*, iii, 174; Edmund Dickinson, *Physica vetus et vera sive Tractatus de Naturali Veritate Hexaëmeri Mosaici*, 4°, London, 1702, 327; Tierie, 59 f.; Jaeger, 71 f.; Francis Bacon had heard of the submarine: *Novum Organum*, II, l; *Works*, ed. Spedding, 1901, iv, 234.

[2] *Ann. Phys.*, 1868, cxxxiii, 680.

[3] Jöcher, iii, 690, with list of works.   [4] Geneva 1628 (not seen).

von der Quintessenz und einer Zueignungs Schrift von Primo Mobili. Wie auch . . . Erzehlungen von denen Winden, Leipzig, 1723 (Pat. Off. BA 90* (28700); BM 8630. bbb. 12. (2.)).

10. Deux Traitez Philosophiqves de Corneille Drebbel. I. De la Nature des Elemens. II. De la Quinte-Essence. Nouvellement traduit en François par un Docteur en Medicine; in Divers Traitez de la Philosophie Naturelle, Paris, 1672, 175–273 (Ferguson, i, 216; my copy has no t.p.; Thorndike dates it 1673).

Drebbel's *Short Tract on the Nature of the Elements* shows[1] a retort filled with air hanging over a charcoal brazier, with the neck dipping in a dish of water, through which bubbles of air escape, and it is said that the water is drawn back into the retort on removing the fire. In another part of the book[2] it is said that: 'saltpetre is broken by the power of the fire, and so changed into the nature of air' (wan der Salpeter gebrochen wirde durch das Feuwer, vnnd also verandert in die Natur des Lüffts, 1608 ed.; soo het lichaem des Salpeters gebroken ende ontbonden wordt, door die kracht des vyers, 1621 ed). Tierie[3] joined the drawing and the statement together (although they are separated in the book), and concluded that Drebbel discovered oxygen by heating saltpetre in a retort. This is quite unjustified, as Jaeger had already stated.[4] Tierie[5] thinks Flud[6] had Drebbel in mind when he said: 'Some fraudulent persons maintain that they have extracted a fluid or spirit, hereby arousing still greater admiration.'

Drebbel's main idea was that the elements can be transmuted into one another. The sun's rays turn air into fire and water into air, but in the cold upper atmosphere air condenses to water. Air expands in boiling water but condenses again when the kettle is taken off the fire. Fire is subtle air, air is subtle water, water is subtle earth, earth is crass fire. Earth is of a less simple nature than the other three elements and is impure, being as it were an excrement of them. There are speculations on the origin of winds, thunder and lightning (a cloud by the action of hot dry air is suddenly converted into air, with expansion 600-fold), etc. Earth by the force of fire or the innate efficacy of nature is transformed into water and is made salt; salt dissolved by fire is transformed into water. These specimens are sufficient to indicate the profundity of Drebbel's theories. He was evidently a good practical workman; he had charge of the fireships and water petards in the expedition to La Rochelle (1627), and was one of a company formed to drain the fens in eastern England.[7] Like his kind, he tried to impress wealthy men by vague hints of wonderful inventions and became even more attractive by his secrecy and obscurity. His foreign origin also helped him in England.

Drebbel is said to have introduced into England the manufacture of sulphuric acid by burning sulphur with saltpetre afterwards patented by Dr. Joshua Ward.[8] Romocki thinks Drebbel may have discovered mercury and

---

[1] Chapt. iv; (1), 1608, fol. a₈ v; (2), 1621, 24; Hoefer, (1), ii, 128; the figure is slightly different in the different editions.

[2] Chapt. vii; (1), 1608, fol. B iii; (2), 1621, 32.   [3] 1932, 65, 114.

[4] 1922, 78 f., 84: De ontdekking van de zuurstof door Drebbel behoort volkmaakt thuis in het land der fabelen.

[5] 1932, 59 f.   [6] *Philosophia Moysaica*, f°, Goude, 1638, lib. i, f. 3.   [7] Thorndike, vii, 497.

[8] Ephraim Reinbold Seehl, *A New Improvement on the Art of Making the True Volatile Spirit of Sulphur*, 8°, London, 1744; Dossie, *The Elaboratory laid open, or, the Secrets of*

silver fulminates, since (4) speaks of dissolving 'metallum aut minerale tuum' in distilled vinegar (which Romocki thinks meant dissolving mercury or silver in aqua fortis), crystallising and drying, and digesting the solid with rectified spirit: et erit tibi Quinta Essentia metallorum et mineralium, valens adversus quodcumque vitium. There is, however, no mention of an explosive product, and Jaeger[1] does not think one was meant.

Drebbel's most useful discovery (Kopp says about 1630) was that of a tin mordant for dyeing scarlet with cochineal, which he communicated to his son-in-law, Dr. Abraham Kuffeler, a dyer in Bow (or the Minories), London. The colour was known as *color Kufflerianus* and was afterwards made known by Gülich and van der Vecht to the brothers Gobelin in Paris.[2] Kuffeler is also (incorrectly) called Kieffer, etc., etc.[3] He left a large manuscript of over 700 pages[4] which contains no mention of the use of the *tin* mordant for dyeing scarlet but describes a furnace with thermostatic control. Others say the process was invented by an otherwise unknown Dutchman, Niklas Drebbel.[5] De Francheville says a Flemish painter, Peter Koeck, travelled in Turkey and brought back to Flanders a knowledge of dyeing wool and silk; he died in 1550. Hoefer,[6] who calls him Kloeck, made him a discoverer of the scarlet dye, but this may have been the Turkey red madder and not cochineal. Borrichius[7] says of Drebbel's weather-glass or thermoscope and his scarlet dye (coloris ignei, Scarletto Italis dicti) 'common artificers imitate both with equal success'.

Boyle in 1664[8] says it is essential in dyeing scarlet with 'the Bow-dye' that 'the vessels, that immediately contain the tinging ingredients, are to be made of or to be lined with tin', and also[9] that the 'true scarlet dye' was invented by Cornelius Drebbel, . . . 'a mechanician, and a chemist, not a dyer', who discovered the process from a hint given him by some merchants about a process 'a while before casually lighted on in Holland'. The 'Bow-scarlet' is mentioned in an interesting 'Apparatus to the History of the Common Practices of Dying [*sic*]' drawn up by Sir William Petty.[10]

FLUD

Robert Flud or Fludd (de Fluctibus) (Milgate House, Bearsted, Kent, 1574–London, 8 September 1637), of Welsh descent (Lloyd), studied in St. John's College, Oxford, from 1592, B.A. 1596, M.A. 1598, then travelled on the Conti-

Modern Chemistry and Pharmacy Revealed, London, 1758, 44, 158 f.; 162; Kopp, (1), iii, 305; the process is described by Lemery (see Vol. III).

[1] 1922, 77.

[2] Sprat, *History of the Royal Society*, 4°, 1667, 391; De Francheville, *Hist. Acad. Berlin*, 1767 (1769), 41–128 (67); F. Hoffmann, pref. to *Observationum physico-chymicarum selectiorum*, 4°, Halle, 1722; Wiegleb, (1), 1792, 179; Beckmann, (1), i, 402; C. A. Browne, *Isis*, 1935, xxiii, 415.

[3] Tierie, 1932, 76 f.; Jaeger, 1922, 88 f., 93, etc.; Kopp, (1), iv, 131, 398.

[4] Cambridge U.L. 2206, L. l. V. 8; dated 1666, and by Kuffeler 1690; I checked the extracts in Jaeger, 1922, 85, 135 f., with the MS.

[5] Poggendorff, (1), i, 602.   [6] (1), ii, 102.

[7] *De Ortu et Progressu Chemiæ*, Copenhagen, 1668, 10.

[8] *On Colours*; *Works* ed. Birch, 1744, ii, 76, 80.

[9] *Usefulness of Natural Philosophy*, 1671; *Works* ed. Birch, 1744, iii, 174.

[10] Sprat, *History of the Royal Society*, 1667, 284.

nent, where he learnt medicine. He returned to Oxford to graduate in medicine (M.B. and M.D.) in 1605, when he became a member of Christ Church, Oxford, and in 1609 he became a Fellow of the Royal College of Physicians.[1]

Flud was a remarkable figure; with undoubted scientific ability he combined belief in alchemy, astrology, occult medicine, and ideas borrowed from Neoplatonism, the Jewish *Qabbalah*, and Paracelsus. Much more learned than Paracelsus but less scientific than Van Helmont, he belonged to their circle. He was criticised by Gassendi,[2] who gave a summary of Flud's teachings.[3] Flud was also criticised by Kepler, Mersenne (who had called him in correspondence an evil and heretical magician, but seems to have got the worse out of a controversy),[4] and Libavius (p. 245). Van Helmont, who met him in England, thought Flud was a poor physician and worse alchemist, only superficially learned.[5] Flud also had a lively controversy with William Foster, a parson, on the weapon salve of Paracelsus (p. 424).[6] Flud was a Rosicrucian and defended the fraternity against attacks, e.g. by Libavius.[7] He defended geomancy.[8]

The bibliography of Flud's works is difficult, since several were published together in five or six folio volumes at Oppenheim from 1617.

I. Utriusque Cosmi Maioris scilicet et Minoris Metaphysica, Physica atqve Technica Historia . . . Avthore Roberto Flud aliàs de Fluctibus . . . f°, Oppenheim, Ære Johan-Theodori de Bry Typis Hieronymi Galleri, 1617 (206 pp., iii ll.; sep.t.p. Tractatus Secundus De Naturæ Simia seu Technica macrocosmi historia, . . . (788 pp., v ll., with sep t.ps. to tracts); Tomus Secundus, 1619.

II. Svmmvm Bonvm, quod est

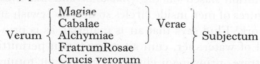

Verum { Magiae / Cabalae / Alchymiae / FratrumRosae / Crucis verorum } Verae } Subjectum

---

[1] Tennemann, 1814, ix, 216; Morhof, (1), 1714, ii, 246 (habebat ingenium phantasmatum valde); Sprengel, (1), 1815, v, 6; Hoefer, (1), ii, 177; Harcourt, *Phil. Mag.*, 1846, xxviii, 491; Anon., NBG, 1857, xviii, 15; Gordon, DNB, 1889, xix, 348–50; Anon., *Brit. Med. J.*, 1897, ii, 408 ('all his speculations are vitiated by his gross ignorance'); Gunther, (1), 1926, iii, portr. opp. p. 37; Ferguson, i, 283; Pagel, *Bull. Johns Hopkins Inst. Med. Hist.*, 1935, iii, 277; Bayon, *Ann. Sci.*, 1938, iii, 66; Josten, *Ambix*, 1949, iii, 91; Kiesewetter, (1), 230 f., 252 (list of works); F. Freudenberg, *Paracelsus und Fludd, Die beiden grossen Okkultisten und Ärzte des 15 und 16 Jahrhunderts, mit einer Auswahl aus ihren Okkulten Schriften*, Berlin, 1918 (vol. xvii of *Geheime Wissenschaften* series — slight); Thorndike, vii, 98, 439, 497, and index, viii, 695.

[2] *Petri Gassendi Theologi Epistolica Exercitatio. In qua Principia Philosophiæ Roberti Fluddi Medici reteguntur*, Paris, 1630; in *Opera Omnia*, Lyons, 1658, iv, 21.

[3] *Opera*, 1658, iii, 221–8; Thorndike, vii, 441–2.   [4] Thorndike, vii, 439 f.

[5] *Correspondance de Mersenne*, ed. Tannery and de Waard, 1936, ii, 584 (fluctuantem Fluddum).

[6] William Foster, parson of Hedgerley, Bucks., *Hoplo crismaspongvs: or a Sponge to wipe away the Weapon-Salve. A treatise wherin is proved that the cure late taken up amongst us, by applying the salve to the weapon, is magicall and unlawful*, 4°, London, 1631 (56 pp.) (CUL Dd*. 4. 6⁶ (E)); *Dr Fludds answer to M. Foster, or, the squeezing of Parson Fosters Sponge, ordained by him for the wiping away of the Weapon-Salve*, 4°, London, 1631 (CUL Syn. 7. 63. 88); Latin in Flud's *Philosophia Moysaica*, Gouda, 1638: *Responsum ad Hoplocrisma-Spongum M. Fosteri . . . ab ipso ad unguenti armarii validitatem delendam ordinatum. hoc est Spongiae M. Fosteri expressio seu elisio*; Rodwell, *Chem. News*, 1870, xxi, 136.

[7] Flud, *Apologia Compendiaria, Fraternitatem de Rosea Cruce . . .*, Leyden, 1616; *Tractatvs Apologeticvs, integritatem Societatis de Rosea Crvce defendens. In qua probatur contra D. Libavii et aliorum ejusdem farinæ columnias*, sm. 8°, Leyden, 1617; Waite, *The Real History of the Rosicrucians*, 1887, 301; id., *The Brotherhood of the Rosy Cross*, 1924, 271–309.

[8] *De Animæ Intellectualis Scientia seu Geomantia Hominibus . . .*, 8°, Verona (Heidelberg ?), 1687; BM 1141. a. 16.

f°, Frankfurt, 1629, with design of a rose and bees and the motto: dat rosa mel apibus.

III. Medicina Catholica seu Mysticvm Artis Medicandi Sacrarivm, f°, Frankfurt, 1629.

IV. Sophiæ cvm Moria Certamen in quo Lapis Lydivs a falso Strvctore Fr. Marino Mersenno . . . accurate examinat, f°, Frankfurt, 1629.

V. Clavis Philosophiæ et Alchymiæ Flvddanae . . . , f°, Frankfurt, 1633.

VI. Philosophia Moysaica Avthore Rob. Flvd, alias de Flvctibvs, f°, Gouda, 1638 (an English tr. by Flud himself is said to have been printed in 1659).

An alchemical *Truth's Golden Harrow*, in an Oxford MS. (Ashmole 766) described by Josten, is apparently a criticism of a *Tillage of Light* by Patrick Scot (1623), and says that alchemy is an allegory expressing, in incomprehensible terms, the process of obtaining and perfecting wisdom.

Flud's obscure philosophy assumed that the primordial chaos was a *nihilum*, first matter, or Ens, the *mysterium magnum* of the Paracelsists. A *potentia divina* as light is the *actus divinus*; it was informed by the Maker of the world with a universal essence, the 'light' of Moses, first evolved in the highest region of the world, a region of form and immaterial. There is a second spiritual heaven, the *sphæra æqualitatis*, corporeal in respect of the other and the abode of the four elements. Earth is a conglomeration of material darkness and the refuse of the heavens; water is the most gross spirit of the darkness of the inferior heaven, nearly devoid of light; air is the spirit of the second heaven; fire is the spirit of the darkness of the empyrean heaven. The universe was formed after the pattern of an archetypal world existing in the Divine ideality, which was made by emanation and regression. Flud also had a system of spiritual evolution based on the *Qabbalah* and his works are full of the cross-shaped figures of men inside circles so dear to Jewish authors.

In the first work[1] Flud says that air is material, as is proved by inverting a glass in a vessel of water: aër, cum sit corpus, non permittit aliud corpus in suum locum intrare, priusquàm ejus pars aliqua aut totum à praedicto loco recedat. By burning a candle under a globe inverted over water he concluded that air nourishes fire and in the nourishing is consumed, the water, which is the third element, takes the place of the air consumed, a vacuum not being admitted:[2]

In secunda demonstratione candela infundo vasis alicujus aqua repleti affigitur, cujus flamma per orificium phialæ ingrediens depresso ejus orificio ad angulos rectos cum candela in vasis aqua sursum attrahet tantam aquæ proportionem, quantam aëris in phiala inclusi consumpserit: Aër enim nutrit ignem, & nutriendo consumitur, ac ne vacuum admittatur, aqua, quæ est tertium elementum, locum possidet aëris comesti.

These experiments come from works by Philo of Byzantium and Heron of Alexandria (Vol. I).

Flud mentions the deflagration produced when powdered sulphur is thrown on fused nitre,[3] also an empty eggshell filled with a mixture of equal parts of nitre, sulphur and quicklime, and the orifices stopped with wax, which emits flames when thrown into water;[4] and a stone composed of a mixture of 1 lb. of *calamitha*, 4 oz. of asphalt (*aspalthae*), 4 oz. of nitre (*salis nitri*), 3 oz. of

[1] (I), Tract. II, lib. iii, pt. 7, p. 469.　　[2] *Ib.*, p. 471, Fig. 2.
[3] (I), Tract. I, lib. vii, ch. 6, Experimentum I, p. 193 and fig.
[4] *Ib.*, Experimentum II, p. 194 and fig.

sulphur, and 6 oz. of liquid varnish, made into a paste and formed into a cake (*panis*) which is coated with quicklime, kept in a box, and dried by heating for 9 days and nights: when spat upon the stone inflames.[1]

The substance of saltpetre is nothing but air congealed by cold, which air breaks out when saltpetre deflagrates with sulphur: Salis Petræ substantiam nihil aliud esse, quàm aërem frigore congelatum, cui, si accedat sulphuris aliqua portio, licèt exigua admodùm, strepitum ingentem edit, fulguraque artificialia emittit.[2] Heat is different from light:[3] Hic autem calor, licèt naturaliter huic parti insit, attamen, quia non est de vera lucis essentia, sed quasi ultimus ejus actionis effectus, immediatè à materiæ motu profluentis, ideò ad vitæ functionem nihil facit.

In his *Philosophia Moysaica*[4] he describes a thermometer from a source which he says is 500 years old, but this is probably said with the object of removing the priority of Drebbel (see p. 323), who is mentioned in the book for a perpetual motion apparatus.

Another Oxford Rosicrucian was William Backhouse (1593–1662), who adopted Elias Ashmole (1617–92) and taught him the 'secret'.[5]

DICKINSON

Edmund Dickinson (Appleton, Berks., 26 September 1624–London, 3 April 1707), B.A. Oxford 1647, M.D. 1656, Fellow of St. John's College and later of Merton College, Oxford, practised medicine in Oxford and from 1684 in London, and was physician to Charles II and James II.[6] Charles II is said to have watched Dickinson's experiments in a laboratory fitted up for him in St. James's Palace. Hanckewitz[7] says Dickinson 'toiled and laboured many years in experiments on the stercus humanum; and has several times with the greatest pleasure showed me metallic reguluses, he had extracted from it . . . and no wonder . . . for we take in daily with our food . . . metallic substances, besides what metallic vessels, kettles, pots and dishes furnish.' Dickinson claimed to have learned the secret of the philosophers' stone from Mundanus, a French alchemist, whom he got to know about 1656.[8]

Evelyn in June 1705 had a long conversation with Dickinson on the 'Philosopher's Elixir, which he believeth attainable, and hath seen projected himselfe by one who went under the name of Mundanus, who sometimes came among the adepts, but was unknown as to his country or abode'. [This is

[1] *Ib.*, p. 195 and fig.; ch. vii, p. 197; this is old material, Partington, (4).
[2] *Ib.*, 193.   [3] *Ib.*, Tract. I, ch. xi, p. 63.   [4] VI, lib. i, f. 3.
[5] Gunther, 1926, iii, 56; Josten, *Ambix*, 1949, vi, 1.
[6] William Nicolas Blomberg, *An Account of the Life and Writings of Edmund Dickinson, Physician in Ordinary to King Charles II and King James II*, 4°, London, 1737 (140 pp.); 2 ed., 8°, 1739, *To which is added, a Treatise on the Grecian Games, printed from the Doctor's Manuscript* (in Latin); Harrison, DNB, 1888, xv, 33; Brucker, 1766, IV, i, 617.
[7] *Phil. Trans.*, 1733, xxxviii, 58.
[8] *Edmundus Dickinson, Medicus Regius, Et Theodorus Mundanus, Philosophus Adeptus, de Quintessentia Philosophorum Et Vera Physiologia . . . Editio altera*, 8°, Rotterdam, 1699 (Duveen, 170); Ferguson, i, 210, says it was first publ. in Oxford, 1686, and gives an ed. *De Chrysopoeia sive de Quintessentia Philosophorum. Juxta exemplar Oxoniense editio hoc exemplari longè castigatior*, s.l.e.a. (? 17–   ).

incorrect, see above.] He found Dickinson 'very old and infirm, yet continuing chymistry'.[1]

Dickinson wrote a very obscure work intended to show that all science is to be found in the writings of Moses,[2] in which he has much from the Bible and Greek authors. He denied that metals grow from seeds: metalla, cùm non fiant à semine; nec in se (quicquid in contrarium dicant Hermetici) gerant semen,[3] also the spontaneous generation of animals (animalculæ can be seen in the microscope, and seeds pass into the earth, water, air, and flesh).[4] He thought that Moses dissolved the golden calf by chemical means, since he was learned in all the wisdom of the Egyptians, including physics, chemistry, and astrology: maximè cùm certum sit, Chemiam fuisse non exiguam partem istius sapientiæ, in quâ Moses educatus fuit.[5] The book is notable in defending the atomic theory (ch. II. Pro vindicanda Philosophia Corpusculari) since he thought Moschos or Mochos the Phœnician, who taught it long before the Trojan war (Vol. I), was Moses.[6]

KIRCHER

Athanasius Kircher (Geisa, nr. Fulda, 2 May 1602–Rome, 28 November 1680), a Jesuit father, professor in Würzburg and later in Rome, was the author of many large works on various subjects.[7] His collection and museum still exist in the Jesuit College in Rome.[8] Views on Kircher's merits are varied. Torrey held that he 'established no useful generalization. He made no stimulating suggestions for research. In his own time he belonged to the past'. Although Ferguson said: 'His works in number, bulk, and uselessness are not surpassed in the whole field of learning', Kircher had his good points. His vigorous criticism of alchemy at a time when men like Boyle believed in it must be put to his credit. Some of his publications are listed below:

I. Oedipvs Aegyptiacvs. Hoc est Vniuersalis Hieroglyphicæ Veterum Doctrinæ temporum iniuria abolitæ Instavratio, 3 vols., f°, Rome, 1652–3, printed partly at the expense of the Emperor Ferdinand III, which 'disappointed his contemporaries'[9] but is 'packed with learning'.[10]
II. Mundus Subterraneus In XII Libros digestus; Quo Divinum Subterrestris

[1] Diary, ed. Bray, 1870, 589.
[2] Physica Vetus & Vera: sive Tractatus de Naturali veritate hexaëmeri Mosaice, 4°, London, 1702 (engr. t.p., t.p., ii ll. dedic., ii ll. with figs. 1–2 Diacosmus Mosaicus, 340 pp., ii ll. index); Rotterdam, 1703; 12°, Leoburg, 1705.
[3] Ib., 1702, 109.   [4] Ib., 157.   [5] Ib., 316 f.   [6] Ib., 8–16.
[7] J. L. Pfaff, Vita Athenasi Kircherii, Fulda, 1831; K. Brischar, P. Athenasius Kircher. Ein Lebensbild, in J. B. Stamminger, Katholische Studien, Würzburg, 1871, iii, pt. 5 (91 pp.; dates 2.5.1601–30.10.1690); E. G. in NBG, 1858, xxvii, 769; Hoefer, (1), ii, 330; Müller, Catholic Encyclopaedia, 1910, viii, 661 (b. 2.5.1601); Stirling, Some Apostles of Physiology, 1902, 93 (portr.); Ferguson, i, 468; Torrey, Osiris, 1938, v, 246; B. Szczesniak, Osiris, 1952, x, 385 (portr.); Thorndike, vii, 566; Fasciculus Epistolarum A. Kircheri, ed. Langenmantel (with autobiogr.), 8°, Augsburg, 1684 (iv, 100 pp.; BM 1165. b. 15; BN Z. 14195); 5 ed., 1901 (not seen).
[8] G. de Sepibus, Romani Colegii Societatis Jesu Musæum celeberrimum . . . A. Kircherus . . . instruxit, f°, Amsterdam, 1678; E. de Ruggiero, Catalogo del Museo Kircheriano, vol. i, 8°, Rome, 1878.
[9] Mosheim, in Cudworth, The True Intellectual System of the Universe, tr. Harrison, 1845, i, 537.
[10] Ruska, Tabula Smaragdina, 1926, 49, 216.

Mundi Opificium, ... exponuntur, 2 vols., f°, Amsterdam, 1665, 2 ed. 1668 (re-issue of 1664 ed., with prelim. matter reprinted; cited below from 1665 i and 1668 ii); 3 ed., 1678.

III. Ars Magnesia, hoc est disquisitio ... de Naturis, Viribus, et prodigiosis effectibus Magnetis, 4°, Würzburg, 1631.

IV. Magnes Siue De Arte Magnetica, 4°, Rome, 1641; 4°, Cologne, 1643; f°, Rome, 1654 (uses the name 'electromagnetism'; 1643, p. 563).

V. Musurgia Universalis sive Ars Magna Consoni et Dissoni, 2 vols., f°, Rome, 1650 (mentioning the transmission of sound by solids).

VI. Ars Magna Lucis et Umbræ, f°, Rome, 1646; 2 ed. (enlarged), f°, Amsterdam, 1671 (observations on fluorescence).

VII. Scrvtinivm Physico-Medicvm Contagiosæ Luis, quæ Pestis dicitur, 4°, Rome, 1658; 12°, Leipzig, 1659; Frankfurt, 1663 (contagion due to microscopic organisms).

VIII. (a) Itinerarivm Exstaticvm qvo Mvndi Opficivm ... Interlocvtoribvs Cos-miele et Theodidacto ad Serenissimam Christinam ... Reginam, 4°, Rome, 1656 (iv. ll., 464 pp., xii ll.).

(b) Iter Extaticvm II. Cui & Mundi Subterranei Prodromvs dicitur. Qvo Geocosmi Opificivm sive Terrestris Globi Structura, vnà cum abditis in ea constitutis arcanoris Naturæ Reconditorijs ... In III. Dialogos dis-tinctum. Ad Serenissimvm Leopoldvm Ignativm ... Regem, 4°, Rome, 1657 (xii ll., 237 pp., vi ll.).

(c) Iter Extaticum Coeleste, Quo Mundi opificium ... Cosmiele et Theo-didacto: Hac secundâ editione Prælusionibus & Scholiis illustratum; ac schematismis necessariis ... exornatum; nec non à mendis, quæ in primam Romam editionem irrepserant, expurgatum, ... a P. Gaspare Schotto ... Accessit ejusdem Auctoris Iter Exstaticum Terrestre, & Synopsis Mundi Subterranei, 4°, Würzburg, 1660 (xii ll., 689 pp., ix ll., engr. f.p. with portrait of Kircher, arms on t.p. v, 12 pl.).

IX. Arca Noë in tres libros digesta, f°, Amsterdam, 1675.

X. Turris Babel, sive Archontologia, f°, Amsterdam, 1679.

XI. China Monumentis, qua sacris quo profanis ... illustrata, f°, Amsterdam, 1667; f°, Antwerp, 1667; Monumenta Sinica ... Planò uti A. Kircherus in China sua illus-trata, ... edidit ... A. Müllerus, 2 pts., 4°, Berlin, 1672.

XII. Physical works summarised by J. S. Kestler: Physiologia Kircheriana Ex-perimentalis ... ex vastis Operibus Adm. Rev. P. Athanasii Kircheri extraxit, et in hunc ordinem per classis redigit, f°, Amsterdam, 1680 (summarised under Physics, Mathematics, Medicine, Chemistry, Music, Magnetism, and Mechanics). The Biblio-thèque Nationale has a large collection of Kircher's works: Catal. Gén., 1924, lxxxi, 821–30.

Much of his work on the magnet is unscientific, deals with toys, retails some old superstitions, and had little scientific influence.[1] Kircher, like Boyle, was too credulous and too proud of his supposed scepticism: he says[2] he is so constituted by nature that he does not easily put faith in statements handed down by authors about the virtues of natural things and prodigies, unless convinced by his own experience and observation.

In his Oedipus Aegyptiacus (II, ii, 432) Kircher (quoting Diodoros Siculus on the gold mines) argued that Egyptian alchemy was derived from the art of extracting gold from earthy materials and not by the use of the philosophers' stone, the idea of which was then unknown. He gives (II, ii, 406–17) a good summary of the theory of alchemy, and quotes Arabic texts. His Mundus Subterraneus, largely written around his pet theory of vast underground re-servoirs of water in the earth, contains a good deal of interesting chemical

---

[1] Rosenberger, 1884, ii, 91; cf. ib., 120, where he is called a physicist of the old school, deficient in mathematics; Thorndike, vii, 269.
[2] Mundus Subterraneus, 1668, Pref. II, f. *** 1 v.

information, and illustrations of apparatus in the 'pharmaceutical' laboratory (so named to disguise its real function) in the Jesuits' College in Rome. It deals with the analysis of mineral waters by evaporation on the sand bath and heating the residue on an iron plate (i, 253), the hydrometer (i, 255), salts (i, 299), nitre beds (i, 305), the cold produced by dissolving salts in water (i, 306), the composition and explosion of gunpowder (including 'silent gunpowder') (i, 306), the manufacture of alum (i, 313 f.), the supposed transmutation of iron into copper by vitriolic waters (i, 319), coloured flames (ii, 18), asbestos paper (ii, 74), gems and their properties (ii, 78), poisons (ii, 104), metals (ii, 145), mercury mines in Carniola and Spain (ii, 152), metallurgy (ii, 162), mines in Hungary (supplementing Agricola) (ii, 183), Peru and America (ii, 208), the amalgamation process for silver (ii, 211), the separation of gold from silver by aqua fortis according to Andreas Schaffer (ii, 215), salt-making (ii, 224), general chemistry and alchemy (ii, 231), coloured indicators in testing for metals (ii, 299), recipes and accounts of transmutation (ii, 300), distillation (de arte stalactica sive distillatoria) (ii, 390), a table of the proportions of salt, sulphur, and mercury in various plants gathered at appropriate astrological times and a plate of correspondences in the microcosm and megacosm (ii, 406), the revival of plants from their ashes (ii, 414), potable gold (ii, 419) and other arcana, metal trees (ii, 431), the hydrostatic balance (ii, 439), glass, enamels, and imitation gems coloured with smalt and metallic oxides (ii, 450, quoting Baptista Porta and Cardan), the pyrotechnic or pyrabolic art (ii, 467, giving the composition of gunpowder and describing fulminating gold, fireworks, etc.), and finally (ii, 481) mechanical artifices, which include chemical (parting gold and silver, calces, artificial gold and silver).

The long section on poisons (De venenis eorumque Natura, Origine & admirandis proprietatibus, ii, 104–45, with Tabula Synoptica, 140–5) defines a poison as something non-natural (Res non naturalis). Animal, vegetable, and mineral poisons are discussed, the first two because, since they are composed of salt, sulphur, and mercury, they are ex Subterraneis originem suam primordialiter. Poisons are generated in corpses [ptomaines]. Poisons have sympathies and antipathies, and occult qualities, and may act by emanations (ἀπορρεία). Much of the text is based on Porta (see p. 16) but there are additions, such as the theory of diseases from Paracelsus, and American poisonous plants.

Kircher believed in the divining rod (i, 245; ii, 181), the theory of signatures (i, 217), the presence of demons in mines (ii, 101), barnacle geese (ii, 346), and Paracelsus's theory of diseases produced by sulphur, mercury, and salt (ii, 135), but rejected perpetual motion (ii, 233).

The most important part of the book is its criticism of alchemy (ii, 250 f., 280 f.) (Chymotechnicus),[1] in which, while not denying that alchemy is possible and may one day be achieved, he divides the alchemists into four groups. The first believe that alchemy is an impossible science (the disappointed alchemists); the second are the metallurgists; the third sell imitation gold and silver as the true metals; the fourth (the alchemists proper) pretend to

[1] In Manget, i, 54–109 (De Lapide Philosophorum Dissertatio).

make pure gold and silver by the philosopher's stone, but are swindlers (Pseudochymicos, homines ad omne fraudis genus fictos). He was told by a friend that he had turned 300 lb. of mercury into gold, but this, says Kircher, was only because the Devil wished to blind him (ii, 284; the chapter is entitled: Quod dæmon utplurimum se Alchymiæ cultoribus immisceat). Kircher's criticisms of alchemy were answered by Borrichius.[1] John Webster[2] called Kircher 'that universal Scribbler and Rhapsodist', and said his *Mundus Subterraneus* was disappointing and 'stuffed with Scandals and Lies against Paracelsus, Arnoldus, and Lully, whose Art of Transmutation . . . he laboureth to prove to be false'. Kircher's book is mentioned very unfavourably by Morhof[3] who himself wrote a defence of alchemy.[4] It was also 'answered' by professional alchemists, such as Salomon de Blawenstein (Kestler refers to 'fictitio nomine de Blauenstein') and Gabriel Clauder:

Interpellatio Brevis ad Philosophos veritatis tam Amatores, quam scrutatores pro Lapide Philosophorum contra Antichymisticum Mundum Subterraneum. P. Athanasii Kircheri Jesuitæ . . . à Salomone de Blawenstein Artis huius vero Alumno, Biennæ, 4°, 1667 (pp. 28); Duveen, 83; repr. in Manget, i, 113.

Gabriel Clauder, Dissertatio de Tinctura Universali (vulgo Lapis Philosophorum dictâ). In qua 1, Quid Hæc sit. 2, Quod detur in Rerum Natura . . . ; 3, è qva Materia; & 5, quo modo præparetur . . . , 4°, Altenburg, 1678 (272 pp.); in Manget, i, 119 (Tractatus de Tinctura Universali, ubi in specie contra R.P. Athanas. Kircker. pro existentia Lapidis Philosophici disputatur); repr. as Schediasma de Tinctura Universali, vulgo . . . etc., 4°, Nürnburg, 1736 (Sotheran *Cat.* 800 (1926) No. 10486); German as Dissertation von der Universal-Tinctur oder dem Stein der Weisen, Nürnburg, 1682, with other works.

There is no doubt that Kircher's attack shook up the alchemists disagreeably, and since he was a man of considerable influence it must have had some effect. Boyle (who believed in alchemy) quotes Kircher frequently; after thumbing over the *Mundus Subterraneus* he wrote in 1665 to Oldenburg that: 'I do much fear, he gives us rather collections, as his custom is, of what is already extant and known, than any considerable new discoveries', and demurred at paying forty shillings for it.[5]

In a discussion of perpetually burning lamps said to have been found in tombs, Kircher[6] quotes an Arabic author ('Schiangia Arabs in historia memorabilium Ægypti') that liquid bitumen is conveyed in pipes (canales) from the source to the lamps in the crypt, and[7] he gives a picture of a lead pipe connecting the petroleum well (fons petroli) with such a lamp as a possible contrivance (dico, hujus ope quempiam ignem perpetuum fovere posse, hoc artificio) — the first (albeit imaginary) oil pipe-line. In his *Ars Magna Lucis et Umbræ* Kircher shows no knowledge of Descartes' law of refraction (1637). He describes burning mirrors (bk. x, pars 3; 1671, 764), fireworks (bk. x, pars

---

[1] *De ortu et progressu Chemiæ*, Copenhagen, 1668, 73, 79; in Manget, i, 1–37.

[2] *Metallographia*, London, 1671, 30.

[3] 1747, i, 357, 725, ii, 156, 402–3 (crambem coctam multoties recoquit, nova parca manu serit), 419 (operose solidque refutavit Valerius Bonvincus in Lance peripatetica adv. Kircherum, 8°, Patav, 1676; Kestler in the preface to XII calls him Valesianus Bonvicenas, professor of Physica in Padua.

[4] *De Metallorum Transmutatione ad . . . Joelem Langelottum . . . Epistola*, Hamburg, 1673; in Manget, i, 168 f.

[5] *Works*, 1744, v, 336.   [6] I, 1654, iii, 548.   [7] II, 1665, ii, 73.

2; 1671, 722), and a magic lantern (bk. x; 1671, 769). He and his pupil Schott (p. 333) tried at Syracuse to imitate the burning mirror of Archimedes.[1]

The magic lantern is first described in the second edition (1671). In 1653-4 the Jesuit Father Andreas Tacquet in Leyden had arranged Kircher's earlier apparatus, described in the first edition (1646), apparently based on Porta's concave mirror (p. 25), by the addition of a lens in the course of the rays reflected from the mirror. The invention of the projection lantern with a glass slide has been ascribed to Huygens (1656); it was developed by his associate, the Dane Walgenstein, who published a description of it in 1668.[2]

Kircher describes the fluorescence of an infusion of *lignum nephriticum* (bk. i, pars 3; 1646, 77; 1671, 56)[3] which had been mentioned by Monardes in 1569.[4]

He mentions a cup of the wood given him by the procurator of the Jesuits in Mexico. It coloured water in it at first a deep blue, the colour of a Bugloss flower, 'but if poured into a glass globe and held against the light, no trace of blue colour is seen. In a more shady place, the liquid becomes a beautiful green, and in a more shady place a reddish colour, and thus it will change colour in a wonderful way according to the nature of its background.' He says he was the first to observe this chameleon-like colour, an apparent colour produced by the various modification of the light, nor a true or real colour, since no colour is seen when it is held up against the light. By various experiments he had discovered the true cause, which he would publish later, but apparently never did. Kircher's account of the source of the wood was probably taken from Ximinez' translation of a manuscript of Hernandes.[5] Kircher presented the cup to the Emperor. A second cup was described by Bauhin.[6] Another Jesuit, Father Grimaldi, the discoverer of the diffraction of light,[7] says the decoction shows two colours, blue and yellow, and explains this by supposing the blue is: reflexum ab interioribus particulis aquæ sic infectæ, whilst the yellow is: refractum quidem est per aquam prædictam — not a bad guess for the time.

Ordinary fire is air caused to glow by the vehement collision of two bodies, by the heat of which combustible matter is changed into flame:[8] Ignis igitur nostris usualis nihil aliud est, quàm aër ex vehementi duorum corporum collisione accensus, cujus ardore combustibilis materiæ fomes arreptus in-flammam abit. Only matter which can be volatilised can produce flame.

In his book on the plague[9] Kircher described seven experiments on putrefaction, postulated the existence of 'worms' invisible to the naked eye in the blood of sufferers from the plague, and suggested that a *contagium animatum* is the cause of infectious diseases. He thought[10] that flies and other insects were formed by the coalescence of putrid particles in the atmosphere.

Gentile da Foligno (d. 1348) in a consilium on the plague at Genoa in 1348 (of which he died) regarded it as caused by the stars, corruption of the air by putrefaction, evil smells from stagnant water, and infections (*semina, reliquiae*, suggesting 'germs' of disease).[11] Giovanni della Penna (d. 1387) in two consilia on the same plague, maintained that it was spread by air polluted by the breath of diseased persons, not by the causes

[1] J. Parsons, *Phil. Trans.*, 1754, xlviii, 621.
[2] Eder, *History of Photography*, tr Epstean, New York, 1945, 46, 51.
[3] Emsmann, *Ann. Phys.*, 1868, cxxxiii, 175; Burckhardt, *ib.*, 680.
[4] Partington, *Ann. Sci.*, 1955, vi, 1.
[5] *Qvatro Libros. De la Natvraleza, y Virtvdes de la plantas, y animales que estan receuidos en vso Medicina en la Nueua España*, sm. 4°, Mexico City, 1615.
[6] *Historia Plantarvm Vniversalis Nova*, f°, Yverdun, 1650, i, 492.
[7] *Physico-Mathesis de Lvmine, Coloribvs, et Iride*, Bologna, 1665, 246, 327; Burkhardt, *Ann. Phys.*, 1868, cxxxiii, 680; Berthold, *ib.*, 1876, clviii, 620.
[8] VI, Bk. I, pars i, c. 5; 1671, 12.
[9] VII, 1658; Torrey, *Osiris*, 1938, v, 246; Pagel, *Paracelsus*, Basel, 1958, 184.
[10] II, Bk. IX, sect. i, c. 2; 1668, ii, 106.   [11] Sarton, (1), iii, 848.

given by Foligno; he prescribed syrup of roses, sugar mixed with powdered gems, bone of a stag's heart, etc.[1]

Girolamo Fracastoro (Verona; 1478–1553) spoke[2] of seeds (*seminaria*) of contagion borne through the air and the cause of infection by fomites; the particles from dry fevers do not adhere to bodies and are not contagious, those from sordid diseases are sticky and contagious. Poison is not contagious. The seminaria can also be carried by water, and they spread rapidly in the human body, but perish with it on death. The seeds are given off from pores as odours, especially from moist and volatile bodies and carried a great distance.[3] The idea comes from Lucretius, who had spoken of 'seeds of death', and Fracastoro used the corpuscular theory to explain chemical actions;[4] Varro (116–28 B.C.), before Lucretius, spoke of minute invisible organisms (animalia quædam minuta, quæ non possunt oculi consequi) as the cause of marsh fever.[5]

Kircher[6] still believed in the flying dragons described by Roger Bacon (Vol. I) specimens of which were in museums; he had the head of one, in poor condition, sent to him for his own museum.

Schott

Gaspar Schott (Königshofen, 1608–Würzburg, 22 March 1666), a Jesuit pupil of Kircher in Rome, professor of physics and mathematics in Würzburg,[7] produced several bulky works in the style of Kircher's, e.g.:

(1) Mechanica. Hydraulico-Pneumatica . . . Accessit Experimentum Novum Magdeburgicum, 4°, Würzburg, 1657 (with the first published account of Guericke's experiments with the air pump); (2) Thavmatvrgvs Physicvs, Siue Magiæ Uniuersalis Naturæ et Artis, 4 pts. 4°, Würzburg, 1657–9; (3) Physica Curiosa sive Mirabilia Naturæ et Artis libri XII, 4°, Würzburg, 1662, 1664, 1667 (1389 pp.), 1697; (4) Technica Curiosa, sive Mirabilia Artis . . . Quibus varia Experimenta, variaque Technasmata Pnevmatica, Hydravlica, Hydrotechnia, Mechanica, Graphica, Chronometrica, Automatica, Cabalistica, aliaque Artis propununtur, 4°, Nürnberg, 1664 (1044 pp.),

and similar works of little value, the emphasis being on the 'wonderful'. Thorndike says (1) outlines experiments, some of which seem scarcely true; (3) is particularly disappointing; it deals with demons, spectres, monstrosities, and 'varied marvels' with little or no true physics; (4) is more interesting; (2) includes unpublished notes prepared by Kircher for such a work and Pt. IV (pp. 91–223) is on 'Magia Pyrotechnia'.

Lana

Francisco Lana Terzi (Brescia; 13 or 31 December 1631–26 February 1687), a Jesuit, associate of Kircher in Rome (1652), professor of physics in Brescia and founder of an Academia Philexoticorum Naturæ et Artis there, mineralogist, experimenter on the barometer (1665) and on ballistics, inventor of clocks, projector of an airship raised by vacuous copper globes, and student of dynamics.[8] He published:

---

[1] Sarton, (1), iii, 859; on bone of the stag's heart, see Kremers, *Isis*, 1935, xxiii, 256.
[2] *De Contagionibus*, 1546.
[3] Stones, *Isis*, 1928, x, 448; Thorndike, v, 488–97; Greenwood, in Singer, (1), 1953, 501.
[4] Lasswitz, (1), 1890, i, 306.   [5] Kortenhaus, *A. Med.*, 1928, xx, 129.
[6] II, Bk. VIII, sect. iv, c. 2; 1668, ii, 89; Thorndike, *Speculum*, 1953, xxviii, 692.
[7] Thorndike, vii, 590–608.
[8] Louvet, NBG, 1859, xxix, 301; Hoefer, (1), ii, 265; Thorndike, vii, 610.

I. Prodromo overo saggio de alcune Inventioni nuove, f°, Brescia, 1670 (BN Rés. R. 208).

II. Magisterium naturae et artis, opus physico-mathematicum . . . in quo occultiora naturalis philosophiae principia manifestantur, 3 vols. f°, Brescia, 1684–86–92 (BN R. 394–6).

(I) describes the airship and a fountain worked by water made artificially by the distillation of air; (II) was to have been in 9 vols. but vol. 3 was posthumous. Hoefer gives 'philosophico-mathematicum', 2 vols., 1686; it is not in the BM and since I have not seen it I copy Hoefer's description.

The first volume of II describes Lana's theory of dynamics and opposes the Copernican system (tract. iii, p. 409). The second volume, including chemistry, speaks of the transformation of rubies, sapphires, etc., into diamonds by means of steel filings (perhaps by heat-treatment removing the colour), the production of mercury from air (Ex communi aere hydrargyrum seu argentum vivum prolicere) (Bk. ii, p. 75), and concentrating alcohol by passing the vapour through pig's bladder, when the phlegm is retained (Bk. i, c. 2, p. 32; this is a process mentioned by Libavius, etc., and depends on selective absorption). All sorts of tricks and wonders are described, such as sticking a needle into an arm or leg without pain (Bk. ii, p. 35). The production of water from air is amplified from I and Lana is often quoted for this (it depended on the condensation of moisture from air on a cold vessel); see Porta p. 21.

The solidification of a mixture of concentrated solutions of calcium chloride and potassium carbonate (from precipitation of calcium carbonate), described by Lana in 1686, was known as the 'chemical miracle'; he ascribed it to Dr. Hieronymus Alegri of Verona.[1] Lana thought some hexangular crystals found in a meadow, said to be generated from dew, were nitre (saltpetre), which he extracted from the soil, since nitre is 'the natural coagulum of water'.[2]

THE BOLOGNA PHOSPHORUS

A very interesting chapter in the history of chemistry and physics is concerned with the preparation and investigation of phosphorescent barium sulphide, called the Bologna phosphorus, said to have been discovered by a shoemaker-alchemist, Vincenzo Casciorolo of Bologna, in 1602–4.[3] The Bologna phosphorus is first mentioned, as well known then, by Julius Cæsar

[1] Lana, in Acte Novæ Academiæ Philexoticorum Naturæ et Artis, 1686, 8°, Brescia, 1687, no. 17; excerpted in Acta Eruditorum, 1686, v, 556–65 (564); Gmelin, (1), ii, 224; Thorndike, viii, 230.
[2] Phil. Trans., 1672, vii, 4068; no. 83.
[3] Priestley, History of Vision, Light and Colours, 1772, i, 360–83 (361: mis-spells the name Cascariolo; date 1603 misprinted 1630; refs. confused); Hoefer, (1), ii, 328–9; Poggendorff, (2), 1883, 247; Joseph (Placidus) Heinrich, Die Phosphorescenz der Körper oder die im Dunkeln bemerkbaren Lichtphänomene der anorganischen Natur, 2 pts., Nürnberg, 1811–12 (BM 432. k. 6); id., Die Phosphorescenz der Körper nach allen Umständen untersucht und erklärt, 5 pts. (sep. t.ps.), Nürnberg, 1811–12–15–20–20 (BM 8760. f. 10); id., J. Chem. Phys., 1820, xxx, 218–39; Heinrich (1758–1825) was a Benedictine monk in the Royal Monastery of St. Emmeran near Regensburg; in 1791–8 he was professor of natural science, mineralogy, and meteorology in the University of Ingolstadt; in the preface he says he became interested in the subject by a study of Priestley's Vision, Light and Colours; H. Kayser, Handbuch der Spectroscopie, Leipzig, 1908, iv, 599–838 (bibl.); E. N. Harvey, A History of Luminescence (American Philosophical Society, Memoirs, xliv, Philadelphia, 1957, xxiii, 692 pp.), 306 f.; Thorndike, viii, 380.

La Galla.[1] La Galla, who mentions Marcus Antonius Prosper a Paliano, says there is a stone, translucent like talc, of a caustic arsenical nature, found in the fields near Bologna, which when calcined by art acquires the property of shining in the dark, after exposure to sunlight or secondary light, with a reddish light like a glowing coal; after a time it ceases to shine. The cause of the luminescence was the inclusion of much igneous or luciferous substance in the luminous matter:

Est hic lapis, qui in Bononiensi agro reperitur scissilis, ac pellucidus aliquantulum, ita ut talco videatur adsimilis, Arsenicalis naturæ, & calidissimus, ac causticus. Talis sua natura est hic lapis, qui ita comparatus non lucet, sed ut lumen concipiat, atque conceptum retineat per aliquam temporis moram, et referat, quemadmodum initio narravimus nos vidisse, necesse est ipsum calcinari, sive artificiose ad ignem vri, ita ut in calcem vertatur, atque ita secundum eam partem, quæ in calcem versa est, lumen concipit et fulget cum secundum reliquam partem non luceat, lumen concipit Solis tantum, ut ego expertus sum, et a cæteris accepi, neque necesse est solis radiis, aut luci primiariæ exponatur, sed sufficit exponatur lumini, siue secundariæ luci, unde satis est lumen crepusculi: lux, quam refert, est punicea, et adsimilis ignitis carbonibus. . . . ego puto eandem esse causam luminis in hoc lapide, quæ est in cœteris noctu fulgentibus, de quibus diximus nempe multam copiam igneamque lucentis substantiæ in candida materia inclusam.

The preparation of the phosphorescent material from the stone, of which there were three kinds, was first described by Pierre Potier (Pierre de la Poterie), a native of Anjou who went early to Italy and was still living in Bologna in 1640 but, it is said, was soon afterwards assassinated by his friend Sancassani.[2]

Potier was famous for a remedy called *Antihecticum Poterii*,[3] the preparation of which, by oxidising a mixture of tin and antimony with nitre, was first clearly described by Rolfinck.[4]

Potier published the recipe in his *Spagirical Pharmacopœia*.[5] Potier says there were three kinds of the stone, the best being translucent and very like gypsum (pellucidus, gypso valdè similis). He gives a long account of the place where the stone was found, on Monte Paterna, four miles from Bologna, says it was thought by a certain alchemist (quidam Argyropœi) that it would serve for transmutation, and Scipio Bagatello, a well-known alchemist of Bologna,

---

[1] *De Phoenominis in Orbe Lvnæ* (*Novi Telescopii vsv a D. Gallileo Gallileo*) . . . *necnon De Lvce, et Lvmine Altera disputatio*, 4°, Venice, 1612, 71; reprinted in Galileo, *Opere*, Florence, 1843, iii, 239–368 (357); this is said to be the first use of the word 'telescope'.

[2] Gmelin, (1), i, 592; Ferguson, ii, 219; Thorndike, viii, 83; he is different from the alchemist Michael Potier, eleven works by whom are listed by Gmelin, i, 505, 523–4; Ferguson, ii, 220–1, although alchemical works by P. Potier, *De salem extractione et præparatione in genere*; *De magisteriis*, and *De quinta essentia*, are said to be contained in earlier eds. of his works. A *Libri duo de quinta essentia solutiva*, 4°, Panorm., 1613, is attributed to an A. Potius by Hoefer, (1), ii, 321, and *Manes Poteriani i.e. Petri Poterii . . . Inventa Chymica*, publ. by J. C. Ettner, 4°, Frankfurt and Leipzig, 1692 (dated 1689 at end) is given by Ferguson, i, 252.

[3] Potier, *Opera*, Frankfurt, 1666, 35, 225, 285.

[4] *Chimia in Artis formam redacta*, Jena, 1662, 378; König, *Regnum Minerale*, 4°, Basel, 1686, 44 (diaphoreticum joviale seu Antihecticum Poterii).

[5] *Pharmacopœa Spagirica*, bk. ii, c. 27, Ferguson, ii, 219, says this was publ. at Bologna, 8°, 1622 (copy without t.p. 308 pp.) and 8°, Frankfurt, 1628; Thorndike gives Cologne, 1624, Bologna, 1635; I have used the eds. in Potier's *Opera Omnia Medica et Chemica*, 8°, Lyon, 1644, 533; Frankfurt, 1666, 498; and in F. Hoffmann, *Opera Omnia*, f°, Geneva, 1749, Suppl. i, 135 f., 217 (De lapide quodam incognito admirabilis virtutis, à paucis annis in agro Bononiensi reperti). Hoffmann published an ed. of Potier's works in 1698, 4°, Frankfurt (BM 542. c. 21).

first used this solar stone (lapidem nostrum solarem) in making gold. It had some arsenical properties (proximè ad sandaracam) and a fœtid sulphureous smell, and a lixivium made from it removed hair.

To make it luminous it was calcined in two ways; in the first a fine powder was heated very strongly in a crucible, in the second the powder, as fine as flour, was made into tablets as big as a thaler with water or white of egg, these were dried, stratified with charcoal, and then very strongly heated in a wind furnace for four or five hours:

in pollinem redactus, in placentulas, thaleri instar compingitur, vel solâ aquâ communi, vel albumine ovi. Hæ per se exsiccatæ in furno venti cum carbonibus stratificantur, & dato igne validissimo per quatuor, vel quinque horas, calcinantur: furno per se refrigerato placentulas exime. . . . Ter nonnunquam reiteratur dicta calcinatio.

Potier does not name Casciorolo, who seems to be mentioned first in two letters, of Count Majolino Bisaccione (1582–1663), a doctor of law of Bologna, and Ovidio Montalbani (1602–71), a doctor of medicine, a botanist, and professor of logic, physics, and mathematics in Bologna. These letters were published in Bologna as an 8-page pamphlet in 1634 (lent to me by E. Weil):

De / Illvminabili / Lapide / Bononiensi / Epistolæ familiares duæ. / Bononiæ, Typis Clementis Ferronij 1634. Superiorum permissu (1v blank, pp. 1 and 2 unnumb., 7·8 × 5·3 in., paper and typography poor) 8 pp.; at end: D. Homobonus de Bonis Pœnitentiarius, pro Eminentiss, & Reuerendiss. Card. Archiepisc. Imprimatur / Fr. Hieronymus Onuphrius Consulator S. Offitij, pro Reuerendiss. P. Inquisit. Bonon.

Bisaccione had seen some specimens of a stone not unlike gypsum thirty or more years ago, found in a mountain not far from the outskirts of Bologna and shown to him by a chemist Vincentius Casciarolo (sic), which when burnt to a kind of lime and mixed, in a way he did not know, with white of egg and then exposed to sunlight, shone by night like a carbuncle. Montalbani says Maginus got this 'solar sponge' from Casciarolo, Galileo did much with it, La Galla showed its effects, and Potier published the method of making it. The direct or reflected light of the sun, or fire, or something very subtle emitted in the diaphanous, separates by calcination the most apt parts of the stone, as if by ignition. These are capable of taking up light or other inflammation and becoming luminous. But the luminosity sooner or later becomes extinguished by what surrounds the preparation, depending on how many of the resolved particles in the whole body have been ignited.

Montalbani was inclined to think the stone if not totally at least for the most part arsenical, with some admixture of sulphur and vitriol. For, when exposed to great heat the stone, smelling abominably of orpiment [arsenic sulphide] turns from a pale leaden colour to yellowish, reddish, whitish, and finally blackish, while formerly it had the appearance of common flint or rather rounded gypsum. Taken internally it causes vomiting, applied externally it is depilatory.

There are four kinds of the stone depending on the arrangement of striations on it, the fourth, black and friable, with striations spreading from a centre, being, 'if I am not mistaken, our stone.' Montalbani sent various specimens of the genuine stone; some showed a dark red vivid light, others a light like the lambent blue flame of sulphur, others like glowing embers.

Evelyn[1] in Bologna 'enquired out a priest and Dr. Montalbano [sic], to whom I brought recomendations from Rome [probably Kircher]; this was he who invented or found out the composition of the *lapis illuminabilis*, or phosphorus. He shew'd me their property (for he had severall), being to retaine the light of the sun for some competent time, by a kind of imbibition, by a particular way of calcination. Some of these presented a blew colour like the flame of brimstone, others like the coals of a kitchen fire.'

Fortunio Licetus or Liceti (Rapallo, 3 October 1577–Padua, 17 May 1657), professor of logic and Aristotelian physics at Pisa, Padua, and Bologna, and of medicine at Padua gave an account of the Bologna stone in 1640:

Litheosphorvs, sive de Lapide Bononiensi Lucem in se conceptam ab ambiente claro mox in tenebris mire conseruante Liber Fortvnii Liceti Genvensis Pridem in Pisano, nuper in Patauino, nunc in Bononiensi Archigymnaso Philosophi Eminentis. Vtini, N. Schiratli, 1640. Sm. 4°, pp. iv, 280; BM 987. h. 23. Pref. dated Bologna, October, 1639, dated at end (p. 280) 5 Feb. 1639; Liceti's book, stuffed with classical quotations on stones in general, etc., is a sorry performance; Kayser says: 'man kann sich schwerlich etwas Alberneres denken.' He mentioned the Bologna stone in another work: De Reconditis Antiquorum Lucernis, f°, Utini, 1653, 283.

He gives three dates for the discovery: 1604 (p. 2, side note); 1602 (p. 12, side note), and in text (p. 12): Porro triginta sex circiter ab hinc annos (i.e. $1639 - 36 = 1603$). He says (p. 31) he saw the stone in 1638 and $1638 - 36 = 1602$. It was discovered, he says, by a humble man of Bologna called Vicentius Casciorolus (a quosdam humilis conditionis homine. ... Vincentius Casciorolus cognominabatur, genere Bononiensis) (p. 12). He describes the preparation, the native stone being heated with white of egg, flour paste, or other liquor (pp. 99, 120 f.). He mentions its use as a depilatory, says it has a fœtid odour and great density (pondere plumbum lapis Bononiensis valde superat) (p. 103), and deals with its phosphorescence (pp. 102–3): most of rest of book is on phosphorescence and the explanation of it.

Liceti says Casciorolo called his material the solar stone (*lapis solaris*), and showed it to an alchemist Scipio Bagatelli, who seemed to see the sun, the symbol of gold, fixed in this stone, which had been used to make gold. Bagatelli made the discovery known to G. A. Magini, professor of mathematics in Bologna, who sent specimens to Galileo and other scientists, and even to several European sovereigns. Liceti rejected the explanation given by Montalbani that the light was due to an actual combustion of sulphureous matter, and that of La Galla that light is absorbed and then re-emitted, and proposed a fantastic new theory. The stone when ignited becomes impregnated like a uterus, fire being the sperm, and then bears a child, light. The ignition also removes impurities and brings the purer part to the surface, where it is more easily impregnated.

[1] *Diary*, May 1645; ed. Bray, 1870, 156.

Experiments with the Bolognian phosphorus were made by Kircher[1] and Christian Mentzel.[2] Hooke[3] mentions both 'the Bononian stone' and 'the preparation lately found out of common chalk by Dr. Baldwin', i.e. calcium nitrate.

The merchant and alchemist, Christian (or Christoph) Adolph (or Adam) Balduin (or Baldewein) (Doebeln, nr. Meissen, 1632– ? 31 December 1682), who lived at Grossenhain, Saxony, a member of the Academia Naturæ Curiosorum in 1673, taking the name of Hermes, published in the *Miscellanea Curiosa* of this society[4] several alchemical tracts, most of which appeared separately, including one on a 'Hermetic phosphorus', which was calcium nitrate:

(i) Circa regeraninationem argenti novo artificio inventum.

(ii) Aurum Auræ, Vi Magnetissimi Universalis Attractum, also printed in 1673 (BM 1036. a. 4. (1.)), twice in 1674 (BM 1034. c. 16. (2.) and 1036. a. 4. (2.)) and 1675, Colonia ad Spream (i.e. Berlin) (53 pp.); on the extraction of an astral gold from the atmosphere by universal magnetism, potable gold, the virtues of the atmospheric gold in the three kingdoms of Nature, and other similar matters.

(iii) Aurum Superius & Inferius Auræ Superius & Inferioris Hermeticum, also 12°, Frankfurt and Leipzig, 1675 (173 pp., folding title, 2 folding plates; item iv prefixed), and Amsterdam, 1675 (96 pp.).

(iv) Phosphorus Hermeticus, Sive Magnes Luminaris, also Frankfurt and Leipzig, and Amsterdam, 12°, 1675, unpaged (20 pp.); in the 1675 publs. this is part of iii).

(v) Hermes Curiosus, sive Inventa et Experimenta Physico-Chymica Nova, also 12°, Leipzig, 1680 (58 pp.) and Nürnberg, 1683 (58 pp.). Ferguson mentions eds. of 1667 (Leipzig) and 1679 (Haynæ, sm. 8°, 56 pp.); Ferguson, i, 68; Duveen, 41; Sotheran *Cat.* 879 (1947) no. 2427; Thorndike, viii, 380; BN R. 27427.

Balduin had thoroughly muddled ideas about a supposed 'immortali anima nitri' in saltpetre, which appeared as red fumes in distilling nitric acid, and Stahl[5] says Becher held the same view.

Balduin prepared what he called 'Hermetic phosphorus' by a process he does not describe clearly. He says: 'When a few years ago I was engaged in making the alkahest, after the distillation was over I found the cooled glass retort shining inside like red-hot iron.' Kunckel,[6] who dates the discovery in error 1677, says Balduin was trying to separate the spiritus mundi from air and use it as the philosophers' stone. He made a solution of chalk in nitric acid and distilled it to dryness in a retort. The residue (calcium nitrate) was exposed to

---

[1] *Magnes, sive de Arte Magnetica Libri tres*, f°, Rome, 1641, lib. iii, pars 3, quaest, 2, p. 463; *Ars Magna Lucis et Umbræ*, f°, Rome, 1646, lib. i, pars 1, ch. 8, pp. 26–9 (De photismo lapidum. De lapide Pheggite, seu Phosphoro minerali); König, *Regnum Minerale*, 4°, Basel, 1686, 118.

[2] *Lapis Bononiensis In obscuro lucens collatus Cum Phosphoro Hermetico Clariss. Christiani Adolphi Baldvini . . . nuper edito, Et cunctis Naturæ Indigatoribus Vlterioris scrutinii ergo exhibitus à Christiano Menzelio . . .*, Bielefeld, 1675 (BM 1033. e. 16. (4.), the facsim. t.p. in Harvey, 1957, fig. 34 opp. p. 347, is dated 1676, but the I in MDCLXXVI has obviously been added by hand; in the bibliography, p. 643, it is dated 1675); Mentzel, *Miscell. Acad. Curios.*, 1673–4 (1688), Ann. IV–V, Appendix, 158–89.

[3] *Cutlerian Lectures on Light*, 1680–82, in *Posthumous Works*, 1705, 122; *Philosophical Experiments and Observations of the late Dr. R. Hooke and other eminent Virtuosos, Publish'd by W. Derham*, 8°, London, 1726, 174–83 (BM 232. g. 33).

[4] *Miscell. Curiosa Medico-Physicæ Academiæ Naturæ Curiosorum*, Nürnberg, 1673–4 (reprint, 1688), Appendix, 82–9, 90–146, 147–51, 152–89, with plate opp. p. 90. The same volume, Appendix, 69–81, contains the anonymous alchemical *Tumba Semiramidis*; see Ferguson, ii, 477.

[5] *Fundamenta Chymiae*, 1747, iii, 242.   [6] *Laboratorium Chymicum*, 1716, 656.

air and deliquesced, and the water distilled from the liquid was the spiritus mundi. Once, after overheating, something yellow deposited in the neck of the retort, which was broken off and thrown into a dark place, when it shone like a coal. When this disappeared it was renewed after exposure to sunlight. Balduin at first kept the preparation secret, but it was soon discovered by Kunckel, who says Balduin was associated with a 'Medico, Doct. Fruben', perhaps Frobenius (p. 546). Balduin sent an account and a specimen to Oldenburg, Secretary of the Royal Society, in September, 1676[1] and was elected F.R.S. The preparation of the 'phosphorus Balduini' was described by Boyle.[2]

Georg Caspar Kirchmaier[3] followed Elsholtz (see p. 372) in distinguishing Kunckel's phosphorus (our phosphorus) from the Bologna stone, emeraldine phosphorus (green fluorspar) and Balduin's hermetic phosphorus (calcium nitrate). He gives Potier's preparation, saying that he had omitted one essential, which Mentzel had given him but he does not disclose it. Balduin's phosphorus can be duplicated with nitre, sugar, or Cretan earth. Although Kirchmaier says true phosphorus was known to Bartholomaeus Anglicus (13 cent.) the passage he quotes[4] does not bear this out.

N. Lemery's account of the Bologna stone in his *Cours de Chymie* up to the 5 ed.[5] merely says the secret of preparation had been lost, but in the 7 ed.[6] there is a long account of the preparation based on information from Homberg, who went to Italy to discover the method. Homberg gave an account of it in 1694.[7] Other experiments on phosphorescence were published by Louis Ferdinand Marsigli,[8] C. F. Du Fay,[9] Marggraf,[10] Giacomo (or Jacopo) Bartolomeo Beccari of Bologna,[11] and Giacomo Battista Beccaria of Turin.[12]

Further experiments were made by Benjamin Wilson (see footnote 11),

[1] *Phil. Trans.*, 1676-7, xi, 788, no. 131 ('Baldwin'); Abgd., 1809, ii, 368.
[2] *The Aerial Noctiluca*, 1680; *Works*, ed. Birch, 1744, iv, 37.
[3] *De phosphoris et natura lucis nec non de igne: commentatio epistolica*, Wittenbergae apud Johannem Ellingerum Bibl. Anno cIc Icc LXXX (1680; dedication dated 20 August, 1679), illustr. t.p., 3 sheets (in a collection of *Dissertationes Chemicæ*, 1680-93, BM 1033. h. 20); Thorndike, viii, 380.
[4] Bartholomaeus Anglicus, *De Proprietatibus Rerum*, bk. viii, ch. 40: de luce.
[5] *A Course of Chymistry*, tr. W. Harris, 8°, London, 1686, 525.
[6] *Cours de Chymie*, 7 ed., 1690, 657-85.   [7] AdS 1730, x, m 33; 1733, ii, h 214.
[8] *Dissertatione epistolare del fosforo minerale ò sia della pietra illuminabile Bolognese*, 4°, Leipzig, 1698, BM B. 396. (16.); 2 ed. 1702.
[9] AdS, 1730, h 48 m 524; 1735, h 1 m 347 (diamond).
[10] *Hist. Acad. Berlin*, 1749, 56; 1750, 144.
[11] *De Quamplurimis Phosphoris nunc primum detectis commentarius*, 4°, Bologna, 1744 (xii, 85 pp., i l.; approbation dated 30 March 1744) (CUL IV. 15. 38); summary in *Phil. Trans.*, 1746, xliv, 81-91; repr. with same title (last word omitted) in *Bonon. Comment.*, 1746, II, ii, 136-79; Zanotti and Beccari, *Bonon. Comment.*, 1748, i, 181-205; Beccari, Di vi, quam ipsa per se lux habet, *Bonon. Comment.*, 1757, iv, 74; B. Wilson, *A Series of Experiments relating to Phosphori, and the prismatic colours they are found to exhibit in the dark . . . With a translation of two Memoirs from the Bologna Acts, upon the same Subject, by J. B. Beccari*, 4°, London, 1775 (BM 8715. ee. (1.)); 2 ed. with Additions, 4°, 1776 (BM 537. d. 20. (1.)); Wilson's *A Series of Experiments on the Subject of Phosphori . . .*, 4°, London, 1776 (BM 31. d. 6) is a different book; *Obs. Phys.*, 1780, xv, 92.
[12] *Phil. Trans.*, 1771, lxi, 212; Poggendorff, (1), i, 123, distinguished Jacopo Bartolomeo Beccari (Bologna; 25 July 1682-18 January 1766), professor of medicine, anatomy, and chemistry in the Institute at Bologna and later president of it, and Giacomo Battista Beccaria (or Beccharia) (Mondovi, 3 October 1716-Turin, 27 May 1781), professor of physics in Turin (previously lecturer in rhetoric and philosophy in Rome and Palermo).

Giovanni Marchetti (d. 1817), professor of medicine and chemistry (1790–1815) in Bologna,[1] Thomas Wedgwood,[2] and Grotthuss.[3] A very good theoretical explanation of phosphorescence was given by Euler.[4] Friedrich Hoffmann seems to have been the first[5] to have mentioned obscurely the phosphorescence of calcium sulphide:

Singularis species talci, nostra inventione præparata, lucida reddi potest, non secus ac lapis Bononiensis, ita ut phosphori lucentis Germanici titulum mereatur

if the 'kind of talc' is gypsum and if he reduced this, but he does not say this. The credit for the first clear description of phosphorescent calcium sulphide, therefore, belongs to John Canton.[6] He calcined oyster shells in an open fire for half an hour, separated the whitest part of the lime, powdered and sifted it, mixed three parts with one of flowers of sulphur, and heated the mixture, rammed into a crucible $1\frac{1}{2}$ in. deep till almost full, red-hot for at least an hour. The mass, when cold, was turned out and broken up, the white part being powdered and kept in a dry stoppered bottle. Most of the modern phosphori are mainly calcium or barium sulphide.[7] The phosphorescence of strontium sulphide was described by J. F. John[8] and that of (hexagonal) zinc sulphide by Theodor Sidot.[9]

[1] *Bonon. Comment.*, 1791, vii, 289.   [2] *Phil. Trans.*, 1792, lxxxii, 270.
[3] *J. f. Chemie* (Schweigger), 1815, xiv, 133.
[4] *Acta Acad. Petropol.*, 1777, i, 71 h; Partington, *Advanced Physical Chemistry*, 1953, iv, 80.
[5] *Demonstrationes physicæ curiosæ, experimentis et observationibus curiosis mechanicis ac chymicis illustratae*, 4°, Halle, 1700; Demonstr. x no. 3; *Opusc. phys. med.*, i, no. II, 153–222; *Opera*, 1740, v, 5.
[6] *Phil. Trans.*, 1768, lviii, 337.
[7] Recipes in Partington, *Text-Book of Inorganic Chemistry*, 1957, 784.
[8] *Ann. Phys.*, 1817, lv, 453–60.
[9] *Compt. Rend.*, 1866, lxii, 999–1001 (prep.); 1866, lxiii, 188–9 (phosph.).

CHAPTER X

GLAUBER AND KUNCKEL

GLAUBER

Johann Rudolph Glauber (Karlsstadt, Franconia (Bavaria), 1604 (or 1603)–Amsterdam, 19 March 1670) was the son of a barber and, apparently, self-taught, without university education and also without training as an apothecary. He read books on alchemy, made experiments, and conversed with others, whom he found less informed than himself. He travelled and worked in various parts of Germany, Austria, and Switzerland. In 1624 or 1625, when nearly dying of the 'Hungarian disease' (hospital fever ?) in Vienna he cured himself by drinking the water of a mineral spring in which he discovered what he called the *sal mirabile*, which he thought was the same as Paracelsus's *sal enixum*, a salt later named after him 'Glauber's salt' (sodium sulphate).[1] After many years of travel, study and experiment, during which he acquired an extensive knowledge of chemistry, pharmacy, geology, mineralogy and technology, Glauber in 1646 went to Holland; he settled in 1648 in Amsterdam, where he had a large laboratory, called a 'Hermetic Institute', in a house formerly inhabited by an alchemist. In this town he published most of his books. In 1649 he returned to Germany and in 1651 set up a laboratory in a large house in Kissingen (where there are mineral springs), where he worked out some technical processes. One of his assistants, Farner, who was bound by a promise of secrecy, afterwards offered for sale some of Glauber's processes as his own, at the same time ridiculing his master, so that in 1655–7 Glauber published his defences against Farner and made known the secrets. He seems to have felt this ingratitude keenly, since he had, apparently, so far escaped this very common annoyance of gifted men. He left Germany again for Amsterdam in 1655–6, and set up another large laboratory, with several work-rooms and a garden for testing mineral manures.[2] Glauber's health now began to fail and from 1660 became gradually worse. The date of his death is usually given as 1668, but Vreeswyck says Glauber died in Amsterdam on 19 March 1670 and that he attended the funeral.[3]

[1] Glauber, *De natura salium* 1658; *Works*, transl. Packe, 1689, i, 260; Paracelsus, *Opera*, 1658, ii, 170.

[2] Jorissen, *Chem. Ztg.*, 1927, li, 17.

[3] Goosen van Vreeswyck, *Silvere Rivier ofte Konings Fontein. Waar-in ontdekt worden veele notable Medicijnen der oude Philosophen*, 8°, 's Gravenhage, 1684, 117 (on Vreeswyck, a mineralogist who wrote on that subject as well as alchemy, see Ferguson, ii, 519); W. P. Jorissen, *Chem. Weekbl.*, 1914, xi, 1076–86; on the date of Glauber's death, *id.*, *ib.*, 1918, xv, 268; Jorissen and J. Postma, *ib.*, 1927, xxiv, 30–3; Jorissen, *Chem. Ztg.*, 1927, li, 17; Gmelin, (1), i, 626–57; Thomson, (1), i, 226; Hoefer, (1), ii, 182–91; W.R. in NBG, 1857, xx, 798; Kopp, (1), i, 128; *id.*, (2), iii, 160; *id.*, (4), i, 50, 251; Picton, 97; Ferguson, i, 322; W. Brieger, *Chem. Weekbl.*, 1918, xv, 984–7 (portr.); L. Darmstaedter, *Chem. Ztg.*, 1926, l, 585–6; Szathmáry,

Glauber's later writings are full of bitter complaints and charges against his contemporaries; men are false and treacherous, everywhere returning evil for good. Often, when he thought he had found an honest assistant and had taught him some process, the base creature imagined that he knew more than his master and left him on some pretext, or even without permission, and Glauber says he had learnt by experience the truth of the old proverb that whoever would have his affairs go aright must be himself both master and servant (wer

FIG. 11. J. R. GLAUBER, 1604–1670.
(Deutsches Museum, Munich)

seine Sachen will gethan haben recht muss selbsten seyn Herr und Knecht). 'If I have not done in this world all the good I would have done, the perversity of men is the reason.'[1]

He says:[2] 'Is there any reason why we should cast pearls before swine? If what others obscurely treated of, I should here openly communicate to enemies, would they, think you, cease to do evil, and begin to do well?'

Glauber lived in a restless age: the Thirty Years War (1618–48) was devastating Germany, and the poverty of his country was an impulse towards some of his technological studies, although much of his time was spent in Holland

ib., 1927, li, 305; Walden, Z. angew. Chem., 1928, xli, 622; Kotowski, ib., 1939, lii, 109; Paterson, Dyer and Calico Printer, 1927, lviii, 226; Armstrong and Deischer, J. Chem. Educ., 1942, xix, 3; Read, (2), 92; Thorndike, vii, 197; for correspondence of Glauber and Otto Sperling (1602–81), see Isis, 1926, viii, 761.
    [1] Menstr. universal.; Opera Chymica, Frankfurt, 1658, i, 167 f.
    [2] Mirac. mund. II, pref.; Works, tr. Packe, i, 223.

and most of his books were published there. He was essentially a technical chemist, preparing materials for sale, and in his writings he often extols his preparations in the ridiculously exaggerated fashion of the industrialist. He is too fond of praising himself and posing as a benefactor of mankind in general and Germany in particular.

At the end of the seventh part of his *Pharmacopoea Spagirica* (1667)[1] Glauber says he is 'now ready to be laid in my grave', but 'If the most wise God will prolong my life until the next Summer, and enable me to write out of bed, my purpose is to publish some other new wonderful works.' Since he published some appendices to this work in 1668, and was 'in some small measure recovered', he proceeded with his writing, dying two years after he completed this work.

Glauber is an extremely verbose, untidy, and often obscure author, as he himself sometimes admits, with the excuse that he is trying to be clear. He usually begins and ends his treatises with prayers and moralising, but his chemical works are more profitable than those of his great hero Paracelsus, that 'most potent lion and monarch of the North'.[2] His works are very numerous,[3] some small in size and value, others with an importance fully appreciated at the time, as the Latin, English, and French translations from the German show. They are most conveniently read in the collected editions. Glauber sometimes divides his description of a process between two or more treatises, omitting some essential step or operation in one and supplying it in another, or else he gives an obscure description in one work and a clearer one in another.

In the preface to his English translation Packe says the Latin works were then very scarce and expensive in London. He purchased the copperplates in Amsterdam and they have legends in German. Packe knew no German, translated the Latin works, and had the German ones done by 'a person well skill'd both in the High-Dutch, and also in Chymistry'. In the list of subscribers are 'The Honourable Ro. Boyl, Esq.', Daniel Cox, William Penn, and the Lord Mayor of London (Sir John Shorter). Packe's own book[4] is of no chemical interest; at the end is a price list of medicines and of books sold by Packe, who says he still had some copies of his translation of Glauber's 'Works' for sale at a reasonable price.

The following list includes all the numerous works of Glauber known to me, beginning with the collected editions; they are quoted in the account following by letter and number.

A. Opera Chymica, Bücher und Schrifften, so viel deren von ihme bisshero an Tag gegeben worden. Jetzo von neuem mit Fleiss übersehen, auch mit etlichen neuen Tractaten vermehrt, und umb mehrer Bequemlichkeit willen, in diese Form zusammen getragen, sampt ein darzu verfertigten volkommenen Register. 2 vols. 4°, Frankfurt. In Verlegung Thomae-Matthiae Götzens, 1658 (xxiv, 574 pp., 2 pl.) with Continuatio Operum Chymicorum, . . . , 1659 (xii, 444, xviii pp., engr, pl.) (BM 1400. i. 25; Ferguson, i, 322; Davis and Orioli, Cat. 139 (1950), no. 129, gives 7 plates. Another ed., 4°, Amsterdam, 1659, is mentioned by Graesse, Trésor de livres rares et précieux, Dresden, 1862, iii, 93). Works in this ed. are marked G in the list below.

[1] *Works*, tr. Packe, ii, 186. [2] *Prosper. Germ.*, iii; *Works*, tr. Packe, i, 351.
[3] Boerhaave, (4), i, 51–2: list of 36 titles.
[4] *Medela Chymica, or an Account of the Vertues and Uses of a Select Number of Chymical Medicines . . . as also an Essay upon the Acetum Acerrimum Philosophorum, or Vinegar of Antimony*, 8°, London, 1708.

B. French tr.: La Description des Novveavx Fovrneavx Philosophiqves ov Art Distillatoire, Par le moyen duquel sont tirez les Esprits, Huiles, Fleurs, & autres Medicaments: Par vne voye aisée & avec grand profit, des Végétaux, Animaux, & Mineraux traduit en nostre Langue, Par Le Sieur dv Teil, 8°, Paris, Chez Thomas Iolly, 1659; my copy, in the old binding, contains: xvii ll. (1 errata), pp. 71, 174, 74, 92, 53 (5 pts. of Fourneaux, and Appendix), 62 (Annotations sur l'Appendix); 64, 48, 111 (3 pts. Oeuvre Minerale); 22 (+ 1 l. blank) (De l'Or Potable); 62 (+ 1 l. blank) (La Medicine universelle); 64 (La Consolation des Navigants); all parts have sep. t.ps.; 3 folding plates. The translation from the Latin is by Bernard du Teil, Sieur de Saint-Leonard. Works in this ed. are marked F in the list below. The treatises have separate t.ps. and are sometimes (e.g. by Ferguson) listed as independent works.

C. The Works of the Highly Experienced and Famous Chymist, John Rudolph Glauber: Containing, Great Variety of Choice Secrets in Medicine and Alchymy ... Translated into English ... by ... Christopher Packe, Philo-chymico-Medicus, f°, London, 1689 (3 pts. in 1 vol., sep. pagin.; pp. 440; iv, 220; 92, xi, 11 plates on wood and copper; contents in Bolton, i, 483). Many passages of religious or patriotic interest were omitted by Packe, 'on the advice of an honourable person.' Imprimatur of Thos. Witherly, 'Præses. Coll. Med. Lond.' and four censors; dedicated to Edmond Dickenson, Physician to the King.

D. Glauberus Concentratus, oder Kern der Glauberischen Schrifften, worinnen alles unnöthigen Streit-Wesen weggelassen, was nutzbar ist, in die Enge gezogen, und was undeutlich oder verstecket, so viel möglich klar gemacht ... von einem Liebhaber Philosophischer Geheimnisse, 4°, Leipzig and Breslau, Michael Hubert, 1715 (862 pp.; Ferguson, i, 322).

E. Latin translations of Glauber's works in 4 vols. 8°, Amsterdam, 1651–56 (Bolton, (1), 1893, 483, gives 1650–70, with list of contents) and 7 vols. 8°, Amsterdam, 1661, are mentioned.[1] They probably consist of collections of the separate tracts listed below,[2] some of which are often bound together.

De Villiers[3] gives a list of 56 German works of Glauber, not all of which he had seen in the first editions quoted, and says they would form 8 to 10 vols. in 8°; the titles only are often in Latin but the text in German. Latin translations appeared in many cases almost simultaneously; according to de Villiers the 14 works marked with an asterisk below were not translated into Latin. Works marked with § are *not* contained in C, which is otherwise complete. The long titles of many works (given by Gmelin and Ferguson) have been abbreviated. Editions not seen but quoted are shown in square brackets.

(F, G). 1. De Auri Tinctura sive Auro Potabili Vero Was solche sey, und ... wo zu solche in Medicina könne gebraucht werden, 8°, Amsterdam, Johann Fabel, 1646, [1650], 1651 (BM 1033. b. 11. (2.)), 1662; [Frankfurt, 1652]; Latin: De Auri Tinctura Sive Auro Potabili Vero. Quid sit & quommodo differat ab auro potabili falso, & Sophistico, 8°, Amsterdam, 1651 (22 pp.); Sotheran *Cat.* 773 (1919), no. 2514 f., gives 12°, Amsterdam, 1658, but this is probably no. 15. This is Glauber's first published work, the least important but the only one dealt with in detail by Thorndike.

(F, G). 2. Furni novi philosophici oder Beschreibung einer Newerfundener Destillirkunst, 8° (Johann Fabel), Amsterdam, 5 parts; I 1646 pp. 102, ii; II 1647 pp. 183, v; III 1648 pp. 64; IV 1648 pp. 106, ii; V 1649 pp. 56, viii Appendix (BM 1033. b. 9); also Amsterdam, I 1648, II 1649, III 1650; all five parts, sm. 8°, Frankfurt, Matth. Meriani Erben, 1652 (each part paginated separately but signatures A–Zz₈ incl. Appendix continuous; Quartich Cat. 1957, no. 762); 5 pts., Amsterdam, Jannson, 8°, 1661 (Ferguson, i, 324); Prague, 1700.[4] Latin: Furni Novi Philosophici,

---

[1] Lenglet du Fresnoy, iii, 175; Gmelin, (1), i, 643; Graesse, *Trésor de livres*, 1862, iii, 93.
[2] See, e.g., Duveen, 254–7, in 8 vols.
[3] In Spielmann and Cadet, *Instituts de Chymie*, 1770, ii, 354 f.
[4] Gmelin; Speter, *Chem. Ztg.*, 1929, liii, 237.

Sive Descriptio Artis Distillatoriæ Novæ . . . , 5 parts, with Appendix and Annotationes in Appendicem quintæ partis . . . , 8°, Amsterdam, J. Jasson, 1651; reprint
(rare) 1658 (Sotheran *Cat.* 800 No. 10903); 2 ed. with Appendix, Amsterdam,
J. Jasson, 1661; Pars tertia 1664; Pars quarta 1658; Annotationes in Appendicem,
1658, 1664. The 1651 and 1661–4 eds. contain: I 67 pp., i l., 1 fold. pl.; II 148 pp.,
ii ll., 1 fold. pl.; III 55 pp., 1 fold. pl.; IV 83 pp., i l., 1 pl.; V 54 pp. (Appendix
49–54); Annotationes 72 pp. English: A Description Of New Philosophical Furnaces, Or A New Art of Distilling, divided into five parts, Whereunto is added a
Description of the Tincture of Gold, Or the true Aurum Potabile [*i.e.*, No. 1
above]; also the First Part of the Mineral Work [*i.e.*, No. 3, I below] . . . by
John Rudolph Glauber. . . . Set forth in English by J[ohn] F[rench] D.M., sm. 4°.
London, 1651: sep. t.ps. for each part dated 1652 (pp. xvi, 452, xii: contains 5 pts.,
Appendix, and Annotations (BM E. 649. (3.); French tr., 8°, Paris, 1674, and
Brussels, 1674, are quoted by Gmelin.
(G) 3. Operis Mineralis, oder vieler künstlichen vnd nutzlichen Metallischen Ar-
beiten Beschreibung . . . 3 parts [I, 1650; II, III, 1651], 8°, Amsterdam, I 1651,
II–III 1652 (BM 1033. b. 10);[1] Latin: Operis mineralis, 8°, Amsterdam, 3 pts.
[I, 1651], II–III, 1652; I–III: 1657, [1658], 1659 (I 67 pp. i l.; II 47 pp.; III
110 pp.); Pt. III is a commentary on Paracelsus's Cœlum Philosophorum.
(G) 4. Miraculum Mundi oder Ausführliche Beschreibung der wunderbaren Natur,
Art, vnd Eigenschafft des Grossmächtigen Subiecti . . . , 8°, Part I,[2] Amsterdam,
1653 (with copperplates); Miraculi Mundi Ander [Part II] Theil. Oder Dessen
Vorlängst Geprophezeiten Eliæ Artistæ Triumphirlicher Ein Ritt. . . . Dieses
alles durch die grosse Gnad vnd Barmhertzigkeit Gottes erfunden . . . , Amsterdam,
J. Jansson, 1660 (BM 1033. b. 21; 1033. b. 24. (1.)). Latin: Miraculum Mundi sive
Plena Perfectaque descriptio admirabilis Naturæ, ac Proprietatis potentissimi
Subjecti, 8°, Amsterdam, I 1653 (87 pp.), 1658; II 1660 (I 64 pp., II 101 pp.). The
work q. by Gmelin, i, 637 as Von Tugend, Krafft und Eigenschaft des Menstrui
universalis, is only the beginning of Pt. I.
(G) 5. Explicatio oder Aussführliche Erklärung vber das vorlangsthin . . . Auss-
gangnes (Miraculum Mundi) intitulirtes Tractätlein, 8°, Amsterdam, 1656;
Frankfurt, 1656 (Ferguson, i, 325); Latin: Explicatio Tractatuli, qui Miraculum
Mundi inscribitur, 8°, Amsterdam, 1656 (71 pp.); Frankfurt, 1656 (62 pp.).
(G) 6. Miraculum Mundi Continuatio, Darinnen die gantze Natur entdecket, und der
Welt nackent und bloss vor Augen gelegt, 8°, Amsterdam, 1657; Latin: Miraculi
Mundi Continuatio, in quo tota natura denudatur, & toti Mundo nudè ob oculos
ponitur, 8°, Amsterdam, 1658 (133 pp.).
7. Annotationes vber Diessen jüngst-heraussgegebenes (Continuatio Miracul
Mundi intitulirtes) Tractätlein, 8°, Amsterdam, 1659 (BM 1033. b. 21. (6.)). Latin:
Annotationes in Nuper editam Continuationem Miraculi Mundi, 8°, Amsterdam,
1659 (37 pp.; BM 1033. b. 14; Ferguson, i, 325).
(G) 8. Gründliche und wahrhafftige Beschreibung wie man auss den Weinhefen
einen guten Weinstein in grosser Menge extrahiren soll . . . , 8° [Nürnburg, 1654];
Amsterdam, 1654 (BM 1033. b. 23. (5.)); Latin: Vera ac perfecta Descriptio, Qua
ratione ex Vini Fecibus Bonum plurimumque Tartarum sit extrahendum, 8°,
Amsterdam, 1655 (28 pp.).
(G) 9. Pharmacopoea spagyrica oder gründlicher Beschreibung, wie man aus den
Vegetabilien, Animalien und Mineralien, auff eine besondere und leichtere Weise,
gute, kräfftige und durchdringende Artzneyen zurichten und bereiten soll, in 7
pts. and 3 Appendices, 8°, Amsterdam: I, 1654 and 1668 (also Nürnberg, 1654),
Pt. I has the title Pharmacopaeae Spagyricae; II 1656; III 1657; IV 1661; V 1663;
VI 1664; VII 1667; 3 Appendices to Part VII: (1) 1667; *2 1668; *3 1668. The Ger-
man collected works (A, 1658–9) contains only Pts. I–III. Latin: Pharmacopoea
Spagyrica, Sive exacta descriptio. Quâ ratione ex Vegetabilibus, Animalibus &
Mineralibus modo haud usitato faciliorique . . . medicamenta fieri præpararique
possint, 8°, Amsterdam, I 1654; II 1656; III 1657 and 1661; IV 1661; V 1663; VI
1664; VII 1668 (BM 1033. b. 19 and 1033. b. 22). (Pts. II and III have title
Pharmacopœa Spagyricæ, I, 76 pp., II 48 pp.)

---

[1] Frankfurt, 1651 (Ferguson, i, 326), 1655, 1695; Arnheim, 1656; Prague, 1705 (Ferguson, i,
326 for Pts. II–III).
[2] Frankfurt, printed Hanau, 1653 (Ferguson, i, 324); Rotenburg an der Tauber, 1653.

10. Apologia Oder Verthädigung, Gegen Christoff Farners Lügen und Ehrab-
schneidung, 8°, [Maintz], 1655; Latin: Apologia contra mendaces Christophori
Farnneri Calumnias, 8°, Frankfurt, 1655, 1665; § *. Zweyte Apologia oder Ehren-
Rettung gegen Christoff Farneri Lügen, 8°, Frankfurt, 1656 (BM 1414. a. 44;
Gmelin, i, 616).

§ *11. Glauberus Redivivus; Das ist: Der von Falschen und Gifftigen Zungen
ermordte . . . [against Farner], 8°, Amsterdam, 1656; Frankfurt, 1656 (Ferguson,
i, 328).

§ *12. Testimonium veritatis. Oder Gruendlicher beweis, dasz Farners Wiederlegung oder Warnung, ueber Glauberi Miraculum Mundi genantes Tractaetlein
. . . in geringsten keiner Wahrhafften Wiederlegung gleich, sondern nichts als auss
lauterem Neidt und Hass . . . ein zusammengeschaffte schmehcharten sey . . .
Und derer Unerhoerten Farnischen Luegen und verwegener Treulosigkeit voi
aller Weldt ein Offenbarung, 8°, Amsterdam, 1657 (320 pp., BM 1033. b. 24);
Farner replied to Glauber: [Ehrenrettung Christoff Fahrners Spagyrischen
Thumbstiffts Schaffners zu Löchgen wider die genandte Apologi, vielmehr aber
lugenhaffte Lästerschrifft Johann Rudolph Glaubers . . . 8°, Stuttgart, 1656];
Glauberus Refutatus . . . Das ist Ein Hundert Lugen . . . Auss Glaubers selbst
eigenen Schrifften . . . Durch Antiglauberum . . . , *s.l.* 1661, is probably by Farner.
A work by Glauber, Apologetische Schrifften in 280 Aphorism. gesetzt durch H. J.
Macle, in four parts, is contained in A (1658–9).

(G) 13. Dess Teutschlands-Wohlfahrt (Teutsch-landts Wohlfart on t.p. of vol. 1), in
6 parts and appendix to V; 8°, Amsterdam, I 1656 (also Arnheim 1656), II 1657,
III 1659, IV 1659, Annotat. to Part IV 1659, V 1660, Appendix to Part V 1660,
VI 1661 (complete in German in BM 1033. b. 12; also Prague, 1704, Ferguson, i,
327). The German collection A (1658–9) contains only Parts I–II. Latin: Pros-
peritatis Germaniæ, 8°, Amsterdam: I 1656, II 1657 and 1659, III 1659, IV 1659
(Nourry-Thiébaud *Cat.* 66 (1938) No. 882 gives an ed. of 1669), V 1660, Appendix
to Part V 1660, VI 1661 (complete in Latin in BM 1033. b. 13; pts.I–II, 1139. b.
8). According to Gmelin the Curieuser Tractat vom Gebrauch und Nutzen des
Weins, Korns und Holtzes . . . , 8°, Amsterdam, 1686, is really only part I of
Teutsch-Lands Wohlfahrt; an ed. of it was publ. in Prague, 1704 (Ferguson, i,
327, all six pts. and Appendix to V).

(F, G) 14. Trost der Seefahrenden, 8°, Amsterdam, 1657; Latin: Consolatio navi-
gantium, Amsterdam, 1657 (BM 1033. b. 15. (4.)); Dutch: Der Zee-Luyden
Gesontheydts-welvaren, Amsterdam, 1659 (BM 1033. b. 25. (1.)).

(F, G) 15. Tractatus de Medicina Universali, sive Auro Potabili Vero oder ausführliche Beschreibung einer wahren Universal-Medicin, 8°, Amsterdam, 1657 and
1658. (Gmelin also gives 1653; Sotheran, *Cat.* 839 (1934) No. 462 gives 18°, Amsterdam, 1658, as the first ed.); Latin: Tractatus De Medicina Universali, sive Auro
Potabili Vero, hoc est accurata Descriptio verae Medicinae Universalis, . . . 8°,
Amsterdam, 1658.

(G). 16. Tractatus de natura Salium oder ausführliche Beschreibung, deren be-
kanten Salien . . . und absonderlich von einem der Welt noch gantz unbekantem
wunderlichem Saltze . . . , 8°, Amsterdam, 1658; Latin: Tractatus de Natura
Salium. Sive Delucida descriptio, perfecta explanatione declarans naturam . . . 8°,
Amsterdam, 1659.

(G) 17. Tractatus de Signatura Salium, Metallorum et Planetarum oder gründlicher
Unterricht wie oder auff was Weise man gar leichtlich nicht allein der Salien,
Metallen und Planeten, sondern auch der Wörter und Nahmen ihre verborgene
Kräfften, Bedeutung und Natur . . . erlernen . . . kann, 8°, Amsterdam, 1658;
Prague, 1703 (Ferguson, i, 327); Latin: Tractatus de Signatura Salium, Metallorum
et Planetarum, 8°, Amsterdam, 1659. (The De Signatura Vegetabilium, Animalium
et Mineralium, mentioned in the above work, was probably never published,
according to Gmelin.)

18. Reicher Schatz- und Sammel-Kasten Oder Appendix Generalis ueber alle
dessen herausgegebener Buecher . . . in Decem Conturiis Treuherzig beschreiben
und an Tag geben, 5 pts. 8°, Amsterdam; I 1660 [and 1690], II 1660 [and 1690],
III, IV and V with one t.p. as * Continuatio Centuriarum, 1668 (BM 1033. b. 16);
Latin of I: Arca Thesavris Opvlenta, sive Appendix Generalis Omnium Librorum
hactenus editorum . . . , in Decam Centurias distributum, 8°, Amsterdam, 1660

(189 pp.); and of II as Opulenti Thesauri, et Arcæ Thesaurariæ ... Centuria Secunda, 8°, Amsterdam, 1661 (149 pp.). At the end of the German ed. the publication of a sixth 'century' is promised, and this appeared in 1669 as no. 20.

*19. De Tribus Lapidibus Ignium Secretorum. Oder von den drey Alleredelsten Gesteinen, so durch drey Secrete Fewer gebohren werden ... Von dem obern vnd vntern Donnerstein. Vnd wie des Basilii stein Ignis auss dem Antimonio durch kunst zu bereiten sey ..., 8°, Amsterdam, 1667, and 1668 (BM 1033. b. 20. (2.)); 8°, *s.l.* [Prague ?], 1703 (Ferguson, i, 328).

20. De Lapide Animali, Oder von dieser Animalischen Materi oder Subjecto ... und wie eine wahre universal Medicin daraus bereitet werden könne, ... 8°, Amsterdam, 1669 (irregular signatures: BM 717. a. 58); see no. 18.

*21. De Igne Secreto Philosophorum. Oder geheimen Fewr der Weisen ... 8°, Amsterdam, 1669.

*22. Libellus ignium: oder Feuer-Büchlein, darinnen von unterschiedlichen Frembden und biss dato noch gantz unbekandten Feuern gehandelt ..., 8°, Amsterdam, 1663.[1]

23. Libellus dialogorum oder Gespräch-Büchlein ..., 8°, Amsterdam, 1663;[2] Latin: Libellus dialogorum sive Colloquia, 8°, Amsterdam, 1663.

§ 24. Explicatio oder Auslegung über die Wörte Salomonis: In Herbis, Verbis et Lapidibus Magna est Virtus. Sampt beygefügtem Tractätlein de quinta essentia metallorum ..., 8°, Amsterdam, 1663; Latin: Explicatio verborum Salomonis ... una cum adjuncta tractatincula entia metallorum in gratiam ..., Amsterdam, 1664, [1675].

25. Novum Lumen chymicum: oder eines ... hohen Secreti Offenbahrung ... sondern auch die wahrhafftige Materia Lapidis Philosophorum zu finden ..., 8°, Amsterdam, 1664 (BM 1033. f. 34); Latin: Novum Lumen Chymicum. Hoc est, cujusdam recens inventi & Mundo unquam patefacti Secreti ardui Revelatio ... ubi non tantùm Aurum. Sed vera etiam Materia Lapidis Philosophorum subministretur, 8°, Amsterdam, 1664 (Ferguson, i, 325; 45 pp.); tr. by W.[illiam] C.[ooper], The Golden Ass Well managed, and Mydas Restored to Reason. Or a new Chymical Light ... Written at Amsterdam, 1669. by John Rudolph Glauber ..., in The Philosophical Epitaph of W. C. Esquire ..., sm. 8°, London, 1673, vi ll., pp. 37–56.

26. Von den Dreyen Anfängen der Metallen, alss Schwefel Mercurio und Saltz der Weisen, wie dieselbige in Medicina, Alchymia, und andern Neben-Künsten nützlich zu gebrauchen ..., 8°, Amsterdam, 1666, [1668]; Latin: Tractatus de tribus principiis Metallorum, videlicet Sulphure, Mercurio et Sale Philosophorum, 8°, Amsterdam, 1667.

*27. Kurtze Erklährung über die höllische Göttin Proserpinam, Plutonis Hausfrawen ... allen Liebhabern, der unbetrüglichen Alchimiae zu gefallen beschrieben und an Tag gegeben, 8°, Amsterdam, 1667 (BM 1033 .b. 20).

*28. De Elia Artista. Oder wass Elias Artista für einer sey und wass Er in der Welt reformiren oder verbesseren werde, wenn Er kombt? Nemblich die Wahre Spagirische Medicin, 8°, Amsterdam, 1668 (BM 1143. a. 3. (1.)).

*29. De Purgatorio Philosophorum oder von dem Fegfewer der Weysen ... von den alten Philosophis Ysopaica genant worden ... Ars lavandi per Ignem, 8°, Amsterdam, 1668.

§ *30. Glauberus concentratus. Oder Laboratorium Glauberianum, ... Durch den Authorem vnd Besitzer obgedachter Raritäten, den Vnwissenden zur Nachricht beschrieben vnd an Tag gegeben, 8°, Amsterdam, 1668 (BM 1143. a. 3. (5.) and (1.)); 75 pp., 15 p. catalogue of books at end; a list of preparations, apparatus, etc., for sale by Glauber, published by himself; Ferguson, i, 323; partly repr. in D.

Glauber's principal work, *New Philosophical Furnaces* (1646–9), described as 'certainly one of the most remarkable books on chemistry of the seventeenth century',[3] contains most of his important chemical discoveries. As a political economist Glauber was well in advance of his time; he made many

---

[1] Prague ?, 1703, Ferguson, i, 324, *s.l.*, 64 pp.   [2] Prague, 1703, Ferguson, i, 328.
[3] Ferguson, i, 329.

suggestions as to how materials then imported into Germany could be made from native ores and raw materials by processes which he worked out, and suggested that German goods should be sold to other countries for gold:[1]

Deutschland ist von Gott sonderlich hoch begabet, mit allerhand Bergwercken von andern Ländern und Königreichen; mangelt nur an erfahrnen Leuten, welche dieselbe zu recht wissen zu bringen . . . Inden wir andern Nationen unserm Ueberfluss für Gold verkauffen könten, führen wir dasselbe auss dem Land, andere damit zu bereichern, und vns zu entblössen.

He insisted on the value of experimental work and says: 'those that stick to so many books, will hardly ever come to get any good, but are led out of one Labyrinth into another, spending their life miserably in watching and cares:

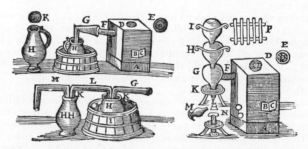

FIG. 12. APPARATUS USED BY GLAUBER. NEW PHILOS. FURN.
ON THE RIGHT IS A FURNACE FOR DISTILLATION, WITH RECEIVERS G, H, I. ON THE LEFT IS A RECEIVER COOLED IN A TUB OF WATER, AND BELOW IS SHOWN THE METHOD OF CONNECTING TWO RECEIVERS TOGETHER.

but if they would first seriously consider things, and learn to know nature, and then take their work in hand, then they would sooner attain to true knowledge.'[2] This practical bent is found in nearly all his works, and is certainly praiseworthy.

In his theoretical and philosophical views, however, he is far too much influenced by Paracelsus and is much inferior to Boyle, or even Van Helmont. He believed firmly in alchemy, as is seen from some titles and many passages in his works, especially in his *Opus minerale* (1651) and his *Miraculum Mundi* (1653).[3] He published a supposed proof of the transmutation of silver into gold.[4] He also believed in the *alkahest* or universal solvent of Van Helmont[5] and in the efficacy of potable gold and other nostrums (tinctures of corals, etc.), and the universal medicine, all of the Paracelsan kind. He does not, however, claim much success in the transmutation of metals, but he says that when copper precipitates silver from solutions, if 'the business is managed knowingly and skilfully', some of the copper is converted into silver, and similarly when iron precipitates copper, some of the iron is 'exalted' into copper.[6] He accepted the theory of salt, sulphur and mercury of Paracelsus, but laid especial emphasis on the importance of salt: he speaks of 'these two creatures of God, fire and salt' as being really one,[7] and says: 'in the sun and in salt are all things'

[1] (3), III; A, 1658, 424 (not in C); Gmelin, (1), i, 643; cf. (13) I; C, i, 294.   [2] (2), II; C, i, 50.
[3] Kopp, (2), iii, 161 f.; (4), i, 50 f.   [4] (5), 1656; C, i, 177.
[5] (3), (4), (10); C, i, 108, 152, 163.   [6] (4), II; (13) II; C, i, 228, 334.   [7] (16); C, i, 250 f.

(in sole et sale omnia).[1] He obtained much curious information about the planetary symbols for the seven metals by enclosing them in squares,[2] but thought the planets had no influence on the generation of metals, also rejecting the efficacy of the divining rod.[3]

FIG. 13. APPARATUS USED BY GLAUBER: THE 'IRON MAN.'

A good example of Glauber's rambling style is his description of the deflagration of tin amalgam with saltpetre in the red-hot belly of his 'iron man'.[4] In this process, he says, 'the noxious and superfluous sulphur of the tin is burnt by the saltpetre', when the tin acquires 'a more compact and better body'. The amalgam is more easily powdered and mixed with the nitre than tin alone (Baptista Porta had used tin filings). On heating the product with coals, the tin is again obtained as a metal. Paracelsus and Basil Valentine had 'involved this operation in obscure words' but Glauber says he had made it manifest 'openly and clearly'.

In Glauber's time the experts in other subjects such as mathematics, mechanics, and astronomy had realised clearly that they had no authority in chemistry. Galileo was no chemist. Kepler said (1609): Vnd ob ich mich wol noch nie resolvirt, alweil ich kein Chymicus bin, so wil mich noch geduncken, das Fewer sei materialiter nicht anders, dann der Schwebel, sulphur in motu constitutum.[5] The historians of chemistry have nothing to say about Kepler.

Glauber was a very skilled practical chemist. He improved and invented many kinds of furnaces and stills, and used a chimney (an iron pipe 5, 6, 8 or 12 ft. high) at the top of a furnace to increase the draught, instead of using bellows.[6] He made use of cheaper wooden apparatus when this would serve

[1] (18); I Cent.; C, ii, 1, 32.   [2] (17); C, i, 270.
[3] (3), II; C, i, 120.   [4] (6); C, i, 201, and plate.
[5] Kepler, *Opera*, ed. Frisch, 1858, i, 541; q. by Lasswitz, (1), i, 328.
[6] (2), V; C, i, 68; it has been said that Glauber first used a chimney on a furnace.

instead of metal, and tin-glazed pottery instead of glass.[1] He describes and illustrates the U-shaped 'safety tube' containing mercury for allowing gases to escape (later called 'Welter's tube').[2] He used an annular mercury seal with a bell-shaped cover,[3] ground in glass stoppers with emery,[4] used lutes for broken glass, describes the making of crucibles and cupels,[5] recommends Hessian crucibles for high temperatures,[6] and frequently describes the use of filter paper and glass funnels.[7] He also used an apparatus very similar to the Woulfe's bottle.[8]

Glauber's descriptions of acids are very noteworthy. He gives the preparations and properties of the three mineral acids very clearly.

Hydrochloric acid (spiritus salis) was first made on the large scale by different methods:

(1) by quenching hot wood charcoal in common salt solution, then burning it in a special furnace and condensing the fumes in a glass receiver, or a series of receivers connected by tubes;[9]
(2) by mixing common salt, green vitriol and alum in a mortar, putting the mixture on a fire in his furnace, and condensing the vapours as before;[10]
(3) by distilling salt with clay, a little water being put in the receiver;[11]
(4) by distilling common salt with oil of vitriol.

(4) is obscurely mentioned in 1658;[12] in 1660 the oil of vitriol is denoted by 'A',[13] whilst in the same year Glauber[14] describes the process clearly, specifying equal weights of kitchen salt and oil of vitriol. Boerhaave[15] calls the product made by this process *spiritus salis Glauberi*, but before this Van Vreeswyck (who knew Glauber in Amsterdam: see p. 341) had given a recipe 'Om den Spiritus Salis van den Philosoph Glauberus te maken', by mixing 1 lb. of oil of vitriol with 2 lb. of common salt dissolved in 6 parts (deelen) of water and distilling.[16] Glauber knew that the acid obtained by the different processes was the same: its cost is given as 6 stivers (2½d.) per lb.[17] It is said to dissolve all metals and minerals except silver, and nearly all stones, converting them into useful medicines. In the dilute form it is recommended as a medicine and also as a drink, and in the kitchen as a substitute for vinegar, for making meat tender, and mixed with sugar as a sauce.[18] It also prevented scurvy.[19] Glauber also used double lead cisterns, the outer filled with cold water, to condense

[1] (2), V; C, i, 92.
[2] (2), V; C, i, 85 and plate; cf. Berzelius, *Traité de Chimie*, Paris, 1833, viii, 341, and plate vi, fig. 39.
[3] (2), V; C, i, 85 and plate; Nicholson, *Nicholson's J.*, 1803, iv, 6.
[4] (2), V; C, i, 87.   [5] (2), V; C, i, 90 f.   [6] (13), IV; C, i, 404.
[7] (2), II; (9); (18) Cent. II; C, i, 51; ii, 59, 102, etc.
[8] (2), I, plate; C, i, 2, and plate; Nicholson, *Nicholson's J.*, 1803, iv, 6.
[9] (2), I; C, i, 4; Boyle, *Works*, ed. Shaw, 1725, i, 68, said the process 'failed both with me and some of my acquaintance'.
[10] (2), I; C, i, 4.   [11] (14); C, i, 283.   [12] (16); C, i, 261.
[13] (4), II; C, i, 225.   [14] (18), II Cent.; C, ii, 53.
[15] (2), 1732, ii, 408; hoc experimentum utilissimum Glauberianae quoque industriae imprimis debetur unice.
[16] Vreeswyck, *Het Licht der Mane of Glans der Sonne*, Rotterdam, 1678, 74: many references to Basil Valentine.
[17] (2), Appendix to V; C, i, 95.
[18] (2), I; (14); (13), IV; C, i, 4, 283 f., 378.   [19] (14); C, i, 284.

the spirit of salt; three cisterns in his laboratory contained 1040 lb. of sheet lead.[1] The residue from processes (2) and (3) when dissolved in water and crystallised was *sal mirabile* (p. 341).

Glauber says that if oil of calamine (concentrated zinc chloride solution) is mixed with sand and distilled with a very strong fire, it gives a 'spirit like fire' (dat spiritum planè igneum), which is so strong that it can hardly be kept and dissolves all metals and minerals except silver and sulphur:[2] it has been supposed that chlorine is meant,[3] and since Glauber says the 'strong spirit of salt' dissolves gold[4] this is possible. Since, however, he speaks also of the product as a thick, fiery and strongly fuming oil,[5] he also meant it sometimes to be anhydrous zinc chloride.

Nitric acid (aqua fortis) was made:

(1) by heating 1 of saltpetre with 1 of bole or brickdust in the furnace;[6]
(2) better, by heating 1 of saltpetre with 2 of alum, giving *spiritus acidus nitri*;[7]
(3) by heating 1 of saltpetre with 2 of green vitriol, giving *aqua fortis*.[8]

In methods (1)–(3) some water was put in the receiver and the product is said to be practically the same. During the distillation, the glass receiver appears dark red in the middle of the process, when the strongest product is collected. If no water is put in the receiver, which must be well luted to the retort, a blood-red strong spirit of nitre is obtained,[9] which would be fuming nitric acid rich in nitrogen peroxide. A similar product is a 'fiery smoke of saltpetre' obtained by distilling zinc nitrate.[10]

(4) By distilling saltpetre with oil of vitriol:
Boerhaave[11] says the product, called *spiritus nitri fumans Glauberi*, was first obtained in this way by Glauber, who kept the process secret. Hoffmann[12] gives the process without naming the discoverer; König[13] gives it as Glauber's. Glauber says the acid colours hair, nails and feathers golden yellow and brightens the colour of cochineal when added to the dye-bath;[14] it dissolves iron and zinc easily,[15] and can be used for etching copper plates[16] and for separating gold and silver, leaving the gold as a powder.[17]

By distilling equal weights of white arsenic and saltpetre, Glauber says, a blue spirit comes over, which is very strong, but no water must be put in the receiver, otherwise it is turned white.[18] He must have obtained nitrous anhydride (N_2O_3), and the residue would be potassium arsenate: he says it makes copper brittle. He wrongly thought the blue colour came from the arsenic. *Aqua regia* was obtained by distilling aqua fortis with calcined common salt

---

[1] (13), Appendix to V; C. i, 418.   [2] (2), I; Amsterdam, 1651, 44; C, i, 9.
[3] Hoefer, (1), ii, 186.   [4] (9), V; C, ii, 149.
[5] (18), I Cent.; C, ii, 4.   [6] (2), II; (18), I Cent.; C, i, 23; ii, 6.
[7] (2), II; C, i, 23.   [8] (2), II; (5); C, i, 29, 180.
[9] (13), IV; C, i, 385.   [10] (18), I Cent.; C, ii, 6.
[11] (2), 1732, ii, 392 f.: mortalium primus Joannes Rudolphus Glauberus reperit hanc artem, arcanum prorsus, raro hinc pretio vendidit.
[12] *Observat. phys.-chem. select.*, 1722, ii, 3; *Opera*, Geneva, 1740, iv, 482.
[13] *Regnum minerale*, 4°, Basel, 1686, 138.
[14] (4), I; (5); 9, VI; C, i, 179; ii, 169.   [15] (2), II; C, i, 28.
[16] (5); C, i, 179.   [17] (2), IV; C, i, 70.   [18] (2), II; C, i, 30.

in a glass retort on a sand bath; it dissolves gold and other metals (except silver, and sulphur) better than that made from aqua fortis and sal ammoniac.[1]

Sulphuric acid (oil, or spirit, of vitriol) was made by distilling green vitriol or alum. It dissolves iron and copper only when water is added and precipitates [calcium sulphate] from a solution of lime in aqua fortis [calcium nitrate].[2] The usual process of burning sulphur under a bell can be much improved by using a pottery dish cooled with water placed over the burning sulphur.[3] Glauber mentions that if nitre is mixed with sulphur in due proportion and the mixture burnt, a strong spirit (sulphuric acid) comes over.[4] After Lemery's description (see Vol. III) this process was used in making sulphuric acid by the bell process. The acid obtained by distilling green vitriol and rectifying the product was very strong and charred wood;[5] it may have been fuming sulphuric acid. Glauber's 'moist fires' to be used against Turks, either projected by sprays or in bombs,[6] were apparently concentrated mineral acids, although he may have known the inflammation of oils by nitric acid.[7]

FIG. 14. PREPARATION OF OIL OF VITRIOL BY GLAUBER BY DISTILLING FERROUS SULPHATE.

In his memoir on the inflammation of essential oils by nitric acid, Rouelle[8] obviously had these 'flying fires' in mind when he says Glauber 'me paroît être le premier qui en a parlé, & même assez au long', since he gives the references to Glauber's *Prosper. German. VI, Explicatio verb. Salomonis*, and *Centuria prima*, mentioning 'les vaisseaux & des espèces de grenades' to contain 'ces feux liquides'.

Among the alkalis, Glauber attached great importance to salt of tartar (potassium carbonate), ascribing to it exaggerated powers.[9] He describes the distillation of ammonia from sal ammoniac and lime, potash (potassium carbonate), or (better) zinc oxide, and calls the product *sal volatile urinæ*. He states that the spirit distilled from human hair dissolves sulphur,[10] and must have obtained ammonium sulphide. He mentions that four immiscible liquid layers may be obtained with oil of tartar (concentrated potassium carbonate solution), spirit of wine, ammonia and an essential oil.[11]

Glauber's experiments on salts are especially important. He gives a long description of his *sal mirabile* (sodium sulphate, Na_2SO_4, $10H_2O$, 'Glauber's salt'), which he first discovered in the water of a mineral spring near Vienna (p. 341). This water was said to be 'nitrous', but Glauber separated the salt in crystals by evaporation and showed that it was quite different from saltpetre. He thought it was the same as Paracelsus's *sal enixum*, and also called it 'the universal salt of the philosophers'. Its long transparent crystals do not

[1] (2), II; C, i, 23.   [2] (2), II; C, i, 17, 18, 21, 22.   [3] (2), II; C, i, 54.
[4] (2), II; C, i, 29.   [5] (18), I Cent.; C, ii, 2.   [6] (13), VI; C, i, 437 f.
[7] (24); Kopp, (1), iv, 395.   [8] AdS, 1747, m 34–56.
[9] (9), II; C, ii, 93 f.   [10] (2), II; C, i, 49, 52.   [11] (2), II; C, i, 51.

deflagrate or decrepitate in the fire, they melt on the tongue like ice, and are not bitter but have a peculiar saline taste. When dried in a fire sal mirabile loses $\frac{3}{4}$ of its weight;[1] it should be 0·56. It can be used in medicine either externally or internally — when it acts as a purgative. He says when fused with gold in a glass retort it forms a greenish mass which gives a green solution, of great medicinal virtue, with rain water.[2] He knew that the natural salt was the same as that obtained as a by-product in making spirit of salt from common salt and green vitriol or oil of vitriol; it can be used as a flux.[3]

Glauber mentions the intense cold produced when spirit of salt (hydrochloric acid) is poured upon sal mirabile (Glauber's salt), which he used for strengthening wine by freezing out the water. He suggests that poor wines or weak vinegar should be strengthened by dissolving his dry *sal mirabile* in them and crystallising it out, when it acts as a 'water magnet'. The dry salt was also used for removing water from oils, mineral acids, etc. (all these processes have been patented in quite recent times).[4] When sal mirabile is fused with charcoal, the residue with acid forms sulphur, which Glauber thought came from the charcoal.[5] Glauber's recognition that salts contain an acidic and a basic constituent was in advance of his time, although not so clearly expressed as by Tachenius in 1666 (p. 293). He says that sal ammoniac, for example, contains, and can be prepared from, a volatile salt of urine (i.e. ammonia) and a common acid salt (i.e. hydrochloric acid):[6] Darauff berichte ich, dass in dem Sal Armoniac zweyerley Salien seyn, nemblich ein Sal Acidum, commune, und ein Sal volatile Urinæ, welche beide ohne dess einen tödtung nicht wol zu scheiden seyn. This artificial sal ammoniac is the same as that obtained from urine, common salt, soot and ox-blood, and that dug in some mountains.[7] A *sal ammoniacum secretum* (ammonium sulphate) is prepared from ammonia and volatile spirit of vitriol,[8] and a 'most secret and fiery sal ammoniac' (afterwards called *nitrum flammans*, ammonium nitrate)[9] was prepared from ammonia and aqua fortis.

Glauber explains that large crystals of a salt, e.g. tartar, can be obtained only when a large amount of solution is used.[10] He paid special attention to crystal forms, which he often describes; e.g. he says that common salt and potassium chloride crystallise in cubes,[11] vitriol and alum in knotty uneven masses unless highly purified, when they form cubes, saltpetre in long six-sided crystals,[12] and *sal mirabile* (Glauber's salt) in long crystals.[13] Pure saltpetre can be obtained by adding a solution of salt of tartar (potassium carbonate) to aqua fortis (nitric acid) till the noise and ebullition cease.[14] Glauber thought the fiery part of saltpetre came from the air.[15] He says he knew a way of converting hydrochloric into nitric acid,[16] and mentions a saltpetre made from common

---

[1] (18), Cent. II; C, ii, 53.   [2] (4), II; (16); C, i, 223 f., 259 f.
[3] (2), I; (4), II; (18), II Cent.; C, i, 4, 225; ii, 53.
[4] (18), II Cent.; C, ii, 44 f., 55 f.   [5] (26), 1666; C, iii, 4; Boyle, see p. 539.
[6] (2), II, *c*. 87, 1647, 160; A, 1659, ii, 137; C, i, 49, 51.
[7] (16); C, i, 258.   [8] (2), II; (9), VII; C, i, 51; ii, 178.
[9] (2), II; (9), VII, Appendix 3; C, i, 23; ii, 8; Kopp, (1), i, 129; iii, 250.
[10] (2), II; C, i, 38.   [11] (16); C, i, 259 f.   [12] (17); C, i, 275.   [13] (18), II Cent.; C, ii, 53.
[14] (17) (1658); (18), I Cent. (1660); C, i, 275; ii, 31; see Boyle, p. 541.
[15] (13), IV; C, i, 389.   [16] (13), III; C, i, 374.

salt,[1] so that it has been supposed[2] that he was acquainted with potassium chlorate. He may have boiled common salt with nitric acid and obtained sodium nitrate. He gives some details of the production of saltpetre on the large scale in 'nitre beds', but he incorrectly thought that lime, common salt, and alum, etc., could be converted into saltpetre. He recommends saltpetre as manure and for steeping grain before sowing.[3] By deflagrating nitre with charcoal, 'the Egyptian bird' flies away and the residue is similar to calcined tartar (potassium carbonate).[4] Glauber called the product of deflagrating nitre with charcoal 'fixed nitre' (nitrum fixum).[5] A mixture of nitre, sulphur and salt of tartar (potassium carbonate) explodes violently when fused, but when kindled it burns rapidly and metals are fused by the heat developed.[6] Glauber used fused saltpetre in refining metals, e.g. in separating copper and bismuth from gold and silver,[7] and calls it 'the true universal dissolvent'.[8] By exposing oil of tartar (concentrated potassium carbonate solution) to the air for a long time he obtained small star-shaped crystals arranged in circular clusters (potassium bicarbonate).[9]

Glauber made many experiments with what he calls 'soluble glass', i.e. potassium silicate, obtained as a clear, white, transparent glass by throwing a mixture of salt of tartar (potassium carbonate) with sand or powdered rock crystal or flint into a red-hot crucible, when the mixture 'boils like alum' (evolution of carbon dioxide) and fuses. This deliquesces in moist air to an oily liquid called 'oil of flints' or 'liquor of flint' (liquor silicum).[10] It precipitates metals from solutions of their salts, but the 'calx' precipitated is different from that obtained with salt of tartar since it is much heavier, 'because the flints (silices) mix with it:'[11]

Dieses Oleum oder Liquor Silicum hat die Natur, dass er alle Metalle die in Corrosivischen menstruis solviret seyn præcipitiret, aber nicht auff solche weiss, gleich wie ein Sal Tartari thut, dann der Calx metallorum, welcher mit diesem Liquore ist niedergeschlagen, viel schwerer davon (weiln sich die Silices damit vermischen) worden ist, als wann er nur mit Sale Tartari allein wäre präcipitiret.

The aqua regia holding gold in solution 'kills' the salt of tartar of the liquor of flints and causes it to abandon the silica, and in exchange the salt of tartar paralyses the action of the aqua regia so that it lets go the gold which it has dissolved. Thus the silica and the gold are both deprived of their solvents and precipitate together:

Als zum Exampel, Solvire in aqua regis so vil Gold du wilt, und giesse dieses Liquoris [Silicum] so viel darauff, bis alles Gold in Form, eines gelben Pulvers zu Boden gefallen, und die Solution weiss und klar worden ist, welche du abgiessen, und das gefällte Gold mit süssem Wasser absüssen und trucknen sollst . . . und noch einmal so schwer wigen wird als das Gold vor der Solution . . . das Aqua regis hat durch sein aciditat das Sal Tartari getödtet, und krafftlos gemachet, dass es sein angenommene Kissling oder Sand hat müssen fallen lassen, hergegen hat auch das Sal Tartari bey dem Liquore silicum die schärpffe dess Aquae regis zunicht gemacht, dass es sein bey

[1] (6); (13), I, II, V; C, i, 186, 312, 335, 416.　　　　[2] Kopp, (1), iii, 362.
[3] (6); (16); (13), III, IV, V, etc.; C, i, 186 f., 259, 309 f., 335 f., 338 f., 409, 416; ii, 41.
[4] (2), II; C, i, 33.　　　　[5] (9), II; C, ii, 99.
[6] (2), II; C, i, 31; T. L. Davis, Chymia, 1949, ii, 99.　　[7] (5); C, i, 172 f.
[8] (9), II; C, ii, 98.　　　　[9] (17); C, i, 275.　　　　[10] (2), II; C, i, 44.
[11] (2), II, c. 82; 1647, 144; A, 1659, 125; C, i, 46.

sich genommenes ☉ [gold] nicht länger hat halten können, dadurch also zugleich das ☉ und Kissling, von ihrem solvente entlediget seyn.

Glauber says that when the precipitate (containing silica, gold oxide, and potash) is heated, a purple solid is formed:

dieses Pulver thue in einen reinen Tigel, und setze denselben zwischen glüende kohlen, dass es beginne zu glüen, aber nicht lang, so wird sich die gelbe in die aller schönste Purpurfarbe verwandeln, welches mit Lust zu sehen ist.

He emphasises that the precipitate made with salt of tartar is not explosive, as is that made with ammonia (spiritus urinæ).[1]

The description of the precipitation of a solution of gold in aqua regia (gold chloride) by liquor of flints (potassium silicate) illustrates Glauber's very clear idea of the play of elective affinities in solution, as that quoted on p. 357, dealing with the formation of butter of antimony from stibnite and corrosive sublimate, is concerned with affinities in the dry way. Another clear example is that explaining the displacement of ammonia from sal ammoniac by heating with zinc oxide: the latter 'loves acids very much and is loved by them', so that it combines with the acid salt and sets the ammonia free:[2]

Galmei . . . eine scheidung der salien gibt . . . weilen der Galmei oder Zink solcher Natur ist, dass er grosse Gemeinschafft mit allen acidis hat, dieselbe sehr liebet, und auch von ihnen geliebet wird . . . also hencket sich das sal acidum in der Wärme an denselben, verbindet sich damit, dadurch das Sal Volatile ledig gemacht, und zu einem subtilen spiritu destilliret wirdt.

The liquor of flints may be kept liquid by pouring over it a layer of alcohol.[3] Glauber described the tree-like growths ('chemical garden') formed when liquor of flints is poured over various metallic salts,[4] an effect due to the formation of semipermeable membranes.[5] Glauber describes the preparation of fulminating gold (aurum fulminans) by adding salt of tartar to a solution of gold in aqua regia (which must have contained ammonium chloride),[6] and he explains how potable gold is made by fusing gold with sal mirabile (sodium sulphate) — perhaps in presence of some reducing agent which would give sodium sulphide; the solution is green, but turns yellow or red on standing:[7]

mein Sal mirabile nicht allein alle Metalle, sondern auch alle Steine und Beine, ja die Kolen, welche sonst durch kein corrosiv zu solviren, radicaliter solviret, und meist allen dingen, die es solvirt, so wol Metallischen, als Vegetabilischen und Animalischen, eine grüne Solution gebe, darunter etliche grün bleiben, etliche aber mit der Zeit in eine Gelbe, oder Röthe verwandeln, von welcher wunderbaren solution ich ein gross Buch machen könte.

A green solution, giving small green crystals, is obtained by mixing lemon juice with a solution of gold, and adding ammonia, when only part of the gold is precipitated.[8] Glauber mentions the purple precipitate of gold produced from a solution of the chloride by tin.[9] He prepared a concentrated solution of

[1] (2), II, c. 82; 1647, 144 f.; A, 1659, 125; C, i, 79, 83, 114.
[2] (2), II, c. 87; 1647, 166; A, 1659, ii, 137.   [3] (9), II; C, ii, 102.
[4] (2), II; C, i, 7, 11, 48; see also Digby, Chymical Secrets, ed. Hartman, 1683-2, 136: To make metals vegetate.
[5] Fordham and Tyson, J. Chem. Soc., 1937, 483.
[6] (2), II; (5); C, i, 25, 182; cf. Kunckel, p. 375.
[7] (16); A, 1658, i, 501; C, i, 265.   [8] (2), II; C, i, 50.   [9] (13), IV; C, i, 384.

gold chloride and recommended it as an internal remedy without specifying the dose, although it is a violent poison; he prescribed it for old ulcers of the mouth, tongue, and throat arising from venereal disease.[1] He mentions the 'silver tree' formed when mercury is put in a solution of silver nitrate.[2]

Ammonia gives a blue solution with a solution of silver [containing copper] in aqua fortis[3] and also dissolves calcined copper to a deep blue solution[4] which deposits crystals called by Glauber vitriol of copper (vitriolum veneris).

A solution of silver nitrate can be used to blacken wood, furs and feathers, and to dye hair, skin, nails, etc., red to black.[5] The white precipitate (silver chloride) thrown down from the solution by common salt is very fusible, melting in a candle flame, and is volatile:[6] the precipitate dissolves in ammonia.[7] Ammonia throws down a black precipitate (silver oxide) from the silver solution, but the clear solution on evaporation deposits white crystals, which he called 'vitriol of silver' (vitriolum lunæ).[8]

Glauber[9] was apparently the first to describe the production of brass from copper and metallic zinc (which he says came from the East Indies), and to recognise that zinc is the metallic basis of calamine (which is nothing but 'infusible zinc'). Prince Rupert, who was associated with Glauber for a time, made use of an alloy of metallic zinc and brass made with calamine; this was harder than calamine brass.[10] Speculum metal is made by fusing copper with arsenic, then fusing with brass and finally tin: a description of casting the mirror is given.[11] Tin is hardened by melting 12 parts with 1 of antimony or zinc.[12]

Iron filings kill intestinal worms. When a bar of red-hot steel is touched with sulphur it melts and the fused product [ferrous sulphide] may be allowed to drop into water.[13] If a metallic ore containing sulphur is melted with iron, the sulphur deserts its native metal and joins to the iron, for which it has more affinity and similarity (cum quo majorem habet affinitatem et similaritatem).[14] Glauber describes the preparation of a solution of ferric chloride and recommends it for application to ill-conditioned ulcers and cancers.[15] Glauber prepared several metallic salts by dissolving the metals (or calces) in acids, as green vitriol ($FeSO_4$, $7H_2O$), blue vitriol ($CuSO_4$, $5H_2O$), white vitriol ($ZnSO_4$, $7H_2O$), copper and silver nitrates, and silver sulphate,[16] and he says that zinc displaces iron from a solution of green vitriol ($Zn + FeSO_4 = Fe + ZnSO_4$).[17] The green precipitate (basic copper carbonate) thrown down by salt of tartar (potassium carbonate) from a solution of copper in aqua fortis can be used as a pigment instead of verdigris.[18] Materials containing potassium manganate and

[1] (2), II; C, i, 23; Thomson, (1), i, 228, said this use, therefore, did not originate with Chretien, of Montpellier.
[2] (13), II; C, i, 334; see Eck of Sulzbach, p. 8.   [3] (2), II; C, i, 27.
[4] (2), II; C, i, 50.   [5] (2), II; (5); C, i, 27, 180.   [6] (9), III; C, ii, 127.
[7] (2), II; C, i, 18: known to Van Helmont, see p. 226.   [8] (2), II; C, i, 51.
[9] (13), II, 1657; C, i, 319.
[10] Smith and Gnudi, *The Pirotechnia of V. Biringuccio*, New York, 1942, 71.
[11] (2), IV; C, i, 79 f.   [12] (11); C, i, 155.   [13] (2), II; (9), IV; C, i, 20; ii, 136.
[14] (2), IV; C, i, 74.
[15] (2), II; C, i, 28; Thomson, (1), i, 228, says it had about 1830 been recommended as a remedy for cancers.
[16] (2), II; C, i, 18, 26.   [17] (2), II; C, i, 35.   [18] (5); C, i, 179.

permanganate were obtained by Glauber, since he says that when 'magnesia' (pyrolusite, manganese dioxide) is fused with fixed saltpetre (potassium carbonate) the mass when dissolved in water and filtered gave a solution of a 'dainty fiery purple' colour (potassium permanganate, $KMnO_4$), which on standing in the cold changed colour every hour, becoming green (potassium manganate, K_2MnO_4), blue, and red.[1]

Glauber made many experiments with coloured glasses, and he obtained a gold ruby glass (p. 355). He says that when liquor of flints (potassium silicate) is added to a solution of gold in aqua regia, the precipitate on heating changes to a most beautiful purple colour (in allerschönste Purpurfarbe verwandeln). When fused with glass this gives an azure colour and with iron (regulus Martis) a ruby coloured glass.[2] He mentions the blue glass containing cobalt made by fusing sand, potash, and cobalt minerals (bereitet von flüssiger Sand, Pott-Asche und zuthun Kobolt oder Kraupen von Wissmut-Erzt).[3]

Glauber was acquainted with tartar emetic.[4] His *panacea antimonialis*, a wonderful medicine,[5] was apparently the golden pentasulphide of antimony (Sb_2S_5). His sudorific *bezoardicum minerale*, also a precious remedy, was antimony pentoxide precipitated from antimony trichloride solution by nitric acid.[6] By dissolving antimony oxide in the acid obtained by distilling tartar (pyrotartaric acid) Glauber obtained what he called a panacea or universal medicine, which he claimed would cure the most virulent diseases, including all kinds of cutaneous eruptions; it might, he says, be the alkahest of Paracelsus and Van Helmont.[7]

Glauber gives a very clear description of the preparation of 'butter of antimony' (antimony trichloride, $SbCl_3$) by distilling stibnite (antimony sulphide, Sb_2S_3) with corrosive sublimate (mercuric chloride, $HgCl_2$); the reaction is: $Sb_2S_3 + 3HgCl_2 = 2SbCl_3 + 3HgS$. The same product is formed from antimony oxide and hydrochloric acid:

for sublimed mercury being mixed with antimony, feeling the heat of the fire, is forsaken by the corrosive spirits associating themselves with the antimony, whence comes the thick oil; at the same time the sulphur of the stibnite is joined to (conjugirt sich) the mercury and yields cinnabar, sticking to the neck of the retort. . . . Whence it necessarily follows that the thick oil is nothing but (metallic) antimony dissolved in spirit of salt. For the flowers of antimony [antimony oxide] being mixed with spirit of salt [and distilled] make an oil in all respects like the butter made from antimony and mercury sublimate.

He also showed by experiment that the white precipitate formed from butter of antimony and much water [antimony oxychloride, SbOCl], called *mercurius vitæ*, is really free from mercury, since on melting in a crucible 'it yields partly a yellow glass but no mercury at all':[8]

Oleum Antimonii: wann der mercurius sublimatus mit Antimonio vermischt, die Hitze empfind, so greiffen die Spiritus welche bey dem Mercurio sublimato seind, den Antimonium lieber an, und lassen also den Mercurium wieder fallen, und steigt also

[1] (13), III; C, i, 353: Scheele's 'mineral chameleon', Vol. III.
[2] (2), IV; C, i, 82 f.; Jorissen and Postma, Johann Rudolph Glauber, Andreas Cassius en het 'Purper van Cassius', *Chem. Weekblad*, 1927, xxiv, 30.
[3] (5), I; A, 1658, 187. [4] (2), II; C, i, 41. [5] (9), II; C, ii, 109. [6] (2), I; C, i, 8.
[7] (3), I; C, i, 106-9. [8] (2), I; 1646, 53; Latin, Amsterdam, 1651, 36; C, i, 8.

dick Oleum über: Der Sulphur Antimonii aber conjungirt sich mit dem Mercurio vivo, und gibt einen Cinnober, welcher im Halss dess Retorten bleibt, der übrige Mercurius bleibt zum theil zu rück . . . zum theil steigt mit über, doch wenig.

Dieses hab ich darumb angezeygt, weilen viel der Meynung seind, als wann es ein Oleum Mercurii were, und nennen also das weisse Pulver, welches sie machen, wann sie viel Wasser auff das Butyrum schütten, vnd sich das Antimonium wieder von den Spiritibus scheidet, und als ein weiss Pulver zu boden felt, einen Mercurium Vitae, da doch kein Mercurius darbey ist, gleich als nun bewiesen, sondern ein lauter Regulus Antimonii, welches man also erfahren kan, wenn man solches abgesüsste weisse Pulfer in einem Tiegel schmeltzet, so geht ein Theil in ein geel Vitrum, das ander wird ein Regulus, vnd findet sich kein Mercurius. Darauss zu schliessen, dass solches dicke Oleum nicht anders sey, als ein Solutio Antimonii cum Spiritu Salis.

In advancing these new, correct, and advanced opinions, Glauber says: 'let every one be free in his own judgment, for those things I have written I have not written out of ambition, but to find out the truth.'

He also obtained butter of antimony ($SbCl_3$) by distilling a mixture of stibnite, common salt and green vitriol (ferrous sulphate),[1] and similarly a butter of arsenic (arsenic trichloride, $AsCl_3$) by using white arsenic (arsenious oxide) or orpiment (arsenic sulphide, As_2S_3) instead of stibnite.[2] Several other metal chlorides were prepared by Glauber. Oil of lapis calaminaris (zinc chloride) was made by dissolving powdered calamine (native zinc carbonate) in spirit of salt, filtering, and evaporating till a thick red oil (containing ferric chloride) remained (the spirit of salt being almost mortified with the lapis calaminaris is deprived of its acidity). It was used internally and externally in medicine, and to dissolve birdlime.[3] Glauber also prepared stannous chloride crystals,[4] ferric chloride,[5] cupric chloride,[6] lead chloride by dissolving lead in spirit of salt or precipitating a solution of lead in aqua fortis (lead nitrate solution) with common salt[7] (the precipitate being recommended as a pigment in place of white lead), and gold chloride by dissolving gold in aqua regia.[8] Glauber proposed to precipitate the salt from sea water by adding salt of Saturn (sugar of lead; lead acetate), but admitted that the water was not rendered drinkable.[9]

Mercury dissolves metals from their ores in the order of gold, silver, copper and iron (with great difficulty); tin and lead are very easily dissolved.[10] Since gold and silver easily dissolve in mercury, their compounds are given for mercurial poisoning.[11] Red precipitate (mercuric oxide) was obtained by heating mercuric nitrate.[12] All mercury compounds are poisonous and calomel should not be given to children.[13]

Glauber describes several qualitative analytical reactions, both dry and wet tests. Thus, metals give characteristic colours when melted with fusible Venice glass (a precursor of the borax-bead test): copper, sea-green; copper + iron, grass green; iron, rusty colour; tin, yellow; silver, ruby; gold, blue (azure); gold + silver, emerald; gold + silver + copper + iron, amethyst.[14] Solutions of salts of metals give different coloured precipitates with ammonia and with salt of tartar (potassium carbonate).[15] In the fourth part of his *Philosophical*

[1] (2), II; C, i, 35.   [2] (2), II; C, i, 35: first obtained by Glauber, Kopp, (1), iv, 97.
[3] (2), I; C, i, 9.   [4] (2), I; C, i, 8.   [5] (2), II; C, i, 28.
[6] (2), II; C, i, 27.   [7] (2), II; (5); C, i, 28, 179.   [8] (2), II; C, i, 23.
[9] (14); C, i, 285; lead chloride and sulphate would be precipitated.
[10] (2), IV; C, i, 74.   [11] (2), II; C, i, 29.   [12] (18), I Cent.; C, ii, 28.
[13] (2), II; C, i, 28.   [14] (2), IV; C, i, 70.   [15] (2), II; (9), II; C, i, 50 f.; ii, 102.

Furnaces Glauber deals with assaying and docimastic processes,[1] and in the fifth part with lutes for glass vessels, grinding glass stoppers, the preparation and qualities of crucibles, antimony cups, and the glazing or vitrification of earthen vessels.[2] In the first part of his *Mineral Work* he deals with the separation of gold, which otherwise cannot be removed, from flints, sand, clay and other minerals, but the second and third parts are purely alchemical.[3]

Glauber prepared milk of sulphur by adding an acid to a filtered red solution of liver of sulphur.[4] He mentioned the peculiar efficacy of applying solutions of sulphur, etc., to the skin, and anticipated the various vapour and gaseous baths introduced in Vienna and other places early in the nineteenth century. A portable Turkish bath consisting of a tub or chest supplied with steam is shown.[5] Sir Thomas Browne[6] in a letter of 1679 says: 'you have seene a sweating tubbe of myne, wherof the figure is in Loselius *de podagra* . . . wherein the steeme of water doth all, as in some the steeme of *aqua vitæ*.'

Guichard[7] says that Glauber in 1658 knew that neutral salts remain neutral on mixing, and Rodwell[8] that he suggested that the gain in weight of metals on calcination 'may arise from the coagulation of heat by the metal during calcination'. I do not happen to have found these two items in Glauber's writings.

In Glauber's time the distinction between mineral and organic chemistry had not been made. He describes a number of organic compounds, mostly in a crude and impure form. He mentions mineral lakes of dyes,[9] fruit vinegars[10] and wood vinegar obtained by distilling wood, the same as ordinary vinegar but sharper, and concentrated by freezing out water.[11] By dissolving salt of tartar or wood ash (potassium carbonate) in wood vinegar he obtained crystalline potassium acetate; he also dissolved zinc and lead oxides in vinegar to obtain the acetates, which on dry distillation gave an 'oil' (containing acetone).[12] He describes in some detail the destructive distillation of wood in closed beehive-shaped ovens, obtaining charcoal, and recovering tar and spirit (pyroligneous acid) with an air condenser: a dark red oil (creosote) obtained from the tar prevents wood from rotting.[13] By distilling fixed oils soaked in burnt clay balls he would obtain crude acrolein, and he also distilled sugar, honey, amber, etc.[14]

By distilling coal he obtained a sharp spirit and a blood-red oil. The red oil (containing phenol and cresols) he says is a balsam which heals ulcers: the spirit when purified by distillation with spirit of salt yields a white aromatic oil (containing benzene) and a less volatile oil (toluene and xylenes).[15]

Aromatic oils were obtained from flowers, seeds, plants, etc., by first grinding with salt water and then distilling. The oil was removed as an upper layer by means of a 'separating glass' (a separating funnel), distilled, dried with a 'calcined salt' (potassium carbonate, K_2CO_3) and distilled again.[16] Woods and

[1] (2), IV; C, i, 67.   [2] (2), V; C, i, 85.   [3] (3), I; C, i, 101–47.   [4] (9), II; C, ii, 102.
[5] (2), III; C, i, 55, 63.   [6] *Letters*, ed. Keynes, 1946, 139.
[7] *Essai historique sur les mesures en Chimie*, 1937, iii, 76.
[8] *Phil. Mag.*, 1868, xxxv, 20.   [9] (5); C, i, 179.   [10] (2), Appendix to V; C, i, 94.
[11] (2), I; (6); C, i, 189, 191.   [12] (2), I, II; C, i, 10, 36.
[13] (2), I; (6); C, i, 10, 189, and plate; Partington, *Chem. and Ind.*, 1923, xlii, 636.
[14] (2), II; C, i, 52 f.   [15] (2), II; (9), III; C, i, 30; ii, 126.   [16] (2), II, III; C, i, 52, 59 f.

gum resins could also be distilled with spirit of salt, and this process made old essential oils fresh again.[1] Animal horns and claws, and human hair were also distilled.[2] Glauber seems to have known that water is formed by the combustion of spirit of wine.[3]

FIG. 15. BEEHIVE OVEN FOR RECOVERY OF WOOD TAR (GLAUBER, 1657).
NOTE THE AIR CONDENSER AND TAR COLLECTOR.

When concentrated zinc chloride solution is mixed with the best rectified spirit of wine and the mixture digested some while, the spirit of salt will separate the spirit of wine and make the oil of wine swim to the top (vini oleum innatare faciet).[4] This would be ethyl chloride.

Malt extract dissolved in water was recommended as a cure for scurvy.[5] Crystalline grape sugar was obtained from honey, raisins, etc.[6] Plants, nux vomica, opium, toads, etc., were extracted with dilute nitric or sulphuric acids and a powder precipitated with salt of tartar (potassium carbonate), containing the concentrated virtue of the materials (alkaloids ?).[7]

Linen thread boiled with alkali or salt of tartar becomes lustrous like silk ('Mercerising'), and linen garments are waterproofed by soaking in linseed oil boiled with zinc or lead oxide ('oilskins'). Glue when made with spirit of salt and oil of calamine (zinc chloride solution) remains liquid when cold.[8]

Glauber introduced the Germans to 'Ersatzstoffe', since he describes how

[1] (2), I; C, i, 5 f.   [2] (2), II; C, i, 52.   [3] (9), VI; (28); C, ii, 158; iii, 55.
[4] (2), I; C, i, 9.   [5] (14); C, i, 279 f.
[6] (2), V Appendix; C, i, 95; *Annotat. in Append. V Pars Fornacem*, 1651, 14 f.
[7] (9), II; C, ii, 101, 111.   [8] (5); C, i, 180–2.

wines and spirits may be made from fruits and vegetables, how sour wines may be sweetened, vinegar made from fruits or by distilling wood, how bad cheese may be made good by spirit of salt, etc., the imitations being usually described as better than the genuine, or at least as competent to serve the good of Germany by avoiding imports.[1] He is also a precursor of 'Gasangriff' or chemical warfare; he describes how spirit of salt and corrosive acids might be sprayed or shot over 'Turks' so as to blind or incapacitate them,[2] giving the familiar excuse (with invocations of the Almighty) that 'no man is slain', and asking: 'Is it not lawful for us to smite our Capital Enemies the Turks with blindness, and to defend ourselves, our Wives and Children?' The 'Turks' would accommodate other troublesome neighbours of Germany. The sub-titles of the various parts of the *Prosperity of Germany*[3] show how many ideas, good and useless, Glauber had for the benefit of his native land; the third part claims to give 'a succinct explanation of Paracelsus's prophecy; that is to say, in what manner it is to be understood the northern lion will institute or plant his political or civil monarchy; and that Paracelsus himself will not abide in his grave, and that a vast quantity of riches will offer itself. Likewise who the artist Elias is, of whose coming in the last days, and his disclosing abundance of secrets, Paracelsus and others have predicted.' When he wrote this, Glauber was in Amsterdam, but he had a genuine desire to be of service to his native land.

KUNCKEL

Johann Kunckel (or Kunkel) (Hütten near Rendsburg, Schleswig-Holstein, 1630 (or 1638)–Stockholm (?), 20 March 1703)[4] was the son of an alchemist to the Duke Frederick of Holstein, and was his assistant; he also worked for pharmacists and in glass-works and had no scholastic training. Kunckel was throughout his life a believer in alchemy (but not in the universal medicine) and worked for several notable persons. In 1659 (perhaps in 1658) he was in the service of Duke Franz Carl of Sachsen-Lauenburg in his castle at Neuhaus, and of his brother Julius Heinrich, and was chamberlain, court apothecary and chemist to the first; some accounts say this appointment dated from 1654. He made experiments on metals, on the question as to whether there was a 'spirit' in the air which was attracted to plants and animals like a magnet (he often speaks of chemical affinity as 'Magnet'), and on the colours of flowers. About 1667 he entered the service of the Elector of Saxony, Johann Georg II, at Dresden, whose predecessors August and Christian I were very interested in alchemy and had the alchemists David Beuther and Sebald Schwärtzer in their service. Kunckel owed this appointment to the recommendation of Dr.

---

[1] (2), III; (4); (6); (8); (13), I, IV; (18), III Cent.; C, i, 67, 157 f., 186 f., 290 f., 298 f., 380; ii, 62; *Annotat. in Append. V Pars Fornacem*, 1651, 9 f.

[2] (13), VI; C, i, 432 f., 437 f. [3] Given by Thomson, (1), i, 230–2.

[4] Ganzenmüller, 1956, 46, 105, 192–203; Gmelin, (1), ii, 154; Hoefer, (1), ii, 192; A. W. Hofmann, (1), 1882, 30–6; Kopp, (1), i, 173; *id.*, (2), iii, 193; *id.*, (4), i, 58; H. Maurach, Johann Kunckel: 1630–1703, Deutsches Museum Abhandlungen und Berichte, V, pt. 2, Munich, 1933, 31–64, with 3 figs. and portrait; Peters, *A. Nat.*, 1912, iv, 178–214 (bibl.); Saverien, 1769, vii, 71 (who says, p. 95, that Kunckel died soon after 1696); Thomson, (1), i, 233; Thorndike, viii, 379 (dates Kunckel *c.* 1612–1702).

Langelott and Counsellor Vogt. He worked in the laboratories in Dresden and Annaberg at the 'Profession von der Anatomia metallorum'[1] and he says: 'Es ist bekandt, dass ich in Dresden bey 10 Marck Lunæ (silver) in Solem (gold) maturiret, andere sagen transmutiret.'[2] He claimed to have extracted mercury from all metals, but not much; he had made it from silver, lead, and antimony in less than six hours.[3] In the time of the Elector August of Saxony, in 1680–90

FIG. 16. J. KUNCKEL, 1630–1703.

(he died in 1686), sophists claimed to convert silver into gold and gold into silver, also mercury and copper into silver and gold, but the Elector had a tincture which coloured 1604 times its weight of mercury into the best gold.[4] Kunckel's process for extracting mercury from silver (or lead) was to dissolve it in nitric acid, precipitate with common salt, and heat the washed precipitate with quicklime and potash, when a little sublimate, which whitened gold, was obtained.[5] He converted silver into gold by heating it in thin leaves in a crucible with rock salt and repeating the process seven times.[6]

In his last work,[7] however, he did not claim any success; he says 'will ich niemanden Anlass geben nach dem Lapide Philosophorum zu trachten, denn

[1] I, ch. vii; in VII, 264; see list of works, p. 364.   [2] V; in VII, 175.
[3] I, ch. iii; in VII, 196–8.   [4] I, chs. v, vii; in VII, 237, 259.
[5] I (Chymische Brille); in VII, 141; VI, 1716, 204.   [6] I; in VII, 147.
[7] VI, 1716, 563–625 (Historia de Transmutatione Metallorum) 641–9 (Von der Thorheit der Chymicorum).

ich habe ihn selber nicht'.[1] He gives an interesting account of the large laboratory ('gold house') in Dresden, as big as a church, with furnaces and tall chimneys, of the old manuscripts, and of the harsh treatment of former alchemists who failed to achieve results.[2]

Kunckel made use of an old alchemical manuscript, *Scriptis Chymicis Saxonicis*, which Engelleder says was written by Abraham Riesse senr., from which he gives a recipe for transmutation,[3] also a process due to Sebald Schwärtzer.[4] The first process had in 1584, he says, 'tinged' 1024 parts to gold, but he himself found that 'die Augmentation ist geringe'. Christoph Grummet was Kunckel's assistant in Dresden and, in the belief that Kunckel had discovered the secret of transmutation, was annoyed that the process had escaped his notice. In Kunckel's absence he pretended that he had performed a transmutation and this caused a great sensation.[5]

Kunckel lost his situation and in 1677 (or 1676) he became a teacher in the University of Wittenberg, where he discovered the method of making phosphorus (see p. 372). He says he was assisted in experiments by Christian Vater (1651–1732, who later became professor of medicine in Wittenberg) but he had no facilities for work on metals (i.e. transmutation), and he obviously did not feel at home in academic work, saying: 'Ich fand gleichwohl auch dass es ein sauer Bissen Brot ist von Studiosus sich zu ernehren.'[6]

Georg Caspar Kirchmaier (Uffenheim, Franconia, 20 (29) July 1635– Wittenberg (?), 28 September (October) 1700), who was professor of rhetoric in Wittenberg but in his spare time studied numismatics, physics, chemistry, metallurgy, mineralogy, zoology, history, and theology, on many of which subjects he published a large number of works,[7] was interested in Kunckel and had him provided with a laboratory in which he taught practical chemistry.[8] Kunckel[9] says there was no professor of experimental chemistry in Wittenberg when he went there; Prof. Sennert could have given the course but he was then too old and infirm. Many medical students attended Kunckel's lectures.

In 1679 Kunckel went to Berlin as director of the alchemical laboratory of Frederick William of Brandenburg, the 'Grosse Kurfürst'. A visit to Kunckel's laboratory in Berlin, and a conversation with him on alchemy, are recorded by Jacob Toll.[10] On the death of his master in 1688, Kunckel's laboratory was accidentally burnt, and in 1689 he went to Sweden as Bergrath (minister of mines) to Charles XI, by whom he was ennobled as Baron von Loewenstern in 1693. He died on 20 March 1703, either in Stockholm or on a journey there, and it is not known where he was buried. A less likely account says he retired in 1703 to an estate in Livonia and died there.

Although Kunckel knew some Latin he wrote his works in German, giving some of them Latin titles, as was then customary. His style is very prolix,

---

[1] *Ib.*, 185. [2] VI, 1716, 568–625. [3] VI, 1716, 289. [4] VI, 1716, 591 f.
[5] VI, 1716, 607; he speaks of 'dieser Vogel [Grummet] und sein bosshafftiges Weib', *ib.*, 611.
[6] VI, 1716, 616. [7] Jöcher, ii, 2097–9.
[8] I am unable to find any confirmation for the statement of Peters, *A. Nat.*, 1912, iv, 178 (187), that Kirchmaier was professor of medicine and chemistry.
[9] VI, 1716, 615. [10] *Epistolae Itinerariae*, 1700; 2 ed., Amsterdam, 1714, 46.

rambling, involved, and difficult to read, especially as it mixes German with Latin in the manner then usual. He had a high opinion of Becher (Der unvergleichliche und Hoch-erfahrne D. Becher ... keiner so accurat),[1] although he criticised his views; he says[2] they never met. He thought 'Basil Valentine' was a good man but he never achieved the transmutation of metals (ob ich gleich unmöglich glauben kan, dass er den Lapidem, ja nicht eimahl ein Particular gehabt habe).[3] As a good German, Kunckel held himself in high esteem.[4]

A description of Kunckel's writings will now be given; some of the very long titles are abbreviated. The most important is the posthumously published *Laboratorium Chymicum* (1716).

I. Nützliche Observationes oder Anmerckungen von den Fixen und flüchtigen Salzen, Auro und Argento potabili spiritu mundi ... , 8°, Hamburg, 1676 (BM 1034. c. 17. (3.)); Latin tr. by C. A. Ramsay; Utiles Observationes sive Animadversiones de Salibus fixis & volatilibus, Auro & argento potabili, Spiritu mundi, & similibus. Item de colore & odore metallorum, mineralium aliarumque rerum quæ à terra producuntur, 12°, London and Rotterdam, 1678 (BM 1037. a. 17; Saverien, 89; with a list of the Royal Society).

II. Chymische Anmerckungen: darinn gehandelt wird von denen Principiis Chymicis, Salibus Acidis und Alkalibus, Fixis et Volatilibus, in denen dreyen Regnis, Minerali, Vegetabili und Animali ... mit Anhang einer Chymischen Brille contra Non-Entia Chym. ... , 8°, Wittenberg, 1677; Latin: Philosophia Chemica Experimentis Confirmata In qua agitur De Principiis Chymicis, Salibus acidi & alcalibus, fixis & volatilibus, in tribus illis Regnis, Minerali, Vegetabili, & Animali, itemque de odore & colore, &c. Accedunt Perspicilium Chymicum contra Non-entia Chymica, 12°, Amsterdam, 1694 (iv ll., 333 pp., iv ll.); Ferguson, i, 484; English: Pyrotechnical Discourses. Containing I. An Experimental Confirmation of Chymical Philosophy, treating of the several Principles in the Animal, Vegetable and Mineral Kingdoms. With a Perspective Against Chymical Non-entities, by John Kunkel. II. A Short Discourse on the Original of Metallick Veins, by George Ernest Stahl, M.D. III. The Grounds of Pyrotechnical Metallurgy, and Metallick Essaying, by John Christian Fritschius, all faithfully translated from the Latin: 8°, London, B. Bragg, 1705; 2 ed. 1730 (BM 1035. i. 3 and 8715. aa. 24).

III. Oeffentliche Zuschrift von dem Phosphoro Mirabili und Dessen leuchtenden Wunder-Pilulen. Samt angehängten Discurs von dem weyland recht benahmten Nitro ... , Leipzig, bey Michael Rustwurm, Gedruckt Joh. Wilh. Krüger, herausgegeben in Wittenberg, 1678.

IV. (a) Ars Vitraria Experimentalis, oder Vollkommene Glasmacher-Kunst ... samt einem II Haupt-Theil, so in drey unterschiedenen Büchern ... mit einem Anhang von denen Perlen und fast allen natürlichen Edelsteinen ... , 4°, Frankfurt and Leipzig, 1679 (BM 58. f. 29; for the very long title see Duveen, 328), dedic. to Elector Frederick William of Brandenburg, 2 parts: Pt. I, portr. (not in my copy), vii ll., pp. 1–200 Antonii Neri von der Glasmacher-Kunst (with Kunckel's notes), 201–12 Kunckels Sonderbahre Zugabe der Glas-Kunst, 213–337 Merrett's notes on Neri, 338–50 Kunckel's notes on Merrett. Pt. II, t.p. incl. in pp. 1–5, pp. 1–44 a hundred experiments (numbered), 45–71 Zugabe of miscellaneous recipes (with sev. t.ps. incl. in pagin.), 72–141 Drittes Buch ... Kunst-Stücken und Experimenten, xxxv pp. index and errata (unpaged), 18 plates; also 4°, Amsterdam and Danzig, 1679 (BM 563. a. 2); 2 ed. (incorrectly called 1 ed. by Bolton, (1), i, 594), 4°, Frankfurt and Leipzig, 1689 (Hoefer); 3 ed. 4°, Nürnberg, 1743 and 1756 (BM 1400. h. 6).

(b) Tr. by 'M.D ***' [i.e. P. F. Dietrich, Baron d'Holbach), Art de la Verrerie, de Neri, Merret et Kunckel, Auquel on a ajouté Le Sol Sine Veste D'Orschall; L'Helioscopium videndi sine veste solem Chymicum; Le Sol Non Sine Veste; Le Chapitre XI.

---

[1] VI, 1716, preface, 5 v.   [2] VI, 1716, 415.   [3] Ib., 476, 481.
[4] IVa, 1679, dedication, fol. Biii: wie denn meine Experientz, die ich in der Chymie erlangt, ohne Ruhm zu melden, in und ausser Deutschland bekannt und in aestim ist.

du Flora Saturnizans de Henckel, Sur la Vitrification des Végétaux; Un Mémoire sur la maniere de faire le Saffre; Le Secret des vraies Porcelaines de la Chine & de Saxe, 4°, Paris, 1752, t.p., i l., pp. lv, 630, i l., 16 plates. The work on zaffre is by Zimmermann, that on Chinese and Saxon porcelain is tr. from an anonymous German work (Berlin, 1750). The section on gems in IV*a* is omitted.

V. (*a*) Johann Kunckels ... Chymischer Probier-Stein / de Acido & Urinoso, Sale Calid. & Frigid. Contra Herrn Doct. Voigts Spirit. Vini Vindicatum, An Die Weltberühmte Königl. Societät in Engeland / als hierüber erbätene hohe Richter, Berlin, 6 July 1684, sm. 8°, viii ll., 204 unnumb. pp., errata, followed by:

(*b*) Johann Kunckels ... Epistola contra Spiritum Vini sine Acido An ... Johannes Voigt, t.p., 30 unnumb. pp. (BM 1033. a. 19; in item VII below, pp. 155–78, this is dated at end Berlin, 1681; Hoefer, (1), ii, 193, gives as a separate publication, 12°, Berlin, 1681; there was another issue of the whole book in 1686 (Sotheran *Cat.* 851 (1937), no. 1199; Hoefer dated it 1685) and again in 1696: Chymischer Probier-Stein, de Acido & Urinoso, Sale Calid. & Frigid, contra Herrn Doct. Voigts, Spirit. Vini Vindicatum, an die Weltberühmte Königl. Societät in Engeland, als hierüber erbätene hohe Richter. Worbey angefüget die Epistola contra Spir. Vini sine Acido, so an Herrn D. Voigten abgelassen, 8°, Berlin, 1696, no pagin. Ferguson, i, 483. The Royal Society printed a long review of the book in *Phil. Trans.*, 1684–5, xv, 896, no. 168, without expressing any opinion on the matter.

VI. Collegium Physico-Chymicum Experimentale, oder Laboratorium Chymicum, In welchem, Deutlich und gründlich Von den wahren Principiis in der Natur und denen gewürckten Dingen so wohl über als in der Erden, Als Vegetabilien, Animalien, Mineralien, Metallen ... Nebst der Transmutation und Verbesserung der Metallen gehandelt wird ... herausgegeben Von Johann Caspar Engelleder, Med. Doct und Pract. in Hamburg, 8°, Hamburg and Leipzig, Samuel Heyl, 1716; portr. and one plate, pp. xxxvi, 737, Index xxxvii (BM 1034. a. 16). My copy belonged to J. W. Baumer (1719–88), whose signature and the date 1758 is on the t.p.; he was then professor of physics in Erfurt. There are several MS. notes by him in the book. 2 ed. Hamburg and Leipzig, Samuel Heyl, 1722 (very rare); identical with first ed. in pagination;[1] 3 ed., Johann Kunckels Collegium Physico-Chemicum Experimentale, oder Laboratorium Chymicum ... Hamburg bei Gottfried Richter, 1738, identical with 1 ed. in pagination (BM 8907. a. 37). 4 ed. Johann Kunkels von Löwenstern Vollständiges Laboratorium Chymicum, worinnen von den wahren Principiis in der Natur, des Erzeugung, der Eigenschaften und der Scheidung der Vegetabilien, Mineralien und Metalle, wie auch von Verbesserung der Metalle gehandelt wird. Vierte verbesserte Auflage. Berlin, 1767, in Rüdigerschen Buchhandlung: rather tall 8°, 671 pp., 1 plate, index. Kunckel refers to Thurneisser as living in the preceding (16th) cent. (1716, 527) and (*Ib.*, 151) says he himself had worked at chemistry for sixty years, so that the book was probably written in Stockholm about 1700, although Peters, *A. Nat.*, 1912, iv, 178 (195) thinks it was written in Wittenberg in 1677–9. Engelleder in his preface, dated Hamburg, 25 April 1716, says he divided the text into chapters and improved the style in places without altering Kunckel's opinions, processes and experiments, although he had supplied the weights of the ingredients where they were omitted; on Engelleder see Gernet, Mitteilungen z. älteren Medicinalgeschichte Hamburgs, 286 f. A rearrangement and commentary, by Engelleder, is:

Königliche Hermetische Special-Concordanz ... Seines A. 1716 ... herausgegebenen Laboratorii Chymici, und zwar in Specie desselben 42. Capitels, ... von einem Liebhaber der reinen Wahrheit ... durch öffentlichen Druck an der Tag gegeben, 8°, Breslau and Leipzig, 1724 (703 pp., BM 1034. e. 29; Ferguson, i, 476; Sotheran *Cat.* 800, no. 1124).

VII. V Curiose Chymische Tractätlein ... nebst einer Vorrede ... D. Johannis Philippi Burggravii ..., 8°, Frankfurt and Leipzig, W. C. Multz, 1721. Contains I–III and V above (II, 1–154; I, 179–286; III, 287–326); V*b*, 155–78 (Epistola contra Spiritum Vini sine Acido); V*a*, 327–488 (Chym. Probier-Stein); also the Blut der Natur of Grummet (here called Brummet), 489–512; Index xxiv ll. The preface (iv ll.),

---

[1] Dörling Auction Catalogue 53, Hamburg, 1936, No. 219; Sotheran *Cat.* 832 (1932), No. 5388; Saverien, *op. cit.*, 97, who mistook it for the first edit.

dated Frankfurt, 21 April 1721, is by Johann Philip Burggrav, either the elder (1673–1746) or the younger (1700–75), Ferguson, i, 131, thinks the younger (he says he never knew Kunckel).

As a theorist Kunckel is not successful, and Stahl[1] criticised him on this ground (er zu der Wissenschaftlichen Betrachtung, oder Theorie, die nöthige Hülfe nicht genug inne gehabt), and also because he gives only such of his experiments as agree with his theory — a common failing even to-day. Kunckel believed that both light and darkness, and heat and cold, were real, not that darkness and cold were mere negations, and he explains a great many phenomena as due to the collision and struggle between heat and cold (kein Feuer kann formiret werden, wo nicht zwei Dinge, als Hitze und Kalte mit einander streiten), and saltpetre brings about deflagration because it contains much cold.[2] Kopp[3] found it difficult to extract any meaning from Kunckel's theoretical dissertations.[4] Kunckel accepted air and water[5] as principles; not ordinary water, but rather 'eine gewisse Materiam unctuosam & viscosam, welche ich auch Materiam cœlestem nenne . . . Universal-Sperma bestehet aus einem dicken, klebrichten, zehen, fetten und unctueusen Wesen'.[6] He says river water on keeping turns from hard (hart Wasser) to soft (weich Wasser) by absorbing celestial matter (so wird es von der Materia coelesti geschwängert).[7] He recognised that air is necessary for fire (nun ist die Lufft dessen Trieb, dann wo selbige nicht hin kan, da kan auch kein Feuer werden noch lichte brennen),[8] and says that tartar when strongly heated in a retort remains black but is converted into a white salt when air is admitted.[9] He believed that metals are generated in the earth by coction from water and a universal sperm,[10] and that combustibles contain a peculiar viscous matter (nun brennet kein Ding in der Welt, es brenne dann vermittelst dieser Materia viscosa), commonly called sulphur. He made the mistake of denying the presence of sulphur in several sulphide ores of metals, although he recognised its presence in cinnabar and some other minerals.[11] He denied the presence of fixed sulphur in metals: Ich, als so ein alter Mann, der bey der Chymia etliche sechzig Jahre zugebracht, habe noch nicht finden können, was Sulphur fixum, oder was es in den Metallen sey? . . . Denn obgleich alle Vorfahren vom Sale Sulphure & Mercurio viel Wesens gemacht, und solche als Principia auff die Bahn gebracht, so will an seinem Ort erwiesen, dass es falsch sey.[12] All kinds of things have been called sulphur but this does not make them so: es hat wohl ein jeder Macht sein Kind zu nennen wie er will; wann ich aber einen Esel wolte einen Ochsen nennen, so kan es mir zwar keiner wehren, kein Mensch aber würde sich doch überreden lassen, dass der Esel deshalben Ochse wäre.[13]

Kunckel at first regarded sulphur as a fatness of the earth, which contains a combustible oil, since it not only burns but also combines with alkalis and dis-

[1] *Von dem Sulphure*, 1718, 58. [2] VI, 1716, 105. [3] (2), iii, 197 f.
[4] VI, I Theil, Von denen Principiis Naturalibus, e.g. ch. ii, Von der Finsternüs als dem andern Principio; ch. v, Von der Wärme und Kälte, auch Feuer und Bewegung.
[5] *Ib.*, ch. iv: Vom Wasser als dem einigen Material-Principio.
[6] *Ib.*, 35. [7] *Ib.*, 49. [8] *Ib.*, 58. [9] II; VII, 1721, 90.
[10] VI, 1716, 72 f., 260. [11] I, II; VII, 1721, 76 f., 196; VI, 1716, 151, 188.
[12] VI, 1716, 151; cf. 198 f., 191 f. (vom Sulphure Metallorum). [13] *Ib.*, 190.

solves in oils,[1] but later experiments showed him that it is a compound of a combustible and an acid (ich durch andere experimenta befunden, dass er in solcher Fettigkeit bestehe, wie die Olea vegetabilia sind; sondern dass sein Principium sey ein Acidum, und sein Lumen oder Flamma in einem Volatili nur).[2] He denied the truth of the statement: ubi ignis ibi sulphur et calor, item ubi flamma ibi sulphur (where there is fire there is sulphur and heat, and where there is flame there is sulphur),[3] which is sometimes[4] erroneously attributed to him. Lemery[5] also pointed out that heat could arise without sulphur, e.g. by the action of water on quicklime, which contains igneous particles.

Kunckel believed that mercury is a constituent of metals, but doubted its presence in vegetables and animals.[6] He criticised the vague statements about an 'internal sulphur' in mercury, etc. (es jammert mich aber sehr der blinden Wort-Gelehrten, wann sie schreiben: Wo bleibet des mercurii sein sulphur internum? &c. Antwort: Er bleibet da er gewesen, nemlich nirgends).[7]

Berzelius[8] says Kunckel observed that metals when heated with sulphur produce a fire which he compares with that in saltpetre and concluded that sulphur participates in its nature, but this observation was forgotten until it was rediscovered by the Dutch chemists (Vol. III). Kunckel[9] says that when powdered tin and sulphur are heated in a crucible, 'so bald der Schwefel anfängt zu brennen / und das Zinn berühet / so entzündet es sich / als wann Nitrum darunter wäre / und das Zinn wird zu Pulver.' In a similar experiment with copper[10] he does not mention the incandescence, but reports it for lead and sulphur.[11]

Kunckel gave a severe but fair criticism of the views of Van Helmont,[12] for whom, in general, he entertained great respect. He criticised the *alkahest* of Paracelsus and Van Helmont, since if it dissolves everything, it should dissolve the vessel which contains it. 'I must give its true name (since such a solvent cannot be what Helmont writes of it) and it is really this: Alles Lügen heisst, oder: Alles Lügen est' (it is all lies).[13] He also denied the efficacy of potable gold, saying that many preparations owed their colour only to burnt sugar, etc.[14]

Kunckel, as a professional alchemist, did not think the transmutation of metals contradicted 'Aristotle's' dictum (see Vol. I): *species in speciem non transmutatur*, since there is no transmutation but only improvement: 'In der Chymie sind vielerhand Scheidungen und dadurch Verbesserungen, aber keine Transmutationes . . . Ein anders ist transmutatio, ein anders propagatio und maturatio.'[15] He relates that his assistant Grummet once claimed to have converted, in Kunckel's absence, some silver into gold,[16] but he knew that many alchemists were fraudulent: a red projection powder was found to contain only sulphur, arsenic and antimony, and the gold and silver were to be put

---

[1] I; VII, 185.　　　　[2] II; VII, 1721, 10.　　　　[3] II; VII, 1721, 5 f., 16 f., 80 f.
[4] Mellor, (1), i, 64.　　　[5] *Cours de Chymie*, 1690, 318.
[6] II; VII, 1721, 55, 131, 133, 196, 280; VI, 1716, 202 f.　　　[7] VI, 1716, 483.
[8] *Essai sur la Théorie des Proportions Chimiques*, 1819, 63.　　　[9] VI, 1716, 386 f.
[10] *Ib.*, 397.　　　　[11] *Ib.*, 419.　　　　[12] VI, 1716, 247–55, 491–563.
[13] VI, 1716, 506, 527 (al Lügen est).　　　[14] *Ib.*, 280 f.　　　[15] *Ib.*, 567 f.　　　[16] *Ib.*, 606.

in by a trick (könte man dergestalt das Gold und Silber durch einen Handgriff hinein bringen);[1] in spite of this, the transmutation of metals can only be denied by people who know of Nature only from books (dieses zu negiren steht nur solchen Leuten zu die in der Natur weiter nichts als aus Büchern wissen).[2]

Kunckel had great enthusiasm (es ist die Chymie das edelste Studium in der Welt),[3] ample opportunities for experiment, a capacity for keen observation, great patience and stubborn application — in fact all the qualities which are found in a great chemist. He was a man of transparently honest character,[4] and in cases where his word is set against that of men such as Leibniz and Stahl, it may be accepted without hesitation.[5]

Glass

Kunckel's book on glass (IV), *Ars Vitraria Experimentalis*, incorporates a small early work by Antonio Neri,[6] a priest, perhaps born in Florence, who probably worked in Murano, travelled a good deal, and died at Pisa in 1614.[7] Neri's work was translated with large additions[8] by Christopher Merret or Merrett (Winchcomb, Glos., 16 February 1614–London, 19 August 1695), F.R.S.[9] Merrett enumerates twenty-eight properties of glass which distinguish it from all other bodies.[10] Neri describes the preparation of lakes of Brazil wood and madder,[11] also of kermes, 'which is my invention'.[12]

Thomson says Kunckel's *Ars Vitraria* 'till nearly the end of the eighteenth century, constituted by far the best account of glass-making in existence'. It is divided into two parts, the first containing the seven books of Neri and the notes of Merrett, and the second is by Kunckel. The second part, by Kunckel, is divided into three books, the first giving 100 experiments on calcination, gilding and painting glass, and glazing pottery, the second giving 60 experiments on making and painting faience in the Dutch style, and the third book gives 50 experiments on casting various models of plants from silver, colouring gypsum, marbling paper, making plastic wood, etc. In the first book there are recipes for colouring glass yellow with silver sulphide, iron ochre, and anti-

---

[1] *Ib.*, 620.   [2] II; VII, 143 (Chymische Brille).   [3] VI, 1716, 210.
[4] Kopp, (4), i, 60.   [5] Partington, *Sci. Progress*, 1936, xxx, 402.
[6] *L'Arte Vetraria distinta in libri sette*, 4°, Florence, Giunti, 1612 (iv ll., 114 pp., iii ll.); 8°, Florence, Marco Rabbuiati, 1661; 8°, Venice, Iacomo Batti, 1663; Latin, *De Arte Vitrariâ Libri Septem, & in eosdem Christoph. Merretti . . . Observationes & Notæ*, 12°, Amsterdam, 1668; German tr. by F. Geissler, *Sieben Bücher Handlend von der künstlichen Glass- und Crystallen-Arbeit . . .*, 8°, Frankfurt and Leipzig, 1678. The full title of Neri's book (which I have not seen) is given as: *L'Arte Vetraria distinta in libri sette, ne quale si scoprone, Effeti maruigliosi, & insegnano Segreti bellissimi del Vetro nel Fvoco & altra Cose curiose.*
[7] P. in NBG, 1863, xxxvii, 686; Ferguson, ii, 134; Neri also worked as a menial assistant in several laboratories. Rodwell, *Phil. Mag.*, 1868, xxxv, 10, mentions an unpublished MS. of Neri, written before 1613, containing 35 names and 22 symbols for mercury, 16 names and 14 symbols for lead, 2 names and 16 symbols for sulphur.
[8] *The Art of Glass . . . translated into English, with some Observations on the Author . . .*, 8°, London, 1662 (BM 1043. c. 20); reprinted at Middle Hill, Worcs., ed. Sir T. Phillipps, f°, 1826, BM 577. l. 28. (41.); Latin, *Antonio Neri De Arte Vitrariâ libri septem et in eosdem . . . Observationes & Notæ*, 12°, Amsterdam, 1668 (see note 6).
[9] Boulger, DNB, 1894, xxxvii, 288; Merrett also published *Pinax rerum naturalium Britannicarum, continens vegetabilia, animalia, et fossilia, in hoc Insula reperta inchoatus*, 8°, London, 1666, most copies dated 1667; and other works; Account of the Tin Mines in Cornwall, *Phil. Trans.*, 1678, xii, 949, no. 138; The Art of Refining, *ib.*, 1678, xii, 1046, no. 142.
[10] IV*b*, p. xxv.   [11] IV*b*, 250.   [12] IV*b*, 251.

mony, recipes for varnishes, sealing wax, etc. The faience glazes in the second book contain lead. Kunckel[1] gives a description, with a very incorrect plate, of blowing small glass toys with the lamp provided with foot-bellows, and says metal oxides may be reduced on charcoal with the flame. The glass mouth-blowpipe is mentioned in the *Saggi di naturali experienze* of the Accademia del Cimento (1667) for use in blowing thermometer bulbs.[2] Merrett gives a description and illustration of the 'Rupert's drop'.[3] Kunckel describes an invention of Johann Daniel Kraft for blowing bottles in copper moulds.[4]

Another work on glass is that by Haudicquer de Blancourt (Picardy; *c.* 1650–? 1708).[5] Peder Månsson's earlier work is mentioned in it.[6] Blancourt is described as a 'gentleman glassblower'. The second French edition has a section entitled 'De tirer la couleur des métaux, minéraux, herbes et fleurs'. Blancourt also wrote on genealogy. In 1701 he was sent to the galleys for forging titles of nobility, the sentence being later commuted to imprisonment for life. It is not known when he died but his papers were confiscated in 1708 and are in the Bibliothèque Nationale.[7]

In the time of Louis IX (1214–70) a law allowed only gentlemen or the sons of nobility to establish a glass-house or work in one, and for long after the workers were called 'gentlemen glass blowers'. The French artists were instructed by Venetians, incorporated by royal charter with many privileges, and were established by the government at Tourlaville, near Cherbourg, in 1665, the site being selected in imitation of the island of Murano, since the quality of Venetian glass was supposed to be due to the direction of the prevailing winds.[8]

Blancourt, who refers to Colbert as a reviver and encourager of arts and sciences, and to Jacques de Paroy, a glass painter who died at the age of 102, attributes the invention of glass to Tubal Cain and Hermes and says 'to have the name of a chymist is enough to render a man detestable among honest men'.[9] He mentions the use of ash of fern, cut in May and June in the increase of the moon,[10] and says lead glass was little known in his time.[11] Gold ruby glass requires annealing to develop the colour.[12] Blancourt also mentions mirrors of an alloy of copper, tin and arsenic,[13] often attributed to Newton.

Melchior Frieben[14] found that gold could impart either a golden or amethyst

[1] IV*a*, 1679, Pt. II, 66; IV*b*, 429.
[2] *Essays of Natural Experiments*, tr. R. Waller, London, 1684, 2: 'blowing with his own mouth (instead of bellows) through a glass pipe upon the flame of a lamp.' Boyle, *An Essay of the Great Effects of Even Languid and Unheeded Motion*, 1685; *Works*, 1744, iv, 258: the 'small crooked pipe of metal or glass such as tradesmen for its use call a blow-pipe'. A mouth-blow-pipe is shown used for sealing the neck of a flask in the *Mutus Liber*, 1677, pt. 10; in Manget, 1702, i, at end.
[3] IV*a*, 1679, Pt. I, 320.   [4] IV*a*, Pt. II, 93; IV*b*, 468.
[5] *L'Art de la Verrerie* . . . , 12°, Paris, 1697; 2 vols. 12°, 1718; tr. *The Art of Glass . . . with an appendix containing Exact Instructions for making Glass Eyes of all colours*, 8°, London, 1699.
[6] Peder Månsson, 1460–1534; *Skrifter* in *Samlingar utgifne af Svenska Fornskrift-Sallskapet*, Stockholm, 1913–15, cxliii–cxlviii.
[7] NBG, 1858, xiii, 549; Ferguson, i, 367.
[8] C. Tomlinson, *Cyclopædia of Useful Arts*, 1854, i, 759, says 'the idea is not altogether futile'.
[9] *Art of Glass*, 1699, 10.   [10] *Ib.*, 25.   [11] *Ib.*, 136.   [12] *Ib.*, 177.   [13] *Ib.*, 347.
[14] *Ephem. Acad. Cæs. Nat. Curios.*, 1677 (1702), Dec. I, Ann. VIII, App., 281–5; *Epistola, sive brevis enumeratio hactenus à se in Chemia actorum*, in Manget, ii, 875–6; Wiegleb, (2), 1790, I, i, 59. Frieben (or Fribe), Friedland, Silesia, 24 November 1629–Mittweide, 1690, was a practising M.D. and also wrote on medical subjects; Gmelin, (1), ii, 139; Ferguson, i, 294.

colour to glass; silver a citron yellow, blue, or emerald green; copper or bismuth a sapphire or azure blue; antimony a hyacinth; tutia a sea-green; zinc a
pale yellow. Grummet also reported that saltpetre coloured glass red[1] but
Kunckel[2] showed that this occurs only when the glass contains manganese
(mit der Magnesia geschmoltzen und præpariret sey, deren noch ein ver-
steckter Theil darinnen enthalten).

Kunckel's assistant in Dresden, Christoph Grummet, published there in
1677 a work on saltpetre.[3] In this it is said that there is in Nature a 'Rosin-
farbenes Blut' which served 'zu leiblicher Reinigung aller erschaffenen Dinge';
it is also contained in Nitrum (saltpetre), and its first generation is from air,
'ex Aëre empfangen' (an expression reminiscent of Mayow's nitro-aerial
spirit).[4] Kunckel attacked this in an appendix to his work on phosphorus[5]
and Grummet published a reply[6] and also a book with a title based on that by
Orschall (p. 371)[7] claiming that gold could be recovered from ruby glass,
which Kunckel denied.

Gmelin identified Grummet with another author, Theophorus Gummert[8]
but Ferguson thought the two were different. The place and date of publication and the words *Notification-Schrift* in both titles, suggest, however, that
this book and the *Blut der Natur* are both by Grummet.

Kunckel gives the important recipe for the manufacture of gold ruby glass.[9]
He says Cassius prepared a *præcipitationem Solis cum Jove* (the so-called
purple of Cassius, finely divided gold and tin oxide),[10] perhaps from a hint from
Glauber (wozu vielleicht Glauber mag Anlass gegeben haben).[11] Kunckel
found that when fused with glass the mass remained clear, but on working at
the lamp it became ruby red. Kunckel points out that the colour develops
only when the glass is re-heated,[12] and he made specimens of this glass for
various people, including a chalice for the Elector of Cologne for 800 thalers.[13]
He says 1 part of gold will colour 1280 parts of glass.[14]

Gold ruby glass was known before Kunckel's time and was apparently discovered in
Italy; it is mentioned by Antonio of Pisa (14 cent.). Kunckel seems to have been influenced by ψ-Lull (see Vol. I) and Isaac of Holland (p. 203),[15] but the impulse for his
researches was undoubtedly Cassius. Stahl[16] says that when he was aged sixteen (in 1676)
an old glassmaker told him that 'Venetian ruby glass' in a strong fire becomes colourless

[1] *Das Blut der Natur*, 1677; in Kunckel, VII, 497.   [2] III; in VII, 318.
[3] *Nitrum oder Blut der Natur aus eigener Erfahrung handgreiflich augewiesen, darzu mit
gewissen Experimenten zum Verfolg seiner Notification-Schrifft auffgesetzet und herausgegeben . . .*, 4°, Dresden, 1677; 8°, Wittenberg, 1678 (Sotheran *Cat.* 839 (1934), no. 348; Gmelin,
(1), ii, 155); repr. in Kunckel, VII, 489–510 (where the name is mis-spelled Brummet).
[4] VII, 494–6.   [5] III, 1678; VII, 313–26.
[6] *Defension-Schrift über das Nitrum oder sogenannte Blut der Natur und seine Person wider
Kunckels Phosphoros mirabiles und dessen andere Schriften*, 8°, s.l. (Leipzig), 1679, q. by
Gmelin, (1), ii, 28, 155.
[7] *Sol non sine veste, oder überwundenes Gold in seiner Tapferkeit triumphirend aufgeführt*,
12°, Rotenburg, 1685; French tr. in IV*b*.
[8] *Treuhertzige Notification-Schrift von Ursprung und Ende, das ist: Von der Generation und
Vitrification der Metallen, Mineralien und allerhand Steine . . .*, 4°, Dresden, 1674 (and again
in 1679 ?); Ferguson, ii, 355.
[9] VI, 1716, 650.   [10] Partington, *General and Inorganic Chemistry*, 1960, 355.
[11] VI, 1716, 650; Jorissen and Postma, *Chem. Weekbl.*, 1927, xxiv, 30 (bibl.), think the purple
was obtained by Glauber in 1659, four years before Cassius.
[12] VI, 1716, 4.   [13] VI, 1716, 651.   [14] VI, 1716, 4.
[15] Ganzenmüller, (1), 1956, 77, 85–128.   [16] *Von dem Sulphure*, 1718, 136.

but recovers its colour in a smoky flame, and this is probably from Neri. Kunckel's contribution was to work out the process in detail and make it applicable to blown glass. Ganzenmüller thinks Orschall at first worked independently but without success until Cassius revealed his secret to him.

Andreas Cassius the elder (Schleswig, ?–Hamburg, 1673) a physician of Hamburg and one of the executors of Jungius's will (p. 417),[1] is the reputed discoverer of 'purple of Cassius'. He did not publish the process, which was first disclosed by Orschall, who says he learnt it from Cassius and that it consisted in precipitating gold with tin.[2] Cassius's son, also named Andreas, published a pamphlet on gold.[3] Beckmann thought that Cassius was not the discoverer of gold purple, but he was not very sure of this.[4]

The younger Cassius thought metals were composed of mercury and sulphur. Gold is masculine and silver feminine. He deals with antimony, bismuth, zinc, marcasite (bismuth), manganese and cobalt as imperfect metals. Under menstrua he has sulphur, arsenic, realgar, cinnabar and quicksilver, vitriol, alum, borax, and sal ammoniac; pearls, shellfish and testacea are zoo-mineral; amber, coral and petrified wood phyto-mineral. He has a curious theory of the circulation of waters inside the earth from the north to the south poles; on their passage north on the surface their salty particles receive impressions from the planets which turn them into metals and minerals when they are heated inside the earth.

Johann Christian Orschall, a Hessian mining official, was in Dresden in 1682 learning the amalgamation process which he later worked in Bohemia. He was mining inspector in Frankenberg in 1684–7 and then vanished; he is said to have died in a monastery in Poland. He also wrote other works.[5]

Kunckel was important in the history of the discovery of phosphorus. He tells us[6] that in Hamburg in 1675 he saw a phosphorus which shone in the dark without previous illumination and tried to buy the process of its preparation from an alchemist who pretended to be a doctor of medicine, Hennig Brand, who had recently discovered it. Kunckel's friend Kraft, whom he told this in a letter, then went to Hamburg (where Kunckel accidentally met him) and bought the secret of the preparation, together with some phosphorus, from Brand. Johann Daniel Kraft (usually given as Krafft) (Miltenberg,

---

[1] Jöcher, i, 1734, who says he had a bezoar essence curing the plague; Gmelin, (1), ii, 235, gives his publication *De triumviratu intestinali cum suis effervescentiis disputatio*, 4°, Groningen, 1668; 12°, Nijmegen, 1669.

[2] Orschall, *Sol sine Veste. Oder Dreyssig Experimenta dem Gold seinen Purpur auszuziehen*, 12°, Augsburg, 1684: 12°, Cassel, 1742; tr. in IV*b*, 471 f. There was an anonymous criticism of this: *Apelles post tabulam observans maculas in Sol Sine Veste: ob J. C. O.[rschall] die wahre Auffschliessung dess Goldes und den Rubinfluss gnugsam erwiesen?*, 16°, Cölln, 1684; Kopp, (4), ii, 372; Ferguson, i, 38.

[3] *De extremo illo et Perfectissimo Naturæ Opificio ac Principe Terrænorum Sidere Auro de admiranda ejus natura Cogitata Nobilioribus experimentis illustrata*, 8°, Hamburg, 1685 (viii, 152 pp.); Ferguson, i, 148.

[4] Beckmann, (1), i, 123; J. C. Fischer, *Dinglers Polytechn. J.*, 1866, clxxxii, 31–40, 129–39; Roscoe and Schorlemmer, *Treatise on Chemistry*, 1923, ii, 524, 538; Ferguson, i, 148; ii, 156; Ganzenmüller, Beiträge zur Geschichte des Goldrubinglases, *Glastechnische Berichte*, 1937, xv, 346, 379, 417; *id.*, (1), 1956, 85–128 (bibl.); abstr. in *J. Soc. Glass Technol.*, 1938, xxii, 287.

[5] *Wunder Drey*, 12°, Cassel [Marburg], 1685; *Wunder-Dreyes Continuatio*, 12°, Cassel [Marburg], 1686; *Ars Fusoria Fundamentalis et Experimentalis. Das ist, Gründlich und auss Erfahrenheit stammende Schmeltz-Kunst*, 12°, Cassel, 1687, 1689, 1730, 1750; tr. [by Baron d'Holbach] as *Oeuvres Metallurgiques. Contenant I. Art de la Fonderie; II. Un Traité de la Liquation; III. Un Traité de la Maceration des Mines; IV. Le Traité des Trois Merveilles*, 12°, Paris, 1760 (xxxii, 394 pp., errata leaf, 1 plate); Ferguson, ii, 156.

[6] VI, 1716, 656 f.

Franconia, 1624–Amsterdam, 1697), an M.D. who became interested in commercial projects and travelled extensively, finally settled in Amsterdam, where he was deceived by alchemists and died in extreme poverty.[1]

Kunckel obtained from Brand a hint that phosphorus was obtained from urine, and he returned to Wittenberg and set to work. In March, 1676, Kunckel obtained solid white phosphorus, a short account of which was published by Kirchmaier, the preparation not being disclosed.[2] He says the 'noctiluca constans' was shown to him by Kunckel six months before but he did not know how it was made. In July 1676 over half an ounce of it was glowing for hours on end:[3]

sextus propemodùm elapsus mensis est, ex quo signicavit mihi primum, Luminis perpetui se possessorum esse. . . . Quamdiu artifex collegerit in materia ritè præparandâ, jam non explanabo; id tantem contentus memorasse, cum laborem iteraret die XXV Julii haud ita pridem, vix ultra uncià dimid. elicuisse igne valido, per horas plurimas continuato. Testabuntur de Herculeo labore, qui tùm interfuerant post cœna tempus, cum Amicis aliis, egregii quidam studiosi juvenes, chymiae sub ejusdem ductu dediti. . . .

Johann Sigismund Elsholtz (Frankfurt an Oder, 26 August 1623–Berlin, 28 February 1688), who had studied medicine in Wittenberg and Königsberg, M.D. Padua, physician and botanist to the elector of Brandenburg, Frederick William, in Berlin, was in touch with Kraft and published a slight account of the properties of phosphorus in 1676.[4] Elsholtz says Kraft, 'recently returned from Batavia', exhibited phosphorus to the Margrave of Brandenburg and his court in Berlin on 2 April 1676, at 9 p.m., taking from a little phial a bit of what he called 'perpetual fire', which shone in the dark like a glow-worm.

A fuller account of phosphorus (without disclosing the method of preparation) was given by Kunckel in 1678.[5] Kraft showed phosphorus to Boyle in 1677 and gave him a hint of its preparation. In 1680 Boyle published some experiments with a solution of phosphorus.[6] Hooke in a letter of April 1680, to Sturm at Altdorf, said: 'We have ye phosphoro: Baldwini, pray send that of Kunkell'.[7] Boyle did not obtain solid phosphorus until 1682.[8]

A different account of the discovery of phosphorus is given by Leibniz, who says it was discovered by Brand, who was formerly a soldier, in 1669.[9]

[1] Peters, A. Nat., 1916, vii, 85 (105); J. Ince, Pharm. J., 1853, xiii, 280–2.
[2] Kirchmaier, Noctiluca constans & per vices fulgurans, diutissimè quæsita, nunc reperta; Dissertatione brevi prævia de Luce, Igne, ac Perennibus Lucernis, Publicata à Georgio Caspare Kirchmajero, In Electorali Academ. Witteberg. Prof. Publ., Wittebergæ, Typis Matthæi Henckelii, Acad. Typogr. Anno M.DC.LXXVI, 4°, 25 pp. incl. t.p., sign. 2 blank, A₁–[C₃]. (BM 1033. h. 11. (16.)). Pref. dated 11 September 1676: Mittam Tibi Noctilucam vitreo inclusam & Hermeticè signatam vasculo, Kunckelianam; ut inter rariora tua extet.
[3] Ib., ch. III.
[4] De phosphoris quatuor observatio, Berlin, 1676; Miscell. Curiosa Academiæ Naturæ Curiosorum, 1702, 32, 37; Ferguson, i, 238 (2 ed., 8°, Jena, 1706); Prantl, J. Chem. Educ., 1948, xxv, 414 (the information had already been given by Partington, Sci. Progr., 1936, xxx, 402); the four kinds of phosphorus are the Bolognian, Baldwin's, 'smaragdinus' (fluorspar) and fulgurans.
[5] III; VII, 1721, 287.   [6] The Aerial Noctiluca, 1680, 95 (method of preparation).
[7] Gunther, (1), 1930, vii, 552.
[8] Observations made upon the Icy Noctiluca, 168½ (1682), 16; for Boyle's work see p. 542.
[9] Leibniz, Historia inventionis phosphori, Miscell. Berolin., 1710, ii, 91; Opera, 1768, II, ii, 102 (this part contains Leibniz' chemical papers); tr. in James, Medicinal Dictionary, 1745, iii, Art. Phosphorus; Anon., Pharm. J., 1895, xxv, 937; German tr., Peters, A. Nat., 1912, iv, 178 (196–203; the paper is in a confused order); 1916, vii, 85; id., Chem. Ztg., 1902, xxvi, 1190; see

Leibniz received from Tschirnhaus the method of preparation of phosphorus, which he communicated to the Paris Academy in 1682. In the printed account some experiments with phosphorus made by Cassini are mentioned.[1] Since Leibniz's letter[2] mentions Boyle's method of preparation, published in 1682 (see above), the priority of publication of the preparation of phosphorus belongs to him. The method is described in great detail by Homberg in a paper read to the Paris Academy on 3 April 1692.[3] The method so described in 1692 for the preparation of what is called 'the phosphorus of Kunckel', is the same as that described in 1682, with one or two slight modifications. The urine (that of a beer-drinker gives a better yield of phosphorus) is first evaporated to a syrup and then allowed to putrefy (this, as Leibniz said, is not essential). The black residue obtained by evaporation and heating is then distilled at a very high temperature in an earthen retort. Sand, used by Boyle (p. 542) and a useful addition, is not specified. Leibniz, who describes Boyle's process in detail, incorrectly said his phosphorus was 'not so strong' and his process was 'not instructive' (!). Homberg thought that phosphorus was the fatty part of the urine concreted to a very combustible earth.

Kraft, described as M.D. and 'Handelsrat' in Mainz, visited Leibniz in Hannover in 1677 and showed him two phials containing a liquid phosphorus which could be put on the hands, clothes, etc., without injury, and a morsel of solid; both ceased to glow unless air was admitted. Leibniz, who reported this, said a friend of Oldenburg's had sent him some of the phosphorus as a present to M.B. (Boyle).[4]

In this account Brand is not mentioned, since Leibniz first met him in Hamburg in July 1678, and Brand apparently then told him he had discovered phosphorus in 1669. It was not until 1682 that Leibniz was able to send what he thought was Brand's process to Tschirnhaus in Paris. Becher[5] also in 1682 reported that 'D. Brand zu Hamburg die Noctiluca oder einen leuchtenden Liquorem [sic] erfunden'. Boyle's two books on the 'Noctiluca' had then appeared. Becher was another who had tried to learn the preparation from Brand. Leibniz says that, 'as far as he knew', Brand was still alive when the communication of Homberg appeared in 1692; he had written to Homberg asking him to correct his statements, but without effect. (He does not name Homberg but speaks of 'a famous man', his 'friend'.) He admits that Kunckel's discovery was independent of Brand's, and apart from the date 1669 his account does not contradict Kunckel's. This date 1669 does not seem to me ever to have been satisfactorily established and rests solely on some recollection of Leibniz.

Guyton de Morveau[6] pointed out that Leibniz described only what was

also Jettel, *ib.*, 1892, xvi, 919; Franck, *ib.*, 1898, xxii, 240; Palet, *An. Soc. Quim. Argentina*, 1917, v, 238; Speter, *Chem. Ztg.*, 1929, liii, 1005; Clark, *School Sci. Rev.*, 1933, 142; Partington, *Sci. Progress*, 1936, xxx, 402; Weeks, *Discovery of the Elements*, 1956, 109, 121–39 and bibl.; G. Mielke, Ostwald's *Klassiker*, 1913, clxxxvii, 40 f.

[1] *Hist. de l'Acad.*, 1682; AdS, 1733, i, h 342.
[2] Gerhardt, *Leibniziens mathematische Schriften*, Halle, 1859, iv, 496–8.
[3] *Mémoires de Math. et Phys. Tirez des Registres de l'Académie Royale des Sciences*, Paris, 1692, 74; AdS, 1730, x, m 84.
[4] *Journ. des Sçavans*, Paris, 2 August 1677, pp. 190–1.
[5] *Närrische Weisheit*, 1682, 41.   [6] *Ency. Méthod., Chimie*, 1786, i, 203.

known to him and his account brought to light some important circumstances, but Kunckel's independent discovery cannot be doubted, and it was not accidental but the result of research. Leibniz was wrong in saying that Kraft had made his process known to Boyle, who would not have wished to appropriate the discovery of another, and Boyle's discovery was independent. Fourcroy[1] says Kraft gave his process, after having sold it several times, 'dans un Traité de phosphores de l'abbé de Commines, publié dans le Mercure de juin 1683'; that Brand's process was published in 1726;[2] that Homberg published a process he says he had seen used by Kunckel,[3] and that the process described by Hellot[4] was one sold to the French government by 'a stranger' in 1737, which was tested and confirmed on behalf of the Academy by Dufay, Geoffroy, Duhamel, and Hellot, after Teichmeyer, Hoffmann, Niewentyt, and several other chemists had described processes which nevertheless were not practised in laboratories. Hanckewitz (who made the phosphorus for Boyle) says Leibniz and the Duke of Brunswick tried to obtain phosphorus by Brand's process but all they ever got was 'a confused form, as a chaos', not hard solid phosphorus.[5]

Besides a number of minor discoveries,[6] Kunckel described the increase in weight of antimony on calcination, which he at first ascribed to the fixation of igneous corpuscles:[7] 1 lb. of antimony increased by 6 scruples or even an ounce, since 'die particulæ igneæ haben sich darein insinuirt'; but afterwards he explained the increase in weight by the matter becoming denser and expelling the air between its pores, as happens also in the calcination of lead (die Theile dicker in einander fallen, und also die darzwischen hebende Lufft weggetrieben wird, so druckt es mehr durch selbige und vermehrt das Pondus welches auch an der Calcination des Bleyes zu sehen dass solches viel Pfund auff einen Centner zuninunt).[8] He denied that any material corpuscles could penetrate glass, as in Boyle's experiments (p. 529): keine Particulae so klein dass sie durch ein Glass dringen;[9] and he says he had long rejected the idea that in calcining antimony any igneous particles can penetrate the earthenware vessel containing the metal: *Particulae igneae* sollen durch die steinerne Pfanne gekrochen seyn, und sich mit dem *Antimonio* vereiniget haben . . . ich aber diese *Phantasie* schon längst widerleget.[10]

Kunckel in 1677[11] said that when metallic antimony is calcined it diminishes in bulk but increases in weight (so hat sich mein Maass verringert, und mein Gewich-Gemehret). This is because porous bodies are buoyed up by the air (alle porose corpora sind leicht, und werden von der Lufft gehoben), but when they become compact the air presses upon them, and thence the weight results (und daher rühret die Schwere). Boyle, however, had shown that lead calx is specifically lighter than lead, the densities being as 9 to 11·5.[12]

[1] *Système de Connaissances Chimiques*, 8°, 1801, i, 186.
[2] *Philosophical Experiments and Observations Of the late Eminent Dr. Robert Hooke*, publ. by W. Derham, 1726.
[3] AdS, 1692, 74.   [4] AdS, 1737, m 342; dating Brand's discovery 1677.
[5] J. Ince, *Pharm. J.*, 1853, xiii, 280–2.   [6] Gmelin, (1), ii, 159 f.
[7] II, 1677; VII, 29.   [8] VI, 1716, 14.   [9] *Ib.*, 7.   [10] *Ib.*, 455.
[11] II; VII, 29; Guyton de Morveau, *Digressions Académiques*, Dijon, 1772, 92 f.
[12] A Discovery of the Perviousness of Glass to Ponderable Parts of Flame, in *Essays of Effluviums*, 1673; *Works*, ed. Birch, 1744, iii, 351.

Kunckel praised Lemery for giving precise details and weights in processes but thought his theory of pores and points was unproved (so wäre auch
sein Judicium wegen der pororum der Metallen und spitzigen Stachelgen,
die nur in einer Meynung und keiner wahren Demonstration bestehen).[1]

Kunckel, although he knew little of mathematics, considered it very important and esteemed it highly.[2] He made many quantitative experiments. He
determined the strength of nitric acid by saturating it with silver, evaporating
to dryness, and weighing the residue:[3] 1 oz. of silver gave 2 oz. of salt (actually
1·7 should be obtained). The acid is pure when it gives a clear solution with
silver, but if it contains spirit of salt it gives a white precipitate (weissen
Kalck fallen lässet).[4] Pure silver is obtained by heating with potash the white
precipitate obtained by adding common salt to a solution of silver in aqua
fortis.[5] Silver is dissolved by boiling with oil of vitriol[6] whilst gold is not.[7]
Pure gold is precipitated from solution by vitriol (ferrous sulphate).[8] He says
that 12 parts of silver, when dissolved and precipitated with common salt or
sal ammoniac, give exactly 16 parts of silver chloride (weissen flüchtigen
Silber-Kalck),[9] which is very near the true weight of 15·9. He gives a process
which involves the sublimation of gold chloride (destillir und sublimire das
Gold auff, so siehet es wie ein Rubin aus . . . hier hast du nun wie das Gold
über den Helm zu destilliren, aber deswegen ist es noch nicht zerstöret).[10]

He describes the preparation of fulminating gold by adding oil of tartar
(potassium carbonate) to a solution of gold chloride mixed with ammonia or
sal ammoniac (so fällt auch ein ☉ fulminans), or by digesting precipitated
gold oxide with ammonia. He gives an interesting theory of the nature of
fulminating gold, which also contains his ideas on elective affinity. On adding
the potash solution to the mixture of gold salt and sal ammoniac, the ammonia
is set free and 'insinuates' itself with the gold calx, which the acid is no longer
able to hold:

wann das Sal acidum in die Terram alcali greiffet, so wird das Urinosum frey, und
insinuiret sich mit der Terra Solis, also kan das Acidum das Gold nicht länger halten-
sondern lässet es fahren . . . weil eine Ungleicheit vom Acido und Urinoso da est . . .
Hieraus kannst du sehen, worinnen die Krafft im Auro fulminante gesteckt, nehmlich im Sale volatile concentrato.[11]

He gives the preparation of fulminating silver by digesting silver oxide with
ammonia (dieser kan das Silber zum Fulmen præcipitieren, wenn es nemlich
in rechter Proportion bey einander ist).[12] He prepared copper sulphate by
heating thin sheets of copper with oil of vitriol and noticed the evolution of
gas (so gehet ein Theil Spiritus Vitrioli herüber, das andere solviret so viel
vom Kuppfer. Wann es auffhöret Blasen im Glase zu kriegen, und gantz stille
stehet, so ist es ein Zeichen, dass es genug solviret hat). By cooling, adding
water, filtering and crystallising, 'so bekommstu einen Wunder-schönen
Vitriol'.[13]

Kunckel[14] described, long before Woulfe, the preparation of mosaic gold

[1] VI, 1716, 370.   [2] VI, 1716, 5.   [3] II; VII, 48.   [4] VI, 1716, 170.   [5] Ib., 310.
[6] Ib., 300.   [7] Ib., 680.   [8] Ib., 274.   [9] Ib., 309.   [10] Ib., 287.
[11] VI, 1716, 271 f., 288; Kopp, (1), iv, 214.
[12] VI, 1716, 308.   [13] Ib., 397.   [14] IVa, Pt. II, 95; IVb, 465.

(aurum musicum), crystalline stannic sulphide, by heating tin amalgam, sulphur, and sal ammoniac, or tin, bismuth, sulphur, and sal ammoniac; an amalgam of tin and bismuth he calls mosaic silver (argentum musicum).

Kunckel (1676) distinguished calamine (*Galmey*) from *tutia* (zinc oxide): he says in making brass (from tutia or calamine, charcoal and copper), the copper takes the 'mercurial' (metallic) part of the calamine or tutia (i.e. the zinc) and becomes yellow and heavier: von der Galmey und Tutia nimmt es den Mercurium in sich;[1] and der Galmei seinen mercurialischen Theil in das Kupfer fahren liesse, und es zu Messing machte.[2] A good account of brass manufacture was given by Merret in his notes to Neri.[3]

Kunckel set great store on the medicinal use of antimony, but he mentions a case in which a patient was almost poisoned because the ignorant apothecary had calcined the crude antimony (stibnite) prescribed in order to 'drive the poison from it', thus converting it into the poisonous oxide:[4] Ey, sagte er, behüte Gott! das is zu roh und grob, wir wollen es ein wenig corrigiren und calciniren, damit das Gifft hinweg gehe. He prepared metallic antimony (Regulus Antimonii) by heating calcined stibnite with oil or butter and charcoal powder, and then throwing on some saltpetre.[5] He explains the reduction as due to the conversion of the acid in the calx into alkali by the fat or charcoal: wann aber gesagtes Fett und die Kohlen zusammen kommen, so wird es ein Sal alcali, und läst den Regulum als partem Mercurialem fahren.

Kunckel believed that acids could be converted into alkalis and vice versa.[6] He showed that any alkali from plant ash is the same as salt of tartar, since, e.g., they all yield the same tartarus vitriolatus (potassium sulphate) with oil of vitriol.[7] He mentions the preparation of caustic ammonia (ammonium hydroxide) by treating sal ammoniac with caustic lime as something well known, and compares the reaction with the caustification of potash with lime, when an acid passes from the quicklime to the alkali. He explains the burning of limestone as due to expulsion of volatile salt, the acid only remaining.[8] He mentions the smell of ammonia produced by the action of quicklime on (ammonia) alum (so gehet ein Spiritus Urinosus davon), and says the acid (of the ammonium salt) combines with the quicklime (das Sal acidum hält sich an die Terra des Kalcks).[9] He says alum is a double salt containing ammonia salt (Allaun ist ein Sal duplicatum, mit dem Sale Urinae componiret).[10] He described the preparation of nitric acid.[11]

Kunckel's work was mostly on inorganic chemistry, but he has some interesting observations on organic chemistry. He says that some old specimens of essential oils from Thurneisser's laboratory which came into his possession had deposited a 'salt' (darinne ein Sal angeschossen):[12] this so-called stearop-

[1] I; VII, 276 f.   [2] VI, 1716, 235, 404; see Glauber, (1657), p. 356.
[3] *The Art of Glass*, 1662; Kunckel, IV*b*, 66–70.   [4] VI, 1716, 432, 442.
[5] *Ib.*, 455 f.   [6] II; VII, 104 f., 113 f.; VI, 1716, 145 f.
[7] II; VII, 106 f.; I; VII, 182 f.: von Gleichförmigkeit der alcalischen Saltze.
[8] VI, 1716, 484 f.   [9] VI, 1716, 150.
[10] *Ib.*, 239: the meaning of *Sal duplicatum* in old authors is not usually that of the modern 'double salt'.
[11] *Ephemer. Acad. Nat. Curios.*, Dec. II, An 1, 1694, 291–4, and plate; reprod. in VI, 1716, 669.
[12] V*a*; VII, 397; VI, 1716, 527.

tene was distinguished from camphor in 1775.[1] Kunckel describes the production of a very volatile 'oil' (ethyl nitrite) on distilling alcohol with nitric acid: ein oleum das so subtil als ich eins auf der Welt gefunden, schwimmt etliche Tagen oben, hernach fällt es zu Boden.[2] He calls this 'oil' by the name 'sweet spirit of nitre' (spiritus nitri dulcis), and he was the discoverer of this, since although ψ- Lull (Vol. I) had described the violent action of alcohol on aqua fortis, and Huygens and Papin[3] found that much 'air' is extricated, Kunckel in 1681 first described the liquid product. Kunckel obtained mercury fulminate but did not isolate it, the product of the reaction exploding violently.[4] He dissolved mercury in aqua fortis, poured in highly rectified spirit of wine and warmed gently in horse dung, when on the next day there was a violent explosion, so that the groom in the stable thought someone had shot at him through the window, or that the Devil was in the stall: that es einen solchen Donner-Knall, mit Zerschlagung des Glases, dass der Knecht im Stalle . . . vermeynte entweder es hätte einer nach ihm durchs Fenster geschossen, oder der leibhaffte Teufel wäre im Stalle.

Kunckel considered that fermentation and putrefaction are similar processes; both take place in presence of moisture and warmth, whilst acids and cold prevent fermentation. In slow fermentation acid is produced at the expense of the alcohol: vekehret sich so viel in eine Säure, die hernach nicht als ein Spiritus Vini übergehen kan.[5] At first he thought that spirit of wine is an acid (denn sein meistes ist ein Acidum),[6] even though it does not act on indicators, but he later maintained that it is not an acid (Spiritus vini ist kein Acidum).[7] It is not an oil, as some theorists say, since it does not swim on water, does not dissolve sulphur, fats, or wax, and does not form a soap with alkalis.[8] Following Sala (whom he mentions), he prepared tinctures by fermenting a solution of sugar with yeast, adding the flowers (such as lilies) and distilling (so steiget solch ein anmuthiger Spiritus aus den Kräutern oder Gewürtze mit über).[9]

He describes observations of fish-spawn under the microscope and believed that the fish was 'von einer blossen Materia unctuosa [or viscosa], wie alle andere Thiere, generiert werden', and he believed in barnacle geese (aus einer gewissen Muschel oder Baum-Frucht, wann die ins Wasser fällt, eine Endte wird).[10]

BARNER

Jacob Barner, Elbing (W. Prussia); 1641–86, a pupil of Sennert, and an adherent of Van Helmont, was professor of medicine and chemistry at Padua from 1670, then Leipzig, and the author of a popular text-book.[11] He published several other works.[12] Gmelin and Kopp mention no discoveries made by

---

[1] Wiegleb, (2), 1790, ii, 166.   [2] V b; VII, 167; Gmelin, (1), ii, 163.
[3] Phil. Trans., 1675, x, 443.   [4] VI, 1716, 213 f.   [5] VI, 1716, 101 f., 696 f.
[6] II; VII, 97.   [7] V a–b; VII, 155, 390.
[8] VI, 1716, 703 f.   [9] VI, 1716, 710 f.   [10] VI, 1716, 44–5.
[11] Chymia Philosophica perfecte delineata, . . . cum brevi sed accurata & fundamentali salium doctrina. Medicamentis etiam sine igne culinari facile parabilibus, . . . , 8°, Nürnberg, 1689 (560 pp.).
[12] Exercitium Chymicum delineatum, Padua, 1670; Spiritus Vini sine Acido, hoc est: In Spiritu Vini & oleis indistinctè non esse acidum, nec ea proptereà à Spiritu Urinae revera coagulari,

Barner, who published a work professing to teach all medicine in six weeks.[1]

Barner[2] thought the cause of fermentation was 'the action and reaction of acid and alkali of the internal parts, by which oils are changed into spirit'.

STISSER

Johann Andreas Stisser, who became a teacher of chemistry in Helmstäct in 1688, published three parts of *Acta* of the chemical laboratory there, in the first of which he dealt with the transmutation of metals and potable gold. He described the preparation of gold by fusing verdigris, tutia, and some salts (which would produce brass).[3]

DIPPEL

Johann Conrad Dippel (Frankenstein, nr. Darmstadt, 10 August 1672–3— Witgenstein, 25 April 1734) studied theology at Giessen and Strassburg and medicine at Amsterdam, graduating M.D. at Leyden in 1711. On account of his opinions as a Pietist he led a wandering life in Holland, Denmark, Sweden, and Germany. He was a brilliant man of agreeable manners but made many enemies. Dippel wrote under the name Christianus Democritus a number of alchemical works which I have not seen.[4]

Dippel's best-known chemical discovery is the 'animal oil' named after him, obtained by distilling bones, in which pyridine and other important substances were long afterwards discovered. The description of the animal oil is in his M.D. thesis.[5] He obtained it first by distilling hart's blood but soon found that it can be made from bones and all animal materials.[6]

Dippel was reported to have made after eight months' study so much al-

Demonstratio curiosa. Cum Modo conficiendi Salia volatilia oleosa, Leipzig, 1675 (40 pp.). Ferguson (i, 74) and Duveen, 45, also give a *Dissertatio Epistolica . . . Seu Prodromus Vindiciarum Experimentorum ac Dogmatum . . . de Volatilisatione Salis Tartari . . . ac Meditationibus circa Principia naturalia*, . . . Augustæ Vindelicorum (1674–5 ?).

[1] *Prodromus Sennerti novi seu Delineatio novi Medicinæ Systematis*, 4°, Augsburg, 1674.

[2] *Chymia Philosophica*, Nürnberg, 1689, 157.

[3] *Actorum Laboratorii Chemici authoritate atque auspiciis Serenissimorum Potentissimorumque Ducum Brunsv. et Luneburg. in Academia Julia editorum*, 3 pts. 4°, Helmstädt, 1690–3–4 (BM 1033. h. 20. (14.)); Gmelin, (1), ii, 29, 134, also q. Stisser, *Commentatio Chemiæ instituta die XVII Augusto Anno 1688*, 4°, Helmstädt, 1689.

[4] *Weg-Weiser Zum verlohrnen Licht und Recht*, etc., Berlin, 1704, partly theological but alchemical in the second part, Duveen, 174; *Analysis Cramatis Harmonici Hyper-Metaphysico-Logico-Mathematica, das ist: Chymischer Versuch zu destillieren per descensum, per ascensum & per latus, und in ihr Sal, Sulphur & Mercurium zu resolviren die drey harmonischen Systemata der heutigen Philosophie, nehmlich des Cartesii, Spinosæ und Leibnitzens . . . Zweyte Edition . . .*, 4°, s.l., 1734, pp. (2), 86 (Kopp says 1 ed. 1729); *Christiani Democriti . . . Auffrichtiges Glaubens-Bekänntnüss . . .*, 8°, s.l., 1732.

[5] *Vitæ Animalis Morbus et Medicina, suæ vindicata origini disquisitione Physico-Medica, quâ simul Mechanismi & Spinosismi deliramenta funditus deteguntur . . . & integrum universi motus. Systema concinnis vinculis nectitur . . .*, 8°, Leyden, 1711 (BM 784. c. 29); tr. with additions: *Christiani Democriti Kranckheit und Artzeney des Animalischen [thierisch-sinnlichen] Lebens . . . mit umständlicher Beschreibung aller Chymischen und Medicinischen Experimenten des Autoris . . . Zerlegung, Zusammensetzung, Verbesserung und Veränderung der Metallen . . .*, 8°, Frankfurt and Leipzig, 1736 (Sprengel says Hamburg).

[6] Gotthold Ernestus Loeber, *Dissertatio . . . de præparatione olei animalis Chrisaniti Democriti ejusque usu febribus intermittentibus medendi*, 4°, Göttingen, [1747] (BM T. 52. (14.)); Gmelin, (1), ii, 364, also refers to J. W. Baumer, *Acta Acad. Elect. Mogunt. Erford.*, i, 297; for the discovery of Prussian blue, see Vol. III.

chemical gold that he bought a large estate; he worked at chemistry in Berlin in 1705. He combined the spiritualism of Van Helmont with the iatro-chemistry of Sylvius, but differed from the latter in supposing that animal heat arises from bilious particles in the blood. He was 'an alchemical vaga-bond' who in 1733 printed a patent at Darmstadt saying that he would not die until 1808, but the next year was found dead at Witgenstein.[1]

[1] Jöcher, ii, 149–51; J. C. G. Ackermann, *Das Leben J. C. Dippels*, Leipzig, 1781 (118 pp.; BM 10707. c. 37. (3.)); Gmelin, (1), ii, 329; Sprengel, (1), v, 114; (2), iv, 400; Kopp, (1), iv, 370, 394; (4), i, 136; Wilhelm Bender, *Johann Konrad Dippel. Der Freigeist aus dem Pietismus*, Bonn, 1882 (on D's alchemy, 80 f., only slight); NBG, 1855, xiv, 315; Ferguson, i, 214; Dippel's complete works were publ. in several vols. in Berleburg but I have not seen them.

CHAPTER XI

FRANCIS BACON AND SOME CONTEMPORARIES

SUBSTANTIAL FORMS

When Boyle[1] contrasted the Aristotelian doctrine of 'forms' with the atomic or 'corpuscular' philosophy he said the modern Aristotelians or Peripatetics had got a way:

> of referring all natural effects to certain entities, that they call real qualities . . . in some cases separable from all matter whatsoever . . . as if (for instance) it be demanded, how snow comes to dazzle the eyes, they will answer, that it is by a quality of whiteness, which makes all very white bodies produce the same effect: and if you will ask what this whiteness is, you will find . . . that they either speak of it much after the same rate as they do of their substantial forms . . . or at least they will not explicate it more intelligibly.

The unsatisfactoriness and barrenness of the school philosophy, he says:

> have persuaded a great many learned men, especially physicians, to substitute the chymists three principles [salt, sulphur, and mercury] . . . yet as it is by chymists pretended to contain a system of theoretical principles of philosophy, I fear it will afford but very little satisfaction to a severe inquirer into the nature of qualities . . . without recourse to the more comprehensive principles of the corpuscularian philosophy . . . by such corporeal agents as do not appear to work otherwise than by virtue of the motion, size, figure, and contrivance of their own parts.

We have now reached a stage in the development of philosophical thought when the old teachings of Aristotle and their development in the Middle Ages, of which a detailed account is given in Volume I, were replaced by those of Bacon, Descartes, and Gassendi. A brief summary of the older views is necessary in understanding the position taken by Boyle and others treated in the present volume, and this will now be given.[2]

Aristotle had taught that every specific thing consists of a union of 'matter' ($\H{y}\lambda\eta$) and 'form' ($\epsilon\hat{\imath}\delta\text{os}$). Very roughly speaking a property of a body such as its colour was called an 'accident'. Copper has a 'substantial form' and tin another, in virtue of which they are copper and tin. When melted together they form bronze, which is a homogeneous body and has another substantial form. Yet copper and tin can be recovered again from bronze. The opposite properties (hot and cold; moist and dry) of the components must exist in a mean state between actuality and potentiality, whilst at the same time the combined substances are not actually present but are potentially present. The essential existence (*actus primus*) of each constituent remains potentially in the compound, whilst its operation or action (*actus secundus*) is removed.

---

[1] The Origin of Forms and Qualities, according to the Corpuscular Philosophy (1666); *Works*, 1744, ii, 451 (459).

[2] Summary in Partington, *Ann. Sci.*, 1939, iv, 245; detail in Vol. I.

Avicenna (Ibn Sīnā, A.D. 980–1037) said that in a 'mixture' (usually meaning a chemical compound) the substantial forms of the components remain unchanged and only the opposite properties suffer change, i.e. the compound contains its elements *in actu*. Averroës (Ibn Rushd, A.D. 1126–98), another commentator of Aristotle, maintained that the forms are not present *in actu*, when the compound would be merely a mechanical mixture, nor are the forms wholly lost but they are capable of gradual change (as black changes to white through grey) and exist in the compound in a state nearer actuality than potentiality (potentia propinqua ad actum), thus transferring Aristotle's mean state of properties to the substances themselves.

Roger Bacon (1214–92) explained the variety of forms by an equal variety of material substrate, thus denying the existence of a primary matter. Albertus Magnus (1193–1280) in the main followed Aristotle. Thomas Aquinas (1225–1274) disagreed both with Avicenna and Averroës. He proposed that the elements in a compound are not wholly destroyed but somehow (aliqualiter) remain in it. The substantial forms of the elements are present in the compound neither actually nor potentially but in virtue (in virtute), and the qualities of the elements in the compound, which are somewhat different from the substantial forms, remain and take the place of the substantial forms (sunt igitur virtutes formarum substantialium simplicium corporum in corporibus mixtis non actu sed virtute). The difficulty that an element which no longer existed could possess properties and develop activity as postulated for its essential form was not explained by Thomas and has never been explained since.

The doctrine of substantial forms as it was understood by the average student was somewhat as follows.[1] The substantial form is what gives a thing its reality and makes it what it is, by attracting certain cognate accidents and repelling other unrelated accidents; in this way it explains individuality and is more essential than the matter of the thing. Clay is the matter of a cup, but only in potentiality; it is the form given by the craftsman which makes the cup what it is, and (as Thomas Aquinas said) the form is 'immersed in matter'. When phosphorus is burnt, the Schoolman would say it is corrupted and its substantial form is displaced to make way for that of a new body, phosphorus pentoxide. The substantial form of phosphorus exists potentially in phosphorus pentoxide, since phosphorus can be educed out of the potentiality of the matter of the latter.

BRUNO

Giordano Bruno (Nola, kingdom of Naples, 1548–Rome, 17 February 1600) entered the Dominican order in Naples in 1565. At first an Aristotelian, his study of the works of Ramon Lull (*c.* 1232–*c.* 1315), which he greatly admired, including the spurious alchemical works, led him into a kind of pantheism in which he supposed that one spirit or sense is diffused throughout the universe, which is a manifestation of God and is divine, and every soul or spirit is a part of it. Spirits inhabit the bodies of men and animals and also plants, stones, and

---

[1] J. Masson, *Lucretius, Epicurean and Poet*, 1909, ii, 44 f., 47 f.

minerals, and they also live in mines. All diseases are evil demons. Bruno believed in the efficacy of images, signs and characters, which act physically.

Bruno, holding such views, came into collision with the Church and he apostasised from his Order. After a long imprisonment by the Inquisition he was burned in Rome in 1600. He defied the Inquisition to the end, but Lucilio Vanini (1585–1619), who submitted, was still burnt, well into the seventeenth century. Bruno's fate has very naturally attracted much attention to him but as a scientist he is negligible; he is eminent rather as a philosopher.[1]

The real reason for Bruno's condemnation is unknown (the history of the Inquisition in his time is very obscure),[2] but it probably had nothing to do with his scientific opinions. What counted most was his apostasy from his Order, his long association with heretics, and his questionable attitude towards the Incarnation and the Trinity.[3] Of eight propositions culled from his books which he refused to abjure only two are known: one is said to bear on the Novatian heresy and the other affirmed that the soul is in the body as a sailor is in a boat.

Bruno possessed the same kind of mentality as Paracelsus (whom he cited, with the Talmudists and Qabbalists, in a work *De monade numero et figura*, discussing the pentacle, key of Zoroaster, and palmistry), and Cornelius Agrippa. His works on the art of memory; images, signs, and ideas; and a *Lampas triginta statuarum*, are, as Thorndike said, 'redolent of mythological, astrological and magical names, figures and characters.' The Jewish theory of the macrocosm and microcosm, in which the earth is compared with the human body (see Vol. I), appears in his works.[4]

He had a high opinion of Paracelsus, classing him with Zoroaster, the Gymnosophists, and Plato, as builders of his Temple of Wisdom.[5] His commentaries on Aristotle are careless and inaccurate,[6] and although he wrote much on mathematics, his knowledge of it was very imperfect and out of date.[7] His metaphysical and pantheistic speculations played no effective part in the development of scientific theory. He opposed the Aristotelian doctrine of substantial forms but offered no fruitful alternative to it.

He recognised no dualism of matter and form, but supposed that matter developed from some internal power, which is a form of the demiurgos of Plato.[8] The only aspect of his philosophical ideas of any interest to us is his treatment of the atomic theory.[9] He recognised a minimum of every species of being, metaphysically the monad or unit of all existence, in space the point

[1] *Opere di Giordano Bruno Nolano*, 2 vols., Leipzig, 1830 (portr.); *Jordani Bruno Nolani Opera Latine*, Naples and Florence, 1879–91 (3 vols. in parts); Rixner and Siber, 1824, v; Rosenberger, 1882, i, 144; Sigwart, *Kleine Schriften*, Freiburg i.B., 1889, i, 49; Lasswitz, (1), 1890, i, 359–403; id., *Vierteljahrsschrift für wissensschaftliche Philosophie*, 1884, viii, 18–55; J. L. McIntyre, *Giordano Bruno*, London, 1903; Ueberweg ,(1), 1924, iii, 48; Stones, *Isis*, 1928, x, 450; Thorndike, 1941, vi, 423, 459; D. W. Singer, *Giordano Bruno. His Life and Thought*, New York, 1950 (with tr. of *De l'infinito universo et mundi* (1584)); Graubhard, *Isis*, 1951, xlii, 247.
[2] Thorndike, vi, 149.   [3] McIntyre, 1903, 257.
[4] Thorndike, vi, 424; Singer, 1950, 318.
[5] McIntyre, 1903, 128, 149 f.   [6] *Ib.*, 116, 121 f.   [7] *Ib.*, 241 f.
[8] Bruno, *De causa, principio et Una*, 'Venice' (really London, J. Charlewood), 1584.
[9] Bruno, *De triplici minimo et Mensvra ad trivm specvlatiuarum scientiarum & multarum actiuarum artium principia, libri V*, sm. 8°, Frankfurt, 1591.

(*punctus*) in substance the atom (*atomus*). These are special cases of a general idea.

According to Lasswitz, Bruno's atomic theory has three aspects, not clearly separated: (i) the metaphysical, in which the atom is the ultimate, indeterminate, substance of things, (ii) the physical, in which it is a hypothesis to explain the difference among material bodies, although only earth among the four elements is atomic in nature; and (iii) the critical, in which the 'minimum' is used as a measure of things, yet only God is a true monad, the others being relative. In an unusually long section in his book, Lasswitz[1] concluded: 'Seine phantastische Naturanschauung sucht Befriedigung des Gemüts in metaphysischer Dichtung . . . für eine rein physikalische Erklärung der Vorgänge in der Körperwelt hat er kein Interesse.'

The atoms are spherical. There are three physical principles, dry earth, water and ether, ether being the *spiritus universi* filling physical space. The atoms are animated virtually if not actually (a Scholastic distinction, see p. 381) and their motion is due to the action of a soul in each, operating in obedience to a final cause (an Aristotelian conception, see Vol. I). The four Peripatetic elements Bruno replaced by water (abyss or styx), earth (atis or atom), spirit (air or soul) and light, which are not transformable into one another but readily 'concur' or have intercourse with one another.

Eilhard Lubin (Westerstädt, Oldenburg, 24 March 1565–Rostock, 2 June 1621), professor of theology in Rostock, followed Bruno's idea of an 'atomistic continuum' but postulated two principles, God and Nothing. The physical atom is a point and has no parts.[2]

TELESIUS

Bernardino Telesio (Telesius) (Cosenza, 1509–Naples, 1588) supposed[3] that all phenomena proceed from the interaction of passive matter (*hyle*) and two active principles, heat and cold, heat being the cause of motion and cold of rest.[4] He believed that all bodies are animated. In making heat and cold two fundamental principles of nature he followed Parmenides (Vol. I). They were immaterial until joined to the third factor, matter. Heat preceded motion in time, nature, and dignity; motion was merely an operation of heat, no new heat being produced by motion but only pre-existing heat excited. Heat was associated with the sky, cold with the earth. Telesio rejected the Aristotelian distinction between rational, sensitive, and vegetative soul, holding that all faculties of the soul are equally rational, although plants have crasser spirits than animals, the spirits in the brain and body being informed by the soul. He extended the mediaeval conception of spirits, and explained intellectual and moral qualities by the difference of the spirits in heat, tenuousness, and purity.

---

[1] (1), i, 391.

[2] Lubin, *Phosphorus, de prima causa et natura mali . . . tractatus hypermetaphysicus*, 12°, Rostock, 1597; Jöcher, ii, 2554; E.G. in NBG, 1860, xxxii, 102; Lasswitz, (1), i, 403.

[3] *De Natvra Ivxta Propria Principia* (Books i–ii), 4°, Rome, 1565; complete, 9 books, *Varii de Natvralibvs Rebvs Libelli*, ed. Ant. Persius, 4°, Venice, 1590 (sep. t.ps.) (CUL M. 15. 52).

[4] Morhof, (1), 1747, ii, 230–8; Rixner and Siber, 1820, iii; Spedding and Ellis, *Works of Francis Bacon*, 1857, i, 51 f., 564; Ueberweg, 1924, iii, 42; W. Frost, *F. Bacon und die Naturphilosophie*, Munich, 1927, 454.

His theory of spirits was adopted by Francis Bacon (p. 396). He believed in the spontaneous generation of certain animals, and in occult qualities.[1]

PATRICIUS

Francesco Patrizi (Patricius) (Cherso, Dalmatia, 1529–Rome, 1597), who studied in Padua from the age of nine, was professor at Ferrara (1578–92), and in the Sapienza in Rome, and was a Platonist. In his *New Philosophy*,[2] dedicated to Pope Gregory XIV, draws on Egyptian, Chaldaean, Alexandrian, and Neoplatonic sources, and leans heavily on Telesio. The four parts of the new philosophy are called Panaugia, Panarchia, Pampsychia, and Pancosmia, and the four elements are replaced by space, light, heat, and humour. The sun is the sole generator of earthly things by its seeds and light. The stars receive from the empyrean light, heat, humour, life, soul, mind, and ideas. Their heat and seeds go to the sun; the moon receives from them a fluid or ether, and passes it to the earth, which is immovable at the centre of the universe. Patrizi's opposition to Aristotle was not successful but he discredited the Peripatetic school. He accepted all past reports on Zoroaster, supposing there were Persian, Bactrian, Armenian or Pamphilian, and Medo-Persian bearers of the name, and thought he was really a Chaldaean, the *Chaldaean Oracles* (Vol. I) containing true magic. The works of Telesio and Patrizi were put on the Index.

Godefroy Chassin (Chassinus) studied under the Jesuits at Lyons and Tournon, then law at Padua, then made an intensive study of Aristotle. In his book on *Nature*[3] he adopts the dictum that nature abhors a vacuum. Like Van Helmont (p. 222) he takes water as the matter of things and heat the instrumental cause, the *causa agens* being the form of the world soul. He gives a *scala naturæ* with thirteen steps.

CAMPANELLA

Tommaso Campanella (Stilo, Calabria, 5 September 1568–Paris, 21 May 1639), a Dominican, although a faithful Catholic spent twenty-seven years of his life in the prisons of the Inquisition, and some physical means of persuasion seem to have been applied to bring him to a proper frame of mind.

Gaffarel, who visited Campanella in the Inquisition prison in Rome, says he found him grimacing and then noticed that his legs were all bruised and most of the flesh had been torn off his seat bit by bit to induce him to confess to charges made against him.[4] He supported Paracelsus in general but thought

---

[1] Thorndike, vi, 370–1.

[2] *Nova de universis philosophia, libri L comprehensa . . . Quibus postremo sunt adjecta Zoroastris Oracula . . . Hermetis Trismegisti . . . Asclepii . . . mystica Ægyptiorum . . . in quibus Plato consors, Aristoteles vero catholicæ fidei adversarius ostenditur*, f°, Ferrara, 1591 (extremely rare); Rixner and Siber, 1823, iv; Z. in NBG, 1862, xxxix, 342; Ueberweg, 1924, iii, 43; Thorndike, vi, 373, 460.

[3] *De natura sive de mundo libri octo*, 8°, Lyons, 1614, 1619; Thorndike, vi, 382.

[4] Gaffarel, *Cvriositez Innovyes svr la Scvlptvre talismaniqve des Persans*, Pt. II, ch. 6, § 13; 8°, *s.l.* [Paris ?], 1637, 127; *Vnheard of Curiosities*, tr. E. Chilmead, 8°, London, 1650, 175; Rixner and Siber, 1826, vi (q. E. S. Cypriani, *Vita Campanellæ*, 2 ed., Amsterdam, 1722); Aubé, NBU, 1854, viii, 365; Lasswitz, (1), 1890, i, 340; Ueberweg, 1924, iii, 45; Thorndike, vi, 121, 173–6; vii, 291–301; L. Blanchet, *Campanella*, Paris, 1920.

he was somewhat given to superstition.[1] Campanella wrote a large number of works, now very rare (probably most copies were burnt).[2]

Campanella said that heavy and light bodies would fall equally fast in a vacuum[3] and that all colours can be derived from black and white.[4] He adopted Seneca's explanation (see Vol. I) of condensation and rarefaction as due to intension or internal tension (intensio id est interna tensio), and not to atomic attraction (non tamen atomorum coitio) as Demokritos and Epikouros supposed.[5] He rejected the four elements and the three alchemical principles[6] but believed that transmutation is possible,[7] mercury by killing its spirit being converted into gold, which does not rust because its parts are very uniform; silver has parts of tin in it. Repeated fusion changes lead into tin, silver, and gold. Transmutation is also possible by means of the spirit of gold.[8] Campanella believed in the divining rod.[9] In the seventh book of his work on astrology[10] he deals with 'peculiar times of applying remedies' so as to catch or avoid specific influences of the stars. In a chapter (vii) on more secret remedies he explains that there are stones, metals, plants, colours, tastes, and other things peculiarly endowed with the forces of the planets which, if applied under certain constellations, guard us from evil events, and that natural magic had to do with these.

Francesco Sanchez (Braga, Portugal, 1552–Toulouse, 1632), educated at Toulouse, M.D. Montpellier 1574, professor of medicine at Montpellier 1576, then physician and royal professor of medicine at Toulouse, composed in 1576 at the age of twenty-four a work entitled 'Of the Right Noble and First Universal Science, That Nothing is Known', published in 1581,[11] in which he opposed the scholastic method, and he may be regarded as a precursor of Descartes and Francis Bacon. He proposed to take up the investigation of nature and scientific method in further works, which never appeared.

Another sceptic was Lucilio Vanini (Taurisano, Otranto, 1584–burnt at Toulouse, 9 or 19 February 1619)[12] who was a pantheist. His works[13] show ignorance of recent

---

[1] Thorndike, vii, 300.

[2] Works which I have seen are: (1) *Prodromus Philosophiæ Instaurandæ, id est Dissertationis De Natura Rerum Compendium*, 4°, Frankfurt, 1617; (2) *De Sensv Rervm et Magia*, 4°, Frankfurt, 1620; (3) *Apologia pro Galileo*, 4°, Frankfurt, 1622; (4) *Vniversalis Philosophiæ sev Metaphysicarvm Rervm, Ivxta Propria Dogmata, Partes Tres*, f°, Paris, 1638; (5) *Realis Philosophiæ Epilogisticæ*, 4°, Frankfurt, 1633; (6) *Philosophiæ Rationalis Partes Qvinqve*, 4°, Paris, 1638 (dedic. dated Paris, 15 March, 1635); (7) *Medicinalium juxta propria principia Libri septem. Opus non solum medicis, sed omnibus naturæ et privatæ valetudinis studiosis utilissimum*, 4°, Lyons, 1635 (690 pp.; sometimes dated in error 1636).

Among his many other works (list in Rixner and Siber, vi, 29 f.) are: (8) *Physiologia*, ed. T. Adami, 4°, Frankfurt, 1623: (9) *De Libris propriis et recta studendi Syntagma*, 8°, Paris; *Lettere*, 1927, modern eds. and *Opuscoli Filosofici*, 1927, are quoted but I have not seen them. The works are quoted in the footnotes by the numbers given above.

[3] Rixner-Siber, 92.   [4] *Ib.*, 69.   [5] (4), 1638, Bk. II, ch. v, art. 9, p. 214.
[6] (4), I, ix, 12; Rixner-Siber, 58.   [7] (8), viii, 5; Rixner-Siber, 130.
[8] (2), i, 11; Rixner-Siber, 201.   [9] (2), iii, 13; Rixner-Siber, 133.
[10] *Astrologicorum Libri VI*, 4°, Lyons, 1629 (BM 718. e. 19. (1.)); bk. vii was added to the six named in the title, with separate pagination; Thorndike, vi, 173–5.
[11] *De multum nobili et prima universali scientia quod nihil scitur*, 4°, Lyons, 1581, Frankfurt, 1618 (BM 528. b. 3. (2.)); Sprengel, (2), 1827, iv, 30, gives Rotterdam, 1647; P. in NBG, 1864, xliii, 254 gives 8°, Frankfurt, 1628; Thorndike, vi, 560–8.
[12] M. in NBG, 1866, xlv, 920; Thorndike, vi, 560, 568.
[13] *Amphitheatrum æternæ Providentiæ divino-magicum christiano-physicum necnon astrologo-catholicum adversus veteres philosophos Atheos Epicureos Peripatheticos et Stoicos*, 8°, Lyons,

scientific discoveries and he relies mainly on Pomponazzi and Cardan (whom he sometimes criticises).

BODIN

Jean Bodin (Angers, 1530–Laon, 1596) speaks[1] of atoms (*atomi*) as indivisible bodies; he does not admit a distinction between mathematical and physical indivisibility, but supposes an infinite force (potestas in infinitum crescerent) would be necessary to divide the (physical) atoms. He ascribes motion to the atoms, which varies according to the circumstances (*motus vagus*).[2]

Nicholas Hill (London, 1570–on Continent, 1601),[3] a Lullist,[4] gave a confused mixture of short statements on all kinds of subjects, with no plan or conviction, and very little on atoms.

Julius Cæsar La Galla (Padula, kingdom of Naples, 1576–Rome, 15 March 1624), in a work which influenced Jungius (p. 416),[5] gave a summary of some of Demokritos's opinions.

GORLÆUS

David Van Goorle (Gorlæus) (Utrecht, 15 January 1592 (or 1591)–Cornjum, 21 April 1612), of an Antwerp family, studied in Leyden (1609–11).[6] In a book published posthumously[7] he classified properties into those of the 'second kind', not inherent in the atoms but appearing in their aggregates, viz. hardness, softness, liquidity (*liquor*), aridity, flexibility, friability, fluidity (*fluor*), stability, rarity, density, roughness, smoothness, slipperiness and shape; the 'third kind' of properties belonged to the atoms themselves (in ipsis atomis existunt), viz., moistness, dryness, fineness (*tenuitate*), largeness, opacity and transparency.[8] Weight is not a property but a force (gravitatem esse vim corporibus à Deo impressam) inherent in the atoms.[9] The section on atoms[10] is on metaphysical lines.

Earth and water are the only elements;[11] air, which has weight,[12] is not an element but only fills the spaces in earth and water.[13] Fire is only an accident, generated by the power of heat, and is not a substance.[14] One element cannot

1615 (BM 224. e. 34); *De Admirandis Naturæ Reginæ Deæque Mortalium Arcanis libri quatuor*, 8°, Paris, 1616 (BM 976. b. 1: the running title at the top of the pages is *Dialogi* and the speakers are Alexander and Vanini, who calls himself Julius Caesar).

[1] *Vniversæ Natvræ Theatrvm*, Lyons, 1596, 76, 80; Partington and McKie, *Annals of Science*, 1937, ii, 365; Lasswitz, (1), i, 411; Hoefer, NBU, 1853, vi, 325, speaks of Bodin's *Theatrum Naturæ*, Lyon, 1590 (*sic*) as 'ouvrage supprimé, et aujourd'hui très-rare'.

[2] *Ib.*, 1596, 109.

[3] Robinson, DNB, 1891, xxvi, 404.

[4] *Philosophia Epicvrea Democritana, Theophrastica proposita simpliciter, non edocta*, sm. 8°, Paris, R. Thierry, 1601 (pp. vi, 118, ii; very rare); 12°, Geneva, 1619; Jöcher, ii, 1604; Lasswitz, (1), i, 465.

[5] *De Phoenominis in Orbe Lunæ Novi Telescopii Vsv a D. Gallileo Gallileo* . . . , 4°, Venice, 1612 (72 pp.), ch. viii, p. 21 f.: Democryti Opinio: quod plures sunt mundi; Jöcher, ii, 2205; Lasswitz, (1), i, 465.

[6] Lasswitz, (1), i, 333, 455–63; F. M. Jaeger, *Historische Studien*, Groningen, 1919, 51.

[7] *Exercitationes Philosophicæ quibus Vniversa fere discutitur Philosophia Theoretica*. . . . *Post mortem Auctoris editæ cum gemino jndice*, Leyden, 1620 (352 pp.).

[8] *Exercit.*, 1620, 139 f., 143 f.   [9] *Ib.*, 146 f.

[10] *De Atomis, ib.*, 235–49.

[11] *Ib.*, 314.   [12] *Ib.*, 154, 332.   [13] *Ib.*, 329 f.   [14] *Ib.*, 318 f.

be converted into another,[1] and water vapour is not air.[2] Respiration cools the blood.[3]

A supplementary work by Gorlæus[4] was not available to me; Jaeger says there was no copy in Holland but there were copies in the libraries of the Universities of Greifswald and Königsberg, and he gives a summary of the contents.

BASSO

An important author in the history of atomism is the French physician Sebastian Basso, who studied under Petrus Sinsonius at the academy of Pont à Mousson (Academia Mussipontana).[5] He proposed a theory of matter based on the ideas of Demokritos, Plato, Anaxagoras, and Empedokles as opposed to Aristotle's views, and assumed that all bodies are composed of exceedingly small atoms of different natures:[6] omnes ex minimis, divertissimisque particulis res contrui, quæ ut ab invicem sejunctæ naturas haberent dissimiles, eandem naturæ differentiam conjunctæ retinerent, quocunque tandem nomine res illas voces. These were created by God:[7] censemus eas à Deo creatas, quod fuit præmonendum. The formation of a compound (mistio, crama) from different constituents and its resolution into these is an argument for the existence in it of real parts (actu naturali) retaining their form, the mixture, such as wine diluted with water, being only homogeneous in appearance:[8] crama namque illud, id est aquâ dilutum vinum, non est unum formâ, sed continuatione sola. This he disputed against Scaliger.[9] In opposition to Aristotle (Vol. I), whose theory of forms he (unlike Sennert, in 1619) (p. 271), completely rejected, Basso supposed the constituents of mixtures to exist actually in them, although their separation might be more or less difficult:[10] quod scilicet de vini & aquæ mistorum partibus compertum est, eas etsi minutissimas, & alias cum aliis continuas, in sua quamque natura persistere, idem de omnibus mistis esse dicendum; discremenque solum esse, quod alia aliis facilius dissolvantur. By chemical processes, spirit, oil, salt, earth and phlegm are separable from bodies.[11]

The transmutation of the elements is impossible; the ultimate particles have different natures which cannot be changed.[12] If one element, e.g. fire, can be changed into earth, this would have to occur continuously, and when the fire has become denser than water but not so dense as earth, is it still fire or has it

---

[1] Ib., 255–6.
[2] Ib., 127; according to Lasswitz, (1), i, 335, Gorlæus was the first to deny the conversion of water into air; see Van Helmont, p. 222.
[3] Ib., 330.
[4] Idea Physicæ, cui adjuncta est Epistola cuiusdam Anonymi de Terræ Motu, 12°, Utrecht, 1651 (77 pp.).
[5] Basso, Philosophia Naturalis adversus Aristotelem Libri XII. In quibus abstrusa Veterum Physiologia restauratur, & Aristotelis Errores solidis Rationibus refelluntur, 8°, Geneva, 1621; 8°, Amsterdam, 1649; Brucker, 1766, IV, i, 467, 513; Lasswitz, (1), 1890, i, 467–81; id., (2), 1884, viii, 18–55; Ueberweg, 1924, iii, 173; Thorndike, vi, 386; I have not found any particulars of Basso's life; Jöcher, i, 847, says the work was published in Rome, 4°, 1574.
[6] Phil. Nat., 1630, 11 f., 26; 1649, 10 f., 23.   [7] Ib., 1621, 14; 1649, 13.
[8] Ib., 1621, 28; 1649, 24.   [9] Exotericarvm Exercitationvm, Exere. ci, Paris, 1557, 143 v. f.
[10] Phil. Nat., 1621, 26–34, 31; 1649, 23–30, 27.
[11] Ib., 1621, 36; 1649, 31; see p. 458.   [12] Ib., 1621, 40 f.; 1649, 35 f.

become earth?[1] Water by evaporation is not changed into air, but its particles have been driven apart by fire particles, and when these are removed by cooling the vapour becomes water again.[2] Basso speaks of particles [atoms] of fire, air, water and earth,[3] which can combine to particles of the second, third, etc., orders; this explains the great diversity of bodies:[4]

Non tantum prima elementa in misto seu mavis composito manere, sed diversissimas quibus mistum constat, particulas, ex iis primis rerum principiis diversimode constructas; quas secundas, docendi gratia vocare liceat. Ex his secundis varie coëuntibus tertiæ fiunt non minus quàm secundæ inter se differentes. Eundem in modum, & ex tertiis quartæ, et ex quartis quintae fieri intelliguntur. . . . Atquè compositum naturale non primo resolvitur in prima illa elementa, sed in partes quasdam inter se natura discrepantes; quarum singulæ species rursus in alias multiplices dividuntur; et hæ in alias minutiores conciduntur. Sæpiusque hæc partium diversarum in minutiores semper diversas subdivisio repetitur.

All this was published forty years before Boyle's *Sceptical Chymist*. Basso, however, retained some Aristotelian ideas: he thought that hot water freezes faster than cold water and that a manure heap keeps its heat longer in winter than in summer. Basso distinguished four states of inorganic aggregation: solids (solida et firma), liquids (liquida et fluxa), fusible bodies (fusilia) intermediate between solids and liquids, and aëriform (meteora quæ sursum efferuntur); their constituents are mainly earth, water, earth +less water, and fire, respectively:[5]

corpora [inanima] omnia composita, in quatuor genera commode possunt distribui; ut alia sint liquida & fluida; alia firma et constantia; alia utramque naturam participantia, qualia sunt fusilia omnia; alia denique meteora quæ sublimè feruntur; ut halitus & vapores.[6]

The extinction of fire is due to the compression and condensation of its parts by water and air.[7] Basso rejected the existence of a vacuum and supposed, with the Stoics (Vol. I), that the spaces between the particles of bodies are filled with a subtle spirit:[8]

ni concedamus vacuum inter partes à quo natura abhorret, admittendam esse substantiam aliquam corpoream, tenuissimam quidem, quæ in aëris, verbi gratia, rarefactione, in partes aëris sese insinuans. . . . En tibi Stoici clarè manifestarunt.

Fire consists of this subtle spirit together with fine and sharp corpuscles (aculeis subtilissimis).[9] Perhaps these ideas influenced Francis Bacon (p. 395).[10] Basso seems to have regarded the subtle fluid (which is the same as the ether) as a continuum; it produced all material changes by causing motion and arrangement of the atoms.[11] The idea of qualities as due to motion was extended by Galileo.[12] Descartes[13] was certainly influenced by Basso, who stands between him and Bruno.[14]

[1] *Ib.*, 1621, 59; 1649, 52.   [2] *Ib.*, 1621, 74 f.; 1649, 66 (preceding Van Helmont).
[3] *Ib.*, 1621, 125; 1649, 112.
[4] *Ib.*, 1621, 79 f.; 1649, 70 f.: *De diversitate partium compositarum, ex quarum harmonia totum resultat*; cf. 1621, 126; 1649, 113; Lasswitz, (1), i, 473 (cf. 479) says: 'dürfte Basso als der erste unter den Erneueren der Physik genannt werden, welcher den Begriff der chemischen Molekel völlig klar erfasst hat.'
[5] *Ib.*, 1621, 126; 1649, 113.   [6] *Ib.*, 1621, 80; 1649, 71.   [7] *Ib.*, 1621, 127; 1649, 113–14.
[8] *Ib.*, 1621, 335; 1649, 300.   [9] *Ib.*, 1621, 337; 1649, 304.   [10] Lasswitz, (1), i, 476.
[11] Basso, 1621, 430 f.; 1649, 387 f.
[12] *Il Saggiatore*, Rome, 1623; Partington and McKie, *Ann. Sci.*, 1937, ii, 365 f.
[13] *Oeuvres*, tr. Cousin, 1824, vi, 146.   [14] Lasswitz, (1), i, 480 f.

FRANCIS BACON

Francis Bacon (London; 22 January 1561–9 April 1626) came of a very distinguished family. In 1573 he entered Trinity College, Cambridge, and in 1576 became a student in Gray's Inn, London. He took up the practice of law. He was assisted by the Earl of Essex (whose execution in 1601 owed much to Bacon's legal skill). In 1618 he became Lord Chancellor and Baron Verulam, in 1621 Viscount St. Alban. Soon afterwards he was convicted of accepting bribes, fined £40,000, lost office, and (after a few days' imprisonment in the Tower) retired to his estate at Gorhambury. He died from a chill contracted at Highgate on a journey, from an experiment of stuffing a fowl with snow to find the effect of refrigeration in delaying putrefaction.

Although Bacon lived in the period of transition from scholastic philosophy to experimental science, his writings show an optimistic belief in the possibilities of science, and a firm insistence on the necessity for special planned experiments as opposed to formal logical argument based on insufficiently established generalisations.[1]

Bacon insists on the worth and dignity of experiments (he died as a result of making an experiment) and on the danger of relying on authority or preconceived notions; for 'rightly is truth called the daughter of time, not authority',[2] and since knowledge is finite, everything can in time be known — as was said by Roger Bacon also (Vol. I). His views on experimental science generally place him in a notable position for his time. What distinguished him most from his Continental contemporaries, such as Galileo, was the religious earnestness of his works and their freedom from cynical insincerity, but even at that time England and Italy were not comparable localities for the free expression of personal convictions. In many ways Bacon's ideals anticipated those of the French Encyclopædists,[3] but he had much less material to work upon.

Bacon's philosophical writings[4] of interest to us are the following:

A. *Advancement of Learning*, 1605 (in English); the first book was written in 1603 and was printed (not published) before the second was sent to the press.

[1] Baden Powell, 1834, 195–212 (good); C. D. Broad, *Nature*, 1926, cxviii, 487, 523; J. C. Crowther, *Francis Bacon. The First Statesman of Science*, London, 1960; J. W. Draper, *History of the Conflict between Religion and Science*, 1875, 233; Fowler, DNB, 1885, ii, 350; F. Frost, *Bacon und die Naturphilosophie*, Munich, 1927; Gardiner, DNB, 1885, ii, 328; R. W. Gibson, *Francis Bacon, a Bibliography of his Works and of Baconiana to the year 1750*, Oxford, 1950; J. C. Gregory, *Ambix*, 1938, ii, 93; W. Hale-White, *Bacon, Gilbert and Harvey*, 1927; A. Heller, *Geschichte der Physik*, Stuttgart, 1882, i, 310; P. Janet, *Baco Verulamius alchimicis philosophis quid debuerit* (Paris thesis), Angers, 1889 (57 pp.); Kopp, (4), i, 254; Sir S. Lee, *Great Englishmen of the Sixteenth Century*, 1907, 262; J. Levine, *Francis Bacon*, 1925; Libri, (1), 1841, iv, 159; Lippmann, (2), i, 374; Macaulay, *Essay on Bacon*, 1837; I. Masson, 1925, 12 f., 17 f.; Morin, NBU, 1852, iv, 93; Poggendorff, (2), 1883, 122; Rodwell, *Chem. News*, 1863, viii, 186; Rosenberger, 1884, ii, 70; Thorndike, vii, 63–88; Ueberweg, (1), 1924, iii, 193; *id.*, (2), 1874, ii, 33, 518; Whewell, (2), 1847, ii, 226–51; A. Wolf, (1), 1935, i, 632.

[2] *Novum Organum*, i, 83–4; *Works*, 1857 f., I, 190; IV, 81.   [3] Frost, 1927, 145 f.

[4] *Philosophical Works*, ed. and tr. by Peter Shaw, 3 vols., 4°, London, 1773; *The Works of Francis Bacon*, collected and edited by J. Spedding, R. L. Ellis and D. D. Heath, 7 vols., 1857–9, and later reprints (e.g. 1883–92) ('a splendid and carefully annotated edition'; Fowler, DNB, 1885, ii, 353) this edition is the one quoted below; *Life and Letters of Francis Bacon*, ed. Spedding, 7 vols., 1861–74.

B. *Novum Organum*, as *Pars Secunda* of the *Instauratio Magna* (f°, London, 1620); begun in 1608 and never completed. Ed. with notes by T. Fowler, Oxford, 1889.
C. *De Augmentis Scientiarum*, 1623; an enlarged edition of A; the translation was by Bacon himself.
D. *Historia Naturalis et Experimentalis . . . sive Phænomena Universi, Pars Tertia (Historia Ventorum)*, 1622.
E. *Historia Vitæ et Mortis*, January, 1622–3.
F. *Sylva Sylvarum* [= Collection of Collections ?], published by Rawley in 1627 (in English; printed for W. Lee; 266 pp.) and repeatedly reissued, e.g. 1650–1, 1664, 1670, and the last, 10th, ed. in 1676. The full title is: *Sylva Sylvarum or a Naturall History. In Ten Centuries*. It contains 1000 paragraphs and was regarded by Bacon as mere raw material from which the new philosophy was to be built up.
G. *New Atlantis*, written before 1617 but unfinished; appended to Rawley's edition of F (47 pp.) and Bacon's most popular philosophical work; it suggests the formation of scientific societies, such as the Royal Society.

Some smaller works were first issued by Isaac Gruter,[1] and others by Bacon's chaplain and secretary, the Rev. Dr. William Rawley:[2]

α. Historia Densi et Rari (publ. by Rawley, 1658).
β. Cogitationes de Natura Rerum (written *c.* 1605 ?).
γ. De Principiis atque Originibus secundum Fabulas Cupidinis et Cœli (with the alternative title: Parmenidis et Telesii et præcipue Democriti philosophia tractata in fabula de Cupidine).
δ. Parasceve (publ. with Novum Organum, 1620).
ε. Descriptio Globi Intellectualis (before 1612).
ζ. Cogitate et Visa (1607).
η. Redargutio Philosophiarum (1607–8 ?).
θ. Filum Labyrinthi sive Formula Inquisitionis (in English; almost the same as ζ).
ι. Thema Cœli (before 1612).
κ. Historia Soni et Auditus (1608 ?).
λ. Inquisitions touching the Compounding of Metals; printed from Bacon's papers in: Baconiana. Or, Certain Genuine Remains of Sr. Francis Bacon, 8°, London, 1679, by Thomas Tenison (Archbishop of Canterbury).
μ. Articles of Enquiry touching Metals and Minerals.
ν. Of the Interpretation of Nature (in English).
ξ. Inquisitions concerning the Versions, Transmutations, Multiplications, and Effections of Bodies (in English) (publ. by Tenison, 1679).
ο. Temporis Partus Masculus (*c.* 1608 ?).
π. Topica Inquisitionis de Luce et Lumine.
ρ. Catalogue of Bodies Attractive and Non-Attractive (publ. by Tenison, 1679).
σ. Experiments about Weight in Air and Water (publ. by Tenison, 1679).
τ. Phaenomena Universi (after 1608, before 1622).

Item μ was found among Bacon's manuscripts by Rawley (who corrected the proofs, and said 'there is nothing more of that subject to be found'); printed by W. Lee in an edition of F.[3] These small works (many of them mere pitiful scraps) were probably intended by Bacon to be worked up and incorporated in a completion of B which never appeared. In what follows, the works are quoted by capital or Greek letters, as above, and the volumes of Bacon's works in Spedding's edition in Roman numerals.

[1] *Scripta in Natvrali et Vniversali Philosophia*, 12°, Amsterdam, 1653.
[2] *Opuscula Varia Posthuma*, 8°, London, 1658.
[3] *Articles of Enquiry touching Metals and Minerals. . . . Thought fit to be added, to this Work, of his Natural History. Newly put forth this yeare 1661, by the former Publisher*, London, 1662; in *Sylva Sylvarum*, 8 ed., London, t.p. dated 1664, with sep. t.p. but contin. pagin. 221-8; *Works*, III, 806 f.

Bacon believed in the essential unity of science, and enforced the necessity of laying aside preconceived notions and following Nature; he claimed that his method led to absolute truth, and that it could be used by all men for the attainment of that end in a reasonable time. His method of drawing up lists, collecting 'instances', and bringing in as many facts as were known, at the same time perceiving where new experiments are necessary, has some practical foundation and is partly followed intuitively in scientific research.[1] Bacon says:[2] consilium est, universum opus Instaurationis potius promovere in multis, quam perficere in paucis (my design is rather to advance the universal work of renewal in many things than to perfect it in a few).

Bacon had the Arabic passion for classification; his 'schemes of matter' are[3] the pairs of opposites: dense, rare; heavy, light; hot, cold; tangible, pneumatic; volatile, fixed; determinate, fluid; moist, dry; fatty (pingue), crude (crudum); hard, soft; fragile, tensile; porous, close; spirituous, jejune; simple, compound; absolute, imperfectly mixed; fibrous and venous, simple of structure or equal (æquum); similar, dissimilar; specific, nonspecific; organic (organicum), inorganic (inorganicum); animate, inanimate — 'further I do not go.' He has nineteen types of motion:[4] resistance (antitypiæ materia, a name used by Aristotle), connexion, liberty, of matter (hyles), continuity, for gain or of want (ad lucrum sive indigentiæ), of the greater congregation, of the lesser congregation (congregationis), magnetic, of flight, of assimilation or self-multiplication or generation, excitation, impression, of configuration or position, of transition or passages (per transitionis, sive secundum meatus), royal or political, spontaneous rotation, trepidation, and repose or aversion to move. These are the species or simple elements of motions; they are not abstract divisions and others may be added or some taken away 'according to the true veins of nature'. While it is quite true to say[5] that Bacon 'never really understood' what motion was in the sense of the simple mathematical definition used by Galileo, it must be admitted that he was looking rather beyond this sort of thing, and in deciding that 'heat is motion' he got far ahead of Galileo.

Francis Bacon's division of natural philosophy into speculative and operative is the same as Roger Bacon's (Vol. I). Speculative natural philosophy as it considers efficient causes is physics, as it considers ends it is metaphysics. Operative natural philosophy considered as the application of physics is mechanics, considered as the application of metaphysics it is natural magic.[6] Bacon's insistence on the value of experiment, although probably directly derived from Telesius (1508–88), also goes back to Roger Bacon.[7] It is doubtful if Francis Bacon had read any of the works of Roger Bacon, some of which were printed in his lifetime;[8] he is mentioned[9] for an optical trick, according to 'an old tale in Oxford', and in another place he is (as Ellis said) at least 'faintly praised'.[10]

[1] Ellis, in Works, I, 84.   [2] D, pref.; II, 15; V, 133.   [3] C, iii, 4; I, 560; IV, 356.
[4] B, ii, 48; I, 330; IV, 214.   [5] Lasswitz, (1), i, 419.
[6] Ueberweg, History of Philosophy, 1874, ii, 37 f.   [7] Thorndike, vii, 63–88.
[8] Ellis, Works, II, 98.   [9] F, viii, 762; II, 586.
[10] o; III, 534: utile genus eorum est, qui de theoriis non admodum solliciti, mechanica quadam subtilitate rerum inventarum extensiones prehendunt; qualis est Bacon.

Boyle frequently refers to Bacon[1] as having improved apparatus and devised and made experiments, and as having pointed out the way of arriving at truth, which Boyle consciously followed. He calls him 'the illustrious Lord Verulam (one of the most judicious naturalists, that our age can boast'), who 'though not a more florid, than a judicious writer, has, much to the satisfaction of his readers, frequently made use of comparisons, in whose choice and application he was very happy', thereby anticipating 'that severe philosopher, monsieur Des Cartes'.

Hooke[2] says 'the incomparable Verulam' had perfected with respect to the intellect, 'some Method or Engine, which shall be as a guide to regulate its Actions, so as that it shall not be able to act amiss', and had shown that 'even Physical and Natural Enquiries as well as Mathematical and Geometrical, will be capable also of Demonstration; so that henceforward the business of Invention will not be so much the Effect of acute Wit, as of a serious and industrious Prosecution'. Playfair[3] emphasised that Bacon 'traced not merely the *outline* but the *ramifications* of science that did not yet exist'. Macaulay's criticism[4] that Bacon's rules are never consciously followed in discovery has often been repeated,[5] but his method of drawing up lists, etc., was consciously used in the early days of the Royal Society and the results were not too bad: ἀπὸ τῶν καρπῶν αὐτῶν ἐπιγνώσεσθε αὐτούς.

The very unfavourable criticisms of Bacon by Kuno Fischer[6] and Liebig[7] were answered by Sigwart,[8] and modern opinion is decidedly more favourable.[9] Mersenne, in the best Continental tradition, censured Bacon for not mentioning foreigners enough, at the same time making extensive use of Bacon's writings without naming him.[10] The harsh criticism by Liebig is unfairly presented. Frost[11] says that Liebig was annoyed with the reception of his agricultural theories by the Royal Agricultural Society, and wished to show up the 'unscientific mode of thought of the English (die unwissenschaftlichen Geistesart der Engländer)' by taking the writings of one of their national heroes. He picked out the weak and foolish parts (einiges ganz Drollige herausfischt), especially from the *Sylva Sylvarum* — a work which Bacon himself said would probably injure his reputation,[12] thus pouring ridicule on Bacon's scientific attainments.

Bacon's famous division of the 'idols' (*idolum* = εἴδωλον, image or spectre)[13]

---

[1] *Works*, ed. Birch, 1744, i, 57, 215, 233, 581; ii, 232; iii, 154, 519; iv, 48; v, 2, 39, 77.

[2] A General Scheme or Idea of the Present State of Natural Philosophy, and How its Defects may be Remedied by a Methodical Proceeding in the Making of Experiments and Collecting Observations, in *Posthumous Works*, 1705, 1 f., 6–7.

[3] Q. by Harcourt, *Phil. Mag.*, 1846, xxviii, 513.

[4] *Essay on Bacon*, ed. Salmon, 1904, 123.   [5] Spedding, in *Works*, I, 38; etc.

[6] *Franz Bacon von Verulam. Die Realphilosophie und ihre Zeitalter*, Leipzig, 1856, tr. Oxenford, *Francis Bacon of Verulam. Realistic Philosophy and its Age*, London, 1857; 2 ed., *Francis Bacon und seine Nachfolger*, Leipzig, 1875.

[7] *Francis Bacon von Verulam und die Geschichte der Naturwissenschaften*, Rede [28th March 1863] in die öffentliche Sitzung der h. [Bavarian] Akad. Wiss., Munich, 1863; *Rede und Abhandlungen*, Leipzig and Heidelberg, 1874, 220 f.; id., *Lord Bacon as a Natural Philosopher*, London, 1863; answered by Rodwell, *Lord Bacon as a Natural Philosopher*, London, 1866.

[8] *Preussische Jahrbücher*, 1863, xii, 93; 1864, xiii, 79.

[9] See, e.g., Farrington, in Singer, (1), 1953, i, 439.

[10] Thorndike, vii, 66, 72.

[11] 1927, 33 f.   [12] *Works*, II, 335.   [13] B, i, 52 f.; I, 169; IV, 58.

obstructing right reasoning was into (1) *idola tribus* (idols of the tribe), inherent in human nature; (2) *idola specus* (idols of the den), those 'pet ideas' of
the individual in his own den or cave, obstructing the light of nature (a simile
from Plato's *Republic*); (3) *idola fori* (idols of the market-place), formed in
associations of men, or society, the 'treasured traditions'; and (4) *idola theatri*
(idols of the theatre), embodied in language and ultimately derived from the
dogmas of old philosophical systems.[1]

Bacon uses the name *form* in the sense of a primary quality; the form of heat
is the local motion of the particles of a body; that of colour is a mode of
arrangement of these particles. He calls it a *law*, in fulfilling which the existence of a particular quality is determined, and also the real thing (ipsissima
res), a true physical cause, we might say. It is the business of science to find
these forms, which cannot be done by argument but only by observation and
experiment. The number of forms should be reduced as much as possible;
there might even be only one ultimate form.

Bacon's inductive method consisted in drawing up three tables: (i) a table of
positive instances, giving all known cases in which a phenomenon (e.g. heat) is
present; (ii) a table of *negative instances*, comprising *related* cases in which it is
absent; and (iii) a table of *degrees of comparison*, in which the nature is present
in different degrees, more or less. The form of the given nature must be
present when this nature is present, absent when it is absent, and must vary
quantitatively when it varies. In such a way Bacon arrived at the correct
deduction that 'Heat itself, its essence and quiddity, is motion and nothing
else', and is a particular kind of motion, 'expansive, restrained, and acting in its
strife upon the smaller particles of bodies.'[2] The various special aids proposed
by Bacon must be sought in his writings. Only one of his twenty-seven
prerogativa instantiarum or comparative values of facts, the *instantiæ crucis*,
has survived in half-understood form as the 'crucial experiment'; it was to
serve as a 'guide-post' where a road forks into two roads, when a phenomenon
can be explained in only one of two alternative ways.

Bacon seems to have had a fairly competent knowledge of very recent work
in chemistry, mentioning Paracelsus (often), Isaac Hollandus,[3] Oswald Croll,[4]
George Agricola,[5] and Basil Valentine.[6] If Bacon wished to know anything
significant about chemistry he would have to go to the experts, the contemporary alchemists, which he did, and the above are all good authors. The
alchemical-theosophical background of much of Bacon's work, with its
theories of sympathy and antipathy and the microcosm and macrocosm, and
interest in the Jewish *Qabbalah*, although firmly grounded in contemporary
England,[7] were much more prominent in Germany under the influence of
Paracelsus (p. 127), who has come in for as much praise as Bacon for blame.

Frost[8] thought that Bacon's lack of money interested him in alchemy, but it
was widespread in England in his period; his criticisms of it are sharp and

[1] Baden Powell, 1834, 198.　　　　[2] B, ii, Aph. 10–20; I, 235–68; V, 126–49.
[3] Bacon, *o*; III, 534: Isaac Hollandus et turbæ chymistarum.
[4] F, x, 998; II, 671.　　　　[5] C; I, 512; IV, 366.
[6] *ε*; III, 747; V, 523: similia Valentini iconibus et somniis, images and dreams of Valentinus.
[7] Lange, 1882, 177.　　　　[8] 53 f., 99 f.

advanced for their time and he goes further than Boyle or Newton later; his numerous allusions to chemistry, often with accounts of his own experiments, brought its study into academic and polite circles. Boyle read the *Novum Organum* with care, and designed many of his experiments as a continuation of the *Sylva Sylvarum*,[1] calling Bacon 'one of the first and greatest experimental philosophers of our age', and 'the great architect of experimental history'.[2]

From the 'Catalogue of Particular Histories' which Bacon proposed to write[3] it is clear that he intended to deal with chemistry in considerable detail: the titles include histories of flame, air, water, earth, metals and mines, quicksilver, vitriol, sulphur, gems, stones; chemical histories of metals and minerals, vegetables, and 'things taken by animals', medicines; histories of wine, honey, sugar, perfumes, dyeing, tanning, working in metals and glass, the history of salts, and 'common experiments which have not grown into an art'. Of this ambitious programme he was able to accomplish little. He collected a large number of what were then regarded as 'facts' from various authors: in his *Sylva Sylvarum* he draws largely on Baptista Porta's *Magia Naturalis*. In his *De Augmentis Scientiarum*[4] Bacon speaks of 'that natural magic . . . embracing certain credulous and superstitious traditions and observations concerning sympathies and antipathies . . . which flutters about so many books (quæ in libris plurimorum volitat)'; yet Book X of the *Sylva Sylvarum* is full of such material, with personal observations by Bacon confirming it. He spoke of 'purification of the word magic'.[5] He also relied to a lesser extent on such standard works as Cardan's *De Rerum Varietate* and *De Subtilitate*, Scaliger's *Exotericarum*, and Sandys' *Travels*; of ancient authors he used Pliny and the *Problems* and *De mirabilibus auscultationibus* attributed to Aristotle,[6] but he often gives his own solutions to problems suggested by these authors, and made many experiments himself. Although the *Sylva Sylvarum* copies many absurd statements from the recognised authorities of his time, 'it is probably the best and most complete single collection of the kind that, up to that time, had been published.'[7] Bacon's observations on natural history are weak and frequently erroneous, being mostly derived from books,[8] as would be expected of a city lawyer.

In a world obsessed by Plato and Aristotle, Bacon frequently speaks of Demokritos with great respect; his school 'went further into nature than the rest'.[9] Bacon's attitude towards the atomic theory varied.[10] In earlier works he speaks favourably of it and admits the existence of a vacuum. He says: 'I know not whether this inquiry I speak of concerning the first condition of seeds [Lucretius's name for atoms, Vol. I] or atoms be not the most useful of all, as being the supreme rule of act and power, and the true moderator of hopes and works.'[11] The doctrine of Demokritos about atoms is either true or is useful

[1] Boyle, *Works*, ed. Birch, 1744, i, 196; iii, 154; Frost, 62.
[2] Boyle, *Works*, 1744, v, 41, 51.   [3] δ; I, 405–10; IV, 265–70.
[4] C, v; I, 573, IV, 367.   [5] C; I, 57; IV, 277, 365.   [6] *Works*, II, 326 f.
[7] Fowler, DNB, ii, 350.   [8] Ellis, *Works*, II, 575 f.
[9] B, i, 51, 57; I, 168; IV, 58; γ; III, 84; V, 466.
[10] Summary in Lasswitz, 1890, i, 413; C. T. Harrison, Bacon, Hobbes, Boyle, and the Ancient Atomists, *Harvard Studies in Philosophy and Science*, 1933, xv.
[11] β; III, 18; V, 423.

for demonstration, since otherwise it is not easy to comprehend the genuine subtlety of nature. There is in things a much more subtle distribution than is observable by the senses, but this is not infinite nor perpetually divisible. The minute parts in continuous bodies, such as solutions of colours or air infected with odours, are demonstrably far more subtle than in broken up or discontinuous bodies.

The atom had been regarded either as the last term in the division of bodies or as a body without vacuum. Heron had denied the existence of a continuous vacuum but had maintained that of a dispersed vacuum, which would explain compressibility.[1] This could happen by forcing out a finer body (a process which would seem to have no end), or by exclusion of a vacuum, or by some natural (whatever that may be) condensation and rarefaction of bodies. Bacon inclines to the existence of a vacuum, and thought the conjecture of Heron, 'a mechanical man', was inferior to that of Demokritos, 'a distinguished philosopher.'[2] Lasswitz[3] regarded Bacon's views on the corpuscular theory as stimulating others; it was for him an applicable and useful aid in physics, and even the vacillating opinions in the Novum Organum represented a great advance over scholastic physics. His conception of the physical universe as an aggregate of matter, form, and motion was a negation of the scholastic system of substantial forms, and his introduction of 'spirits' is an attempt to refer the visible changes of bodies to motion and material influences. It might be added, also, that for Bacon 'spirit' often meant what we call 'energy' rather than some occult principle; this will appear in what follows. As Lasswitz[4] said: 'Er wollte gar kein fertiges Natursystem liefern, und daher ist es nicht zu verwundern, dass wir unverinbare Widersprüche bei ihm finden.'

Bacon's view that the properties of bodies should be explicable in terms of the size and motion of the corpuscles, not necessarily indivisible atoms, is the same as Boyle's and the resemblance can hardly be accidental. Pythagoras assumed that atoms are all alike, when everything comes to their number and arrangement; Demokritos assumed specific differences among the atoms, and denied that everything could come from everything else — which Bacon thought possible. Bacon attributed the idea of the weight of atoms to Demokritos, whom he criticised for his explanation of motion, although his philosophy was much weightier than those of Plato and Aristotle — which perhaps explains why it sank into oblivion after Roman times, whilst the latter floated to the surface like scum.[5] Bacon[6] disproved by experiment Demokritos's statement that a vessel full of ashes holds as much water as an empty vessel. Demokritos and Epikouros were criticised for neglecting God and mind (mens) in the world[7] — which they did not (Vol. I).

Bacon's mature judgment of the atomic theory in the Novum Organum (1620) was unfavourable: 'Men cease not . . . from dissecting nature till they reach the atom; things which, even if true, can do but little for the welfare of

---

[1] See Vol. I.
[2] β; III, 15 f.; V, 419 f.; in ε; III, 744; V, 520, Bacon says it was Demokritos who denied a collective vacuum but proposed an interspersed one.
[3] (1), i, 435.   [4] (1), i, 431.
[5] γ; III, 83; V, 465.   [6] F, i, 34; II, 354.   [7] C, 4; I, 569; IV, 363.

mankind.'[1] He rejected the doctrine of atoms (although not absolutely the physical part of it) on the ground that it implies 'two false assumptions, the hypothesis of a vacuum and the unchangeableness of matter' (e.g. that water cannot be converted into air),[2] and maintained that 'there is no vacuum in nature, either collected or interspersed', rather there is, 'within the bounds of dense and rare, a fold of matter (plica materiæ), which folds and unfolds itself without creating a vacuum.'[3] The spirits or pneumaticals of tangible bodies had been taken for vacuum, whereas they are really the most active bodies.[4]

Bacon[5] asserted that fire is 'merely compounded of the conjunction of heat and light in any substance', and that 'heat itself, its essence and quiddity, is motion and nothing else', a motion which is expansive, restrained, and acting in its strife upon the smallest particles of bodies. His ideas on the nature of this motion are necessarily not very precise and the examples he gives to demonstrate his theory are not to us very convincing. He believed that heat was not material, since 'ignited iron and other metals, which communicate heat to other bodies . . . lose none of their weight or substance'.[6] Quicklime retains some latent heat from the fire in which it is made.[7] Bacon, who derived many ideas from Telesius,[8] criticised the theory of Telesius (p. 383); his own views were as follows.

'Heat and cold are nature's two hands, whereby she chiefly worketh'; cold is produced in seven ways: (1) by coming out of the inside of the earth (the primum frigidum) in winter — a theory which Bacon attributes to Parmenides,[9] (2) by contact with cold bodies, as in 'a conservatory of snow and ice; such as they use . . . to cool wine in summer', (3) as the primary nature of all tangible bodies, as 'all things whatsoever, tangible, are of themselves cold', (4) by the density of the body, dense bodies being colder than rare, and 'earth, dense, tangible, holds all of the nature of cold', (5) a quick spirit enclosed in a cold body, as nitre or snow, (6) the expulsion of spirits, as by opium, which might show its cold on the bulb of a thermoscope, (7) the exhaling of warm spirits, as the moon draws in heat like a magnet, as might be tried by the cooling of warm water exposed to, and screened from, the moon.[10] The greatest producible cold is not comparable in degree with the greatest producible heat[11] — a vague anticipation of absolute zero. Heat and cold in small masses kill one another but in large masses dislodge one another.[12] Bacon evidently thought a great deal about the nature of heat and cold, some of his earlier speculations[13] contain germs of the treatment in the Novum Organum but not the theory of motion. Paracelsus is quoted on strengthening wine by freezing (p. 150).

[1] B, i, 66; I, 178; IV, 68.   [2] B, ii, 8, 48; I, 234, 348; IV, 126, 231; F, i, 98; II, 381.
[3] α; II, 303; V, 398; C. de Waard, L'Expérience Barométrique, Thouars, 1936, 32, translated 'plica materiæ' as 'subtle matter' (of Descartes), but the expression is reminiscent of Boyle's little 'coiled springs'; see 523.
[4] F, i, 98; II, 380.
[5] B, ii, 11 f., 20; I, 236 f.; IV, 127 f., 150; Novum Organum, ed. Fowler, Oxford, 1889, 42, 361 f.; cf. Rosenberger, 79 f.
[6] B, ii, 18; I, 259; IV, 148.
[7] B, ii, 13; I, 248; IV, 138; St. Augustine, De Civitate Dei, xxi, 4; in Hoffmann, Corpvs Scriptorvm Ecclesiasticorvm Latinorvm, Leipzig, 1900, xl, 518: 'miraculum calcis.'
[8] See his account of the views of Telesius in γ; III, 94; V, 476; Frost, 1927, 454.
[9] F, i, 69; II, 370.   [10] F, i, 69–75; II, 370–1.   [11] B, ii, 50; I, 353; IV, 237.
[12] B, ii, 48; I, 338; IV, 223.   [13] Inquisitio legitima de calore et frigore; Works, III, 643–52.

Bacon distinguishes radiant heat from light: it is 'the concomitant of light, not the effect of it'.[1] This had been suggested by Epikouros (300 B.C.).[2] Bacon gives the stock illustration of the insufficiency of sense impression in comparison of temperatures:[3] 'tepid water feels hot if the hand be cold, but cold if the hand be hot.' He mentions and made experiments with a vitrum calendare,[4] which is a thermoscope (see below). Much might be done by the prolonged action of a gentle fire instead of hurried application of strong fire[5] — a good chemical idea.

Bacon identified magnetic force and gravitation, and considered that the former requires time for transmission, which is a proof of the existence of essences and substances separate from matter, and incorporeal.[6] He mentions the microscope and telescope with reserved praise[7] as 'noble discoveries . . . which I regard with suspicion chiefly because the experiment stops' with seeing the exact shapes of fleas and of spots on the sun, 'and many other things equally worthy of investigation are not discovered.' He did not believe in the rotation of the earth, but he thought that light travels with a finite velocity.[8] The rise of water in pumps he thought was due to what 'the Schoolmen call "motion to prevent a vacuum" '.[9] Electricity, of which Gilbert and others had devised such stories, is nothing but the appetite (appetitus) of a body when excited by gentle friction;[10] Bacon gives a list of materials which become electrified by friction.[11] He suggested trying an experiment with a spring clock and one worked by weights, on a high steeple and in a mine, to see if the weight or heaviness varies[12] — as it does.

Bacon made many measurements of specific gravities by weighing cubes of metals etc. of the same size as a cube of gold weighing 1 oz. Troy (24 grains = 1 pennyweight (dwt.), 20 dwt. = 1 ounce Troy) and weighing liquids in a hollow cube of silver holding 1 dwt. 3 grains of water;[13] it is said the ratio never exceeds 21 : 1, 'so limited is nature' — this is about right (see p. 398).

A table of the specific gravities of eleven or twelve substances was published in 1603 by Ghetaldus,[14] who gives the relative volumes for equal weights of bodies: oil $20\frac{8}{11}$, wax $19\frac{19}{21}$, wine $19\frac{19}{59}$, water 19, honey $13\frac{3}{29}$, tin $2\frac{11}{37}$, iron $2\frac{3}{8}$, copper $2\frac{1}{9}$, silver $1\frac{26}{31}$, lead $1\frac{18}{23}$, mercury, $1\frac{38}{95}$, gold 1; he weighed in air and water.

Porta[15] had given a confused account of Archimedes' method of weighing in air and water. The papers of Thomas Harriot (1560–1621) in the British

[1] π; II, 315; V, 409; B, ii, 12, 18; I, 238 f., 259; IV, 129 f., 148.
[2] Vol. I; Gassendi, *Philosophiæ Epicuri Syntagma*, London, 1668, 64–8; Baden Powell, 1834, 25.
[3] B, ii, 13; I, 256; IV, 145.   [4] B, ii, 13; I, 254; IV, 143.   [5] B, ii, 35; I, 290; IV, 177.
[6] B, ii, 37, 45; I, 305, 321; IV, 191, 207.
[7] B, ii, 39; I, 308; IV, 192 f.
[8] B, ii, 46; I, 325; IV, 210 f.   [9] B, ii, 48; I, 330; IV, 215.   [10] B, ii, 48; I, 334; IV, 218.
[11] ρ; III, 824–6.   [12] B, ii, 36; I, 299; IV, 185.
[13] α; II, 245; V, 341; D; III, 691; the table is mentioned in B, ii, 40; I, 312; IV, 198.
[14] *Promotvs Archimedis sev De varijs corporum generibus grauitate & magnitudine comparatis*, 4°, Rome, 1603 (4 ll., 72 pp.), 32 f., calculations for mixtures, 54 f.; Ellis, *Works of F. Bacon*, II, 229, 819; Marinus Ghetaldus (or Getaldus), (Dubrovniki, 1566 or (more probably) 1568– Venice (?), 1626 or 1627); Mohrovičic, *Arhiv. Hem. Farm.*, 1927, i, 49; a good history of specific gravities is given by Richard Davies, *Phil. Trans.*, 1748, xlv, 416.
[15] *Magia Naturalis*, 1588, bk. xviii, ch. 8 f.

A Table showing the Contraction (coitionis) and Expansion of Matter in Respect of Space in Tangible Bodies . . . with a Computation of the Proportions (rationum) in Different Bodies. The same space is occupied by a quantity of:

	Dwt.	Gr.		Dwt.	Gr.
Pure gold weighing	20	0	Oil of vitriol	1	21
Quicksilver	19	9	Oil of Sulphur	1	18
Lead	12	1½	Aqua fortis	1	7
Pure silver	10	21	Sheep's blood	1	5
Tin (tyn) glass (Plumbi			Cow's milk	1	4½
cinerei) [bismuth]	10	13	Camphor	1	4
Copper	9	8	Vinegar	1	3½
Brass (aurichalci)	9	5	Amber	1	3
Steel	8	10	Urine	1	3
Common brass (æris			Common water	1	3*
communis)	8	9	Oil of cloves	1	3*
Iron	8	6	White sugar	1	2½
Tin	7	22	Yellow wax	1	2
Marble	2	22¾	Myrrh	1	0
Glass	2	20½	Butter	1	0
Crystal	2	18	Almond oil	0	23½
Rock salt	2	10	Petroleum	0	23
Nitre	2	5	Spirit of wine	0	22
Sulphur	2	2	Oak wood	0	19½
White vitriol	1	22	Fir wood	0	15
Alum	1	21			

(The complete table lists 78 materials)

* A little less.

Museum show that he had determined specific gravities by this method before 1603.[1] Libri[2] quotes a letter from Toby Matthew to Bacon in April, 1619, 'Brussels, from my bed', mentioning some experiments of Galileo, apparently on specific gravities, in 'a discourse of the mixture of metals' (never published), and thinks Bacon may have got some ideas from Galileo. Some values in a table of 13 materials given by Jacobus Wenceslaus Dobrzensky of Negropont, assistant professor of medicine in Prague,[3] differ from Bacon's: water $5\frac{2}{3}$, gold 100, mercury $71\frac{1}{2}$, lead $60\frac{1}{2}$, silver $54\frac{1}{2}$, copper $47\frac{1}{2}$, iron 42, common tin 39, and pure tin $38\frac{1}{2}$. Mersenne[4] gives in a table: gold 100, mercury $71\frac{1}{2}$, lead $60\frac{1}{2}$, silver $54\frac{1}{2}$, copper $47\frac{1}{2}$, iron 42, tin $38\frac{1}{4}$, water $5\frac{1}{3}$, etc., and shows how the composition of a binary alloy may be calculated from the specific gravity (the old problem of Archimedes). A table of specific gravities was given by Baptista Villalpando (Cordova, 1552–Rome, 1608).[5]

Bacon also gives a 'table of the bulk of matter within a given space or dimension in the same bodies, whole or powdered'[6] and 'in bodies crude and in bodies distilled':

---

[1] Ellis, *loc. cit.*

[2] 1841, iv, 160, 466.

[3] *Nova et amoenior de admirando fontium genio . . . philosophia*, f°, Ferrara, 1657; *Nova philosophia de fontibus*, f°, Prague, 1659 (same contents and pagin., 123 pp.), 13; q. by Thorndike, viii, 202 (table, 203).

[4] *Hydravlica Pnevmatica; Arsqve Navigandi*, 4°, Paris, 1644, 189–92: de Gethaldi [sic] tabulis; 211 (alloy).

[5] *In Ezechielem explanationes et Apparatus Urbis ac Templi Hierosolymitani*, 3 vols. f°, Rome, 1596–1606; 1604, ii (not in BM).

[6] II, 697; V, 347–8; cf. σ, α; III, 819 and note.

	Dwt.	Gr.		Dwt.	Gr.
mercury in body	19	9	sublimate in powder	3	22
lead ,, ,,	12	1½	white lead powder	4	8½
steel ,, ,,	8	10	steel in medicinal powder	2	9
crystal ,, ,,	2	18	crystal ground and compressed	2	20
oak ,, ,,	0	19½	oak in ashes	1	2
sulphur ,, ,,	2	2	sulphur in a chymical oil	1	18
vitriol ,, ,,	1	22	in oil	1	21

Bacon says, erroneously, that although the density ('weight compared with the dimension') will detect an adulteration of gold by silver it 'will not be detected' in the adulteration of silver by lead 'if you take so much the more silver as will countervail the over-weight of the lead'.[1] He explained varying density as the distribution of matter in varying space; although he criticises Aristotle as settling 'the whole matter by that frigid distinction between act and power',[2] this is incorrect, since Aristotle held the same view as Bacon. Bacon says his table disproves the theory of the four elements, since many bodies such as gold are much denser than the heaviest element (earth); the explanation that 'elementary earth' is heavier than any compound, and is different from common earth, is trifling and dictatorial.[3] Since quicksilver is heavier than diamond, 'the form of heaviness or weight depends simply on quantity of matter and not on compactness of frame.'[4] Gilded silver stretches to a great length of gilt wire.[5]

The transformation of concrete bodies from one into another, so far as this is possible (intra terminos Possibilis), is a legitimate object of inquiry.[6] It is also necessary to inquire under what climates, in what earth, and at what depth the several metals are generated, this being part of the general relation (consensus) between primary bodies and their supports (fomitum), i.e. their menstrua and foods.[7] It is one of the greatest magnalia naturæ (a Paracelsan term) to turn water into oil, but it is greater than nature to turn silver or quicksilver into gold.[8] Alchemy pretends to separate 'the unlike parts of bodies which in mixtures of nature are incorporate'.[9] Bacon's definition of chemistry is:[10]

Chymica in se suscipit partes rerum heterogeneas, quæ in corporibus naturalibus latent et implicantur, separare et extrahere; corporaque ipsa inquinata depurare, impedita liberare, immatura perficere.

Chemistry takes upon itself the task of separating and extracting the parts which are hidden and confused in heterogeneous bodies, of purifying bodies from their defilements, of liberating the encumbered, and perfecting the immature.

The alchemists say nature has an intention to make all metals gold but is prevented by impediments, and call in astrology, natural magic, superstitious interpretations of the Scriptures, auricular traditions, feigned testimonies of ancient authors, etc., although they have brought to light not a few profitable experiments and thereby made the world some amends[11] — not a bad judgment.

[1] F, viii, 798; II, 599.
[2] α; II, 243; V, 339; Ellis's note, II, 236.
[3] α; II, 248; V, 344.
[4] B, i, 24; I, 273; IV, 159.
[5] B, ii, 43; I, 319; IV, 204.
[6] B, ii, 1; I, 227; IV, 119.
[7] B, ii, 50; I, 360; IV, 243.
[8] F, iv, 355; II, 459.
[9] A, i; III, 289.
[10] C, i; I, 457.
[11] F, iv, 327; II, 448.

'The alchemist discharges his art upon his own errors, either supposing a misunderstanding of the words of his authors, which makes him listen after auricular traditions, or else failing in the true proportions and scruples of practice, which makes him renew his trials infinitely and, finding that he lights upon some mean experiments and conclusions on the way, feeds upon them, magnifies them to the most, and supplies the rest in hopes.'[1]

The race of chemists, out of a few experiments, have built up a fantastic philosophy, framed with reference to a few things;[2] the empiric philosophy has not found its basis in common notions but in the narrowness and darkness of a few experiments; to those who are daily busied with these experiments, and have infected their imagination with them, such a philosophy seems probable and all but certain, to all other men incredible and vain; of this there is a notable instance in the chemists and their dogmas, though it is hardly to be found elsewhere in these times, except perhaps in the philosophy of Gilbert:

itaque talis philosophia (in paucorum experimentorum angustiis et obscuritate fundatum) illis qui in hujusmodi experimentis quotidie versantur atque ex ipsis phantasiam contaminarunt probabilis videtur, et quasi certa; cæteris, incredibilis et vana. Cujus exemplum notabile est in chimicis, eorumque dogmatibus.[3]

It is not to be denied, however, that not a little has been produced by the industry of chemists, but this accidentally, or by a kind of variation of experiments such as mechanics use and not by art or theory. The alchemist nurses eternal hope and when the thing fails lays the blame on some error — not but that the alchemists have made a good many discoveries and presented men with useful inventions (neque tamen negandum est alchymistas non pauca invenisse, et inventis utilibus homines donasse) but this was accidental.

The analogy between the alchemists who sought the philosophers' stone and made chemical discoveries, and the sons in Æsop's fable digging for supposed treasure and so cultivating the land, was instituted by Bacon, for 'assuredly the search and stir to make gold hath brought to light a great number of good and fruitful inventions and experiments, as well for the disclosing of nature as for the use of man's life'.[4]

Alchemy belongs to the sciences (including also astrology and natural magic) which hold too much imagination and belief, but of which the aims are noble; the conversion of silver, mercury or any other metal into gold is difficult to believe, yet it is more probable that it will be effected by a diligent study of the natures of weight, colour, malleability and extension, volatility and fixedness, and of the first seeds and menstruums of minerals, than that a few grains of an elixir should in a few moments turn other metals into gold by its power to perfect nature and free it from all impediments.[5] Similarly, he who knows something of the spirits is more likely to 'prolong life or restore some degree of youth or vivacity' by 'diets, bathings, anointings, medicines, motions, and the like', than can be done with the use of a few drops or scruples of a liquor or receipt'.[6] In the late experiment of artificial freezing, salt is discovered to have great powers of condensing, and this may be transferable to metals, since

[1] θ; III, 497.   [2] B, i, 54; I, 169; IV, 59.   [3] B, i, 64; I, 175; IV, 65.
[4] A, i; III, 289; B, i, 73, 75; I, 183; IV, 74, 84; ζ; III, 605; τ; III, 685; η; III, 575.
[5] A, i, ii; III, 289, 362; C, iii, 5; I, 574; IV, 367.   [6] A, ii; III, 362.

it is known that strong waters (aquas fortes) composed of certain salts precipitate a little sandy gold (præcipitare arenulas auri) from certain metals not so
dense as gold itself.[1] Mercury put into a linen bag set into the middle of
molten lead which is solidifying will become solid, and might, by many
repetitions of the operation, become fixed and malleable.[2]

Inquiry should be made 'from what beginnings and by what method and by
what process gold or any other metal or stone is generated from its first
menstrua and rudiments up to the perfect mineral'.[3] Although alchemy is 'in
the practice, full of error and imposture; and in the theory, full of unsound
imaginations', yet 'we conceive that a perfect good concoction or digestion or
maturation of some metals will produce gold'. Transmutation, or rather 'the
maturing of metals, and thereby turning some of them into gold', might be
effected (as a Dutchman, 'that had wrought himself into the belief of a great
person', taught), by the use of a temperate, digesting heat, quickening and
spreading uniformly the spirit of the metal but not emitting it, using the most
promising metals (silver and copper, not mercury), a tenth part of mercury
and a twelfth part of nitre, with some injection of an oiled substance, and
allowing time enough (six months at least) and a closed vessel.[4] 'Alchemists of
the reformed school (ex reformatis) conceive that by the equable warmth of
lamps and the like, burning uniformly, they can attain their end, whereas in the
generation of metals in the earth heat is applied and withdrawn gradually and
periodically,[5] as Aristotle had perceived.[6]

Since matter cannot be annihilated it is useless, as 'an obscure writer of the
sect of the chemists' has well said, to try to transmute bodies by reducing them
to nothing.[7] The so-called 'drowning' of metals, in which one metal is converted into another with which it is alloyed in small quantity (Aristotle's idea)[8]
is false, although $\frac{1}{15}$ of silver mixed with gold cannot be separated by aqua
fortis unless more silver is put in.[9] It is possible that metals such as iron, brass
and tin could be refined more than is commonly done.[10]

Bacon does not suggest (as Newton did later) that affinity is a *force*, but he
says all bodies, though they have no sense, yet have perception:

'for when one body is applied to another, there is a kind of election to embrace that which
is agreeable, and to exclude or expel that which is ingrate: and whether the body be
alterant or altered, evermore a perception precedeth operation.'

This may act at a distance, as when a magnet attracts iron.[11] The proneness or
reluctance of bodies to draw together or unite by composition or simple
opposition, by inner consents and aversions, or friendships and enmities ('for
I am almost weary of the words sympathy and antipathy on account of the
superstitions and vanities associated with them') are worthy of careful
attention.[12] Bacon says he does not 'share the idle notion of Paracelsus and the
alchemists, that there are to be found in man's body certain correspondences
and parallels which have respect to all the several species (as stars, planets,

[1] C, v, 2; I, 628; IV, 417.   [2] C, v, 2; I, 626; IV, 415; F, ix, 847; II, 619.
[3] B, ii, 5; I, 231; IV, 122.   [4] F, iv, 326–8; ed. 1627, 86; II, 448–50.
[5] B, ii, 50; I, 357; IV, 241.   [6] B, ii, 135; I, 290; IV, 176.   [7] F, i, 100; II, 383.
[8] *De generatione et corruptione*, i, 10.   [9] F, viii, 798; II, 599.
[10] F, ix, 849; II, 620.   [11] F, ix, 801; II, 603.   [12] B, ii, 50; I, 361; IV, 244–5.

minerals) which are extant in the universe' (from the old Jewish notion of the microcosm) yet 'of all substances which nature has produced, man's body is the most multifariously compounded'.[1]

Writers on natural magic and alchemy are 'a sort of suitors and lovers of fables'.[2] Paracelsus, 'blinded by his distillations', had set up the theory of the Archeus and 'such trifles'.[3] Bacon classes Paracelsus among 'some darksome authors of magic',[4] yet he himself suggests that the imagination can act upon 'dead bodies, as plants, wood, stone, metal, &c.'[5]

Bacon accepted the theory of Paracelsus and the chemists that 'sulphur and mercury run through the whole universe', but found that 'what they add about salt [their third principle] is absurd, and introduced merely to take in bodies earthy and fixed'.[6] Salt itself, in fact, is composed of mercury and sulphur.[7] There is consent between (constiunt) sulphur, oil and greasy exhalation, flame, and perhaps the body of a star (corpus stellae), and also between mercury, water and water vapours, air, and perhaps the pure interstellar ether; these two quaternions or great tribes of things differ immensely in density and quantity of matter but agree very well in configuration (schematismo).[8]

Sulphur is commonly supposed to be the father of metals.[9] Sulphur mixed with a large quantity of steel is able to melt it.[10] Some metals such as lead are melted by fire simply; others such as gold and silver require a fire blown by bellows, others require admixture of some other ingredient, such as steel, which does not melt without a mixture of sulphur or something of that kind.[11] Bacon was acquainted with metal 'trees', which he calls the 'sproutings, branchings or arborescences' of metals, important but 'a kind of toy or pleasure.'[12]

Bacon[13] suggested incorporating iron with flint or other stone ('like not to rust so easily') — silicon steel (which does not rust!); iron with brass; brass, iron, calaminar stone and sulphur, and perhaps lead; andiron (or white) brass contains tin, and 'for the golden colour [of brass ?], it may be by some small mixture of orpiment [arsenic sulphide], such as they use to brass in the yellow alchemy'; silver and tin; various alloys and glasses, including one containing *galletyle*,[14] and one with 'some portion of the glass of metal vitrified'.

To make gold seems impossible, as it is the heaviest of metals, but silver might be made from the heavier quicksilver and lead (as the Chinese are 'mad upon making');[15] quicksilver in molten lead is 'stupefied', and further treatment might take the courses of (i) iterating the melting of the lead, (ii) putting hot

---

[1] C, iv, 2; I, 587; IV, 379.   [2] B, ii, 29; I, 283; IV, 169.   [3] B, ii, 48; I, 339; IV, 224.
[4] F, x, pref.; II, 641.   [5] F, x, 945; II, 654.
[6] B, ii, 50; I, 359; IV, 242; F, iv, 355; II, 459.
[7] *Historia Sulphuris, Mercurii, et Salis*, in D; cf. II, 82; V, 205; ι, III, 769.
[8] B, ii, 50; I, 359; IV, 243; Boyle's word 'schemes'; Janet, 1889, 44, 47: est Baconem ab alchemistis qui in medio ævo florebant parum discessisse.
[9] τ; III, 695.   [10] C, 2; I, 625; IV, 414.   [11] α; II, 269; V, 364.
[12] μ; III, 813–14.   [13] λ; III, 799–805.
[14] The *Oxford Dictionary* does not include this word; the *Century Dictionary*, New York, iii, 2441, with reference to Bacon, says it, or *gallitile*, is a small coloured tile; yellow glaze from antimony? Bacon says: 'Enquire of the substance of *galleytyle*'; III, 805.
[15] F, iv, 327; II, 448.

realgar [arsenic sulphide] into the midst of the mercury, to condense it within as well as without, (iii) try quicksilver in the midst of molten iron or steel.[1] By 'brass' Bacon means copper; brass is 'latten', made from 'brass and the calaminar stone'.[2] Bacon said: 'I heare much of turning Iron into Copper: I heare also of the Growth of Lead in weight, which cannot be without a Conversion of some Body into Lead.'[3]

Bacon clearly recognised the conservation of mass:

'There is nothing more true in nature than the twin propositions, that "nothing is produced from nothing" and "nothing is reduced to nothing", but that the absolute quantum or sum total of matter remains unchanged, without increase or diminution.[4]

There is no reduction from nothing or to nothing, but 'the sum total of matter remains always the same, without addition or diminution'.[5] 'That all things are changed, that nothing really perishes and that the sum of matter remains exactly the same, is sufficiently certain.'[6]

Bacon says 'the weight answers to the quantity of matter in the parts of a tangible body; whereas spirit and the quantum of matter which it contains cannot be computed by weight, for it rather diminishes the weight than increases it', and mentions his table of densities, which shows only a variation in the ratio of 1 to 21. He also tried to find 'the proportions . . . which intangible or pneumatic bodies bear to bodies tangible (si forte capi possint rationes corporum non-tangibilium sive pneumaticorum, respectu corporum tangibilium)' by connecting a small phial containing a weighed amount (about 1 oz.) of spirit of wine with an oiled bladder squeezed out, and heating the phial till the bladder, holding about a quart, filled with vapour. The liquid remaining was weighed, and hence it was found that the liquid had expanded to 100 times its volume of vapour[7] — a vapour density determination. In another description, the bladder had the capacity of a gallon or eight pints; $\frac{1}{2}$ oz. of spirit of wine was put in the phial and, when the vapour filled the bladder, had lost 6 dwt., occupying $\frac{1}{40}$ pint, hence the expansion of the liquid when turned into vapour (in auarm versi) was $40 \times 8 = 320$ times.[8] In a similar experiment, 2 dwt. of water produced vapour which filled a $\frac{1}{2}$ pint bladder; the proportions of vapour from spirit of wine and water might give the ratio of densities of flame and air, to which the vapours of these two liquids are closely related.[9]

Air or material spirits cannot escape through solid vessels, as had been thought, and this makes it possible in operations on natural bodies to be certain of the total quantities.[10] Although in one place[11] Bacon says air can never become fluid, in another he suggests that it is worth trying whether when left compressed for a long time it will not lose its pressure (as a bent stick finally assumes this shape), or will even turn into water.[12] When moisture evaporates into the air it is converted into air,[13] yet air in the upper regions must be

---

[1] Ib.; λ; III, 803. [2] μ; III, 807. [3] λ, in F, 1664, 227.
[4] B, ii, 40; I, 311; IV, 197; F, i, 100; II, 383. [5] α; II, 243; V, 339–40.
[6] β, v; III, 22; V, 426 f., where Bacon confuses absolute and specific gravity.
[7] B, ii, 40; I, 312; IV, 197–9. [8] α; II, 257; V, 352–3. [9] τ; III, 705, 710.
[10] B, ii, 50; I, 351; IV, 235; β, v; III, 23; V, 428–9.
[11] B, ii, 33; I, 288; IV, 174. [12] B, ii, 50; I, 353; IV, 236. [13] α; II, 281; V, 376.

turned into water 'as a necessary conclusion from the conservation of things';[1] Van Helmont denied this (222). 'Tangible bodies have no pleasure in the consort of air, but endeavour to subact it into a more dense body'; bulbs sprout in air and become heavier by magnale naturæ, 'for it sheweth that air may be made so to be condensed as to be converted into a dense body', whilst the tendency is 'to extenuate and turn things to be more pneumatical and rare'; the observation 'sheweth also that air can nourish, which is another great matter of consequence'.[2] As there are pestilential airs which can suddenly kill a man in health, there may be sovereign airs able suddenly to cure a man in sickness.[3]

Air when too hot is suffocating, perhaps because it becomes thickened (Jean Rey's idea, 1630), as when persons are suffocated by burning coals or charcoal.[4] It is certain that air is at least 100 times rarer than water, but flame is not 10 times rarer than air.[5] Air is dilated by heat, this property being used in the thermoscope (in *vitro* quod appellamus *calendare*) to mark the degree (gradus) of heat and cold in the weather.[6] The construction of thermoscopes 'those glasses which indicate the state of the atmosphere in respect of heat and cold' is fully described,[7] and Bacon often proposes experiments in which they are to be used to detect heat and cold in bodies. He tried to measure the dilatation of air by 'external violence' by sucking air from a glass egg (ovum vitreum) with a small hole in it, quickly stopping the hole with the finger, and then opening under water; the hole was stopped with wax and the dilated air left for a day, to see if it would 'no longer care about restoring itself', but the water entered as before.[8] The same should be tried with air dilated by heat.[9]

The air thermoscope or vitrum calendare probably became known to Bacon through Drebbel (321) or Flud, who brought it from Italy in 1605 (327). It is usually said to have been first devised by Galileo about 1595, but Porta had described it in 1589.[10] Porta says:

Vas inversum aquam hauriat, ita efficies. Longissimi colli paretur vas, & quanto longius fuerit, eo mirabilius videbitur, vitreum vero, & pellucidum, ut ascendentem perspicias aquam . . . hinc artificia . . . nunc vero in domesticum permeavit usum.

Libri[11] and Cajori[12] discussed the claims of Galileo, Bacon, Flud, Drebbel, Sanctorius, and Sarpi to the invention of the air thermoscope and decided in favour of Galileo before 1597; 1595 or even 1592 are now proposed, but Galileo's claim (he made none himself) is based only on much later letters to him (1613, 1615) by Sagredo and a statement in 1638 by Castelli.

The name 'thermometer' is first used by the Jesuit Jean Leurechon[13] in a section

[1] α; II, 293; V, 388.   [2] F, i, 27, 29; II, 349–50.   [3] C, iv, 1; I, 585; IV, 378.
[4] E; II, 205; V, 313; F, x, 919; II, 647.
[5] α; II, 259; V, 354; B, i, 45; I, 165, and note [6]; IV, 55.   [6] α; II, 267; V, 362.
[7] B, ii, 12, 13; I, 241, 254 f.; IV, 131, 143.   [8] α; II, 283; V, 379.   [9] α; II, 290; V, 385–6.
[10] *Magia Naturalis*, 1589, xix, 3; Ellis, *Works* of F. Bacon, I, 254; Wolf, (1), 1935, 82; F. S. Taylor, *Ann. Sci.*, 1942, v, 129; Chaldecott, *ib.*, 1952, viii, 195; E. H. Browne, *J. Chem. Educ.*, 1934, xi, 448–53; L. D. Patterson, *Isis*, 1953, xliv, 51 (Royal Society thermometers and scales of temperature, 1663–1709); M. K. Barnett, *Osiris*, 1956, xii, 269–341 (development of thermometry, to Regnault); T. Thomson, *Outline of the Sciences of Heat and Electricity*, 1840, 35–42 (Sanctorio; Galileo not mentioned); Poggendorff, (2), 154; *A Story of Temperature Measurement*, Negretti and Zambra, London, 1958.
[11] (1), iv, 189, 468.   [12] *History of Physics*, New York, 1929, 97.
[13] *Recreation Mathematicqve*, published in 1624 under the pseudonym of H. van Etten; ed. 8°, Lyons, 1627, problem 76, p. 101; Hellmann, *Neudruck von Schriften und Karten über Meteorologie und Erdmagnetismus*, No. 7, Berlin, 1893, 8.

headed: 'Du Thermometre, ou Instrument pour mesurer les degrez de la chaleur ou du froidure', with two pictures of air thermometers with graduations.

Bacon thought that water by intense and prolonged cold turns into crystal and never recovers its form,[1] and stalactites are formed from congealed water, although crystals sometimes form on bare rocks without water.[2] Water is compressed only with great difficulty: corpora tangibilia (quale est aqua) multo ægrius et ad minus spatium partiuntur compressionem. Bacon filled a strong lead sphere, holding 2 pints, with water, stopped the hole with melted lead, and flattened two opposite sides of the globe with a heavy hammer and then with a press, 'till the water impatient of further pressure exuded through the solid lead like a fine dew (per solida plumbi instar roris delicati exstillaret)'. He 'computed the space lost by the compression'.[3]

The Florentine Academicians used a silver vessel,[4] but Tyndall[5] emphasised Bacon's priority.

Thorndike has followed some earlier censorious authors in supposing that Bacon's 'spirits' were some sort of occult beings, like ghosts or demons, although Lasswitz[6] and others who had read Bacon with sufficient knowledge had clearly recognised that they were 'effluvia' or pneumatica, which although weightless were material. They correspond, in fact, with what Van Helmont called 'gas' and have a perfectly sensible and meaningful physical significance. In the 16 cent. the idea was in vogue that spirits are a refined form of matter and are a motive force in the human body; they 'govern nature principally'.

Bacon probably got his notion of animal spirits from Telesius; in the 17 cent. they were very generally believed to be circulating in the motor and sensory nerves[7] and his views are quite 'scientific'. Johannes Argentarius (Castelnuovo, Piedmont, 1514–Turin, 1572), who professed to follow Galen, held[8] that men breathe in air and breathe out spirit, which is crasser than air and is produced from matter composed of all the elements. Spirit is a vaporous substance essential to the performance of the bodily functions; it is all of one kind and is not differentiated as animal, vital, and natural. Domenico Bertacchi of Campo Reggio (d. 1596)[9] accepted the Galenic classification of animal, vital, and natural spirits, associated with the brain, heart, and liver.

Bacon proposed to 'inquire what power the mixing or coupling of a light body with a heavy one has in lessening the gravity of a body (ad elevandam corporis gravitatem), as in the weight of animals alive and dead'.[10] The spirit which pre-exists in bodies adds nothing to the weight but rather takes away from it, by turning into itself that moisture and juice of the body which previously had weight[11] — Cardan's idea (p. 13). Bacon thus distinguished between the crude spirits present in tangible bodies and the animal spirits

---

[1] B, ii, 48; I, 332; IV, 217.   [2] ξ; III, 818; α; II, 294; V, 389.
[3] B, ii, 45; I, 324; IV, 209; τ; III, 703.
[4] *Saggi di Natvrali Esperienze fatte nell' Accademia del Cimento*, f°, Florence, 1666, 204 (CUL xxii. 27. 20); *Essayes of Natural Experiments*, tr. R. Waller, 4°, London, 1684, 117.
[5] *Heat a Mode of Motion*, 6 ed., 1880, 180.   [6] (1), i, 431.
[7] Thorndike, *Speculum*, 1953, xxviii, 692.
[8] *De Somno et Vigilia libri duo*, 4°, Florence, 1556, BM 1039. 1. 33.
[9] *De Spiritibus libri quattuor; necnon de Facultate Vitali libre tres* 4°, Venice, 1584; Thorndike, vi, 226, 228.
[10] C, v, 3, 11; I, 638; IV, 426.   [11] E; II, 120; V, 232.

peculiar to living creatures. The latter have positive levity, a dead body being heavier than a living body.[1] The atmospheric air is devoid of levity, since a bladder filled with air is not lighter than when empty.[2]

Bacon's ideas on 'spirits' anticipated some of Van Helmont's on gases and Boyle's on 'effluviums'.[3] Fermented liquors close confined often burst casks and bottles by the force of the native spirit expanding itself.[4] Experiment will show 'whether there can be such a heterogeniety in pneumatic bodies (inter spiritalia) as we find there is in liquids';[5] the spirits or pneumaticals in tangible bodies are scarcely known and have been mistaken for vacuum or for air, 'from which they differ exceedingly'; they are not natural heat or cold, or virtues and qualities, but 'things by themselves', and 'nothing else but a natural body, rarefied to a proportion, and included in the tangible parts of bodies, as in an integument'.[6]

In mines there are damps which kill either by suffocation or by the poisonous nature of the mineral, as the spirits of quicksilver fly to the skull, teeth and bones, so that gilders hold a piece of gold in the mouth to draw the spirits of quicksilver, which gold becomes whitened.[7] Pneumatic bodies appear to be of three kinds: (1) imperfect (inchoata, inopes), (2) fixed (devincta), and (3) pure (pura, divites). The imperfect comprise all kinds of fumes (fumi omnigeni), including volatile fumes from metals and some minerals, easily coagulated by sublimation or precipitation; vaporous fumes from water and liquids (aqueis); fumes (fumorum) from dry bodies; exhalation (halitum) from oily bodies; breaths (aurarum) from bodies watery in substance and inflammable in spirit, as wines, distilled liquors (liquores exaltati) and strong drinks. Another kind of fumes, called after-fumes (post-fumos) or secondary fumes, exhale from combustibles after flame; there are also after-vapours (post-vapores), after-breaths (post-halitus) and after-volatiles (post-volatiles).

Bacon gives a:

Table of Pneumatic Bodies in Order of Bulk.

Volatilia metallorum et fossilium	Auræ
Post-volatilia ipsorum	Post-auræ
Vapores	⎰Spiritus crudi, devincti in tangi-
Fumi	⎱bilibus
Post-fumi	Aër
Halitus	⎰Spiritus vivi, sive incensi, devincti
Post-halitus	⎱in tangibilibus
	Flamma.

Unmixed pneumatic bodies are of two kinds, air and flame.[8] Fixed airs (pneumatica devincta), commonly called spirit (spiritus vulgo vocant), occur only enclosed in tangible bodies (tantum corporibus tangibilibus inclusa); they are at the same time oily and watery, and on being converted into a pneumatic substance constitute a body composed as it were of air and flame and comprising the mysterious properties of both; they are near to breaths such as rise from wine and salt, and have two natures, of crude and vital spirits. Air and flame are the only pure pneumatic bodies, existing in great

[1] E, α; II, 112, 119, 254; V, 224, 232, 349.   [2] α; II, 254–8; V, 349–52.
[3] Frost, 1927, 159 f.   [4] α; II, 262; V, 357.   [5] B, ii, 42; I, 318; IV, 204.
[6] F, i, 98; II, 381.   [7] F, x, 918; II, 647.   [8] ι; III, 769; V, 547.

variety and unequal degrees of bulk. After-fumes are thinner and rarer than fore-fumes, as 'they are the carcases and solutions of flame, which is itself so subtle a body' (sint flammæ (corporis tam subtilis) cadavera et solutiones). Air in a room lighted by many candles and torches can be breathed after many hours, whilst the fore-fumes from such candles and torches, when extin-guished and smoking without flame, would be unendurable in a much shorter time. Crude spirits fixed in tangible bodies are denser than air, as odours escaping gradually from vegetables and dead animals, manifestly retaining something gross. Living spirits are lighter than air, and last of all comes flame, which mounts upwards and is thinner, softer and more yielding than air, for the least breath makes a candle flame tremulous, and as oil (the pabulum of flame) is rarer than water, so is flame rarer than air and spirit.[1] As it is a kind of froth composed of air and a finer substance than air, flame would be white but for the admixture with smoke.[2] In another place,[3] Bacon says flame is not ignited air (aërem incensum) but differs from air as much as water differs from oil, or sulphur from mercury; also[4] 'let no one dream that lighted flame is air, when in fact they are quite different bodies'.

A flame is compressed by the air around it and is every moment generated and extinguished; extinction begins at the sides, where the flame is compressed and troubled by the air, but the heart of the flame, which is not touched by the air but is surrounded by other flame on all sides, is not extinguished until gradually compressed by the air, hence the pyramidal shape of the flame.[5] Flame, if too much compressed, is extinguished, as may be seen by putting a glass over a candle, for the air expanded by the heat compresses the flame and thereby lessens and extinguishes it, just as a candle flame is put out, or a burn-ing coal, by pressing it with tongs (etenim aër per calorem dilatatus contrudit flammam, eamque minuit et extinguit).[6] Burning a candle in a glass vessel over water is 'a common experiment but the cause is mistaken', since the rise of water in the vessel had been explained as due to the drawing action of heat, or the flame drawing the liquor as nourishment, whereas when the flame actually goes out the water rises more copiously, because it now takes up the space previously occupied by the flame.[7] 'The air is not diminished in quan-tity but contracted in space' since the water does not rise much till the flame is extinguished;[8] this is a correct observation.

In an experiment 'on the secret nature of flame', a candle in a holder is put in a porringer of spirit of wine, and both candle and spirit kindled: the candle flame will 'open itself and become four or five times bigger than otherwise' and also globular and not pyramidal, and flickering.[9] The tallow or wax candle flame is more luminous than the spirit flame because it has a greater density:[10] nam flamma sevi aut ceræ magis luminosa est, et (si ita loqui licet)

---

[1] α; II, 254–6; V, 349–52.   [2] v; III, 236.   [3] ι; III, 771; V, 550.
[4] B, ii, 36; I, 304; IV, 189.   [5] B, ii, 36; I, 303; IV, 189; ε; III, 763; V, 538.
[6] E; II, 203; V, 311.   [7] F, ix, 889; II, 635.   [8] B, ii, 50; I, 351; IV, 235.
[9] B, ii, 36; I, 304; IV, 190; F, i, 31; II, 352; the explanation, as Ellis remarks, is that 'in impure air flames increase in size because the heated vapour of which they are composed diffuses itself before it meets with sufficient oxygen for complete combustion'; Liebig ridi-culed the experiment as impossible; see Partington, *Ann. Sci.*, 1945, v, 229.
[10] ε; III, 758, 763; V, 533, 539.

magis ignea; at flamma spiritus vini magis opaca, et tanquam aërea, præsertim si in parva sit quantitate, ut flamma seipsam non inspisset. This is an anticipation of Frankland's theory of the luminosity of flame.[1]

In a set of experiments 'touching the continuance of flame', a spoonful of spirit of wine was kindled and the time taken for it to burn away was measured as 116 pulses. Nitre, bay-salt, gunpowder, yellow wax, milk, water, a pebble, and wood were added in measured amounts and the times taken. The result was that 'the spirit of wine simple endureth the longest; and the spirit of wine with the bay-salt, and an equal quantity of water, were the shortest'.[2] Flames burn better in cold air, which irritates them; dry air is indifferent but moist air partly quenches the flame (as lights will go out in the damps of mines), hence the flame lasts longer.[3] The outer part of a flame, in contact with the cold air which is in conflict with it, is hotter than the inside, as can be shown by putting a stick in the flame ('hold an arrow in flame'), when it is burnt more quickly at the sides.[4]

Nitre (nitrum) is the spirit of the earth, since it is generated either naturally or (in some parts of Europe) artificially in any earth, even though pure and unmixed with nitrous matter, when laid up free from the rays of the sun.[5] Nitre (or rather its spirit) is very cold, and hence nitre or salt when added to snow or ice intensifies the cold of the latter, the nitre by adding its own cold but the salt by supplying activity to the cold of the snow. It is said that in hot countries where there is no snow, congelation is produced by nitre alone instead of by these congealing mixtures of ice and the salts, 'but this I have not proved.'[6]

Gunpowder was 'suggested by the pot lid of the monkish chemist [Berthold Schwartz; see Vol. I] suddenly flying up with great force and a loud report'.[7] A white gunpowder which propels without sound is a fiction,[8] or 'a dangerous experiment, if it should be true'.[9] The explosion of gunpowder is not simply due to expansion but is owing to the conflict of two natures, the highly inflammable sulphur and the flame-abhorring crude spirit in the nitre. In this strange conflict the sulphur kindles into flame with all its might (for the charcoal only combines the other two bodies) and the spirit of the nitre bursts forth with all its might and dilates itself by heat, and by thus flying and bursting out fans the flame of the sulphur on all sides as with hidden bellows.[10] In this way, by an internal mixture in a body before it is set on fire, a mixed body may be made of flame and air, as the flame of gunpowder may be compared with a powerful froth of flame and air, which cannot be produced by blowing a flame with bellows.[11]

Although other things penetrate one another on account of their restless

[1] Partington, *op. cit.*   [2] F, iv, 366; II, 463; also ridiculed by Liebig.
[3] F, iv, 374–5; II, 466.
[4] B, ii, 13, 20, 36; I, 254, 265, 302; IV, 143, 153, 188; F, i, 32; II, 353; Partington, *op. cit.* (quotation).
[5] E; II, 166–7, V, 273–4; α; II, 263; V, 358.
[6] B, iii, 5; I, 575 (sal nigrum); IV, 369; F, i, 83; iv, 354; II, 375, 459.
[7] C, v, 2; I, 627; IV, 416.   [8] κ; III, 662.   [9] F, ii, 120; II, 392.
[10] B, ii, 36; I, 302; IV, 188; E; II, 167; V, 274; β, ix; III, 32; V, 436; Romocki, *Geschichte der Explosifstoffe*, Berlin, 1895, i, 159.
[11] α; II, 261; V, 356; F, i, 30; II, 351.

nature and desire for change, as metals and strong waters, and gold and quicksilver, 'as it were with consent' and without violence, yet flame is not content to take in any other body; either it overcomes the other body and turns it into itself, or itself dies and goes out.[1] When a candle is blown out, the fume rising seems to occupy about half the volume of the flame, which gives some idea of the ratio of densities.[2]

Fire, when very strong, will dry up things, such as metals, which it has melted; the metals (except gold) lose their volatile part in a strong fire and become lighter and more brittle.[3] The rusting of metals is due to the escape of an imponderable spirit which is 'compelled to push and drive before it the tangible parts themselves, so that they go out along with it'.[4] When the spirit is detained and yet expanded and excited by heat or something analogous thereto, fusion of metals, etc. results (whilst other bodies harden on heating because the spirit escapes); when the spirit is neither wholly detained nor wholly discharged, an organic body is formed, as in 'the first beginnings and rudiments or essays of life in animalculæ generated from putrefaction'.[5] It should be an experiment on the vitrifaction of metals 'what weight the vitrified body bears, compared with the crude body' and, 'because vitrifaction is accounted a kind of death of metals, what vitrifaction will admit of turning back again, and what not.'[6] Lead increases in bulk and weight, especially if stored in cellars, where things rust.[7]

Pure and perfect metals, though vexed and altered by sublimations, precipitations, amalgamations, dissolutions, calcinations, etc., are restored (restituuntur) by fire and conflation, and turned into the same kind of body as before; this is nothing but the emission and exclusion of the air which was mixed with them or of the waters in which the metals had been dissolved (esse nihil aliud quam emissio et exclusio aëris qui se miscuerat, aut aquarum in quibus dissoluta erant).[8]

Mineral medicines are extolled by chemists yet, although they are safer for outward application, no one has tried to imitate natural baths and mineral fountains, which owe their virtues to the mineral veins through which they flow, as it is possible to find by analysis (distinguere per separationes) what such waters dissolve (hujusmodi aquæ inficiantur), such as sulphur, vitriol, steel (chalybe), etc.[9]

In distillation, which was unknown to the ancients,[10] a body is 'opened' or 'attenuated' in two different ways, in one of which the original body is recovered from the vapour, and in the other a rarer, more subtle, body is obtained from the crude body distilled. Every distillation is performed with varying degrees of heat and in alembics or in retorts (in retortis) with receivers luted on, and occurs in two phases, first rarefaction into a pneumatic body and secondly condensation and restoration into a tangible body as the heat

---

[1] F; viii, 800; II, 600.   [2] τ; III, 711.   [3] E; II, 115; V, 227.
[4] Cf. Plato, Timaios 59 c; Opera, ed. Schneider, Paris, 1846, ii, 225; Oeuvres, tr. Cousin, xii, 170 f.
[5] B, ii, 40; I, 310; IV, 195; E; II, 120; V, 232; α; II, 264; V, 359.
[6] μ; III, 813.   [7] α; II, 251; V, 347.   [8] α; II, 286; V, 381.
[9] A, ii; III, 376; C, iv, 2; I, 597; IV, 389.   [10] B, i, 85; I, 192; IV, 83.

slackens.[1] The separation of a compound by distillation and other modes of analysis, and the bringing together of its several homogeneous parts, may lead to knowledge of the simple natures and forms, but this is not to be effected by fire, for many *new* natures are brought out by fire and heat, and other modes of solution, which things are falsely supposed to be merely separated from the compound, in which they are thought to have subsisted.[2] 'When bodies are tormented by fire or other means, many qualities are communicated by the fire itself, and by the bodies employed to effect the separation, which did not exist previously in the compound.'[3] This was insisted upon later by Jungius, Van Helmont, and especially Boyle (*Sceptical Chymist*, 1661, see p. 501).

Bacon thought that if a cube of wood were heated in a strong iron vessel which it just filled, and tightly shut so that no moist and pneumatic part of the wood could be expelled, one of two things would happen; either the body of the wood would be converted into some kind of amalgam (in quoddam amalagma), or it would be resolved into air or a pure pneumatic body, leaving some dregs (coarser than ashes) at the bottom, and some incrustations on the sides, of the vessel. Water in the same apparatus might be altered in colour, smell, taste, or oiliness, achieving some great things. The amount of pneumatic material formed in a distillation could be found from the difference in weight between the original body and the solid and liquid products.[4]

Mercury contains a 'flatulent spirit' and explodes when heated in a closed vessel, so that it resembles gunpowder, with which a little mercury is mixed to make the powder stronger; chemists also say that gold, in certain preparations, when vexed and confined, makes dangerous explosions, almost like thunder; but Bacon says he had no experience of these things.[5]

Gold is used medicinally in three forms: potable gold, wine in which red-hot gold has been quenched, and in substance such as leaf and filings. Potable gold 'is now given as a strong cordial in dangerous or desperate maladies with tolerable success', but (although this fact was carefully suppressed) it seems that the spirits of salt used to dissolve the gold really supply the virtue, and if gold could be 'opened' (aperiri) without corrosive waters, or by corrosive waters without poisonous properties, it would be a good thing. Powdered gems and pearls as powder or dissolved in lemon juice are also given as medicine; but pearls may have nearly the same properties as crayfish shells (testis cancrorum fluviatilium).[6] There was then, however, little confidence in such medicines, to which the Arabs, Greeks, and 'moderns' attributed fantastic virtues.[7] It is uncertain if gold can be made volatile and pneumatic (like mercury when heated), or even potable, as they call it, which does not mean soluble (for that is easily done by aqua fortis) but digestible by the human stomach.[8]

Corrosive liquids, which possess acridity, act like heat in tearing bodies asunder, but their operation is relative, depending on the porosity of the

[1] α; II, 273; V, 367.   [2] B, ii, 7; I, 234; IV, 125.   [3] B, ii, 40; I, 314; IV, 199.
[4] α; II, 274; V, 368.   [5] α; II, 282; V, 378; F; i, 30; II, 351; D; II, 74; V, 196.
[6] E; II, 156; V, 264.   [7] E; II, 181; V, 289.   [8] α; II, 269; V, 364.

bodies acted upon, for aqua regia dissolves gold but not silver, and aqua fortis dissolves silver but not gold, and neither dissolves glass.[1]

Bacon described in detail some *quantitative* experiments on dissolving gold in aqua regia, and mercury, lead, silver, copper, tin, and iron in aqua fortis,[2] and the phenomena attending the processes. He noted that a given quantity of acid dissolves only a certain weight of metal and no more; that a copious saffron-coloured fume is evolved with iron and aqua fortis; that the solution of copper and iron is attended by evolution of heat, in the case of iron more than the hand can bear, and with a very great internal tumult; that the greater part of the lead is deposited in a 'calcined form', whilst in the case of silver 'icy particles, either from the metal or the water [acid], or both, shoot across' in the solution [silver nitrate]; and in the case of tin, 'the whole metal is turned into a body like cream or curds.'[3] A solution of quicksilver might be performed quantitatively to see if the weight of the product was equal to the weight of the components; quicksilver is the most suitable metal, as it dissolves without much heat.[4] When the experiment was tried with iron in aqua fortis, there was no loss in weight although much thick vapour came off; this experiment (tried once or twice, 'but I do not know whether there were any error in the trial', says Bacon), shows that 'the opening of a body doth increase the weight'.[5] Some experiments on dissolving metals in acids and 'the commixture of liquids' (e.g. spirit of wine and oil of vitriol, which 'gathereth a great heat, and a sweetness in the taste'), were published in 1679 by Tenison.[6]

Gold dissolving in aqua regia, and lead and mercury dissolving in aqua fortis, do not generate heat, but silver, copper, tin, iron and steel give out heat, increasing in this order.[7] The various colours of the solutions of the metals are emphasised, as well as those of their 'rusts' such as vermilion, azure, verdigris, bice, cirrus, etc., and in their vitrifactions; they are able to resist fire or strong waters, and to be 'put in an equal posture' and retain part of their spirit, both of which are required to make colours.[8]

Bacon found that a solution of two drachms of quicksilver ('for that charge the aqua fortis will bear') in 2 oz. of aqua fortis will not bear a flint as big as a nutmeg; hence the weight of the quicksilver more than the weight of the stone does not compensate the excess of the weight of the stone over that of aqua fortis.[9]

Sir Thomas Browne[10] says Bacon had asserted that

'a dissolution of iron in aqua fortis, will bear as good weight as their bodies did before, notwithstanding a great deal of waste by the thick vapour'. Browne, however, says: 'we cannot find it to hold neither in Iron nor Copper, which is dissolved with less ebullition; and hereof we made trial in Scales of good exactness: wherein if there be a defect, or such as will not turn upon quarter grains, there may be frequent mistakes in experiments of this nature.'

[1] B, ii, 12, 20; I, 246, 262; IV, 136, 150.　　[2] α; II, 278 f., 301; V, 372 f., 396.
[3] Metastannic acid, see Boyle, p. 536.　　[4] α; II, 279; V, 374.
[5] F, viii, 789; II, 595; cf. Bacon's statements on the indestructibility of matter and the *gain* in weight by loss of spirit.
[6] *Baconiana*, 1679, 140; III, 822.　　[7] B, ii, 12; I, 246; IV, 135.　　[8] F, ii, 291; II, 437.
[9] F, viii, 790; II, 596; the experiment is suggested for stones and tin in α; II, 280; V, 374.
[10] *Pseudodoxia Epidemica*, bk. iv, ch. 7; 1658, 169; *Works*, ed. Sayle, 1927, ii, 141; ed. Keynes, 1928, iii, 36.

Browne[1] also says: 'thus also in a solution of one ounce of Quick-silver in two of *Aqua fortis*, the liquor will bear Amber, Horn, and the softer kinds of stones, as we have made triall in each.'

Bacon describes some experiments in which wheat was steeped in (*a*) water mixed with horse and pigeon dungs, or in urine, (*b*) in water mixed with chalk, ashes, or bay salt, (*c*) in wine, and (*d*) in spirit of wine, and then left to germinate. When compared with unsteeped wheat, that which had been steeped in water mixed with dungs of horses and pigeons, in urine, in water mixed with soot, chalk, ashes and salt, came up in six days; the wheats which grew best were those steeped with urine, dungs, chalk, soot, ashes and salt in this order; wheats steeped in wine and spirit of wine did not come up at all.[2] Nitre promotes the sprouting of vine buds, 'for nitre is (as it were) the life of vegetables.'[3] Bacon mentions the soap bubbles which boys blow into a wonderful tower-like fabric with a pipe or tube dipped into water mixed with a little soap.[4]

Spirit of wine, more pungent and stronger than wine itself, is made from wine by one distillation; if itself distilled will it become again stronger?[5] Spirit of wine probably expands more than water on heating in thermoscopes (in vitro calendari);[6] it is the lightest liquid.[7] When very strong and well rectified it has the same effect as heat in coagulating white of egg and in hardening bread.[8]

Putrefaction is caused by the innate spirit of a body, which is not simply discharged but is partly detained, whence it produces strange effects.[9] The mould from a cut lemon consisted of tufts of hair an inch high, and on the top of each hair was a kind of head like the head of a small snail, plainly beginning to imitate a plant.[10] Wetting hastens rusting or putrefaction by softening the crust and allowing the spirits to come forth; hence putrefaction may be inhibited by cold, astringents, exclusion of air, motion or stirring, drying, strengthening the spirits (say by salting or adding aromatics), separation of cruder parts by distillation, embalming, mixing with sugar or oils, and smoking.[11] The turning of wine into vinegar is a kind of putrefaction, due to the escape of the more oily spirits leaving the liquor more sour and hard; to make vinegar vessels of wine are exposed to the noon-day sun.[12] Living creatures are generated by putrefaction by the spirit driving the glutinous substance into shape and members.[13]

Some good experiments with phosphorescent wood[14] and the phosphorescence of the sea, insects, etc., are described.[15] Sugar has displaced the use of honey and preparations of honey, such as mead (which was still made in Russia and Wales).[16] All hard sugar, raw or refined, sparkles when broken or scraped with a knife in the dark (probably the first mention of tribolumines-

---

[1] *Pseudodoxia Epidemica*, bk. vii, ch. 15; 1658, 313; *Works*, ed. Keynes, 1928, iii, 30.
[2] F, v, 402; II, 475 f.   [3] F, v, 444; II, 485.   [4] β, vi; III, 27; V, 431.
[5] III, v, 2; I, 626; IV, 415.   [6] α; II, 276; V, 371.   [7] B, ii, 34; I, 288; IV, 175.
[8] B, ii, 11; I, 238; IV, 128; α; II, 289; V, 384.   [9] E; II, 121; V, 233.
[10] α; II, 264; V, 359; F, vii, 606; II, 529.   [11] F, iv, 329–50; II, 451 f.
[12] F, ix, 898; II, 637.   [13] F, ix, 900; II, 638.   [14] F, iv, 352; II, 456 f.
[15] C, iv, 3; I, 612; IV, 404.
[16] F, ix, 848; II, 619; suggesting a sugar-mead — the Spanish-American *guarapo*.

cence).[1] Boyle (p. 546) also described the luminescence of sugar on scraping with a knife.

The smell of fresh earth is very beneficial, and it might be tried whether pouring some Malmsey or Greek wine into the new earth would improve the effect, the vapours of the earth and the wine together comforting the spirits more; 'provided always it is not taken for a heathen sacrifice, or libation to the earth.'[2] Bacon suggests hot-houses for plants, not known in his time.[3] Leaven, yeast, curd, and 'certain poisons' excite and invite a successive and continued motion in dough, beer, cheese, or the human body, 'not so much by the force of the exciting as by the predisposition and easy yielding of the excited body.'[4] This is a suggestion of catalysis, and the editors refer to Liebig's theory of 'communication of motion' in fermentation.[5] Bacon[6] criticised Paracelsus's theory of nutrition,[7] viz. that the nutriment of bodily parts is present in the food and is merely separated by the Archeus. Bacon thought the parts of the body assimilate the juices, which are nearly alike for all of them, and then turn these into their own nature (et vertere in naturam suam). The object of respiration is cooling[8] — this was Harvey's idea too (p. 440).

Bacon's doctrine of two souls in man, the animal soul and the immortal soul, was derived from Telesius. St. Augustine, St. Thomas Aquinas, and the Schoolmen had taught that there is only one.[9]

Bacon has been criticised on the ground that he was 'not fully abreast of the scientific knowledge of his time'; he does not mention the circulation of the blood, which Harvey began to teach in 1619; did not know of Kepler's calculations or Napier's invention of logarithms (Bacon was weak in mathematics and mechanics), rejected Copernicus's theory, and (although he gives him full credit) was not very enthusiastic about the work of Gilbert.[10] Much of this criticism, although it is regularly repeated, is ill-informed.[11] Most of Bacon's important works on the 'advancement of learning' were written in the early years of the seventeenth cent. when neither Kepler's laws nor Galileo's law of falling bodies (1612) were known. The main discoveries which were known to Bacon, such as Gilbert's De Magnete (1600),[12] and Harvey's on the circulation of the blood (1619), were non-mathematical and the few mathematical works available to him were very specialised. The Discours de la Méthode (1637) of Descartes was written when much of the best work in astronomy and physics had been achieved by measurement and calculations were available. Bacon objected to the idea that mathematics, which is an instrument or hand-maid, should 'almost domineer over physics'[13] — as it does to-day. It is generally agreed that Bacon's ideas were influential in the creation of the Royal

---

[1] B, ii, 12; I, 242; IV, 132; C, iv, 3; I, 612; IV, 403.   [2] F, x, 928; II, 649.
[3] F, v, 412; II, 479.   [4] B, II, xlviii; I, 341; IV, 225.
[5] Liebig, Letters on Chemistry, 1851, 209.   [6] B, ii, 48; I, 339; IV, 224.
[7] Paracelsus, Modus Pharmacandi, iii; Opera, 1658, 815; De Morbis Tartareis, iii; Opera, 1658, 294.
[8] E, 10; II, 205; V, 312–13.   [9] Ellis, in Works, 1857, I, 50 f.
[10] Fowler, DNB, ii, 357; Spedding, Works, III, 510 f.; Lippmann, (2), i, 390.
[11] Rosenberger, 1884, ii, 76; Merz, 1902, iii, 322; Butterfield, Bull. British Soc. Hist. Sci., 1950, i, 49.
[12] He had read at least the part on electricity in this; D. H. D. Roller, Isis, 1953, xliv, 10.
[13] C, iii, 6; I, 577; IV, 371.

Society, which in a way reduced to practice the vision of the *New Atlantis*.[1] Bacon has been credited[2] with an influence on the development of mechanical arts in England in the 18 cent. He certainly undervalued mathematics, but the criticism[3] that he laid insufficient emphasis on hypothesis and deduction would seem to apply also to the earlier period of the Royal Society, a body which Bacon foreshadowed but did not live to see.

Bacon has been compared unfavourably with Gilbert, and a few words on the latter, although he is of no importance in the history of Chemistry, may be said.

GILBERT

William Gilbert (1544–1603) is best known for his researches in magnetism and electricity. He rejected the ideas that the force of a magnet is removed by garlic (Porta had already disproved this by experiment, p. 18), and the medicinal use of powdered magnet in plasters. He recommended the medicinal use of iron powdered and soaked in vinegar and then dried, a preparation later extolled by Willis (p. 309). He mentions that Galen, Rhases, and Montagnana had said that iron is of a hot quality, whilst Manard, Curtius, and Fallopio said it is cold: he does not decide what it is.[4] Gilbert followed Aristotle's views in general, although often chiding the Peripatetics and denying (before Boyle) the doctrine of the chemists and alchemists that metals are composed of mercury and sulphur. These are bodies of a different order from metals, and metals are formed from an exhalation hardened in the veins of earth, in which were germs (*primordia*) of metals and stones from which they grew. Earth is not a simple substance, but the best iron contains true and genuine earth, while other metals contain not so much earth as fixed salts (*fixo sales*), which are efflorescences of earth. The metals do not correspond with the planets either in number or properties (numero aut proprietate). Gilbert rejects the view of the chemists that all metals can be perfected into gold, which is as absurd as to think all stones could be changed into diamonds (quare vani sunt illi Chemici, qui putant naturam velle omnia metall in aurum perficere);[5] but he believed that the magnetic force of the earth is due to a soul imprisoned in it.[6]

A book published after Gilbert's death, from papers collected by his brother, by William Boswell, who was agent at The Hague (knighted 1633, d. 1647),[7]

---

[1] Baden Powell, 1834, 260; Rosenberger, 1884, ii, 77: ich glaube, man darf nicht anstehen, Bacon als einen Mitbegründer der neueren Naturwissenschaft anzuerkennen, wenn man nur dabei weniger an die Schöpfung als an das Geltenmachen und die Verbreitung ihrer Methode denkt.

[2] R. C. Cochrane, *Ann. Sci.*, 1956 (1957), xii, 137.

[3] B. Russell, *History of Western Philosophy*, 1947, 563.

[4] *Gvilielmi Gil- | berti Colcestren- | sis, Medici Londi- | nensis, | De Magnete, Magneti- | cisqve Corporibvs, et de Mag- | no magnete tellure; Physiologia noua, | plurimis & argumentis, & expe- | rimentis demonstrata*, f°, London, Peter Short, 1600; i, 15, p. 33 (Ferri medicinales); tr. P. M. Mottelay, Gilbert, *On the Loadstone and Magnetic Bodies, and on the great Magnet the Earth*, London, 1893, 55 f.

[5] *Ib.*, i, 7; pp. 19–24; Mottelay, 33 f.   [6] *De Magn.*, v, 12; Mottelay, 308 f.

[7] *De Mundo nostro Sublunari Philosophia Nova. Opus posthumum, Ab Authoris fratre collectum pridem & dispositum . . . Ex duobus MSS. codicibus editum . . . Gvilielmi Boswelli*, 4°, Amsterdam, Elzevir, 1651.

has been reputed to advocate the Copernican theory but actually rejects it.[1] In it Gilbert rejects the four element theory (as Cardan had done before). Fire is not an element since it requires fuel (quod pabulo egeat) — a common argument at the time.[2] Celestial and terrestrial heat are the same and cold is only a privation of heat (frigus est privatio caloris).[3] Flame is a vehement action of sulphur dissolved and fused together with water;[4] there is no heat without humour (moisture) and all fire is the action of attentuating humour.[5]

Spirit in the arteries is attenuated humour seeking an exit with violence, and finding none is reflected back to the heart, is ventilated in the lungs, receives aliment, and surges out again, 'which reciprocal movement is called the pulse.'[6] The Chaldaeans and Magi were first in knowledge, which declined in the Middle Ages when the schools were filled with the errors of Aristotle and Galen.[7] Gilbert in his general scientific views does not seem to me in any way superior to Bacon.

JUNGIUS

Joachim Jungius (Lübeck, 21, 22 or 28 October 1587–Hamburg, 22 or 23 September 1657),[8] studied first at Rostock, then went in 1608 to the recently founded university of Giessen, where he graduated master in philosophy; he followed the Peripatetics in preference to the Thomists or Scotists, and lectured in 1609 on philosophy and mathematics. He studied medicine in Padua in 1618–19. In 1622 he founded in Rostock a short-lived philosophical society, Societas Ereunetica or Zetetica, independent of the University.

Jungius was wrongly said[9] to have written the *Fama Fraternitatis . . . des R.C.* (Cassel, 1614), which led to the foundation of the Rosicrucians, but he belonged to the circle which included the real founder Johann Valentin Andreae.[10]

Guhrauer[11] thinks Jungius may have read and been influenced by Bacon's *De augmentis scientiarum* (1605) although Bacon's writings were without

---

[1] Thorndike, vi, 61.   [2] *De Mundo*, i, 4–12, 19.   [3] *Ib.*, i, 17; ii, 30, p. 215.
[4] *Ib.*, ii, 29, p. 215.   [5] *Ib.*, ii, 29–30; pp. 214–15; an Aristotelian idea, Vol. I.
[6] *Ib.*, i, 32; ii, p. 218.   [7] *Ib.*, i, 3, 17; pp. 4–7, 45; an echo of Paracelsus.
[8] C. G. Guhrauer, *De Joachimo Jungio commentatio historico-literaria*, Breslau, 1846; *id.*, *Joachim Jungius und seine Zeitalter*, Stuttgart and Tübingen, 1850 (383 pp., with biography and reprint of a piece by Goethe on Jungius; Guhrauer, *ib.*, 213, says Jungius, not Jung or Junge, is the correct form of the name); Lindau, NBG, 1858, xxvii, 242; R. C. B. Avé-Lallemant, *Dr. Joachim Jungius aus Lübeck. Briefwechsel mit seinen Schülern und Freunden*, Lübeck, 1863, 216, 375; *id.*, *Das Leben des Joachim Jungius aus Lübeck*, Breslau, 1882 (not available); E. Wohlwill, Joachim Jungius und die Erneuerung atomistischer Lehren im 17 Jahrhundert, in *Festschrift zur Feier des fünfzigjährigen Bestehens des Naturwissenschaftlichen Vereins in Hamburg, Abhandlungen aus dem Gebiete der Naturwissenschaften, Naturwiss. Verein*, Hamburg, 1887, x, 1–66 (contains Jungius's Disputations on the Principles of Natural Bodies (Hamburg, 1642), p. 31 f.); *id.*, *Joachim Jungius, Festrede zur Feier seines dreihundertsten Geburtstages am 22 Oktober, 1887*, Hamburg and Leipzig, 1888; E. von Meyer, in *Kultur der Gegenwart*, 1913, Theil III, Abt. ii, Band 2, p. 2 (he does not mention Jungius in his *History of Chemistry*, 1906); A. Meyer, in *Naturforschung und Naturlehre im alten Hamburg. Erinnerungsblätter zu Ehren der 90. Versamml. Ges. Deutscher Naturforscher und Ärzte in Hamburg*. Staats-und-Universitäts-Bibliothek, Hamburg, 1928, 81 f., also 10 f. (bibl. of Junge), portrait of Junge; Polvani, *Nuov. Cim.*, 1924, i, 1 (41), on a copy of the *Doxoscopia* in the Public Library at Lucca; J. H. S. Green, *Nature*, 1957, clxxx, 570; Guthrie, *ib.*, 1959, clxxxviii, 1435.
[9] *Acta Eruditorum*, 1698, 172.
[10] Guhrauer, 1850, 53–66, 230; *id.*, *Z. histor. Theol.*, 1852, xxii (N.F. xvi), 298–315; Thorndike does not mention Jungius.
[11] 1850, 52, 75, 129, 230.

influence in German universities; he later criticised Bacon. Bacon was eulo-
gised by Tobias Adami of Weimar in his edition of Campanella's *Realis
philosophiæ epilogisticæ*, Frankfurt, 1623. The study of mathematics was at a
low level in German universities (his predecessor in Giessen, Hermann,
taught only elementary arithmetic) and Jungius first heard of Vieta's
writings in 1613.[1] In 1624 he became professor of mathematics in Rostock. He
then succeeded Gottfried Vogler as professor of medicine at Helmstädt (1625),
was appointed physician in Brunswick and Wolfenbüttel, again became professor of mathematics at Rostock (1626), and finally (from 1628–9) was rector
of the Hamburg Gymnasium. Hamburg was then in close relations with England and Holland and was a centre of active intellectual life. Part of his duty
was to lecture on Aristotelian physics. He did so faithfully, at the same time
pointing out its defects and introducing more correct opinions on the nature
of the elements, based on the atomic theory of Demokritos. Jungius had no
children and his wife (whom he married in 1624) died, after a prolonged
mental illness, in 1638.

Jungius dissipated his energies over too wide a field — theology, logic, philosophy,
mathematics, physics, chemistry, mineralogy, botany, and zoology all claimed his
attention. He had a very orderly and clear mind but his ideas were expressed in too
concise and dry a form to be attractive, and he used too many unnecessary new names.

He failed to press forward into prominence, had little or no direct influence on
contemporary or later scientific development, and was so largely forgotten that he has
only recently been rescued from oblivion with considerable persistence and enthusiasm.
He left much manuscript material in Hamburg,[2] some of which was destroyed in a fire
in Vaget's house in 1691[3] but it was probably mostly composed of rough notes and
excerpts from books, Fogel and Vaget having previously gone through the manuscripts
and extracted what they considered important.[4]

On 15 May 1654 Samuel Hartlib (d. ? 1670), son of a Polish refugee who
came to England about 1628 and took up educational reform after failing in
various business and agricultural enterprises, sent to Boyle what he called a
'rude draught of Dr. Jungius's Protonœtical Philosophy, which as it lyes in a
pack bound about with such coarse expressions and terms as he useth makes
no great show; but if it were fully opened, a great deal would appear to be
rich cloth of Arras'.[5]

Guhrauer[6] gives quotations to show that Jungius was critical of Aristotle.
Wohlwill[7] asserted that Jungius, 'the German Bacon', anticipated Boyle in the
revival of the atomic theory (gewiss ist dass er in origineller Weise die alte
demokritische Lehre bearbeitet und verwertet und von ihr aus namentlich
über die künftige Entwicklung der chemischen Forschung Andeutungen
gegeben hat).

Ramsauer[8] thought the influence of Jungius on Boyle had been exaggerated
by Wohlwill; Boyle's main sources were Bacon, Gassendi, and Descartes.
Jungius, although vacillating, mainly favoured the type of atomism adopted
by Sennert (1619, see p. 273), having Aristotelian features, atoms having

[1] Guhrauer, 1850, 21.
[2] List in Guhrauer, 1850, 280; incomplete according to Wohlwill, 1887, 4.
[3] Beckmann, (3), 1795, 97; he frequently quotes Jungius.   [4] Wohlwill, 1887, 6 f.
[5] Boyle, *Works*, ed. Birch, 1744, v, 266; Guhrauer, 1850, 130; Stones, *Isis*, 1928, x, 457.
[6] 1850, 42, 331 f.   [7] 1887, 4, 60 f.; 1888, 24.   [8] *Z. f. Naturwiss.*, 1936–7, ii, 373.

qualities as well as the purely mechanical properties involved in the atomism of Gassendi, Descartes, and Boyle. Boyle did not distinguish sharply between the two views, saying that although they (Gassendi and Descartes) 'differed in some material points from one another, yet in opposition to the Peripatetick and other vulgar doctrines, they might be looked upon as one philosophy'.[1]

In his most elaborate comparison of Aristotelian and corpuscular physics, Boyle[2] does not mention Jungius. He criticised the notion of 'form' as understood by Sennert and came down clearly and decidedly in favour of the mechanical atomism of Gassendi, whilst Jungius, in trying to combine atomism with the Aristotelian idea of 'form', followed Sennert.[3]

Jungius may have become interested in the atomic theory partly from his knowledge of the theory of Asklepiades of Prusa (Vol. I) acquired in his medical studies, or more probably by reading La Galla's *De Phoenominis in Orbe Lunæ* (1612), all the passages in which dealing with atomism are underlined in his copy.[4]

Jungius published very little. He left directions in his will that his very large collection of papers (which were difficult to read) should be arranged and published, and a legacy for this to be done. Some of these appeared.[5] The works listed below are referred to by the numbers given to them.

(1) *Doxoscopiæ Physicæ Minores, sive Isagoge Physica Doxoscopia. In qua præacipuæ Opiniones Physica passim receptæ breviter quidem, sed accuratissime, examinantur*, Ex recensione et distinctione M.[artini] F.[ogelii] H.[amburgensis], cujus Annotationes quædam accedunt, 4°, Hamburg. Typis Pfeifferianis, 1662 (BM 462. b. 10), unpaged; reissued from unsold sheets with new t.p., as: Joachim Jungii Lubecensis præcipue Opiniones Physicæ passim receptæ, breviter quidem sed accuratissime examinatæ, ex Recensione & Distinctione M. Fogelii . . . cujus Annotationes quædam accedunt. Accessit nunc primum ejusdem Autoris Harmonica et Isagoge Phytoscopica, 4°, Hamburg, 1679 (BM 537. e. 9), with portrait and four indexes; M.F.H. Indices quatuor in annotationes suas.[6]

This book is based by Fogel (d. 1675) on Jungius's notes for lectures probably given in the early period (*c.* 1630) in Hamburg, and Wohlwill[7] thinks the published version contains only unimportant additions by Fogel.

Fogel, in his life of Jungius, gave as the content of his physics: 'Physicum vero studium stupebant omnes qui versabunt aliquando Logicam Physeoscopicam, Auctores Physicae, Physicam, καθολικὴν, Definitiones Reflexivas et Rectas Syndiacriticus, Syndiacrisin, Democritica. Admirabilis est Textuarum θεωρια, modo sciendi Physico inserviens. Adde Observationes de corporibus similaribus, observationes Terrae, Aquae, Aëris, Ignis, lixivii, muriae, aceti, vini, fermenti, sebi, cretae, etc. de Mineralibus generalia. Fossilia, Lapides in genere, Fossilium loca, Dictionarium Docimasticum, Metallurgicum Chimicum.' He adds: 'Et Chimica transeant, quia sunt pauca et quaedam sub Physicis comprehensa.'[8]

(2) *Joachimi Jungii . . . Scheduarum fasciculus* (32) *inscriptus Mineralia, concinnari in Systema cœptus à Christiano Bunckio . . . ita atque ab eo mox defuncto relictus erat, ita editus, recensente Johanne Vagetio*, 4°, Hamburg, 1689, 344 pp. and plate (BM 990. h.

[1] Boyle, Some Specimens of an Attempt to make Chymical Experiments useful to illustrate the notions of the Corpuscular Philosophy; *Works*, 1744, i, 228.
[2] The Origin of Forms and Qualities according to the Corpuscular Philosophy (1666); *Works*, 1744, ii, 451.
[3] Wolff, *Z. ges. Naturwiss.*, 1935, i, 357; Ramsauer, *ib.*, 1936–7, ii, 373.
[4] Wohlwill, 1887, 15 f.   [5] Guhrauer, 1850, 137, 273, 313.
[6] Guhrauer, 1850, 313.   [7] 1887, 26.   [8] Guhrauer, 1850, 294.

3); attention was directed to this work by Beckmann,[1] who says it was very rare at that time; it frequently mentions Jungius's friend Andreas Cassius junr.

This consists mainly of excerpts from printed books and criticises Agricola principally on philological points;[2] it also mentions Zacharias, alchemist of Lübeck, Bodd, and the *Illuminirbuch* of Bolzen (see Vol. I). The third chapter of Part II, sect. 2, is concerned with a pedantic refutation of Agricola's classification of minerals into earths, concrete juices, stones, and metals, substituting one into metals, salts, sulphur, etc.,

(3) *I. Iungii Opuscula Botanico-Physica ex recensione et distinctione Martini Fogelii et Ioh. Vagetii*, 4°, Coburg, 1747. This contains the botanical works (*a*) *Isagoge Phytoscopica*, (*b*) *Monenda Vegetiana*, (*c*) *De plantis doxoscopia*, (*d*) *Addenda*, and (*e*) *Annotationes*, and is of botanical interest only. The *Isagoge Phytoscopica* first appeared in 1679 (see no. 1) and would be available to John Ray in the preparation of his *Historiæ Plantarum* (3 vols. f°, London, 1786–88–1704).

(4) *Auctarium Epitomes Physicæ Clarissimi atque Experientissimi Viri, D. Daniellis Sennerti. . . . Ex alius ejusdem libris à viro quodam docto excerptum*, Hamburg, 1635; Amsterdam, 1651; this small anonymous work by Jungius consists mostly of excerpts from Bk. xi of Sennert's *De Galenicorum et Peripateticorum Chymicis Consensu ac Dissensu* (1619).[3]

(5) *Logica Hamburgensis . . .* , 8°, Hamburg, 1638 (BM 527. b. 12); *ib.*, ed. Vagetius, 8°, Hamburg, 1681 (BM 527. b. 1. (3.)).

(6) *Phoranomia, seu Doctrina de Motu Locali*, ed. Heinrich Siver (professor of mathematics in Hamburg), 4°, *s.l.e.a.* [Hamburg ?, 1650 ?] (BM 580. e. 2. (8.)).

(7) *Historia Vermium*, ed. J. Vagetius, 4°, Hamburg, 1691 (BM 954. i. 25.).

An excellent account of Jungius's chemical views is given by Wohlwill (1887), who also gives a translation of important parts of two dissertations (*Disputatione*) of 1642; about forty of these were published by Jungius himself in Hamburg, and they mostly contain criticisms of Aristotelian physics. It is just possible that some of these were the material sent to Boyle by Hartlib; they certainly anticipate some ideas in the *Sceptical Chymist*. Jungius, as would be expected for his time (Bacon's *Novum Organum* appeared in 1620) was quite clear on the value of experiment (Modus sciendi Physicus est Phænomena non ad præconceptas Opiniones, sed Hypotheses ad Phænomena accommodare),[4] although he does not seem to have made experiments himself. His revival of the atomic theory[5] was called by himself *syndiacritic* (from *synkrisis*, mixing, and *diakrisis*, separation), as opposed to the old Aristotelian theory, which he calls *actupotential*.[6] Sennert[7] had already opposed atomistic to Aristotelian ideas, whilst retaining some of the latter, and Sennert's work of 1619 was known to Jungius,[8] whose views on the elements are expounded in two of his printed dissertations (*Disputationes*) of 1642 (see above), in which he criticised the Aristotelian four elements and the alchemical three principles.[9] In a dissertation of 1639 the views of Aristotle

[1] (3), 1795, 94–108.   [2] Guhrauer, 1850, 302 f.
[3] Sennert, *Operum*, 1656, i, 1 f.; Wohlwill, 1887, 63; Lasswitz, (1), 1890, ii, 250; Wolf and Ramsauer, *Z. f. gesamte Naturwiss.*, 1935, i, 357, say it is by Sennert.
[4] (1), P. II, sect. i, Proem., Ass. 1; fol. Aa 3.
[5] Wohlwill, 1887, 13 f.; Lasswitz, (1), 1890, ii, 245–61; E. Bloch, *Isis*, 1913, i, 377.
[6] (1), P. II, sect. i, cap. 12, Ass. 1–20, f. Oo 1 *v* f.
[7] *De Galenicorum et Peripateticorum cum Chymicis Consensu ac Dissensu*, 1619; *Opera*, 1656, I, 180 f., 230; Lasswitz, 1890, i, 436–54; an annotated copy of the 2 ed. of Sennert's book (1624) was in the Hamburg collection of Jungius's papers.
[8] Wohlwill, 1887, 13 f., 18, 63.   [9] Wohlwill, 1887, 27–9, 40 f.

and his modern commentators, e.g. Zabarella, on the transmutations of the four elements and on steresis (privatio) are said to be erroneous.

Jungius says the ash, salt and oil formed by burning wood are not the hypostatic principles of wood, since by distillation of wood a different oil, a spirit and acid are obtained: 'what hypostatic principles, therefore, we assume as first for homogeneous bodies is not to be founded on speculations but rather by unabated diligence in scientific observation, going into detail.'[1] Many of these views go back to Jungius's manuscript of 1630. In a dissertation of 1634 it is said that bodies contain many more than four elements, and in the separation of a mixt not always the primary elements are obtained; it is incorrect to suppose that a body is 'by nature' composed of the things into which it is resolved, but correct to say that it is composed of the bodies into which it is *ultimately* resolved.[2]

Those parts of a body which can exist independently (e.g. threads of a piece of cloth) are called *hypostatic*;[3] parts which exist only as parts of a whole (e.g. heat in water) are *synhypostatic*. A *syndiacritic* change arises from separation (*diacrisis*) or conjunction (*syncrisis*), or both, of invisible particles (e.g. salt and water; plaster made from vinegar, litharge and oil; alloy of gold, silver and copper).[4] The change may be conceived as ultimately due to the coming together or separation of the smallest parts of the bodies, which are for each absolutely similar (exquisite similares); only when analytical observations have reached the first hypostatic principles (absolutely similar) of bodies composed of atoms of the same kind, can it be said if there are any synhypostatic principles. The assumption of these will probably be unnecessary on the basis of the atomic theory.[5] Internal change of bodies without addition of atoms from outside is called *metasyncrise* or 'metaschematism' — a foreshadowing of isomerism, as illustrated by different arrangements of four letters, ABCD.[6] The change of water into vapour may be metasyncrisis, but is more probably syncrisis, since fire atoms may be added; rusting of metals and formation of white lead and verdigris are not changes of decomposition (diacrisis) but of syncresis or metasyncrisis.[7]

Jungius criticised the alchemical theory of three principles[8] as well as the Aristotelian theory of the four elements. He denied especially that salt is a principle of bodies, said that nobody had ever extracted mercury from a metal, or combined mercury and sulphur to form a metal, and gold, silver, asbestos, talc, and mercury had never been separated into their supposed component principles.[9] It is not known how many completely uniform or simple bodies exist.[10] 'It does not follow that all which has not so far been

---

[1] Wohlwill, 1887, 42 f., who draws attention to the close analogy with Boyle's experiments and statements in the *Sceptical Chymist* (1661).
[2] Wohlwill, 1887, 27.
[3] In Boyle, hypostatic has quite a different meaning of the three chemical principles.
[4] *Disputationum de principiis corporum naturalium*, 1642, i, §§ 56–9; Wohlwill, 1887, 34.
[5] *Ib.*, §§ 68, 71; Wohlwill, 1887, 35–6.   [6] *Ib.*, §§ 73–7; Wohlwill, 1887, 36–7.
[7] (1), P. II, sect. i, cap. 19, Ass. VI, §§ 4–7.
[8] De principiis Hermeticis; in (1), P. II, sect. iC, cap. 8, Ass. 1; fol. Ll 1; Wohlwill, 1887, 55 f.
[9] *Disputat. de Princip. corp. nat.*, 1642, ii, § 49 f.; Wohlwill, 1887, 40 f.
[10] (1), P. II, sect. ii, cap. 2, Ass. 2; fol. Aaa 2 *v*.

decomposed is not compounded, since armenian salt [sal ammoniac] had formerly not been decomposed; when, however, anything cannot be decomposed (of which it is not known that it is a compound), this can be regarded as a simple or fully homogeneous body.'[1] The resemblance between this and Boyle's *Sceptical Chymist* seems almost too close to be accidental. The views of Jungius on affinity[2] are less advanced than Boyle's. He says:

Est quidem in Corporibus Naturalibus aliqua sive *Potentia*, sive Appetitus, quo *se* ea, quae Specie aut Genere *Cognata* sunt, mutuo *appetetunt*, attrahunt, conjungunt, in aliis Robustior & *Evidentior*, in aliis Debilior & *Obscurior* . . . ex Hydrargyro Aurum amplexante.

There is in natural bodies some power or appetite, such that those which are cognate in species or genus have a mutual appetite for and attract one another, and combine; this is in some stronger and more evident, in others weaker and more obscure . . . as mercury embraces gold.

He does, however, recognise a mechanical cause as an alternative to *appetitus*, but this is a violent agitation (*agitatio*) of the atoms, as may happen when lead and silver are fused together;[3] or else, as when moist and dry things combine, a result of the shapes of the atoms.[4] These are put forward only as alternatives to the 'appetite'. It is noteworthy that Jungius realised that mere juxtaposition (juxtapositio) of parts, or mere mechanical mixture, is not sufficient to explain a chemical change; there must be a more intimate cohesion (*cohaesivitas*) in order that the parts may readily and permanently (*et promte et constanter*) remain in union. This he seems to have regarded as a result of the shape of the particles (as Boyle did), and he had no idea of an attractive *force*. In his corrections to his manuscript, Jungius writes in succession: 'familiaritas sive affinitas', but struck these out; 'cohæsio partium, cohæsivitas permistorum hoc est Aptitudo Cohærendi.'[5] Wohlwill is wrong in seeing an idea of molecular forces here, since Jungius is thinking only of a suitable disposition of the surfaces of the particles, as in the old atomic theory (Vol. I).

Jungius recognised that the air plays some part in combustion. The reason why fire seems to fly out of some combustibles, such as naphtha, is that the flame, which draws air to itself (dum Aërem ad se trahit) also draws out the fatty vapour from the bituminous body, which is seen rising from a blown-out candle (sicut Halitum Pinguem e recens exstincta Candela corripit Flamma, etiam si ipsum Fumigans Ellychnium non contigat).[6] Fire is not the 'lightest element' (non probatur, ignem esse elementum levissimum).[7]

The other elements are not transmutable:[8] the precipitation of copper from vitriol-water by iron is not a transmutation but a permutation and an equal amount of iron passes into solution.[9] Similar to Van Helmont's and Boyle's

[1] Q. from a MS. of 1630; based on *Disputatio* II, 67; Wohlwill, 1887, 43; Lasswitz, (1), ii, 255.
[2] (1), P. II, sect. i, cap. 17, Assert. 9, f. Yy 4; Wohlwill, 1887, 58.
[3] (1), P. II, sect. i, cap. 17, Assert. 10, f. Yy 6.
[4] *Ib.*, P. II, sect. i, cap. 17, Assert. 20; f. Zz 3; Wohlwill, 1887, 64.
[5] (1), P. II, sect. iC, 16, Assert. 25, f. Xx 4; Wohlwill, 1887, 65; Lasswitz, (1), ii, 259.
[6] (1), P. II, sect. i, cap. 13, Ass. 18; f. Rr 3.
[7] (1), P. II, sect. i, cap. 13, Ass. 18; Wohlwill, 1887, 53, thinks Jungius did not know of Van Helmont's ideas, see p. 222.
[8] (1), P. II, sect. i, cap. 14, Ass. 1–8, f. Rr 4 f.; Wohlwill, 1887, 53 f.
[9] (1), P. II, sect. i, cap. 19, Ass. 6; f. Bb II, i; Wohlwill, 1887, 58.

statements (pp. 221, 500) is Jungius's that gold remains the same after chemical changes:[1]

Quod si in Auro, quod est Corpus notissimum, & hactenus in Partes Mistitias non Dissolubile, quamvis multis modis tractatum, examinatum, immutatum, id tentare refugiat, sumat aliud quodcunque Corpus, sive Rarum, sive Frequens, dummodo Tractatione meae obnoxium;

and that gold (as well as silver) after conversion into powder, salt, liquor, or fume, still remains gold:[2]

Post enim Aurum & Argentum Speciem Pulveris, Salis, Liquoris, Halitûs induere, & tamen manere Aurum.

Lead may be converted into white lead (cerussa) and white lead into red lead (sandyx), but although red lead cannot be reconverted into white lead, both can be reconverted into lead, which remains in both substances.[3] Metals when dissolved in acid spirits are not destroyed but may be recovered with their original fusibility, malleability, etc., by driving off the spirits by fire.[4] In all such changes the total weight remains unchanged.[5] On heating lead the volatile part goes off as a fume and the fixed part is left behind.[6] When litharge (Bley-Glette) is reduced to lead, 130 parts of litharge give 100 of lead, and the question is whether the lead ash (litharge) is heavier than the lead, or if it has been mixed with ash (of the fire) (Ob die Bleiasch schwerer ist als das blejs das da wider aus werden kan / oder obs daher komme / weil die Glette mit asch vermenget ist).[7] Jungius quotes Bodin[8] that lead increases in weight on calcination while other things become lighter — the latter statement not being believed (hoc vix credo);[9] he says the lead increases by one-tenth in weight (decima sui parte ingravescit), and Bodin's theory that the light airy matter is driven out by the fire and thus the calx is made more compact (solidior) is nugatory, since wood when divided into sawdust is not make lighter (the original has 'heavier' but the argument requires 'lighter') than wood, and yet in wood air is enclosed but more between the atoms of the sawdust; air in air is neither heavy nor light, and not for this reason is calx of lead heavier than lead:

haec ratio nulla est, nam lignum in scobem rasum non est gravius [? levius] ligno, quamvis enim aër in lignum inclusus, tamen plus aëris f. inter scobis atomos. & utut fit // aër in aëre nec gravis nec levis, ε. hac ratione calx plumbi gravior esse nequit.

A saturated solution of a salt in water is one which will not dissolve any more of that species of salt (saturata sale aqua dicitur, ubi plus salis ejusdem speciei non liquat).[10]

The long section on fossil bodies in the *Doxoscopia*,[11] like the descriptions in the *Mineralia*, is mostly copied from Classical authors, Agricola, Cæsalpinus,

[1] (1), P. II, sect. i, Proem., Assert. 7, § 14, f. Bb 3.
[2] (1), P. II, sect. i, cap. 19, Assert. 5; Wohlwill, 1887, 59.
[3] (1), P. II, sect. i, cap. 12, Assert. 18. [4] (1), P. II, sect. i, cap. 22, Assert. 7; f. Dd II.
[5] (1), P. II, sect. i, cap. 20, Assert. 6. [6] (1), P. II, sect. i, cap. 17, Assert. 10.
[7] (2), 1689, 130. [8] *Vniversæ Natvræ Theatrvm*, Lyons, 1596, 263; see p. 14.
[9] (2), 4 i; Wohlwill, 1887, 50, who also refers to Galileo's *Il Saggiatore* (see p. 14).
[10] (1), P. I, sect. ii, port. 2, cap. 6, def. 2; f. L 4.
[11] (1), P. II, sect. ii, caps. 1–22; ff. Aaa 1–Kkk 2.

Ercker, Beguin, Libavius (frequently), and the Lübeck alchemists Zachariæ and Cassius. It contains, probably, the first explanation of the name (used in the 16 cent.) potash (=pot-ash) as made by boiling the extract of 'clavellated' ashes in pots (Potasch e clavellis doliorum sive cadorum cinere infectorio refertorum fiat).[1]

The chapters deal with: (6) stones (lapidibus Ignis invictis), (7) salts, (8) nitrum (soda), (9) saltpetre (sal Petræ), (10) vitriols, (11) alums, (12) Reliquis Salibus (tartar, clavellated ashes, glass), (13) sulphurs, (14) arsenics, (15) bitumens, (16) mineral oils, (17) other bitumens (cafura, benzoin, amber, spermaceti), (18) fossils, (19) fatty earths (terra pinguibus), (20) stones, (21) gypsum, (22) quicklime (calx viva Leodicensi).

Jungius[2] mentions zinc (speóter, zincum) as a metal brought from India to Holland and sold in Nürnberg; it forms with tin an alloy like silver; he also mentions the golden alloy of copper and zinc (brass) made in Lübeck,[3] calamine,[4] and orichalcum,[5] and suggests that vitriols can be formed by imperfect metals such as zinc and bismuth. Like Agricola, he confuses arsenic and cobalt.

BERIGARD

Claude Berigard, born at Moulins in France in 1578 or 1591, left Paris for Pisa in 1628, and died in 1663 at Padua. In his collection of four treatises,[6] each has a separate title-page specifying a work by Aristotle, e.g. *Circulus Pisanus in Aristotelis libros octo Physicorum*, etc. The opposition to Aristotle is cautiously put in the form of a dialogue. Berigard supposed that there is no vacuum but that all bodies, including e.g. gold, contain pores (meatus) which are always filled with subtle bodies which can enter and leave them.[7] The number of simple substances (substantiae simplices) is infinite, since every property represents one of such.[8] The atoms are spherical and of different sizes, and always in contact.[9] Air is not an element but a panspermia (πανσπερμία), a mixture of all possible substances, having the pores filled with finer and finer particles which can flow in and out on dilatation and compression.[10] Subtle bodies such as light (which is corpuscular) can pass through the pores of glass.[11] The ancients explained compression and dilatation by the smaller or greater mobility of the parts produced by the propinquity or admixture of others,[12] but Berigard refers them to the difference and mixture of the indivisible points which are the principle of simple bodies.[13] He describes an air thermoscope.[14]

Weight (gravitas) is due to the mutual action of bodies, produced by efflux of corpuscles by the earth and heavy bodies.[15] He discusses the nature of the

---

[1] (1), P. II, sect. ii, cap. 12, def. 3: De Reliquis Salibus; Speter, *A. Nat.*, 1910, ii, 201–13; Lippmann, (1), ii, 318–57.
[2] (2), 140 f., 144; q. by Pott, *Dissertations Chymiques*, Paris, 1759, iii, 445, 491.
[3] *Ib.*, 145.   [4] *Ib.*, 153.   [5] *Ib.*, 156 f.
[6] *Circvlvs Pisanvs Clavdii Berigardi Molinensis . . . De veteri & Peripatetica Philosophia*, 4°, Vtini, 1643; 2 ed., 4°, Patavii, 1660–1 (portr., contin. pagin.); Brucker, 1766, IV, i, 463–86; Ueberweg, (1),1924, iii, 173.
[7] *Circ. Pis. in Arist. lib. de Ortu et interitu*, III, 1643, 17.   [8] *Ib.*, XX, 125 f.
[9] *Ib.*, VIII, 61 f.: De atomis Democriti.   [10] *Ib.*, V, 31 f.   [11] *Ib.*, IX, 1661, 434.
[12] *Ib.*, V, 1643, 38.   [13] *Ib.*, VII, 55.   [14] *Ib.*, 80.   [15] *Circ. in prior. lib. phys.*, IX, 61.

elements in compounds[1] and describes (before Van Helmont, p. 232) an experiment of heating charcoal in a long-necked flask, when it does not burn.[2] The book is mentioned by Boyle,[3] but not for this experiment.

Berigard, who at first disbelieved in alchemy, was given a drachm of a powder of the colour of wild poppies and smelling of calcined sea salt, with which, taking every precaution against fraud, he himself converted ten drachms of mercury into the finest gold, as he could faithfully testify:[4]

Referam tibi fideliter quod olim mihi contigit cùm vehementer ambigerem an aurum ex hydrargyro fieri posset, accepi a viro industrio, qui hunc mihi scrupulum auferre voluit, drachmam pulueris colore non absimilis flori papaueris siluestris, odore uerò sal marinum adustum referentis . . . Decem istius drachmas inieci subjecto igne satis valido statimq; omnia exiguo intertrimento in decem ferè drachmas auri optimæ notæ coaluerunt . . . nam fidanter testari possum, rem ita esse.

He also[5] refers to the herb lunaria, which solidifies mercury (to silver).

COMENIUS

John Amos Komeský (Comenius) (Uherský-Brad, Moravia, 28 March 1592–Naarden, Amsterdam, 15 November 1671), visited England in 1641–2 to plan a Baconian College of Sciences and was in relation with Hartlib, Petty, etc. His ideas on chemistry and alchemy are based on Aristotle and other Classical authors, Sennert, Vives, Campanella, Francis Bacon, Paracelsus, and Libavius, and are of no real interest.[6] He supposed that the four elements are the same matter in different states of density and transmutable with proportions by volume (air: water = 100 : 1). He assumed vital and animal spirits, omitting natural spirits; assumed as principles salt, sulphur, and mercury, associated with matter, spirit, light (or fire) and an occult quality in each body, and had the old idea (due to Plato) that metals produce rust (rubigo) by a corruption in the interior escaping through pores to the surface.

DIGBY

Sir Kenelm Digby (Gayhurst, 11 July 1603–London, 11 June 1665)[7] after a successful career as a privateer (pirate) retired to study alchemy. He became a favourite at the court of Charles I but later was imprisoned under the Long Parliament. He went to France in 1643, returning to England after the Restoration to become one of the founders of the Royal Society. He was a curious mixture of real ability in science and a capacity for clear thinking with

[1] Circ. in de Ortu et inter., 142. [2] Circ. in de Ortu et inter., XXII, 135, and fig.
[3] History of Cold, 1665; Works, ed. Birch, 1744, ii, 342.
[4] Circ. in de Ortu et inter., de Chrysopœa, 153 f.; Lenglet du Fresnoy, 1742, ii, 31.
[5] Circ. in de ortu et inter., 39: lunaria herba communicat hydrargyro soliditatem.
[6] Comenius, Physicæ ad lumen divinum Synopsis, 12°, Amsterdam, 1643; Strunz, in Diergart, 1909, 325 f.; id., (1), 1906, 33; (2), 1913, 119–38; (3), 1928, 267; R. F. Young, Comenius in England, 1932; Hujer, Isis, 1953, xliv, 67; Thorndike, vii, 410.
[7] [T. Longueville], The Life of Sir K. Digby, by one of his descendants, London, 1896; S. Lee, DNB, 1888, xv, 60; J. F. Fulton, Sir Kenelm Digby, London, 1937 (trivial); Miles, Chymia, 1949, ii, 119; Ferguson, i, 213; R. T. Petersson, Sir Kenelm Digby, 1956; Thorndike, vii, 498; Sprengel, (1), 1815, v, 9; NBG, 1855, xiv, 166.

credulity and superstitious beliefs such as we found in Paracelsus and Van Helmont.

Evelyn, who frequently mentions Digby, visited him on 7 November 1651 and 'had much discourse of chymicall matters. I shew'd him a particular way of extracting oyle of sulphur, and he gave me a certaine powder with which he affirm'd that he had fixed ☿ (mercury) before the late King; he advis'd me to try and digest a little better, and gave me a water which he said was onely raine water of the autumnal equinox exceedingly rectified, very volatile; it had a taste of strong vitrioliq, and smelt like aqua fortis. He intended it for a dissolvant of calx of gold; but the truth is, Sir Kenelm was an errant mountebank.'[1]

While in France, Digby lectured to an 'assembly' (really an academy) at Montpellier[2] on the 'powder of sympathy' or 'weapon salve', which cured wounds when applied to the weapon which had produced them. This was an older idea on which Nicolas Papin, uncle of the more famous Denis Papin (p. 519), had written.[3] Digby claimed to have got the recipe for the powder from a Carmelite in Florence in 1622. As Hartman[4] explained, it consisted of dried green vitriol (ferrous sulphate). Digby's discourse was printed first in French and in the same year in English, in 1658:

Discovrs fait en vne celebre Assemblé par le Chevalier Digby ... tovchant la Gverison des Playes par la Poudre de Sympathie, sm. 8°, Paris, 1658 (CUL Hh. 18. 41); also 1660, 1666, 1669, 1678, 1681, 1700, 1715, 1749 (var. places); A Late Discourse Made in a Solemne Assembly of Nobles and Learned Men at Montpellier in France ... Touching the Cure of Wounds by the Powder of Sympathy ... Rendered faithfully out of French into English By R. White, Gent., 12°, 1658; The Second Edition, sm. 8°, London, 1658 (with index); 3 ed. 1660, 4 ed. 1664; Ferguson, i, 213. German tr.: Eröffnung unterscheidlicher Heimlichkeiten der Natur, tr. Hupka, Frankfurt, 1560 [=1660], 1684 (BM 1034. f. 33; CUL Acton. d. 47–458), 5 ed., 1700.

Digby's book mentions magnetic and electric attractions,[5] acoustic resonance,[6] and the ripples formed on the surface of water when the glass containing it is rubbed with the fingers.[7]

A more important book by Digby is:

Two Treatises. In the one of which The Natvre of Bodies; In the other the Natvre of Mans Sovle; is looked into: in the way of discovery, of the Immortality of Reasonable Sovles, enormous 4°, Paris, G. Blaizot, 1644; 4°, London, 1645, 1658, 1669; Latin, Demonstratio immortalis animæ rationalis, sive tractatus duo philosophici ..., Ex Anglico in latinum versa operâ et studio J.L., Frankfurt, 1664 (used by Lasswitz, (1), ii, 188–207).

This deals with the elements and describes experiments on the circulation of the blood. A later edition (1669) includes a Discourse concerning the Vegetation of Plants.[8] In the preface he remarks that 'the best wittes of Christendome, which flock to the Vniuersities', are sent home with nothing but 'a faculty, and readynesse to talk like parrots'. He says the parts of fire, like sharp needles, violently assail its fuel and penetrate its pores. Fire is identical with light and

---

[1] Diary, ed. Bray, 1870, 215.　　　　　　[2] Harcourt Brown, 1934, 210.
[3] Papinius, De Pulvere Sympathico, Patavii, 1655 (earlier eds., 1650 or 1651); a collection of 27 authors (Papin, Digby, Goclenius, Van Helmont, Robertus, Flud, Becher, Borellus, Bartholinus, Kircher, Sennert, Fracastorius, Wecker, etc.) appeared as Theatrum Sympatheticum, 2 ed., by A. Tentzel, 4°, Nürnburg, 1662; Robertson, Ann. Med. Hist., 1925, vii, 387.
[4] The True Preserver of Health, 1682.　　　　　[5] 2 ed., 1658, London, 54.
[6] Ib., 95.　　　[7] Ib., 112.　　　　　[8] T. L. Davis, Isis, 1931, xvi, 86.

its minute atoms are absorbed by humid air and then bear no resemblance to fire.[1] Light is not a substance.[2] Earth and water are the basis of all permanent mixtures but some bodies are resolved by fire into spirits, waters, oil, salts, earth and glass.[3] Digby put forward some views on the cause of the varying densities of bodies and calculated (from results of Galileo and Ghetaldus) that gold should be 7600 times denser than air, hence the air particles can no longer touch one another, which he thought was improbable.[4] His main concern was an explanation of denseness (densitas) and rareness (raritas). The first results from compression, the second from expansion. With these two fundamental properties, weight is associated, and according to the degrees in which weight is greater or less than denseness or rareness various states of matter result:[5]

$$\text{Weight} \begin{cases} \text{greater than} \begin{cases} \text{denseness} \\ \text{rareness} \end{cases} \text{produces fluidity} \begin{cases} \text{dense fluids (liquids)} \\ \text{thin fluids (gases)} \end{cases} \\ \text{less than} \begin{cases} \text{denseness} \\ \text{rareness} \end{cases} \text{produces dryness} \begin{cases} \text{dense dry bodies (solids)} \\ \text{thin dry bodies (heat, fire)} \end{cases} \end{cases}$$

A criticism of Digby's two works of 1644 by Alexander Ross,[6] deals with magnetism, the electric torpedo-fish, etc.

Digby in a lecture at Gresham College on 23 January 1661[7] refers (p. 8) to the Archeus, the increase in weight of antimony calcined by a burning glass (p. 40), and (pp. 62-4) his own experiments and those of others on the promotion of plant growth by solutions of 'salt-peter', saying that plants receive their fecundity not only from a nitrous salt, a balsamic saline juice of the earth which causes a plant to 'Swell, Germinate, and Augment it self', but also from a similar substance in the air. The saltpetre of the earth attracts to itself, like a magnet, a similar salt in the air, 'that gave cause to the Cosmopolite to say, there is in the Aire a hidden food of life': this refers to Sendivogius (see p. 426). Airs 'as are most impregnated with this benigne fire, are healthfull to live in'; others having little of 'this balsamick Salt in them', which is 'the food of the Lungs, and the nourishment of the Spirits', are 'unsound'. Digby refers to the experiment of Drebbel (see p. 321) by which he claimed to 'revive his languishing guests, in his straight house under water' by 'opening a Fiole' (p. 65) — as in all other accounts of this, it is hearsay. He describes in great detail, mentioning witnesses, his experiments on freezing water infused on the ashes of nettles, the ice showing the figures of the nettles, as Quercetanus had found (p. 75; see Quercetanus, p. 169). Digby is said to have been the first to use saltpetre as a fertiliser (suggested by Glauber, see p. 354).[8] In

---

[1] *Two Treatises*, i, ch. v; pp. 32 f., 36. [2] *Ib.*, i, ch. vi, pp. 39–75.
[3] *Ib.*, i, ch. v, p. 36 f.; ch. xv, p. 130 f.
[4] *Ib.*, i, ch. iii, p. 20; Lasswitz, (1), ii, 188–207. [5] Lasswitz, (1), ii, 193, 202.
[6] *The Philosophical Touch-Stone: or Observations upon Sir Kenelm Digby's Discourses of the Nature of Bodies, and of the reasonable Soul*, 4°, London, 1645.
[7] *A Discourse Concerning the Vegetation of Plants. Spoken by Sir Kenelm Digby at Gresham College, on the 23. of January, 1660* [O.S.]. *At a Meeting of the Society for promoting Philosophical Knowledge by Experiments*, 12°, London, 1661; French tr. by P. de Trehan, Paris, 1667; Latin tr. by O. Dapper, *Dissertatio de Plantarum Vegetatione*, 12°, Amsterdam, 1669; republished in English with the *Two Treatises*, 1669.
[8] Mehring, Ross, and Merz, *Ind. Eng. Chem.*, 1929, xxi, 379.

1660 he reported that he had seen soil at Arcueil turn successively into salt-petre, vitriol, lead, tin, copper, and (after fourteen months) gold.[1]

Digby in 1633–5 made chemical experiments at Gresham College, and many processes, including those given him by others, were published by one of his operators, Georg Hartman:

Choice and Experimented Receipts in Physick and Chirurgerie, 8°, London, 1668, 1675; Chymical Secrets and Rare Experiments in Physick and Philosophy, 8°, London, 1683–82, two pts., pp. 1–143; sep. t.p. 1682, pp. 147 (BM); A Choice Collection Of Rare Chymical Secrets And Experiments In Philosophy; As Also Rare and unheard-of Medicines, Menstruums, and Alkahests; with the True Secret of Volatilizing the fixt Salt of Tartar. Collected and Experimented by the Honourable and truly Learned Sir Kenelm Digby . . . Hitherto kept Secret since his Decease, but not Published for the good and benefit of the Publick, by George Hartman, sm. 8°, London, Printed for the Publisher, and are to be Sold by the Book-sellers of London, and at his own House in Hewes Court in Black-Fryers, 1682, 4 plates (Quaritch *Cat.* 742 (1955), no. 157); German: Ausserlesene, seltzame Philosophische Geheimnüsse und chymische Experimente . . . , tr. J.L.M.C. [Johann Lange, Medical Candidate], Hamburg, 1684 (with portrait) (q. by Stahl, Traité des Sels, 1783, 216, etc.; Ferguson, i, 213; Miles, 121).

In one of the 'Choice Experimental Receipts', silver is converted into gold by heating silver amalgam with red precipitate (mercuric oxide) repeatedly grinding and heating in a sand-bath till it becomes yellow, and after 21 days, melting with borax, when a weight of 24-carat gold rather more than that of the silver was obtained. This could be tried by anyone in a modern laboratory. Digby's alchemical manuscripts are in the British Museum and the Bodleian, Oxford.[2]

A book of recipes and on cookery (sack posset, syllabub, clouted cream, flommery) was published posthumously:

The Closet of the Eminent Learned Sir Kenelme Digby Kt. Opened: Whereby is Discovered Several ways for making of Megethlin, Sider, Cherry-Wine &c. Together with Excellent Directions for Cookery . . . , Published by his son's Consent, 8°, London, 1669, 1671, 1677; ed. A. Macdonnell, 1910 (portr.).

SENDIVOGIUS

Ideas like those in Digby are contained in works attributed to Michael Sendivogius (Sedziwój), a Moravian or a Pole, whose dates are given as 1556–1636 or 1646. He is said to have received a book from Alexander Seton, a Scottish alchemist who was imprisoned and tortured at Dresden, but was rescued by Sendivogius and taken to Cracow, where he died in 1604. Sendivogius married his widow. Seton is reputed to have carried out several trans-mutations, and to have given some of the philosophers' stone to Sendivogius, who used it until the stock was exhausted.[3]

---

[1] Boyle, *Works*, 1744, v, 302.   [2] *Isis*, 1930, xiv, 493.
[3] P. Borel, *Tresor de Recherches et Antiqvitez Gavlois et Françoises*, 4°, Paris, 1655, 474–88 (Cosmopolite), 581–6 (Sendivogius); Schmieder, 1832, 341; Kopp, (1), ii, 204; (4), i, 127, 164, 198; Figuier, *L'Alchemie et les Alchimistes*, 1860, 254; Ferguson, i, 257, 293; ii, 364, 374; Guerlac, *Actes du 7e Congrès Internat. d'Histoire des Sciences*, Jersualem, 1953, 332; Waite, *The Secret Tradition in Alchemy*, 1926, 237; Ostachowski, *Archives*, 1954, xxxiii, 267; Read, (2), 1947, 37, 52 (portr. on plate 15, 16); *id.*, (3), 1957, 87, plate fig. 23 (calls him a Pole, b. 1556 or 1566 at Sacz); *id.*, *William Davidson of Aberdeen*, Aberdeen, 1951, 22 (Estreicher of Cracow

In 1604 the Emperor Rudolph II at Prague, under the guidance of Sendivogius, carried out a transmutation with some of Seton's powder, and had fixed to the wall of the room where the experiment was made a marble tablet with the inscription:

Faciat hoc quispiam alius
Quod fecit Sendivogius Polonus

(Let somebody else do what Sendivogius of Poland has done), and Schmieder says this was still to be seen in 1650. In another story, Sendivogius showed the Emperor Ferdinand II a silver medal partly converted into gold; Kopp thinks a gold medal was amalgamated to make it white like silver, then on heating, the mercury volatilised and the gold appeared. Even the existence of Sendivogius is doubtful.

In the French translations of his writings, Sendivogius is called the 'Cosmopolite'. Of the many editions of his writings I have seen the following:

I. Novum Lumen Chymicum, e Naturæ Fonte et manuali experientia depromptum, & in duodecim tractatiis diuisum. Cui accessit Dialogus Mercurij, Alchymistæ & Naturæ, perquàm vtilis, 12°, Cologne, 1614, 1619; also in Albineus, Bibliotheca Chemica Contracta, Cologne, 1653, 68 f. (without t.p. or pref.); and M. Maier, Tripus Aureus, Frankfurt and Leipzig, 1749, 545–600; other eds. in Duveen, 308, 542. Although this was said to have been published in Frankfurt in 1604 and Paris in 1606, the earliest known ed. is of Paris, 1608, issued by Jean Beguin; Thorndike, vii, 158, gives 'Prague, 1604, Paris, 1608', etc.; see Patterson, *Ann. Sci.*, 1937, ii, 243, who thought it was 'filled with learning and erudition', and says MS. copies are extant: Read, (2), 1947, 57. The dialogue was issued separately as: Dialogus / Mercurii, / Alchymistae / et / Naturae / Scriptis in Gratiam / amici / Coroades. / Auctore eo, Qui / Divi Leschi Genus Amat. / Cologne, Seruatius Erffens /, 8°, 1607, Ai–8, Bi–vi, Bvii blank, pp. 1–28.

II. A New Light of Alchymie: Taken out of the fountaine of Nature, and Manuall Experience. To which is added a Treatise of Svlphvr: Written by Micheel Sendivogius ... Also Nine Books Of the Nature of Things, Written by Paracelsus ... Also a Chymicall Dictionary explaining hard places and words met withall in the writings of Paracelsus, and other obscure Authors. All which are faithfully translated out of the Latin into the English tongue, By J.F.M.D., sm. 4°, London, 1650 (xvi, 1–147 pp., xiii, 1–145 pp., l; sep. t.p.s to the three parts); 2 ed., 8°, London, 1674. The translator was John French who in his The Art of Distillation, 4°, London, 1651, 167, 171, 188–9, quotes Sendivogius; The Hermetic Museum, ed. Waite, 1893, ii, 79–129; Treatise on Sulphur, *ib.*, 130–58.

III. Les Oevvres dv Cosmopolite, Divisez en trois Parties. Avec un Dialogue du Mercure, de l'Alchymiste, & de la Nature, sm. 8°, Paris, 1669. Les Oeuvres du Cosmopolite divisez en trois Traitez, dans lequel sont clairement expliquez les trois Principes de la Philosophie naturelle, Sel, Soufre, et Mercure. Augmentée de la Lettre Philosophique d'Antoine Duval, 12°, Paris, 1723. In the 1669 edit. the Lettre Philosophique is said to have been translated from German into French by Du Val. Thorndike, vii, 158, lists French trs. of 1609, 1618, 1639, 1669, 1691, and 1723.

Since Digby refers to Cosmopolite, he probably read these works; the treatise on Sulphur is cited by Sir Thomas Browne.[1] The tract *On Nature in General* has in the Epilogue[2] the passage cited by Digby:

pointed out that the anagram *Divi Leschi genus amo* means 'I love the Poles', Lech, or Leszek, was the legendary founder of the kingdom of Poland; and Sendivogius is a Latinised form of a Polish name meaning literally 'he who judges warriors').

[1] *Pseudodoxia Epidemica*, ii, 3; *Works*, ed. Sayle, 1927, i, 240.   [2] III, 1669, 63; II, 1650, 40.

Man was created of the Earth and lives by virtue of the Air. For there is in the Air a secret food of life, which in the night we call dew, and in the day rarefied water, whose invisible congealed spirit is better and more precious than the whole universal earth.

In the tract *On Sulphur*[1] it is said:

[Air] contains the vital spirit of every creature, which spirit lives by all, penetrates all, and gives the seed to the other elements . . . nourishes them, impregnates them, and preserves them, and this daily experience teaches . . . not only minerals, vegetables, and animals, but also the other elements live by means of the air. For we see that all waters putrefy and become filthy if they do not receive new air, fire is also extinguished if it has not air. . . . The pores of the earth are also conserved by air, and the whole machine of the world is maintained by means of the air. Man, like all other animals, dies when deprived of air, and nothing will grow in the world without the force and virtue of the air, which penetrates, alters, and attracts to itself the multiplying nutriment.

The tract *On Nature in General* also speaks[2] of 'the water of our dew, from which is extracted the saltpetre of the philosophers', and it attributes[3] the fertilising power of rain to the same agency:

Thus when it rains, the rain takes from the air a certain vital force and joins it to the nitrous salt (*sel nitre*) of the earth (since the nitrous salt of the earth by its dryness attracts the air to itself, when the air is reduced to water, as happens to calcined tartar, and this nitrous salt of the air, since it was the air itself, and which was joined to the fatness of the earth) . . . and in consequence a great abundance of corn grows on the earth, as daily experience teaches.

The comparison of the attraction of the magnet for iron:[4] 'The air engenders this magnet and this magnet engenders or causes to appear our air', is also given by Digby.

A long commentary on the *Novum Lumen* written by an otherwise un-known Orthelius and 'translated from German into Latin' in 1624, was issued as an appendix to the edition of Sendivogius in that year.[5] It was reprinted in 1661[6] with thirteen alchemical woodcuts. Orthelius also wrote commentaries on the 'words of Maria'[7] and on a letter of John Pontanus on the philosophers' stone[8] which throw no light on them. What Hoefer[9] calls a 'Novum Lumen Chymicum' of Joachim Polemann is a *Novum Lumen Medicum* in German[10] printed later in Latin[11] as *De Mysterio Sulphuris Philosophorum*. It deals with the solution of copper in ammonia, etc.

The reputed work of Seton, which Sendivogius is said to have received from him and published as his own work, was printed under Seton's name:

IV. Alexand. Sitonii / aus Schottland / eines wahren Besitzers der Kunst / Zwölf Bücher / von dem rechten wahren / Philosophischen Steine. / Aus einer sehr alten Handschrift. / Als des grossen und kleinen Bauers / Chymischer Bücher / Zwyter Theil. / Franckfurt und Leipzig, 8°, 1751, pp. xii, 76: on p. xii is stated: 'NB. Dass Alexand. Sitonius, ein Schottländer, ein wahrer Besitzer der Kunst gewesen, in Pohlen gestorben, und vorher seinem Freunde Sendvogio seine Frau, sein Verwandlungs-Pulver und dieses sein Buch aus zwölf Büchern bestehend, gegeben; Sendvogius aber diese zwölf Bücher unter seinen eigenen Nahmen ausgehen lassen, bezeuget das Teutsche Fettefeuer der Schiede-Kunst,

[1] II, 96; III, 1669, 22 in the sep. pagin.; *Hermetic Museum*, 1893, ii, 136.
[2] III, 1669, 63; II, 1650, 41.   [3] III, 66; II, 43.   [4] III, 63; II, 41.
[5] Ferguson, ii, 157.   [6] *Theatrum Chemicum*, 1661, vi, 397–458.
[7] *Theatrum Chemicum*, vi, 480–7.   [8] *Ib.*, vi, 489–96.   [9] (1), ii, 326.
[10] Ferguson, ii, 210.   [11] *Theatrum Chemicum*, vi, 600–24.

das es die wahren Besitzer anfuhret, und unter denen den Sendivogium einen Pohlen sub numero 45. pag. 88. gedruckt zu Hamburg 8. Anno 1702. bey Gottfried Libernickel.' The text is the same as the Latin of Sendivogius' Novum Lumen in Albineus, Bibliotheca Chemica Contracta, pp. 3–68, but omitting pp. 12–13, and the present book does not include the *Dialogue* and later tracts. It is very probably merely a German translation of the printed Latin text.

A Lucerna Salis Philosophorum. Hoc est: Delineatio nuda desiderati illius Principii tertii mineralium Sendivogiani . . . , 8°, Amsterdam, 1658, is ascribed to J. F. Hautnorthon, 'son of Sendivogius', by Ferguson, i, 368; ii, 45.

Morhof[1] says Seton transmuted lead into gold in Holland in the presence of Vander Linden and his friend Hanssen, and Morhof himself saw a morsel of this gold in the possession of J. A. Vander Linden (the grandson), who marked it with the information that the transmutation was effected at 4 p.m. on 13 March 1602.

[1] *De metallorum transmutatione*, Hamburg, 1673, 148.

CHAPTER XII

DESCARTES

René du Perron Descartes, Latinised as Renatus Cartesius, whence his philosophical system is called 'Cartesianism' (La Haye, Tours, 31 May 1596–Stockholm, 11 February 1650), was trained until 1612 in the Jesuit College of La Flèche, where he showed great aptitude in languages and mathematics. He soon became dissatisfied with the scholastic philosophy and resolved to work out a new method. He served in the army in Holland, Bohemia, and Hungary. He retired in 1621 and from 1629 lived in seclusion in Holland, where he composed his works. In 1648 he went at the invitation of Queen Christina of Sweden to Stockholm, where he died. His remains were transferred in 1666 to Ste. Geneviève, Paris, and in 1819 to St. Germain-des-Prés, where they now rest.

Descartes' name is memorable both in mathematics, as the founder of analytical geometry, and in philosophy. As a philosopher Descartes is of outstanding importance. He represents a complete break with Scholasticism and the introduction of the rational explanation of phenomena on the basis of mathematical physics. Although always careful not to come into collision with the Church, and devoting a large part of his philosophy to a proof of the existence of God (taking, as Bossuet said, 'precautions which reached even to excess' to escape criticism), yet his works were nevertheless placed on the Index at Rome and in Paris in 1663, and in 1671 the King prohibited the teaching of Cartesian doctrines in the University of Paris. Descartes' works were removed from the Paris *Index* in 1740 to provide an alternative to the Newtonian philosophy then becoming popular.[1]

Cartesianism was particularly developed in the universities of Holland[2] but it was forbidden by Dutch theologians in 1656.[3]

[1] Adam, Bréhier, Brunschvicg, etc., *Descartes* (*La Revue Philosophique*), Paris, 1937; F. Bouillier, *Histoire de la Philosophie Cartésienne*, 2 vols., Paris and Lyons, 1854; Chevalier, *Descartes*, Paris, 1921; Dingle, *Nature*, 1950, clxv, 213; Hoefer, NBG, 1855, xiii, 756; Lasswitz, (1), 1890, ii, 55–126; Lippmann, *Abhl. Naturforschenden Gesellschaft zu Halle*, 1901, xxii, 1–35; *id.*, (1), i, 488; Mahaffy, *Descartes* (in Knight's *Philosophical Classics*), 1880; J. Millet, *Histoire de Descartes avant 1637*, Paris, 1867; Poggendorff, (2), 184; Rosenberger, 1884, ii, 99–116; J. F. Scott, *The Scientific Work of René Descartes*, 1952 (mostly on mathematics and superficial and unsatisfactory otherwise); Sprengel, (1), 1815, v, 43–58; *id.*, (2), 1827, iv, 318–36; Stones, *Isis*, 1928, x, 452; Tannery, *Mémoires Scientifiques*, 1926, vi; Tennemann, *Geschichte der Philosophie*, Leipzig, 1817, x, 198–285; Thorndike, vii, 544–66; Ueberweg, (1), 1924, iii, 219; Wolf, EB[14], 1929, vii, 244–53; I have not seen *The Method, Meditations, and Selections from the Principles*, with introd. essay by J. Veitch, Edinburgh, 1880, reissued by F. Sewell, New York, 1901, said to be valuable.
[2] Bouillier, 1854, i, 240 f., 251 f.; C. L. Thijssen-Schoute (ed.), Nederlands Cartesianisme, in *Verhl. K. Nederl. Akad. Wetens.*, *Afd. Letterkd.*, 1954, lx (742 pp., summary in French, 651–79).
[3] Ueberweg, (2), 1874, ii, 54.

The basis of Descartes' philosophy, *cogito ergo sum*, was apparently anticipated by John Scotus (Erigena) in the 9 cent.[1] Descartes' main contributions to science were in mathematics; those to physics, chemistry, and physiology are purely speculative; he threw out the most extraordinary opinions as to the shapes and motions of small particles which are entirely imaginary. These nevertheless had a great influence on many chemists until they were displaced by Newton's hypothetical atoms and attractions and repulsions. Descartes' idea that, if we knew enough, chemistry and biology could be reduced to departments of mechanics, had a great influence, e.g. on Boyle and on Borelli.

Descartes was familiar with the new scientific knowledge of his time and took account of it, but in the main his system is his own. It was an attempt towards a general synthesis of knowledge, an explanation of the universe on the basis of a few postulates; in spite of its many shortcomings it was a triumph of method and had a profound influence on the development of contemporary experimental science.[2] Writings of Descartes of interest to us are:

I. Principia Philosophiæ, 4°, Amsterdam, 1644 (bk. i, 1–33, ii 33–70, iii 70–189, iv 190–310), 1650, 1654, 1663, 1664, 1672, 1678–7; 8°, London, 1664; in IV, 1905, viii; French tr. in V, 1824, iii.
II. Le Monde, publ. 1664, prob. written 1630 (A. Wolf, (1), 1935, i, 251); in V, iv, 215–332.
III. De Homine, figvris et latinitate donatus a F. Schuyl, 4°, Leyden, 1662; Traité de l'homme et de la formation du fœtus, 4°, Paris, 1664; prob. written 1630–3 (Chevalier, 1921, 69).
IV. Oeuvres de Decartes, ed. C. Adam and P. Tannery, 13 vols., 4°, Paris, 1897–1911.
V. Oeuvres de Decartes, French tr. by V. Cousin, 11 vols. 8°, Paris, 1824–6.
VI. The Philosophical Works of Descartes, tr. E. S. Haldane and G. R. T. Ross, 2 vols., Cambridge, 1911 (incomplete).
VII. Traité des Météores (publ. with the Discours de la Méthode, 1637).
VIII. Passiones Animæ.
　　References to I below are to the 1664 Amsterdam ed. by page; for the translations the volume and page of V are usually given.

The ideas of Descartes, which are not usually mentioned by historians of chemistry,[3] are particularly important in understanding the views of Boyle, Mayow, and Lemery, to mention only three chemists whose opinions, usually presented as novel and peculiar to themselves, are more or less largely founded on the Cartesian philosophy. In 1628 Descartes became acquainted in Paris with the chemist de Chandoux, who worked on the decomposition of metals and was hanged in 1631 on the charge of making false money, being condemned by a special court which had been established at the Arsenal to try coiners. The plausible eloquence of Chandoux deceived Mersenne and others, but Descartes was sceptical.[4]

Sir Charles Cavendish and John Peel corresponded on Descartes' philosophy in 1627 and it is mentioned that Hobbes, who had read Descartes' works

---

[1] Dum ergo dico, Intelligo me esse, nonne in hoc uno verbo, quod est intelligo, tria significo a se inseparabilia? Nam et me esse, et posse intelligere me esse, et intelligere me esse, demonstro; *De divisione naturae*, i, 50, q. by Lane Poole, *Illustrations of Medieval Thought*, 1920, 56–7.
[2] Lasswitz, (1), ii, 124–6.
[3] Kopp, (1), ii, 386 (12 lines); Gmelin and Hoefer do not mention him.
[4] NBU, 1854, ix, 663; Thorndike, vii, 188.

in manuscript, had little admiration for it. Petty reported that Toncher Hooghland (Hogheland ?), a chemist and physician, was a friend of Descartes,[1] but, unlike Newton (470), Descartes does not seem to have dabbled in alchemy. In his earliest work[2] he says he thought he knew enough not to be deceived by 'the promises of an alchemist, the predictions of an astrologer, the impostures of a magician',[3] but later[4] he said that in the sciences based on rare and well thought-out experiments we should have to know all the herbs and stones brought from India, have seen the phœnix, and have knowledge, which is useful, of the secrets of arts, apparitions, illusions, and other wonderful effects due to magic, many of which, it is true, are due to automata and mere conjuring tricks. All occult qualities, and effects of sympathy and antipathy, provided they proceeded from purely material causes, could be explained on the basis of his philosophy.[5]

The main features of the philosophy of Descartes of interest to us may be summarised as follows. The nature of body consists not in weight (in pondere), nor in hardness, nor colour, and so on, but in extension alone.[6] 'The same extension in length, breadth, and depth which constitutes space, constitutes body.'[7] Weight is not essential to the nature of body, since fire although very light is yet body (quamvis ignis sit levissimus, non ideo putatur esse corpus).[8] It is contrary to reason to say that there is a vacuum or space in which there is no body. A space is said to be empty only when it contains no sensible body; if God removed all the body contained in a vessel without permitting its space to be occupied by another body, the sides of the vessel would come into immediate contact.[9]

Although Whewell[10] says Descartes first devised an account of the universe on the assumption of a vacuum, but remodelled it on the assumption of a plenum when Mersenne told him that the vacuum was no longer in fashion in Paris, Lasswitz[11] was unable to find any reference for this story, which is perhaps only a Cambridge tradition. The corpuscular theory of Descartes was probably suggested by the work of Basso (1630), whom he mentions in a letter[12] with Telesius, Campanella, Bruno, Vaninus, 'et tous les novateurs', perhaps including Gassendi.[13] Bacon's writings were known on the Continent in Descartes' time, and he was treated by Descartes with respect. Since Descartes wished to arrive at results from a few axioms he treated induction and experiment as occupying only a subsidiary place.[14]

The material particles are not atoms, as they may be worn away by attrition.[15] Atoms have no existence, for even if God had rendered the particle so small that no creature could divide it, he still could not deprive Himself of His power of division, and therefore its divisibility remains, because it is so from its nature.[16] Motion is the action by which any body passes from one place to

---

[1] J. O. Halliwell-Philipps, *A Collection of Letters*, 1841, 77–88.
[2] *Discours de la Méthode*, 1637.   [3] VI, i, 86.
[4] *The Search after Truth*, date unknown; VI, i, 300 f.   [5] I, iv, 187.
[6] I, ii, 4; 1664, 22; V, 1824, iii, 123; VI, i, 255; II, ch. iv, in V, 1824, iv, 230 f., 255.
[7] I, ii, 10; 1664, 24; V, 1824, iii, 128; VI, i, 259.
[8] I, ii, 11; 1664, 24; V, iii, 129; VI, i, 259.
[9] I, ii, 16–19; 1664, 26; V, iii, 133–6; VI, i, 262–3; in II, in V, 1824, iv, 231 f., 234, Descartes does not deny the possibility of vacuous parts in bodies, particularly solids, but thinks the assumption unnecessary.
[10] (1), 1857, ii, 105.   [11] (1), 1890, ii, 95.   [12] V, 1824, vi, 146.
[13] Lasswitz, (2), 1886, x, 166–89; *id.*, (1), 1890, ii, 87 f.   [14] Baden Powell, 1834, 225f.
[15] VII, i, 9; V, 1824, v, 160 f.   [16] I, ii, 20; 1664, 27; V, iii, 137; VI, i, 264.

another.[1] If a body (which is something moveable as a whole) moves from A to B then, since space is full of matter, another body must move from B to A; hence space is full of circular or vortex motions.[2]

Descartes' name, *tourbillon*, for a vortex had been used in a similar sense by Jean Belot.[3] A supposed anticipation of the 'subtle matter' of Descartes by Isaac Beeckman (who kept a journal)[4] is unlikely.[5]

The quantity of motion (*motus*) in the universe remains constant, although it may vary in the separate parts;[6] by 'motion' he understood momentum =mass × velocity.[7] Although Descartes would not question the account of creation in the Bible, he offered an explanation of the present state of the universe on the assumption that it first consisted of portions of the same kind of matter equal in size, each turning about its centre and all revolving about several centres corresponding with the fixed stars, 'in such a way that God has produced so many vortices as stars (sicque tot varios vortices componerent, quot jam astra sunt in mundo).'[8] Whatever figure these parts had initially, they would tend to become spherical by attrition, their corners being rubbed off. Thus two kinds of matter arose: (i) the first matter (*materia primi elementi*) consisting of the fine dust abraded from the original particles, at first moving with great velocity and filling the interstices, but becoming finer and finer and losing its velocity and so tending to accumulate in the centre of the vortex; and (ii) the second matter (*globuli secundi elementi*), consisting of small spherical globules formed from the original particles, having a circular motion and tending to recede from the centre as they swing round the axis of revolution. The second matter (*materia cœlestis*) constitutes the atmosphere of the sun or star.[9] A third matter (*particulæ tertii elementi*) is formed from parts which, by reason of their size and shape, are not so easily moved; its particles are neither square nor spherical but are partly rounded by abrasion, still retaining some of their angles.

Although Descartes' theory is plerotic (i.e. assumes that all space is full of something) it did not exclude the existence of corpuscles and hence could take over many aspects of the atomic theory,[10] as Boyle recognised (p. 502). The fact that solid bodies completely filling space originally (e.g. cubes) could not begin to revolve round their centres must have been known to a mathematician like Descartes, and his assumptions are often superficial and could not have been thought out in detail.

What Descartes calls *soliditas* is density, the ratio of the quantity (*quantitas*) of inertial matter to the volume.[11] Whereas in Newton's theory of gravitation, a denser

---

[1] I, ii, 24; 1664, 28; V, iii, 139; VI, i, 265.
[2] I, ii, 33; 1664, 31; V, iii, 147; the germ of this idea is in Plato's *Timaios*, 80 c., ed. Martin, Paris, 1841, i, 214.
[3] *Les Fleurs de la Philosophie Chrestienne et morale ou Refutations de Henry Corn. Agrippa et de P. d'Albano en leur philosophie occulte*, 12°, Paris, 1603, 83 r (BM 702. b. 6. (1.)): un petit tourbillon de Matiere Meteorique qui n'occupe aucun lieu; Thorndike, vi, 362.
[4] *Journal tenu par Isaac Beeckman de 1604 à 1634*, ed. C. de Waard, 4 vols., The Hague, 1939–53; Beeckman, d. 1637, was principal of the college in Dordrecht and wrote *Mathematico-Physicæ Meditationes*, 4°, Utrecht, 1644 (posthumous).
[5] Thorndike, vii, 547–8.   [6] I, ii,36; 1664, 33; V, 1824,iii, 150; II, *c.* vii; in V, 1824, iv, 256 f.
[7] Lasswitz, (1), 1890, i, 104 f.   [8] I, iii, 46; 1664, 57; V, iii, 211–12.
[9] I, iii, 48–64; 1664, 58 f.; V, iii, 214 f.   [10] Lasswitz, (1), ii, 71.   [11] I, iii, 121.

body would have greater gravitation towards the sun, in Descartes' theory the less dense bodies tend towards the centre. This depends on whether the centrifugal force of a body is greater or less than that of its environment, when it tends to recede from, or approach, the sun, respectively. The centripetal force, by which a body in a vortex is thrown to the centre, depends on the volume, since this has to be replaced by the celestial matter displaced by the body. The translational force of the vortex, viz. in its revolution, depends on the magnitude of the surface of the body, and the larger this is, the more matter can act upon it. The inertial property of a planet depends neither on surface nor volume, but only on that part of the volume filled by the third element, since the quantity of the matter of the first and second elements filling the pores of the body is indifferent towards the conservation of proper motion, since it is constantly varying and does not belong specifically or permanently to the body.[1]

The first matter is the fire element, constituting the sun and fixed stars; the second matter is the air element, constituting the atmospheres of the sun and stars, and hence the sky; the third matter is the earth element, forming the earth, the planets, and comets.[2] Some parts of the first element join together and in passing through the triangular spaces between the particles of the second element, acquire a channelled and spiral figure, like screws.[3] These parts (*particulæ striatæ*) settle like a scum upon the inner ocean of solar dust and form spots on the sun.[4]

The channelled particles (*particulæ striatæ*) of the first element can link together and with other particles of irregular shapes to form larger particles which constitute the element of earth; thus the third element does not appear to be regarded as independent but can be formed from the first.[5] The *three* elements first appear in the *Principia philosophiæ*, there being only two, a fine and coarse, in *Le Monde*.

Lasswitz[6] says there is no trace of the corpuscular theory in 1619–20; in 1619–24 Descartes became acquainted with the writings of Sennert, Bacon, Basso, d'Espagnet, and Gassendi; he was in Paris in 1625–8 and must have got to know of them there (he mentions Basso in a letter of 1630). Descartes made a notable extension of the corpuscular theory by considering the *motion* of the particles and their attrition. The detailed theory was mentioned in a letter of 1639, but the idea of screw-like particles (particulæ striatæ) is later, since it is not mentioned in *Le Monde*.

The speculations of chemical interest are mostly contained in the fourth part of the *Principia philosophiæ*, dealing with the earth. This is composed of three parts: (i) the innermost, containing only the first matter, (ii) a second region containing a very solid and opaque matter with pores allowing the passage only of channelled parts of the first matter; (iii) a third outer region composed of a confused aggregate of particles of the third element with much of the second matter in their interstices, with diverse figures.[7] The particles of the second element are present everywhere between those of the third, and when the particles of the third element are very fine, so that the celestial matter can move freely between them, they constitute transparent liquids (e.g. water); when they are coarse, the liquid is opaque (mercury).[8]

---

[1] Lasswitz, (1), ii, 70.
[2] I, iii, 52; 1664, 59; V, 1824, iii, 217–18; II, *c.* v, in V, 1824, iv, 237 f.; VII, i, 3, in V, 1824, v, 160.
[3] I, iii, 88 f.; 1664, 69 f.; V, 1824, iii, 255 f.   [4] I, iii, 94 f.; 1664, 86 f.; V, 1824, iii, 260 f.
[5] I, iii, 94; 1664, 87; V, 1824, iii, 260.   [6] (1), ii, 87 f.; *id.*, (2), 1886, x, 166 f., 179 f.
[7] I, iv, 1–13; 1664, 121–4; V, 1824, iii, 330–8.
[8] I, iii, 55, 63 f.; iv, 16, 28; 1664, 61, 65 f., 124, 129; V, iii, 220, 228 f., 332, 339 f.

Descartes explains the clarification of liquids such as wine, and the globular form of liquid drops, by the action of subtle matter in the pores.[1] Gravity (gravitus) is due to the subtle matter pressing the parts towards the centre.[2] At the same time the celestial matter tends upwards to take the place of the matter which descends.[3] The different gravities of bodies are due to the different amounts of the celestial matter in their pores and are not always in the ratio of the quantities of their terrestrial matter.[4]

There are three main kinds of terrestrial particles: (1) branched, (2) spherical or cubical, and (3) long and thin.[5] The particles of air are slender and detached and easily set in motion by the celestial matter, each particle moving in the small space about its proper centre and pushing away all others which try to enter this space (occupatque totam illam exiguam sphæram, quam ad motum circularem circa proprium suam centrum requirit, & ex ea vincas omnes expellit).[6] Expansion by heat results from the increased violence of motion. The air is compressible and dilatable because its parts are soft and flexible like small feathers or pieces of very fine string, and when compressed other parts are constrained to occupy the space taken by each particle (unaquæque ejus particula sphæricum illud spatiolum, quod ad motum suam requirit, sibi soli non habeat, sed aliæ vicinæ in ipsum ingrediantur).[7]

The particles of water are of two kinds, one soft and flexible, the other hard and inflexible, both kinds being long and united. The first kind compose sweet water, the second when separated compose solid salt. There is no essential difference between water and air, and one may be converted into the other.[8] the first kind of particles separate by evaporation but they can recondense to water.[9]

Earth is composed of particles of all kinds of figures, which are so coarse that the matter of the second element cannot carry them with it in its ordinary movements, as it does those of air and water.[10] The particles of salt, vitriol, alum, and other minerals which are sharp and corrosive, are sharp-pointed and polished like little blades, having been beaten out by collision with other particles;[11] those of oils, sulphur, bitumen and other fatty or oily minerals are less hard and have been divided into thin and flexible branches.[12] In this way, says Descartes, he explains the bodies which the chemists have taken for the three principles, salt, sulphur and mercury, from which metals are generated in mines, which process he says he will better explain when he has had the opportunity of making the requisite experiments.[13]

Heinrich Gerhard Herfeld[14] combined the three elements of Descartes with the three chemical principles (salt, sulphur, and mercury); he cites Mayow. Descartes' mention

---

[1] I, iv, 18–19; 1664, 125–6; V, 1824, iii, 343–5.   [2] I, iv, 20–1; 1664, 126; V, 1824, iii, 345.
[3] I, iv, 22–3; 1664, 127; V, 1824, iii, 346–8.
[4] I, iv, 24–5; 1664, 127–8; V, 1824, iii, 348–9.   [5] I, iv, 33 f.; 1664, 131 f.; V, 1824, iii, 356 f.
[6] I, iv, 45; 1664, 138; V, 1824, iii, 369; this passage was q. by Boyle, see p. 523.
[7] I, iv, 46; 1664, 139; V, iii, 370; This idea was adopted by Boyle, see p. 523.
[8] I, iv, 48; 1664, 139; V, iii, 370.   [9] I, iv, 64; 1664, 145; V, iii, 384.
[10] I, iv, 57; 1664, 139; V, iii, 378.   [11] I, iv, 61; 1664, 144; V, iii, 382.
[12] I, iv, 62; 1664, 144; V, iii, 383.   [13] I, iv, 63; 1664, 144; V, iii, 383.
[14] *Philosophicum Hominis ... Willisii Bartholini Malpighii Fracassati Harvæi aliorumque methodo illustrissimi D. Cartesii concinnatum*, 8°, Leyden, 1687; Thorndike, viii, 443.

of 'requisite experiments' suggests that he did not feel that his general speculations were likely to interest or assist professional chemists.

What are called exhalations, vapours and spirits, although of different species, are composed of thin and branched particles of the third element. By penetrating the pores of earthy bodies they form the different kinds of gems. The vapours of mercury rising in the earth carry with them particles of gold, silver, lead or other metals; the mercury may ascend or descend, leaving the metals, but when it meets with more subtle exhalations it forms minium. Other spirits and exhalations may carry copper, iron and antimony.[1] Descartes tries to explain why metals are found only in certain places by assuming that the exhalations pass only through certain 'faults' in the earth.[2] When the exhalations, joined with the most subtle parts of the spirits, are too agitated to form bitumen and naphtha, they form a fatty fume like that rising from the wick of a candle when it is blown out, and by taking fire inside cavities in the earth they give rise to earthquakes, and on breaking out, volcanoes are produced.[3]

Descartes gives a long discussion of the production of fire, on purely mechanical principles.[4] Light is apparent without heat in phosphorescent bodies (sea-water, rotten wood, salt fish, etc.) when the first matter, unhampered by the presence of a large quantity of the third element, is able to set in motion the globules of the second element, present in larger amount, but cannot move the particles of the third element. Heat is apparent without light (as in slaking lime) when the first matter can move the particles of the third element but is so entangled in them that it cannot move the globules of the second element. Heat and light are simultaneously produced in flame and rapid combusion when there are many globules of the second element present, and the first matter is so abundant that it can agitate both these and the particles of the third element.

All particles of earthy matter, of whatever shape, take the form of fire when they are separated from one another and agitated by the matter of the first element, as they become air when agitated by the matter of the second element. The principal difference between fire and air is in the much swifter agitation of the particles of fire.[5]

Heat is a motion of the particles of the third element which is so brisk that it becomes sensible. It is produced mostly by the action of light but when once set up is maintained.[6] When for any reason the particles of the second element are driven from the pores of the third element, leaving only the particles of the first element, fire is produced. The particles of the third element are thus set into a particularly violent motion, being whirled in vortices by the motion of the first element, since they are no longer surrounded by those of the second element, as they are in air.[7] By striking flint with steel, or another flint, the

---

[1] I, iv, 70–72; 1664, 146–7; V, iii, 389–90.   [2] I, iv, 73–5; 1664, 147 f.; V, iii, 391–2.
[3] I, iv, 77–8; 1664, 148; V, iii, 393–4.
[4] I, iv, 81–92; 1664, 149–54; V, iii, 397–409; Rodwell, *Phil. Mag.*, 1868, xxxv, 14 f.
[5] I, iv, 80; 1664, 148; V, iii, 395.
[6] I, iv, 20 f.; 1664, 130; V, iii, 353; VII, i, 7, in V, 1824, v, 160.
[7] I, iv, 80 f.; 1664, 149; V, iii, 396 f.

particles of the second element are pressed out of the interstices of the hard flint particles, leaving the latter surrounded by particles of the first element which agitate them and produce fire.[1]

The force of light (*vix luminis*), propagated from the sun, produces a motion of light (*lumen*) in a medium.[2] Light is an action propagated with immense velocity as a pressure due to the centrifugal force set up in the particles of the second element by the rotation about the sun. The famous law of refraction of light[3] is said to have been really due to Willebrord Snell (Leyden; 1591–1626), but some think Descartes discovered it independently.[4] Huygens was in general a follower of Descartes, although he rejected the view that light travels instantaneously, and he introduced the theory of the ether (corps éthéré) as a subtle medium transmitting waves of light.[5] He also rejected Descartes' theory that animals are automata.[6]

'Every invisible and impalpable body is called *air* in its most ample signification.'[7] Wallis[8] said:

By Air, I find, Mr. Hobbes would sometimes (*Dialogus physicus*, p. 4) have us understand a pure Æther or (as his words are): 'Aërem ab omni Terræ Aquæque effluviis purum, qualis putatur esse Æther'; to which, I suppose, answers the *Materia subtilis* of Des Cartes, and M. Hugens his 'more subtile matter' than Air. On the other hand, M. Hugens here, by Air seems to understand that feculent matter arising from those the Earths and Waters Effluvia, which are intermingled with this subtile Matter. We mean by *Air* the Aggregate of both these, or whatever else makes up that heterogeneous Fluid wherein we breathe, commonly called Air, the purer part of which is Mr. Hobbes Air, and the feculent of it is Monsieur Hugen's Air.

Wallis[9] says: 'whether that subtile body, be (as Dr. Garden seems to suppose,) much heavier than our common Air,[10] I much doubt . . . it may, for ought I know, be void as well of weight as spring.'

Descartes supposed that a flame, like all other bodies, will continue to exist once it is formed if its parts are not dissipated, hence the sun, which is of the nature of flame, requires no aliment.[11] In a flame the parts are continually agitated and hence it liquefies most other bodies. When it melts metals it acts with the same power as when it burns wood, but the particles of a metal are nearly equal, whilst those of wood are unequal, the smallest being separated to form liquid, i.e. to cause them to fly away as smoke, whilst the grosser particles are not agitated. After flame, there is nothing more liquid than air, its parts being seen to be in motion by the motes in sunlight. Something similar happens when liquids are mixed with various colours, and when strong waters dissolve metals, separating and agitating their particles. The air particles differ in size; in a flame there are parts both larger and smaller than in air; the smallest ones can penetrate the pores of many bodies which are too small for the air as a whole to enter, and only the larger parts burn, the flame from spirit of wine or

---

[1] I, iv, 84; 1664, 150; V, iii, 399.   [2] I, iv, 28; 1664, 129; V, iii, 352.
[3] *Discours de la Méthode*, 1637, 20.
[4] Whewell, (1), 1857, ii, 276; Poggendorff, (2), 1883, 189; Cajori, 1929, 83.
[5] *Traité de la Lvmiere*, Leyden, 1690 (written in 1678); Lasswitz, (1), ii, 341–84 (355).
[6] Thorndike, vii, 637.   [7] V, 1824, vii, 237.
[8] *Phil. Trans.*, 1672, viii, No. 91, p. 5160; Harcourt, *Phil. Mag.*, 1846, xxviii, 129.
[9] *Phil. Trans.*, 1685, xiv, No. 171, p. 1002 (1004).
[10] Garden, *Phil. Trans.*, 1685, xiv, No. 171, p. 991.   [11] I, iii, 22; 1664, 48; V, iii, 191.

other subtle bodies hardly burning (the hand) like those of harder and heavier bodies.[1]

Descartes is quite unaware of the part played by the air in the maintenance of flame; he says air would tend to replace the particles of the second element in the pores of the burning body (p. 436) and hence extinguish the flame; since particles of the third element are emitted as smoke, a body is necessary to maintain the supply of these, and without such nourishment the particles of the first element cannot be protected from the entry of the second.[2] There are fires which burn under water because they contain particles of the third element so solid, in such large number, and so agitated that they can repel the water on all sides.[3] Flame tends upwards because it contains a large amount of the first matter, which is lighter than air and is the cause of levity in all bodies.[4]

Descartes gives a very poor figure of a candle flame (showing lack of ordinary observation) and explains that the flame is composed of small particles of the wax agitated by those of the second element, following the course of the first element. The particles of air descending would suffocate the flame if they were not pushed away by the first element. The particles of air circulate about the flame and enter its base, thus supporting it mechanically, and, as is said, 'nourish' the flame.[5] Flames become more violent when water is thrown upon them, and even more so by salt, the long particles of which, provided with points like arrows, have much force when inflamed, hence certain salts are mixed with metals to make them melt more easily.[6] The heat of slaking of quicklime is due to the expulsion of the particles of the second element from the pores of the lime by the water.[7]

Common salt consists of long and straight particles. The rigid corpuscles of salt are not easily separated, but salt liquefies in water because the slippery and flexible water corpuscles wrap themselves round the sharp points of the salt and carry these away with them. Salt water becomes fresh on filtration through sand.[8] The differences between salts arise from the different figures of their particles or from the presence of some small earthy particles.[9]

Descartes explains the explosion of gunpowder as follows.[10] The sulphur is composed of particles of sharp or corrosive juices surrounded by branched particles of oily matter, through which only particles of the first matter can pass, hence in medicine it is very hot. The nitre (nitrum) is composed of long and rigid particles, pointed more at one end than the other (those of common salt are equally pointed at both ends): the pointed ends whirl round in circles whilst the heavier bases serve as supports [like the points of a peg-top]. The particles of sulphur, which do not turn in this way, pass more easily between the particles of nitre when the latter are spinning in an obtuse cone, and inflame them, driving the second element before them. Each particle of nitre drives out all others from the circle of its motion; since it is only the points which rotate, the flame of the powder is upwards only, and it may be burnt on

[1] II, iii; V, 1824, iv, 227–30.   [2] I, iv, 100 f., 107; 1664, 155–7; V, iii, 414 f., 419.
[3] I, iv, 100; 1664, 155; V, iii, 414.   [4] I, iv, 97; 1664, 155; V, iii, 412.
[5] I, iv, 95–9, 116; 1664, 154–5, 159; V, iii, 411–14, 426.
[6] I, iv, 105; 1664, 156; V, iii, 418.   [7] I, iv, 93; 1664, 154; V, iii, 409.   [8] VII, iii, 3, 7.
[9] I, iv, 69; 1664, 146; V, iii, 388.   [10] I, iv, 109–15; 1664, 157–8; V, iii, 420–5.

the palm of the hand without injury. Charcoal has pores into which the sulphur and nitre enter; for this reason the powder is moistened and formed into grains. The charcoal offers resistance to the dilatation of the parts of the nitre. A feebler explanation than this could hardly be imagined. Calcination is due to the separation of finer parts of a body by the action of fire on the surface:[1] ex corporibus, quæ uruntur, tenuiores omnes particulæ avulsæ ac rejectæ sunt, cæteræ quæ pro calce vel cineribus manent, tam solidæ sunt & crassæ.

Descartes explains the properties of glass,[2] or iron, steel and the magnet,[3] and magnetic and electrical attractions.[4] He gives diagrams of lines of force, formed by chains of particles of the first element, around and inside the magnet.[5]

Descartes supposed that animals are mere automata, the sole principles of physiology being motion and heat. His physiology is essentially a mechanisation of that of Galen prevalent in his time.[6] His views on animal heat are as follows:[7]

The flesh of the heart contains in its pores one of those fires without light, and when the blood enters the chambers of the heart it suddenly inflames and dilates, as you can show by dropping blood or milk into a very hot vessel. The fire in the heart serves to dilate, heat, and subtilise the blood. The flesh of the lung is thin and soft and is refreshed by the air as the vapour of the blood enters one side of the heart, where it thickens and falls drop by drop into the left cavity. Respiration is not less necessary for the maintenance of this fire and serves for the conservation of life, at least in full-formed animals with lungs.

Vopiscus Fortunatus Plemp (Amsterdam, 23 December 1601–Louvain, 12 December 1671), professor of medicine in Louvain, who censured Descartes in the fourth edition of his *Foundations of Medicine*,[8] included two unpublished letters of Descartes proving that the movement of the heart is caused by the rarefaction of the blood, which dilates it, and not by any pulsific virtue of its own. This theory was criticised by Digby,[9] who upheld Harvey's view that the heart beats of itself. Descartes was not acquainted with Harvey's *De Motu Cordis* until five years after its publication in 1628, when he was completing his *Physics*, but he had got to know of Harvey's book previously (1633 ?) through Mersenne.[10]

Descartes says:[11]

The parts of the blood passing to the brain serve not only to nourish its substance but also to produce a very subtle wind, or rather a very lively and pure flame called the animal spirits. These spirits pass into the pores of the brain, and from these to the nerves, and from these to the muscles, which they cause to move.

The air in respiration mixes in some way with the blood before this enters the left ventricle of the heart and produces more active and agitated spirits in

[1] I, iv, 123–4; 1664, 161; V, iii, 431.   [2] I, iv, 124–32; 1664, 161–4; V, iii, 431–42.
[3] I, iv, 133–83; 1664, 164–85; V, iii, 440–92.   [4] I, iv, 184–6; 1664, 185–6; V, iii, 492–7.
[5] I, 1664, 173.   [6] Foster, 1901, 59, 260–8; A. G. Berthier, *Isis*, 1914, ii, 37–89.
[7] III; V, 1824, iv, 339–40.
[8] *De Fundamentis Medicinæ ad scholæ acribologiam adapta*, f°, Louvain, 1664 (3 ed. 1654; BM 544. h. 24–5); Thorndike, viii, 408.
[9] Thorndike, vii, 501–2.
[10] V, 1824, i, 179 f. (*Discours de la Méthode*); vi, 235 (letter to Mersenne, 1633 ?); Lasswitz, (2), 1884, 166 f.
[11] V, iv, 345–7.

dry weather, as a flame is hotter in such weather. Changes in the spirits may be compared with the modification of the heat of those closed lamps used by the alchemists.[1] The 'vegetative' part of the soul assumed by Aristotle (Vol. I) was removed by Descartes from the soul and transferred to the body in the form of vital spirits (*spiritus vitales*), which are 'nothing but material bodies ... of extreme minuteness', formed in the cavities of the brain from the most animated and subtle parts of the blood rarefied by heat in the heart. They are never at rest but move with great speed and cause movements of the muscles. All the bodily members can be moved by objects of the senses without the aid of the soul, and 'there is nothing in us that we ought to attribute to our soul excepting our thoughts'. The sensitive soul of Aristotle is thus also rejected, and of the three parts only the rational and immortal soul is retained.[2]

'One cannot doubt that there is heat in the heart, one can feel it by the hand when the body of a living animal is opened; and there is no need to suppose that this heat is of any other nature than is, in general, all that which is caused by the mixing of any liquor or any ferment, which causes the body in which it is to be dilated.[3]

'The blood and spirits in an animal are agitated by the heat of a fire which burns continually in the heart, and is of no different nature from all the fires which are in inanimate bodies.[4]

'The blood is cooled and condensed in the lungs, but as it stays there only a short time and does not mix with any grosser matter, it retains more facility for dilating and heating that it had before entering the heart, as is seen in experiments with oils passed several times by the alembic, which are easier to distil the second time than the first. ....[5] The more subtle parts of the blood, like spirit of wine, or strong waters, or volatile salts, at the same time more solid and more agitated, form the animal spirits.'[6] The motion of the heart is due to the action of this fire on its fibres, which are agitated.[7]

The blood, heated and rarefied in the heart, engendered 'the very subtle air, or rather the very lively and pure flame, called the animal spirits'. In the brain and nervous system this carries out, according to simple mechanical and physical laws, the motions of the body in response to changes of environment, and also, by supplying the physical basis for, and working on, the rational soul, gives rise to modifications of thought. The animal spirits are a kind of fluid, very subtle but obeying the physical laws of fluids and flowing along the nerves as tubes. The nerves are like 'the tubes of the machines in grottoes and fountains in our royal gardens' [Versailles], and the rational soul resides in this machine in the pineal gland in the brain, directing the operations of the body. The nerves also contain delicate threads determining the outflow of spirits from the gland and the ventricles of the brain which form a secondary reservoir of the spirits. These threads open the pores of the skin through which sensations pass and at the same time pull upon the parts of the brain; they act like bell-cords. In this way Descartes explained in a mechanical way all the psychical functions.[8]

Harvey was also quite ignorant of the function of respiration, considering[9] that the chief function of inspiration is to cool the blood:

Inspiration is a means by which the blood in its passage between the two ventricles of the heart is tempered by the cold of the ambient atmosphere, lest, getting heated, and blown up by a kind of fermentation, like milk or honey set over the fire, it should so distend the lungs that the animal got suffocated.

The heart, for him, was 'the laboratory, fountain, and perennial focus of heat, comparable to a hot kettle'.[10]

---

[1] V, iv, 389–90.   [2] VIII, chs. x–xi, xvi–xvii; VI, i, 335–40.   [3] III, ii; V, iv, 437.
[4] III, 1664, 107; V, iv, 428.   [5] III, ii; V, iv, 447.   [6] V, iv, 475.
[7] V, iv, 501.   [8] Foster, 1901, 260–8.
[9] *Second Disquisition to John Riolan*, 1649; tr. Willis, revised by Bowie, London, 1889, 123.
[10] *Ib.*, 143.

Descartes explained smell and taste in terms of the sizes, shapes, and motion of the particles.[1]

Descartes' physiological theories, although very erroneous, were better than earlier ones. Barchusen[2] said many physicians had put a new face on rational medicine (hinc orta nova medicinæ rationalis facies) by borrowing many hypotheses from the physics of Descartes and combining them with the principles of Galen and the chemists; Descartes' main contribution was his hypothesis of the first element and its passage through pores. Sprengel[3] thought it would have been possible to combine the idea of vortices formed by the small atoms of subtle matter around the large globules with Van Helmont's ferments, the result of continual internal change producing active gases; the fermentescible particles might have been given particular forms. Descartes had explained animal heat as the result of a fermentation of the same kind as that produced when the juice of black grapes forms red claret wine, or when a mineral acid acts on iron, which he calls a fire without light.[4] The cause of this fermentation resides in the ether, a subtle element, which was substituted for the gas of Van Helmont.[5] The secretions preserve their natural state because their particles traverse tubes corresponding with their shapes, round particles in cylindrical canals, pyramids in triangular tubes, cubes in square conduits.[6] It is probably true[7] that Descartes 'a introduit dans la physiologie et maintenu dans l'anatomie plus de nouvelles erreurs qu'il n'en a détruit d'anciennes', but they were at least errors which could be refuted by experiments and they suggested these. Gilson[8] too cleverly said that Descartes' philosophy was in large part a clear explanation of facts which did not exist, and Thorndike thought that Descartes attempted to deal with century-old problems and solve them by a new method appealing to natural reason. But Descartes was trying to come to grips with real facts, and many of them new facts, and to evolve a philosophical system based on them. He failed but his attempt stimulated young men with open minds, like Mayow, to try to do better in restricted fields, and after his influence had sunk in, it put a 'new face' not only on medicine but also on science. Newton superseded Descartes in astronomy and dynamics, but Newton was no chemist.

In France, a Cartesian society was established about 1664 by Pierre Michon (the Abbé Bourdelot; Sens, 1610–Paris, 1685).[9] They discussed water and salt as primary substances, salt being volatile or composed of fire. Volatile salt has perfectly round particles, salt composed of fire having elongated and square atoms. The theory of acids and alkalis, and the origin of diseases, were explained on these principles. There are two kinds of water, sulphur, and mercury, the first derived from several materials and the second containing aqueous particles.[10] Nicolas Malebranche (1638–1715) combined Cartesianism with theology.[11]

[1] I, iv, 194, 199; 1664, 189–92; V, iii, 504 f.
[2] Historia Medicinæ, 8°, Amsterdam, 1710, 524.   [3] (1), v, 51.   [4] V, iv, 338, 345.
[5] Sprengel, (1), v, 52.   [6] III; V, iv, 344, 415, 460, 464, 477, 484.   [7] Daremberg, 1870, ii, 701.
[8] Études de Philosophie Mediévale, 1921, q. by Thorndike, vii, 555.
[9] Conversations de l'Académie de M. de l'Abbé Bourdelot, ed. de Gallois, Paris, 1672; Harcourt Brown, 1934, 231–53; Sprengel dates the work 1675; I have not seen it.
[10] Sprengel, (1), v, 56.   [11] De la Recherche de la Vérité, 1674.

Pierre Sylvain Regis (1632–1707), professor of philosophy at Toulouse, Montpellier, and Paris, was a pupil of Rohault and an enthusiastic Cartesian. His encyclopaedic work[1] contains sections on metals, mineralogy and chemistry,[2] the magnet and electrics;[3] flame, gunpowder, and the theory of explosion;[4] glass and the Rupert's drop;[5] acids (eaux fortes) and alkalis;[6] fermentation;[7] and 'general reflexions on chemistry'.[8] Sprengel[9] says Regis, a pupil of Renerius, was very superficial, and after gaining his professorship in 1665 on the basis of his enthusiasm for the new philosophy, he publicly abjured it; his introduction to medical practice (4°, Utrecht, 1657) is mediocre.

IATROMATHEMATICS

The application of Descartes' ideas to medicine was taken up by a number of physicians, resulting in the formation of a school of Iatromathematics (or Iatromechanics), opposed to the chemical school of Paracelsus and Van Helmont and their followers, the exponents of Iatrochemistry (p. 135).[10] Some steps in the direction of Iatromathematics (probably influenced by Galileo) were taken by Santorio Santorio (Sanctorius Sanctorius, 1561–1636), professor at Padua and Venice, who discovered insensible perspiration (perspiratio insensibilis) by living on the platform of a large balance, on which he worked and took his meals. With a daily diet of 8 lb. of food and drink he lost 5 lb.[11] Sanctorius invented an air-thermometer, a string hygrometer, a pulse-meter and other instruments, a list of which he gave in his commentary on Avicenna.[12]

Descartes' ideas were applied to medicine by the Dutch physician Cornelius Hogeland, a friend of Descartes,[13] who compared the human body with an alembic, in which the vital spirits are separated from the blood by a true distillation, and the gastric juice and the blood are compared with a fermenting mixture of butter of antimony and aqua fortis[14] or aqua fortis and steel filings;[15] the blood is expelled from the heart into the arteries by an effervescence like that produced by butter of antimony prepared with corrosive sublimate.[16] Fever is due to a fermentation of viscous matter composed of large particles.

William Croone (or Croune) (London; 15 September 1633–12 October

[1] *Système de Philosophie, contenant La Logique, La Métaphysique, La Physique et La Morale*, 3 vols. 4°, Paris, Thierry, 1690 (portrait); Gmelin, (1), ii, 242; Hoefer, (1), ii, 240.
[2] Bk. IV, pt. 2; 1690, Vol. ii, 183 f.   [3] *Ib.*, 220 f., 251.   [4] *Ib.*, 265, 269.
[5] *Ib.*, 281–7.   [6] *Ib.*, 301 f., 310 f. (solution of metals).   [7] *Ib.*, 306.
[8] *Ib.*, 333 f.   [9] (2), 1827, iv, 330.
[10] Daremberg, 1870, ii, 735–887, who says the account of Iatromathematics in Sprengel, (1), 1815, v, 131–95; *id.*, (2), 1827, iv, 418–50, is very superficial, although it contains most of what he gives.
[11] *Ars Sanctorii Sanctorii . . . de Statica medicina, aphorismorum sectionibus septem comprehensa*, 12°, Venice, 1614, and 20 more eds., the last in Paris, 1770; Daremberg, 1870, ii, 735; Haeser, 1881, ii, 316.
[12] *Comment. in primam fen Avicennae*, f°, Venice, 1625 (BM 542. h. 11); 4°, Venice, 1646 (BM 541. b. 5); Sprengel, (2), 1827, iv, 422–3 (16 items); the book is very rare; for the thermometer, F. S. Taylor, *Ann. Sci.*, 1942, v, 129.
[13] *Cogitationes, Quibus Dei Existentia; Item Animæ Spiritalitas*, 12°, Amsterdam, 1646, 29, 50, 59, 70, 75, 81, 89, 103, 118, 151, 153, 172, 212, 236, 285; Sprengel, (1), 1815, v, 55, quotes from an ed. of Leyden, 1676.
[14] *Ib.*, 89.   [15] *Ib.*, 118.   [16] *Ib.*, 81, 103.

1684)[1] professor at Cambridge, then physician in London, professor of rhetoric at Gresham College (1659), a founder fellow of the Royal Society and founder of the Croonian Lecture, was also interested in Cartesian ideas. In an anonymous work[2] he compares the vital spirits with the subtle spirits of the chemists.[3] They flow along the nerves to the muscles and by mixing with the spirit, like spirit of wine, in the blood, produce muscular motion by a kind of fermentation or commotion, like that between oil of vitriol and water, or butter of antimony and spirit of nitre:[4]

Ex admistione liquoris hujusce sive spiritûs cùm spiritibus sanguinis, continuò spirituosarum omnium particularum, quæ in vitali totius Musculi succo insunt, magnam agitationem contingere, uti cùm spiritus vini spiritui sanguinis humani admiscetur . . . Ut in Exemplo modo allato, ac etiam in aquâ communi oleo vitrioli, aut Butyro Antimonii spiritui Nitri affuso. He mentions Hogeland and Ent (aut flammæ vitalis).

The use of Cartesian ideas by Boyle (p. 502) and Mayow (p. 584) will be considered later.

BORELLI

The real founder of Iatromathematics was Giovanni Alfonso Borelli (Castelnuovo, Naples, 28 January 1608–Rome, 31 December 1679), professor of philosophy and mathematics in Messina (1649) and Pisa (1656), and a member of the Accademia del Cimento in Florence. When the Accademia was dissolved in 1667 he lived at first in Messina but then retired to a cloister in Rome, where he died. His book on natural motions depending on gravity[5] contains earlier material presented to the Accademia del Cimento. He maintained, against Aristotle, that there is no positive levity in nature,[6] that fire is not positively light,[7] that an experiment proved that smoke falls in a Torricellian vacuum,[8] that it is a collection of fine particles,[9] and that flame is not ignited smoke.[10] He devoted much attention to flames;[11] the shape of a flame is due to the pressure of the surrounding air[12] — much of this is in Francis Bacon. He maintained the necessity of a vacuum and refuted in detail Aristotle's arguments against it,[13] also dealing with Torricelli's barometer.[14] His statements on fermentation and the solution of metals in acids, etc.,[15] contain nothing of note. He mentions Descartes,[16] Gassendi,[17] and Boyle,[18] and criticises some of Descartes' ideas without naming him.

His long section on the air[19] refers to Roberval's experiment on the dilatation in a vacuum of a bladder containing some air,[20] and says that in 1660 he (Borelli) had found the densities of air and water in the ratio 1 : 1175.[21] He

---

[1] Cooper, DNB, 1908, v, 207.
[2] De Ratione Motus Musculorum, 4°, London, 1664 (34 pp.).   [3] Ib., 46.   [4] Ib., 21–6.
[5] Io: Alphonsi Borelli De Motionibvs Natvralibvs a Gravitate Pendentibvs, Liber, 4°, Regio Ivlio, In Officina Dominici Ferri, 1670, Superiorum permissu. Pp. viii, 566, vi.
[6] Cap. IV, p. 79.   [7] Prop. LV, p. 115.   [8] Prop. LXII, p. 128.
[9] Prop. LXIV, p. 132.   [10] Prop. LXV, p. 133.
[11] Props. XL, LXVII–LXXI, pp. 124, 136–45.   [12] Props. LIX–LX, pp. 121–5.
[13] Cap. XII, p. 501 f.; Prop. CCXLVIII, p. 504.   [14] Prop. C, p. 206.
[15] Prop. CXLVII.   [16] Ib., pp. 325, 542, 551.   [17] Ib., p. 550.   [18] Ib., p. 212.
[19] Cap. V, p. 205 f.: De Structura, Gravitate, Æquilibrii, & Vi Elateria Aeris.
[20] Prop. CV, p. 220.   [21] Prop. CXX, p. 251.

assumed that air is composed of little 'machines' which can be compressed by force but when released expand again like bent bows:[1] Aer videtur compositus ex machinalis, quæ stringi quidem ad hibita violentia possint, sed postea sponte resilire ad instar arcus valeant; ex machinis flexibilibus, & resilientibus ad modum arcus. The air particles are hard, flexible, and resilient, and have the figures of tubes, hollow cylinders composed of sheets, or thin threads, like curled branching particles:[2] particulæ sint duræ flexibiles, & resilientes, vel cylindri excaui composite ex laminis, vel filis lævibus, aut ramosis obliquè in se ipsos circumductis.

In considering the nature and cause of fluidity[3] Borelli says the particles of a given liquid are all of the same weight and each can move without causing motion of others. The particles do not form a continuum but are separated from one another[4] (corporis partes diuisæ inter se); they are not themselves fluid but can move over one another,[5] and such particles cannot form a hard body[6] (duritiem creare non possunt), the particles of which Descartes thought to be at rest. The smallest parts of a flexible body are all inflexible, rigid, and hard.[7]

A long and important section deals with the rise of liquids in capillary tubes[8] and capillary phenomena generally. Borelli showed that the rise is not due to the pressure of the air, and explained it by the assumption that the water particles are surrounded by a down of flexible and elastic 'machines' which act like levers, the branches insinuating themselves into the pores of the glass tube, and hence their pressure on the particles below is relieved and the water rises:[9]

aquæ particulæ adhærentes parieti vasis insinuant ramos suarum machinularum intra porositates, & foueolas parietis, à cuius eminentijs, & asperitatibus fulciuntur extremitates particularum aquæ, quarum oppositi termini sustinetur, à subjecta collaterali aqua, proptereà efficientur veluti totidem vectes conuertibiles circa eorum fulcimenta parieti annexa.

The smallest component particles of water (minimæ particulæ aquaæ) are smaller than those of air, since water can pass through a porous jar which retains air.[10] Borelli mentions experiments with the thermometers of the Accademia del Cimento.[11] He explains the expansion of water on freezing by assuming that the liquid contains cylindrical particles of air which contain a number of smaller water particles, and on freezing these water particles pass out and increase the volume.[12] In a solution of a salt in water the salt particles are not moving in the interstices of the water particles, but the latter are firmly 'glued' to the salt particles:[13] completa dissolutione salis particulæ eius innatantes non suspenduntur ab intestina aquæ commotione, sed ab eius naturali glutine validùs operante in superficieculis particularum salium.

[1] Prop. CXXIII, p. 257.   [2] Prop. CXXV, p. 261.
[3] Cap. VII, p. 285: De Natura & Causa fluiditas, mentioning Boyle.
[4] Props. CXXXVIII–IX, pp. 292–3.   [5] Prop. CXL, p. 294.
[6] Prop. CXLIII, p. 302.
[7] Prop. CCLXI, p. 528.   [8] Prop. CLXXXV f., p. 377 f.; J. C. Fischer, 1801, i, 312–22.
[9] Prop. CLXXXII, pp. 366–73, esp. 371.   [10] Prop. CCLXXIV, p. 553.
[11] Prop. CCLXXI, p. 546.
[12] Prop. CCLXXII–III, pp. 548–53.   [13] Prop. CLII, p. 320.

Borelli's posthumous book on the motion of animals[1] deals in the first volume with the movements of bones and their attached muscles on good mechanical principles. The second volume only is of interest to us and all the references below are to it (1680–1).

Borelli calculated that the motive force (vis motiva) of the muscle of the heart is 3000 lb.[2] and he took the resistance of the arteries as 60 times this, or 180,000 lb.[3] If the power of the heart (potentia cordis) was not only to dilate the arteries but also drive the blood through them (sed insuper portionem aliquam immisi sanguinis extra arterias expulerit), the total force of the heart in expelling three ounces of blood comes to 135,000 lb.[4] The motion of the heart is automatic (motus Cordis fieri posse organica necessitate, ut automa movetur).[5] The digestion of food in the stomach is mainly due to trituration (trituratio) and the force of the muscular walls of the stomach of a turkey-cock is given as 1350 lb.[6] Borelli tried to disprove Iatrochemical theories by quoting experiments on the injection of acids, alkalis, and sulphur preparations into animals, but he accepted some of them, e.g. the anomalies in the mixture of body fluids.[7]

Borelli believed that muscular motion was due to 'something like a fermentation or ebullition, by which the sudden inflation of the muscle is brought about', and such an action 'is rendered clear by innumerable experiments which are continually being made in chemical laboratories, as when spirits of vitriol are poured on oil of tartar, and indeed all acid spirits when mixed with fixed salts at once boil up with a sudden fermentation'. In the muscle there may occur 'a somewhat similar mixing from which a sudden fermentation and ebullition results, with the mass of which the porosities of the muscle are filled up and enlarged, thus bringing about the turgescence and the inflation' (ex qua fermentatio & ebullitio subitanea subsequatur, à cujus mole porositates musculorum replenitur & amplientur & inflatio, & consequantur turgentia).[8] Francis Glisson (1596–1677), Regius Professor of Medicine in Cambridge, physician in London,[9] first proved experimentally (by contracting muscle under water and observing the fall in level) that muscles *contract* when brought into action, and do not expand, as Borelli thought.

The analysis of blood by distillation is not a true one since it is made by fire, the particles of which, acting as wedges, break up the particles of the bodies it acts upon and alters them, as Boyle had shown,[10] whilst otherwise the labours of chemists can produce wonderful operations. The true parts of blood, as observation shows, are the albumen and red clot separating like cheese from milk:[11] subitò albumen à rubicundo cruore secernitur, eodem modo, ac serum lactis à caseosa ejus portione grumefacta separatur . . . ab albumine, fluiditatem retinente, ut nil prorsus ab aqueo sero lactis videatur. The red part consists of a glutinous or slippery part and a purple juice, which can be

[1] *De Motu Animalium*, 2 vols. 4°, Rome, 1680–1; Leyden, 1685; Leyden, 1710 (ed., with corrections, by the printer, Peter vander Aa); Foster, 1901, 62–83, 179; H. Boruttau, *A. Med.*, 1909, ii, 301 (318).
[2] Prop. 67.   [3] Props. 72–3.   [4] Prop. 76.   [5] Ch. VI, Prop. 79.
[6] Props. 189–91.   [7] Prop. 224.   [8] Props. 22, 27, 28; Foster, 75.
[9] *Tractatus de Ventriculo et Intestinis*, 4°, London, 1677 (written in 1662); Foster, 289–90.
[10] Prop. 131.   [11] Prop. 130.

washed from the first part by water, leaving a white fibrous part (in fibras candidas), the red part subsiding from the water as a powder.[1] This is a recognition of the colouring matter as distinct from the protein.

The fibrin in blood is present as a liquid in the blood vessels but coagulates when blood is exposed to air, as cheese forms from milk:[1]

deindè sicut in lacte adest succus concrescibilis in caseum, sic in sanguine reperitur succus viscosus, & glutinosus, qui postmodum facta concretione, abit in fibras, vel membranas reticulares; quodque tales fibræ sic condensatæ non præextiterint intra vasa animales viuentis.

Urine is separated from the blood by a sieve action of capillaries, other explanations (by acids, fermentation, etc.) proposed being refuted at length.[2] Borelli had some idea of the separation of liquids by osmosis in passing through animal membranes, explaining it as a result of the adaptation of the sizes of the molecules and pores: quia nimirum figuræ molecularum prædictorum fluidorum congruunt, adæquanturque figuris porulorum per quos pertransire possent.[3]

In criticising Helmont's willow-tree experiment (see p. 223), Borelli says water molecules are not simple but composed of atoms of primary elements (aquæ moleculæ non sunt corpora prima simplicia, sed sunt congeries, compositae ex atomis primis elementaribus).[4] The principal cause of the vegetation of plants is air (præcipuam causam vegetationis plantarum esse aerem), but the reason Borelli gives, that they grow upwards and hence need something light, is not very good.[5] Plants take in air by an imperfect kind of respiration, and their life depends on and is conserved by it, by its oscillatory motion.[6]

Borelli made constant use of the theory of animal spirits (introduced by Galen, Vol. I). He regarded them as very subtle but still material fluids or juices, subject to the laws of hydrodynamics. The nerve juice (succus nerveus) participates mainly as nutritive juice (succus nutritivus), governing the processes of nutrition; the spiritual juice (succus spirituosis) is concerned with movement and sensation; but a seminal spirit (succus spirituosis seminalis) is concerned with the generation and nutrition of both animals and plants, and even of some kinds of diseases.[7]

Ch. VII is on the motion in respiration (De motu respirationis). In it[8] the residual air is clearly recognised: In expiratione non evacuantur pulmones omninò, sed semper in eis remanet non exigua moles aeris. It was also recognised by Thomas Bartholinus senr. (Copenhagen; 20 October 1619–4 December 1680)[9] who says that it causes drowned persons to rise after three

---

[1] Prop. 132.   [2] Props. 140–42.   [3] Prop. 138; Foster, 81; cf. Asklepiades of Prusa, Vol. I.
[4] Prop. 179.   [5] Prop. 181.   [6] Prop. 182.
[7] Props. 24–8, 79, 116, 122–3, 128, 134; Ch. XI, Props. 154 f., 200 f., 213, 289; Foster, 82–3.
[8] Prop. 94.
[9] *Thomæ Bartholini De Pulmonum Substantia & Motu Diatribe. Accedunt Cl. V. Marcelli Malpighij de Pulmonibus Observationes Anatomicæ*, sm. 8°, Hafniæ, 1663, Sect. II. The book contains the following sections: I Substantiam pulmonum ex Hippocratis sententia non esse carneam (mentioning, p. 9, the blackening of the lungs by tobacco smoke), II Pulmonum substantiam ex membraneis vesiculis constare, III Motus pulmonum contra Helmontium astruitur, IV Motus causam non esse cor, sed thoracem seu diaphragma, V Aerem a thorace non

days, and hence pirates cut out the lungs of a corpse before throwing it into the sea: unde pulmonis eximere solent piratae, ne submersa cadavera fundum linquant. Borelli's Ch. VIII on the use of respiration (De usu respirationis), says that this is not the cooling and ventilation of the flame and heat in the heart:[1] non esse ad refrigerium, & ventilationem flammæ, & caloris cardis. He found by inserting a thermometer into the left ventricle of a living stag's heart that it registered only 40°, which is the ordinary summer heat in Italy.[2] No soot is given off in the breath, and respiration cannot serve the purpose of expelling smoke or soot from a fire in the heart:[3] respiratio non est ad expellendas fuligines genitas ab igne in corde existente. In a detailed discussion[4] Borelli concludes that the purpose of respiration is to churn the blood mixed with chyle: duo diversi fluores misti, ope contusionis. The air itself is necessary for animal life[5] and is the most important cause of it: aer, per respirationem receptus, est causa potissima vitæ animalium. This had been proved in experiments in which air is removed by Boyle's air pump, or better by the Torricellian vacuum: remotio aeris in machina pneumatica Boyliana, & melius in vacuo Torricelliano ope hydrargyri. Gassendi's experiment on freezing water (see p. 465) also showed that air is necessary for the life of fish. The air is mixed with the blood but it does not act chemically by producing effervescence, nor by its elastic force, nor (especially) by its nitrous nature:[6] aeris particulis, sanguini immistas, non augere ejus fluxilitatem, nec producere effervescentiam in corde ob vim ejus elasticam, aut nitrosam ejus naturam,[7] and the supposition of some recent authors that air is of a nitrous nature is false: ergo illa aeris nitrosa natura à recentioribus introducta, vana omnino est.[8] This seems to refer to Mayow.

The true action of respiration is a tremulous or oscillatory motion produced by the air mixed with the blood:[9] Exponitur ratio mechanica continuæ motionis tremulæ, quam aer, sanguini immistus, producere potest. The air particles are small elastic spirals or machines producing oscillations like small pendulums, or waves, and regulated like the beating of a pendulum clock:

tremulus ille motum machinularum aeris; machinæ spirales, quæ comprimi à vi externa possunt, & deinceps spontè resilire ad instar arcus, ut in sclopeto pneumatico patet; motum oscillatorium, ad instar undarum, & pendulorum.

The air mixed with the blood by respiration produces and conserves animal life, and life is a mechanical process, automata and animals both moving according to mechanical laws (Descartes' idea):[10]

Commistio aeris per respirationem intra sanguinem immisti vitam animalem producit et conservat. Videtur automa umbratilem quandam similitudinem cum animali-

pelli in pulmones contra Cartesium (in which he gives Plato's theory in the *Timaios* that inspiration is caused by the expanding chest pushing in the surrounding air, and the same theory is given, with experiments to prove it, in Swammerdam's *Tractatus physico-anatomico-medicus de respiratione usque pulmonum*, Leyden, 1667); Boruttau, *A. Med.*, 1909, ii, 301 (322).
   [1] Prop. 96, 1681, p. 187–264 (187).
   [2] *Ib.*, p. 189: the arbitrary scale must have been similar to the Centigrade scale; in Prop. 175 he describes, and in Plate xviii, 13, illustrates an air thermometer with a bulb and tube dipping into a liquid, which he ascribes to Sanctorius (see p. 442).
   [3] Prop. 97, 1681, p. 192.   [4] Props. 99–109, 1681, pp. 194–209.
   [5] Prop. 112, 1681, p. 212 f.   [6] Props. 113–14, 1681, pp. 215–19.
   [7] P. 219.   [8] P. 223.   [9] Prop. 115, 1681, p. 223.   [10] Prop. 116, 1681, p. 226.

bus habere, quatenus ambo sunt corpora organica se moventia, quæ legibus mechanicis utuntur, & ambo à facultatibus naturalibus moventur. Videamus modo an ex artificialium cognitione rerum naturalium proprietates indagare aliquo pacto possimus.

The death of animals in rarefied air or in a vacuum is due to the destruction of the blood-vessels by expanding air (embolism):[1] naturalis vis elastica, libertatem nacta, resiliendo expandi potest. Breathing is faster with exercise because the blood circulates faster and loses its air content faster, and this must be renewed.[2] The suffocation of animals in a closed space containing burning charcoal is not due to thick (crassus) and moist air, but to fiery particles (particulæ igneæ) from the charcoal fumes entering through the nose, infecting the brain, and causing stupefaction and death: per nares cerebrum mordicando & inficiendo, stupiditatem inducunt, & deindè mortem.[3]

MALPIGHI

Marcello Malpighi (Crevacuore, 10 March 1628–Rome, 29 November 1694), professor of theoretical medicine at Pisa (where he met Borelli),[4] in two letters to Borelli (whom he praises fulsomely)[5] deals with circulation in the lungs of frogs and accepts Borelli's vibration theory: probabiliter credam pulmones à natura fabrefactos esse ad sanguinaria molis miscellam.

BAGLIVI

A prominent Iatromathematician was Georgio Baglivi (Ragusa, 8 September 1668 (or 1669)–Rome, 17 June 1707),[6] physician to Pope Innocent XII and professor of anatomy in the Sacred College in Rome.[7] Baglivi, who was an exponent of the experimental method taught by Francis Bacon,[8] says that the mathematical-mechanical and the experimental physico-mechanical and chemical systems of medicine see in all natural actions in the body only a complex of chemico-mechanical motions, the principles of which depend on mathematics. The teeth are compared with pincers, the stomach with a phial, the blood vessels with hydraulic tubes, the heart with a piston, the intestines with a filter, the chest with bellows, the muscles with levers, the corners of the eyes with pulleys, etc. Chemists give explanations in terms of fusions, sublimations, precipitations, etc.; philosophers in terms of wedges, equilibria, levers, and moving forces.[9] Baglivi paid special attention to the solids in the body instead of the liquids (humors) and his followers were called 'solidists'.[10]

[1] Prop. 120.   [2] Prop. 121.   [3] Prop. 125.
[4] Gaetano Atti, Notizie Edite ed Inedite della Vita e delle Opere Marcello Malpighi e de Lorenzo Bellini, Bologna, 1847.
[5] Printed in Bartholinus, De Pulmonum, 1663, 103 f., 111 f., 126; dated Bologna, 1661; other letters in Malpighi, Opera Posthuma, f°, London, 1697, 6 f., 38 f.; also mentioning Borelli's and Bellini's theory of the separation of urine by a sieve action, 103 f.
[6] Hoefer, NBU, 1853, iv, 160; Stemm, Ann. Med. Hist., 1941, iii, 183.
[7] Baglivi, Opera Omnia Medico-Practica et Anatomica, 6 ed., 4°, Lyons, 1704 (pref. dated 1696) (portr. and life, summary of medical system); ed. C. G. Kuhn, in Scriptorum Classicorum de Praxi Medica, 2 vols., 12°, Leipzig, 1827–8.
[8] Praxeos Medicæ, i, 11; Opera, 1827, i, 150.   [9] Prax. Med., i, 11; 1827, i, 154–5.
[10] Canones de Medicina Solidorum ad rectum statices usum; Opera, 1828, ii, 133–149.

He said that hot lemonade is a more wholesome drink than coffee or choco-
late.[1] He often mentions Paracelsus, Van Helmont, and Boyle, and occasionally Mayow. He criticises the acid-alkali theory of Sylvius.[2] In his treatise on
blood, respiration, etc.,[3] he gives (without naming him) Mayow's theory of the
mechanism of respiration,[4] describes the barometer experiment, and gives
(again without naming him) Mayow's theory of 'nitrum aeris' in respiration.[5]
At the end of the treatise are experiments on the action of various reagents
(ammonia, oil of tartar, a solution of crabs' eyes in vinegar, powdered alum,
spirit of wine, powdered cantharides, nitric and sulphuric acids, etc.) on
blood.[6] He made similar experiments with bile[7] and saliva,[8] including solutions
of mercury sublimate and tin. He also allowed saliva to putrefy for several days
and distilled it. The residue was a whitish slightly acrid salt, and Baglivi
thought that saliva contains a nitrous salt to which it owes its activity (continere in se sal nitro-salinum universali sali analogum), which took part in the
fermentation of food, purification of chyle, sanguinification, etc. A similar
nitrous salt was obtained by distilling snow and rain water. He thought a
nitrous spirit was diffused in all nature (imo spiritum illum nitrosum infusum
esse in omni natura).[9]

In his essay on blood and respiration[10] he mentions the theory that aerial
nitre is filtered off by the lungs and mixes with the blood, and says some but
not all of it is perhaps so filtered off, but most of it is dissolved in the saliva and
passes by way of the stomach to the blood:

portionem aliquam salium aëris filtrari per solidas pulmonem partes et sanguini
commisceri concederem in gratiam eorum, qui talem tuentur opinionem, sed totam
nitri quantitatem omnino nego. Crederem potius . . . aëris salia fundi et imbibi a
saliva ac lympha oris . . . et ita per ventricululum in sanguinem traduci.

Although it is reasonable to suppose from its effects that the nervous fluid is in
some way fiery, it is rash to assume (with Mayow, who is not named) that it is
sulphureous and nitrous like gunpowder, and if bodily movements were so due
to continuous explosions excited in the muscles, men would be constantly
convulsed (sulphureum, nitro-salinum et impetuosum ad instar pulveris
pyrii . . . si enim corporis motus fierent per . . . explosionem continuam . . .
homines continuas . . . convulsiones paterentur).[11]

Baglivi also wrote on blistering agents[12] and on the tarantula, the poisonous bite of
which he thought was curable by music.[13] In his essay on the vegetation of stones[14] he
mentions cases of the apparent growth of stones, and he described an earthquake in
Rome in 1703.[15]

[1] De Morborum et Naturæ Analogismo; Opera, 1828, ii, 157–8.   [2] Ib., ii, 10; 1827, i, 270 f.
[3] De Sanguinem, de Respiratione, de Statice aeris & liquidorum; Opera, 1704, 442–66; 1828,
ii, 97–128.
[4] Ib., 1704, 455; 1828, ii, 101.   [5] Ib., 1704, 459–60; 1828, ii, 120.
[6] Ib., 1704, 463–5; 1828, ii, 124–6.   [7] Ib., 1704, 436–9; 1828, ii, 90–6.
[8] Ib., 1704, 422–8; 1828, ii, 78–9.
[9] De vegetatione lapidum; Opera, 1828, ii, 174; q. Duhamel and Sendivogius.
[10] Opera, Lyons, 1704, 459–60; 1828, ii, 120.
[11] De fibra motrice specimen, i, 7; Opera, 1827, i, 375.
[12] De Usu & Abusu Vesicantium; Opera, 1704, 581–606; 1828, ii, 344–68.
[13] Dissertatio de Anatome, Morsu & Effectibus Tarantulae; Opera, 1704, 539–80; 1828, ii,
294–339.
[14] De Vegetatione Lapidum; Opera, 1828, ii, 158–92.   [15] Opera, 1828, ii, 192–245.

PITCAIRNE

Archibald Pitcairne (Edinburgh; 25 December 1652–17 or 20 October 1713) studied theology, law and mathematics in Edinburgh, then medicine in Montpellier (or Paris). In 1692 he lectured at Leyden on medicine, but in 1693 he returned to Scotland, ostensibly for his marriage, but it is said on account of the poor reception of his applications of geometry and mechanics to medicine. Boerhaave and Mead were his pupils in Leyden.[1]

Pitcairne, an expert mathematician and a great admirer of Borelli, opposed the use of philosophy and chemistry in medicine.[2] He supposed that all physiological and pathological phenomena depend on the varying sizes of the pores in the organs (cf. Asklepiades of Prusa, Vol. I). Animal heat is due to the friction of the blood against the walls of the vessels, and digestion is a mechanical trituration of food in the stomach, and not the result of the action of a ferment. Pitcairne supported the claims of Harvey to the discovery of circulation of the blood.[3]

He criticised the Iatrochemical theory of acid and alkali[4] and also criticised Mayow's views (p. 621).

The famous physician Thomas Sydenham (Wynford Eagle, Dorsetshire, 1624–London, 29 December 1689), a friend of Boyle, made no contributions to chemistry; he was opposed to both iatrochemical and iatromathematical theories and counselled a return to the methods of Hippokrates.[5]

BELLINI, ETC.

After Borelli, the most famous exponent of iatromathematical theories was his pupil Lorenzo Bellini (Florence; 3 September 1643–8 January 1704), professor at Pisa and Florence. He wrote on respiration.[6] He explained the tastes of salts by the shapes of their particles, and fevers as due to a viscosity (*lentor*) of the blood. Bernard Ramazzini (1633–1714) combined the theory of acid and alkali of Sylvius with astrology, believing that the sky sent volatile spirits to the earth. Jean Bernoulli (1667–1748; see p. 628) studied effervescence and fermentation. Domenico Guglielmini (Bologna, 27 September 1655–Padua, 12 July 1710), professor of mathematics at Bologna and from 1702 of medicine

[1] Thin, *Edin. Med. J.*, 1928, xxxv, 368; T. Thomson, (1), i, 207; NBG, 1862, xl, 340; Sprengel, (1), 1815, v, 151–94; Daremberg, 1870, ii, 850; Guthrie, *A History of Medicine*, 1945, 196; Comrie, *History of Scottish Medicine*, 1932, i, 273.

[2] *Oratio, qua ostenditur medicinam ab omni philosophorum sectâ esse liberam*, Leyden, 1692, Edinburgh, 1696; printed in his *Dissertationes Medicæ*, 4°, Edinburgh, 1713, 1; *Opera Omnia Medica*, 4°, Leyden, 1737, 197.

[3] *Elementa Medicinæ Physico-Mathematica libri duo. Quorum prior Theoriam, post, Praxim exhibet*, 2 vols., The Hague, 1722, 4°, Venice, 1740; in *Opera Omnia Medica*, 4°, Leyden, 1737, 1 f., with unpaged *Brevis Conspectus*.

[4] *Dissertatio brevis de Opera quam præstant corpora acida vel alcalica in curatione morborum*, in *Dissertationes Medicæ*, 4°, Edinburgh, 1713, 150; *Opera Omnia Medica*, 4°, Leyden, 1737, 298.

[5] Comrie, *Selected Works of Thomas Sydenham*, London, 1922; Daremberg, 1870, ii, 706; Riseman, *Ann. Med. Hist.*, 1925, vii, 171; Sprengel, (2), 1827, iv, 492.

[6] *Laurentii Bellini Opuscula Aliquot, ad Archibaldum Pitcarnium . . . in quibus Præcipue Agitur de Motu Cordis in & extra uterum, ovo, ovi aere & respiratione*, . . . , 4°, Leyden, 1696, 1714, 1737 (BM 783. f. 12, 15 (1), 16).

at Padua, F.R.S. 1697, established the law of constant interfacial angles for salt crystals.[1] He believed that the blood contains sulphureous morsels (sulfuris ramenta) and that air taken in by respiration agitates the blood and separates the vital spirits which are taken in by the food.[2]

Giambattista Mazini (d. 1743) explained the red colour of arterial blood as due to its rapid motion. He spoke of rays of light and aerial particles penetrating to the stomach, the vesicles of the lungs, and the arterial system, and of the participation of sulphureous and nitrous salts in the process of chylification, but he rejected Mayow's theory of nitro-aerial spirit. He took as active principles air, light, and sulphur, and as inert principles water, salts, and mercury.[3]

The British school of Iatromathematics included William Cole (time of Pitcairne), and James Keill of Northampton (1673–1719). Keill[4] calculated the force of the heart as 8 to 12 oz. instead of Borelli's 135,000 lb. (p. 445) and estimated the weight of the blood in a man of 160 lb. as 100 lb., instead of the true figure of about 16 lb. for 130 lb. body weight. He made use of the Newtonian theory of attraction in physiology (as his brother, John Keill, did in chemistry, see p. 408) and tried to explain the cause of diabetes.

Other iatromathematicians, whose theories are given by Daremberg, are John Freind (1675–1728), historian of medicine and lecturer on chemistry at Oxford (see p. 479), Richard Mead (1673–1754),[5] Bryan Robinson (see p. 626), and Clifton Wintringham senr. and junr. This eighteenth-century school probably owed its mechanical bent to Newton rather than to Descartes. We may, however, now take leave of the subject.

Hartsoeker

Nicolas Hartsoeker (Gouda, 26 March 1656–Utrecht, 10 December 1725), who left Holland for Paris with Huygens in 1678, worked mostly on microscopy but wrote on chemistry, etc.[6] Hartsoeker[7] opposed the Newtonian

[1] *Riflessioni Filosofiche dedotte dalle Figure de' Sali*, 4°, Bologna, 1688, Padua, 1706; Mieleitner, *Fortschr. Min. Krist. Petr.*, 1923, viii, 199; Guglielmini, *Opera omnia, mathematica, hydraulica, medica, et physica; accessit vita auctoris a J. B. Morgagni scripta*, 4°, 2 vols. Geneva, 1719, 2 ed. 1740.

[2] *Exercitatio physico-medica de Sanguis natura et constitutione*, 8°, Venice, 1701.

[3] Mazini, *Mechanices Morborum desumptæ a* (i) *Motu Sanguinis* (ii) *Motu Solidorum* (iii) *Motu Febricum*, 3 pts. 4° (sep. t.ps.), Brescia, 1723, 1725, 1727 (BM 789. k. 5); *Edit. secunda post Brixianam primam diligenter correcta*, 4°, Paris and Leyden, 1731 (BM 783. f. 18); *Conjecturæ Physico-Medico-Hydrostaticæ De Respiratione Fœtus*, 4°, Brescia, 1737 (BM 790. m. 27); not available to me were: *Mechanica Medicamentorum*, 4°, Brescia, 1734; *Institutiones Medicinæ Mechanicæ*, 4°, Brescia, 1739; *Opera Omnia nunc primum tribus tomis distributa*, 4°, Brescia, 1743; Daremberg, 1870, ii, 839, q. *Opera Omnia*, i, §§ 83, 123, 146 f.

[4] *An Account of the Animal Secretion, the Quantity of Blood in the Human Body, and Muscular Motion*, sm. 8°, 1708; a *Tentamina medico-physica quinque*, London, 1718, Leyden, 1730, is q. by Daremberg, 1870, ii, 866.

[5] *Mechanical Account of Poisons*, 8°, London, 1702; *Mechanica Expositio Venenorum*, 8°, Leyden, 1737; including poisonous vapours infecting the atmosphere.

[6] Saverien, 1773, viii, 93; NBG, xxiii, 477; Thorndike, vii, 694; Lasswitz, (1), 1890, ii, 432.

[7] A. *Principes de Physique*, 4°, Paris, 1696; B. *Conjectures physiques*, 4°, Amsterdam, 1706; C. *Suite des Conjectures physiques*, 4°, Amsterdam, 1708; D. *Eclaircissemens sur les Conjectures physiques*, 4°, Amsterdam, 1710; E. *Suite des Eclaircissemens physiques*, 4°, Amsterdam, 1712; F. *Cours de Physique*, 4°, La Haye, 1730; correspondence (1706–12) with Leibniz, in G. Leibniz, *Philosophischen Schriften*, ed. Gerhardt, 1875–90, 1887, iii, 488–535.

theory, criticised Descartes for professing to start with only matter and motion and then assuming an infinity of things, corpuscles soft as paste or hard as steel, rigid as needles or flexible as eels,[1] and proceeded to simplify Descartes' system by making the subtle matter a continuum, an infinite perfectly homogeneous fluid (the 'first element'), 'pure fire', which is in motion at every point, and in which swim hard, indivisible corpuscles (the 'second element'), infinite in number and various in size and shape, always separated from one another by the first element. The motions of the hard particles in the first matter (which is 'the vehicle and prime mover of these minute bodies') is examined from the point of view of the laws of collision; the smaller particles acquire greater velocities and are driven outwards, whilst the heavier collect in the centre and form the heavenly bodies.[2] Weight is due to the acceleration, increasing in a progression, due to the collisions of the minute corpuscles of the second element with the heavy body.[3] Cohesion is due to the pressure of weight assisted by the shapes of the corpuscles; in solids these have projections which prevent them from sliding over one another; in liquids they are spherical or ellipsoidal and mobile; air particles are hollow and elastic, and made up, as it were, of three rings (see I below); these air particles can contain water particles, which emerge on freezing, causing an increase in volume.

Salts and vitriols have particles which are heavy balls studded with sharp pointed blades or cutting knives, or else pointed needles.[4] Tastes are explained by the various shapes of the particles.[5] Acids have long particles pointed at each end and alkalis hollow cylindrical particles through which the acid particles penetrate (see II).[6]

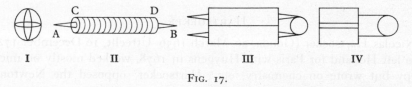

FIG. 17.

The solution of salts in water is explained by the fitting of globular water particles between the points of the salt particles (see III).[7] In the solution of metals, e.g. gold, in acids the acid penetrates the metal particles and then water particles fit in between each pair of salt particles (see IV).[8] The descriptions are accompanied by numerous diagrams.

Hartsoeker afterwards modified his views on neutralisation, putting forward a peculiar theory.[9] His discussions of combustion and inflammable bodies[10] and his account of antimony[11] are of some interest. He argued for the existence of hard corpuscles by the indestructibility of elements:[12]

Faites fondre de l'or autant de fois qu'il vous plaira; vous trouverez toûjours de l'or. . . . Faites boüillir de l'eau plusieurs fois de suite, vous trouverez toûjours de l'eau. . . . Comment donc se pourroit-il faire que les parcelles, par exemple, qui com-

[1] B, Avertiss.   [2] A, 1 f., 66 f.; E, 2 f.   [3] A, 78 f.; C, 12 f.
[4] A, 86–112; B, 76 f., 89 f., 101 f.; D, 56–7; F, 56 f., 137; 156 f.   [5] C, 113 f.   [6] B, 102 f.
[7] B, 105.   [8] B, 119 f., 125.   [9] F, 166 f.
[10] F, 64 f., 153 f.   [11] B, 135 f.   [12] A, 6, 95; D, 168 f.; F, 172 f.

posent l'or, & que la violence du feu auroit brisées à l'infiny pendant les diverses, fusions, reprissent la même figure, la même grandeur, & le même arrangement qu'elles avoient auparavant.

Metals are not transmutable and do not grow in mines.[1] The particles of gold cannot be closely-packed cubes (as its density would suggest) since the metal is permeable to magnetic matter.[2] The artificial preparation of gold is impossible:[3]

... on peut conclure que les Chimistes qui travaille à en faire, doivent perdre inutilement leurs peines, & que ceux qui se vantent d'avoir ce secret, sont des charlatans & des fourbes, qui ne cherchent qu'à attraper des personnes credules.

Flame is produced by the 'fermentation' of particles of saltpetre and other salts which occur plentifully in the atmosphere with the irregularly shaped particles of sulphureous or combustible bodies.[4] Hartsoeker has a long chapter on the magnet;[5] the particles of iron are long hollow prisms through which the extremely subtle magnetic matter passes.[6]

Hartsoeker[7] criticised the views of Homberg on the principles (see Vol. III); metals contain neither the mercurial nor the sulphureous principle, which cannot be extracted from them. The increase in weight of metals on calcination is due to the fixation of 'salts and other bodies which fly about constantly in the air, some of which insinuate themselves into the regulus during the calcination and augment the weight'.[8] When iron rust is heated with oil, the oil 'absorbs the salts and other heterogeneous bodies which hide and envelop a true iron, and so allows it to reappear in the form of iron to our eyes'.[9] Gold remains unchanged in weight when heated by a burning glass[10] and in the calcination of other metals something comes from the support.[11]

I conclude ... that the metals are not composed of several principles like the vegetables, and do not grow in the entrails of the earth from some seed, but that each metal is a mass of simple parts, specific, homogeneous and eternal, and that all that the chemists have proposed of their mercury, their sulphur, their salt and their earth, are only chimeras.[12]

The four reasons given for the view that metals grow in mines (that a matter which is on the way to becoming a metal is found with metals; that the gangue grows metal when out of the mine; that ores grow and passages close up in mines; gold and and silver occur in arborescent forms) are, says Hartsoeker, all fallacious.[13]

Hartsoeker[14] denied the formation of the world from 'a fortuitous concourse of an infinity of atoms', using the old argument of the letters of the alphabet forming a poem. He showed[15] that Mexican cochineal consists of the dried bodies of female insects, full of red eggs: la cochenille ... paroist être le cocon

[1] D, 168 f.   [2] A, 95.   [3] A, 96; G, iii, 503.   [4] A, 115 f.
[5] A, 151 f.   [6] A, 110, 154 f.   [7] D, 62 f., 166 f.
[8] D, 68 f.; F, 179 f.: 'une matière étrangère entoure leurs parcelles & les séparent les unes des autres', and this comes from the atmosphere.
[9] D, 74.   [10] D, 167 f.   [11] F, 1730, 70 f.
[12] D, 173.
[13] D, 173-5.   [14] A, 65.   [15] *Essay de Dioptrique*, 4°, Paris, 1694 (233 pp.), 51-2.

d'un insecte, lorsqu'on l'examine avec une loupe aprés l'avoir trempé quelques jours dans de l'eau. He gives a picture. Cochineal was formerly regarded as a 'berry'.[1] Leuwenhoeck[2] later confirmed Hartsoeker's result (without mentioning him).

[1] Anon., *Phil. Trans.*, 1668, ii, 796.   [2] *Phil. Trans.*, 1704, xxiv, 1614.

CHAPTER XIII

THE REVIVAL OF ATOMISM: GASSENDI AND NEWTON

In previous chapters of this volume many cases of the use of atomic and corpuscular theories have been given, and this applies even in the case of Descartes, whose philosophical system is based on a plenum. There was, how-ever, especially with Bacon, more or less scepticism, and the question at issue was more often that of the existence of an extended vacuum than of atoms. The revival of the old atomic theory of Leukippos, Demokritos, Epikouros, and Lucretius is particularly associated with Gassendi, although it was never lost sight of.[1] Before considering Gassendi, however, something will be said of a writer who occupies an intermediate position, on the one hand using the Scholastic doctrine of substantial forms (p. 380) and on the other making extensive use of indivisible atoms.

MAGNENUS

Johann Chrysostom Magnenus, a patrician of Luxeuil in the Franche Comté of Burgundy, who was a student at Dôle, went to Italy and became professor of medicine in the University of Pavia; besides some writings on tobacco[2] and manna,[3] he composed a remarkably interesting book on the revival of Demokritos and on atoms.[4]

Magnenus generally retained the doctrine of substantial forms as presented by Averroës (p. 381). He denied the existence of a single primary matter (materia prima), which he thought Aristotle had borrowed from the Egyptians, and followed Avicenna in supposing that the primary matter is consti-tuted by the separate elements,[5] which 'experiments in chemistry' showed cannot be converted into one another.[6] An element is a simple body, purely homogeneous, and combining with other elements to form compound bodies, and the elements are independently (formaliter) present in compounds.[7]

---

[1] See Vol. I; Partington, *Ann. Sci.*, 1939, iv, 245.

[2] *De Tabaco Exercitationes XIV*, 4°, Pavia, 1648, 1658; 12°, Amsterdam, 1669: 'ouvrage utile et rempli d'observations neuves' according to K. in NBG, 1860, xxxii, 714.

[3] *De Manna*, 8°, Pavia, 1648; 12°, The Hague, 1658; works on the air of Pavia, *Aere Ticinensi*, and on the powers of imagination, *De Viribus Imaginationis*, are also attributed to him.

[4] *Jo: Chrysostomi Magneni Burgundi, Philosophi, Medici, & in celeberrima Ticinensi Vni-versitate Regij Medicinæ Professoris. Democritvs Reviviscens sive De Atomis. Addita est Democriti vita cum Indicibus necessarijs*, la. 8°, Papiæ, 1646 (276 pp. and index); Jöcher, iii, 40; Brucker, 1766, IV, i, 504, who quotes eds. of 12°, Leyden, 1645, and The Hague, 1658 (K. in NBG, 1860, xxxii, 714, adds 'La Haye et Londres', 1688), and gives a long account of the book, knew nothing of the author, saying: cuius quoque viri docti memoria in historia medicinæ literaria haud obscura est; Ueberweg, 1924, iii, 173; Lasswitz, (1), i, 501.

[5] *Democr. Revivisc.*, 1646, 35 f., 48, 52 f.   [6] *Ib.*, 37 f.   [7] *Ib.*, 33 f., 48 f.

In a review of modern opinions on elements Magnenus mentions one which supposes an element to be compounded of three: humor, succus, and solida substantia. A Hungarian nobleman explained to him another view which regarded elements as composed of mass and an influx of ethereal substance which related them to the planets and these to the fixed stars (Van Helmont's blas, p. 229). The Hungarian also had seven elements: earth, water, fire, spirit essence (essentia), rule (regula) and number (numerus), each in sympathy with a planet.[1] The chemists thought there were two, water or phlegm, and earth or caput mortuum (illi duo dari volunt elementa, Terra quam damnatã, maledictam, & caput mortuum vocant, & Aquam vel insipidum phlegma, quæ omni sale, mercurio, & sulphure careat). Others admitted five elements, fire (or ether), water, earth, influx (influxus) from the stars, and glutinous tartar (glutinosus tartarus); these cannot be obtained pure by natural methods and have very potent qualities and simple primordial motion.[2]

Magnenus adopted the view of Demokritos that the elements are composed of atoms, the same for each, which are the first seeds (seminarium primum) and produce minimal forms under the influence of substantial forms, the revolution of the heavens (Magnenus believed in astrology), etc., and entered into mixtion (formed compounds).[3] There are only three elements, fire, water and earth.[4] Air is not an element, since it has no specific properties and does not enter into compounds;[5] it has no weight (experiments to prove the contrary are disputed); it can assume all primary properties, and its function is to transfer all properties among the elements,[6] and fill the pores of bodies and so prevent a vacuum.[7]

The elements are atoms,[8] physically indivisible although having extension.[9] They are finite in number, finitely different from one another and of finite size; they are the simple atoms, the root and beginning of the material and physical extension of the continuum:

> Continum componitur ex atomis, sive corpusculis finitis numero, adæquate inter se distinctis, certæ & determinatæ areæ.[10]
> Atomus substantialis est Entitas corporea substantialis simplex, et purissime homogenea indivisibilis ex natura sua per se primo exigitiva quantitatis cujus beneficio fit impenetrabilis, et ad continuum physicum componendum ordinata.[11]

Magnenus[12] gives eight arguments for the existence of atoms, including some based on natural magic (from Jacques Gaffarel, *Cvriositez Inovyes*, 1629) and some on chemistry (from Sennert).[13] He disagrees with Sennert's view that the *mixta corpuscula* are also atoms, and disproves the mathematical objections by distinguishing between the mathematical continuum and physical bodies.[14]

The elementary atoms have specific properties: those of fire are hot and sometimes luminous, those of water moist and transparent, those of earth cold and usually (but not always) opaque. Atoms of compounds and organic bodies are best called natural minima; they are small, differently conditioned particles,

---

[1] *Ib.*, 50.　　[2] *Ib.*, 51–2.　　[3] *Ib.*, 53 f.　　[4] *Ib.*, 65, 105 f.　　[5] *Ib.*, 70.
[6] *Ib.*, 86 f.　　[7] *Ib.*, 115.　　[8] *Ib.*, 94 f.: De compositione rerum ex atomis.
[9] *Ib.*, 98.　　[10] *Ib.*, 104.　　[11] *Ib.*, 114.　　[12] *Ib.*, 105 f.
[13] *Hypomnemata*, III, ii; 1636, 108; *Opera*, 1650, i, 119 f.　　[14] Magnenus, 1646, 188 f.

divisible only when they retain their form (forma), and there is an indefinite number of them according to their number, shape and size, like different individuals of the same species of animal.[1] Three kinds of atomic motion are recognised: (1) to and from the centre of the universe, (2) by reason of a vacuum, the avoiding of a vacuum, and impenetrability, (3) from inclination to combination. Explanations based on supposed 'sympathies' of the atoms are fabulous.[2]

Opinions on the sizes of the atoms vary; they are not apprehensible by the senses. An attempt is made to obtain a numerical estimate from the diffusion of smell from incense, but the result is regarded as uncertain; it cannot be said with certainty if fire atoms are greater or smaller than earth or water atoms. The air atoms never unite with one another; there is no resistance offered by air and hence its atoms at most touch one another but do not adhere.[3]

Combination of atoms is explained by the Aristotelian concept of 'form' (p. 380); they have an inherent tendency (amor) to union and are at rest only when combined. This tendency is especially exerted between different atoms, atoms of earth may unite to atoms of fire but probably do not, as they are usually spherical, and fire is never found in coherent masses like water, air, and earth.[4] Earth atoms are originally cubical and on account of their solidity they retain this shape; water atoms can take any shape but are spherical when left to themselves; air atoms are indifferent to shape but *per accidens* accumulate in a spherical form.[5] The whole discussion of the forms of atoms[6] is referred to Demokritos.

Magnenus's own theory of varying shape of atoms is based on the assumption that a vast number of forms, each occupying a different 'space', can be produced from the same atom, which retains its mass. He calls these 'isoperimetric figures' (tota hæc mea doctrina in isoperimetrarum figuram propositionibus inititur).[7] An atom may even be made to occupy an infinite 'space' in this way:[8]

Unica atomus sine rarefactione, sine inflatione aut reproductione potest naturaliter occupare maiorē, & maiorē locum in infinitum. . . . Cum enim figuræ regulares in isoperimetris sint magis collectæ minoremque locũ occupent, sequitur quod quo irregularior erit figura eo maiorē occupabit locu.

His interpretation of *locum* is peculiar since he does not admit a vacuum[9] (non datur vacuum in natura); he seems to be thinking, e.g., of the expansion of a cube into an infinite plane, and vacant spaces filled with air atoms.

Combination of atoms involves the insinuation of atoms into the pores of bodies.[10] In free space (i.e. in air) the atoms exert their influence by propagation (propagatio) of their properties by way of the indifferent air atoms. This cannot happen in compact bodies, in which there is a mutual hindrance of opposite properties, e.g. fire and water atoms balance each other's properties. The first degree of combination is to form minima of elementary atoms; the *prima* so formed are the actual results of the decomposition of more complicated

---

[1] *Ib.*, 114–15.   [2] *Ib.*, 118.   [3] *Ib.*, 122–5.
[4] *Ib.*, 126–8; cf. Boerhaave, p. 749.   [5] *Ib.*, 143–9, 153.
[6] *Ib.*, props. XXVII–XXX; 138–55.   [7] *Ib.*, 157.
[8] *Ib.*, 247.   [9] *Ib.*, 226; Lasswitz, (1), i, 505 f.   [10] *Ib.*, 166 f.

compounds.[1] These form secondary minima, and these tertiary minima, which are organic materials utilised by living organisms.[2] This aggregation can go further; the more complex the aggregate, the more pores it contains, and through these pores (e.g. in glass) the effluvia of spirituous substances can pass;[3] these are of the nature of flame or exhalation from water.[4] All motions of atoms proceed in the shortest and easiest way:[5]

Mobilia quæ naturaliter movĕ[n]tur, ad locū[m] que[m] appetŭ[n]t illuc tĕ[n]dŭ[n]t quā[m] fieri potest breuissimè & facillimè, natura en¹[m] compendiosa est suaq;[ue] per lineas breuissimas omnia mouet.

The processes of the Schoolmen are explicable by atomic motions: alteratio by motion through invisible pores and channels, intensio by arrangement and place of atoms, remissio by resolution of this order.[6] Magnenus also discusses the 'theory of colours founded by Demokritos', which regards colour as the result of internal refractions and darkenings of the light of the body, due to the emission of fire atoms and the influence of the atoms of the body on them,[7] and many other matters which cannot be considered here.

The ideas of Magnenus, with their denial of a vacuum, the retention of the doctrine of substantial forms, and the theory of change of 'shape' without explanation of how it arises, are really in conflict with consequent atomism and in that sense a retrograde step. His criticism of Sennert is based on a misunderstanding, since Sennert had also assumed the physical indivisibility of the minima, or true atoms, and distinguished them from the *prima mixta*.[8]

Before the revival of atomism by Gassendi and Magnenus, Francis Bacon had turned to Demokritos as an alternative to Aristotle (p. 395), and Galileo, who did not give atomism a prominent place, did make some use of it and some references to Demokritos have been traced in his works.[9]

GASSENDI

Pierre Gassendi (Sprengel[10] said the correct form was 'Gassend' and he himself always wrote 'Gassendus', but Gassendi is now usually preferred) (Champtercier (or Digne) in Provence, 22 January 1592–Paris, 24 (or 14) October 1655), of peasant family, studied and taught at Aix. He was ordained in 1617. He revolted from the scholastic philosophy and in 1624 produced a criticism of Aristotle.[11] Of the seven books in the work, only the first is printed in full, the rest being briefly summarised. The second book was printed in 1658, after the death of Gassendi.[12] He probably suppressed the remaining books on the advice of his friends, since in 1624 the Parliament of Paris, on the appeal of the Theological Faculty, had decreed that 'no person should either

[1] *Ib.*, 170.   [2] *Ib.*, 172 f.   [3] *Ib.*, 177.   [4] *Ib.*, 179; with physical and chemical examples.
[5] *Ib.*, 226.   [6] *Ib.*, 170 f.; see Vol. I.   [7] *Ib.*, 264 f.   [8] Lasswitz, (1), i, 511 f.
[9] Löwenheim, *Archiv Gesch. Philos.*, 1894, vii, 230–68; Burtt, 1925, 77.
[10] (2), 1827, iv, 30.
[11] *Exercitationes Paradoxicæ adversvs Aristoteleos. In quibus præcipua totius Peripateticæ doctrinæ fundamenta excutiuntur: Opiniones verò aut Novæ, aut ex vetustioribus Obsoletæ stabiliuntur*, 8°, Grenoble, 1624; sm. 8°, Amsterdam (Elzevir), 1649, pref., 208 pp.
[12] Gassendi, *Opera omnia*, Lyons, 1658, iii, 149 f.

hold or teach any doctrine opposed to Aristotle', and this 'on penalty of death'.[1] Gassendi enjoyed the protection of powerful friends; in 1624 he became Provost of Digne cathedral and in 1645 professor of mathematics in the Collège Royale in Paris. He was more a philosopher than a scientist, and lacked interest in experiments. Rosenberger did not rate him high as a mathematician, and he was much below Descartes in speculative power.[2]

Gassendi severely criticised Flud (p. 324).[3] He also criticised the rival system of Descartes.[4] In polite circles in Paris the systems of Descartes and Gassendi were actively discussed.[5]

Gassendi's interest in the atomic theory came from his study of Epikouros, by whom he was influenced 'in a way which is almost abnormal'.[6] He published a life of Epikouros[7] in which he cleared the name of this philosopher from the obloquy which had gathered around it (see Vol. I). He thus smoothed the way for an exposition of the philosophy of Epikouros which he published in 1649 in the form of an edition of the tenth book of Diogenes Laertios, with notes.[8] Gassendi was a poor Greek scholar and his edition is uncritical.[9] This work contains a small 'syntagma', also published separately.[10] This gives a concise epitome of the old atomic theory. It was the atomic theory in its form as improved by Epikouros (who took account of Aristotle's criticisms of Demokritos) which was adopted by Gassendi,[11] and he also modified it in the important particular that the motion of the atoms was assumed to have been bestowed by God at the creation,[12] thus mitigating the atheistic tendency of the theory. (This had been done long before by the Arabs, Vol. I.) Gassendi's views were well known before the publication of the Syntagma (1660) from his correspondence with Mersenne and others.[13] Boyle[14] remarked, with approbation, that 'the learned and subtle Gassendus . . . waves the common practice

[1] Text in de Launoy, De Varia Aristotelis in Academia Parisiensi Fortvna, Paris, 1653, 137; Gassendi, Opera, 1732, IV, i, 220 f.
[2] Aubé, NBG, 1857, xix, 564–88; G. S. Brett, The Philosophy of Gassendi, 1908 (superficial); Brucker, 1766, iv, 510; EB[11], 1910, xi, 503; EB[14], 1929, x, 53; Lange, 1882, 184; Lasswitz, (1), 1890, ii, 126; id., Ann. Phys., 1874, cliii, 373; Mabilleau, Histoire de la philosophie atomistique, Paris, 1895, 400; J. Masson, Lucretius, Epicurean and Poet, 1909, ii, 14; R. Pintard, Le Libertinage Érudit dans la première moitié du XVIIe Siècle, 2 vols., Paris, 1943; id., La Mothe de Vayer, Gassendi, G. Patin. Études de Bibliographie et de Critique, Paris, 1943; Poggendorff, (2), 1883, 181; P. Rochot, Les Travaux de Gassendi sur l'Épicure et sur l'Atomisme, Paris, 1944 (212 pp., bibl.); id. in Actes du Congrès du Tricentenaire de Pierre Gassendi (August, 1955), [Paris, 1957], 227–47 (see also Koyré, ib., 175–90); Rosenberger, 1884, ii, 116; Sorbière, in Gassendi, Opera, 1658, i, pref. (life of G.); Stones, Isis, 1928, x, 460; Tennemann, 1817, x, 141; Thorndike, vii, 426; Ueberweg, (1), 1924, iii, 174.
[3] Examen Philosophiæ Roberti Flvddi Medici, 1631; Opera, Lyons, 1658, iii, 211 f.
[4] Disqvisitio Metaphysica sev Dvbitationes et Instantiæ adversvs Renati Cartesii Metaphysicam et Responsa; Opera, 1658, iii, 269 f., pref. dated 1643.
[5] Molière, Les femmes savantes, act 3, scene 2, ed. in Gombert's French Drama, London, 1876, 49 f.
[6] Masson, 1909, ii, 14.
[7] De Vita et Moribus Epicvri Libri octo, 4°, Lyons, 1647, 236 pp., index.
[8] Animadversiones in Decimvm Librvm Diogenis Laertii, Qvi est De Vita, Moribus, Placitisque Epicvri, 3 vols., f°, Lyons, 1649, pref. dated 1646; Opera, 1658, v, 1 f.
[9] Bailey, Epicurus, Oxford, 1926, 12.
[10] Philosophiæ Epicuri Syntagma, continens Canonicam, Physicam, et Ethicam, London, 8°, 1660; 12°, 1668; first as appendix to Animadversiones, 1649, III, pp. xcvij–cclxij; Opera, 1658, iii, 1–94; atomic theory, ib., iii, 15 f.
[11] Dyroff, Demokritstudien, Leipzig, 1899, 157.
[12] Masson, 1909, ii, 42–3.   [13] Lasswitz, (1), i, 487.   [14] Works, 1744, iii, 358.

of troubling his readers with a multitude of authorities . . . and betakes himself to arguments'.

Gassendi's complete works were published as edited by Sorbière[1] and by N. Averanio.[2] The first contains (Vols. I–II) a detailed *Syntagma Philosophicum* by Gassendi; the *Animadversiones* was not reprinted as such but part (text of Diogenes Laertios and notes) was included in Vol. V and much of the rest dispersed in Vols. I–II.

Gassendi's philosophy is much simpler than Descartes', since he left out the 'celestial matter' (ether) of the latter and contented himself with atoms and vacuum. In seeking for an authority to oppose to Aristotle, he took Epikouros. He was busy studying Lucretius in 1621 and in 1629 was lecturing on Epikouros; his friends urged him to publish these lectures. His studies on the atomic theory appear to have begun late in 1642 and his *Syntagma* of 1649 was his first publication on the subject.[3]

Gassendi was able to base the existence of a vacuum on Torricelli's experiments of 1643 (p. 513), which he discusses in detail.[4] He does not think the space above the mercury is completely vacuous, since light and heat (which are atomic) pass through it. The mercury is held up by the pressure of the atmosphere, due to its weight (or rather the densities of its atoms), as is shown by the relative heights of the mercury and water barometers being inversely as the densities of the two liquids. Gassendi recognised the vacuum separatum (outside the world), the vacuum disseminatum (in bodies), and the vacuum coacervatum (too large for nature to produce in bodies and only realised artificially), of Heron (see Vol. I). In the atmosphere, the atoms are closer together in the lower parts, as follows from the atomic interpretation of density, and this increased density hinders the fall of the mercury in the barometer.[5] This revival of the old theory of a vacuum (due to Demokritos or Leukippos) by Gassendi was of the greatest significance.[6]

Gassendi gives a review of the theories of matter from antiquity to Descartes, and adopts the theory of atoms, for which he gives the various names.[7] The four ancient elements (elementa) and the three (salt, sulphur, mercury) or five (these with water and earth) principles (principia) of the chemists are resolvable into atoms, which must be regarded as the prima materia, having a definite form. Matter is a necessary substrate for the forms of bodies; every body has a fixed mass (moles) which remains unchanged when the forms change; nothing can be produced from nothing and no body can become nothing, except by an act of the Creator.[8] Arguments against the existence of atoms are refuted, the distinction between mathematical and physical divisibility being emphasised.[9]

Each atom is a plenum, and division and separation of matter is possible

---

[1] *Opera Omnia in VI tomos divisa*, 6 vols., f°, Lyons, 1658 (portr.); all refs. are to this ed.
[2] *Opera Omnia*, 6 vols. f°, Florence, 1727 (pagin. difft. from 1658 ed., some textual corrections).
[3] Lasswitz, (1), ii, 128–32; Rochot, 1944, 139, 167.
[4] *Opera*, 1658, i, 203 f.; Rochot, 1944, 153–4 (appendix in 1649 book).
[5] *Ib.*, i, 186 f., 192 f., 196 f., 203 f.   [6] Lasswitz, (1), ii, 168 f.
[7] *Opera*, i, 234 f., 256 f.; ii, 70.
[8] *Ib.*, ii, 220 f., 244 f., 247 (q. Digby), 323.   [9] *Ib.*, i, 261 f., 265 f.

only because of empty space contained in it. The atoms are primordial, impenetrable, simple, unchangeable and indestructible bodies;[1] they have extension and magnitude (hence they may be called, following Cicero, corpuscula), but they are the smallest bodies which can exist. Atoms and vacuum, the absolutely full and the absolutely empty, are the only true principles, and there is no third principle possible.[2]

Atoms differ in size (magnitudo), shape (figura), and weight (pondus), the last added by Epikouros, and these are the sole possible differences; in respect of shape they might be called rough and smooth, but they do not possess such qualities as heat or cold, colour, taste, smell, etc.[3] Even the largest atom is invisible, and is much smaller than the mote in the sunbeam, which contains myriads of them; in addition to the old arguments[4] for the very small size of atoms (e.g. the anatomy of midgets), Gassendi mentions observations with the microscope (engyscopius), the dilution of colours, large flames from small burning bodies, etc.[5] As proofs for the smallness of atoms, he mentions the parts (including muscular fibres) of microscopic insects, the parts of the smallest dust particles seen under the microscope, the smoke from green wood, the great amount of light from a little oil in a lamp, and the motes in the sunbeam. He mentions the idea of the 'smallest parts' ($\tau\acute{\alpha}$ $\dot{\epsilon}\lambda\acute{\alpha}\chi\iota\sigma\tau\alpha$) of atoms (see Vol. I).[6]

As to shapes, he agrees with Epikouros against Demokritos (see Vol. I) that these are immeasurably numerous, but yet not infinite, although the number of atoms of each shape is infinite; microscopic observations are again mentioned as revealing differences of figure inappreciable to the naked eye:[7]

Deinde, cùm sint figurarum in Atomis species numero incomprehensibiles; sunt enim rotundæ, onatæ, lenticulares, planæ, gibbæ, oblongæ, turbinatæ, hamatæ, læves, asperæ, hispidæ, tetrahedricæ, pentahedricæ, hexahedricæ, &c. tam regulares, quàm irregulares, absque vlla determinatione Intellectui possibili; non sint illæ tamen numero simpliciter infinitæ habendæ . . . tametsi species figurarum infinitæ non sint; sunt tamen in vnaquæve speciè Atomi numer infinitæ simpliciter.

As evidence for the great numbers of shapes of atoms, Gassendi mentions that no two grains of wheat, no two leaves of the same tree, etc., are identical.[8] The atoms may possess hooks and other excrescences, but these cannot be removed by breaking off or by attrition, as the atom is always indivisible and absolutely hard.[9]

The weight (pondus) of the atom is an innate force (interna facultas seu vis) with which it was endowed by God in the creation (since atoms are not eternal as Epikouros said), and it is necessary for its motion, which may take place in all directions and not only in straight lines up or down, with deviations, as Epikouros incorrectly supposed.[10] This motion is the sole cause which must be assumed to explain physical phenomena; it is in a sense secondary, since the only first cause is God, and since order is recognisable in the Universe, there

[1] Ib., i, 266 f.   [2] Ib., i, 143, 256; ii, 71.
[3] Ib., i, 266 f.; ii, 74; Syntagm. philos. Epicuri, ib., iii, 15 f.: dari in natura rerum atomos, quæ sint concretarum corporum principia.
[4] Ib., iii, 16.   [5] Ib., i, 268 f.; ii, 560.   [6] Ib., i, 267; Rochot, 1944, 174.
[7] Ib., iii, 17.   [8] Ib., i, 270.
[9] Ib., i, 271 f., 273, thus answering Lactantius; ib., iii, 17.   [10] Ib., i, 273 f.; iii, 17.

must be an ordering Intelligence. In the realm of secondary physical causes, however, the moving atoms are alone.[1] The moving impulse (impetus; energia) is constant and of the same magnitude as it was at the creation. The velocities may seem to vary, but this is because the atom, which when it is moving travels with a constant speed, is subject to periods of rest in its path, brought about by collisions with other atoms, and hence the times for describing equal distances are variable;[2] the theory (which goes back to Epikouros, who spoke of the ἀντικοπή, 'check', suffered by an atom in its motion) thus differs from the modern kinetic theory of gases.[3]

A long section is devoted to the motion of atoms.[4] Even in bodies apparently at rest the atoms are in motion, as may be seen from motes in a sunbeam, spirits of nitre (fumes ?) and those experiments which chemists make with a liquid obtained from tin, mercury, and sublimate (ex mercurio, stanno et sublimato præparatis eliciunt);[5] he means the fuming of stannic chloride.

The atoms first form very small corpuscles (corpuscula), small concretions (concretunculæ), or molecules (moleculæ), which then aggregate into larger and larger bodies.[6] Gassendi recognised the existence of molecules, and uses this name:[7]

ex Atomis conformari primùm moleculas quasdam inter se diuersas, quæ sint semina rerum diuersarum: ac deinde res quasque ex seminibus suis ita texi, atque constitui vt neque sint neque esse possint ex aliis.
. . . sunt moleculæ, sive mavis, concretiunculæ quædam perexiles, quæ factæ quibusdam perfectioribus, indissolubilioribúsque coalitionibus, sint quasi rerum semina diu perdurantia[8]
vt ex dulci fiat aliquid amarum, aut ex albo nigrum; oportet moleculas, seu corpuscula, quæ ipsum constituunt, transponi, & alium vice alterius, ordinem suscipere.[9]
. . . atque ea quidem, seu moleculæ ex Atomis conflatæ dumtaxat misceantur, seu moleculis etiam resolutionis in Atomos misceantur ipsæ Atomi; idque proinde, non sine molecularum, corporúmque ex iis constantium, vt vini, aquæ, mellis, similiúmque interitu; & corporis misti, molecularúmque ipsius exortu. Videlicet, non quasi aqua, & vinum, verbi gratiâ, sed quasi aquificæ, vt sic loquar, & vinificæ Atomi misceantur.[10]

A body is not resolved immediately into atoms but into molecules, and the parts of which it is composed, which are a kind of species of concrete bodies (parteisve ex ipsis compositas, quæ sint species quædam concretorum corporum), as wood on combustion into fire, smoke, aqueous humour, and ash.[10]

The production of colours and heat on mixing liquids in chemical experiments shows that new qualities may arise from the arrangement and position of atoms.[11] Boyle[12] mentions that Gassendi had described the changes of colour on adding oil of vitriol and oil of tartar (potash) to an infusion of red rose leaves, which Boyle had met with in 'turning over the leaves' of Gassendi's book, 'my eyes being too weak to let me read such voluminous books quite through.'

The qualities, which are the properties apprehensible by the senses, are

[1] Ib., i, 280 f., 287, 334.   [2] Ib., i, 279 f.; iii, 18.
[3] Lasswitz, (1), ii, 174 f.; Bailey, Greek Atomism, Oxford, 1928, 329.
[4] De motu, et mutatione rerum; Opera, i, 338–71.
[5] Ib., i, 277; iii, 18 (quasi palpitationes intestinæ).   [6] Ib., i, 280, 384; iii, 18.
[7] Ib., i, 282; Lasswitz, (1), ii, 182; Masson, 1909, ii, 95, says Lucretius's semina rerum are atoms, Gassendi's are molecules.
[8] Ib., iii, 18.   [9] Ib., iii, 20.   [10] Ib., iii, 25.   [11] Ib., i, 367 f.   [12] Works, 1744, ii, 62–3

explained in detail on the basis of the atomic theory.[1] The transparency of dense bodies such as water or glass is due to the regular arrangement of pores (like many sieves arranged in 'register'), through which light can pass; since salt on solution does not impair the transparency of water, its very small particles must fall in line with the water particles without impairing their arrangement.[2] The solution still contains pores, since Gassendi found that water saturated with salt will still dissolve alum as freely as pure water:[3]

. . . experiundi gratiâ Alumen conicci in Aquam per complureis dies sale imprægnatam; ac tum, non sine quodam stupore succedere coniecturam vidi: scilicet Alumen perinde, ac si aqua sale carnisset, exsolutum fuit.

Gassendi's statement is translated by Walter Charleton[4] as if it were his own, but Digby[5] correctly attributed this experiment to Gassendi.

In his long account of generation and corruption,[6] Gassendi says these processes do not really occur, but only change of place of atoms (as in the evaporation of water), or addition of new atoms (as in organic growth), or the separation of atoms:[7]

. . . præfuere omnes Atomi, & moleculæ, siue semina, ex quibus contexitur; vt cùm domus dicitur fieri, intelliguntur lapides, ligna, & alia, ex quibus construitur, præexistitisse: sed contendo solum eius Atomos, semináque sic commiscere, eaque ratione adunare, vt nouo sint modo, sine nouâ formâ, qua nullatenus antè fuerat. . . . Quamobrem & fit, vt Generatio & Corruptio sola Principiorum concretione, & secretione fiat; non item verò transmutatione, quod Atomi sint, vt iam dictum est, omnis mutationis, ac ideò transmutationis incapaces.

He mentions the theory of transmutation held by the chemists, 'or as some call them, alchemists.'[8]

The four elements, although not true elements but aggregates of atoms, can be used in explanations of properties when their own qualities have been explained atomistically. Heat is due to the rapid motion of very small spherical heat atoms (atomi caloris); when a body sends out these atoms it is actually (actu, formaliter) hot; when it contains them in its pores it has the possibility of becoming hot. Besides heating by conduction, Gassendi recognised that produced by internal atomic motions set up by putrefaction or by friction.[9] Boyle[10] says: 'For, not only the learned Gassendus, but I know not how many other Atomists (besides other Naturalists) antient and modern, expressly teach the sun-beams to consist of fiery corpuscles, trajected through the air, and capable of passing through glass'; a doctrine which Boyle himself adopted.

Gassendi supposed that cold is due to cooling atoms (atomi frigorificæ), larger than heating atoms, and tetrahedral in shape.[11] Boyle[12] suggests that Gassendi regarded air as the primum frigidum (which is not the case) but he himself 'did not think fit . . . to make the water indifferent, as to heat and

---

[1] Gassendi, *Opera*, i, 372 f.   [2] *Ib.*, i, 195 f., 375 f., 379 (glass).
[3] *Ib.*, i, 195; Ettmuller, *Nouvelle Chymie raisonné*, Lyon, 1693, 32.
[4] *Physiologia Epicuro-Gassendo-Charltoniana*, f°, London, 1654, 31; Stones, *Isis*, 1928, x, 462.
[5] *A Late Discourse Made in a Solemne Assembly . . .* , 1658, 74.
[6] De ortu et interitu; *Opera*, i, 366 f., 458 f.; iii, 24 f.   [7] *Ib.*, iii, 25.
[8] *Ib.*, i, 243.   [9] *Ib.*, i, 394 f.; iii, 23.
[10] *Works*, 1744, i, 141 b.   [11] *Opera*, i, 401; ii, 66.   [12] *Works*, 1744, ii, 311.

cold'. Boyle[1] also deals at great length with Gassendi's 'new doctrine' that 'the cold we meet with in the air, water, and other bodies, proceeds from the admixture of nitrous exhalations, or corpuscles introduced into them', but whereas other 'eminently learned men, as well of our own, as of other nations, have resolutely enough embraced it . . . whereas they pitched upon nitre, as the grand universal efficient of cold, I confess I cannot yet fully acquiesce in that tenet'. Boyle elsewhere[2] deals in detail with the views of Gassendi on cold.

Gassendi in his discussion of heat and cold[3] says:

Ac addiquidem fortassis posset, præcipua frigoris semina, siue quæ constant potissimum ex frigorificis Atomis, abire in halinitrum, corporáque ipsi affinia; quando experimur non exsolui halinitrum, quin & penetrando in aquam, ipsam congelit; & vniuersa à se contacta refrigeret; & abeundo in halitum, creet gelidum, seu frigidum ventum . . . aliqua esse corpuscula . . . ex quorum introductione in aërem, aquam, terram, carnem, lignum, lapidem, alia, frigus in ipsis concitetur, seu ipsa dicantur frigefieri.[4] Ex quibus dico, qualitatem Frigoris requirendam esse non in natura aëris, in natura aquæ, in natura terræ præcisè; sed in natura corpusculorum, cuiusmodi, exempli causâ, nitrosa sunt.[5]

He assumes that these nitrous particles can penetrate glass.[6] Gassendi's theory was summarised by Charleton:[7] 'a particular species of Atoms (of which sort those whercof Salnitre is for the most part composed) which being introduced into Earth, Water, Aer, or any other mixt Bodie, imprægnate them with cold.'

Vapours consist of the atoms of a liquid carried off by the fire atoms, and more widely separated.[8] The atoms in solids are rigidly held together, either by hooks (hamuli uncinulive) or by pressure of the flat surfaces of the cold atoms, or by the exclusion of the round and smooth particles which are favourable to motion.[9] Light (lucifica) and heat (calorifica) atoms are identical, as is proved by the burning-mirror. The light-atoms are emitted with great speed from a source; Descartes' theory of light as due to pressure is rejected.[10]

The various salts, saltpetre, alum, vitriols, etc., classed as 'juices' (succi) include chalkanthon (χάλκανθον) and atramentum 'newly named copperas' (recentius est nomen, quo Vitriolum vocant, cùm & coparosam vulgus dictitet). The reason why aqua regia dissolves gold but not silver, and aqua fortis dissolves silver but not gold, is explained in terms of the sizes of the pores of the metals and the sizes of the acid corpuscles.[11]

The sole possible method of transmission of motion between atoms is by collision, and hence all forces must be explained in this way; 'tension' is merely a convenient expression. The explanation of the fall of bodies towards the earth and of magnetic attraction is then a difficulty. Gassendi contented himself at first with vague speculations about chains of atoms, linked one to another by hooks, stretching between the attracting bodies,[12] something in the manner of Faraday's electrically polarised dielectric; but later he gave an explanation based on the emission of quasi-rigid jets of atoms from the attracting body.[13]

[1] Op. cit., ii, 313 f.   [2] Op. cit., iii, 358 f.
[3] De Calore, et Frigore; Sect. I, Lib. VI, cap. vi; Opera, i, 395 f., 399–401.   [4] Ib., i, 399 b.
[5] Ib., i, 400.   [6] Ib., i, 401.   [7] Op. cit., 1654, 310 f., 313.
[8] Gassendi, Opera, i, 398 f.; iii, 23.   [9] Ib., i, 394 f.; iii, 23.   [10] Ib., i, 422 f.; on colours, 432 f.
[11] De succis intra Globum Terra conclusis; Opera, ii, 33 f., 38–9.
[12] Ib., i, 347, 478 f.   [13] Epistolæ tres de Motv Impresso, i, 14; in Opera, iii, 493.

The virtues of many bodies may be due to a very fine active part or spirit (spiritus); in organised bodies the virtues are in the seed and develop with it. Organic bodies require nourishment, since the natural heat consumes something from all the parts and these must be replaced by nourishment. Perhaps forgetfulness is due to alteration of the brain by nourishment.[1] Actions of sympathy and antipathy, usually explained by occult qualities (qualitates occultæ), probably have a mechanical origin.[2] The magnet[3] possesses virtues which pass through hard stone, a force something like life in plants.

The possibility of the transmutation of metals by atomic rearrangement cannot be denied, although the alchemists practise many frauds.[4] The artificial prodution of gold, however, must imitate the natural:[5] sicque germen auri nihil aliud facit inter manus artificicis, quàm quod facturam fuisse in viceribus Terræ. Gassendi discussed the elixir of life, which was claimed by Roger Bacon, Artephius, Flud, and the Rosicrucians, and (giving ten arguments) thought this not impossible (quid chimæras tamen insequi est necesse ?). It was thought that the medicina catholica of incorruptible gold, having received the rays of the sun and dissolved into potable gold, bestowed homogeneity with the soul of the world, giving immortality and universal knowledge. Some ideas of the Rosicrucians, Gassendi thought, were very impious,[6] and the absurd names and medical theories of Paracelsus and his followers are sharply criticised.[7]

Gassendi's 'Scale of Being'[8] is:

$$
\text{Atoms in}
\begin{cases}
\text{Inorganic} & \begin{cases} \text{primary groups (earth)} \\ \text{higher groups (metals)} \end{cases} \\
\\
\text{Organic} & \begin{cases} \text{primary groups (plants)} \\ \text{higher groups (animals)} \end{cases}
\end{cases}
$$

He accepted spontaneous generation, e.g. of mites in cheese.[9] Respiration is mainly for the purpose of freeing the blood from foreign humours and spirits and to cool the heart.[10] Vital heat (calor vitalis) is a kind of flame (quasi vita flamma quædam sit).[11] Borelli[12] says Gassendi[13] proved by an experiment of freezing water that air is necessary for the life of fish, but this observation had previously been described by Scaliger.[14]

Gassendi says that each atom when originally created was provided with such a power or quality (vis, energia, indoles) as would be necessary in all *future* actions which were foreseen by God. The atoms may, as the Bible says, have been originally in a state of chaos, an assumption against which no reasonable objection can be made. The formation of rock crystal is due to an inner seed which works upon the stony matrix like a ferment and so orders the

---

[1] *Opera*, i, 387; ii, 296 f., 407.　　[2] *Ib.*, i, 449 f.　　[3] *Ib.*, ii, 122 f.; full summary of early views.
[4] *Ib.*, i, 243; ii, 135–43: De Metallis, ac eorum transmutatione.　　　　　　　　　[5] *Ib.*, ii, 142–3.
[6] *Ib.*, ii, 614–16.　　　　　[7] *Ib.*, ii, 567 f.　　　　　[8] *Ib.*, i, 280; Brett, 1908, 256.
[9] *Opera*, ii, 260 f. (De animalibus sponte nascentibus); iii, 25.
[10] *Ib.*, ii, 318 f.; Anon., EB[14], 1929, x, 54.　　　　[11] *Ib.*, ii, 584.
[12] *De Motu Animalium*, Rome, 1681, ii, 212 f., Prop. 112.
[13] *Opera*, ii, 318 f.　　　　[14] *Exotericarum Exercitationum*, CCLXXII, 2; Paris, 1557, 346 v·

corpuscles that these arrange themselves into a definite shape.[1] The vegetable and animal souls are corporeal, consisting of the finest and most mobile atoms, unless there are special soul-molecules, but the rational soul of man is immaterial and was specially created by God.[2] this is also the view of Descartes (p. 440).

MORIN

Gassendi was attacked by the French astrologer Jean Baptiste Morin (1583–1656)[3] in a small pamphlet:

Dissertatio Io. Bapt. Morini Doctoris Medici, et Parisiis Mathematvm Professoris. De Atomis, et Vacvo contra Petri Gassendi Philosophiam Epicuream. Ad serenissimvm Principem Henricvm Borbonivm Metensivm Episcopvm, S. Germani a Pratis Abbatem, &c. Parisiis, Apvd Avthorem, in Svbvrbio D. Marcelli, jvxta ædem Patrvm Doctrinæ Christianæ: Tvm apvd Macævm Boüillette, in Collegio Regio. MDCL. 4°, 32 pp. (BM 538. d. 2 (3)). Morin had previously attacked the Copernican theory in his: Alæ Tellvris Fractæ. Cvm Physica demonstratione, quòd opinio Copernicana de Tellvris motu sit falsa . . . , 4°, Paris, 1643. Gassendi's reply, which was not intended for publication, was published by Neuræus in 1649.[4] Morin replied by his De Atomis et Vacuo.

He did not accept the hypothesis that the primary matter of all atoms was the same; the smallest particles of water, earth, glass, etc., still consist of these bodies:[5] in partes quantùm fieri poterit minimas, earum tamen pars quælibet restabit eiusdem naturæ cum suo toto. Gassendi's assumption that air cannot be changed into water is incorrect.[6] The different shapes of the atoms are said to be incompatible with their material identity.[7] The assumption of a vacuum is not necessary to explain motion, since displacement may occur simultaneously with motion.[8] Morin found by experiments in which salt, alum and sugar were added to water in a flask with a graduated neck that, in apparent opposition to Gassendi's result (p. 463), the volume of water increased when substances dissolve in it.[9] The assumption of a vacuum is not necessary to explain evaporation, since space expands along with the matter it contains; when a drop of water evaporates in a sealed flask full of air, the volume which contained the air and water now contains the air and vapour, so that the water particle takes up no more space in the state of vapour.[10]

Morin upheld the doctrine of substantial forms (p. 380) by arguments; e.g. there are only seven metals, that the nature is retained when atoms are taken up in growth; and the assumption of varying shapes of atoms of the same primary matter is really a statement that atoms consist of matter and form.[11] Gassendi is also charged with holding impious and heterodox views, and opposing astrology.[12] Morin also attacks Descartes, whose atoms are nothing but uncreated empty space, which he nevertheless makes the sole principle of

[1] *Opera*, ii, 112 f., 114 f.; Van Helmont, p. 236.   [2] *Ib.*, ii, 144 f., 193 f., 237 f.
[3] Lasswitz, (1), ii, 183; Thorndike, vii, 477.
[4] Gassendi, *Opera*, iii; De motu impresso a motore translato, part 3.
[5] *De Atomis et Vacua*, 9.   [6] *Ib.*, 19.   [7] *Ib.*, 10–11.
[8] *Ib.*, 13–14: this was realised by Descartes.
[9] *Ib.*, 19 f.; also repeated in Morin's *Defensio suæ Dissertationis de Atomis & Vacuo; aduersus Petri Gassendi . . .* , 4°, Paris (136 pp.), 1657, 59; see Grew, p. 567.
[10] *De Atomis et Vacua*, 16–17.   [11] *Ib.*, 20–4.   [12] *Ib.*, 26–8.

physical things: Imò eius atomi nihil aliud sunt quàm merum inane increatum, quod tamen facit vnicum principium rerum Physicarum.[1] Morin's *Astrologia Gallica* was posthumously published in 1661, at the expense of the Queen of Poland.[2]

A bitter and violent personal attack on Morin was made by François Bernier, a pupil of Gassendi, in a book with a punning title[3] and Morin replied under the name of Vincentius Panurgus,[4] and in his *Astrologia Gallica*.[5] Bernier later published an epitome of Gassendi's philosophy.[6] Morin's *Astrologia Gallica* has an interesting chapter on the temperature of a mixture.[7] In the book Morin denied that the Torricellian experiment produced a vacuum or proved its existence.[8]

G. B. de Saint-Romain, who wrote on natural science, free from the chicanes of the schools,[9] adopted atoms or corpuscles in preference to the four elements, the three chemical principles, and the three elements of Descartes; he used them to explain sympathies and antipathies as due to emission of atoms or spirits and their reception by pores. He mentions the star on regulus of antimony made with iron and the use of the antimonial cup (see Vol. III).

CHARLETON

An English work on the atomic theory is that of Walter Charleton:

Physiologia Epicuro-Gassendo-Charltoniana: or, a Fabrick of Science Natural, Upon the Hypothesis of Atoms,

$$\left.\begin{array}{c}Founded \\ Repaired \\ Augmented\end{array}\right\} By \left\{\begin{array}{l}Epicvrvs \\ Petrvs \ Gassendvs \\ Walter \ Charleton\end{array}\right.$$

The First Part

f°, London, 1654 (xvii ll., 475 pp., ii ll.; all publ.).

Charleton deals with the barometer,[10] 'the existence of Atoms evicted',[11] the magnitude of atoms,[12] the 'origine of qualities',[13] substantial emanations,[14] gravity and levity,[15] heat and cold,[16] fluidity and siccity, etc.,[17] occult qualities made manifest,[18] the loadstone,[19] generation and corruption,[20] and motion.[21] He

---

[1] *Ib.*, 31.   [2] *Astrologia Gallica*, f°, Hague, 1661, with portr. and life of Morin.
[3] *Favilla Ridicvli Mvris* . . . , 4°, Paris, 1653, 297 pp.
[4] *Vincenti Panvrgi Epistola de Tribus Imposteribvs ad.* . . . *Ioan. B. Morinvm*, 4°, Paris, 1654 (120 pp.).
[5] 1661, 160 f.
[6] *Abregé de la Philosophie de Gassendi en VIII tomes*, 8 vols. 12°, Lyons, 1678; and enlarged, 7 vols., 1684.
[7] *Astrologia Gallica*, 1661, bk. viii, *c.* 15, pp. 158–9; McKie and Heathcote, *The Discovery of Specific and Latent Heats*, 1935, 54, 149.
[8] Thorndike, vii, 482.
[9] *La Science Naturelle dégagés des Chicanes de l'École: ouvrage nouveau enrichi de plusieurs Expériences curieuses tirées de la Médecine et de la Chymie; et de quelques observations utiles à la Santé du Corps*, 12°, Paris, 1679 (BM 1035. a. 25); *Physica sive Scientia Naturalis Scholasticis Tricis liberata*, 12°, London, 1684 (BM 445. a. 6); his *Discours touchant les merveilleux effets de la Pierre Divine*, 12°, Paris, 1679 and later eds., deals with the use of jade as an amulet and is not alchemical; Gmelin, (1), ii, 19; Thorndike, vii, 264; viii, 294.
[10] *Ib.*, 36.   [11] *Ib.*, 84 f.   [12] *Ib.*, 113.   [13] *Ib.*, 127.   [14] *Ib.*, 136.   [15] *Ib.*, 275 f.
[16] *Ib.*, 293 f., where he discards the 4 or 8 'degrees of heat' and says, p. 302, 'the Degrees of Fire are so various, as to arise even to innumerability'.
[17] *Ib.*, 316 f.   [18] *Ib.*, 341 f.   [19] *Ib.*, 383 f.   [20] *Ib.*, 415 f.   [21] *Ib.*, 435 f.

says: 'of them [atoms] are first composed certain Moleculæ, small masses, of various figures, which are the seminaries of various productions.' Archimedes assumed 10,000 atoms in the diameter of a poppy-seed, but perhaps a million atoms in the smallest particle.[1] There may be differences in size and weight between the atoms ('some may be more, and others less ponderous').[2] Further calculations on the size of atoms are made from the small amount of colour necessary to colour water, the small quantity of oil consumed by a burning lamp, smoke from frankincense, the microscope, etc.,[3] mostly from Magnenus. The atoms were 'created by God', who also gave them an 'internal energy', or a 'Faculty Motive', or an 'internal Motive Virtue', which 'necessitates their perpetual Commotion among themselves'.[4]

NEWTON

Sir Isaac Newton (Woolsthorpe, Lincs., 25 December 1642 O.S. (=5 January 1643)–London, 20 (=31) March 1727) entered Trinity College, Cambridge, in 1661, graduated B.A. 1665, returned to Woolsthorpe in the Plague year 1665–6 (where, tradition says, he evolved the theory of gravitation in an orchard), became fellow of Trinity College, 1667, Lucasian professor of mathematics 1669, Master of the Mint 1699, M.P. 1689–90, and 1701–5, president of the Royal Society 1703–27, and was knighted in 1705.

Newton (like John Locke and, later, Priestley) was a Unitarian; some of his statements, e.g. on the Deity being 'everywhere present, and by existing always and everywhere, He constitutes duration and space' (durat semper et adest ubique, et existendo semper et ubique durationem et spatium)[5] approach the mechanical pantheism of Spinoza.[6]

The works of Newton of interest to us are:

I. Philosophiæ Naturalis Principia Mathematica, 4°, London, 1687; 2 ed. (Cotes), Cambridge, 1713; 3 ed. (Pemberton), London, 1726; tr. Motte, Mathematical

---

[1] *Ib.*, 97, 114.   [2] *Ib.*, 111–12.   [3] *Ib.*, pp. 113 f.   [4] *Ib.*, 126.
[5] *Principia*, iii, Scholium Generale, 1723, 483.
[6] Andrade, *Roy. Soc. Newton Tercentenary Celebrations*, 1946, Cambridge, 1947; *id.*, *Nature*, 1950, clxvi, 284; Sir David Brewster, *Memoirs of the Life, Writings and Discoveries of Sir Isaac Newton*, 2 vols., Edinburgh, 1855; *id.*, *The Life of Sir Isaac Newton*, 1858; S. Brown, *Lectures on the Atomic Theory, and Essays*, 1858, i, 86; Cajori, *Isis*, 1927, ix, 159; *A Catalogue of the Portsmouth Collection of Books and Papers written by or belonging to Sir Isaac Newton*, Cambridge, 1888; *Catalogue of the Newton Papers sold by order of the Viscount Lymington*, Sotheby, London, 1936; I. B. Cohen, *Franklin and Newton*, Philadelphia, 1956; *id.*, *Isaac Newton's Papers and Letters on Natural Philosophy*, Cambridge, 1958; W. C. Dampier, *A History of Science*, Cambridge, 1946, 164, 194; Geoghegan, *Ambix*, 1957, vi, 102; A. R. Hall, *The Scientific Revolution, 1500–1800*, 1954 (see Partington, *History*, 1956, xci, 216); *id.*, and M. Boas, *Archives*, 1958; *Ambix*, 1959, vii, 118 (two CUL MSS., Add. 3973, 3975, with expts. on alloys, etc.); W. V. Harcourt, *Phil. Mag.*, 1846, xxviii, 478; Hiscock, *David Gregory, Isaac Newton and their Circle*, Oxford, 1937; Hoefer, NBG, 1863, xxxvii, 840; *Isaac Newton: A Memorial Volume*, edited for the Mathematical Association by W. J. Greenstreet, 1927; Koyré, *Isis*, 1950, xli, 114; 1952, xliii, 312–37 (Hooke and Newton); McKie, *Phil. Mag.*, 1942, xxxiii, 847; Metzger, *Newton, Stahl, Boerhaave, et la Doctrine Chimique*, 1930; L. T. More, *Life of Sir Isaac Newton*, New York, 1934 (ch. iv, on alchemy and chemistry); *Nature*, 1927, cxix, Suppl. 26 March; L. C. Newell, in *Sir Isaac Newton, 1727–1927, a Bicentenary Evaluation of his Work*, publ. by the History of Science Society, Baltimore and London, 1928; Pelseneer, *Bull. Acad. Roy. Belg.*, 1952, xxxviii, 219 (first ed. of *Principia*, only one impression, correcting Gray, *Bibliography of . . . Newton*, 2 ed., Cambridge, 1907); Poggendorff, (2), 1883, 403; Thorndike, viii, 588, 597.

Principles of Natural Philosophy, 2 vols. 1729 and later eds., revised Cajori, Cambridge, 1934.
II. Opticks: or, a Treatise of ... Light, 4°, London, n.d. (advertisement dated 1 April 1704), contains 16 Queries; 2 ed. 8°, 1717 (reissued 1718), 31 Queries; 3 ed. 1721; 4 ed. 1730 (with addits. to Qu. 31); repr. with foreword by Einstein and intr. by E. T. Whittaker, 1931.
III. Opuscula Mathematica, 3 vols. 4°, Lausanne and Geneva, 1744.
IV. Opera quæ extant Omnia, ed. Samuel Horsley, 5 vols. 4°, 1779–85 (it is actually far from complete).

Newton made chemical experiments in Cambridge in 1667[1] and was greatly interested in speculative and mystical alchemy, leaving a mass of manuscripts containing transcripts from printed works on that subject. His own copies of these books have the leaves turned down (in his characteristic way) in the most obscure and unintelligible parts.[2] Brewster[3] found that in Newton's papers 'many chemical observations and experiments are recorded, but it is sometimes difficult to distinguish what is his own from what he has copied from other writers'. Newton's alchemical MSS. (dating from 1676 to 1696) were sold in 1936 and most are now in King's College, Cambridge. He mostly copied out printed works but one MS. is an attempt to compile from various authors (Mundanus, Philalethes, Flamel, etc.) a coherent account of alchemical doctrine.[4]

Keynes, from the Portsmouth Papers (see above) and Newton's private notes, concluded that Newton was 'the last of the magicians', that 'his deepest instincts were occult, esoteric, semantic', and that Newton was 'a wrapt, consecrated solitary, pursuing his studies by intense introspection'.[5]

Hoefer, in his two volumes, does not mention Newton on chemistry (his name is not in the index); Kopp, in his four volumes, mentions Newton fourteen times: for his introduction of the idea of attraction as chemical affinity,[6] for his inclusion of water among salts,[7] for his explanation of flame as burning smoke (in Aristotle and Albertus Magnus),[8] for his doubt as to the element fire (in Van Helmont),[9] for his view that water vapour is 'a sort of air',[10] for his explanation of the action of gunpowder as due to the generation of gas (in Van Helmont),[11] for the belief in the convertibility of water into earth (a commonplace of his time),[12] for his suggestion (from its high refractive index) that diamond is combustible,[13] for his invention of a fusible alloy (see p. 470), and for the preparation of ether (see p. 546). Brewster[14] said that: 'Although Sir Isaac had directed his attention to chemistry at various periods of his life, yet his name has not been associated with any striking discovery in the science.'

Newton's early notebooks contain accounts for the purchase of chemical books and apparatus, miscellaneous recipes on colours, 'to make birds drunk',

[1] Brewster, 1855, ii, 85 f.   [2] Zeitlinger, in Sotheran Cat. 800 (1926), no. 12098; Duveen, 539.
[3] 1855, ii, 367 f.
[4] F. S. Taylor, Ambix, 1956, v, 59–84 ('Newton was in the fullest sense an alchemist'); Forbes, Chymia, 1949, ii, 27.
[5] Keynes in Newton Tercentenary Celebrations, Cambridge, 1947 (an account of proceedings of the Royal Society).
[6] II, Qu. 31.   [7] II, Qu. 30.   [8] II, Qu. 10.   [9] II, Qus. 9, 18.   [10] II, Qu. 30.
[11] II, Qu. 10.   [12] II, Qu. 30; I, bk. iii, prop. 41, probl. 21; Amsterdam, 1723, 473.
[13] II, bk. II, pt. iii, prop. 10.   [14] 1855, ii, 360 f.

incantations, etc.[1] In 1661–96 he made chemical experiments in a laboratory in the garden behind his rooms in Trinity College. In a letter of 1669 to a young friend about to tour the Continent, Newton[2] advised him to pay particular attention to mining and metallurgy, particularly:

'any transmutations out of their species into another, (as out of iron into copper, out of any metall into quicksilver, out of one salt into another, or into an insipid body, &c.) these, above all, will be worth your noting, being the most luciferous, and many times lucriferous experiments too in philosophy . . . whether at Schemnitium, in Hungary, (where there are mines of gold, copper, iron, vitriol, antimony, &c.,) they change iron into copper by dissolving it in a vitriolate water, which they find in cavitys in rocks in the mines, and then melting the slimy solution in a strong fire, which in the cooling proves copper.' Roman vitriol is no longer sold because it has 'a nobler virtue than that which is now called by that name', as 'they make a greater gain by some such trick as turning iron into copper with it, than by selling it'.

It seems that Newton believed (as was common at the time) that iron is really 'turned into' copper. In his 'busy period' (1675–6) Newton was 'intent upon chemical studies and practices'.[3]

Newton invented an arsenical copper alloy for telescope mirrors,[4] and left a long account of its preparation and the method of casting the mirrors, in his own handwriting.[5] He used alloys of 11–12 copper, 4 tin and 1 white arsenic; or 6 copper, arsenic 1, tin 2; or better with some zinc (zineti seu margaritæ [? marchasitæ] albæ) and regulus of antimony. He also invented a fusible metal composed of 2 lead, 3 tin and 5 bismuth.[6] The scale of temperatures[7] is Newton's, as he told Gregory in 1706.[8] It is based on the so-called 'law of cooling'.[9]

In correspondence with Locke in 1692 Newton refers to Boyle's process for 'multiplying gold' by combining a certain unspecified red earth with mercury. Boyle had communicated his 'secret under conditions' and given Locke some of the earth. Newton, to whom Locke gave some of it, writes that though he has 'no inclination to prosecute the process', yet as he had 'a mind to prosecute it' he would 'be glad to assist him' [Locke] though he 'feared he had lost the first and third of the process out of his pocket'.[10]

Boyle, he says, had convinced him that 'mercury, by this recipe, may be brought to change its colour and properties but not that gold may be multiplied thereby'. Several chemists had worked on the secret; two had given it up, and a third, 'the chief artist . . . was so far run into debt that he had much ado to live.' Newton hints that Locke might have been told more about it than he, and might like to disclose the first part of the recipe.[11]

[1] Brewster, 1855, i, 33; Greenstreet, 16 f.   [2] Brewster, 1855, i, 34, 388–9.
[3] Brewster, 1855, i, 127.
[4] Birch, (1), 1757, iii, 4–5 (18 January 1782); Newton, *Phil. Trans.*, 1672, vii, No, 81, 4004; Abridged ed., 1809, i, 693.
[5] Brewster, 1855, ii, 361, 535 (text).
[6] *Phil. Trans.*, 1701, xxii, 824 (in water in 'strong ebullition'); Roscoe and Schorlemmer, *Treatise on Chemistry*, 1923, ii, 1035, give the composition $8Bi + 5Pb + 3Sn$ by weight for 'Newton's metal' of m.pt. 94·5° C.
[7] *Phil. Trans.*, 1701, xxii, 824 (in Latin); Abrdg., 1809, iv, 572 (in English).
[8] Hiscock, 1937, 32.
[9] Partington, *Advanced Treatise on Physical Chemistry*, 1949, i, 477; 1952, iii, 268.
[10] Newton used mercury in some experiments; Brewster, 1855, ii, 89.
[11] Lord King, *Life and Letters of John Locke*, 1884, 221 f.; T. S. Kuhn, *Isis*, 1951, xlii, 296.

In further correspondence, Newton dissuaded Locke against incurring any expense by 'a too hasty trial of the recipe', on which several chemists were engaged, and Boyle had also, in sending the recipe, 'reserved a part of it . . . though I knew more of it than he has told me.' When Boyle once exchanged two experiments for one, 'he cumbered them with such circumstances as startled me [Newton], and made me afraid of any more.' Newton says that a company was established in London to multiply gold by this recipe, which he 'takes to be the thing for the sake of which Mr. Boyle procured the repeal of the Act of Parliament against multipliers'.[1] Boyle had not himself tried the process but 'a certain gentleman was now about it, and it succeeded very well as far as he had gone'.

The story in Huygens' diary that Newton lost his reason in 1694 by over-study, 'or from excessive grief at having lost, by fire, his chemical laboratory and several manuscripts', is said[2] to be a fiction, but he certainly behaved rather oddly then.

Newton's assistant Humphrey Newton (no relation) recorded in 1728[3] that:

He very rarely went to bed before two or three of the clock, sometimes not till five or six . . . especially at spring and fall of the leaf, at which time he used to employ about six weeks in his elaboratory, the fire scarcely going out either night or day, he sitting up one night and I another, till he had finished his chemical experiments, in the perform-ance of which he was the most accurate, strict, exact . . . the elaboratory . . . was well furnished with chymical materials as bodyes, receivers, heads, crucibles, &c., which was made very little use of, ye crucibles excepted, in which he fused his metals; he would sometimes, tho' very seldom, look into an old mouldy book wch lay in his elaboratory, I think it was titled *Agricola de Metallis*, the transmuting of metals being his chief design, for which purpose antimony was a great ingredient.

This may refer to Newton's experiments on alloys for mirrors used in reflecting telescopes, which contained antimony,[4] and Agricola's *De Re Metallica* is not an alchemical book.

Newton's speculation on the combustibility of the diamond is well known:[5] it was 'an unctuous substance coagulated', because of its high refractive index, and 'it seems rational to attribute the refractive powers of all bodies chiefly, if not wholly, to the sulphureous particles with which they abound'.

Newton's famous experiment on the dispersion of white light into a spectrum of coloured rays was published in 1672,[6] and in 1675 he suggested to the Royal Society that 'rays of light' are composed of 'small bodies emitted every-way from shining substances'.[7] Newton is usually supposed to have originated the corpuscular theory of light, in which it is regarded as material, and this view of light as an 'imponderable element' was of importance in chemistry in the eighteenth and early nineteenth centuries:[8]

Are not the Rays of Light very small Bodies emitted from shining Substances? . . . Bodies of different Sizes, the least of which may make violet the weakest and darkest of

[1] Brewster, 1855, ii, 121–2, 461–2.   [2] Brewster, 1855, ii, 131 f.
[3] Brewster, 1855, ii, 93, 95–6; Newell, 1928, 203–55.   [4] Brewster, 1855, ii, 361, 535.
[5] *Opticks*, Bk. ii, prop. 10; 1730, 249; Brown, *Essays*, 1858, i, 86 f., says, this is 'a prosperous guess which it is customary to extol as sagacious'; similar criticism by Brewster, 1855, i, 213.
[6] *Phil. Trans.*, 1672, vi, 3035, no. 80; Birch, (1), 1757, iii, 9 (Newton, 6 Feb., 1672), 10–15 (Hooke); II, 1931, 20.
[7] Brewster, 1855, ii, 391.   [8] *Opticks*, Qu. 29; 1730, 345.

the Colours . . . and the rest as they are bigger and bigger, may make the stronger and more lucid Colours, blue, green, yellow, and red. Also, Query 30: The Changing of Bodies into Light, and Light into Bodies, is very conformable to the Course of Nature.

Descartes[1] had previously supposed that light consists of small particles emitted by luminous bodies, which he compared with balls and so explained reflexion and refraction. To explain the production of colours by refraction he supposed the balls to have an alternating rotatory motion.

Newton mentions Descartes in a letter to Hooke[2] in 1676, in which he uses the famous (but not novel) simile of 'standing on the shoulders of giants',[3] and in his other speculations Newton was considerably influenced by Descartes, whose philosophical system he was ultimately to dethrone.

David Gregory in 1705 reported that Newton believed that the 'Rays of Light enter into the composition of most Natural Bodys, that is the small particles that are projected from a Lucid body in form of Rays. Its plain this may be the case with most combustible, inflammable bodys'. He adds that 'gun-powder fired in vacuo produces common air'.[4]

Some speculations about the nature of light, the subtle but strongly elastic aethereal medium, vibrating like the air, flame 'as particles of smoke turned by the access of light and heat to burning coals, little and innumerable' (cf. Hooke's theory, p. 563), the action of the soul on 'the whole aether in any part of the body', the animal spirits of an aethereal nature able to pervade the animal juices, etc., etc., some quite mediaeval in character, were sent by Newton to the Royal Society in December 1675,[5] Hooke saying when it was read that 'the main of it was contained in his *Micrographia*'. Many things subsequently published in the *Opticks* were also read in January 1676,[6] with a reply to Hooke, who in 1678 said he had 'hundreds of experiments' to prove the reality of aether.[7]

In December 1675, in a letter to the Royal Society[8] Newton suggested that a 'spirit' rising from the centre of the earth may turn back in the upper regions and in descending press upon bodies, causing them to gravitate towards the earth. The sun imbibes this spirit to conserve his shining and keep the planets from receding further from him, but in another place it is said that the unsociableness 'between the æthers in the vortices of the sun and planets' keeps these apart. Newton is still using Descartes' theory of vortices and his later ether theories owe their inspiration to Descartes. Newton in the *Principia* proved the inadequacy of the theory of vortices to explain the motions in the solar systems, but he was much influenced by it.

In a remarkable letter to Boyle of 28 February 1679[9] Newton says:

the particles of vapours, exhalations, and air, do stand at a distance from one another, as the pressure of the incumbent atmosphere will let them: for I conceive the confused mass of vapours, air, and exhalations. which we call the atmosphere, to be nothing else but the particles of all sorts of bodies, of which the earth consists, separated from one another, and kept at a distance, by the said principle.

[1] *La Dioptrique*, 1637, 13, 23; *Les Météores*, 1637, viii, 256.   [2] Brewster, 1855, i, 142.
[3] Sarton, *Isis*, 1935, xxiv, 107; Klibansky, *ib.*, 1936, xxvi, 147.   [4] Hiscock, 1937, 31.
[5] Birch (1), 1757, iii, 247–69.   [6] Birch, (1), iii, 272–305 (296).   [7] Birch, (1), iii, 373.
[8] Birch, (1), 1757, iii, 247–69 (251–3).
[9] Boyle, *Works*, edit. Birch, 1744, i, *Life*, 71–2; reprinted in Brewster, 1855, i, 409–19.

This 'principle' is 'an endeavour of receding from one another', which Newton there explains on the hypothesis of an ether which is *rarefied* between bodies when they are brought near to one another (why, is not clear) and thus presses them together.

Newton *published* such like speculations only as 'queries' in his *Opticks*, and was far from laying down dogmatic hypotheses as 'facts'. In the 'Scholium Generale' added to the 1713 edition of his *Principia*, after some detailed explanations of the meaning of Deus (God), he says of 'the spirit which pervades crass bodies' and is the cause of the attraction of their particles to the minimum distances, and also the action of electrified bodies, which attract over greater distances, 'these are things which cannot be explained in a few words, neither is there a sufficiency of experiments which are required to determine accurately and demonstrate the laws by which this spirit operates.'[1]

Influenced both by Descartes and Gassendi, Newton varied in his attitude towards an ether. The hypothesis of an ether (which he regarded as corpuscular) set out in his letters to the Royal Society (1675)[2] and to Boyle (1679)[3] he apparently abandoned before 1702[4] but he revived it again in 1717,[5] when the density of ether is calculated as $1/6 \times 10^8$ that of water. In this vacillating attitude towards the ether, for which he has been reproached,[6] Newton was obscurely anticipating the modern conceptions of wave-mechanics. His brilliant suggestion that experiment alone should decide whether a single atom is divisible,[7] also condemned as unphilosophical,[8] has been justified by the modern experimental division of atoms. Newton, in a letter to Bentley (February, 1693), said that he did not then believe (as Epikourus did) that gravity is a property inherent in matter: it 'must be caused by an agent acting constantly according to certain laws, but whether this agent be material or immaterial, I have left to the consideration of my readers'.[9]

In 1675[10] Newton supposed that a vacuous receiver contained not only 'the main phlegmatic body of æther' but also 'other various ætherial spirits', for 'the electric and magnetic effluvia, and the gravitating principle, seem to argue such variety'. In fact, 'the whole frame of nature may be nothing but various contextures of some certain ætherial spirits or vapours, condensed as it were by precipitation. . . . Thus perhaps may all things be originated from æther.' Gravitation might be caused by the 'condensation of some . . . ætherial spirit, not of the main body of phlegmatic æther, but of something very thinly and subtilely diffused through it, perhaps of an unctuous, or gummy tenacious and springy nature; and bearing much the same relation to æther which the vital aërial spirit requisite for the conservation of flame and vital motions does to air', and capable of condensing in the pores of bodies just as 'this ætherial

[1] I, Amsterdam, 1723, 484.   [2] Brewster, 1855, i, 390.
[3] Boyle, *Works*, ed. Birch, 1744, i, *Life*, 70 f.; Harcourt, *Phil. Mag.*, 1846, xxviii, 478.
[4] Brewster, 1858, 304–5.   [5] II, 1717, Qus. 18–24; 1730, 323 f.
[6] Lasswitz, (1), 1890, ii, 559 f.
[7] I, Bk. iii, *Regulæ Philosophandi*, 3; Amsterdam, 1723, 357.   [8] Lasswitz, (1), 1890, ii, 558.
[9] VI, 1782, iv, 438; cf. II, 1717, Qu. 31; 1730, 377; Cajori, 1934, 632 f.; Lasswitz, (1), ii, 576; Partington and McKie, *Ann. Sci.*, 1938, iii, 9.
[10] Birch, (1), 1757, iii, 247–69; Brewster, 1855, i, 392–7; Harcourt, *Phil. Mag.*, 1846, xxviii, 480.

spirit may be condensed in fermenting or burning bodies'. The ætherial vibrations were the cause of combustion, for 'flame is nothing but the particles of smoke turned by the access of light and heat to burning coals, little and innumerable'. He speaks of 'the gas' of spirit of wine, so that he had evidently read Van Helmont.

In a letter to Oldenburg, 25 January, 1675 (1676 N.S.), Newton asks that a statement that 'the frame of nature may be nothing but æther condensed by a fermentable principle' should be altered to read 'certain ætherial spirits or vapours condensed, as it were, by præcipitation, much after the manner, that vapours are condensed into water, or exhalations into grosser substances, though not so easily condensable'; and not by a fermental principle but 'at first by the immediate hand of the Creator, and ever since by the power of nature' at His command. He says: 'there is a parenthesis, in which I mention volatile salt-petre. Pray strike out that parenthesis, lest it should give offence to somebody' (perhaps Hooke).[1]

Newton's chemical reputation rests largely on some 'Queries' added to his *Opticks*, of which Black, for example, had a high opinion.[2] Whetham thought that Newton's chemical interests were chiefly concerned with the nature of metals, the causes of chemical affinity, and the structure of matter. The first edition of the *Opticks* (1704) contained only 16 Queries, the second (1717) contains 31 Queries,[3] and in these (especially No. 31) Newton's views on chemical processes and on atoms are given in detail.

Newton's dictum, 'I frame no hypotheses (hypotheses non fingo)', was applied to the specific case of his inability to 'discover the cause of . . . gravity from phenomena',[4] and not intended to apply generally. Particularly in the *Opticks*, Newton proposed numerous hypotheses, but he usually distinguishes them from facts. He made extensive use of the atomic hypothesis.

Although Daubeny[5] suggested that most of them came from Lucretius, Newton's views on atoms were probably derived directly from Boyle, and thence ultimately from Gassendi.[6] Voltaire[7] reported that Newton told a Frenchman then living 'qu'il regardait Gassendi comme un esprit très-juste et très-sage, et qu'il fesait gloire d'être entièrement de son avis dans toutes les choses dont on vient de parler'.

In 1679[8] Newton explained the 'sociability' of particles in chemical actions by an excess of the 'principle of acceding' over the 'principle of receding'. In the *Opticks*,[9] he says: 'particles attract one another by some force, which in immediate contact is exceeding strong, at small distances performs the chymical operations, and reaches not far from the particles with any sensible effect.'

Giles Persone de Roberval (Roberval nr. Senlis, 8 August 1602–Paris, 27 October 1675), professor of mathematics in the Collège Royale and one of the foundation members of the Académie des Sciences, who was on bad terms with

---

[1] Boyle, *Works*, 1744, i, *Life* 74.   [2] Lord Brougham, 1855, 450.
[3] Brewster, 1855, i, 247.   [4] I, Bk. iii, Scholium gen.; Amsterdam, 1723, 484.
[5] *Atomic Theory*, Oxford, 1850, 44 f.
[6] Mabilleau, *Histoire de la Philosophie Atomistique*, Paris, 1895, 435 f.; Lasswitz, (1), ii, 555 f.
[7] *Œuvres*, 1784, xxxi, 37; Bloch, *Isis*, 1913, i, 377; Marwan, *Wiederaufnahme der griechischen Atomistik*, 1935, 32.
[8] Letter to Boyle, *Works*, 1744, i, *Life* 72.   [9] 1717, Qu. 31; 1730, 364.

Descartes and Torricelli but a friend of Mersenne, Pascal, and Gassendi, in 1644[1] had proposed a universal attraction between the smallest particles of matter, which causes them to aggregate into one mass, which, according as it contains many or few particles, is commonly called heavy or light:

Prætereà toti illi materiæ mundanæ et omnibus atque singulis ejus partibus insit quædam proprietas, seu quoddam accidens, vi cujus tota illa materia cogantur in unum. . . . Toti autem illi Systemati Terræ et elementorum terrestrium atque singulis ejus partibus insit quædam proprietas, sive quoddam accidens, quale toti Systemati mundano convenire supposuimus, vi cuius scilicet, cogantur in vnum omnes illius partes, & ad inuicem ferantur, seséque reciprocè attrahant, vt arctè cohæreant; nec se patiantur diuelli, nisi vi maiori, & violentiâ quâdam . . . vt hoc pacto corpus ipsum Terræ quia densissimum est . . . plus habeat ipsius proprietatis . . . ea est quam vulgò vocamus grauitatem vel leuitatem.

According to Lasswitz[2] Roberval was the first to postulate a *universal* attraction between *the smallest particles* of matter. It should also be noticed that Newton did *not* extend the inverse-square law to these smallest particles (p. 483).

By making use of hard atoms with forces between them, Newton[3] was able to strip the atoms of the hooks and cyes of the old atomic theory and of Descartes. He says:

. . . it seems probable to me, that God in the Beginning form'd Matter in solid, massy, hard, impenetrable, moveable Particles, of such Sizes and Figures, and with such other Properties, and in such Proportion to Space, as most conduced to the End for which he form'd them . . . should they wear away, or break in pieces, the Nature of Things depending on them, would be changed. Water and Earth, composed of old worn Particles and Fragments of Particles,[4] would not be of the same Nature and Texture now, with Water and Earth composed of entire Particles at the Beginning. . . . God is able to create Particles of Matter of several Sizes and Figures, and in several Proportions to Space, and perhaps of different Densities and Forces.

The particles are now hard atoms, not indefinite corpuscles, and they are not 'variously mov'd' as in Boyle's statement (see p. 505).[5] The scientific part of Newton's statement is a paraphrase of Lucretius;[6] the theological idea of a Divine creation of the atoms comes from Gassendi (p. 459) and originated among the Arabs (Vol. I). Voltaire, an enthusiastic Newtonian, said in 1728:

'When a Frenchman arrives in London he finds a very great change in philosophy as well as in most other things. In Paris he left the world full of matter; here he finds absolute vacua. In Paris the universe is seen filled up with ethereal vortices, while here the same space is occupied with the play of the invisible forces of gravitation.'[7]

In 1687[8] Newton gave a formal proof that a 'fluid' consisting of particles repelling one another with a force varying inversely as the distance between

[1] *Aristarchi Samii de Mundi Systemate Libellus. Adjectæ sunt Æ. Personii de Roberval Notæ,* Paris, 12°, 1644; also in Mersenne, *Novarvm Observationvm Physico-Mathematicarvm Tomus III Qvibvs accessit Aristarchvs Samivs de Mvndi Systemate. Adjecta sunt Æ. P. de Roberval . . . Notæ in eundum libellum. Editio Secvnda Correctior,* 4°, Paris, 1647, 2–4.
[2] *Ann. Phys.,* 1874, cliii, 373 (383–4).   [3] II, Qu. 31; 1730, 375–9.
[4] Newton here probably has Descartes in mind; Partington, q. by Meldrum, *Manchester Mem.,* 1910, lv, No. 4, 6.
[5] Gregory, *Short History of Atomism,* 1931, 51 f.
[6] *De Rerum Nat.,* i, 603–8: sunt igitur Solida Primordia . . . reservans semina rebus.
[7] *Lettres sur les Anglais,* 1728; Ueberweg, (2), 1874, ii, 124.
[8] I, Bk. ii, prop. 23, theorem 18; London, 1687, 301; Amsterdam, 1723, 270; tr. Cajori, 1934, 300; the argument is given by J. C. Fischer, 1802, ii, 291.

them would obey Boyle's law. In the statement he brings in centrifugal forces and it is not clear whether he thought the particles were at rest or in motion:

If for a fluid composed of mutually repulsive particles the density is proportional to the pressure, the centrifugal forces of the particles are inversely proportional to the distances between their centres. And conversely, particles the repulsive forces between which are inversely proportional to the distances between their centres, compose an elastic fluid the density of which is proportional to the compressing force.
si Fluidi ex particulis se mutuo fugentibus compositi densitas sit ut compressio, vires centrifugæ particularum sunt reciproce proportionales distantiis centrorum suorum. Et vice versa, particulæ viribus quæ sunt reciproce proportionales distantiis centrorum suorum se mutuo fugientes componuut Fluidum Elasticum, cujus densitas est compressioni proportionalis.

At the end of the section Newton says:

Whether elastic fluids do really consist of particles repelling one another is a physical question. We have here demonstrated mathematically the properties of fluids constituted of such particles so that philosophers may take occasion to discuss that question.
An vero Fluida Elastica ex particulis se mutuo fugantibus constent, Quaestio Physica est. Nos proprietatem Fluidorum ex ejusmodi particulis constantium mathematice demonstravimus, ut Philosophis ansam præbeamus Quæstionem illam tractandi.

He does not examine the relation of this respulsive force to the force of universal attraction of gravitation.

Clerk Maxwell[1] showed that Newton's demonstration requires that the 'repulsive force is inversely as the distance, but is exerted only between the nearest molecules', i.e. 'only between each molecule and a certain definite number of other molecules, which we may suppose to be defined as those nearest to the given molecules'. Jeans[2] said the law of force 'would make the action of the distant parts of the gas preponderate over that of the contiguous parts, and so would not give a pressure which would be constant for a given volume and temperature as we passed from one vessel to another'.

In spite of Newton's cautious statement it was very generally assumed in later times (e.g. by Dalton) that he had proved that a gas consists of particles at rest repelling one another with a force inversely proportional to the distance.

The Jesuit Father Roger Joseph (Ruggiero Giuseppe) Boscovich (Ragusa (Dubrovnik, in Dalmatia), 1 (or 18) May 1711–Milan, 13 (or 12) February 1787)[3] abandoned material corpuscles and replaced them by point-centres of alternating attractive and repulsive forces,[4] a view which commended itself to Priestley,[5] Faraday,[6] Lord Kelvin[7] and others.[8]

---

[1] The Scientific Papers of the Honourable Henry Cavendish, Cambridge, 1921, i, 370.
[2] An Introduction to the Kinetic Theory of Gases, Cambridge, 1940, 73.
[3] Gill, Roger Boscovich, Forerunner of Modern Physical Theories, Dublin, 1941; L. L. Whyte, Ann. Sci., 1954, x, 20; Nature, 1957, clxxix, 284, 458.
[4] Theoria Philosophiæ Naturalis redacta ad Unicam Legem Virium in Natura Existentium, 4°, Vienna, 1758; 2 ed. (enlarged and corr.), 4°, Venice, 1763 (xl + 311 pp.); A Theory of Natural Philosophy . . . Latin-English . . . from . . . the first Venice Edition, tr. Child, Chicago and London, 1922.
[5] Vision, Light, and Colours, 1772, i, 391.
[6] Experimental Researches in Electricity, 1844, ii, 284 (letter of 1844).
[7] Baltimore Lectures, 1904, 675.   [8] Chapman, Nature, 1940, cxlvi, 607.

The idea that gaseous pressure is due to molecular bombardment and not to static forces was reached by Gassendi, Hooke, and Descartes (p. 435), but it was first quantitatively treated by Daniel Bernoulli.[1] Speaking of a vessel of air with a movable piston EF (Fig. 18) he says:

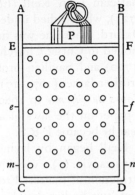

FIG. 18. BERNOULLI, 1738.

So the minute bodies, whilst they impinge on the piston EF, keep it up by their continually repeated strokes, and form an elastic fluid, which expands itself when the weight is removed or diminished.

We shall consider the minute bodies enclosed in the cavity of the cylinder as infinite in number, and when they occupy the space ECDF we shall say that they constitute natural air.

. . . . sic corpuscula, dum impingunt in operculum EF idemque suis sustinent impetibus continue repetitis fluidum componunt elasticum quod remoto aut diminuto pondere P sese expandit.

corpuscula cavitati cylindri inclusa considerabimus tanquam numero infinita, & cum spatium ECDF occupant, tunc aërem illa dicemus formare naturalem.

Bernoulli shows that this hypothesis leads to Boyle's law (ita ut pondera comprimentia sint fere in ratione inversa spatiorum) and attempts to evaluate the correction for the finite size of the particles, and for the pressure increase with rise in temperature (referring to Amontons).[2]

Newton adopted the idea of a static force of attraction between finite portions of matter as produced by the pressure of a corpuscular ether (p. 473). A kinetic atomic theory proposed by George Louis Le Sage (Geneva; 17 (or 13) June 1724–9 November 1803) supposed the atoms to be spherical, hollow and perforated, and bombarded by the very small particles of a fluid or corpuscles gravifique or corpuscles ultramondains.[3]

Newton[4] showed that: (1) 'if the attraction of the body attracted is much stronger when it is contiguous to the attracting body than when it is separated by only a very small interval, the forces of the particles of the attracting body decrease in a ratio more than the square of the distance of these particles', and (ii) 'if the forces of the particles which compose the attracting body decrease as the cube of the distances, the attraction will be much stronger at the place of contact than when the attracting body and the body attracted are separated by only a small interval'.

[1] *Hydrodynamica, sive de viribus et motibus fluidorum Commentarii*, Strasbourg, 4°, 1738, sect. x, §§ 1–4, pp. 200–2; R. A. Smith, Graham's *Chemical and Physical Researches*, Edinburgh, 1876, xiii, says these ideas were worked at when Bernoulli was Professor in St. Petersburg, i.e. before 1733, and hence they might have been known to Lomonosov (see Vol. III), who developed a similar theory.

[2] AdS, 1699, h 103, m 114; 1702, h 1, m 155; 1703, h 6, m 50.

[3] *Essai de Chymie Mécanique*, 4°, *s.l.e.a.* (crowned by the Academy of Rouen in 1758 and privately issued; the Royal Society copy has a MS. title-page and notes in Le Sage's handwriting); *Deux Traités de Physique Mécanique*, Publiés par Pierre Prevost (the first by Le Sage), 8°, Geneva and Paris, 1818. On Le Sage see Thomson, *Ann. Phil.*, 1818, xi, 241; L. L-t, NBG, 1859, xxx, 913; Rosenberger, 1887, iii, 19; W. Thomson, *Proc. Roy. Soc. Edin.*, 1872, vii, 577–89; G. Forbes, *Nature*, 1928, cxxii, 345.

[4] *Principia*, Bk. I, Sect. xiii, props. 85–6, theorems 12–13; 1723, 191–2.

Keill

The first application of these ideas to chemistry was made by the mathematician John Keill (Edinburgh, 1 December 1671–Oxford, 1 September 1721), who studied under Gregory in Edinburgh and in 1694 followed him to Oxford, where he was first an exhibitioner in Balliol College but about 1700 moved to Christ Church. He became deputy professor of natural philosophy (1700) and Savilian professor of astronomy (1710) in Oxford. His younger brother James (1673–1719), a physician in Northampton, translated Lemery's *Cours de Chymie* in 1680 (Vol. III).[1] In 1708 John Keill published in Latin a paper on the laws of attraction and other physical principles,[2] and in that year he became F.R.S.

Keill began by laying down 'three principles, as the foundation of all physics, viz. (1) a vacuum, (2) the divisibility of quantity ad infinitum, (3) the attraction of matter. From these he deduces thirty theorems. The second is that 'two bodies may be given of equal bulk, however unequal in weight and density (i.e. quantity of matter) the sums of whose vacuities or pores may approach a ratio of equality'. This is elucidated in the third theorem: 'the particles which constitute water, air, or similar fluids, if they touch each other, are not absolutely solid but consist of other particles that contain vacuities and pores. The most minute and absolutely solid particles of bodies, i.e. such as have no vacuities at all, may be called particles of the first composition. The molecules (moleculae) arising from the coalescence of several of these particles may be denominated particles of the second composition, and again masses made up of several of these molecules may be called particles of the third composition, and so on, till at length we come to particles which constitute the ultimate composition of bodies, and into which they may be ultimately resolved. That matter is endued with an attractive force, by which its particles mutually attract each other, Sir Isaac Newton first deduced from the phenomena'.

Besides gravity, Keill assumed 'another power in matter', but diminishing in a greater ratio than the inverse square of the distance, by which all the particles of matter mutually attract one another. In the points of contact or at an infinitely small distance, this force will be infinitely great if it has a finite ratio to gravity at a given distance, but if it has a finite ratio to gravity in the points of contact it will vanish at all assignable distances. Keill shows how such a force will explain cohesion, elasticity, crystallisation, solution, fermentation and effervescence, etc.

'Salts are bodies whose particles of the last composition are endued with a great attractive force, though there are several pores interspersed between them that are pervious to the particles of water of the last composition, which being therefore strongly attracted to the saline particles, they violently rush

[1] Gunther, (1), 1926, iii, 109, 143.
[2] *Phil. Trans.*, 1708, xxvi, 97–110; tr. in abrgd. ed., 1809, v, 417; E. Bloch, *Isis*, 1913, i, 377.

upon them, disjoin them from their mutual contact, and dissolve the cohesion of the salts.

'There are three things requisite to make a menstruum dissolve a given body, viz. (1) that the parts of the body attract the particles of the menstruum more than the said particles attract each other, (2) the body has pores open and pervious to the particles of the menstruum, (3) the cohesion of the particles constituting the body shall not be so great that it may not be overcome by the impetus of the rushing particles of the menstruum.

'If corpuscles attracting each other mutually touch no motion will ensue, for they cannot approach nearer. If placed at a very small distance from one another there will be motion, but if at a greater distance there will be no motion, since they will attract each other with no greater force than they attract the intermediate particles of the fluid. . . . Hence appears the reason why so great an ebullition is produced on throwing steel into a mixture of oil of vitriol and water, for the particles of steel have a great elasticity, whence a strong reflection or resilition arises, and why some menstrua if dilute with water act with greater violence upon and sooner dissolve any body.'

FREIND

Keill's applications of mechanical principles to chemical phenomena were extended by his colleague in Christ Church, Oxford, John Freind (Croton nr. Brackley, Northampton, 1675–London, 26 July 1728)[1] who studied in Oxford, was a member of Christ Church College, and in 1703 published, whilst still only M.B., his first medical work.[2] In the preface he complains of the abuse of chemistry in medicine but suggested that chemistry could be improved if reconstructed on mechanical principles. He describes some effects produced by mixing various substances with blood.[3]

In 1704 Freind was appointed reader (prælector) of chemistry in Oxford and delivered a course of lectures in the Ashmolean Museum in which he treated the subject on mechanical lines (before the appearance of Keill's paper, although Keill is mentioned in the preface of Freind's book), and these were published in 1709 'for no other reason but that I have too just a suspicion they would be published by somebody else' and 'they wanted no additional mistakes of a careless transcriber', as he says in the preface, in which he acknowledges the assistance he had in the experiments from Richard Frewin. In 1705 he accompanied the Earl of Peterborough in the capacity of army physician to Spain. Before returning to England in 1707 he visited Rome and met Baglivi and Lancisi. He became F.R.S. in 1712, was for a short time with the army of the Duke of Ormonde in Flanders and then returned to London. He became

[1] Life by Wigan in Freind, Opera Omnia Medica, f°, London, 1733; 4°, Paris, 1735 (BN 4° Te²⁵, 105); 3 vols., 8°, Leyden, 1734 (CUL Hhh. 961); Greenhill, DNB, 1889, xx, 241; Haeser, (1), 1881, ii, 608; Gunther, (1), 1925, iii, 74; Shorr, Isis, 1937, xxvii, 453; Saucerotte, NBG, 1857, xviii, 782.

[2] Emmenologia in qua Fluxus Muliebris Menstrui Phænomena . . . ad Rationes Mechanicas Exiguntur, 8°, Oxford, 1703 (BM 1176. h. 1); English tr. by J. Dale, 8°, London, 1729 (BM 1178. i. 22); French tr. by Devaux, 12°, Paris, 1730.

[3] Opera, 1733, 136.

M.P. for Launceston in 1722 but on the accusation of favouring the Pretender he was imprisoned, with the Bishop of Rochester, in the Tower of London in 1723, where he remained for three months and drew up the plan for his famous *History of Physick* (2 vols. 8°, 1725–6). In 1727 he was appointed by King George II physician to Queen Caroline, but he died a year after of fever. He was buried at Hitcham, near Maidenhead, where he was lord of the manor, and left a legacy of £1000 to the University of Oxford to found a chair of anatomy.[1]

A summary was printed in a review of the publication.[2] In 1710 an unfavourable review in a Cartesian journal[3] attacked the use of attraction as an 'occult principle' and took exception to the use of mv (momentum) rather than mv^2 (vis viva) as the 'quantity of motion'; it was perhaps written by Leibniz. Freind replied.[4] He makes use of nine 'lemmas and postulates from geometry and natural philosophy, which we make no question that the learned will readily grant us, and those who do not understand them are desired to believe them'. He assumed an attractive force between particles which acts only over very small distances, decreasing with distance faster than the inverse square, different according to the various textures and densities of the particles (whilst gravity does not depend on the texture), being greater in one side of a particle than in another. Of two particles A and B the forces are active practically only

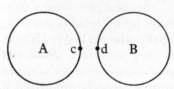

at c and d, the rest of the matter exerting forces next to nothing. The velocities with which the particles move with the same force are inversely as the masses.

Chemical changes may conveniently be divided into two general classes: diacrisis or dissociation and syncrisis or composition. Freind, on the basis of his assumptions of attractions between particles, which may be greater on one side of a particle than another, of the greater velocity of approach of smaller particles, and of the variation of the force with the degree of contact, explained calcination, distillation, and sublimation, which are analytical operations, and fermentation, digestion, extraction, precipitation, and crystallisation, which are synthetical. The increase in weight in calcination is due to fixation of

---

[1] *Prælectiones Chymicæ, In quibus omnes fere Operationes Chymicæ Ad Vera Principia & ipsius Naturæ Leges rediguntur, Ann. 1704. Oxonii, in Museo Ashmoleano habitæ*, 8°, London, n.d. (1709) (BM B. 119. (1.); CUL 7300. d. 9); 8°, Amsterdam, 1710 (93 pp.) (BN R. 36519; CUL Hhh. 232), and 1718 (93 pp., BN R. 36520); 8°, London, J. Bower (ix ll., 176 pp.) n.d. (1726) (Sotheran *Cat.* 800 (1926), no. 10822; BN Rés. R. 2431, printed as part 3 (sep. pag.) of *Emmenologia . . . accedunt ejusdem authoris Prælectiones Chymicæ*, 3 pts. 8°, Paris, 1727 (BM 1176. a. 14); dedicated to Newton; tr. *Chymical Lectures: In which almost all the Operations of Chymistry are Reduced to their True Principles and the Laws of Nature. Read at the Museum at Oxford, 1704. Englished* by J.M. To which is added, An Appendix, containing the Account given of this Book in the *Lipsick Acts*; together with the Author's Remarks thereon, 8°, London, 1712 (viii ll., 200 pp.) (CUL 7360. d. 2; BM 46. m. 10); 1729 (London Chemical Society), 1737 (The Second Edition; viii ll., 200 pp.; 'Englished by J.M.' omitted from t.p. The ed. quoted); also in Latin in *Opera Omnia Medica*, London, 1733, 1–51; summary in Shaw, *The Philosophical Works of Robert Boyle*, 4°, 1725, i, 45.

[2] *Phil. Trans.*, 1709, xxvi, 319.   [3] *Acta Eruditorum*, Leipzig, 1710, 412–16 (Sebtember).

[4] *Phil. Trans.*, 1711, xxvii, 330–42 (in Latin); the review and Freind's reply are printed in the later eds. of his *Prælectiones Chymicæ* and trs. (criticism still in Latin).

particles of fire, which insinuate themselves among the particles of metal and so reduce the specific gravity.

Freind in his lectures criticised the general acceptance of the ideas of Tachenius (p. 292): the corrosive, colorific and fermentative properties are often shared by acid and alkali alike 'and what in respect to one body is named *alkali* is, if compared with some other, by the very same writers call'd an *acid*. So that in vain we endeavour to fix the boundaries which separate each kind'.[1] He is very severely critical of the common 'dirt' chemists, working without philosophical principles. As an example of his application of the theory of attraction the discussion of why aqua fortis dissolves silver but not gold, and aqua regia dissolves gold but not silver may be mentioned.[2] Freind assumes that the diameters of the pores in silver and gold be as 2 to 1. Then corpuscles able to penetrate gold must be eight times less than those which will enter silver.

'Let us suppose the *Attraction* of *Gold* to that of *Silver*, to be as *a* to *b*; and that of *Silver* to *Aqua Fortis*, as *b* to *d*; but that of *Aqua Fortis* to *Aqua Regia*, as *d* to *e*. Let *f* signify the Magnitude of the Particles in *Aqua fortis*, and *v*, those in *Aqua Regia*; *c* the Cohesion of *Gold* and *g* the Cohesion of *Silver*. If the Diameters of the Particles *f*, are greater than the Diameter of the Pores of *Gold*, they can never dissolve the *Gold*, let their *attractive* force be never so strong. But if $\overline{b-d\times f}$ exceeds *g*, then the Silver will yield to that *Menstruum*, whose Particles are *f*, and less than the Pores of the Silver. And if $\overline{b-e\times r}$ is less than *g*, the Silver will never dissolve in that *Menstruum*, the Particles of which are *r*, and the *attractive* Force *e*. But if $\overline{u-e\times r}$, be greater than *c*, the *Menstruum*, made up of the Particles *r*, and whose *attractive* Force is *e*, will be able to penetrate and dissolve the *Gold*.' Arbitrary figures must be assigned to these letters, and several solutions are possible.[3]

At the end of the book are tables of specific gravities of solids and liquids, and a 'table of rarefactions' which is only mentioned incidentally in the text[4] and the meaning of which is not very clear. By way of general criticism, it may be said that attempts to introduce Newtonian mechanics into chemistry led to no useful results. Continental authors[5] who have heard of Keill and Freind make the mistake of supposing that they followed the discussion in Newton's *Opticks*, which they date 1704, whereas the chemical queries first appeared in the 1717 edition, some years after Keill and Freind's publications, which are based on Newton's *Principia*, not containing any chemistry. Newton's chemical queries resemble parts of Freind's work so closely that it is impossible to suppose that they are independent. Kopp and Hoefer mention neither Keill nor Freind; Gmelin[6] just mentions Freind's book but attributes no single chemical discovery to him. The abridged *Philosophical Transactions*[7] says

---

[1] *Chymical Lectures*, 1737, 15; Mills, *Phil. Mag.*, 1869, xxxvii, 461.
[2] *Chymical Lectures*, 1737, 96–102.
[3] This section of Freind is reproduced in the *Nouveau Cours de Chymie suivant les Principes de Newton & de Sthall*, Paris, 1723, i, 210 f.; on p. 74 f., chemical attraction is called the 'magnetism of bodies'; E. Bloch, *Isis*, 1913, i, 377.
[4] *Chymical Lectures*, 1737, 55, 151.
[5] E.g. Metzger, (1), 30, 41.   [6] (1), ii, 695.   [7] 1809, v, 647.

Freind 'in his eagerness to apply the Newtonian philosophy to the phænomena of chemistry, has not duly distinguished elective attraction from the
attraction of gravitation, and the attraction of cohesion. Hence it would be no
ways interesting at this day, to insert . . . even an abstract, of this defence,
grounded on the before-mentioned general properties of matter, and not upon
specific chemical agencies'.

NEWTON'S CHEMISTRY

The practical chemists of Newton's time probably set little store on atomic
speculations. Peter Shaw, the editor of Boyle and F. Bacon, said: 'Leaving,
therefore, to other Philosophers the sublimer Disquisition of primary Corpuscles, or Atoms, . . . genuine Chemistry contents itself with grosser Principles,
which are evident to the Sense', viz. water, earth, salt, sulphur and mercury.[1]

A short memorandum on the nature of acids, *De natura acidorum*, written by
Newton in 1692, and sent to Dr. Pitcairne, was first published (with a translation) by John Harris (1667–1719).[2] It says acid particles are intermediate
in size between those of water and earth, are endowed with a great attractive
force in which their activity consists, and are of a middle nature between water
and terrestrial bodies (corpora terrestria), attracting the particles of both. By
their attraction they surround the particles of metals or earths and can scarcely
be separated by heat. The alkalis are composed of earth joined to an acid
strongly attractive. By rushing towards the particles of bodies, the acid particles move the fluid and excite heat, also 'shake asunder some particles, so
much as to turn them into air, and generate bubbles. . . . In all fermentations
there is an acid latent or suppressed'.

Newton generalised these ideas very freely, considering fats, sulphur and
metallic salts as 'acid particles joined with earthy ones in but a small quantity . . . and hidden as it were in them. . . . Whatever doth strongly attract, and
is strongly attracted, may be called an acid'. When an acid dissolves a metal,
'the particles of the menstruum environ those of the metal, tear them to pieces
and dissolve it.'

Vi magna Attractivâ pollent, & in hoc vi consistit earum Activitas, quâ & Corpora
dissolvunt & Organa Sensuum agitant & pungunt . . . Acidum enim dicimus quod
multum attrahit & attrahitur . . . relictâ scilicet terrâ Subtili cui adhaerebant ob
majorem attractionem ad liquidum linguae, &c. In omni Solutione per Menstruum
particulæ solvendæ magis attrahuntur a Partibus [apartibus] Menstrui quam à se
mutuo.

If gold could be made to ferment and putrefy, it might be turned into any
other body.

Pemberton[3] says: 'Sir Isaac Newton is of the opinion, that wherever any dissolution
is made, there an acid is present, if not manifest to sense, yet latent; in which he only

---

[1] P. Shaw, *Chemical Lectures*, 2 ed., 1755, 146.
[2] *Lexicon Technicum: Or, An Universal English Dictionary of Arts and Sciences*, 2 vols., f°,
1704–10, ii, unpaged introduction; 5 ed., 1736, i, pref. ff. er–fv; Latin in Newton, III, 1744, ii,
413; IV, 1782, iv, 397–400; Shaw, *Works of Boyle*, 1725, iii, 437; Pemberton, *A Course of
Chemistry*, 1771, 73; Newell, 1928, 215; the original seems to have existed in different forms.
[3] *A Course of Chemistry*, 1771, 83.

expresses his sentiment, that acid particles are the active principles, that attract other bodies and are attracted by them.' Inflammable bodies contain an inflammable substance or principle, sometimes called sulphur, the same in all, and 'sir Isaac Newton shews, that light, and consequently heat, operates immediately upon this part in bodies'.[1] He was 'the first, who perceived, that . . . fixt alkali's were an earth with an acid adhering'.[2]

In the *Opticks* Newton[3] asks:

Have not the small Particles of Bodies certain Powers, Virtues, or Forces, by which they act at a distance. . . . What I call Attraction may be perform'd by impulse, or by some other means unknown to me. I use that word here to signify in general any Force by which Bodies tend towards one another, whatsoever be the Cause. . . . The Attractions of Gravity, Magnetism, and Electricity, reach to very sensible distances . . . and there may be others which reach to so small distances as hitherto escape Observation; and perhaps electrical Attraction may reach to such small distances, even without being excited by Friction.

For when Salt of Tartar runs *per Deliquium*, is not this done by an Attraction between the Particles of the Salt of Tartar, and the Particles of the Water which float in the Air in the form of Vapours? . . . And when *Aqua fortis*, or Spirit of Vitriol poured upon Filings of Iron, dissolves the Filings with great Heat and Ebullition . . . effected by a violent Motion of the Parts . . . does not that Motion argue that the acid Parts of the Liquor rush towards the Parts of the Metal with violence, and run forcibly into its Pores till they get between its outmost Particles, and the main Mass of the Metal, and surrounding those Particles loosen them from the main Mass, and let them at liberty to float off into the Water? . . .

When Spirit of Vitriol poured upon common Salt or Salt-petre makes an Ebullition with the Salt, and unites with it, and in Distillation the Spirit of the common Salt or Salt-petre comes over much easier than it would do before, and the acid part of the Spirit of Vitriol stays behind; does not this argue that the fix'd Alcaly of the Salt attracts the acid Spirit of the Vitriol more strongly than its own Spirit, and not being able to hold them both, lets go its own? . . .

When a Solution of Iron in *Aqua fortis* dissolves the Lapis Calaminaris [zinc], and lets go the iron, or a Solution of Copper dissolves Iron immersed in it and lets go the Copper, or a Solution of Silver dissolves Copper and lets go the Silver, or a Solution of Mercury in *Aqua fortis* being poured upon Iron, Copper, Tin or Lead, dissolves the Metal and lets go the Mercury; does not this argue that the acid Particles of the *Aqua fortis* are attracted more strongly by the *Lapis Calaminaris* than by Iron, and more strongly by Iron than by Copper, and more strongly by Copper than by Silver, and more strongly by Iron, Copper, Tin and Lead, than by Mercury? And is it not for the same reason that Iron requires more *Aqua fortis* to dissolve it than Copper, and Copper more than the other Metals; and that of all Metals, Iron is dissolved most easily, and is most apt to rust; and next after Iron, Copper?

When *Aqua fortis* dissolves Silver and not Gold, and *Aqua regia* dissolves Gold and not Silver, may it not be said that *Aqua fortis* is subtil enough to penetrate Gold as well as Silver but wants the attractive Force to give it Entrance . . . ?

T. S. Kuhn[4] thought Newton made a 'slip' in saying that Aqua fortis is able to penetrate gold, but Newton seems to have thought that the particles of the acid *were* actually small enough to penetrate, but did not do so because they were not attracted, and hence did not enter the gold. A large number of other chemical examples, culled by Newton from various unnamed sources, are turned to account in his Queries 30 and 31.[5] They are often credited to him as original.

In his letter to Boyle, (p. 472) Newton says he sometimes thought 'that the true permanent air may be of a *metallic* origin, the particles of no substances

[1] *Ib.*, 87, 248.　　　　[2] *Ib.*, 134.　　　　[3] II, Qu. 31, 1717, 350 f.
[4] *Isis*, 1951, xlii, 296.　　　[5] Harcourt, *Phil. Mag.*, 1846, xxviii, 478.

being denser than metals', and M. Huygens had found that 'the air made by dissolving salt of tartar [carbon dioxide] would in two or three days' time condense and fall down again; but the air made by dissolving a metal continued without condensing or relenting in the least . . . the most permanent part of the atmosphere' may consist of the metallic particles, which being heavy float on the ground and 'buoy up the lighter exhalations and vapours'. This should happen with 'metallic exhalations raised in the bowels of the earth by the action of acid menstruums'.

In Query 31 Newton refers to the inflammation of essential oils by nitric acid (which had been published by Borrichius) and the 'artificial volcano' of Lemery, made by burying sulphur and iron filings, and other well-known experiments, without naming the authors. He says:

Also some sulphureous Steams, at all times when the Earth is dry, ascending into the Air, ferment there with nitrous Acids, and sometimes taking fire cause Lightning and Thunder, and fiery Meteors. For the Air abounds with acid Vapours fit to promote Fermentations, as appears by the rusting of Iron and Copper in it, the kindling of Fire by blowing, and the beating of the Heart by means of Respiration.
. . . in Fermentations the Particles of Bodies which almost rest, are put into new Motions by a very potent Principle, which acts upon them only when they approach one another, and causes them to meet and clash with great violence, and grow hot with the motion, and dash one another into pieces, and vanish into Air, and Vapour, and Flame.

Newton's mention of the beating of the heart in respiration seems to refer to the views of Mayow (*Tractatus Quinque*, 1674). Some of the other crude ideas in the Query seem to have been taken from a little-known book[1] by William Simpson (d. 1680):

Zymologia Physica, Or a brief Philosophical Discourse of Fermentation, From a new Hypothesis of Acidum and Sulphur. Whereby the Phœnomena . . . are solv'd from the intestine duellings and inward collisions of the foresaid principles. Whereby also Various other subterraneal Phænomena, as Damps, Earth-quakes, Eruptions, &c. likewise the appearances of Meteors, &c. and divers other no less remarkable then entertaining, are from the same Doctrine of Fermentation genuinely solv'd, 8°, London, 1675; see preface and pp. 9, 15, 41, 49, 56.

in which it is also said that the heat of slaking of lime is due to fire in it which is an acid, and metals increase in weight on calcination by taking up this acid from the fire,[2] fire and light are due to the collision and fermentation of acid and sulphur set in rapid intestine motion by the air, which imbibes moisture,[3] the light of putrefying wood or fish is due to the same cause,[4] luminous meteors are due to acid and sulphureous particles in the air,[5] or Acido-Nitro-Sulphurous complications floating in the atmosphere,[6] which also cause lightning.

Newton[7] thought that 'Nature seems delighted with transmutations', and water may be converted into earth by distillation. He thought[8] that the matter of the tails of comets was dispersed and entered the atmospheres of the earth

---

[1] It is not mentioned by Gmelin, Kopp, or Hoefer.   [2] *Ib.*, 98–9.   [3] *Ib.*, 108 f.
[4] *Ib.*, 118 f.   [5] *Ib.*, 120 f.   [6] *Ib.*, 124.   [7] II, Qu. 30; 1730, 349.
[8] I, iii, prop. xli, probl. 21; Amsterdam, 1723, 473; tr. Cajori, 1934, 529, 542; H. Pemberton, *A View of Sir Isaac Newton's Philosophy*, 4°, London, 1728, Bk. II, ch. iv, § 19, p. 244; McKie, *Ambix*, 1938, i, 162; *Phil. Mag.*, 1942, xxxiii, 847.

and other planets, where it 'may well be supposed to contribute to the renovation of the face of things, in particular to supply the diminution caused in the humid parts by vegetation and putrefaction', both these tending to convert water into earth. Also, 'the most subtle and active parts of our air, upon which the life of things chiefly depends, is derived to us, and supplied by the comets.'

David Gregory thought that Newton did not mean that the tails of comets restored 'real fluid water' but 'a subtile Spirit that does turn Solids into Fluids. A very small Aura or particle of this may be able to doe the business'.[1]

LEIBNIZ

Gottfried Wilhelm Leibniz (Leipzig, 3 July 1646–Hanover, 14 November 1716) visited Paris, Holland, and London, and was the founder of the Berlin Academy in 1700.[2] Although he served the House of Hanover, Leibniz was left behind when George I became King of England; his dispute with Newton over the discovery of the calculus (which Leibniz evolved in Paris in 1675–6 in ignorance of Newton's previous unpublished work) would have made him unpopular in England. Leibniz's philosophy of 'monads' is said to owe something to Spinoza. He left a mass of philosophical writings, mostly published by Couturet (1901–3). Locke had a poor opinion of his philosophy.[3] He was greatly interested in alchemy, and was in relation with Francis Mercurius Van Helmont (p. 242). In 1654 an alchemical Rosicrucian society was founded at Nürnberg, of which Leibniz became secretary for a year in 1667, making extracts from alchemical writers and recording experiments in the society's laboratory. The society lasted until 1700 and Leibniz's interest in alchemy remained throughout his life. In 1710[4] in a paper on a solution of the alchemical puzzle (see p. 315) which he interpreted as meaning arsenic ($\dot{\alpha}\rho\sigma\epsilon\nu\iota\kappa\acute{o}\nu$), he said it might be possible to extract a quintessence from gold which could convert other metals into gold, although many things make this seem improbable (caeterum quod parum verisimile censeo, non ideo impossibile pronuntiare ausim. Certe esse aliquid in natura, quali pyrius pulvis [gunpowder], nisi experimento convicti, aegre crederemus).

Leibniz[5] said the reaction of vacuum and plenum is the origin of all fermentation, acid and alkali, sympathy and antipathy; and it was foreshadowed by the red and white or masculine and feminine of the alchemists, the three chemical principles, and Helmont's gas, blas, and Archeus. The nucleus of the chemists is constituted by their three principles, their cortex by terra mortua and phlegm. Bullæ or globules, when the air in them is exhausted, constitute alkali or the alchemists' feminine mercury; when they are distended with air, they form acid, masculine sulphur. There is more of this nonsense. Leibniz was a good mathematician but a poor chemist.

[1] Hiscock, 1937, 26.
[2] Chemical papers in Leibniz, *Opera*, 1768, II, ii; Ueberweg, (1), 1924, iii, 299; Ravier, *Bibliographie des Oeuvres de Leibniz*, Paris, 1937 (710 pp.); Kopp, (4), i, 232; Hoefer, NBG, 1859, xxx, 465; Peters, Leibniz als Chemiker, *A. Nat.*, 1916, vii, 85–108, 220–35, 275–87; Hildebrand, *Z. f. gesamte Naturwissenschaft*, Brunswick, 1936–7, ii, 169.
[3] B. Russell, *History of Western Philosophy*, 1947, 592, 633.
[4] *Miscell. Berolin.*, 1710, i, 16.
[5] *Hypothesis Nova . . .* , Mainz, and London, 1671; *Opera*, 1768, II, ii, 3–34; the first part is dedicated to the Royal Society, the second to the Académie des Sciences.

CHAPTER XIV

BOYLE

Robert Boyle (Lismore Castle, Co. Waterford, Ireland, 25 or 26 January 1627–London, 30 December 1691) was the seventh son and fourteenth (or fifteenth) child of Richard Boyle, first Earl of Cork. His mother died in 1630. From the age of eight Robert was educated at Eton and in 1638 he left for a tour on the Continent in charge of a tutor, staying at Geneva for about two years. Boyle there came under Calvinistic protestant influence, which remained with him all his life. He returned home in 1644, living at his sister's, Lady Ranelagh's, house in London for four months, when, after the death of his father and the loss of his fortune, he retired to the family house at Stalbridge in Dorsetshire, where he lived very simply for six years. (The house had disappeared in 1860.) He never married, and in an early letter he says 'the little gentleman [Cupid] and I are still at the old defiance'.[1] In 1648 he completed his first work, *Some Motives and Incentives to the Love of God*, published in 1659 and usually called *Seraphic Love* (from the page-title); it is said this was the result of his disappointment in the marriage of Lady Ann Howard (to whom he was at one time betrothed) in 1645. In 1654 he moved to Oxford and in conjunction with his paid assistant Robert Hooke, appointed about 1655, he worked in lodgings next to University College in the High Street on experiments with the air pump, on combustion, etc.[2] He moved permanently to London in 1668, living with his sister Katharine, Lady Ranelagh, in Pall Mall, until his death there. Lady Ranelagh, married at the age of sixteen to the drunken and brutal Richard Jones, third Viscount Ranelagh, was a woman of strong character. She befriended the poet Milton in the Restoration period, when all Cromwellians were in danger.[3]

[1] *Works*, ed. Birch, 1744, i, *Life*, 86.

[2] L. T. More, 1944, 82, says Boyle worked in rooms in Cross St., now the site of the Shelley Memorial.

[3] Anon., *Nature*, 1927, cxix, 133; *Times Lit. Suppl.*, 19 May 1945; T. Birch, *The Life of the Honourable Robert Boyle*, 1744 (also reprinted in his edition of the *Works* of Boyle, 1744 and 1772); id., *History of the Royal Society*, 4 vols. 4°, 1756–7; E. Bloch, *Isis*, 1913, i, 377 (Boyle and structural chemistry; corpuscles); *Chem. Ztg.*, 1915, xxxix, 481 (calcination); M. Boas, *Isis*, 1950, xli, 261; 1952, xliii, 123; 1954, xlv, 153 (*The Sceptical Chymist*); id., *Osiris*, 1952, x, 412 (mechanical philosophy); id., *Robert Boyle and Seventeenth Century Chemistry*, Cambridge, 1958; G. Burnet, *Lives*, 1833, 325 (funeral sermon, 7 January 1692); E. A. Burtt, *The Metaphysical Foundations of Modern Physical Science*, 1925; A. Cap, *Études Biographiques*, 1857, i, 131–79; A. M. Clerke, DNB, 1908, ii, 1026; G. M. Cullen, *Pharm. J.*, 1927, cxviii, 156; T. L. Davis, *Isis*, 1926, viii, 71–6 (first ed. of the *Sceptical Chymist*); 1931, xvi, 82 (Boyle and Lavoisier on 'element'); H. B. Dixon, *B. A. Rep.*, 1894, 594; E. Färber, *Z. angew. Chem.*, 1927, xl, 948 (the *Sceptical Chymist*); J. C. Fischer, 1801, i, 443, ii, 179, 184, 200; M. S. Fisher, *Robert Boyle Devout Naturalist*, Philadelphia, 1945 (Fisher is a Jew); J. F. Fulton, (1), *A Bibliography of the Honourable Robert Boyle*, Oxford, 1932 (reprinted from the *Oxford Bibliographical Society Proceedings and Papers*, III, pt. i, pp. 1–172); (2), id., *Addenda to a Bibliography of the*

Boyle was 'tall of stature but slender, and his countenance pale and emaciated'. He had weak sight and a bad memory and also had poor health, suffering great pain from a renal disorder, and as a result of a narrow escape from poisoning from a mistake in a prescription he became sceptical of professional medicine and fond of dosing himself and his friends with recipes from very miscellaneous sources, 'being in this way credulous and apt to be imposed upon.'[1] Physicians, grave and ingenious gentlemen from the Continent, experienced technicians, plumbers, gentlewomen, and even 'an old sea captain', provided him with a store of wonders which he seriously records, only occasionally interpolating 'if it be true'. Shaw[2] says that Boyle was in some disrepute at that time for his credulity. Boyle said[3] 'the principal end, for which I study Chymistry, is to relieve some languishing patients the more easily from their sickness; for, certainly, our common remedies are very ineffectual'. His writings show that he had made a careful study of numerous medical authors and had tried a multitude of recipes from all possible sources.

He was made an honorary Doctor of Physic of Oxford in 1665.[4] It is related that 'he had divers sorts of cloaks to put on when he went abroad, according to the temperature of the air, and in this he governed himself by his thermometer'.[5] Boyle devoted much time to theology,[6] writing works on this subject, and throughout his life he spent freely in having translations of the Bible made into Indian, Irish, Welsh, Turkish and Malayan, and also in private charity and Christian missions. Dixon says Boyle's scientific work was very unpopular in Oxford; he was attacked from the pulpit and in print. He may have in mind the Bishop of Oxford, Samuel Parker (1640–88), F.R.S., of whom it is

Honourable Robert Boyle, Oxford [1933] (reprinted from *Oxford Bibliographical Society Proceedings and Papers*, 1933, III, pt. iii, pp. 339–65); *id.*, *Isis*, 1932, xviii, 77–102; 1933, xix, 204; *id.*, *Aviation Medicine in the Preventive Aspects* (Heath Clark Lectures), London, 1948, 4–22; Gmelin, (1), 1798, ii, 34–109; Hanckewitz, in J. Ince, *Pharm. J.*, 1858, xviii, 157–62; W. V. Harcourt, *Phil. Mag.*, 1846, xxviii, 124; F. Hoefer, NBG, 1855, xiii, 756; *id.*, (1), 1869, ii, 146. W. S. James, *Sci. Progr.*, 1928, xxiii, 263 (Boyle's law); H. Kopp, (1), i, 163; (2), 1875, iii, 163; (4), i, 53; T. S. Kuhn, *Isis*, 1952, xliii, 12 (corpuscular theory); C. H. Lea, *Pharm. J.*, 1927, cxviii, 108–9; D. McKie, *Sci. Progr.*, 1934, xxix, 253; 1936, xxxi, 55; *Nature*, 1949, clxiii, 627 (Boyle's library); F. Masson, *Robert Boyle*, 1914; R. E. W. Maddison, *Notes and Records of the Royal Society*, 1958, xiii, 128–201 (A tentative index of the correspondence of the Honourable Robert Boyle); E. von Meyer, *History of Chemistry*, 1906, 109; *id.*, in *Kultur der Gegenwart*, 1913, Theil III, Abt. ii, Bd. 2, 1; L. T. More, *The Life and Works of the Honourable Robert Boyle*, Oxford Univ. Press, New York, 1944; G. G. Perry, *Life of Robert Boyle* (S.P.C.K.), [1863] (48 pp., no scientific work); W. Ramsay, *Gases of the Atmosphere*, 1915, 1; *id.*, *Essays Biographical and Chemical*, 1909, 19; D. Reilly, *J. Chem. Educ.*, 1951, xxviii, 178; G. F. Rodwell, *Chem. News*, 1864, ix, 14, 26, 50; 1864, x, 74; 1865, xii, 62, 74, 293; 1867, xv, 312; 1867, xvi, 29, 43; F. Rosenberger, 1884, ii, 155; G. Sarton, *Chymia*, 1950, iii, 155; M. Speter, *Chem. Ztg.*, 1929, liii, 1005 (phosphorus); Sprengel, (1), 1815, v, 78–9 (On voit combien peu ce grand expérimenteur lui-même, avait secoué le joug des préjugés de son temps'; G. W. Spriggs, *Archeion*, 1929, xi, 1 (primary and secondary properties already in Galileo); T. Thomson, (1), i, 203 (from Sprengel); Thorndike, viii, 170–201; T. E. Thorpe, *Essays*, 1902, 1; W. Tilden, *Nature*, 1921, cviii, 176 (Boyle buried in St. Martin-in-the-Fields but remains lost); *id.*, *Famous Chemists*, 1921, 1; C. R. Weld, *A History of the Royal Society*, 2 vols., 1848; G. Wilson, *Religio Chemici*, London and Cambridge, 1862, 165; F. Wrangham (ed.), *The British Plutarch*, 1816, iv, 324–79.

[1] Birch, *Works*, i, *Life*, 86; J. and W. Thomson and D. Craigie, *An Account of the Life . . . of William Cullen*, 1859, ii, 559.
[2] *Works of Boyle*, 1725, i, pref. xii.
[3] The Usefulness of Experimental Philosophy, *Works*, ed. Shaw, 1725, i, 104.
[4] Wilson, 1862, 232.   [5] Birch, *Works*, i, *Life*, 86.
[6] H. Fisch, *Isis*, 1953, xliv, 252.

said,[1] 'il mourut peu regretté', who was an opponent of Platonism and atomism alike.[2]

Boyle avoided honours and affairs; he repeatedly declined a peerage and died the only untitled member of a large family. He preferred to spend his life in a quiet and dignified study of science, not neglecting its applications to metallurgy, medicine, and the manufacture of chemicals, dyes and glass.[3] His personal character was of the highest[4] and his strict veracity makes his works of great value as historical documents. Burnet[5] says death 'made an end of him; with so little uneasiness, that it was plain his light went out, merely for want of oil to maintain the flame'. He was buried on 7 January 1692, in St. Martin-in-the-Fields. The old church was pulled down in 1721 and Boyle's remains have been lost.[6] Boyle's library was sold and dispersed.

It is uncertain when or how Boyle became interested in chemistry, but one of his teachers is said to have been Frederick Clodius (or Claudius), the son-in-law of Samuel Hartlib, 'a professed adeptus', with a 'pretence of extraordinary arcana.'[7] There were others in England interested in chemistry in Boyle's time; Evelyn[8] met in London 'a gentlewoman called Everard, that was a very great chemist'.

Peter Stahl or Sthael, a Lutheran of Strasbourg and a Rosicrucian, was the first regular teacher of practical chemistry at Oxford, beginning in 1659. He was introduced by Boyle and taught in private houses. In his class was John Locke, who, whilst the other men were taking notes, 'scorned to do it', and 'would be prating and troublesome' (which, Warton said, does not sound likely for Locke). This was in 1663, in which year Sthael had built a laboratory at the back of an old hall or refectory. He went to London in 1664 as operator to the Royal Society, but returned to Oxford to teach again in 1670; he died in London in 1675.[9]

The first University chemical laboratory at Oxford was established by Elias Ashmole, in the cellar of the Ashmolean Museum, which Wood[10] says was 'quite finished' and 'certain scholars went a course of chimistrie', in the middle of September, 1683; in the same year Johann Moritz Hoffmann's

---

[1] P.L. in NBG, 1862, xxxix, 223.

[2] On Boyle's religious and metaphysical views see Burtt, 1925, 160 f.; W. C. Dampier, 1946, 153, says 'Boyle expressed his philosophy in religious terms'.

[3] References in Gmelin, (1), 89 f., 93 f., on chemical industries in England as indicated by Boyle and his correspondents.

[4] Barchusen, *Pyrosophia*, Leyden, 1698, 287, calls Boyle: 'vir vere antiquissimi moris et priscam gravitatem semper humanitate temperans.'

[5] 1833, 362.

[6] A. Wood, *Fasti*, in *Works* ed. Bliss, 1820, iv, 287; Tilden, *Nature*, 1921, cviii, 176; *id.*, *Famous Chemists*, 1921, Pref., and pp. 1 f.

[7] Evelyn, *Diary and Correspondence*, ed. Bray, 1852, iii, 389, 391; Birch, *Works of Boyle*, 1744, i, *Life*, 21 f.; v, 241, 258; K. Digby, *Chymical Secrets*, publ. Hartman, 1683–82, 156; Rowbottom, *Ann. Sci.*, 1950, vi, 376; a Balduin Clodius published an *Officina Chymica, das ist: Künstliche Spagyrischen Zuzubereitung der . . . Medicamenta*, Oppenheim, 1620; Ferguson, i, 164.

[8] *Diary*, 5 July 1650; ed. Bray, 1870, 207.

[9] *Life of Anthony à Wood written by himself* in *Athenæ Oxonienses*, ed. Bliss, 4 vols., 4°, London, 1813–20; I, lii; Gunther, (1), i, 22 f.; Warton, *Life and Literary Remains of Ralph Bathurst*, 1761, 44; Turnbull, *Ann. Sci.*, 1953, ix, 265; S. Ayscough, *A Catalogue of the Manuscripts preserved in the British Museum*, 2 vols. 4°, 1782, i, 494, gives MSS. of Peter Sthalius as *Cursus Chymicus inceptus*, 1668; *Praeparationes Chymicae*, and *Course of Chymistry*.

[10] *Op. cit.*, xcviii; Gunther, (1), 1923, i, 43 f.; 1926, iii, 308 f.

laboratory at Altdorf, and Hjärne's established by Charles XI at Stockholm, were opened. The first professor of chemistry was Robert Plot (Borden, Kent; December 1640–30 April 1696 or 7) and the first demonstrator Christopher White.[1] Plot lectured on Monday, Wednesday, and Friday for a month. He

FIG. 19. ROBERT BOYLE, 1627–1691.

resigned in 1689 and was succeeded by Edward Hannes of Christ Church, knighted in 1705 as physician to Queen Anne.

No manuscript of Plot's lectures on chemistry is known. About 1677 he went into partnership with two other men to make and sell chemical remedies, and later he tried to interest patrons in a great secret which he claimed to have discovered. He published on the lamps supposed to have been found still burning in ancient tombs, which were extinguished when outer air was admitted, although one in a temple of Venus mentioned by St. Augustine was always exposed; Plot thought firedamp or phosphorus might be the explanation.[2] He also wrote on the production of salt and 'sand' (panscale) from brine.[3]

The lectures were continued in 1704 by John Freind (1675–1728), M.D., of Christ Church,[4] who was assisted by Richard Frewin. Salt-glazed stoneware was discovered by John Dwight, B.C.L. (1661) of Christ Church, who set up a manufacture at Fulham.[5] Dr. John Wall (1708–76) of Merton, invented Worcester porcelain in 1751, when the works was set up.[6]

[1] Gunther, (1), i, 43; iii, 308 f.; 1939, xii, 333 f. (lectures, 355; laboratory, 405; writings of Plot, 409); id., Nature, 1927, cxix, 492; Taylor, Ambix, 1949, iv, 67.

[2] Plot, Phil. Trans., 1684, xiv, 806–11; J. Ozanam and M. Montucla, Recreations in Mathematics and Natural Philosophy, tr. C. Hutton, 1803, iv, 496–516.

[3] Phil. Trans., 1682–3, xiii, 96.   [4] Gunther, (1), i, 53; iii, 74 f.

[5] Plot, Natural History of Oxfordshire, 2 ed., Oxford, 1705, 255; Gunther, i, 27.

[6] Gunther, (1), i, 57.

It is not easy to decide which of Boyle's researches were carried out in Oxford, but we know that his first experiments with the air-pump were made there, probably the experiments on burning bodies in vacuum, and the experiments for his *History of Cold*.[1] The *Sceptical Chymist* was published in 1661, and *Experiments on Colours* in 1663/4. The work on the noctiluca (phosphorus) was probably begun in London. Although often away, Boyle did not finally leave Oxford until April 1668. On 13 November, 1668, his sister wrote from Pall Mall, London, that she would 'gladly receive your order to put my backhouse in posture to be employed by you, against your coming, that you might lose no time after'.[2] It was said:

'His greatest delight is chymistrey. He haz at his sister's a noble laboratory, and severall servants (prentices to him) to looke to it. He is charitable to ingeniose men that are in want, and foreigne chymists have had large proofe of his bountie, for he will not spare the cost to gett any rare secret.'[3]

About 1680 Boyle fitted up another laboratory in Southampton Street, Covent Garden, where his assistant was Ambrose Godfrey Hanckewitz (see p. 543), who reported that Boyle was tight with money but not mean.[4]

The origin of the Royal Society has been a subject of controversy and is of no importance to us. On one view, John Wilkins (1614–72) founded a Philosophical College as a group of young scientists which began to meet in London about the end of 1644; this included Wallis, Jonathan Goddard and other medical men, and from 1648 Boyle and William Petty. Most of the members were Puritan and Parliamentary, and when Oxford fell to Cromwell in 1646 several members were appointed to professorships there. Wilkins founded in Oxford a Philosophical Society which lasted until 1690; he was Warden of Wadham College, where Wren, Sydenham, Mayow, and Sprat resided. On the Restoration many scientists appointed by the Commonwealth left Oxford. In November, 1660, the scientists met at Gresham College, London, and proposed the formation of a 'College for the promoting of Physico-Mathematical Experimental Learning', Wilkins being elected chairman. The King's approval was gained by Sir Robert Moray, who was made president, and on 15 July, 1662, King Charles II sealed the charter of the Royal Society for the Improvement of Natural Knowledge, Lord Brouncker being the first president, and Wilkins and Oldenburg the first joint secretaries.[5]

[1] Gunther, (1), i, 16.
[2] *Works*, ed. Birch, v, 563.
[3] Gunther, (1), i, 10.
[4] Ince, *Pharm. J.*, 1858, xviii, 157 (160).
[5] T. Sprat, *The History of the Royal Society of London*, 4°, London, 1667; 2 ed., 1702 (Andrade, *Nature*, 1960, clxxxv, 343); T. Birch, (1), 4 vols. 4°, 1756–7 (containing extracts from the journals not otherwise published); T. Thomson, (3), 1812; Rodwell, *Chem. News*, 1865, xi, 291; C. R. Weld, *A History of the Royal Society, with Memoirs of the Presidents*, 2 vols., London, 1848; M. Ornstein, *The Rôle of Scientific Societies in the Seventeenth Century*, Chicago, 1928 (summary in *Isis*, 1929, xii, 154); D. Stimson, 'Comenius and the Invisible College', *Isis*, 1935, xxiii, 373; Masson, *Three Centuries of Chemistry*, 1925, 23 f.; Sir Henry Lyons, *The Royal Society 1660–1940: A History of its Administration under its Charters*, Cambridge, 1944; L. T. More, 1944, 54, 61; Miss R. H. Syfret, *Notes and Records of the Royal Society*, 1948, v, 75–137; Turnbull, *ib.*, 1953, x, 101–30; on some Royal Society MSS. in the British Museum, S. Ayscough, *A Catalogue of the Manuscripts preserved in the British Museum*, 1782, i, 435–73.

John Evelyn on 1 Sept. 1659[1] 'communicated to Mr. Robert Boyle, son to the Earle of Corke, my proposal for erecting a philosophic mathematic College', and[2] 6 January 1661, 'the first meeting since the King's return', was made F.R.S. and member of the Council of 'the Philosophic Society now meeting at Gressham College . . . but it had begun some yeares before at Oxford, and was continued with interruption here in London during the Rebellion.' On 16 January 1661 he 'went to the Philosophic Club, where was examin'd the Torricellian experiment',[3] and on 3 December 1661 he was thanked by the 'philosophic assembly' for having made 'honourable mention of them by the name of Royal Society' in a dedication of a book.[4] On 29 August 1662 the Council and Fellows went to Whitehall to 'acknowledge his Majestys royal grace in granting our charter, and vouchsafing to be himself our Founder'.[5]

The Royal Society had been anticipated by the Accademia de' Lincei (1603) and Accademia del Cimento (1657) in Italy, and the Collegium Naturæ Curiosorum in Nürnberg (1652).

Another neglected foreigner who is said to have had the idea of the weekly meetings in London about 1645 was a German, Theodore Haak.[6]

Boyle was chosen as president in 1680 but declined to act (probably on religious scruples) and Wren was appointed.[7] The *Philosophical Transactions* began to appear in 1665.[8]

The earlier volumes of the *Philosophical Transactions* contain some very odd material[9] and some of the discussions and experiments recorded by Birch leave little to be desired, e.g. 31 July 1661 'to torment a man presently with the sympatheticall powder'. Cruel experiments with animals were a very popular feature of the earlier meetings. Sarton[10] announced that the academies founded in the seventeenth century were extremely helpful in the development of the experimental method and the sceptical or critical spirit, but Thorndike[11] gave many examples, including a rich collection from the *Philosophical Transactions*, to show that 'their spirit was curious and credulous rather than sceptical and critical'.

Wilkins became Master of Trinity College, Cambridge, in 1659 but lost this post on the Restoration. In 1668, by the influence of the Duke of Buckingham he became Bishop of Chester. Wilkins, a good mathematician, thought the Moon was inhabited, and invented several contrivances for producing perpetual motion.[12]

Henry Oldenburg (Bremen, c. 1626–London, August 1677), who sometimes wrote his name 'Grubendol', Master of Theology of Bremen, came to England as consul. He acted as a tutor at Oxford (he was travelling tutor of Richard Jones, later Lord Ranelagh, who married Boyle's sister Katharine), where he became acquainted with the founders of the Royal Society, of which he became secretary. He published the *Philosophical Transactions* until June, 1677 (no. 136), when he was succeeded by Hooke. He seems to have acquired a very English outlook. He carried on a voluminous correspondence with foreign

---

[1] *Diary*, ed. Bray, 1870, 261.   [2] *Ib.*, 270.   [3] *Ib.*, 271.   [4] *Ib.*, 281.
[5] *Ib.*, 288.   [6] P. R. Barnett, *Ann. Sci.*, 1957 (1959), xiii, 205.
[7] Weld, 1848, i, 270; Evelyn, *Diary*, ed. Bray, 1870, 423, says Boyle was chosen on 30 November 1680.
[8] McKie, *Phil. Mag.*, commemoration number, 1948, 122 (The Scientific Periodical from 1665 to 1798); *id.*, *ib.*, 133 (Scientific Societies to the end of the Eighteenth Century).
[9] Thorndike, viii, 252 f.   [10] *Chymia*, 1950, iii, 155.   [11] viii, 261.
[12] Ch. 9 of his *Mathematicall Magick* (1648, 4 ed. 1691) is 'Of perpetual motion. . . . The several ways whereby it has been attempted, particularly by Chemistry'; Andrade, *Ann. Sci.*, 1936, i, 4; McColley, *ib.*, 330.

scientists and was for a time imprisoned in the Tower.[1] Boyle's letters to Oldenburg were probably burnt.[2]

Boyle's separate works are very numerous and most of them appeared in several editions.[3] If an essay by 'Philaretus' on 'An Invitation to a free and generous Communication of Secrets and Receits in Physick'[4] is by Boyle, as has been supposed, it would be his first published work.

The items in the following list of numbered titles are quoted in the text. The titles are those of the first editions (usually abbreviated) and the format is octavo unless otherwise stated.

I. New Experiments Physico-Mechanicall, Touching the Spring of the Air, Oxford, 1660.

IA. *Ib.*, 2 ed., New Experiments Physico-Mechanical Touching the Air. Whereunto is added A Defence of the Authors Explication of the Experiments, against the Obiections of Franciscus Linus, And, Thomas Hobbes, Oxford, 1662 (contains Boyle's law).

IB. *Ib.*, 3 ed., New Experiments Physico-Mechanical, Touching the Air, . . . Oxford, 1682.

IC. A Continuation of Nevv Experiments Physico-Mechanical, Touching the Spring and Weight of the Air, and their Effects. The I. Part. . . . Whereto is annext a short Discourse of the Atmospheres of Consistent Bodies, Oxford, 1669 (published late in 1668; the Royal Society copy has on the title page 'Presented from ye Author to ye R. Society, Novemb. 30, 1668'; Fulton does not mention this).

ID. Experimentorum Novorum Physico-Mechanicorum Continuatio Secunda . . . , Oxford, 1680; English tr., A Continuation of New Experiments Physico-Mechanical. . . . Together with a Description of the Engines wherein they were made, Oxford (printed in London), 1682.

II. Certain Physiological Essays Written at distant Times and on several Occasions, London, 1661. (Containing: (a) Concerning the Unsuccessfulness of Experiments, (b) Specimens of an Attempt to make Chymical Experiments Usefull to Illustrate the Notions of the Corpuscular Philosophy, (c) The History of Fluidity and Firmnesse Begun).

IIA. *Ib.*, 2 ed. (with additional tract (d) Of Absolute Rest in Bodies), London, 1669.

III. The Sceptical Chymist, London, 1661 (see p. 497 for full title).

IIIA. *Ib.*, 2 ed., The Sceptical Chymist. . . . To which in this Edition are subjoyn'd divers Experiments and Notes about the Producibleness of Chymical Principles, Oxford, 1680.

IV. Some Considerations touching the Vsefulnesse of Experimental Naturall Philosophy, Oxford, 1663, 1664 (written about 1650).

IVA. Some Considerations touching the Vsefulnesse of Experimental Naturall Philosophy. . . . The Second Tome, Containing the later Section Of the Second Part, Oxford, 1671 (mostly written about 1658).

V. Experiments and Considerations Touching Colours, London, 1664 (published in December, 1663; Hall, *Ann. Sci.*, 1955, xi, 27). Latin tr. London, 1664, etc.

VI. New Experiments and Observations Touching Cold, Or an Experimental History of Cold, Begun, London, 1665.

[1] Brewster, *Memoirs of Newton*, 1855, i, 143 (Oldenburg's part in disagreements between Hooke and Newton); Birch, 1757, iii, 353 (d. 1677); Spinoza, *Opera*, ed. Bruder, Leipzig, 1844, ii, 143–204 (25 letters of Oldenburg to Spinoza on the latter's criticisms of Boyle's *Physiological Essays*, 1661, with descr. of expts. and illustrs. of apparatus); *Phil. Trans.* abdgd., 1809, i, 1; H. Rix, *Nature*, 1893, xlix, 9–12; Andrade, *ib.*, 1935, cxxxvi, 358, 603; James, *ib.*, 1935, cxxxvi, 603; McKie, *Notes and Records of the Royal Society*, 1948, vi, 28; letters from Sir Thomas Browne in 1669, in *The Letters of Sir Thomas Browne*, ed. Keynes, 1946, 387.

[2] R. E. W. Maddison, *Nature*, 1950, clxv, 981; *Ann. Sci.*, 1957 (1958), xiii, 90.

[3] Sotheran *Catalogues* 773 (1919), nos. 34–38, 1564–1584; 780 (1922), nos. 403–408; 789 (1924), nos. 4492–4520; 795 (1925), nos. 7397–7405; 9804–9805; 800 (1926), nos. 10307–10367; 806 (1927), nos. 14040–43; 832 (1932), nos. 5073–5083; 837 (1933), nos. 1836–7; Fulton, 1932, 1933.

[4] In *Chymical, Medicinal, and Chyrurgical Addresses*, ed. Hartlib, London, 1655; Rowbottom, *Ann. Sci.*, 1950, vi, 376.

VIA. *Ib.*, 2 ed. Together with an Appendix, containing some promiscuous Experiments and Observations, Oxford (printed in London), 1683.

VII. The Origine of Formes and Qualities, (According to the Corpuscular Philosophy) . . . , Oxford, 1666.

VIIA. *Ib.*, 2 ed., Augmented by a Discourse of Subordinate Formes, Oxford, 1667.

VIIB. Hydrostatical Paradoxes, Made out by New Experiments, (For the most part Physical and Easie), Oxford, 1666.

VIII. Tracts . . . About, (*a*) [An Introduction to the History of Particular Qualities; this is prefixed to the work], (*b*) The Cosmicall Qualities of Things, (*c*) Cosmicall Suspitions, (*d*) The Temperature of the Subterraneal Regions, (*e*) The Temperature of the Submarine Regions, (*f*) The Bottom of the Sea, Oxford, 1671.

IX. Tracts of (*a*) A Discovery of the Admirable Rarefaction of the Air, (*b*) New Observations about the Duration of the Spring of the Air, (*c*) New Experiments touching the Condensation of the Air by meer Cold, (*d*) The admirably differing Extension of the same Quantity of Air rarefied and compressed, London, 1671.

X. An Essay about the Origine and Virtues of Gems, London, 1672.

XI. Tracts . . . Containing New Experiments, touching the Relation betwixt Flame and Air. And about Explosions. An Hydrostatical Discourse . . . To which is annex't An Hydrostatical Letter . . . , Oxford (printed in London), dated 1672 but the 'Hydrostatical Letter' is dated February 13, 1673. (A copy was presented to the Royal Society on 9 April 1673, Birch, 1757, iii, 83.)

XII. Essay of the Strange Subtilty, Great Efficacy, Determinate Nature of Effluviums. To which are annext New Experiments to make Fire and Flame Ponderable: Together with A Discovery of the Perviousness of Glass, London, 1673.

XIII. Tracts Consisting of Observations about the Saltness of the Sea: An Account of a Statical Hygroscope and its uses: Together with an Appendix about the Force of the Air's Moisture: A Fragment about the Natural and Preternatural State of Bodies. To all which is premis'd a Sceptical Dialogue about the Positive or Privative Nature of Cold, Oxford (printed in London), 1674.

XIV. Tracts [six]: Containing Suspicions about some Hidden Qualities of the Air . . . , London, 1674 (presented to the Royal Society 7 January 1675: Birch, 1757, iii, 174)

XV. Experiments, Notes, &c About the Mechanical Origine or Production of divers particular Qualities . . . ; containing (*a*) Heat and Cold, (*b*) Tasts [*sic*], (*c*) Odours, (*d*) Imperfection of the Chemist's Doctrine of Qualities, (*e*) Alkali and Acidum, (*f*) Volatility, (*g*) Fixtness, (*h*) Corrosiveness, (*i*) Precipitation, (*j*) Magnetism [dated 1676], (*k*) Electricity; Oxford (printed in London), 1675. The work is dated 1676 by Birch (Boyle, *Works*, 1744, i, 66); item (*b*) was read to the Royal Society in April 1675 (Birch, (1), 1757, iii, 217) but the complete book was presented in October 1676 (*ib.*, 321).

XVI. The Aerial Noctiluca . . . , London, 1680.

XVII. New Experiments, and Observations, Made upon the Icy Noctiluca, (with title page, A Chymical Paradox, which was intended to accompany IIIA), London, 168½ (*sic*).

XVIII. Memoirs for the Natural History of Humane Blood, Especially The Spirit of that Liquor, London, 168¾ (*sic*).

XIX. Experiments and Considerations about the Porosity of Bodies, London, 1684.

XX. Short Memoirs for the Natural Experimental History of Mineral Waters,. London, 168⅘ (*sic*).

XXI. An Essay of the Great Effects of Even Languid and Unheeded Motion. Whereunto is Annexed An Experimental Discourse of some little observed Causes of the Insalubrity and Salubrity of the Air, London, 1685.

XXII. Of the Reconcileableness of Specifick Medicines to the Corpuscular Philosophy, London, 1685.

XXIII. Medicinal Experiments; or a Collection of Choice Remedies, London, 1692.[1]

[1] According to Birch, *Works*, i, *Life*, 85, this grew out of 'Receipts sent to a Friend in America: printed in 1688', probably *Some Receipts of Medicines for the most part Parable and Simple*, London, 1688 (BM 1038. f. 45), with 'five decads'; 1692 with five more decads; 1693–4; 6 ed. 1718 with additional recipes. Fulton says 'the first two volumes, credulous though they seem, are certainly written by Boyle' (1688 and 1692, presumably), but later issues

XXIIIA. A Disquisition About The Final Causes of Natural Things . . . To which are Subjoyn'd . . . Some Uncommon Observations About Vitiated Sight, London, 1688.

XXIV. Medicina Hydrostatica: or, Hydrostaticks Applied to the Materia Medica. . . . To which is subjoin'd, A Previous Hydrostatical Way of Estimating Ores, London, 1690.

XXV. Experimenta & Observationes Physicæ (in English), London, 1691.

XXVI. The General History of the Air, Designed and Begun, London, 1692.

Besides the above and other works not of interest to us, Boyle published some papers in the *Philosophical Transactions*,[1] including:

XXVII. An Experimental History of Cold, 1664–5, i, 8, 46.

XXVIII. A New Frigoric Experiment, 1666, i, 255, no. 15.

XXIX. New Observations about Respiration, 1670 (2 papers), v, 2011, 2035, nos. 62, 63.

XXX. On Ambergris (Amber Greece), 1673, viii, 6113, no. 97.

XXXI. New Experiments about the weakened spring, and some un-observed effects of the air, 1675, x, 467, no. 120.

XXXIA. A New Essay-Instrument, 1675, x, 329, nos. 115–16 (hydrostatic balance for testing gold and silver coin, etc.; plate); An extract of a letter, relating to the Essay Instrument described in the foregoing tract.

XXXII. Of quicksilver growing hot with gold, 1675–6, x, 515, no. 122.

XXXIII. Account of making phosphorus, 1692–3, xvii, 583 (dated 30 September 1680).

XXXIV. A way of examining water, 1692–3, x, 627.

The most complete collected edition of Boyle's works is by Thomas Birch:

The Works of the Honourable Robert Boyle. To which is prefixed the Life of the Author, 5 vols., f°, London, 1744 (preface dated Nov. 1743); with corrected text, 6 vols., la. 4°, London, 1772 (pagination quite different from 1744 ed.); with full-length portrait by Kersseboom engraved by Baron, and medallion portrait on each t.p. by Gravelot, which is said to be a better likeness than Kersseboom's. This edition has an index which is not reliably complete. Birch's life, published separately in 1744, 8°, contains the incomplete autobiographical 'An Account of Philaretus during his minority', and previously unpublished material collected by Burnet and Wotton. The last volume of Birch's edition of Boyle's *Works* contains letters to Boyle. All refs. in the text are to the 1744 ed.

Wilson[2] said no one but the proof reader had ever been through the whole of Boyle's works in the immense folios of Birch, and I am in no position to contradict him. Wilson[3] reports that Samuel Johnson said everybody praised Boyle but nobody read him. The rambling verbose style is a great impediment to an appreciation of the contents. Boyle repeats himself a great deal both in the same and different works, and the same experiment is repeatedly described — perhaps this happened with experiments he made himself, e.g. the action of oil of vitriol on turpentine and the precipitation of silver from a solution of silver nitrate by copper. Boyle's *Occasional Reflections upon several Subjects, whereto is premis'd a Discourse about such kind of Thoughts* (London, 1665; reprinted, Oxford and London, 1848),[4] dedicated to his sister 'Sophronia' (Lady Ranelagh) and written at Stalbridge, is parodied in Swift's *Meditations*

(1694, etc.) contain spurious material. An ed. of 1685 mentioned by Fulton, in 'A Bibliography of Richard Lower and John Mayow', *Oxford Bibliogr. Soc. Proc. and Papers*, 1936, iv, 28, is probably a mistake for 1688; he says 'no copy . . . was ever traced'.

[1] List in Fulton, 1932, 127 f. [2] 1862, 245. [3] *Ib.*, 183. [4] Birch, ii, 138 ff.

upon a Broomstick (1711)[1] and the suggestion of *Gulliver's Travels* comes from the same source; Boyle also influenced Montesquieu's *Lettres persanes*.[2]

Epitomised collected editions of Boyle's works were issued by Richard Boulton of Brazennose College, Oxford[3] (1), and by Peter Shaw (2):

(1) The Works of the Honourable Robert Boyle, Esq. Epitomiz'd, 4 vols. 8°, London, 1699 (i)–1700 (ii–iv), with portrait by Kersseboom engraved by Van der Gucht; *id.*, The Theological Works of the Honourable Robert Boyle Esq. Epitomiz'd, 3 vols. 8°, London, 1715.

(2) The Philosophical Works of the Honourable Robert Boyle Esq; Abridged, methodized and disposed under the General Heads of Physics, Statics, Pneumatics, Natural History, Chymistry, and Medicine. The whole illustrated with Notes, containing the Improvements made in the several Parts of natural and experimental Knowledge since his time, 3 vols. 4°, London, 1725; 1733 (less esteemed); with the portrait by Kersseboom engraved by R.W.

Shaw's text is easier to read (apart from the punctuation) than Birch's, but jumbles separate works into sections under topics with misleading titles, so that it is very difficult to trace the original.

According to Zeitlinger there is only one *collected* Latin edition of Boyle's works, published in Geneva,[4] with a portrait by F. Diodati differing considerably from the one by Kersseboom in the English works; the first volume has the title *Opera varia*, the others have separate title-pages and pagination for each work; the second volume contains the *Chymista scepticus*, etc.;[5] but a collection of ten works (also issued separately) was published there[6] and another complete Latin edition was published in Venice.[7]

In the prefaces to nearly all his books Boyle apologises for hasty publication: the sheets of his manuscript had been lost, he was moving, plagiarism had hurried him into premature printing, or something else had happened.[8] He seems to have led a rather hectic life, and this, with his frail health, makes it very surprising that he wrote (or dictated) so much. Boyle says his papers were stolen so that the discoveries could be published by others;[9] his 'Advertisement' is addressed to 'Mr. J.W.', perhaps Johann Seger von Weidenfeld, who was received by Boyle and perhaps acted as his assistant; he published an alchemical work.[10]

[1] M. Nicolson and N. M. Mohler, *Ann. Sci.*, 1937, ii, 299, 405.   [2] Cap, 1857, i, 175.
[3] With imprimatur of John Hoskyns, Vice-President of the Royal Society.
[4] *Opera varia . . . cum Indicibus necessariis*, 6 vols. sm. 4°, Geneva (S. de Tournes), 1680–1696.
[5] Sotheran, *Cat.* 839 (1934), nos. 334–335. The Latin Geneva edition was pirated and Boyle objected that various works reprinted in it were not given the dates when they were originally issued, *Phil. Trans.*, 1676, xi, no. 130, p. 766.
[6] *Roberti Boyle . . . Opera Varia . . . Cum Indicibvs necessariis & multis Figvris ænis*, 4°, Geneva, de Tournes, 1677; of eleven treatises, with the same title, *ib.*, 1680–88 (both in BM); the last is, apparently, part of the complete work mentioned above.
[7] *Opera Omnia, Nunc primum in unum Corpus redacta, ac tres in Tomos distributa: Accurate recognita, & à mendis repurgata . . .*, 3 vols. 4°, Venice, 1696–7, with portrait and 15 plates; Quaritch *Cat.* 551, 1938, no. 517; the Bibliothèque Nationale has many Latin works of Boyle; *Catalogue Gén.*, 1908, xviii, 653–6; Gmelin, (1), i, 98 f., who gives a long and detailed bibliography of Boyle's works, refers to collected Latin editions of 'Cologne' (3 vols. 4°, 1680–95–95), Geneva (4–5 vols. 4°, 1714), and Venice (4°, 1695), but the first was really published in Geneva.
[8] Fisher, 1945, 137.
[9] *An Advertisement of Mr. Boyle's about the loss of many of his Writings*, 1688; Fulton, 1932, 117; in *Works*, i, 142.
[10] *De Secretis Adeptorum, sive De Usu Spiritus Vinis Lulliani Libri IV*, 12°, Hamburg, 1685 (BM 1035. a. 31); 8°, Leipzig, 1768 (Ferguson, ii, 538, who says it was first publ. 4°, London,

According to Miss Clerke[1] a French 'collection of Boyle's writings' appeared in Paris in 1679 with the title *Recueil d'Experiences*. Apart from the *Aerial Noctiluca* (German, 1682), *Specific Medicines* (French, 1689), and *Medicinal Experiments* (German, 1692), Fulton gives no early French or German translations of works by Boyle, and the work mentioned by Miss Clerke is a translation of part of XV.[2]

J. C. Fischer[3] had said that Boyle, who had an active correspondence with foreign scientists, 'repeated many of their experiments and published his results, so that his countrymen have ascribed discoveries to him to which he had no claim.' This habit still remains, but has always been more prevalent on the Continent. Condorcet[4] devotes only two pages to Boyle in his éloge, whilst a French mediocrity like Malouin has 13 pages.

Stahl had a high opinion of Boyle but thought he would have done better to have devoted more of his time to chemistry (Boyle, den ich in experimentis wegen seiner accuratesse sehr æstimire, und der besser gethan hätte, dass er an statt seines Elateris die Chymie, die einen gantzen Menschen erfordert, tractiret hätte).[5] Boerhaave[6] praises Boyle highly and says he made great progress from Van Helmont. Boyle was severely criticised by Venel (not one of the most notable French chemists).[7] Fourcroy,[8] who praised Boyle, said the English chemists of the 17–18 cents. had mostly written sparingly, reserving their discoveries, whilst the French published their industrial processes to the advantage of the English. Whatever else can be said of Boyle, he can hardly be accused of writing 'sparingly'. He describes his experiments clearly, unlike many of his foreign contemporaries such as Glauber, only rarely 'reserving' some 'secrets' or adopting a mystifying style. In English authors of the early eighteenth century he is regularly characterised as 'incomparable', but Brande[9] said he 'cannot be said to have fathomed the depths of science'.

Boyle has been called[10] the founder of modern chemistry, for three reasons: (1) he realised that chemistry is worthy of study for its own sake and not merely as an aid to medicine or as alchemy — although he believed in the possibility of the latter; (2) he introduced a rigorous experimental method into chemistry; and (3) he gave a clear definition of an element and showed by experiment that the four elements of Aristotle and the three principles of the alchemists (mercury, sulphur and salt) did not deserve to be called elements or principles at all, since none of them could be extracted from bodies, e.g. metals. In many ways he was anticipated by Van Helmont, whose works he studied with care and to whom he frequently refers as an authority.

1684, from Schmeider, 1832, 455; Jöcher, iv, 1852 gives no date or place); Engl. tr. *Four Books . . . concerning the Secrets of the Adepts*, 4°, London, 1685, BM 1033. i. 18. (1.).

[1] DNB, 1908, ii, 1031.

[2] In *Recueil d'experiences et Observations sur le Combat qui procède du mélange des Corps sur les Saveurs, sur les Odeurs, sur le Sang, sur le Lait*, sm. 8°, Paris 1679, (8 ll., 262 pp., 1 leaf. Engraved fp. and one plate). It contains the three works mentioned in the title, the first by Nehemiah Grew (see p. 567), the second by Boyle (pp. 125 f.), and the third by Leeuwenhoek (on blood and milk).

[3] 1802, ii, 204.   [4] *Œuvres*, 1847, ii, 104–6.   [5] *Fundamenta Chymiae*, 1747, iii, 312.

[6] *Oratio de Chemia suos Errores expurgante*, 1718; in *Elementa Chemiae*, Leyden, 1732, 39–40.

[7] Art. 'Chymie' in Diderot's *Encyclopédie*, reprinted in *Encyclopédie Méthodique*, 1796, iii, 299 f.

[8] *Ency. Méthod.*, 1796, iii, 303, 331–6 (art. 'Chimie') defended him.

[9] *Manual of Chemistry*, 6 ed., 1848, I, xxx.

[10] Rau, *Grundlage der modernen Chemie*, Brunswick, 1877, 81: Wäre es statthaft, die Entstehung einer Wissenschaft an einen bestimmten Namen zu knupfen, so wäre Boyle der Gründer der wissenschaftlichen Chemie.

Boyle's most celebrated book is his *Sceptical Chymist*, III (1661) (p. 492):

1. The Sceptical Chymist: or Chymico-Physical Doubts & Paradoxes, Touching the Spagyrist's Principles Commonly call'd Hypostatical, As they are wont to be Propos'd and Defended by the Generality of Alchymists. Whereunto is præmis'd Part of another Discourse relating to the same Subject. By The Honourable Robert Boyle, Esq.; 8°, London, 1661. Fulton, 1932, 34; T. L. Davis, *Isis*, 1926, viii, 71; E. Färber, *Z. angew. Chem.*, 1927, xl, 948; Sarton, *Chymia*, 1950, iii, plate, Figs. 2, 3, two eds. 1661 with titles (*a*) as above and (*b*) as of the 1680 ed., but Davis and Fulton say the latter was a second t.p. inserted after p. 34 in the copy (or copies) he describes. An Oxford ed. of 1661 mentioned by Cap, *Études*, 1857, i, 151, and Gunther, (1), i, 15, is unknown. It is a common mistake to say this ed. was anonymous.
2. The Sceptical Chymist: or Chymico-Physical Doubts & Paradoxes, Touching the Experiments whereby Vulgar Spagirists Are wont to Endeavour to Evince their Salt, Sulphur and Mercury, to be the True Principles of Things. To which in this Edition are subjoyn'd divers Experiments and Notes about the Producibleness of Chymical Principles, [Anonymous], 8°, Oxford, 1680; printed in 1679 but 'not publickly expos'd to Sale' until the beginning of January, 1680. Birch, *Works*, i, *Life*, 39; Fulton, 1932, 35; the paginations in (1) and (2) are closely similar. (2) was reproduced and ed. by M. M. P. Muir, in *Everyman's Library Series*, 1911 (who wrongly says (1) was publ. in Oxford). The 'Advertisement' about the date of printing and publication is given by Birch, *Works*, i, 39, 293; the date for being 'expos'd for sale' is usually $16\frac{79}{80}$ but in the Patent Office copy is $16\frac{79}{78}$. The imprimatur is dated 30 May 1677. The book was printed in London. *The Producibleness of Chymicall (sic) Principles* has a sep. t.p. and pagin. (268 pp.).
3. Abridged German tr. by E. and M. Färber, Ostwald's *Klassiker*, 1929, no. 229.
4. Latin ed. 1662: Chymista Scepticus vel Dubia ac Paradoxa Chymico-Physica, Circa Spagyricorum Principia, Vulgo dicta Hypostatica..., 8°, London, J. Crooke, and Rotterdam, Arnold Leers, 1662; other eds. Rotterdam, 1668; also included in the Opera Omnia, Geneva, 1677, 1680 (L'Art Ancien *Cat*. aa (1938), 27); the London Library has Beddoes's copy of the 1668 ed.

The *Sceptical Chymist* was soon known in France; it was reviewed for the Académie in 1669 by Duclos[1] but it was not translated. It is written in a good, though rather prolix, style, enlivened with touches of humour, as when the alchemists are compared with 'the Navigators of Solomon's Tarshish Fleet, who brought home ... not only Gold, and Silver, and Ivory, but Apes and Peacocks too', since their theories 'either like Peacock's feathers make a great shew, but are neither solid nor useful; or else, like Apes, if they have some appearance of being rational, are blemish'd with some absurdity or other' which makes them appear ridiculous.[2] It contains the germs of many ideas elaborated by Boyle in his later publications.

A draft of the work, prepared between 1651 and 1657, 'Reflexions on the Experiments vulgarly alleged to evince the 4 Peripatetique Elements, or ye 3 Chymicall Principles of Mixt Bodies', contained in Oldenbourg's commonplace book written late in 1660,[3] contains parts reproduced in the printed work, lays stress on Van Helmont's tree experiment and gives details of Boyle's experiments on this subject, but has little on corpuscular theory. It is more concise and clearer than the printed work and was probably intended for circulation.

The value of 'the registering of doubts' was emphasised by Francis Bacon, who thought 'that use of wit and knowledge is to be allowed, which laboureth

---

[1] *Hist. Acad. des Sciences*, 1733, i, 79; *ib.*, 23, review of Boyle's *De formarum origine*.
[2] *Sceptical Chymist*, 1661, 429.
[3] R. Soc. MS. M.I., text and comment. in M. Boas, *Isis*, 1954, xlv, 153–68.

to make doubtful things certain'; the 'entry of doubts are so many suckers or spunges to draw use of knowledge'.[1]

In an early work (IV, IVA) Boyle argued for the experimental method and for the corpuscular (atomic) theory as opposed to Aristotelian philosophy, and gave examples of the practical utility of science, especially chemistry, in medicine and technical arts. The second part,[2] on the technical arts, is very noteworthy and shows a surprisingly wide knowledge, acquired by reading, conversations with practitioners, and experiments. Boyle's earlier interests seem to have been medical.

Boyle complains of the obscure and enigmatical language of the alchemists and of Paracelsus and his followers and of the equivocal sense of many of their statements: '. . . it seems to me that their writings, as their furnaces, afford as well smoke as light; and do little less obscure some subjects, than they illustrate others. And though I am unwilling to deny, that it is difficult for a man to be an accomplished naturalist, that is a stranger to Chymistry; yet I look upon the common operations and practices of chymists, almost as I do on the letters of the alphabet, without whose knowledge it is very hard for a man to become a philosopher; and yet that knowledge is very far from sufficient to make him one'.[3]

'Now a man need not be very conversant in the writings of chemists to observe, in how lax, indefinite, and almost arbitrary senses they employ the terms of salt, sulphur and mercury. . . . But I will not give the chemists any rise to pretend, that the chief fault, that I find with their hypothesis, is but verbal; though that itself may not a little blemish any hypothesis, one of the first of whose requisites ought to be clearness.'[4]

'And indeed I fear that the chief reason, why chymists have written so obscurely of their three principles, may be, that not having clear and distinct notions of them themselves, they cannot write otherwise than confusedly of what they but confusedly apprehend.'[5]

'The chemist's salt, sulphur, and mercury themselves are not the first and most simple principles of bodies, but rather primary concretions of corpuscles, or particles more simple than they, . . . by the different conventions or coalitions of which minutest portions of matter are made those differing concretions, that chemists name salt, sulphur, and mercury.'[6]

'. . . . there is a great difference betwixt the being able to make experiments, and the being able to give a philosophical account of them.'[7] 'I observe that of late chymistry begins, as indeed it deserves, to be cultivated by learned men, who before despised it.'[8]

'. . . . it has long seemed to me none of the least impediments of the real advancement of true natural philosophy, that men have been so forward to write systems of it, and have thought themselves obliged either to be altogether silent, or not to write less than an entire body of physiology . . . it not unfrequently happens, that . . . a writer, to vent some few peculiar notions or discoveries of his own, presumes to write a whole body of philosophy.'[9]

[1] *Advancement of Learning*, ii; Bacon, *Works*, 1857, iii, 364.
[2] *Works*, iii, 135.   [3] III; *Works*, i, 348.   [4] XV (*d*); *Works*, iii, 595.
[5] III; *Works*, i, 330.   [6] XV (*d*); *Works*, iii, 600.
[7] III; *Works*, i, 331.   [8] III; *Works*, i, 290.   [9] II; *Works*, i, 192.

Boyle, like Helmont, accepted the possibility of transmutation and the reality of alchemy.[1] He says:[2] 'I scruple not to acknowledge, there are things which incline me to suspect that some in the world . . . may have *Arcana*, to which most of the processes I reserve . . . may prove little more than trifles.' He speaks of the possibility of transmutation in several other works[3] and says: 'I am tempted to think, that silver may have in it a sulphur (to speak in the chymists language) which maturation is able to graduate into a golden one.'[4]

Boyle describes an experiment in which he melted gold with copper, then acted upon the alloy with a *menstruum peracutum* made by pouring aqua fortis upon butter of antimony and distilling. There remained a white powder which gave silver on melting with borax.[5] He accepted Van Helmont's alkahest (see p. 218)[6] but was doubtful about the divining rod.[7] Boyle says he had in 1652 extracted a mercury (not common mercury) from antimony and other metals which with finely divided gold ('calx of gold') amalgamated with the production of much heat, as he found by mixing them in the palm of the hand. Such a 'spiritually impregnated mercury' will pass through leather and can be distilled; 'for the sake of mankind resolve not to teach the preparation.' It was much denser than common mercury. On distilling an amalgam of gold with this 'invigorated mercury' in a glass vessel on a sand bath, the bottom of the retort was coloured turquoise inclining to yellow. By long decoction of it, the glass was coloured a beautiful ruby.[8] Boyle's *Historical Account of the Degradation of Gold* (London, 1678)[9] is, as the sub-title describes it, 'a strange chemical narrative.' Boyle is said to have procured the repeal of Statute 5 of Henry IV against 'multiplication of gold' in 1689,[10] as he was aware of its absurdity.

About 1685 an English bishop told Manget[11] a story of a meanly-dressed stranger who visited Boyle and performed an experiment in which antimony and some other common metals were melted in a crucible and a powder projected on them. He went away, promising to return, but did not do so, so that Boyle ordered the lid to be taken off the crucible and found in the crucible a yellow metal having all the properties of gold. As proof of this, the bishop showed Manget about half an ounce of this alchemical gold (hæc est illa ipsa materia cujus portionem non sine admiratione vidi apud Illustrissimum Virum historiam mihi benevole ut in hujus enarrationis initiô dixi communicantem).

In his collection of medical recipes (excluding the doubtful work XXIII), omitted from the Latin works, Boyle shared the credulity of Van Helmont and

[1] Locke's letter to Newton, 1692, sending a recipe from Boyle, who had formed a Company in London to 'multiply' gold, Sotheby, *Catalogue of the Newton Papers*, 1936, 29; Wilson, 1862, 230; Thorndike, viii, 192.

[2] IV (anon.); *Works*, i, 422.

[3] E.g., letters to Glanville and from Worsley, *Works*, v, 244, 258.   [4] II (*a*); *Works*, i, 215.

[5] VII; *Works*, ii, 513 f., where he describes other experiments on transmutation and asserts somewhat guardedly his belief in 'more noble and subtile corpuscles' capable of effecting it.

[6] III; *Works*, i, 314 f., 326, etc.   [7] II (*a*); *Works*, i, 220.

[8] On the Incalescence of Quicksilver with Gold, *Phil. Trans.*, 1675–6, x, 515–33, no. 122 (in Latin, tr. by Oldenburg); IIIA; *Works*, i, 410; the Latin text of the *Phil. Trans.* paper was reproduced by Henrici Screta in the *Miscellanea Curiosa sive Ephemeridum Medico-Physicarum Academiæ Naturæ Curiosorum*, Decuriæ II, Annus Primus (Anni 1682), Nürnberg, 1683, Obs. xxxiv, pp. 83–93.

[9] *Works*, iv, 13; T. S. Kuhn, *Isis*, 1951, xlii, 296; 1952, xliii, 12, 123.

[10] *Works, Life*, i, 83; Parkes, *Chemical Catechism*, 5 ed., 1812, 293.

[11] *Bibliotheca Chemica Curiosa*, 1702, i, pref.

Francis Bacon; he successfully used some of the moss growing on a dead
man's skull, 'a present out of Ireland (where it is less rare, than in most other
countries)', in stopping bleeding of the nose when merely held in the hand,[1]
and often refers gravely to the wonderful cures effected by the most absurd
remedies. He thought that gold and gems might be useful medicines,[2] and did
not doubt the efficacy of talismans, amulets, and suspensions.

A physician who had travelled in cold countries gave him some rings of the true elk's
hoof (some such rings sold as his being counterfeit or of no efficacy) as a cure for cramp;
although the ring did not cure severe cramp it succeeded with a moderate one, and even
if worn on the finger it cured cramp in the foot, so that Boyle kept it by his bed-
side and much regretted that he lost it. 'But enough, if not more than enough', he
concludes.[3]
He reports from Le Févre that the *ens primum* of balm had rejuvenated an old hen,
but he was a little sceptical about the efficacy of the weapon salve.[4] He discourses on
the 'resuscitable plants' which grow from their ashes, as reported by Bartholinus.[5]

The weaker side of Boyle's character and of his writings is mainly emphasised
by Thorndike,[6] whose chapter is a useful corrective to some other recent rather
fulsome accounts.

Boyle says 'it is acknowledged on all hands, that matter cannot be annihilated',[7] and this had, in fact, been emphasised by Francis Bacon (p. 403),
Van Helmont, and others, and goes back to the old Greek philosophers.

'Chymists do universally take it for granted, that in distillations carefully
made, the matter, that passes into the receiver, or at least ascends, together
with the remains, or *caput mortuum*, amount to just the weight, that the entire
body had before distillation.'[8] He says[9] '. . . besides those which the Chymists
are pleased to name hypostatical [i.e., salt, sulphur and mercury], most bodies
contain two others, Phlegme and Earth', and 'I see no sufficient cause why
they should be excluded from the number of Elements'. Salt, sulphur and
mercury cannot be extracted from gold. 'I can easily enough sublime Gold
into the form of red Chrystalls of a considerable length; and many other ways
may Gold be disguis'd, and help to constitute Bodies of very different Natures
both from It and from one another, and nevertheless be afterwards reduc'd to
the self-same Numerical, Yellow, Fixt, Ponderous and Malleable Gold, it
was before its commixture.' The same is true of mercury. Hence 'the Corpuscle of Gold and Mercury, though they may not be primary Concretions of
the most minute Particles of matter, but confessedly mixt Bodies, are able to
concurre plentifully to the composition of several very differing Bodies, without losing their own Nature or Texture, or having their cohesion violated by
the divorce of their associated parts or ingredients'.[10] In copper nitrate also, the
copper is only disguised: the nitric acid may be separated by heat and the

[1] XIX, XXI; *Works*, iv, 212, 322–4; Bacon, *Sylva Sylvarum*, x, 998, says this moss could be
procured in Ireland.
[2] IV; *Works*, i, 505.   [3] XXI; *Works*, iv, 322–4.
[4] IV; *Works*, i, 519, 530.
[5] XXV; *Works*, v, 102; T. Bartholinus, *De Usu Nivis*, Copenhagen, 1661, 57 (not 17, as
Boyle says), quoting 'Quercetanus, Pharmacopoea Dogmaticorum, c. 35, n. 4'; the first book
includes E. Bartholinus, *De Figura Nivis*, sep. pag., p. 24 on Arbor Dianæ.
[6] viii, 170–201.   [7] VII; *Works*, ii, 473.
[8] XVIII; *Works*, iv, 172.   [9] IIIA, 1680, 189.   [10] III, 1661, 40.

copper by precipitation.[1] It must be remembered that this idea had already been expressed by Van Helmont (p. 221).

One of Boyle's main arguments was that substances separated from bodies by fire may not be 'homogeneous' (i.e. all of the same kind), and may vary with the conditions (e.g. heating in closed vessels or in the air). This had been anticipated by Van Helmont.[2] Boyle's statement that not necessarily three principles are separated also comes from Van Helmont,[3] and many of Boyle's examples are given by him. Boyle also dealt with the five elements (salt, sulphur, mercury, phlegm, and earth).[4]

Pierre Guisson, M.D., of Avignon, who had been with Boyle in Oxford, put forward similar views in 1666, saying that he had sweated for weeks volatilising Venetian talc by sublimations, although he was not a son of the art or fully initiated into its mysteries. The chemists never demonstrated the three principles, many bodies are not divided by fire, and some are divided into five heterogeneous parts.[5]

Boyle's definition of an element is as follows:[6]

I mean by Elements, as those Chymists that speak plainest do by their Principles, certain Primitive and Simple, or perfectly unmingled bodies; which not being made of any other bodies, or of one another, are the Ingredients of which all those call'd perfectly mixt Bodies are immediately compounded, and into which they are ultimately resolved.

(By 'perfectly mixt bodies' he means chemical compounds as distinguished from mechanical mixtures.) 'Elements and Principles' are 'those primitive and simple Bodies of which the mixt ones are said to be composed, and into which they are ultimately resolved'.[7] He argues at some length that the action of fire upon bodies, previously used as a method of resolution into elements, is unsatisfactory. Boyle's definition is practically identical with the Stoic doctrine given by Diogenes Laertios:[8] 'an element is that from which particular things first come to be at their birth, and into which they are finally resolved.'

Boyle emphasised[9] that 'there is not any one determinate number of elements to be uniformly met with in all the several sorts of bodies allowed to be perfectly mixt'. His objections to the three alchemical principles were not found convincing by Morhof,[10] and Boyle was not so clear and dogmatic in his discussion of the chemical elements as could have been wished for his time. He seems to regard the different elements as being made up of some primary

[1] III, 1661, 154.
[2] Tria prima chym. princ., 68: *Ortus Medicinæ*, 1652, 332: Quid enim clarius hoc mechanica, ut elucescat, ignem esse confectorum primorum; adeoque nec esse in se prima, neque præ-existere talia in concreto, qualia separantur indĕ per ignem?
[3] *Ib.*, 49; 1652, 329: quædam corpora non continent tria, sed unico vel duobus tantum sunt contenta.
[4] III; *Works*, i, 327, 336.
[5] *Epistolica dissertatio de anonyme libello (circa abbreviatum veræ medicinæ genus) ubi potissimum eventilatur principiorum chymicorum hypothesis*, included with sep. t.p. and pagination (24 pp.) in P. Potier, *Opera Omnia*, 8°, Frankfurt, 1666.
[6] III, 1661, 350; A. Crum Brown, *The Development of the Idea of Chemical Composition*, Inaugural Lecture, Edinburgh, 1869, 9 f.; T. L. Davis, *Isis*, 1931, xvi, 82.
[7] III, 1661, 16.
[8] *Lives and Opinions of Eminent Philosophers*, vii, 137; tr. Yonge, 1891, 309; tr. R. D. Hicks, 1925, ii, 241.
[9] III; *Works*, i, 324; T. S. Kuhn, *Isis*, 1952, xliii, 12.   [10] (1), 1747, ii, 252–3.

matter, and the varying properties of the elements might be due to the different shapes and motions of the particles of the primary matter:[1]

'The greatest part of the affections of matter, and consequently of the Phænomena of nature, seems to depend upon the motion and the contrivance of the small parts of Bodies',[2] so that 'there is no great need that Nature should alwaies have Elements before hand, whereof to make such Bodies as we call mixts',[3] and 'the difference of Bodies may depend meerly upon that of the schemes whereinto their Common matter is put . . . so that according as the small parts of matter recede from each other, or work upon each other . . . a Body of this or that denomination is produced'.[4] If Boyle had made up a table of bodies which he regarded as satisfying his definition of an element, such as gold, copper, and sulphur, some chemists would have followed him, but he left the matter in too indefinite a form and nowhere says what he considered to be elements.

Boyle believed in the atomic theory. He considered chemical combination to occur between the elementary particles and had some good ideas on chemical affinity. He says:[5]

'There are Clusters wherein the Particles stick not so close together, but that they may meet with Corpuscles of another Denomination, which are dispos'd to be more closely United with some of them, than they were among themselves.'

Boyle's knowledge of the atomic theory was mainly derived from Gassendi (p. 459), whose writings were made known to Boyle in a letter from Samuel Hartlib in May, 1648:[6] 'Your worthy friend and mine Mr. *Gassend* is reasonable well, and hath printed a book of the life and manners of *Epicurus* [see p. 459]. . . . He hath now in the press at Lyons the philosophy of Epicurus, in which I believe we shall have much of his own philosophy, which doubtless will be an excellent work.' In 1661, Boyle recommends 'the learned *Gassendus*, his little *Syntagma* of *Epicurus's* philosophy, and that most ingenious gentleman Mons. Descartes his principles of philosophy'.[7] Boyle, in turn, made the theory known to Newton (see p. 474). The very small primary particles aggregate to *corpuscles* which behave as particles of the chemical elements.[8]

Boyle always tried to explain chemical phenomena on 'mechanical' principles, making use of Descartes' ideas or the atomic theory. Sublimation is due to the fine grinding of the particles of bodies produced by their rubbing against one another; particles which are hooked, branched, 'or other very irregular or inconvenient figures', which cause them to be 'stopped or detained by other bodies, or intangled among themselves, and consequently very difficult to be carried upwards', have these excrescences broken off so that the particles become 'smooth or otherwise fitly shaped to clear themselves, or to be disentangled from each other'.[9] When saltpetre is distilled with oil of

---

[1] M. Boas, *Isis*, 1950, xli, 261; T. S. Kuhn, *ib.*, 1952, xliii, 12–36; Boas, *Osiris*, 1952, x, 412–541.
[2] III, 1661, 333.   [3] III, 1661, 411.   [4] III, 1661, 422–3.
[5] *Ib.*, 153; cf. VII, *Works*, ii, 471.   [6] *Works*, v, 257.
[7] II; *Works*, i, 194; E. Bloch, *Isis*, 1913, i, 377; R. S. Westfall, *Ann. Sci.*, 1956 (1957), xii, 63, 103.
[8] III; IIIA, 1680, 37; *Works*, i, 300.   [9] XV*f*; *Works*, iii, 610 f.

vitriol, the latter breaks up the particles of the salt so that 'the disposed particles . . . which amount to a great portion of the whole, will be made easily enough to ascend . . . in the form of spirits'.[1] There is a 'mechanical origin of corrosiveness', the solvent corpuscles entering the body through pores into which they are impelled by the pressure of the atmosphere or 'by the trans-cursion of some subtile ætherial matter' which agitates them so that they, 'like so many little wedges and levers may be enabled to wrench open or force asunder the little parts between which they have insinuated themselves'; these, however, being only conjectures.[2] Kuhn[3] says Boyle emphasised the novelty of his 'corpuscular hypothesis', and thought that it actually differed in some ways from the contemporary atomic theory. Galileo in his *Dialogues concerning two new Sciences* (1638) had 'favored atomism before or contemporary with Gassendi and Descartes and foreran the "corpuscular philosophy" of Robert Boyle', but the work was not 'as widely and rapidly circulated as one might think' (Mariotte had only just read it in 1668); it describes experiments with compressed air and an air-pump, and weighing air.[4]

Some of Boyle's experiments and opinions were criticised by Spinoza (whose qualifications as a chemist are obscure) on the basis of the philosophy of Descartes.[5] Oldenburg in a letter of 1663 to Spinoza[6] told him that 'our Boyle is not of the number of those who hold so fast to their own opinions that they do not need to take account of the agreement between them and the phenomena':

Est noster Boylius ex eorum numero, qui non adeo suæ rationi confidant, ut non velint cum ratione convenire phænomena. Magnum præterea discrimen ait intercedere inter obvia experimenta, circa quæ quid adferat natura quæque interveniant, ignor-amus, et inter ea, de quibus certo constat, quænam ad ea afferantur.

Boyle was inclined to follow the Epicurean notion of the motion of particles as an innate property, since one must begin with some hypothesis. He would not, however, adopt it as his own view although the phenomena can be well explained by it:

quæ volunt, motum particularis inesse connatum . . . quam tamen propterea suam non faciat, sed adhibeat ad sententiam suam contra chymicos et scholas sustinendum, duntaxat ostendens ex hypothesi memorata rem posse bene explicari.

Boyle's atomic theory[7] is more correctly a 'corpuscular' theory, since he disregards the *indivisibility* of the particles. He mentions the works of Basso, Descartes, Magnenus, etc. (see p. 455) and 'the learned Gassendus's little, but ingenious, *Syntagma Philosophiæ Epicuri*' as if he had only glanced at them.[8] The 'corpuscularian' point of view is opposed to the Peripatetic doctrine of

---

[1] XV*f*; *Works*, iii, 617.

[2] XV*h*; *Works*, iii, 624 f.; on the relation of Boyle's corpuscular philosophy to Descartes and atomism, see Burtt, 1925, 162 f., 174 f., 264 f. (ether and relations to Newton).

[3] *Isis*, 1951, xlii, 296; 1952, xliii, 12, 123.   [4] Thorndike, vii, 38, 44.

[5] Letter from Oldenburg to Boyle, Oct. 1665, in *Works*, v, 339.

[6] Spinoza, *Opera*, ed. Bruder, Leipzig, 1844, ii, 166–7; for Spinoza's criticisms of Boyle, *ib.*, 151–62, 170 f.

[7] Lasswitz, (1), 1890, ii, 261–93; Mabilleau, *Histoire de la Philosophie Atomistique*, Paris, 1895, 432 f., Boas, *Isis*, 1950, xli, 261; *Osiris*, 1952, x, 412; Kuhn, *Isis*, 1952, xliii, 12–56.

[8] VII; *Works*, ii, 456.

substantial forms (see p. 380), especially in Boyle's *The Origine of Formes and Qualities, According to the Corpuscular Philosophy* (Oxford, 1666) and in his *Specimen of an Attempt to make Chymical Experiments Usefull to Illustrate the Notions of the Corpuscular Philosophy*, one of his *Physiological Essays* (1661). The theory is also extensively used in other works. Put in a few words, his view was that the properties (qualities) of a body are not due to the possession of a substantial form but to the effects of the size, shape, position (which he calls 'texture' or 'a certain disposition or contrivance of parts in the whole') and motion of the corpuscles of which it is composed.

P. P. Wiener,[1] in a valuable criticism, thought Boyle had 'no true apprecia- tion of scholasticism' because he had not read the Latin works and relied on 'the shallow self-styled Aristotelians around him', but an examination of *The Origine of Formes and Qualities* does not seem to me to bear out this opinion. Boyle says he 'had the curiosity to resort to several both of the more and of the less recent scholastic writers, and to some of the best metaphysicians to boot', but he had 'purposely forborn the reading of some very much'. He names a large number of authors, including the theologian William Pemble,[2] who had criticised the doctrine of forms. Boyle also gives Latin quotations and seems to have had quite a good knowledge of the subject.[3]

The invisible corpuscles [atoms] of the primary matter can form stable groupings of corpuscles of the second order, 'primary concretions', which are the true components, 'seeds or immediate principles' or 'primary clusters', of sensible bodies such as water, earth, salt, etc.[4] Their association forms com- pound bodies. The production of a body from the parts into which it has been resolved by analysis is regarded as a strong argument for the corpuscular theory.[5]

Boyle's idea of affinity is similar to that of Jungius (p. 420), since he con- sidered it a result of the appropriate shapes of the corpuscles as permitting them to adhere together, and not as a result of an attractive force. He is in advance of Jungius, however, in rejecting a *qualitas occulta* as a possible cause and insisting on a purely mechanical explanation.[6] He says:

Nor do I think, it ought to be incredible, that acid salts, as well as others, should be producible by the various splittings, attritions, coalitions, and changes of texture, which may be caused in several ways, and especially by the operations of the fire; which most active agent, making a vehement and various agitation of all the minute parts, that a body consists of, may, consonantly to what hath above been intimated, split or break some of them, and as it were grind others against one another; and in short, so alter their bulk, figure and motions, as to make them fit to stab or cut the tongue, and other bodies, that they work on, after the manner of those bodies we call acid.[7]

Boyle emphasised that 'we must consider each body, not barely as it is in itself, . . . but it is a part of the universe, and consequently placed among a

---

[1] The Experimental Philosophy of Robert Boyle, *Philosophical Review*, 1932, xli, 595–609.
[2] *De formarum origine. Editio posthuma*, 12°, London, 1629 (BM 8403. aaa. 26. (1.)); ed. R. Capel, 12°, Cambridge, 1650 (?) (BM 527 a. 17. (1.)).
[3] Cf. R. S. Westfall, *Ann. Sci.*, 1956 (1957), xii, 103.
[4] VII; *Works*, ii, 461, 466, 470 f., 474 f.   [5] II (*b*); *Works*, i, 227 f.
[6] Lasswitz, (1), 1890, ii, 280.
[7] IIIA; *Works*, i, 378, see also *ib.*, 384, 387 (cleaving the nitrous corpuscles, or rubbing them one against another).

great number and variety of other bodies, upon which it may act, and by which it may be acted on in many ways'.[1] His explanations of the physical properties of liquids and solids are based on the corpuscular theory.[2] In liquids, the particles are mobile and hard (since liquids are practically incompressible) and have many pores between them; in solids they adhere, not by reason of finer particles (spirit) between them but because of the texture of their surfaces. The paper 'On the Superficial figures of fluids'[3] deals with capillary phenomena.

'It seems not absurd to conceive that at the first Production of mixt Bodies, the Universal Matter wherof they among other Parts of the Universe consisted, was actually divided into little Particles of several sizes and shapes variously mov'd.' . . . 'Neither is it impossible ['possible' in original] that of these minute Particles divers of the smallest and neighbouring ones were here and there associated into minute Masses or Clusters, and did by their Coalitions constitute great store of such little primary Concretions or Masses as were not easily dissipable into such Particles as compos'd them.'[4]

Boyle[5] quotes an 'experiment' said to demonstrate the existence of the four elements in wood, viz. its resolution into fire, air (smoke), water (bubbling from the ends of the logs) and earth (ash) on combustion, and criticises it in a way very like that previously published by Gassendi.[6]

Boyle's criticsm of the Peripatetic doctrines is soundly based on chemical experiments. In place of the substantial forms he proposed twelve 'principles of variation in bodies', viz. matter, local motion, bigness, shape, rest, posture or position, order or consecution, texture or modification, pores, effluviums, mixture, and the universal fabric of things.[7] Not one of these has a truly experimental basis.[8] They were proposed in order to get over the difficulty that 'it is incredible that so great a variety of qualities as we actually find in natural bodies should spring from principles so few in number as two, and so simple as matter and local motion'. He clearly recognised that *chemical* properties could not be explained by purely mechanical principles.

The 'Aristotelian' doctrine of qualities is rather loosely stated by Boyle.[9] There is:

but one universal matter of things . . . *materia prima* . . . the portions of this matter seem to differ from one another but in certain qualities or accidents, fewer or more; upon whose account the corporeal substance they belong receives its denomination, and is referred to this or that particular sort of bodies; so that if it come to lose, or be deprived of those qualities, though it ceases not to be a body, yet it ceases from being that kind of body as a plant, or animal, or red, green, sweet, sowre, or the like.

According to Sir William Hamilton[10] Boyle in his works VII and VIII (*a*)

[1] VII; *Works*, ii, 464.
[2] IIc; *Hydrostatical Paradoxes, made out by New Experiments, for the most part Physical and Easy*, Oxford, 1666; *Works*, i, 240 f., ii, 409 f.; Lasswitz, (1), ii, 283 f.; R. A. Smith, *Manchester Mem.*, 1856, xiii, 120 f.
[3] *Phil. Trans.*, 1676, xi, 775; *Works*, iv, 1.   [4] III; IIIA, 1680, 37; *Works*, i, 300.
[5] III; *Works*, i, 350 f.   [6] Gassendi, *Opera*, 1658, i, 241.
[7] VII, VIII, ch. 13; *Works*, ii, 460, iii, 76; Fisher, 1945, 76; Kuhn, *Isis*, 1952, xliii, 12, 123.
[8] Wiener, *Philos. Rev.*, 1932, xli, 595 (602).   [9] III, 1661, 151.
[10] Ed. of *Works of Thomas Reid, D.D.*, 6 ed., Edinburgh, 1863, 2 vols. (contin. pagin.), ii, 833, note D.

clearly distinguished 'primary' and 'secondary' properties before Locke, and probably suggested the nomenclature adopted but deformed by the latter.

Locke's *Essay concerning Human Understanding* was published in 1690 but the outlines were drawn up in 1670. Locke speaks of colours, sounds, etc., as 'secondary qualities' of bodies, although he realised that they are sense impressions and do not exist in bodies at all; and 'it can only confuse the reader when Locke, while seeking to demonstrate this, sanctions a mode of expression that implies the error which he aims to destroy'.[1] The distinction between 'primary' and 'secondary' qualities was known to Galileo,[2] but it really goes back to Demokritos (Vol. I) and Boyle may have got it through Gassendi (see p. 461).

Locke's distinction between primary and secondary qualities was proved to be philosophically unsound by Berkeley, although it still plays a useful part in science. His thesis that all knowledge (except perhaps logic and mathematics) is empirical in that it is derived through the senses, and that there are no innate ideas or principles (as Plato and Descartes assumed) runs into difficulties which Hume avoided by dropping the assumption that sensations have external causes. Locke rejected the scholastic idea of 'essence', which he said is a purely verbal definition of a general term.

In *A Free Inquiry into the vulgarly received Notion of Nature*, apparently directed mainly against Spinoza, Boyle complained that 'nature' had been used with eight different meanings, all of which, he argues, are not in conformity with observation.[3] He also criticised the over-emphasis on mathematics as against experimental science; it is an abstract science dealing with things not really in contact with natural phenomena.[4] The 'corpuscles' were possibly composite and in theory divisible. Boyle did not recognise weight as a primary property of the atoms. Their motions are not spontaneous but guided by God and other 'incorporeal agents'. He added corpuscular 'texture' to the primary or 'catholic' qualities (bulk, figure and motion or rest); the 'secondary' or 'sensible' qualities include colour, smell, sound, hotness and coldness, and depend on the size, shape and motion of the corpuscles. The arrangement and order of the corpuscles make up what 'by one comprehensive name we call the texture of the body',[5] and 'the greatest part of the affections of matter, and consequently of the phænomena of nature, seems to depend on the motion and contrivance of the small parts of bodies'.[6]

Boyle acquiesced in the corpuscular theory of light but considered, with Francis Bacon, that heat is the result of the agitation of the minute parts of bodies,[7] and supposed that 'the grand efficient of forms is local motion'.[8]

Boyle thought that minerals perhaps grew in mines, possibly because of some 'operation of the air'.[9] He drew up a list of 'Enquiries concerning Mines',[10] and some detailed replies were sent to him by Samuel Colepresse, of Underwood, near Plymouth, in 1667.[11] An anonymous account of mines[12] was by Colepresse. Boyle's interesting work on gems[13] develops the hypotheses that they were formed from solutions and that their colours are due to metallic or mineral matters incorporated in them. He does not reject their medicinal virtues.

---

[1] Ueberweg, (2), 1874, ii, 85.   [2] Burtt, 1925, 173; G. W. Spriggs, *Archeion*, 1929, xi, 1–12.
[3] *Works*, iv, 358; Fisher, 1945, 36, 137.   [4] IV; *Works*, iii, 156.
[5] IV, VII, VIII; *Works*, i, 447 f.; ii, 451 f., 474 f.; iii, 76 f.   [6] III; *Works*, i, 353.
[7] IIA, IV; *Works*, i, 282, 476.   [8] VII; *Works*, ii, 483.   [9] XIV; *Works*, iii, 459.
[10] *Phil. Trans.*, 1666, i, no. 19, 330; *Works*, v, 193.   [11] Boyle, *Works*, v, 573.
[12] *Phil. Trans.*, 1671, vi, no. 69, 2096.   [13] X; *Works*, iii, 214.

Boyle drew up an elaborate scheme of enquiries relating to mineral waters, and made some experiments. By weighing them in a thin glass bulb he found that 'as divers mineral waters (that contain salts in them) are considerably heavier, than common water, so some, especially ferruginous waters, are impregnated with so fine a substance, as to be lighter than common water'. The differences for all, however, amounted only to about 19 grains in 3 oz. 4 dr. as a maximum.[1] As chemical tests he used indicators, solution of galls, and evaporation and examination of the residue for crystals. He made artificial mineral waters, including a chalybeate water with solutions of marcasite in acids.[2]

Boyle agreed with Van Helmont (222) that air and water are not interconvertible,[3] but he was doubtful if water is convertible into earth. He repeated Van Helmont's experiment (223). Instead of a willow tree he used a vegetable marrow, which took less time to grow, but he concluded that the substance of the marrow came mostly from the dust particles floating in the air.[4] He obtained earth by distilling rain water in glass vessels, and water by the combustion of spirit of wine. Boyle also grew plants ('vinca pervinca, raphanus aquaticus, spearmint and even ranunculus') in phials of water and was inclined to believe that there was 'a real assimilation and transmutation of the water'.[5] From an ounce of pure water he obtained by repeated distillation 6 drachms of a white, light, tasteless earth, insoluble in water. Boyle expressed some doubts and regretted that the specimen of earth had been lost. A friend had told him that he had obtained the white powder from rain water distilled 200 times in very clean glasses, getting nearly ¾ oz. from 1 oz. water. Boyle thought it ought to be tried 'whether the glass body, wherein all the distillations are made, loses of its weight, anything near so much as the obtained powder amounts to'. His attitude was very cautious.[6]

Such experiments were criticised by Woodward,[7] who thought the water contained 'great numbers of small terrestrial particles', vegetable and mineral; he did not try distilled water in his experiments. The *Nouveau Cours de Chymie*[8] says Helmont's and Boyle's experiments on growing plants from water were fallacious, as they used well water containing dissolved earth. Helmont used rain water, but even this could contain some earth. The conversion of water into earth is denied. Some experiments on distilling water in lead and glass vessels were made by Francesco Redi, more famous as a biologist.[9]

Boyle was the first in England to use a *sealed* alcohol thermometer ('thermoscope' or 'weather glass'),[10] although these had been used previously by the

---

[1] XX; *Works*, iv, 243.
[2] XX; *Works*, iv, 247. Besides the Latin translation (slightly rearranged) of XX in the 1718 ed. of Nicolaus Vallerius's *Tres elegantes Tractatus* mentioned by Fulton, 1932, 101, it also appears in the *Tentamina Physico-Chymica circa aquas thermales Aquiägranenses* [=Aix], Leyden, 1699, of the same author.
[3] I; *Works*, i, 33.　　　　　　　　　　[4] III, 1661, 107; *Works*, i, 312.
[5] VII; *Works*, ii, 498 f., 519 f., 522.　　　[6] Meldrum, *Isis*, 1934, xx, 396 (412).
[7] *Phil. Trans.*, 1699, xx, 193, no. 253; abr. ed., 1809, iv, 382.
[8] Paris, 1723, i, 11 f.
[9] *Esperienze intorno à diverse cose naturali*, 4°, Florence, 1671; Thorndike, viii, 30.
[10] VI, XV (*b*); *Works*, ii, 249, 264; iii, 570.

Academicians of Florence.[1] One of the original Florentine thermometers is now in the Cavendish Laboratory in Cambridge.[2] Libri[3] compared the scale of a Florentine thermometer with the Reaumur scale; $0°$ Fl. $= 15°$ R. and a degree Fl. was $\frac{4}{5}°$ R. Boyle used the freezing of oil of aniseed as a fixed point for an alcohol thermometer.[4]

The Florentine thermometer was hermetically sealed at the top. The graduations were small beads of white enamel sealed on the stem, the intermediate divisions being beads of green glass or black enamel, although 'these lesser divisions are best made by the eye'. They also used a mercury thermometer.[5]

The Accademia del Cimento was founded (as a result of Galileo's discoveries) in Florence on 19 June, 1657, and was dissolved by Prince Leopold in 1667, according to Poggendorff[6] in exchange for a Cardinal's hat. It consisted of nine members only: Giovanni Alfonso Borelli, Candido and Paolo del Buono, Lorenzo Magalotti (who wrote the account of the proceedings), Alessandro Marsili, Antonio Oliva, Francesco Redi, Carlo Renaldini, and Vicenzo Viviani.[7]

A Latin translation of the *Saggi* was made by Peter van Musschenbroek (Leyden; 14 March 1692–19 September 1761), professor of mathematics and physics in Duisburg (1719), Utrecht (1723) and Leyden (1739), who added a valuable commentary and described his own pyrometer and investigations on thermal expansion of solids.[8]

Boyle made some experiments to try if water is compressible. Water in a flask with a long neck ('philosophical egg') was put under an air-pump receiver. The water rose slightly in the neck on pumping out the air, and on letting in the air it subsided. (This is a modern method of measuring compressibility.) A pewter sphere filled with water and soldered up was hammered, then pierced with a needle, when the water spirted out in a jet.[9] Honoratus Fabri[10] compressed water into a globe fitted with a tap, which was closed. On opening the tap, water spirted out. In 1666 the Accademia del Cimento described their experiments (see p. 405).

Boyle says that contrary to the usual opinion, water expands when it freezes.[11] Sir Thomas Browne[12] says water expands on freezing but thought this might be due to the extrication of bubbles of air. Boyle[13] says: 'I know the

---

[1] *Saggi di naturale Esperienze fatte nell' Accademia del Cimento*, f°, Florence, 1666 (some copies dated 1667), 1 f.; 2 ed., 1691; tr. by R. Waller, *Essayes of Natural Experiments*, 4°, London, 1684, 2.

[2] Glazebrook, *Heat and Light*, Cambridge, 1907, 16.

[3] *Ann. Chim.*, 1830, xlv, 354–61; *Ann. Phys.*, 1831, xxi, 325–30.   [4] VI; *Works*, ii, 246.

[5] Poggendorff, (2), 248.   [6] *Geschichte der Physik*, Leipzig, 1879, 351; *id.*, (2), 215.

[7] Summary of the *Saggi* in Rosenberger, 1889, ii, 162 f.; list of members in Poggendorff, (2), 217 f.; of contents of *Saggi*, *ib.*, 230 f.; G. Tiraboschi, *Storia della Letteratura Italiana*, Florence, 1812, viii, 57, 240, 381.

[8] *Tentamina Experimentorum Naturalium Captorum in Academia del Cimento . . . quibus, commentarios nova experimenta, et orationem de methodo instituendi experimenta physica addidit*, 4°, Leyden, 1731 (BM 536. k. 11; with 32 plates); Vienna, Prague and Trieste, 1756 (BM 536. k. 16); French tr. of this in *Collection Académique* (*Étrangère*), 1755, i. A new edition by Vincenzio Antinori of the *Saggi* (terza edizione Fiorentina) contains many additions from previously unpublished manuscripts: *Saggi di naturali esperienzo*, 4°, Florence, 1841 (BM 715. k. 19).

[9] I; *Works*, i, 29; he does not mention Bacon (1620), see p. 405.

[10] *Physica*, Lyon, 1671, q. by J. C. Fischer, 1802, ii, 206.

[11] VI; *Works*, ii, 276.   [12] *Pseudodoxia Epidemica*, ii, 1; Browne, *Works*, 1927, i, 207.

[13] 'Of the positive or privative nature of cold', in XIII; *Works*, iii, 371.

learned Gassendus, and divers other philosophers, teach us that glaciation is performed by the entering of swarms of corpuscles of cold, as they call them, into the liquor', but he objects that water actually contracts up to a point as it becomes colder; other liquids such as pure spirit of wine are still contracting when water freezes, and oil of aniseed does not expand when it freezes. The explanation of the followers of Descartes is that 'the eel-like particles, wherof they suppose water to consist, are very remissly agitated, and their want of pliantness makes their contexture less close'. Even if they 'should lose all their flexibleness . . . it does not thence appear how they should acquire so vast a power to expand themselves in spite of opposition'. Boyle found that water begins to expand before it freezes,[1] i.e. he noticed the existence of a maximum density. Strong metal vessels are burst by the freezing of water contained in them.[2]

In freezing mixtures, nitric acid gave a lower temperature with snow than sulphuric or muriatic acid;[3] 1 lb. of sal ammoniac and 3 pints of water produced a freezing mixture.[4] That ice from sea water gives fresh water on melting[5] had, as Boyle said, been stated by Thomas Bartholinus.[6] It is also mentioned by Kircher[7] and S. Reyher.[8]

Boyle says:[9]

The dispute, which is the *Primum Frigidum*, is very well known among naturalists; some contending for the earth, others for the water, others for the air, and some of the moderns for nitre: but all seeming to agree, that there is some body or other, that is of its own nature supremely cold, and by participation of which, all other cold bodies obtain that quality.

Boyle, as a result of many experiments and much reasoning, came to the conclusion that cold is a privation of that local motion of the particles of bodies which is requisite to constitute heat, and is not a positive entity at all.[10] Gaffarel, de Clave, and Thomas Bartholinus[11] had reported that water impregnated with the saline parts of a plant gives ice in the shape of the plant, but Boyle[12] did not find this: ice from cabbage-water was not at all like a cabbage.

Aristotle[13] and his followers asserted that hot water would freeze sooner than cold, but Boyle in experiments described in detail (out of 'civility' to Aristotle) found that hot water took much longer to freeze than cold; if it was heated and then cooled again before beginning the experiment, it froze appreciably sooner than untreated water.[14] The question had been much discussed in the fifteenth century[15] and experiments on it were published in 1775 by Black.[16]

Roger Bacon[17] had denied that hot water freezes sooner than cold as 'contrary is excited by contrary', but he affirmed that Aristotle really said this occurs if they are

[1] VI; *Works*, iii, 252.   [2] XIII; *Works*, iii, 373.   [3] VI; *Works*, ii, 258 f.
[4] XVIII; *Phil. Trans.*, 1666, i, 255, no. 15; Abgd. ed., 1809, i, 86.   [5] VI; *Works*, ii, 296 f., 301.
[6] *De Nivis usu Medico Observationes variæ, Accessit D. Erasmi Bartholini de Figura Nivis*, Copenhagen, 1661, cap. iv, p. 42.
[7] *Mundus Subterraneus*, 1668, 166: cur glacies marina dulcis sit.
[8] *Experimentum Novum quo Aquae Marinae dulcedo . . . examinata describitur*, 4°, Kiel, 1677 (BM 7004. de. 1. (14)).
[9] VI; *Works*, ii, 307.   [10] XV (*a*); *Works*, iii, 375.   [11] *De Nivis Usu*, 1661, 57.
[12] II, VI; *Works*, i, 217; ii, 349, 384.   [13] *Meteor.*, i, 12, 348 a.
[14] VI; *Works*, ii, 341.   [15] Thorndike, iv, 206-8.   [16] *Phil. Trans.*, 1775, lxv, 124.
[17] *Opus Majus*, ed. Jebb, 1733, 446; tr. Burke, 1928, ii, 584.

poured on ice, 'and this is true'. Giovanni Battista Benedetti (1530–90), although criticising Aristotle in many things, still thought that heated water freezes faster and gives a harder and colder ice than does cold water.[1]

In a long 'Examen of Antiperistasis',[2] Boyle said it had been taught from Aristotle's time that heat and cold are endowed with self-invigorating powers, which each exerts when surrounded by its contrary, so as to prevent their mutual destruction. He filled a large pot with snow, put in a bottle of water, and set it over a fire. The water did not freeze, although the fire should have driven the cold of the snow into the water. Hippokrates said the stomach is hotter in winter, but, said Boyle, this is because 'the vital heat lodged in the heart' is always 'generating out of the blood and juices, that continually circulate through that part, great store of spirits and warm exhalations, which are wont to transpire through the pores of the skin'; he had found much more transpiration than Sanctorius (p. 442) affirmed. In winter, the pores are shut and the warm steams remain in the body and heat all parts of it.[3] He criticised very severely 'Mr. Hobbes's Doctrine touching Cold',[4] which taught, among other things, that ice is formed 'by the endeavour of the wind to raise the parts of the water, joined with the endeavour of the parts of the water towards the centre of the earth, the uppermost parts of the water will be prest together, and coagulated'.

The Florentine Academicians (1666) noticed that oil of vitriol mixed with water produces a great heat, but not when it is mixed with 'strong waters' (nitric acid). Nitre dissolved in water produces cold, and a mixture of sal ammoniac and water can freeze water in a thin phial, previously cooled in ice, put into it. Sal ammoniac dissolves in oil of vitriol with vigorous effervescence and smoke, yet the mixture grows cold.[5] Boyle[6] found that a mixture of sulphuric acid and sublimed volatile alkali (carbonate of ammonia) produces a great effervescence but becomes notably colder.

Boyle found that a cylinder of ice an inch long completely melted in the following times in minutes, in two sets of experiments, in the liquids named: oil of vitriol 5, 3; spirit of wine, 12, 13; aqua fortis $12\frac{1}{2}$; water 12, 26; oil of turpentine 44, 47; salad oil 52; air 64, 152.[7] He showed that, within the limits of experimental error, water does not change in weight on freezing or ice on melting.[8]

Aristotle's theory (Vol. I) that the saltness of the sea is due to the action of the sun's rays on the water, and hence is confined to the surface, was disproved by Boyle[9] by taking samples of sea water at different depths by means of vessels with valves, and showing, by determining the specific gravity, that they contained as much salt as on the surface. Scaliger[10] had reported a similar experiment in which the deeper water was found to be fresh. Boyle showed that sea water is not saturated with salt.

---

[1] *Diversarum Speculationum mathematicarum et physicarum liber*, Turin, 1585, 271; Thorndike, vi, 373.
[2] VI; *Works*, ii, 355.   [3] VI; *Works*, ii, 361.   [4] VI; *Works*, ii, 373.
[5] *Essayes of Natural Experiments*, tr. Waller, 1684, 153–4.
[6] XIII, XV; *Works*, iii, 374, 570.   [7] VI; *Works*, ii, 305.
[8] VI; *Works*, ii, 330.   [9] XIII; *Works*, iii, 378 f.
[10] *Exotericarvm Exercitationvm*, Ex. LI, cur mare salsum; Paris, 1557, 77.

Boyle's theory of cohesion, that it was due to the pressure of the air acting on two plates of glass, etc., which adhered when pressed together,[1] was criticised by Hobbes[2] on the ground that Boyle had shown that the plates do not fall apart in a vacuum, to which Boyle weakly replied that perhaps there was still some air left in the vacuum.[3] Hobbes had the idea that motion is the cause of hardness, whilst Boyle thought it was the cause of softness. So much can be done by 'mechanical principles'!

Boyle measured the force of capillary imbibition by soaking beans in water in a brass cylinder under a weighted piston.[4] He made experiments on magnetism[5] and electricity.[6] He was not the first to use the name 'electricity', which as a noun, along with the noun 'electrics' and adjectives 'electric' and 'electrical', was used by Sir Thomas Browne.[7] Whittaker[8] says Gilbert was the first to use the name electric (*De Magnete*, 1600, in Latin) for the force; Gilbert also put forward the idea that electrifiable bodies contain a 'humour', which was warmed or excited by friction and issued from them as an 'effluvium', forming an atmosphere around them. This idea was taken over by Boyle, who extended it to other 'effluviums', regarded as very attenuated or subtle fluids. Such 'effluviums', regarded as subtle emanations, on which Boyle wrote a special treatise (XII), were, of course, common property in his time and had replaced the Baconian 'spirits'. Meric Casaubon (1599–1671), prebendary of Canterbury, thought 'the greatest secrets of nature do depend from such kind of natural unsensible emanations'.[9] They have been replaced by electromagnetic fields and such things.

Boyle observed the phosphorescence of a diamond,[10] but this had been mentioned by Albertus Magnus[11] (see Van Helmont, p. 221). Boyle says that Italian goldsmiths had a method of colouring rock crystal and he suspected that the colour penetrated into 'thin flaws' or cracks in the stone.[12] The very valuable *oculus mundi* (hydrophane), which became transparent in water,[13] was a variety of opal.[14] Gems are formed from fluids pervaded by a petrific juice or spirit, and their colours are due to mineral juices.[15]

Boyle's book on *Colours*[16] contains material incorporated into Newton's *Opticks* (1704), describes for the first time the iridescence of metallic films and soap bubbles (structure colours), and gives recipes for mixing colours,

---

[1] I, II (a); Works, i, 45, 254.   [2] *Dialogus Physicus*, 1661.   [3] IA; Works, i, 143.
[4] VIII; Works, iii, 84.   [5] II (a); Works, i, 218; IV; XV (j); Works, iii, 643 f.
[6] *Experiments and Notes about the Mechanical Origin or Production of Electricity*, XV (k); Works, iii, 647 f.
[7] *Pseudodoxia Epidemica: Or, Enquiries into Very many received Tenents, And commonly presumed Truths*, f°, London, 1646 (approbation, March, 1645), bk. ii, ch. 1, p. 51 (electricity), ch. 4, p. 78 (of bodies electricall).
[8] *A History of the Theories of Æther and Electricity*, 1951, 35.
[9] *A Treatise concerning Enthusiasme, As it is an Effect of Nature . . .* , sm. 8°, London, 1655, 44 (2 ed. 1656); Thorndike, viii, 515.
[10] About a Diamond that Shines in the Dark, V; Works, ii, 81; X; Works, iii, 234.
[11] Poggendorff, (2), 246.
[12] X; XIX; Works, iii, 221; iv, 223; cf. the Stockholm Papyrus, Vol. I; Partington, *J. Soc. Chem. Ind.*, 1935, liv, 490.
[13] IV, XIX, XXV; Works, ii, 85; iv, 222; v, 95.
[14] Chaptal, *Elements of Chemistry*, 1791, ii, 130; in Boyle's time one the size of a pea sold in London for £200.
[15] X; Works, iii, 214 f.   [16] V; Works, ii, 1 f., 9, 19, etc.; J. C. Fischer, 1802, ii, 65–73.

preparing lakes, etc. This is one of Boyle's most interesting works; the experiments (including some chemical conjuring tricks) are described in such a way that the reader can almost see them being made.

When a tile is half blackened and half whitened, and is exposed to the sun, the blackened half becomes very hot, whilst the white portion remains cool.[1]

Boyle made a number of determinations of the specific gravities of solids and liquids by means of 'the hydrostatical balance' and the specific gravity bottle (used before by Van Helmont, see p. 220).[2]

Gold	19·640	Tin	7·320	Milk	1·030
Mercury	14·000	Sulphur	1·800	Urine	1·030
Lead	11·325	Salt	2·143	Camphor	0·996
Silver	11·091	Borax	1·714	Olive oil	0·913
Bismuth	9·700	Oil of vitriol	1·700	Spirit of turpentine	0·874
Copper	9·000	Spirit of nitre [HNO_3]	1·315	Spirit of wine	0·866
Steel	7·704–7·738	Spirit of salt	1·130	Cork	0·240
Iron	7·645	Human blood	1·040	Air	0·001¼

Since the density of rock crystal is about 2·65 and ice is lighter than water, the theory that the crystal is ice hardened by long and vehement cold is groundless.[3]

Boyle quotes some figures for the relative densities of water and air: Galileo, 400 : 1, Mersenne, 1356 : 1, Riccioli, 10,000 : 1; using different methods, Boyle found 938 : 1;[4] 650 : 1, or 1228 : 1, or $853\frac{17}{27}$: 1.[5] Other early values found with a globe and air pump are: de Volder, 970 : 1, Wolf, 846 : 1, s' Gravesand (using a method proposed by J. Bernoulli, 1685), 798 : 1, Homberg (1693), 800 : 1, Hunksbee, 885 : 1, and Halley, 800–860 : 1.[6] The correct value is 830 : 1 at 20° C.

Galileo[7] first tried to find the density of air. He used a rather large glass bottle with a narrow neck, into which air was forced by a syringe, so that it contained 2 to 3 times its natural volume, then it was counterpoised and the air allowed to escape, when it was found lighter. In another experiment, water was forced into a bottle containing air and the whole weighed. The air was then allowed to come to atmospheric pressure and the loss in weight was equal to the weight of a volume of air at atmospheric pressure equal to the volume of the water. This gave the result that water is about 400 times heavier than air.

Before describing Boyle's experiments with the air-pump an account will be given of the invention of the barometer by Torricelli and of the air-pump by Otto von Guericke.

Galileo[8] measured the 'resistance of a vacuum' by finding the weight

[1] V; *Works*, ii, 29.

[2] X; XIX; *Works*, iii, 237; IV, 219; XX, *Works*, iv, 243; XXIV, *Works*, v, 25 f., table on p. 36; cf. tables in Shaw's ed. of Boyle's *Works*, 1725, ii, 344–6, and see F. Bacon, p. 397.

[3] X; *Works*, iii, 229.   [4] I; *Works*, i, 55 f.; he says his balance turned with ¼ grain.

[5] IC; *Works*, iii, 61–2; Mersenne, *Hydravlica Pnevmatica; Arsqve Navigandi*, 4°, Paris, 1644, 140 f. (with figures of air thermoscope).

[6] J. C. Fischer, 1802, ii, 418.

[7] *Diocorsi e Dimonstrationi Matematicho, intorno à due nuoue Scienze*, Leyden, 1638, 81; *Opere*, Bologna, 1655, ii, 59; Ostwald's *Klassiker*, 1890, xi, 69; *Dialogues Concerning Two New Sciences*, tr. H. Crew and A. de Salvio, New York, 1914, 78 f.

[8] *Dialogues* etc., 1638; 1914, 14; Rodwell, *Chem. News*, 1863, viii, 186; A. Wolf, (1), 1935, (i), 51; Cajori, 1929, 72.

necessary to draw down a piston in a closed cylinder containing water, and he used this to explain why water cannot be raised above a certain height by a pump, thus finding the weight of a water column supported by the atmosphere, but the two ideas were kept separate. Evangelista Torricelli (Faenza, 15 October 1608–Florence, 25 October 1647) in 1643 combined the two ideas and measured the atmospheric pressure by means of a mercury column, in conjunction with Viviani, but his letters to Ricci (dated June 1644) describing the observations were not published until 1663.[1]

The Florentine Academicians describe a mercurial barometric air-pump similar to the much later Geissler pump as 'an experiment of M. Roberval's',[2] and Boyle[3] also suggested this.

Torricelli's experiment, which was well known before publication, did not dispose of the *horror vacui* since some argued that 'spirits' from the mercury filled the apparently empty part of the tube.[4] and the Jesuit Nicolaus Zucchi (1586–1670)[5] felt able to say that the recent experiments had really demonstrated the existence of a plenum rather than a vacuum.

Blaise Pascal (Clermont, 19 June 1623–Paris, 19 August 1662)[6] in his book on new experiments on the vacuum[7] still made use of the *horror vacui*. He heard of Torricelli's experiment from Mersenne through Ricci (Poggendorff says from Pierre Petit), apparently in 1644. This 'experiment made in Italy' gave Pascal the idea that the barometric height should be tested at the top of a mountain, when it should be less, and this experiment was made on the Puy-de-Dôme by his brother-in-law, Perier, on 19 September 1648.[8] The

[1] Evangelista Torricelli, *Esperienza dell' Argento Vivo*, letters to Ricci, 11 and 28 June 1644, with figure of barometers, publ. in *Lettera a Filaleti di Timavro Antiate* [=Carlo Dati], 4°, Florence, 1663 (27 pp. and 4 figs.), 21; *Lezioni Academiche d'Evangelista Torricelli*, 4°, Florence, 1715 (portr.), p. xxvii and figure; reprinted from Dati's work of 1663 by Hellmann, *Neudrucke von Schriften und Karten über Meteorologie und Erdmagnetismus*, Berlin, 1897, No. 7; Roscoe and Schorlemmer, *Treatise on Chemistry*, 1920, i, 589, Fig. 148 (Torricelli's actual tubes in Science Loan Exhibition, South Kensington); Rodwell, *Chem. News*, 1863, viii, 246; Rosenberger, 1884, ii, 95; Cajori, 1929, 72; F. Weiss, *A. Nat.*, 1928, x, 250–81; for earlier experiments of Berti with a water barometer see C. de Waard, *L'Experience Barométrique*, Thouars, 1936; see also Mattheus Campani, *Nova Experimenta Physico-Mechanica pro demonstranda genuina causa Elevationes Aquae, & Mercurii. Supra solitam eorum libellam in Vitreis Fistulis Torricellianis, a se nuper excogitata*, 8°, Rome, Ignatius de Lazaris, 1666 (79 pp., folding plate of thermometers).

[2] *Essays of Natural Experiments*, tr. Waller, 4°, London, 1684, 18.   [3] XI; *Works*, iii, 249.
[4] Gaspar Schott, *Magia Universalis*, Würzburg, 1658, Pars, iii & iv, 568–601. We think this is correct (mercury vapour), but a few decades ago the space was supposed to be filled with ether.
[5] *Nova de Machinis Philosophia*, 2 ed., Rome, 1649 (BM 538. i. 2); Thorndike, vii, 616.
[6] A. Maire, *Opuscules, Lettres, Biographie et Iconographie de Blaise Pascal*, 5 vols., Paris, 1925–7 (the vol. on 'Pascal Savant', 1925, 22 f.); id., *L'Oeuvre Scientifique de Blaise Pascal, Bibliographie*, Paris, 1912, 73 f.; Poggendorff, (2), 1883, 198 f.; M. G. Bishop, *Pascal, the Life of Genius*, Baltimore, 1937; Watson, *Isis*, 1938, xxix, 116.
[7] *Experiences Novvelles tovchant le Vvide*, sm. 8°, Paris, 1647 (4 ll., 31 pp.); complete tr. of the description from this by W. Charleton, *Physiologia Epicuro-Gassendo-Charltoniana*, 1654, 36.
[8] Pascal, *Recit de la Grande Experience de l'Equilibre des Liqueurs. Projectée par le Sieur B.P. . . . Et faite par le Sieur F.P. en vne des plus hautes Montagnes d'Auuergne*, Paris, 1648 (not in BM); facsimile in Hellmann, *op. cit.*, No. 2, Berlin, 1893; the original is extremely rare; the contents are reproduced in only slightly altered form in Pascal's *Traitez de l'Eqvilibre des Liqvevrs et de la Pesantevr de la Masse de l'air. Contenant l'explication des causes . . . attribuez à l'horreur du Vuide*, sm. 8°, Paris (G. Desprez), 1663 (14 ll., 232 pp., 4 ll., 2 folding plates); 2 ed., sm. 8°, Paris, 1664 (13 ll., 232 pp., 3 ll., 2 plates), 165 ff.; letter to Perier, 167; Perier's letter to Pascal, 177; ref. to Boyle, 210; *The Physical Treatises of Pascal: The Equilibrium of*

suggestion for the experiment actually made by Perier was claimed by Descartes as having been made in correspondence with Reneri in June, 1631[1] in two letters to Carcavi of 11 June and 17 August, 1649[2] and Pascal never denied this.[3]

In a letter to Reneri on 2 June 1631, Descartes pictured a tube *dr* closed at the end *d* and supported by a beam AB (Fig. 20). If the tube is filled with mercury this cannot move downwards without some force, and a force at least as great as that needed to raise the air which reaches from AB to above the clouds. Descartes' argument is connected with his idea that air is like fleeces of wool and the wool near the earth is pressed by the appreciable weight of all the wool above it. To move the wool at O, e.g., with all the wool above it, requires a considerable force, which is not ordinarily perceived because the air is pressed upwards by another part. The whole letter must be read to appreciate Descartes' ideas, but there is no doubt that he had the idea of the formation of a space void of air above the mercury in the tube when the weight of the remaining mercurial column was balanced by the pressure of the atmosphere.

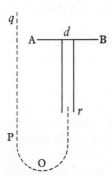

FIG. 20. DESCARTES'
BAROMETER.

The name 'barometer' was first used by Boyle:[4] 'the barometer, if to avoid circumlocutions I may so call the whole instrument wherein a mercurial cylinder of 29 or 30 inches is kept suspended after the manner of the Torricellian experiment.' Fulton's statement,[5] that 'Pascal's celebrated *Traitez de l'équilibre des liqueurs, et de la pesanteur de la masse de l'air*, which described the influence on a mercury column, did not appear until 1663', hardly does justice to the facts, as given above. Torricelli's experiment was described to Boyle in a letter from Samuel Hartlib in May, 1648.[6] Boyle[7] says 'a learned man a while since informed me, that a great Virtuoso, friend to us both, hath, with not unlike success, tried the same experiment [Perier's] in the lower and upper parts of a mountain in the west of England', and this has been supposed to be an experiment by Richard Townley on Winter Hill, near Chorley in Lancashire. Charles Leigh[8] described an experiment in which a bladder a quarter filled with air and tied at the neck was distended when taken up Ingleborough Hill, in Yorkshire.

The air-pump was invented by Otto von Guericke (originally Gericke)

Liquids and the Weight of the Mass of the Air, tr. by J. H. B. and A. G. H. Spiers, with intr. and notes by F. Barry, New York, 1937 (xxviii, 181 pp., 3 plates); Pascal, *Oeuvres complètes*, ed. C. Lahure, 2 vols., Paris, 1858, ii, 310 f.; The *Recit* (1648) was issued only in a small number of copies which were mostly distributed by Pascal rather than 'published'; some have a printed slip pasted in.
    [1] Printed in Descartes, *Oeuvres*, ed. Cousin, 1824, vi, 204.   [2] *Oeuvres*, 1825, x, 344, 351.
    [3] Nourrisson, *Pascal Physicien et Philosophe*, Paris, 1885, 114 f., who says the *Traitez de l'equilibre* was composed in 1653, and that Descartes had used the analogy of wool compressed by its own weight (mentioned in the letter of 1631), used by Pascal and by Boyle, see p. 523; Nourrisson, *Défense de Pascal*, Paris, 1888, 102 f., accepts Descartes' claim, as do Lasswitz, (1), 1890, ii, 92–4, and Hellmann, *op. cit.*; Lasswitz, (2), 1886, 166 f., 181, says Descartes had clear ideas on the pressure of air, and why mercury does not flow out of a tube sealed at the top, in 1629. He had also reached good ideas on hydrostatic pressure before Stevin. On the measurement of the heights of mountains by the barometer see Thorndike, *Isis*, 1927, ix, 426; Cajori, *ib.*, 1929, xii, 499–514 (Boyle, p. 504).
    [4] VI; *Works*, ii, 244.   [5] 1932, 19.   [6] Boyle, *Works*, v, 257.   [7] I; *Works*, i, 10.
    [8] *The Natural History of Lancashire, Cheshire, and the Peak, in Derbyshire*, f°, Oxford, 1700, book I, 13 f.

(Magdeburg, 30 November 1602–Hamburg, 11 May 1686), who studied in Leipzig, Helmstädt, and Jena, travelled in Holland, France, and Germany, and was burgomaster of Magdeburg in 1646–81.[1] Guericke's pump, said to have been invented in 1654, was first made known by Caspar Schott (1608–1666), a Jesuit professor of mathematics in the Gymnasium at Würzburg, in 1657:

Mechanica Hydraulico-Pneumatica, Qua Praeterquàm quòd Aquei Elementi natura, proprietas, vis motrix, atque occultus cum aëre conflictus . . . Experimenta Hydraulico-pneumatica recluduntur; & absoluta Machinarum aquâ & aëre animandarum ratio ac methodus præscribitur . . . Accesset Experimentum novum Magdeburgicum, quo vacuum alij stabilire alij evertere conantur, 4°, Würzburg, 1657, 14 ll., 488 pp., 8 ll. index, engr. f.p., 77 engr. plates, many woodcuts in text; on the pump, pp. 441–84 (no details of it and a poor illustration); Schott, Technica Curiosa, sive Mirabilia Artis, 4°, Nürnberg, 1664, 47 f.: Epistolae Ottonis Gericke ad R. P. Casparum Schotte (letters dated 1661–2).

Guericke's own book was published in 1672:

Experimenta Nova (ut vocantur) Magdeburgica de Vacuo Spatio Primum à R. P. Gaspare Schotto . . . Nunc verò ab ipso Auctore Perfectùs edita, variisque aliàs Experimentis aucta. Quibus accesserunt simul certa quædam De Aëris Pondere circa Terram; de Virtutibus Mundanis, & Systemate Mundi Planetario; sicut & de Stellis Fixis, ac Spatio illo Immenso, quod tàm intra quam extra eas funditur, 4°, Amsterdam, 1672; portr. (missing from many copies), engr. f.p., 7 ll., 244 pp., 3 ll. index and errata dedicated to Frederick William, Marquis of Brandenburg.

It gives an account of the Copernican system, with objections (p. 9). The experiments on the vacuum (p. 73 f.) describe the air-pump (Antlia pnevmatica) (p. 75), the extinction of a flame in vacuum (p. 89), the suppression of sound (p. 91) and the preservation of grapes (p. 93) in vacuum, the famous experiment with the hemispheres, 50 cm. diameter (p. 104, plate opp. p. 100),[2] the water (p. 98) and mercury (p. 117) barometers, weighing air in a previously exhausted globe (p. 100), the air thermometer (p. 122) and the electrification of a globe of sulphur by friction (p. 147).[3] The finis is dated 14 March 1663 (p. 244). J. C. Fischer[4] said Guericke was the first to appreciate the elasticity of the air.

Guericke's theoretical views on the vacuum (p. 55 — misnumbered 57–f.) and on atoms (p. 70) are the usual ones. He regards air not as an element but as an effluvium from the earth (p. 71 f.): there is no true vacuum, since when air is removed from a vessel, air from the water and from the vessels replaces the air pumped out (p. 84). The smell (odor) of things is a kind of air; it cannot pass through solids and is thus different from the incorporeal effluvia (p. 125), which are distinguished from the incorporeal virtues (virtutes), which include virtus conservativa (not attraction, but appetitus) et expulsiva

[1] Poggendorff, (2), 257; E. Hoppe, Otto von Guericke, Berlin, 1927 (x, 66 pp.); H. Schimank, Otto von Guericke, Magdeburger Kultur-und Wirtschaftsleben, No. 6, Magdeburg [1936] (portr.); id., Beitr. zur Geschichte der Technik und Industrie, Berlin, 1929, xix, 12–30; id. Naturwiss., 1953, xl, 397–403; id., Z. techn. Phys., 1936, xvii, 209 (portrs. in Berlin Stadtbibliothek, and Marburg Stadtarchiv MS.); Kossel, ib., 1936, xvii, 345 (usual portr.); good portr. in Experimenta Nova, CUL M. 14. 20. For reputed Guericke pump in existence see G. Berthold, A. Nat., 1916, vii, 426; W. Ahrens, ib., 1918, viii, 82–91 (illustr.); Rosenberger, 1884, ii, 142, 153, dates invention of air-pump 1647–9 or 1651–2.
[2] Andrade, Endeavour, 1957, xvi, 29.
[3] Heathcote, Ann. Sci., 1950, vi, 293.   [4] 1801, i, 441.

(electrical repulsion), virtus directiva (in magnetic phenomena), etc., which act at a distance (in distans) (p. 126). Guerick used an ingenious but rather complicated apparatus to prove that air is diminished in volume by the combustion

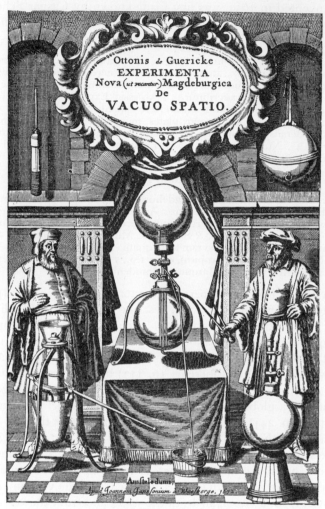

FIG. 21.

OTTO VON GUERICKE'S AIR-PUMP, SHOWN ON THE LEFT BELOW. ON THE RIGHT BELOW IS THE GLOBE FOR WEIGHING AIR. ON THE RIGHT AT THE TOP ARE THE FAMOUS 'MAGDEBURG HEMISPHERES'. (Engraved title of von Guericke's book, Amsterdam, 1672)

of a candle, in which he avoided the bubbling out of the heated air; he thought it should be possible to consume *the whole* of the air (p. 90: 'Experimentum de Consumptione Aëris per Ignem'; ending: 'quæritur, an ignis aërem ita absumat, ut in nihilum redigat').

Josephus de Tertiis[1] contended that von Guericke's experiments show that air is an effluvium, not an element, and experiments in academies in Rome and Florence proved

---

[1] *De Curiositatibus Physicis Tractatus. In quo natura stramentorum fænateorum et qualitates odoris, et effluviorum, elementorumque mutatio, et præcipue aëris examinantur,* 8°, Middleburg, 1686 (BM 1172. e. 6. (4.)); Thorndike, viii, 298.

that it is convertible into water. Hence there are only three elements, earth, water, and fire, which are identified with the three principles, salt, sulphur, and mercury.

In the development of the air-pump[1] Boyle says he started from the announcement of Guericke's 'way of emptying glass vessels'.[2] He could have got an idea of Guericke's pump from the crude picture in Schott's *Mechanica hydraulico-pneumatica* (1657); he says he had heard of this book but had not perused it; on 13 September 1661, Evelyn acknowledged receiving a copy of the book from Boyle,[3] and in January, 1658, Hartlib in a letter to Boyle said 'you still speak of the German vacuum as of no ordinary beauty',[4] so that Boyle must have known Schott's book soon after it was published.[5] In 1658–9 a single-barrel pump was made for Boyle by Hooke.

Boyle says: 'I put both Mr. G. and R. Hook (who hath also the honour to be known to your Lordship, and was with me when I had these things under consideration) to contrive some air-pump . . . and after an unsuccessful trial or two of ways proposed by others, the last named person fitted me with a pump, anon to be described.'[6] Boyle also called this air-pump his 'great pneumatical engine', and, especially abroad, it was named the 'Machina Boyleana'. 'Mr. G.' was Greatorex, or Gratorex, a well-known instrument-maker of the time. Hooke says:[7] '. . . in 1658, or 9, I contriv'd and perfected the Air-pump for Mr. Boyle, having first seen a Contrivance for that purpose made for the same honourable Person by Mr. Gratorix which was too gross to perform any great matter.' Hooke added the globular glass receiver at the top of the pump (Fig. 22). The brass barrel had a hole R at the top which could be closed by a peg P ground to fit, and the globe, holding about 30 wine quarts, had a stopcock N between it and the barrel. The piston was worked by a rack and pinion. During the descent of the piston, which had a ring of leather, the valve R at the top of the barrel was shut and the stopcock N was open; when the piston was raised, R was open and N shut. Boyle called the spherical vessel to be evacuated the 'receiver, for its affinity to the large vessels of that name used by chemists'.[8]

In describing his second air-pump (1667) Boyle refers to 'an illustrious assembly of Virtuosi, which has since made itself sufficiently known under the title of the Royal Society. And having then thought fit to make a present to persons so like to employ it well of the great engine I had till then made use of . . . I applied my studies to other subjects'. He adds: 'in five or six year I could hear but of one or two engines, that were brought to be fit to work.' The first pump was, therefore, presented to 'persons' before the Royal Society was

---

[1] Wilson, *Religio Chemici*, 1862, 195 f.; Rodwell, *Chem. News*, 1864, ix, 14; 1865, xii, 62, 74; Poggendorff, *Geschichte der Physik*, Leipzig, 1879, 470 f.; *id.*, (2), 1883, 286 f.; J. C. Fischer, 1801, i, 442; 1802, ii, 444, 449; Gerland, *Ann. Phys.*, 1878, ii, 534; Andrade, *Endeavour*, 1957, xvi, 29.
[2] I, 1660; in a letter to his nephew, Lord Dungarvan (Richard Boyle, b. 1612, later second Earl of Cork, and Earl of Burlington in 1663); *Works*, i, 4, plate i, fig. 1; Lowry, *Historical Introduction to Chemistry*, 1915, 321, fig. 45; Boyle, *Works*, i, *Life*, 33.
[3] Boyle, *Works*, v, 401.   [4] *Works*, v, 271.   [5] Boas, *Osiris*, 1952, x, 420.
[6] In the Latin, 'air-pump' is *Antlia pneumatica*, a literal translation.
[7] R. Waller, Life of Hooke, in *Posthumous Works of Hooke*, f°, London, 1705, 3; H. D. Turner, *Nature*, 1959, clxxxiv, 395.
[8] IC; *Works*, iii, 1.

founded in 1662. The experiments published in 1669 'were not made at
London, but in places where the want of a glass-house, and other accommo-
dations reduced me to make my trials . . . in the best way I could'. The 'first
engine' was presented, and the experiments with the second made, in Oxford
(where Boyle resided till 1668). The pump with two barrels 'still in possession'

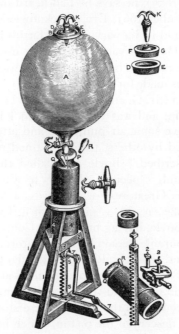

FIG. 22. BOYLE'S FIRST PNEUMATIC ENGINE OR AIR-PUMP (1660).

The air was exhausted from the glass globe A. At the top of A was a brass ring DE cemented to the rim
BC of A. DE had a glass stopper FG with a hole in the middle ground to receive the brass key K (see
inset details). At the bottom of A was a brass stopcock N cemented to it and to the top of the brass
cylinder of the pump PQ, supported on a wooden frame. The cylinder (33 in detail) was open below and
had a hole at the top fitted with a ground plug R. The piston 44 had a ring of leather and was raised and
lowered by a rack and pinion 55 operated by a cog-wheel and handle 7. A little oil or water was put
in the cylinder to make the piston air-tight. When the piston was lowered R was closed and N open.
When the piston was raised R was removed and N closed.

of the Royal Society, and said by Weld[1] to be Boyle's, is a much later one of
unknown origin. Nehemiah Grew[2] mentions 'An Aire-Pump . . . Contrived
and described by the Honourable Rob. Boyle Esq;' as in Gresham College in
1681.

A pump similar to Boyle's, with a brass piston bound with flax, was made
for Huygens in 1668.[3] A 'second engine' mentioned by Boyle in a letter dated
1667, published in 1669[4] was also evolved with the assistance of 'the ingenious
Mr. Hook'. It had a single barrel with a leather piston, now operating under
water, and had an iron plate with a bell-shaped receiver 'whelmed' on it.

[1] *History of the Royal Society*, 1848, i, 97.
[2] *Musæum Regalis Societatis. Or a Catalogue of the Natural and Artificial Rarities Belonging
to the Royal Society And preserved at Gresham Colledge*, f°, 1681, 357.
[3] A. E. Bell, *Christian Huygens and the Development of Science in the Seventeenth Century*,
1947, 163.
[4] IC; *Works*, iii, 1, plates 1 and 2.

Boyle's third air-pump was brought from France in 1676, when he became Boyle's assistant, by Denis Papin, who had previously published an illustrated account[1] of a single-barrel pump with a piston moved by a rack and pinion with a cranked handle. Papin's new pump had two barrels and pistons with valves which, as well as the valves in the pump barrels, were made air-tight by means of water. It had self-acting valves in the cylinders and pistons, and the piston-rods were suspended at the opposite ends of a cord passing over a pulley. At the top of each piston-rod was a stirrup connected with the cord. The pump was worked by the 'exerciser of the machine' putting his feet into the stirrups and, apparently, holding on to the upper frame-work of the pump; he then moved his feet alternately up and down. In this arrangement (as in the later air-pumps), the resistance of the air to the ascent of the piston in one barrel was offset by the air pressure which forced the other piston down, so that only the work of overcoming friction was involved, and the pump also exhausted twice as rapidly as a single-barrel pump.

This apparatus is described in a treatise first written in French by Papin (all the experiments are dated), then translated into Latin by (or for) Boyle and published in 1680.[2] From this an English translation was made under Boyle's supervision and published in 1682.[3] An air-pump of this type, and the first pump to have a plate for a receiver, was devised by Huygens in 1661.[4]

Papin's pump is mentioned again by Nairne.[5] A pump with single barrel and a valve in the piston is described and illustrated by Johann Christoph Sturm (1635–1703), professor of mathematics and physics at Altdorf.[6] The double-barrelled pump is often ascribed to Hauksbee, who, says Wilson, was perhaps the first (in 1704) to use the rack and pinion mechanism for working the two pistons.

Denis Papin (Coudraies, nr. Blois, 22 August 1647), M.D. University of Angers 1669, assistant to Huygens in Paris 1671 came to England in 1675 as assistant to Boyle, F.R.S. 1680, visited Venice 1681 or 1682, returned to London 1684, in 1695 became councillor and physician to the Landgrave of Hesse at Cassel, where he worked at inventions; after some years he returned to London (1707 ?); one account says he left England in 1712 and returned to his family at Cassel in 1714, 'after which nothing more is known of him'; another account says he died in Soho in London in the first half of 1712.[7]

[1] Nouvelles Experiences du Vvide avec la Description des Machines Qui servent a les faire (sm. f°, Paris, 1674, 2 ll., 28 pp., 2 plates).

[2] Experimentorum Novorum Physico-Mechanicorum Continuatio Secunda . . . , London, 1680.

[3] ID; Works, iv, 96 f., plate i; in Works, ed. Shaw, ii, 555, plate xv, Papin is not mentioned.

[4] Gerland, Ann. Phys., 1877, ii, 665–70.   [5] Phil. Trans., 1777, lxvii, 614 f.

[6] Collegium Experimentale sive Curiosum, 2 vols. 4°, Nürnburg, 1676–85; ii, 12 f.: De Novis Antliæ Pneumaticæ; the pump shown in i, 112 f., has a solid piston; Rodwell, Chem. News, 1867, xv, 312.

[7] Rodwell, Chem. News, 1867, xvi, 29, 43; Prosser, DNB, 1895, xliii, 192; L. de Saussaye and A. Péan, La Vie et les Ouvrages de Denis Papin, tome i (all publ.), Paris and Blois, 1869 (portr.), 101 f.; C. Cabanes, Denys Papin Inventeur et Philosophe Cosmopolite, 1647–17 . . . , Galerie d'Histoire Scientifique, Paris, 1935 (portr.); Bibart and De la Quesrerie in Poggendorff, (2), 283; Smiles, Lives of the Engineers. Boulton and Watt, 1874, 41 (portr.) (or 1904, 47); Berthelot, J. des Sav., 1895, 739 (P. b. 22 August 1647); id., Science et Morale, 1897, 453–507 (P. b. 22 April 1647); Dickinson, Nature, 1947, clx, 422 (q. L. de la Saussaye and L. de Belenet, La Vie et les Ouvrages de Denis Papin, Blois, vols. i, 1869 (repr. 1894), ii, 1893 (incompl.), iv, 1894, vii, 1894; it was to have comprised 8 vols.); E. Gerland, Leibnizens und Huygens' Briefwechsel mit Papin, nebst der Biographie Papins, Berlin, Verlag der Königl. Akad. der Wiss., 1881.

Papin was the inventor of a crude steam-engine, the first steamboat, and the 'digester' (1681),[1] with which he prepared hard gelatin from bones, shown to the Royal Society in 1685.[2] His father was Nicholas Papin, who wrote on the powder of sympathy (p. 424).

Boyle showed that warm water or oil of turpentine boils under reduced pressure.[3] He boiled some water 'a pretty while, that by the heat it might be freed from the latitant air', put the warm water under the air-pump receiver, and pumped out the air, when the water boiled 'as if it had stood over a very quick fire', and once it boiled 'so long with prodigiously vast bubbles, that the effervescence lasted almost as long as was requisite for the rehearsing of a Pater noster'. That even solid bodies emit vapours was known to him.[4] He describes apparatus 'to distill *in vacuo*'.[5]

One form was a brass cylinder AA with a polished tin diaphragm separating it air-tight with paper gaskets from another brass cylinder DD and with a connecting tube CC. A stop-cock fastened to the hole in the diaphragm communicated by a tube F with an air-pump. The apparatus was provided with a gauge. The 'evacuated engine' was put over a fire and vapour from a liquid in AA passed through CC and condensed in DD. A second apparatus with pear-shaped bulbs AA and DD was almost entirely of glass, connected by a tube BB polished at both ends. The bulb AA was put in a water-bath.

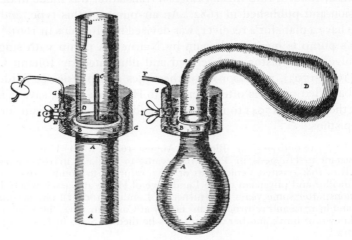

FIG. 23. BOYLE'S APPARATUS FOR DISTILLATION UNDER REDUCED PRESSURE.

Boyle's interest in the effect of pressure on air led him in 1661 to the law named after him, that the volume of a gas is inversely proportional to the pressure. He proved this experimentally both for pressures greater than atmospheric and pressures less than atmospheric, in the first case using the well-known U-tube arrangement with mercury, and in the second case a straight glass tube containing some air confined over mercury, which could be raised

[1] Denis Papin, *A New Digester or Engine for softening Bones*, sm. 4°, London, 1681; *A Continuation of the New Digester . . . together with some Improvements and New uses of the Air-Pump, tryed both in England and Italy*, sm. 4°, London, 1687.
[2] Gunther, (1), 1939, xii, 87; on the digester, see Sir Thomas Browne, *Letters*, ed. Keynes, 1946, 138.
[3] I, 1660; *Works*, i, 74.   [4] IC; *Works*, iii, 64.   [5] ID; *Works*, iv, 105.

in a vessel of mercury.[1] The experiments are contained in a reply to criticism of Boyle's publication of 1660[2] by Franciscus Linus (London, 1595?–Liége, 25 November 1675), a Jesuit teacher in the English College at Liége whose real name is said to be Francis Hall:[3]

Tractatus de corporum inseparabilitate. In quo Experimenta de Vacuo tam Torricelliana quam Magdeburgica et Boyliana examinatur . . . Accessit solutio difficilissimi illius Problematis Aristotelici de duabus Rotis; quae licet valde inæquales, æquales tamen Orbitas describunt. Autore Francisco Lino, 8°, London, Thomas Roycroft for J. Martin, J. Allestry and Tho. Dicas, 1661 (viii ll., 189 pp., i l., 4 fold. plates).

Linus asserted that the mercury was supported in the barometer by an invisible cord or *funiculum* stretching between the surface of the mercury and the top of the tube: he felt this with his thumb applied to the open top of a barometer tube.

Linus was also criticised by George Sinclair (or Sinclar) (E. Lothian–Glasgow 1696), professor of philosophy at Glasgow, who was forced to resign in 1666, but resumed his chair after the Revolution of 1688,[4] in a book.[5] Sinclair says some of his papers sent to the Royal Society were unacknowledged for two years; an unfavourable review of his book[6] says they were given to Sir Robert Moray (a Royalist), a member of the council, who 'did not judge them proper to be exhibited', since they did not seem to contain anything new. The notice in the abridgement of the *Philosophical Transactions* says Sinclair's books were 'not destitute of ingenuity or research', but they, 'and perhaps also his political principles, provoked the indignation of some persons.'

Boyle says:

We took then a long glass-tube, which by a dexterous hand and the help of a lamp was in such a manner crooked at the bottom, that the part turned up was almost parallel to the rest of the tube, and the orifice of this shorter leg of the siphon (if I may so call the whole instrument) being hermetically sealed, the length of it was divided into inches, (each of which was subdivided into eight parts) by a streight list of paper, which containing those divisions, was carefully pasted all along it. Then putting in as much quicksilver as served to fill the arch or bended part of the siphon, that the mercury standing in a level might reach in the one leg to the bottom of the divided paper . . . we took care by frequently inclining the tube . . . that the air at last included in the shorter cylinder should be of the same laxity with the rest of the air above it. This done, we began to pour quicksilver into the longer leg of the siphon, which by its weight pressing up that in the shorter leg, did by degrees streighten the included air: and continuing this pouring in of quicksilver till the air in the shorter leg was by condensation reduced to take up but half the space it possessed (I say, possessed, not filled) before; we cast our eyes on the longer leg of the glass, on which was likewise pasted a list of paper carefully divided into inches and parts, and we observed, not without delight and satisfaction, that the quicksilver in that longer part of the tube was 29 inches higher than the other.

With another tube, with a longer limb several feet long, Boyle made measurements up to nearly 4 atm. pressure and found the twenty-five results to agree closely with 'the hypothesis, that supposes the pressures and ex-

---

[1] IA; *Works*, i, 76 (100, tables, 101–2); Rodwell, *Chem. News*, 1864, ix, 26, 50; 1864, x, 74; 1865, xii, 74; James, *Sci. Progr.*, 1928, xxiii, 263; McKie, *Endeavour*, 1948, vii, 148.
[2] I; *Works*, i, 1.
[3] Cooper, DNB, 1893, xxxiii, 319; Poggendorff, (1), i, 1471 (d. 15 December), gives *De experimento argenti vivi tubo vitreo inclusi et cadentis semper ad certam quandam altitudinem*, London, 16.. [sic], as the work attacked by Boyle, and also dates the *De corporum inseparabilitate* 1662; H. G. Alexander (ed.), *The Leibniz-Clarke Correspondence*, Manchester, 1956.
[4] Anderson, DNB, 1897, lii, 293; *Phil. Trans. abdgd.*, 1809, i, 380; Thorndike, viii, 217.
[5] *Ars nova et magna gravitatis et levitatis*, 4°, Rotterdam, 1669 (BM 538. d. 21).
[6] *Phil. Trans.*, 1669, iv, 1017, no. 50.

pansions [volumes] to be in reciprocal proportion'.[1] By making use of 'a slender glass-pipe about the bigness of a swan's-quill', enclosing about 1 inch of air, shut at the top with sealing-wax, and standing in a vessel of mercury, Boyle was able, by raising the tube, to make measurements below atmospheric pressure down to $1\frac{1}{4}$ in. of mercury, and from 19 results verified the law.

Boyle[2] says the 'hypothesis' was suggested to him by Mr. Richard Townley, who had 'not met with fit glasses' to test it accurately, and that another 'person', having heard him speak of Mr. Townley's suppositions about the proportion, told Boyle he had made observations in 1660–1 'which he acknowledged to agree well enough with Mr. Townley's theory': this was Hooke, who on 10 December, 1662, presented to the Royal Society an 'account of the rarefaction of air', presenting experiments at pressures below atmospheric and giving a table, 'which by reason the tube (as I afterwards found) was somewhat bigger toward the middle than near the upper end, does not exactly agree with the hypothesis, which supposes the degree of rarefaction and force to be in reciprocal proportion, though in other experiments of the same kind, that I have formerly tried with a much more exact tube, I have found it to come very near.'[3] Hooke later published an account of his experiments[4] and said that from them 'we may safely conclude, that the Elater of the Air is reciprocal to its extension, or at least very neer'. He mentions the 'most illustrious and incomparable Mr. Boyle' only for the ratio of the densities of mercury and air. Hooke showed the experiment at lower pressures to the Royal Society in February, 1678.[5] Richard Townley, of Townley, Lancashire, is a very obscure person.[6]

Boyle also replied to a violent attack by Hobbes,[7] as Ellis[8] says, 'with the most devastating ease and equanimity, though he occasionally permitted himself the urbane omission of an *e* from his antagonist's name, a process to which his assistant Hooke was also often subjected.'

It would be unfair to mention Thomas Hobbes of Malmesbury (Malmesbury, 5 April 1588–Hardwick, Derbyshire, 4 December 1679), a critic of Descartes and[9] 'the most remarkable character in the history of materialism', only as criticised by Boyle. He was of great importance in philosophy, and (unlike Bacon) had a good knowledge of mathematics, appreciating fully the teachings of Copernicus, Kepler, Galileo, and Harvey. He differed from Bacon in his insistence on the use in philosophy of the synthetic method, based on mathematics, as well as the analytical. His theory that bodies are composed of small parts, yet not absolutely indivisible, appears also in Boyle. Hobbes reduced all real processes to motions, including those of insensible parts, and

---

[1] Table in *Works*, i, 101, and Lowry, *Historical Introduction to Chemistry*, 1915, 326, also table for pressures below atmospheric.

[2] IA; *Works*, i, 102.   [3] Gunther, (1), 1930, vi, 82–3; Wolf, (1), 1935, 239 f.

[4] *Micrographia*, 1665, 222–8.   [5] Birch, (1), 1757, iii, 384.

[6] In *Phil. Trans. Abridged*, 1809, iii, 619, it is said 'we are not informed of any memoirs of his life'; he invented a rain-gauge, *Phil. Trans.*, 1693–4, xviii, 51, no. 208, and a machine for dividing scales, and observed an eclipse of the sun; Charles Leigh, M.D., *The Natural History of Lancashire, Cheshire, and the Peak, in Derbyshire*, f°, Oxford, 1700, book II, 17, 19 f., 25 (no details of his life); Poggendorff, (2), 293, says the actual formulation of 'Boyle's law' is due to Townley. Rodwell, *Chem. News*, 1865, xi, 74, remarked that Hooke does not mention Boyle and Boyle does not name Hooke.

[7] *Dialogus physicus de natura aeris*, London, 1661; in *Opera philosophica*, ed. Molesworth, London, 1845, iv, 233; Rodwell, *Chem. News*, 1864, ix, 242.

[8] *A History of Fire and Flame*, 1932, 235.   [9] Lange, 1873, 234.

denied action at a distance, supposing that there is some medium when this seems to occur.

Hobbes had an elaborate theory of *Conatus* or 'endeavour', which in his definition (esse motum per spatium et tempus minus quam quod datur) corresponds with the differential coefficient ds/dt (s = space, t = time), and had the germ of action at a distance. He also clearly recognised the composition of several motions in the same place at the same time. He confused 'action' with velocity, leaving out mass. He dealt with the causes of hardness and fluidity, plasticity coming between. His theory of heat (which is distinguished from light) and fermentation is based on centrifugal motions of particles.[1]

Boyle's Law is sometimes called Mariotte's Law, but Mariotte did not publish it until 1679 and did not claim it as new.[2] Edme Mariotte (Bourgogne, ?–Paris, 12 May 1684) prior of Saint-Martin-sous-Beaune, near Dijon, member of the Paris Academy from its foundation in 1666, was one of the outstanding mathematical and experimental physicists of France.[3]

To explain the compressibility of air, Boyle compared its particles with small coiled springs, fleeces of wool, or little sponges, the lower 'springs' in a column of air being compressed by the weight of those above them. Mariotte uses the same analogy, which had been suggested in 1631 by Descartes (see p. 435). Boyle remarks that the pressure could be explained as due to the motion of the particles, as assumed by Descartes. Boyle says[4] that to explain his experiments he will:

... insinuate that notion, by which it seems likely, that most, if not all of them will prove explicable, that there is a spring or elastic power in the air we live in. By which ἐλατήρ or spring of the air, that which I mean is this; that our air either consists of, or at least abounds with, parts of such a nature, that in case they be bent or compressed by the weight of the incumbent part of the atmosphere, or by any other body, they do endeavour, as much as in them lieth, to free themselves from that pressure, by bearing against the contiguous bodies that keep them bent; and, as soon as these bodies are removed, or reduced to give them way, by presently unbending or stretching out themselves, either quite, or so far forth as the contiguous bodies that resist them will permit, and thereby expanding the whole parcel of air, these elastical bodies compose.

There is yet another way to explicate the spring of the air; namely, by supposing with that most ingenious gentleman, Monsieur Des Cartes, that the air is nothing but a

[1] Lasswitz, (1), 1890, ii, 207–42 (214–38); Hobbes, *Opera Philosophica quæ Latine scripsit omnia*, ed. G. Molesworth, 5 vols., London, 1839–45; *English Works*, ed. Sir W. Molesworth, 11 vols., 1839–45; G. Croom Robertson, *Hobbes*, 1886; F. Toennies, *Hobbes Leben und Lehre*, Stuttgart, 1896; 2 ed. as *Thomas Hobbes, der Mann and der Denker*, Osterwieck and Leipzig, 1912; Ueberweg, (1), 1924, iii, 249; A. E. Taylor, *Thomas Hobbes*, 1908; F. Brant, *Thomas Hobbes' Mechanical Conception of Nature*, tr. A. Maxwell and A. I. Fausbøll, Copenhagen and London, 1928; a Hobbes Gesellschaft was established in Kiel by Tennies.

[2] Mariotte, *Essays de phisique ov Memoirs pour servir à la Science des choses naturelles. Seconde essay. De la Natvre de l'Air*, 12°, Paris (Michallet), 1679 (231 pp.); *Ouevres*, 2 vols., Leyden, 1717, i, 149 f.; Poggendorff, *Geschichte der Physik*, 1879, 489; *ib.*, (2), 298; James, *Sci. Progr.*, 1928, xxiii, 263; Rosenberger, 1884, ii, 204; and Cajori, 1929, 80, all date the work 1676, but Poggendorff, (1), 1863, ii, 54, says the 'premier essai (*sic*) de la vegetation des plantes' was published in 1676, and the 'seconde essai (*sic*) ... de la nature de l'air' in 1679, 'Darin das sogen. Mariottsche Gesetz'; Dannemann, 1921, ii, 212, dates the work 1679; in the reprint in Mariotte's *Oeuvres*, 1717, it is said (Avis, ** 2) the *Discours sur les Plantes, la Nature de l'Air, & le Froid & le Chaud* was (or were) reprinted 'sur l'Edition de Paris dc 1676 & 1679', which is ambiguous. The catalogue of the Bibliothèque Nationale gives only the edition of 1679 for the three essays, and 1681 for the one on colours. Mariotte's *Discours de la Nature de l'Air, De la Végétation des Plantes*, and *Nouvelle Decouverte touchant la Vue* were publ. (with a poor introd. by M. Solovine) in the series *Les Maîtres de la Pensée Scientifique*, Paris, 1923.

[3] Condorcet, *Oeuvres*, 1847, ii, 23–33; Merlieux, NBG, 1860, xxiii, 797–805; Rodwell, *Chem. News*, 1864, x, 74; Pelseneer, *Isis*, 1951, xlii, 299.

[4] I; *Works*, i, 8–10.

congeries or heap of small and (for the most part) of flexible particles . . . and by the restless agitation of that celestial matter, wherein those particles swim, are so whirled round, that each corpuscle endeavours to beat off all others from coming within the little sphere requisite to its motion about its own centre . . . their elastical power is not made to depend upon their shape or structure, but upon the vehement agitation, and (as it were) brandishing motion, which they receive from the fluid æther, that swiftly flows between them.

Boyle proved (as Helmont had done, p. 224), that the 'spring' is not impaired by keeping the air long compressed, and that highly rarefied air is also expanded by heat.[1]

In 1660[2] Boyle described the production of 'air' by the action of dilute aqua fortis and dilute oil of vitriol on iron,[3] collecting it in an inverted flask with a long cylindrical neck, which 'seemed manifestly enough to prove, though not that air may be generated out of the water, yet that in general air may be generated anew'. Air was also generated from red coral and spirit of vinegar.[4] Boyle made attempts to weight air.[5] He showed that animals, bees and other insects, and birds, died in receivers from which the air was exhausted.[6] Many of Boyle's experiments on animals would seem to us cruel and some unnecessary, and many of them gave results of little or no value.[7] Boyle began 'exercising myself in making anatomical dissections of living animals' in Dublin in 1653[8] under the direction of William Petty (1623–87), who taught anatomy and chemistry at Oxford in 1648, became physician to the army in Ireland and then surveyor-general there.

Boyle in 1660 included a 'Digression containing some Doubts touching Repiration',[9] in which he summarised prevailing opinions. Respiration might serve to cool the blood and 'ventilate' it in its passage through the lungs, in which it is 'dis-burthened of those excrementitious steams, proceeding, for the most part, from the superfluous serosities of the blood', an 'opinion almost vulgar', due to Moebius and Gassendi. He refers to the opinion of Paracelsus (p. 130) that 'the lungs consume part of the air and proscribe the rest', and that 'there is in the air a little vital quintessence (if I may so call it) which serves to the refreshment and restauration of our vital spirits, for which use the grosser and incomparably greater part of the air being unserviceable, it need not seem strange, that an animal stands in need of almost incessantly drawing in fresh air', which 'opinion', Boyle says, stands in need of being 'explicated and proved'.[10] 'Upon the exsuction of the air, the animal dies a great deal sooner than if it were left in the vessel, though by that exsuction, the ambient space is left much more free to receive the steams that are either breathed out of the lungs of the animal, or discharged by insensible transpiration through the pores of his skin.'[11]

The flame of a lamp is extinguished, like the life of an animal, by removal of air, the gills of fishes seem somewhat analogous to the lungs and if, as is said (see Scaliger, p. 465), fish die in ponds frozen over, air may lurk in water and fish may use it when they strain the water through their gills or in other ways,

[1] IX (b); Works, iii, 206.   [2] I; Works, i, 1–75.   [3] Ib., 35.
[4] Ib., 73.   [5] Ib., 53.   [6] Ib., 63.   [7] Thorndike, viii, 181.
[8] Letter to Clodius; Works, v, 242; Masson, 1914, 185; Tilden, 1921, 13.
[9] I; Works, i, 64.   [10] Ib., 69.   [11] Ib., 67.

although Boyle doubts this.[1] Boyle discusses respiration in the embryo and 'thought of conveying into our receiver young ones, ripped out of the womb of their dams . . . but could not procure them'.[2] That water does contain air (as Galen had assumed (see Vol. I)), was proved experimentally by Bernoulli (1690) (see p. 629). In 1670 Boyle[3] found that water in a vacuous receiver emits bubbles of air, and proposed the 'quere . . . whether in common water there may not be concealed air enough to be of use to such cold animals as fishes; and whether it may be separable from the water that strains through their gills'.

Boyle was the first to collect hydrogen and nitric oxide:[4]

We took a clear glass bubble (capable of containing by guess about three ounces of water) with a neck somewhat long and wide, of a cylindrical form; this we filled with oil of vitriol and fair water, of each almost a like quantity, and casting in half a dozen small iron nails . . . and speedily inverting the phial, we put the neck of it into a small wide-mouthed glass . . . with more of the same liquor in it . . . soon after we perceived the bubbles produced by the action of the menstruum upon the metal, ascending copiously . . . the whole cavity of the glass bubble, and most of its neck, seemed to be possessed by air, since by its spring it was able . . . to hinder the . . . liquor from regaining its former place . . . upon the application of the warm hand to the convex part of the bubble, the imprisoned substance readily dilated it self like air, and broke through the liquor in divers bubbles . . . Having also another time tried the like experiment with a small phial, and with nails dissolved in aqua fortis, we found nothing incongruous to what we have now delivered.
. . . these experiments with corrosive liquors, seemed manifestly enough to prove, though not that air may be generated from water, yet that in general air may be generated anew . . . But if as Leucippus, Democritus, Epicurus and others, followed by divers modern naturalists have taught . . . the difference of bodies proceeds but from the various magnitudes, figures, motions, and textures of the small parts they consist of . . . there appears no reason why the minute parts of water, and other bodies, may not be so agitated or connected as to deserve the name of air.

Van Helmont thought a gas could not be collected in a vessel (see p. 227), but he recognised that there are different gases and that air and water are not convertible into each other, whilst Boyle thought that water may be transmuted into air. He calls the gases 'factitious airs',[5] although he mentions 'gas' or 'blas',[6] and 'the gas (as the Helmontians call it) or the scarce coagulable fumes of kindled and extinguished brimstone'.[7] The name 'factitious air' was used in a meeting of the Royal Society on 14 May 1673;[8] previously 'new air', or 'air generated de novo' (see p. 555) was used.

Boyle was told of the 'sudden damps appearing in mines which stuff up and thicken the subterraneal air' and extinguish lamps and candles, and also of 'hot exhalations which compose their damps', taking fire with explosions, the burning blue of candles giving warning of them,[9] and he mentions an inflammable gas evolved from a ditch in Lancashire,[10] probably firedamp from underground coal. Boyle was the first to publish an account of the combustion of hydrogen, which may have been known before to Turquet de Mayerne (p. 174):

[1] Ib., 70. [2] Ib., 71. [3] Phil. Trans., 1670, v, 2011; Works, iii, 117.
[4] I; Works, i, 35. [5] ID; Works, iv, 96; Harcourt, Phil. Mag., 1846, xxviii, 124.
[6] III; Works, i, 331. [7] X; Works, iii, 243. [8] Birch, (1), iii, 89.
[9] VI; Works, ii, 366. [10] VI, XXI; Works, ii, 368, iv, 282.

A very sharp and piercing saline spirit [hydrochloric acid] was poured upon filings of steel in a small vial, whereupon the mixture grew very hot, and belched up copious and stinking fumes, either of the volatile sulphur of Mars [iron] or metalline steams of a sulphureous nature joined with the saline exhalations of the menstruum. Upon the approach of a lighted candle it would readily enough take fire and burn with a blueish and sometimes greenish flame at the mouth of the vial, for a good while. This flaming vial we conveyed into a receiver, and upon the first exsuction of air it flam'd brisker than before; and likewise upon the second and third; but after it went out, it would not be kindled again, tho' the air was let in upon it.[1]

Boyle obtained factitious air from fermenting dough,[2] fermenting cherries (which 'air' hindered the putrefaction of meat) (pp. 113, 116), grapes, oranges, pears, apricots, plums, gooseberries, peas, etc. (pp. 115–28), and also from coral and vinegar (p. 125).[3]

Huygens[4] experimented on the generation of 'new air' by effervescences in an air-pump receiver containing a pressure gauge, 'the Experimenter being desirous to see, whether these Ebullitions did make new Air.' There was 'a great ebullition' on mixing aqua fortis and spirit of wine, and the gauge ascended 'very nimbly'. But

it was seen that all these kinds of ebullition make an Air which expands it self like common Air. Yet here is something that seems to be very remarkable: which is, that the Air which is made by these ebullitions, is not all of the same nature. For, it hath been found experimentally, that the Air formed by the mixture of *Aqua fortis* and *Copper* remains alwaies Air, and alwaies keeps up the water in the Glass at that height to which it raised it; but on the contrary, that Air which hath been produced by the mixture of *Oyl of Tartar* and *Oyl of Vitriol*, is almost all destroyed of itself in the space of twenty four hours (p. 445); this would be in consequence of the solution of the carbon dioxide in water.

Huygens and Papin noticed (like Boyle, p. 527) that gunpowder burns in a vacuum 'grain by grain, none of the grains kindled firing those which touched'; with less heat it would not burn but only smoked, the smoke condensing to yellow sulphur, the residue burning on coals like saltpetre. There is 'a fifth part of air in gunpowder'.[5]

In 1683 Gould showed the Royal Society the 'easy inflaming of the steams' from steel filings and oil of vitriol.[6]

Boyle found that when air is pumped from a receiver containing a burning candle, 'the flame (except at the very top) appeared exceeding blue, and . . . receded more and more from the tallow, till at length it appeared to possess only the very top of the wick, and there it went out.'[7] After the extinction of an alcohol flame in a receiver 'the air was not visibly altered, and, for aught I

[1] XI; *Works*, iii, 255, abbreviated; Boulton, *Works of Boyle*, 1700, iii, 224; see also XXI, *Works*, iv, 295; XXVI, *Works*, v, 113; Harcourt, *Phil. Mag.*, 1846, xxviii, 127.

[2] ID; *Works*, iv, 112; page references in the text are to this.

[3] See also I; *Works*, i, 73 (to use a 'Helmontian phrase', the acid will 'exantlate itself'); III; *Works*, i, 329.

[4] Some Experiments made in the Air-Pump by Monsieur Papin, directed by Monsieur Hugens (as appears in the Discourse printed at Paris, 1674), in *Phil. Trans.*, 1675–6, x, nos. 119, 120, 121, 122, pp. 443, 477, 492, 524, 544; abridgd. ed., 1809, ii, 239, 257, 271, 272.

[5] On Christiaan Huygens (The Hague; 14 April 1629–8 July 1695), who visited England in 1661, F.R.S. 1663, one of the foundation members of the Académie des Sciences (1666), see Hoefer, NBG, 1858, xxv, 666; J. Bosscha, *Christiaan Huygens. Rede*, tr. Englemann, Leipzig, 1895; A. E. Bell, *Christian Huygens*, 1947; Thorndike, vii, 622; Huygens, *Oeuvres Complètes*, 22 vols. in 23, The Hague, 1889–1950.

[6] Gunther, (1), 1939, xii, 25, 31.   [7] I; *Works*, i, 15.

could perceive by the ways of judging I had then at hand, the air retained either all, or at least for the greatest part of its elasticity, which I take to be its most genuine and distinguishing property'.[1]

On burning amber, camphor, and sulphur in a dry receiver there was no change of pressure when the apparatus had cooled, hence no air was generated.[2]

Boyle suspected the existence of 'ingredients of a more subtle nature, which being extreamly little, and not being in themselves visible, may escape unheeded, at the junctures of the destillatory vessels'; and also of bodies even more subtle, such as the 'little corpuscles that issue out of the loadstone', and 'the effluviums of amber, jet, and other electricall concretes'.[3] He still thought the noxious effects of charcoal fires in rooms with newly plastered walls were due to 'invisible steams issuing out of the walls'.[4]

In his *New Experiments touching the Relation betwixt Flame and Air* (1673),[5] Boyle described experiments on combustion in an exhausted receiver. The method was to put a red-hot iron plate under a bell jar, the air in which could be exhausted by the air-pump, and then drop the combustible material on the hot plate by means of a contrivance fitted in the neck of the bell jar.[6] With sulphur wrapped in paper and lowered on to the plate, fumes were seen but no combustion. On the admission of air, however, Boyle saw 'divers little flashes, as it were, which disclosed themselves by their blue colour to be sulphurous flames'. He describes the extinction of a candle flame and the flame of burning hydrogen, and was inclined to think that a flame could not exist without air.

Boyle, however, obtained very curious results with gunpowder. When dropped upon the heated plate in vacuum the powder burned slowly but did not explode: 'We saw a pretty broad blue flame like brimstone, which lasted so long as we could not but wonder at it'. A ring of gunpowder burned in a vacuum only at the place where it was heated by a burning glass, but on admitting air the whole went off with a flash (Expt. V: About an endeavour to fire gunpowder in vacuo with the sun beams). Gunpowder in a goose-quill would also burn under water, and fulminating gold would explode with a flash when dropped on the hot plate in a vacuum. Boyle at first thought that some air might be mixed with the nitre crystals used to make the gunpowder, but he obtained the same result with gunpowder made from nitre crystallised in a vacuum. He came to the conclusion that substances could burn mixed with nitre even in absence of air, and that nitre on heating gives 'agitated vapours which emulate air', or 'vehemently agitated vapours'. The fulminating gold was made with nitric acid.[7] By casting glowing charcoal into fused saltpetre, Boyle found that 'it presently kindled it, and made it boil and hiss, and flash for a pretty while'.[8]

Boyle had:

a great suspicion of some vital substance, if I may so call it, diffused through the air, whether it be a volatile nitre, or (rather) some yet anonimous substance, sydereal or

---

[1] XIV; *Works*, iii, 467.   [2] IC; *Works*, iv, 131.   [3] III, 1680, 186 f.; *Works*, i, 326.
[4] XII; *Works*, iii, 322.   [5] XI; *Works*, iii, 250; usually misdated 1672.
[6] I; *Works*, i, 19.   [7] XI; *Works*, iii, 253, 257.   [8] II (b); *Works*, i, 230; cf. Hooke, p. 557.

subterraneal, but not improbable of kin to that, which I lately noted to be so necessary to the maintenance of other flames;[1] although I confess I have not been hitherto convinced of all that is wont to be delivered about the plenty and quality of the nitre in the air: for I have not found, that those, that build so much upon this volatile nitre, have made out by any competent experiment, that there is such a volatile nitre, abounding in the air, [and there is likely to be as much common salt in sea air].[2]

Boyle found that when phosphorus is sealed up in a glass tube with air, its glow gradually disappears, hence he concluded that 'the air had some vital substance (if I may so call it) preyed upon thereby or else . . . tamed and rendered at length unfit to continue the flame' by the fumes of the phosphorus'.[3]

Boyle's experiment with the spirit lamp flame (see p. 526), which emitted no 'fuliginous exhalations' such as had been supposed to stifle a flame in a closed vessel, disproved this theory. Sir Thomas Browne[4] refers to Francis Bacon,[5] and Ed. Jorden (1569–1632)[6] for the view that: 'that which substantially maintaineth the fire, is the combustible matter in the kindled body, and not the ambient air, which affordeth exhalation to its fuliginous atomes', which in a closed space 'recoil upon the flame and choak it'. Boyle found that when a spirit lamp burned to extinction in a confined volume of air there was little if any change of *pressure*, and hence there is in the air very little of 'this fine subject, whatever it be', which enables flames to burn.[7]

In his last discourse on the nature of air (1692) Boyle concluded that it is composed of at least three parts,[8] viz.:

(i) vapours from water and living animals;
(ii) a very subtle emanation from the earth's magnetism, producing the sensation of light;
(iii) a fluid, compressible and dilatable, having weight and able to refract light.

He discourses on 'celestial influences or effluviums in the air', not to mention 'exhalations from the planets', in a 'particular apology for astrology', but is sceptical about the nitro-aerial spirit of Mayow (who is not named). Boyle thought air caused diseases when mixed with poisonous exhalations from the earth, plague being caused by arsenical vapours from 'orpimental or other noxious minerals'[9] — a Paracelsan idea. He mentions that food is preserved by exclusion of air.[10]

In 1662[11] Boyle agreed with the ancients and moderns who 'teach the sun-beames to consist of fiery particles, trajected through the air, and capable of passing through glass', and in 1674[12] he 'desired some virtuosi of my acquaintance to assist me in the enquiry, whether any of the spots, that appear about the sun, may not, upon their sudden dissolution, have some of their discussed

[1] XIV; *Works*, iii, 467.   [2] XXVI; *Works*, v, 117.   [3] XVII; *Works*, iv, 86.
[4] *Pseudodoxia Epidemica*, bk. iii, ch. 21 (1646); *Works*, ed. Keynes, 1928, ii, 262 f.
[5] *Of Life and Death* (1623), x, *Works*, London, 1887, ii, 203.
[6] *A Discovrse of Natvrall Bathes and Minerall Waters* . . . , London, 1631 (92 pp.), 59 f., 68 f.
[7] XIV; *Works*, iii, 466.   [8] XXVI; *Works*, v, 107 f.   [9] XXI; *Works*, iv, 279, 284, 290.
[10] IV; *Works*, i, 493; this was known to Columella, 1 cent. A.D.; see Vol. I.
[11] IA; *Works*, i, 141.   [12] XIV; *Works*, iii, 470.

and dispersed matter thrown off, as far as our atmosphere', with what result he does not say. Boyle was not at all clear about the nature of atmospherical air. It was a confused jumble of everything.

Some of Boyle's papers were lost (p. 495) and others ruined by acid spilled over them; among these were: 'Of Fire and Flame', 'Of the Fuel of the Sun's Fire', 'The Mechanical Origin of Inflammability', 'An Historical Dialogue on Flame', and the results of some work 'To produce air out of gunpowder and other nitrous bodies'. Whether these papers advanced his ideas on combustion we cannot say; his mature pronouncements lead us to suspect they did not.

Boyle was not 'sollicitous to ascribe and vindicate to the air so absolute and equal a necessity to the production and conservation of all flames as divers learned men have concluded from my former experiments'. But he was 'content to be kind to the air, but not partial'.[1]

If it is true to say,[2] as it probably is, that: 'Boyle never grasped the true function of the air in combustion', it is certain that he failed to perceive its participation in calcination. Sprat[3] describes some experiments made in the Tower of London for Lord Brouncker in which copper and lead, separate and mixed, increased in weight when calcined in cupels, e.g., 10 dwt. $10\frac{7}{8}$ gr. of lead gained $5\frac{11}{64}$ gr. whilst the cupel alone exposed to the fire lost only 1 to 3 gr. In some experiments made about 1663 on making dross on melted lead exposed to air, 'which by other experiments seems to abound with subtile saline parts, perhaps not uncapable of working upon lead so disposed', Boyle seems to suspect that air was involved in the calcination.[4]

In 1673 Boyle published, as part of his *Essays of Effluviums*, his *New Experiments to make Fire and Flame Stable and Ponderable*[5] in which he describes the increase in weight of metals on calcination in air. This fact was known before his time, and is mentioned by Cardan and others in the sixteenth century.[6] Boyle found that 8 oz. of block tin when heated in an open flask increased in weight by 18 grains. He tried putting the tin in a retort, weighing, then sealing the neck and heating, but owing to the expansion of the air the retort burst 'with a noise like the report of a gun'. He then heated 2 oz. of tin in an open retort and sealed the neck when as much air as possible had been driven out by heat. After heating so as to calcine the tin, the retort was cooled and the neck cut off, when Boyle 'heard the outward air rush in, because when the vessel was sealed the air within it was highly rarefied'. He thus missed the absorption of air from his method of working and concluded that the increase in weight, 12 grains, was 'gained by the operation of fire on the metal'. An experiment to see if mercury gained in weight on conversion into red precipitate did not succeed.[7]

[1] XI; *Works*, iii, 250; O. E. de C. Ellis, *A History of Fire and Flame*, 1932, 237.
[2] H. B. Dixon, *B.A. Report*, 1894, 598.
[3] *History of the Royal Society of London*, 1667, 228: 'Experiments of the Weight of Bodies increased in the Fire'; Lysaght, *Ambix*, 1937, i, 93.
[4] V; *Works*, ii, 10.
[5] XII; *Works*, iii, 340; E. Bloch, Boyles Anschauungen über Metallverkalkung, *Chem. Ztg.*, 1915, xxxix, 481; McKie, *Sci. Progr.*, 1934, xxix, 253; 1936, xxxi, 55.
[6] See p. 13, and Partington and McKie, *Ann. Sci.*, 1937, ii, 364.
[7] XII; *Works*, iii, 346.

Boyle thought 'igneous corpuscles' from the fire passed through the glass and were absorbed by the metal, and hence concluded that fire had weight. In 1673 he published (as part of his *Essays of Effluviums*) his *Additional Experiments about Arresting and Weighing Igneous Corpuscles*.[1] Boyle made the important observation that the density of the calx was less than that of the metal.

The theory adopted by Boyle to explain the increase in weight of metals on calcination was the fixation of ponderable igneous corpuscles or particles of fire. He had previously[2] adopted Bacon's view that heat is the result of an agitation of the small parts of bodies, but he gave this up for what he regarded as a better theory.

Even the roasting of meat may be due to the sticking of igneous corpuscles to it, and 'it seems worthy to be considered, in regard it may concern men's health to know, whether the coction of the meat be made by the fire, only as it is a very hot body, or whether it permanently communicates anything of its substance to the meat', and whether 'the nature of its fuel, may be fit to be considered'. 'And if I had not Weightier Considerations to Discourse to you of, I could name to you, to Countenance what I have newly said, some particular Experiments by which I have been Deduc'd to think, that the Particles of an open Fire working upon some Bodies may really Associate themselves therewith, and add to the Quantity. But because I am not sure, that when the Fire works upon Bodies included in Glasses, it does so by a reall Trajection of the Fiery Corpuscles themselves, through the Substance of the Glass, I will proceed to what is next to be mentioned.'[3]

This theory was adopted by Becher,[4] N. Lemery[5] and others. It was criticised by Cherubin d'Orléans (François Lasseré)[6] on the ground that Boyle should have weighed his retort before opening it, and he argued that ponderable matter could not pass through glass, although Charleton[7] mentions an 'experiment of Sir *Kenelm Digby*, of making a sensible transudation of Mercury mixt with Aqua Fortis in a Bolt-head, through the sides thereof, if gently confricted with a Hares-foot on the outside'. Cherubin[8] criticised Boyle's conclusions in his 'Discovery of the Perviousness of Glass to Ponderable Parts of Flame'.[9] He says there are several reasons why glass cannot be porous. It can be spun in fine threads, and there cannot be pores penetrating from surface to surface, since the threads can be bent without fracture; a glass fibre can withstand torsional vibrations; air may be attenuated under a glass air-pump receiver which will draw out the parts of liquids in ebullition; a tube

[1] XII; *Works*, iii, 347. [2] IIA, IV; *Works*, i, 282, 476.
[3] III, 1661, 212; IIIA, 1680, 216. [4] *Physicae subterraneae*, Frankfurt, 1669, p. 195.
[5] *Cours de Chymie*, 1690, 141, 265. [6] Sotheran, *Cat.* 786 (1923), 227, no. 2983.
[7] *Physiologia Epicuro-Gassendo-Charltoniana*, 1654, 40.
[8] *De l'Impermeabilité du Verre, où est demontré, que le Verre brut, n'a point de pores, qui penetrent ses deux superficies*, appendix in his *Effets de la Force de la Contiguité des Corps. Par lesquels on répond aux expériences de la crainte du Vuide, & à celles de la Pésanteur de l'Air*, sm. 8°, Paris, 1679 (18 ll., 466 pp., 1 l., engr. f.p., 21 plates), 1688 (two edits.), 1689, 1700; Gobet, *Essays de Iean Rey*, 1777, xii, 213; Fourcroy, *Ency. Méthod.*, *Chimie*, 1796, iii, 350; B. H. Paul, in Watts, *Dict. of Chemistry*, 1872, ii, 775–6; Metzger, *Doctrines Chimiques en France*, 1923, 393; McKie, *Sci. Progr.*, 1934, xxix, 253; 1936, xxxi, 55.
[9] In XII, Tract V, *Works*, iii, 350.

filled with water and inverted over a dish of water may be placed under an exhausted receiver without the level falling in the tube. The last experiment is due to Huygens[1] who used mercury in a barometer tube and found that a column of 75 in. was retained. It was repeated by Wallis, Boyle, and Lord Brouncker[2] and was regarded as a serious objection to Boyle's theory of the 'spring' of air.[3] Chemists, says Cherubin, use glass vessels to extract the most spirituous and subtle essences and preserve them 'under the seal of Hermes'. It would be absurd to postulate pores in glass serving to transmit light, since these would have to change their direction with the inclination of the light rays. In Boyle's experiments, Cherubin (this part is reproduced in Gobet) says, Boyle should have weighed the retort and tin after the calcination before opening it to the air. Digby[4] had shown that calcined bodies increase in weight on exposure to air. In Boyle's experiments the metal calcined in the sealed retort had not only been deprived of all humidity but had also been imbued with a very ardent igneous quality, which led to its becoming impregnated with the moist parts of the external air at the moment when, the neck of the retort being broken, it was enabled to exert its attraction upon them.[5] The glass vessel forcibly restrained the air in a state of unnatural attenuation, which could not occur if the glass had pores, for this attenuated air, which, as proved by the noise heard by Boyle, strongly attracted the external air, would not suffer such restraint.

Cherubin's main criticism is perfectly sound but Boyle[6] says he once 'did weigh a sealed retort, with matter in it, and found it encreased in weight, but thought not fit to lay much stress on that circumstance'. He hopes Cherubin 'will give one, that is a piece of a chemist, leave to tell him, that calcined bodies may be of very differing kinds', that salt of tartar absorbs, not air, but 'the moist vapours that rove up and down in the air', and that a pound of tin and copper melted together 'for a pretty while in fusion . . . though a small portion of the mixture was calcined, yet the total had gained in weight no less than 233 grains'. Boyle did not publish these experiments.

Boyle's experiments were also criticised by Pott[7] and Lomonosov,[8] whose *criticism* of Boyle was made in 1744–7, and his *experiments* showing that there is no increase in weight when a metal is heated in a sealed retort, in 1756 (see Vol. III).

The untenability of Boyle's theory was proved by Kunckel,[9] who showed that a mass of iron had the same weight when red hot as when cold, an

---

[1] *J. des Sçavans*, 1672, 12 December, p. 153; *Phil. Trans.*, 1672, vii, 5027, no. 86.
[2] J. C. Fischer, 1801, i, 419.
[3] J. Bernoulli, *De gravitate ætheris*; in *Opera*, Geneva, 1744, i, 116.
[4] *A Late Discourse made in a Solemne Assembly of Nobles and Learned Men at Montpellier in France*, tr. R. White, London, 1658, 66: he actually mentions only the increase in weight of salt of tartar when deliquescing in moist air.
[5] Cherubin did not see that it was the *air in the retort* which acted.
[6] An undated and unaddressed letter in *Works*, v, 233, which is mentioned by Gmelin, (1), ii, 42, and Bloch, *Chem. Ztg.*, 1915, xxxix, 481.
[7] *Dissertations chymiques*, 1759, iii, 429: *De pond. flamm.*; 'elles ne sont plus solides que toutes celles qu'il donne à ce sujet.'
[8] Ostwald's *Klassiker*, No. 178, 26, 50 f.
[9] *Laboratorium Chymicum*, 1716, 31.

similar experiments were made by Boerhaave[1] and others.[2] Mercury heated
for several weeks in a conveniently shaped glass, 'infernal glasses as they call
them',[3] later called 'Boyle's hell',[4] is converted into red precipitate per se, yet
Boyle:

> found by trial, that with a greater and competent degree of heat, this præcipitate *per se*,
> would, without the help of any volatilizing additament, be easily reduced into running
> mercury again. Chemists and physicians who agree in supposing this precipitate to be
> made without any additament, will, perchance, scarce be able to give a more likely
> account of the consistency and degree of fixity, that is obtained in the mercury; in
> which, since no body is added to it, there appears not to be wrought any but a mechani-
> cal change . . . though, I confess, I have not been without suspicions, that in philo-
> sophical strictness this precipitate may not be made *per se*, but that some penetrating
> igneous particles, especially saline, may have associated themselves with the mercurial
> corpuscles.[5]

By heating precipitate *per se* in a glass vessel until it was converted into
mercury, which requires a heat stronger than was used to make the precipitate,
Boyle 'found that there wanted but about a sixth or seventh part of what we
had put in, and we supposed we should not have wanted that neither, but that
the vehemence of the fire had melted the glass, which swallowed up a part of
the powder', which could be seen through it.[6] Hence, 'Without the addition of
any extraneous body, quicksilver may by the fire alone, and that in glass-
vessels, be deprived of its silver-like colour, and be turned into a red body;
and from this red body without addition likewise may be obtained a mercury
bright and specular as it was before.'[7]

'Quicksilver . . . is by the lasting operation of the fire, without external
additaments, at least distinct from the igneous particles, turned into a red
powder, that chymists call *Præcipitate per se*.' . . . 'the bare accession of
igneous particles, is able in time, to turn running mercury into that red
powder, which chymists call *Præcipitate per se*: and I have found by trials
purposely made, and elsewhere related, that this powder without any further
additament may be reduced into running mercury'.[8] Boyle just missed the
discovery of oxygen.

Boyle's long and careful series of experiments on combustion and calcination, described in so much prolix detail, led him to no valid conclusions. He
started with the idea of Paracelsus (p. 130) and he finished with it. In his
experiments with mercury and its oxide he was within sight of the great discoveries of Scheele, Priestley, and Lavoisier, but it was not vouchsafed to him
to make them.

Boyle was also unsuccessful in making out the true part which the air plays
in respiration, in spite of the large number of animals and birds he sacrificed
under the receivers of his air-pumps. In his *New Experiments About the Rela-*

[1] *Elementa Chemiae*, 1732, i, 360.
[2] See Partington and McKie, *Ann. Sci.*, 1937, ii, 378; 1938, iii, 10.
[3] XII; *Works*, iii, 346.
[4] Lavoisier, *Traité de Chimie*, 1789, ii, 520, Pt. iv, Fig. 10, 'enfer de Boyle.'
[5] XV; *Works*, iii, 620; cf. IIIA, 1680, 173, 185; *Works*, i, 404 f.
[6] II, (c); *Works*, i, 272.   [7] III; *Works*, i, 352.
[8] IIIA; *Works*, i, 404–6; the passage is incomplete in IIIA, 1680, 185, where it ends after the
first 'running mercury'.

tion betwixt Air and the Flamma Vitalis of Animals (1673)[1] he describes some inconclusive experiments of enclosing in a receiver with a lighted candle or lamps, either a bird or a mouse (which 'made a shift to blow out the flame'). The bird or mouse lived on after the flame had gone out; even a spirit flame which emitted no smoke could be used.

Glow-worms (or the luminous matter from them) lost their luminosity when the air was pumped out of a receiver but regained it when the air was let in again. A mouse weighed in a noose and then strangled lost $\frac{7}{16}$ grain, and a kitten similarly treated lost 4 grains, probably from 'the avolation of divers subtile particles', whereas it was commonly thought that animals are heavier when dead than when alive. Boyle's vague conclusion was that either 'the common flame and the vital flame are maintained by distinct substances or parts of the air; or, that common flame making a great waste of the aerial substance, they both need to keep them alive, cannot so easily as the other find matter to prey upon, and so expires, whilst there yet remains enough to keep alive the more temperate vital flame; or that both these causes, and perhaps some other, concur to the phænomenon'. In some inconclusive experiments he found that animals live in compressed air.[2]

In 1664 (*The Experimental History of Colours*) and 1675 (*Reflections upon the Hypothesis of Alcali and Acidum*) Boyle gives some general properties of acids and alkalis, such as the sour taste of acids, their action as solvents, their precipitation of sulphur from liver of sulphur, their action on vegetable colours (indicators) such as tournsol, juice of violets and decoctions of cochineal and Brazil wood, the colours being restored by alkalis, and their reaction with alkalis with disappearance of the characteristic properties of each and the formation of a neutral salt. He describes many tests and is one of the founders of qualitative analysis. He mentions the green colour imparted to a flame by copper salts,[3] the white fumes produced with ammonia and nitric and hydrochloric acids[4] (already mentioned by Kunckel), and the black colour produced with iron salts and infusion of galls, powdered galls, infusions of red roses, pomegranate flowers (balustrium), logwood, Brazil wood, and other 'astringent vegetable pigments'.[5] Finely-powdered garnets boiled with aqua regia gave a solution from which on evaporation crystals were obtained which gave the iron test with galls;[6] some dark garnets were attracted by a magnet.[7] For the use of a lady who always inked her fingers when writing, Boyle prepared white paper with a dry powder of galls, calcined vitriol and gum arabic; when written upon with a pen dipped in water this became black.[8]

Boyle mentions the white precipitate (calcium sulphate) formed with sulphuric acid and a solution of calcium carbonate in vinegar (calcium acetate)[9] and the precipitation of silver salts by solutions of chlorides,[10] and the red

[1] XI; *Works*, iii, 261 f.   [2] ID; *Works*, iv, 124.
[3] XXI; *Works*, iv, 298.   [4] XVIII; *Works*, iv, 174.
[5] IVA, XX; *Works*, iii, 193; iv, 240; the reaction was known to Pliny, Vol. I.
[6] X; *Works*, iii, 230.   [7] XXV; *Works*, v, 94.
[8] IVA; *Works*, iii, 150.   [9] XV (i); *Works*, iii, 636.
[10] IV; VII; XVIII; *Works*, i, 496; ii, 506; iv, 171 (where he also mentions the solution of gold leaf in aqua fortis in presence of common salt); v, 201 (Way of Examining Waters, from *Phil. Trans.*, 169⅔, xvii, 627, no. 197.

precipitate from corrosive sublimate and fixed alkali.[1] Many of these tests had been described before, e.g. by Libavius (p. 264), but Boyle's *Short Memoirs for the Natural Experimental History of Mineral Waters* (1685)[2] contains a collection of chemical tests and is a great advance on previous work.[3]

Blue syrup of violets, or violet juice spread on white paper is turned red by acids and green by alkalis.[4] Boyle also used dry test-papers on which drops of solution were placed — the first 'spot-tests'.[5] Other natural colours used as indicators (sometimes in the form of test-papers) were cornflower juice, juice of privet berries, or blackberries or black cherries, decoctions of cochineal, pomegranate flowers, rose petals in dilute sulphuric acid, decoctions of *lignum nephriticum*, Brazil wood, logwood, of various flowers (tulips, auriculas, peach flowers, pea flowers, apple blossom, snowdrop, jasmine, etc., the white flowers becoming yellow or red), or fruits, senna, madder, or litmus (litmase).[6] The Florentine Academicians also describe the red colour produced with various vegetable colours (including also lacca mussa = litmus) by acids (lemon juice, oil of vitriol) and the restoration of the blue colour by potash (oleum tartari).[7]

Once, when 'rummaging in a dark place' among some unlabelled bottles, Boyle says, 'one of them falling down made two or three great stains on the conspicuousest part of a new suit', but on smelling other bottles he found one which by its smell he guessed to 'abound with the volatile salt' (ammonia) and after he had 'bathed the stained parts well with it', it 'in a trice restored them to their former colour'.[8]

Sir Thomas Browne,[9] after describing the black colour formed with vitriol and various astringent materials, says: 'So spirits of Salt upon a blew paper make an orient red. So tartar or vitriol upon an infusion of violets affords a delightfull crimson.' Walter Charleton[10] had shown that oil of tartar turned infusion of senna red, whilst oil of vitriol did not produce this colour; oil of vitriol turned infusion of rose leaves purple or deep scarlet, whilst oil of tartar produced no effect; he also mentions 'the Cerule Tincture caused in White Wine by *Lignum Nephriticum* infused when the Decoction thereof shall remain turbid and subnigricant', by the action of incident light, as a piece of taffaty (*sic*) 'appears of two different dyes'. Boyle[11] describes the fluorescence of solutions of *lignum nephriticum*, the yellow liquid appearing blue in some aspects, mentioning Monardes and Kircher as having published this observation before him (see p. 332), but Boyle used the solution as a sensitive indicator for acids, which destroyed the colour and fluorescence, and this was new.

Poggendorff[11] remarked that many discoveries of others had been wrongly

[1] V; *Works*, ii, 64.   [2] *Works*, iv, 231–50.   [3] G. Rath, *A. Med.*, 1957, xli, 1.
[4] IV; V; VIII (*a*); XVIII; XXV; *Works*, i, 500; ii, 53 f.; iii, 81; iv, 180; v, 85.
[5] XX; *Works*, iv, 239; R. G. Neville, *Isis*, 1958, xlix, 438.
[6] III; V; XX; *Works*, i, 328, 368; ii, 44, 53 f., 60 f., 70 (litmus); iv, 239.
[7] *Saggi*, 1667; tr. Waller, London, 1684, 135; Poggendorff, (2), 1883, 244.
[8] IVA; *Works*, iii, 152.
[9] *Pseudodoxia Epidemica*, 1646; book vi, ch. 12; *Works*, ed. Keynes, 1928, iii, 254.
[10] *Physiologia Epicuro-Gassendo-Charltoniana*, f°, London, 1654, 132 f.
[11] V; *Works*, ii, 44; Partington, *Ann. Sci.*, 1955, xi, 1.   [12] 1883, (2), 292.

attributed to Boyle, who did not himself claim them. In what follows a selection of interesting observations recorded by Boyle is given.

A solution of gold stains the skin and nails, and ivory, purple.[1] Glass in which gold amalgam has been heated appears blue in reflected and golden in transmitted light; the red colour of bits of the windows of old St. Paul's, after its destruction by fire, was found to be on the surface of the glass only.[2] Gold leaf shows a greenish-blue transmitted light.[3] Gold is volatilised [as gold chloride] by dissolving it in a *menstruum peracutum* [aqua regia] obtained by distilling aqua fortis from butter of antimony [$SbCl_3$], evaporating and heating, when a 'good store of large thin crystals, . . . like rubies, very glorious to behold', sublimed, which in moist air 'would run *per deliquium*'.[4] A spirit of salt which attacked gold[5] must have contained chlorine. A fine powder of gold was obtained from a very concentrated solution of gold in aqua fortis by adding alcohol, when a fragrant smell [ethyl chloride] was noticed.[6] Iron may be gilded by first coppering it in a solution of copper in acid and then rubbing with gold amalgam.[7]

Silver gives a yellow colour to glass when fused on it.[8] The separation of silver from its solution in aqua fortis by means of precipitation by copper was well known in London in Boyle's time, and he also showed that the silver is precipitated by zinc.[9] A powder for silvering copper or brass by rubbing on it consisted of a mixture of equal parts of silver nitrate, common salt and crystals of tartar.[10] Fused silver chloride ('resin or gum' of silver) was obtained by heating silver with corrosive sublimate, or by precipitating a solution of silver in aqua fortis with spirit of salt and fusing to *luna cornea* (a name 'already to be met with in the writings of some alchymists'); it could be cut like horn and was 'transparent, though not like glass, yet like good amber'.[11] The blackening of silver chloride on exposure to light he supposed to be due to the action of the air.[12] A solution of silver dyed hair and skin (also ivory) a 'lasting black'.[13]

The 'small crooked pipe of metal or glass, such as tradesmen for its use call a blow-pipe', gives a jet of air which when directed on the flame of a lamp or candle produces a pointed flame which melts silver and even copper.[14]

A 'resin of copper' (cuprous chloride), 'like a lump of good benjamin', was obtained as a residue by distilling copper with corrosive sublimate; on exposure to air the yellow or red mass became green.[15] A solution of copper in aqua fortis was very difficult to crystallise but on careful evaporation gave 'one of the lovliest vitriols that hath perhaps been seen' (copper nitrate);[16] the solution stains ivory a blue colour, solutions of gold and silver staining it purple and black, respectively.[17] Cuprous sulphide was obtained as a black or blue brittle mass by heating in a crucible copper plates stratified with sulphur.[18] A brown solution from copper filings and spirit of salt exposed to air becomes

[1] V; *Works*, ii, 76.   [2] XIX; *Works*, iv, 215, 230.   [3] V; *Works*, ii, 44.
[4] VII; *Works*, ii, 516.   [5] II (a); *Works*, i, 225.   [6] XXV; *Works*, v, 99.
[7] IVA; *Works*, iii, 198.   [8] IVA; *Works*, iii, 193; XIX; *Works*, iv, 229.
[9] II (a), (c); XV (i); XXII; *Works*, i, 217, 250; iii, 640; iv, 313.
[10] IVA; *Works*, iii, 200.   [11] VII; *Works*, ii, 505-7; XXV; *Works*, v, 98.
[12] V; *Works*, ii, 61.   [13] V; *Works*, ii, 34.   [14] XXI; *Works*, iv, 258.
[15] VII; XX; *Works*, ii, 504; iv, 298.   [16] VII; *Works*, ii, 486 f., 490.
[17] XIX; *Works*, iv, 216.   [18] XIX; *Works*, iv, 224.

colourless on standing over copper in a stoppered bottle, when the pressure of the air diminishes, but recovers its colour when exposed to the air.[1] A colourless solution of copper filings in spirit of salt turns an amethyst colour, then green, when exposed to air.[2]

A mixture of iron filings and powdered brimstone heats and smokes when moistened with water.[3] Marcasite (iron sulphide) when exposed to air in a room increased in weight when converted into vitriol (ferrous sulphate), and calcined vitriol also increased in weight when exposed in Boyle's study in Oxford, although one portion 'had met with some mischance, either by mice or otherwise'.[4] Crystals of green vitriol are obtained by dissolving iron filings in dilute sulphuric acid and evaporating, and another kind of iron vitriol (ferrous chloride) is formed in crystals soluble in spirit of wine (perhaps ferric chloride?) from solutions of iron in spirit of salt, but not from aqua fortis.[5]

Iron dissolves in spirit of salt to a green solution, in aqua fortis to a reddish one. Powdered loadstone dissolves in aqua regia or spirit of salt to a golden yellow solution.[6] Sir Thomas Browne[7] found that if aqua fortis is poured on powdered loadstone and the subsiding powder dried, it retains some magnetic virtue, but the 'Icycles or Crystals' obtained on evaporation of the solution are not attracted by a loadstone. The action is due to the 'potential fire' of the acid.

Aqua fortis corrodes more tin than it dissolves and the product (metastannic acid) easily gelatinises like cheese or white of egg.[8] Sir Thomas Browne[9] says: 'upon a solution of Tin by *Aqua fortis*, there will ensue a coagulation, like that of whites of Eggs', and gives this as an illustration that 'many bodies will coagulate upon commixture, whose separated natures promise no concretion'. Bacon[10] said the product was like 'cream or curds'. A 'spirituous liquid' (stannic chloride), strongly fuming in air, is distilled from a mixture of tin with an equal or double weight of Venetian corrosive sublimate.[11]

The nature of white vitriol (zinc sulphate) was disputed and Boyle thought it might contain some copper.[12] He mentions 'zinc or (as in the shops they call it) spelter'.[13] The names speautre, spiauter, spelter, piautre, pewter, etc., for zinc occur from about 1600, and according to Karabaček (1886) are derived from an unusual Arabic name for 'white lead', isbīdāj, from the older Persian name sefīd rūy.[14] The name spiauter may also be derived from that of pewter, O. French piautre, said to be from the Sanskrit pātira,[15] and zinc is called 'pewter' in some earlier publications.

[1] XXXI; *Works*, iii, 553.   [2] XXV; *Works*, v, 86.
[3] XXI; *Works*, iv, 286; Lemery, Vol. III.   [4] XIV; *Works*, iii, 474.
[5] VII; XXV; *Works*, ii, 486 f., v, 94.   [6] XXV; *Works*, v, 82.
[7] *Pseudodoxia Epidemica*, ii, 3; *Works*, ed. Sayle, 1927, i, 237.
[8] V, XV (e); *Works*, ii, 72; iii, 604.
[9] *Pseudodoxia Epidemica*, book ii, ch. 4; *Works*, ed. Keynes, 1928, ii, 138; ed. Sayle, 1927, i, 261.
[10] *Historia Densi et Rari, Works*, ed. Spedding, etc., ii, 279.
[11] XXI; *Works*, iv, 298.   [12] VII; *Works*, ii, 486 f.
[13] XVIII; *Works*, iv, 183; W. Coward, *De Fermento Volatili Nutritio Conjectura Rationis*, 1695, 55: Zink sive Spelter.
[14] Beckmann, (1), 1846, ii, 44; Bucher, *Geschichte der technischen Kunst*, Berlin and Leipzig, 1893, iii, 43 f.
[15] Lenormant, *Les Premières Civilisations*, 1874, i, 148.

Zinc dissolves in ammonia, especially on warming.[1] The lapis calaminaris (zinc ore or zinc ?) changes and improves the colour of copper by turning it into brass; 'and I have sometimes, by the help of zinc duly mixed after a certain manner, given copper one of the richest golden colours, the ever I have seen the best true gold ennobled with. But pray have a care, that such hints fall not into any hands, that may mis-employ them.'[2] Morhof[3] said brass is made by melting together copper (cuprum) and zinc (zincum) in the correct proportions.

Antimony can be obtained in a stellate regulus (exhibiting star-shaped crystals) without iron, previously thought to be necessary: 'my own laboratory hath afforded me divers such parcels of regulus without Mars.'[4] Bismuth or 'tin glasse', which is crystalline,[5] was not much used 'till very lately, unless outwardly, and especially for a cosmetick' but had been used to prepare internal medicines.[6] It is precipitated by water (as oxynitrate) from its solution in aqua fortis.[7] By distilling it with corrosive sublimate a matter 'made up of very thin, smooth, soft and slippery plates, almost like the finest sort of scales of fishes', but of a lovely pearly white colour (bismuth chloride) came over.[8]

The name 'tin glass' is used in 1620 by Henricus Artocophinus, born in Pomerania and town-physician in Stettin.[9] In 1686 Valvasor reported that the addition of one-third of 'bizmuth or zink' to casting brass made it 'run much better'.[10]

Galena is reduced to metallic lead by melting with iron filings.[11] Red lead (minium) loses weight when exposed to sunlight concentrated by a burning glass [i.e. on heating], 1 drachm lost $\frac{3}{4}$ grain; on heating it in the same way in a sealed bulb, the vessel burst with explosion;[12] Boyle had just missed the discovery of oxygen.

Red precipitate of mercury dissolves in spirit of salt;[13] when corrosive sublimate is distilled with sal ammoniac, 'a new kind of sublimate' is obtained, the solution of which is precipitated white (not red) with salt of tartar.[14] Copper amalgam becomes very hard and brittle.[15] An amalgam of 1 part of tin, 1 of lead, 2 of bismuth ('good tinned-glass') and 10 of mercury, strained through linen, was used for 'silvering' glass mirrors.[16] Corrosive sublimate was often adulterated with arsenic.[17]

When corrosive sublimate is 'dulcified' by subliming with mercury (forming calomel), perhaps the little blades of the sublimate particles are sheathed, and so lose their cutting and stabbing qualities; some such explanation may apply to the sweet salt made from lead with aqua fortis, or green vitriol from

[1] XV (h), (i); Works, iii, 628, 640 (zink or speltar).   [2] V (1664); Works, ii, 76.
[3] De Metallorum Transmutatione, Hamburg, 1673, 75.   [4] II; Works, i, 209.
[5] X; Works, iii, 227.   [6] IV; Works, i, 501.
[7] XV (e); Works, iii, 605.   [8] V; Works, ii, 33.
[9] Jöcher, i, 578; he is not mentioned by Gmelin, Hoefer, Kopp, or Lippmann; Prodromus Mysteriorum Naturae Mysteriossisimorum ab Henrico Artocophinus, Stettin, 1620, Tractatus II, 27: Cobaltum Bisemutum quod stannum glaciale nominant.
[10] Gunther, (1), 1939, xii, 121.   [11] XXIV; Works, v, 29.
[12] ID; Works, iv, 149.   [13] XV (h); Works, iii, 632.
[14] VII; XV (e); Works, ii, 506; iii, 604.   [15] II; Works, i, 278.
[16] IVA; Works, iii, 176; mentioning a silvering mixture of Caneparius containing arsenic.
[17] II; Works, i, 205.

oil of vitriol and steel.[1] Mercury is separated from cinnabar by distilling it with iron or steel filings: 'the sulphur of the cinnabar will fasten upon the filings, and let the mercury come over fair and vivid.'[2]

Boyle was acquainted with caustic ammonia, obtained by distilling ordinary ammonia (the carbonate) with quicklime; it does not give a solid on distillation, is not precipitated by alcohol, and does not effervesce with acids although it grows hot when mixed with them:[3] 'alcalizate spirit of urine drawn from some kinds of quicklime being mixed with oil of vitriol moderately strong would produce an intense heat whilst it produced either no manifest bubbles at all, or scarce any, though the urinous spirit was strong and in other trials operated like an alkali.'[4]

Ammonia gives white fumes with the vapours of hydrochloric and nitric acids: when the mouths of bottles containing the acid and ammonia are brought together: 'as soon as the liquors came to be approached, the fumes meeting each other in the air would make coalitions, which would be manifestly visible in the form of ascending smoke, which was wont at first to surprize the delighted spectators.'[5] The volatile alkalis from urine, hartshorn, blood, sal ammoniac, etc., are practically the same.[6] They all give a reddish-yellow colour to saffron and turmeric,[7] and have properties in common with fixed alkalis,[8] but the volatile alkali differs from fixed alkalis in giving a white, instead of a deep orange, precipitate, with a solution of corrosive sublimate.[9] The precipitation of spirit of urine (ammonium carbonate) by spirit of wine requires very well dephlegmated spirits, but then succeeds, so that 'Helmont had not misinformed us'.[10] Sal ammoniac contains as its two constituents spirit of salt and spirit of urine; it is formed from these, and is decomposed by salt of tartar because the latter takes the spirit of salt and sets the ammonia free.[11]

Fresh urine contains a 'native sal ammoniac, much less volatile than the fugitive', since on distilling with a large quantity of salt of pot-ashes it gave a very volatile spirit (ammonia).[12] The volatile alkali precipitates fulminating gold from a solution of gold in aqua regia.[13] It dissolves zinc,[14] and even copper when exposed to air, forming a blue liquid the colour of which disappears when the liquid stands over copper in a stoppered bottle, when the pressure of the air is diminished, but the blue colour reappears on exposure of the liquid to air.[15] The production of this blue colour may be used as a test for copper in gold: this is dissolved in aqua regia and ammonia added, when 'after the urinous spirit had precipitated the gold into a fine calx, the supernatant liquor was highly tinged with blue, that betrayed the alloy of copper'.[16]

Sal ammoniac crystallises 'either like combs or feathers'.[17] Sal ammoniac

[1] XV (h); Works, iii, 630.   [2] IIIA; Works, i, 409.
[3] IV, XV (e), XVIII, XXII; Works, i, 515; iii, 605; iv, 201, 313.   [4] XV (e); Works, iii, 605.
[5] XVIII; Works, iv, 189.   [6] V, XXII; Works, ii, 66; iv, 310.
[7] XVIII; Works, iv, 184.   [8] IV; V; Works, i, 505; ii, 53 f.
[9] V, XV (i), XVIII; Works, ii, 64; iii, 637; iv, 180.
[10] II, III, IV, XV (f), XVIII, XXII; Works, i, 211, 263, 306; iii, 617; iv, 185 f., 313.
[11] III; VII; VIII (a); Works, i, 306; ii, 490; iii, 81; cf. Mayow, p. 606.
[12] XV (b); Works, iii, 617.   [13] IV; Works, iii, 153.
[14] XV (h), (i); XVIII; Works, iii, 628, 640; iv, 183.
[15] XVIII; XXVI, XXXI; Works, iii, 553; iv, 183, 186, 188; v, 119 f., 183.
[16] IV; Works, iii, 153.   [17] VIII (a); Works, ii, 81.

could be made cheaply in England by a process known to Boyle:[1] 'though the sal armoniac that is made in the East, may consist in great part of camel's urine, yet, that, which is made in Europe, (where camels are rarities) and is commonly sold in our shops, is made of man's urine.'[2] A freezing mixture was formed of 1 lb. of sal ammoniac and 3 lb. of water.[3] From nitric acid and ammonia Boyle 'sometimes obtained fine long crystals' shaped like saltpetre (ammonium nitrate).[4]

Boyle criticised 'the doctrine of alkali and acidum' proposed by Sylvius (p. 284) with its assumption of 'a conflict between those two jarring principles, or, if I may so call them, duellists', since 'it seems precarious to affirm that in all bodies . . . acid and alkalizate parts are found'.[5]

The fixed alkalis (potassium carbonate) called fixed nitre, salt of tartar, potash, vegetable and wood ashes, are all practically identical.[6] The fixed alkali is not present (as such) in the vegetable but is produced by burning.[7] This view was adopted by Daniel Coxe,[8] Lemery (see Vol. III), Stahl (see p. 681) and Boerhaave (see p. 755).[9]

The alkalis ('lixiviate salts') will often precipitate pearls, coral, etc., which have been dissolved in acids,[10] but not always.[11] They give a deep orange coloured precipitate with a solution of corrosive sublimate, whereas volatile alkali gives a white precipitate.[12]

When acids and alkalis are mixed, the properties of each disappear, the sharp acid particle being 'mortified or disabled to bite', and its 'power of cutting or pricking' removed by 'having its figure spoiled by the action of a manifest alkali',[13] so that they 'degenerate into a new thing'.[14] Boyle explains in great detail the origin of acid tastes in terms of the sharp or blade-like particles, which have been formed by rubbing together under the action of fire in their preparation (this was a year after Mayow).[15]

Egyptian nitre (soda) is an alkali, quite different from common nitre (saltpetre), since it effervesces with acids.[16] Boyle[17] obtained an alkali (soda) from common salt, which he says was generally supposed not to contain alkali: he twice distilled sea-salt with aqua fortis and obtained a residue (sodium nitrate) which when fused would, with charcoal, 'flash divers times almost like nitre' and the product appeared 'to be brought to an alcalizate nature', since it had a caustic taste, effervesced with acid and turned syrup of violets green.[18]

A way of making alkali out of nitre is to distil it with strong oil of vitriol, powder the dry residue, mix it with charcoal and heat in a crucible. The red mass (liver of sulphur) exposed to air forms an alkaline salt associated with sulphur.[19] A 'follower of Glauber' had, by his master's directions, obtained a real sulphur out of vegetable charcoal in a way 'specious enough to impose

---

[1] XXVIII; *Works*, ii, 549.   [2] XVIII; *Works*, iv, 188.   [3] XXVIII; *Works*, ii, 547.
[4] VII; *Works*, ii, 489.   [5] XV (e); *Works*, iii, 603.   [6] II; *Works*, i, 232.
[7] III, 1680, 52, 81, 235.   [8] *Phil. Trans.*, 1674, ix, 150–8; abridged ed., 1809, ii, 158.
[9] Kopp, (1), iii, 43.   [10] VIIA; *Works*, ii, 537.   [11] XVIII; *Works*, iv, 186.
[12] V, XV (i), XVIII; *Works*, ii, 64; iii, 637; iv, 180.   [13] XXII; *Works*, iv, 311.
[14] IV; *Works*, i, 505.   [15] XV (b); *Works*, iii, 587.   [16] IIIA; *Works*, i, 381.
[17] IIIA; *Works*, i, 382.
[18] See on this Bohn, p. 301; Boerhaave, (2), 1732, i, 44, still denied that common salt contains an alkali (alcali non dant).
[19] IIIA; *Works*, i, 382.

upon those, that either are not chymists, or, if they be chymists, are not cautious men'. This was to distil salt with oil of vitriol, powder the residue, mix it with one-fourth or one-eighth of its weight of charcoal, and heat strongly, when the mass became dark red and 'both smelt and tasted rankly enough of sulphur'. If ammonia was distilled from it, the 'ascending spirit would be manifestly impregnated with sulphur not difficultly separable. . . . But for all this specious separation, I do not take the sulphur, thus produced, to have been the vegetable sulphur of charcoal, but a mineral sulphur, that lay concealed in a liquid form among the saline parts of the oil of vitriol'.[1]

Boyle refers to the different forms of salt crystals and mentions the crystallisation of Venetian borax, saltpetre, and the *caput mortuum* (potassium sulphate) from the preparation of aqua fortis from nitre and vitriol.[2] The shape of the crystals obtained from common salt and oil of vitriol depends on the quantity of the latter (acid and normal sodium sulphates).[3]

From a solution of equal parts of alum and nitre on evaporation alum alone crystallised at first without nitre, but on further evaporation 'at length the nitre shot plentifully into fine little crystals'.[4] Solution is similar to fusion; both are due to the pervasion of a foreign body which separates the particles, a solvent in solution and ' a thin fluid' [fire] in fusion. Powdered alabaster on heating looks like a fluid, rolling about and steaming owing to the agitation of its spherical particles by heat.[5] Limestone on burning becomes lime, which is more soluble in water, because the heat opens the pores of the stone.[6]

Acids produce various effects on coloured indicators and reverse the colour changes produced by alkalis; they precipitate sulphur from liver of sulphur and antimony sulphide from its solution in alkali, and decolorise the blue solution of copper in ammonia.[7] Boyle suspected that white arsenic (arsenious oxide) is an acid body.[8] The three mineral acids were well known to Boyle, and were kept in bottles with ground glass stoppers, which had only recently come into general use in his time,[9] although they were used by the Romans in Pompeii (Vol. I).

Colourless aqua fortis in a partly filled bottle gives off red fumes when exposed to light, or when a metal such as iron or silver is dissolved in it.[10] Concentrated aqua fortis does not dissolve lead or silver but does so on dilution.[11] Aqua fortis usually dissolves mercury, lead, copper and silver;[12] when it acts upon mercury it becomes blue or green.[13] Aqua regia, 'that dissolves gold readily, will dissolve mercury but scurvily, and silver not at all.'[14] Impure silver containing copper gives a blue or green solution;[15] when aqua fortis dissolves silver it increases the weight by one quarter to one third.[16]

Nitre is obtained in prismatic crystals by neutralising aqua fortis with salt of tartar and evaporating. Boyle, who attached great importance to them, says he

---

[1] IIIA; *Works*, i, 395.   [2] III, VII, X, XVIII; *Works*, i, 338; ii, 488; iii, 217; iv, 169.
[3] VII; *Works*, ii, 488.   [4] XXVI; *Works*, v, 189.   [5] II; *Works*, i, 246–7.
[6] XV (*h*); *Works*, iii, 631.   [7] V; *Works*, ii, 66–8.   [8] XX; *Works*, iv, 241.
[9] IV, IVA; *Works*, iii, 197; see Glauber, p. 350.   [10] VIII; *Works*, iii, 75, 80.
[11] II (*a*); *Works*, i, 213; cf. Bohn, p. 301.   [12] XV (*e*); *Works*, iii, 604.
[13] V; *Works*, ii, 72.   [14] XV (*e*); *Works*, iii, 604.   [15] II, V; *Works*, i, 212; ii, 73.
[16] VII; *Works*, ii, 518.

had made these experiments long before Glauber's 'small treatises' (see p. 353) came into his hands.[1] Saltpetre might 'receive divers qualities from the particular soil wherein it grows', since a London physician informed Boyle that the saltpetre of churchyards was peculiarly 'choice'.[2] A powder composed of nitre 'with other ingredients' (sulphur and potassium carbonate) if heated from below detonates but if kindled at the top burns and acts as 'a powerful flux for the reduction of metalline powders mixed with it'.[3] Another 'nitre' (sodium nitrate) was obtained together with aqua regia by distilling common salt with aqua fortis.[4] Boyle describes the preparation of 'phosphorus Balduini' (calcium nitrate).[5]

Oil of vitriol when poured on sal ammoniac gives rise to an 'explosion' (violent evolution of gas).[6] It produces cold when mixed with snow, although Boyle could not freeze oil of vitriol itself (which Merret had declared to be possible), even 'with our frigorifick mixture of ice and salt'.[7] Oil of vitriol corrodes many metals which it will not dissolve;[8] it precipitates a solution of silver in aqua fortis.[9] By distilling oil of vitriol with turpentine in a retort Boyle obtained sulphur, yet he seems to have leaned to the idea that sulphur was a compound of the acid and a combustible principle.[10]

Boyle refers to the 'silent precipitation' of silver by copper, of copper by iron and zinc, and of gold and silver by mercury, from solutions of the salts, saying that 'in these operations, the saline particles may really quit the dissolved body and work upon the precipitant'.[11] When cinnabar (mercuric sulphide) is distilled with iron filings, 'the sulphur of the cinnabar will fasten upon the filings, and let the mercury come over fair and vivid.'[12] Alkalis remove sulphur from cinnabar; 'the corpuscles of sulphur and mercury . . . will rise together in sublimatory vessels without being divorced by the fire', but when the cinnabar is mixed with 'a due proportion of salt of tartar, the parts of the alkali will associate themselves more strictly with those of the sulphur, than these were before with those of the mercury', and in consequence the latter is set free.[13]

Boyle explained the action of substances on one another in terms of the adherence of the particles: 'there are clusters wherein the Particles stick not so close together, but that they may meet with Corpuscles of another Denomination, which are dispos'd to be more closely United with some of them, than they were among themselves.'[14] He also had some idea of the action of mass: 'I have long suspected, that in divers cases, the quantity of a menstruum may much more considerably compensate its want of strength, than chemists are commonly aware of.'[15]

The affinity of acids is greater towards fixed than towards volatile alkali, as may be shown by 'satiating' volatile salt of human blood (ammonia) with spirit of nitre, evaporating, and heating the 'dry concretion' (ammonium nitrate)

[1] II, VII; *Works*, i, 230 f.; ii, 492.   [2] II (a); *Works*, i, 210.
[3] IVA; *Works*, iii, 198.   [4] VII; *Works*, ii, 509; see Bohn, p. 301.
[5] XVI; *Works*, iv, 37.   [6] XI; *Works*, iii, 267.   [7] VI; *Works*, ii, 236, 259.
[8] VII; *Works*, ii, 490.   [9] VII; *Works*, ii, 507.   [10] III, 1661, 218.
[11] XV (i), XXII; *Works*, iii, 640; iv, 313.   [12] IIIA; *Works*, i, 409.
[13] VII; *Works*, ii, 515.   [14] III, 1661, 153; cf. VII; *Works*, ii, 471.   [15] XIV; *Works*, iii, 464.

with salt of tartar and a little water, when it was expected that 'the saline spirits of nitre, being more congruous to the fixed salt than to the volatile, would forsake the salt of blood, (which it detained before from flying away) and give it leave to sublime'; and this was found to occur.[1] The same occurs with a mixture of quicklime or zinc oxide (*lapis calaminaris*) with sal ammoniac:

by making use of such additaments, as to break off, or otherwise divide the particles of the corpuscles . . . and by adhering to, and so clogging one of the particles, to which it proves more congruous, enable the other . . . to ascend . . . when sal armoniac is well ground with lapis calaminaris, or some other fixed alcali, and then committed to dis-tillation . . . the sea-salt that enters the composition of the sal armoniac being detained by the stone or the alcali, there is a divorce made between the common salt and the urinous and fuliginous salts, that were incorporated with it.[2]

Sulphur melted in a small bolt-head formed 'great fibres, almost like little straws' (monoclinic sulphur crystals).[3] Sulphur dissolves to a red liquid in boiling alkali solution or in fused alkali,[4] and the salt from oil of vitriol and salt of tartar (potassium sulphate) becomes red (potassium sulphide) when heated with charcoal.[5] A red liquid 'volatile tincture of sulphur' (ammonium poly-sulphide) with a very powerful odour, emitting white fumes in air, was ob-tained by distilling a mixture of approximately equal weights of sal ammoniac, sulphur and quicklime (or salt of tartar).[6] The fume penetrated a piece of bladder and blackened a silver coin wrapped in it.[7] Liquid ammonium poly-sulphide, although called *liquor fumans Boylei*, was really discovered by Libavius (see p. 264) and again by Beguin.[8] A sympathetic ink was a solution of sugar of lead (lead acetate), writing in which became visible when sponged over with a solution of calcium sulphide (made from orpiment and quicklime) or when exposed to the vapour of tincture of sulphur (ammonium sulphide).[9]

Acting on a hint given him by Kraft (p. 371) Boyle rediscovered phos-phorus.[10] The description of the method of making phosphorus, dated 30 September 1680, was deposited with the Royal Society in October, 1680, and opened after Boyle's death,[11] but it was previously published in his book on the *Aerial Noctiluca* (1680).[12] Putrefied urine was evaporated to a syrup which was mixed with 3 parts of fine white sand. The mixture was heated in a strong retort luted to a large receiver nearly filled with water. After heating as strongly as possible ('NB' is here inserted in the account) for several hours, there finally passed over a substance much of which fell through the water to the bottom of the receiver. In the book on the *Icy Noctiluca* (1682)[13] Boyle says this solid phosphorus was obtained in lumps of various sizes, transparent and colourless like fragments of ice, hence 'I thought it not amiss

[1] XVIII; *Works*, iv, 189.   [2] XV (f); *Works*, iii, 617.
[3] X; *Works*, iii, 227.   [4] V, XX; *Works*, ii, 38, 59, 66; iv, 246.
[5] III, VII; *Works*, i, 382; ii, 512; cf. Glauber, p. 353.
[6] IVA, V, XII, XX; *Works*, i, 570; ii, 59; iii, 330; iv, 240.   [7] XIX; *Works*, iv, 213.
[8] *Tyrocinium Chymicum*, 1610, bk. ii, ch. 6: oleum sulphuris.
[9] VIA, XII; *Works*, ii, 379; iii, 338.
[10] Speter, *Chem. Ztg.*, 1929, liii, 1005; *id.*, in Weeks, 1956, 129; Partington, *Sci. Progr.*, 1936, xxx, 402.
[11] *Works*, ed. Birch, 198; printed in *Phil Trans.*, January 1693, xvii, 583.
[12] XVI, 95; *Works*, iv, 37.   [13] XVII, 16; *Works*, iv, 74.

to call our consistent and self-shining substance, the icy or glacial noctiluca (and for variety phosphorus)'. The experiments described in 1680 were made with a solution or suspension of phosphorus in water, or a 'mud'; those in 1682 with pure solid phosphorus. This work was done in conjunction with Boyle's assistant Ambrose Godfrey Hanckewitz (in 1680 Boyle speaks of a German, '*A.G.* M.D.', having told him that the degree of fire was important, agreeing that 'I knew the true matter').

James[1] refers to some experiments on phosphorus made for Boyle by Bilgar (or Bilger) (who was Boyle's assistant before Hanckewitz),[2] which (since they used fæces) may have been made before the successful preparation from urine; Kraft had, in exchange for one of Boyle's secrets, told him that it was made from 'something to do with the body'.

Boyle's German 'Laborant' Bilger took back to Germany an obscure account of his preparation of a 'hermetic phosphorus' from human excrement and urine, finishing with distillation at a very high temperature (forti igne), when he obtained a buttery mass, light, porous, friable, and dark red, shining in the dark like fire (in butyri forma ascendere quod noctu lucet instar ignis; erat massa levis, porosa, friabilis è fusco rutilans).[3] Hanckewitz says Kraft paid Brand 200 dollars for a specimen of phosphorus, then Kunckel made it, and then 'both these two made it' as 'an unctuous dawbing mass'. Bilger was instructed by Boyle to prepare it but 'long before' this Hanckewitz had made it 'right glacial'. The Duke of Brunswick and Leibniz were working on Brand's process but all they ever got was 'a confused form, as a chaos'. Hanckewitz at first spoke of Brand with respect but changed his tune as time went on.[4]

Ambrose Godfrey Hanckewitz or Hanckwitz (1660–1740 or 1741), presumably a German, assistant to Boyle, F.R.S. 1729, later set up a laboratory for himself where he made and sold phosphorus, which was used (with the original furnaces) by the firm of Godfrey and Cooke until 1862.[5] His sons were Boyle Godfrey (d. 1753), who was an alchemist, Ambrose Godfrey jnr. (*c.* 1685–1756), and John Godfrey (fl. 1747); the two latter carried on a business in Southampton St., Covent Garden, London, but later became bankrupt. Hanckewitz published an *Account of a New Method of Extinguishing Fires by Suffocation and Explosion*, 1724.[6]

About 1685 Ambrose Godfrey Hanckewitz (who then called himself Hanckwitz) issued an advertisement for solid phosphorus, wholesale 50s., and retail £3, an ounce, also flowers of phosphorus (? phosphorus pentoxide), black phosphorus, etc.[7] Hellot[8] says Hanckewitz had a complete monopoly of pure solid phosphorus in Europe, no one else being able to make it.

Hanckewitz's paper on 'some experiments on the phosphorus of urine'[9]

[1] *Medicinal Dictionary*, 1745, iii, Art. Phosphorus.   [2] Anon., *Pharm. J.*, 1895, xxx, 937.
[3] Rosinus Lentillius, *Ephemer. Nat. Curios.*, 1685 (1686), Dec. II, An IV, 312–14: Processu Phosphori Hermetici.
[4] J. Ince, *Pharm. J.*, 1853, xiii, 280–2 (disc. of phosphorus from a pamphlet by Hanckewitz, *Historia Phosphori et Fama* (in English); 1858, xviii, 126–30, 157–62 (mostly on phosphorus), 263–7 (on ether, see p. 546).
[5] Goodwin, DNB, 1890, xxii, 30; Gunther, (1), i, 21; Speter, *Chem. Ztg.*, 1929, liii, 1005 (who says Hanckewitz did not come from Cöthen, as is usually stated); Pilcher, *Ambix*, 1938, ii, 17
[6] Maddison, *Notes and Records of the Royal Society*, 1954–5, xi, 159–88; *Ann. Sci.*, 1955, xi, 64.
[7] La Wall, *The Curious Lore of Drugs and Medicines*, New York, 1927, 336.
[8] AdS, 1737, m 342.
[9] *Phil. Trans.*, 1733, xxxviii, 58; tr. in Crell, *N. Chem. Archiv*, 1785, iii, 1 f.

described the method of preparation of phosphorus by distilling the 'sapon-aceous magma' of urine in 'a closed vessel, with a reverberatory fire, much stronger than that used for the distillation of aquafortis, or the other mineral acid spirits; the rest of the proper encheiresis belongs only to the operator to manage secundum artem'. When the operation succeeds, 'near the end of the distillation, comes over that depurated oil, which constitutes the inflammable part of the phosphorus, which is not raised up till the last, and that by the continuance of a very strong reverberatory fire.' Hanckewitz says Kunckel, Kraft, and Brand obtained only 'a little unctuous opaque phosphorus, . . . not our hard transparent glacial phosphorus', and he claims that he was, 'for these 40 or 50 years, that is, ever since he left the laboratory of his master, the Hon. Mr. Boyle, the only person in Europe able to make and produce in any quan-tity the true solid phosphorus.'

He had also got it from animal excrements, had visited 'hens'-roosts, pigeon-houses, rats-nests, and mouse-holes', and 'had a little phosphorus thence'. From the residuum after the phosphorus is made he extracted a 'particular salt', called *sal phosphori*, which can be sublimed in close vessels, 'as much a secret as the phosphorus itself.' He thought phosphorus was 'a sulphureous body, composed of an acid and depurated oil, joined with a small proportion of earth'. He uses the name 'phlogiston' at the end of his paper.

From 1 oz. (8 drs.) of phosphorus on burning he obtained 10 drs. of 'white sublimed flowers' (P_2O_5)', i.e. 2 drs. more than the phosphorus, so light 'that they just filled a half-pint pot'. These deliquesced to 4 oz. 2 drs. of a 'liqua-men' resembling oil of vitriol but more fixed in the fire than any other acid, and 'having properties peculiar to itself'.

In his work on phosphorus, Boyle established the following important results: (1) the phosphorus glows only in presence of air; (2) a very small quan-tity of phosphorus (1 in 500,000 parts of water) can be detected by the glow; (3) an acid is produced which differs from phosphoric acid in giving little flashes of light on heating (phosphine from phosphorous acid); (4) the glow is exhibited by solutions of phosphorus in olive and some other oils, but oils of mace and aniseed prevent it; (5) after long exposure to phosphorus, the air acquires a strong odour (ozone) distinct from the visible fumes.[1]

The increased luminosity of phosphorus when the pressure of the air is reduced by an air-pump was observed by Frederick Slare[2] and Hauksbee.[3] On 13 December 1685 Evelyn[4] saw some experiments on phosphorus by 'Dr. Sleyer', mixing two cold liquids which produced 'boiling, divers coruscations and actual flames of fire mingled with the liquor', which 'seemed to exhibit a theorie of the eduction of light out of the chaos, and the fixing or gathering of the universal light into luminous bodys'. The experiment (with water, phos-phorus, and oil of vitriol) was described by Slare in 1683.[5]

---

[1] Thorpe, *Nature*, 1890, xli, 523.
[2] *Phil. Collect.*, 1681, 84, no. 4; *Phil. Trans.* abr. Lowthorp, 1705, iii, 347.
[3] *Phil. Trans.*, 1705, xxiv, 1865, no. 296.   [4] *Diary*, ed. Bray, 1870, 494.
[5] *Phil. Trans.*, 1683, xiii, 289–302 (An Account of some Experiments made at several Meetings of the Royal Society . . . , with some short Applications of them to physical Matters); *ib.*, 1683–4, xiv, 523, no. 157 (experiments with a human calculus; nitric acid was the only acid

The preparation and properties of *phosphorus aerëus* were summarised (from Boyle) by Paulo Boccone (Palermo; 24 April 1633–22 December 1704), professor of botany in Padua who afterwards retired to a monastery near Palermo and changed his name to Silvio,[1] in a work[2] also explaining subterranean fires by effervescence of acid and alkali with ethereal matter interposed; a 'smoking liquor' [$SnCl_4$] from mercury and tin; Bolognian phosphorus;[3] panacæa of antimony from crude antimony and fixed nitre,[4] and volcanic sal ammoniac. He thought sal ammoniac was an artificial salt made from the sublimation of a mixture of nitre, sulphur, and vitriol.[5] Johann Christopher Kletwich[6] and Johann Heinrich Cohausen (Hildesheim, 1665– Münster, 13 July 1750)[7] wrote dissertations on phosphorus of no value.

Boyle records many observations of interest in the history of organic chemistry. He reports that coal was charred to make a substitute (coke) for charcoal.[8] Instead of rectifying spirit of wine over salt of tartar, Boyle used quicklime, or else dried the salt of tartar for use again; he says that fixed salt of tartar readily imbibes aqueous bodies but does not mix with pure spirit of wine, hence 'the phlegmatic part of the spirit of wine would be soaked up by the alcalizate salt, whereby the inflammable part would be free from it'.[9] The spirit lamp was used in chemical experiments, and the burning of spirit in such a lamp was a test of its strength.[10] Boyle appears to have been the first to preserve anatomical specimens in alcohol.[11]

Various fermented drinks used in different parts of the world are described.[12] The production of spirit in fermentation is a consequence of the intestine motion, in which the corpuscles by jostling against one another are broken, variously ground, and subtilised until they are qualified to be raised by a gentle heat before the phlegm.[13] By burning highly rectified spirit of wine

which dissolved it); *ib.*, 1694, xviii, 200, no. 213 (inflammation of oil of turpentine by very concentrated nitric acid).

[1] Hoefer, NBU, 1853, vi, 302; Thorndike, viii, 39.

[2] *Osservazioni Natvrali, ove si contengono Materie Medico-Fisiche, et di Botanico, produzioni naturali, fosfori diversi, fuochi sotteranei d'Italia, e altre curiosità, disposte in tratti familiari,* 12°, Bologna, 1684 (400 pp.), Osserv. 1, Intorno al Fosforo Aereo, ò Noctiluca, pp. 3–16; *Phil. Trans.*, 1694, xviii, 33, no. 207.

[3] *Osservazioni*, 1684, 224–48.   [4] *Ib.*, 266–86.

[5] *Phil. Trans.*, 1673, viii, 6158, no. 99; Boccone also published: *Recherches et Observations curieuse sur la nature du corail blanc et rouge . . .*, 12°, Paris, 1671, 69 pp. (BN S 21118); *Recherches et Observations naturelles sur la Production de plusieurs pierres . . . et sur l'Embrasement du Mont Etna*, 12°, Paris, 1671, 112 pp. (BN S 21119); *Recherches et Observations Naturelles . . . touchant le Corail, la Pierre Etoilée, les Pierres de figure de Coquilles, la Corne d'Ammon, . . . le Bezoar Mineral, . . . avec quelques Reflexions sur la Vegetation des Plantes. Examinées à diverses fois dans l'Assemblée de Messieurs de Société Royale de Londres*, 8°, Amsterdam, 1674 (BN S 21114); *Museo di fisica e di esperienze variato . . .*, 4°, Venice, 1697 (CUL M. 15. 38); *Museo di piante*, 4°, Venice, 1697 (with appendix by Cæsalpinus) (CUL L. 3. 42).

[6] *Dissertatio de Phosphoro Liquido & Solido*, Frankfurt on Oder, 1688 (M.D. thesis).

[7] *Lumen Novum Phosphoris Accensum, sive Exercitatio Physico-Chymica De causa lucis in Phosphoris tam naturalibus quàm artificialibus*, 8°, Amsterdam, 1717 (prize essay, Royal Academy of Bordeaux); Cohausen wrote works against snuff and tea, and on the use of Peruvian bark in fevers: *Archeus febrium faber et medicus . . . de usu . . . febrifugorum omnium maximum corticem Peruvianum, seu chinachinam*, 12°, Amsterdam, 1732 (NBG, 1855, ʒi, 67), but is best known for his *Hermippus Redivivus*, 8°, Frankfurt, 1742; tr. J. Campbell, sm. 8°, Dublin, 1744 (Sotheran, *Cat.* 832, no. 5131), 2 ed. (enlarged), London, 1749.

[8] IV; *Works*, i, 514; see Becher.   [9] II (a); *Works*, i, 213.   [10] II (a); *Works*, i, 212.

[11] IV; *Works*, i, 470; Gunther, (1), 1926, iii, 104; F. J. Cole, *Nature*, 1937, cxxxix, 219.

[12] IV; *Works*, i, 490 f.   [13] XV (f); *Works*, iii, 612.

which would burn completely away on a spoon, 'a considerable quantity of downright incombustible phlegm' (water) was obtained.[1] Alcohol precipitates salt from saturated brine.[2]

By distilling spirit of wine with oil of vitriol, a 'very subtle' spirit with a penetrating fragrant odour was obtained (ether), but this was not clearly differentiated from spirit of wine.[3] Besides this 'subtle and odoriferous spirit of wine' Boyle also collected an oil which sank in water and was insoluble in it, but dissolved in alcohol.[4]

The preparation of ether had been described by Valerius Cordus (p. 166). Newton[5] says equal weights of spirit of wine and oil of vitriol digested together and distilled yield two fragrant and volatile spirits which will not mix with one another, since oil of vitriol contains a volatile and a fixed part, the first separated by attraction by the spirit of wine. Sigismund Augustus Frobenius, a German living in London, where he died in 1741 (F.R.S. 1729), described the preparation by distilling alcohol and sulphuric acid by 'Sir Isaac Newton's process' and called it *spiritus vini æthereus*.[6] Cromwell Mortimer[7] published a third paper by Frobenius, saying that in his first communication he described the process, which was not published, but Mortimer gives it. Frobenius said it had been partly described by Caneparius,[8] Boyle, Newton, Stahl and Hoffmann (who knew it from Kunckel). Frobenius (1730) mentions that ether extracts gold from its solution in aqua regia. He removed sulphurous acid from the ether by ammonia solution.

Boyle says that concentrated aqua fortis explodes with alcohol;[9] when strong spirit of wine is added little by little to good aqua fortis and the mixture distilled, the distillate (sweet spirit of nitre) has a pleasing spicy taste and smell.[10]

Sir Thomas Browne[11] says aqua fortis solidifies olive oil. Boyle found that it solidifies almond and olive oils, but dissolves camphor;[12] oils of turpentine and anise produce a great heat with oil of vitriol;[13] oil of vitriol dissolves camphor to a red liquid smelling of camphor, from which the camphor is reprecipitated on adding water.[14] The solubility of sulphur in oils was well known to Boyle.[15]

Two empyreumatic oils, one lighter and one heavier than water, were obtained by distilling tartar.[16] Oil of anise on destructive distillation gave an acid which dissolved coral and minium and effervesced with salt of tartar.[17]

'Knowing [from Francis Bacon, see p. 412] that hard sugar, being nimbly scraped with a knife, will afford a sparkling light', Boyle contrived to scrape a

---

[1] VII; *Works*, ii, 523; cf. Boerhaave.   [2] XV (*i*); *Works*, iii, 642.
[3] IIIA, VII, XV (h); *Works*, i, 394; ii, 524; iii, 627.   [4] IIIA; *Works*, i, 394.
[5] *Opticks*, 1717, Qu. 31; 1931 ed., 384.   [6] *Phil. Trans.*, 1730, xxxvi, 283; 1733, xxxviii, 55.
[7] *Phil. Trans.*, 1741, xli, 864; tr. in Crell's *N. Chem. Archiv*, 1785, iii, 1, 6, 56; Roscoe and Schorlemmer, *Treatise*, 1885, III, i, 324; Kopp, (1), iv, 302; Hoefer, (1), 1869, ii, 389; Ince, *Pharm. J.*, 1858, xviii, 215–22.
[8] *De Atramentis*, London, 1660, 438, 547.
[9] XI; *Works*, iii, 266; Pemberton, *Course of Chemistry*, 1771, 198.
[10] XV, XXII; *Works*, iii, 589; iv, 319.
[11] *Pseudodoxia Epidemica*, 1646, book ii, ch. 4; *Works* ed. Keynes, 1928, ii, 138.
[12] II (c); *Works*, i, 270.
[13] V; XI; *Works*, ii, 60; iii, 267; Sir Thomas Browne, *loc cit.*, says oil of vitriol makes oil of juniper like 'birdlime'.
[14] II, VII; *Works*, i, 251, 270; ii, 502; *A Chymical Paradox*, in XVII; *Works*, iv, 91.
[15] XV (h); *Works*, iii, 628 f.   [16] XXII; *Works*, iv, 335.
[17] *Chym. Paradox*, in XVII; *Works*, iv, 91, 95.

lump of hard loaf-sugar with steel springs in an exhausted receiver and saw 'a good number of little flashes, and sometimes too, though not frequently, there seemed to be struck off little sparks of fire'.[1] About 10,000 tons of sugar were exported annually about 1670 from Barbados.[2]

The distillates from dry wood, honey, and sugar dissolved coral, pearls and even some metals,[3] perhaps because the particles had, during the distillation, been split by the fire into sharp ones, or had become sharp by attrition due to the heat.[4] Boyle made a very careful study of the products of distillation of box-wood. By rectifying the liquid product he separated it into an acid and an adiaphorous (indifferent; a διάφορος) spirit (which would be a mixture of methyl alcohol and acetone). This could be freed from traces of acid by distillation over lime (calcined coral). By heating the solid obtained by saturating the acid (acetic acid) with calcined coral, a red spirit of strong odour and taste passed over, which some chemists called tincture of coral (crude acetone). The last part of the distillate from the liquor of box-wood was yellow and strongly acid, and appeared to be 'radical vinegar' (acetum radicatum).[5]

By the distillation of sugar of lead (saccharum saturni) a liquid came over (containing acetone), which Boyle thought came from the vinegar used to make the sugar of lead, which had left one of its parts combined with the lead, although others had called it the 'sulphur' of the lead.[6]

Plants are nourished by 'a certain nitrous juice harboured in the pores of the earth, or from the excrements of animals, or from the putrifyed bodies, either of living creatures or vegetables, or from other substances of a compounded nature'.[7] Yet the oil formed by olive trees, 'nourished chiefly by rain water, . . . seems to have been made by a transmutation of water'.[8] Boyle measured the very large force produced by the swelling of beans in water.[9]

Opium was 'corrected' by digesting with an equal weight of salt of tartar in wine (when the morphine is set free from its combination with the meconic acid).[10] Attempts were made to extract the 'essential salts' from plants.[11] What 'the chymists call the volatile salt of amber, I found to be really of an acid nature'[12] (succinic acid).

Urinary calculi do not dissolve in acids,[13] but on distilling $2\frac{1}{2}$ oz. of a powdered calculus (which had a small kernel), much volatile salt (ammonium carbonate), reddish spirit, dark oil and 6 drachms of a caput mortuum like soot were obtained, the latter yielding on calcination in an open crucible 2 drachms of insipid white calx which did not slake with water like lime.[14]

Boyle describes the preparation of spirit glue from isinglass and aqueous

[1] I; *Works*, iii, 55–6.
[2] IVA; *Works*, iii, 150; for maple sugar (1685) see Gunther, (1), 1939, xii, 87.
[3] XV (h); *Works*, iii, 625.   [4] V, VI, XV (b); *Works*, ii, 259; iii, 588.
[5] III, IIIA; *Works*, i, 328, 390 f.
[6] III, 1661, 155, 231; *Works*, i, 335, 341, 346; Boyle refers to Beguin, *Tyrocinium Chymicum*; English tr., 1669, 58: 'burning spirit of Saturn'; Patterson, *Ann. Sci.*, 1937, ii, 243.
[7] III; *Works*, i, 332.   [8] IIIA; *Works*, i, 394.
[9] VIII(b); *Works*, iii, 84.   [10] IV; *Works*, i, 517.
[11] IV; *Works*, i, 499.   [12] IIIA; *Works*, i, 379.
[13] IC; *Works*, iii, 67; Slare, *Phil. Trans.*, 1683–4, xiv, 523, no. 157, found one dissolved in nitric acid.
[14] IV; *Works*, i, 474, 500.

alcohol and its use in making 'plastic wood' with wood meal.[1] White of egg, as Bacon said, is coagulated by spirit of wine.[2]

Boyle speaks of 'those many modern philosophers and physicians, that would have life maintained by a *biolychnium*, or vital flame continually burning in the heart, and fed by the spirituous parts of the circulating blood'.[3] He confirmed the action of air in giving blood a red colour, as found by 'an ingenious man in Italy' (this was Fracassati).[4] In his *Natural History of Humane Blood*,[5] dedicated to John Locke, Boyle describes in detail the effects of acids, alkalis and salts on the colour of blood, and sets out thirty 'titles' (heads) of observations which ought to be made to complete a first survey of the subject, followed by thirty-one titles for a natural history of urine. He describes the distillation of blood, producing 'an empyreumatical and very fœtid oil', which he rectified into two immiscible oils, yellow and red. The crude oil grew very hot with oil of vitriol. The spirit obtained by distillation of dried blood seemed like other volatile salts (ammonium carbonate) but Boyle thought it had peculiar medicinal virtues. Preparations from the human body were prized in medicine at that time; Borrichius[6] tested oil of human cranium and found it medically superior to peony or swallow-water — which is not saying much. Boyle found that blood serum deposits a curdy precipitate with acid.[7] The similarity of blood serum and white of egg was first pointed out by Jerome Barbato (Barbatus) of Padua.[8] Boyle[9] found that fresh defibrinated blood and also warm milk froth and boil in a vacuum.

Boyle thought that putrefaction is the result of the slow penetration of 'the air, or some other ambient fluid', among the particles of a body, so loosening and dislocating the parts, changing the texture and perhaps too the figure of its component corpuscles; 'the same agents, that shatter the frame, or destroy the texture of one body, will by shuffling them together, and disposing them after a new manner, bring them to constitute some new sorts of bodies.'[10] Borelli[11] believed that distillation could not reveal the true constituents (salt, sulphur, and mercury) of blood.

Boyle's observations on phosphorescent wood and fish[12] continued the earlier good ones of Francis Bacon (p. 412) on wood, which Boyle does not

---

[1] IVA; *Works*, iii, 175.　　　　　[2] II; *Works*, i, 264.
[3] VIIA; *Works*, ii, 535; the reference is to Willis, see pp. 304, 307.
[4] XIV; XVIII; *Works*, iii, 468; iv, 198; Lower is not mentioned.
[5] XVIII; *Works*, iv, 161 f.; Gunther, (1), 1926, iii, 140.
[6] *Hermetis Ægyptiorum, et Chemicorum Sapientia*, 4°, Copenhagen, 1674, 332.
[7] XVIII; *Works*, iv, 173.
[8] *Dissertatio elegantissima De Sangvine et eivs sero, in qua Præter varia lectu dignissima, Conringii, Lindenii & Barthol. circa sanguinificationem opiniones . . .* , 12°, Paris, 1667 (iv ll., 88 pp.), 15 f., 50; another ed., 12°, Frankfurt am Main, 1667 (i l., 88 pp.) (BM 783. b. 1 and 19. (2.)); Gmelin, (1), ii, 244, gives also 8°, Leyden, 1736; Fourcroy, *Ency. Méthod. Chimie*, 1796, iii, 341; the discovery was first attributed to Willis, Barbato's priority being pointed out by Anduoli.
[9] *Phil. Trans.*, 1670, v, 2035; *Works*, iii, 123.
[10] VII; *Works*, ii, 473.
[11] *De Motu Animalium*, Rome, 1681, ii, 261, prop. cxxxi: sanguinis Anatomia per distillationem facta infida esse videtur.
[12] *Phil. Trans.*, 1668, ii, 581–600, no. 31 (New Experiments concerning the relation between Light and Air in Shining Wood and Fish), 605–12, no. 32 (Comparison between burning Coal and Shining Wood).

mention; those on shining flesh[1] do not refer to the description by Pierre Borel (1620–89), physician of Castres in Languedoc.[2] An account of luminous fish was given to Thomas Bartholin by Olaus Wormius, professor of Greek, medicine, and physics in Copenhagen, and another by Leo Allatius, librarian at the Vatican.[3] Shining meat was described by Puerarus, professor of philosophy in Geneva.[4] Shining fish were described by John Beale.[5] None of these authors is mentioned by Boyle.

Bacon had found that the wood continues luminous under water or oil but was not luminous when dried, it glowed in frosty weather, and 'the putrefaction spreadeth'. Boyle found that meat and fish lost their light in a vacuum but it returned on letting in air. The luminosity of the wood disappeared in a vacuum but reappeared on letting in air. 'Both shining wood and a burning coal need the presence of air' and both 'will be easily quenched by water and many other liquors', but whereas the coal soon goes out in a small confined volume of air, 'a piece of shining wood will continue to shine for some whole days'. He correctly established the necessity for air (oxygen) in the luminescence of wood, fish, and flesh. John Beale later described luminous meat.[6]

[1] *Phil. Trans.*, 1672, vii, 5108–16, no. 89 (Some Observations about Shining Flesh made by Mr. Boyle; December 16, reporting experiments of February 15).

[2] *Historiarvm, et Observationvm Medicophysicarum, Centuriæ IV. Accesservnt D. Isaac Cattieri . . . Observationes Medicinales raræ . . . et Renati Cartesii Vita eodem P. Borello*, 8°, Paris, 1656, Cent. I, obs. 3, p. 5; the life of Descartes has sep. pagin., 59 pp.

[3] Thomas Bartholinus, *De Lvce Animalivm Libri III*, sm. 8°, Leyden, 1647, bk. ii, ch. 15, p. 225.

[4] T. Bartholin, *De Flammula Cordis Epistola cum Jacobi Holstii . . . ejusdem Argumenti Dissertatione. Accessit De Carnibus Lucentibus Danielis Puorarii responsio*, Copenhagen, [1667 ?] (BM 1170. c. 13. (4.)).

[5] *Phil. Trans.*, 1666, i, 226, no. 13.   [6] *Phil. Trans.*, 1676, xi, 599, no. 125.

CHAPTER XV

HOOKE

Robert Hooke (Freshwater, Isle of Wight, 18 July 1635–London, 3 March 1703) was at first intended for the Church but his constitution proved too weakly (he was later hunchbacked). He first became a pupil of the artist Lely, but oil paints injured his health and he went for five years to Westminster School under Dr. Busby. In 1653 he went as Servitor to Christ Church, Oxford. His mechanical inventions attracted the attention of Dr. Wilkins, warden of Wadham College, who introduced him to Willis, whose assistant in chemistry and natural philosophy he became about 1655. He was later assistant to Boyle, and in 1662 became curator of experiments to the Royal Society. After the Great Fire, Hooke became a surveyor of London, in which capacity he amassed a considerable sum of money which was found locked up in an iron chest after his death.[1]

No portrait of Hooke is known, unless he is the favourite pupil shown in the portrait of Dr. Busby of Westminster School, in the hall of Christ Church College, Oxford.

Ward[2] listed 35 works published by Hooke in his lifetime and several published later. Those of interest to us are given below. They are printed in a mixture of roman and italic type interspersed with capital letters; these are not distinguished in the quotations but the original spelling, punctuation, and style in long rambling sentences, are preserved.

I. An Attempt for the Explication of the Phænomena, Observable in an Experiment Published by the Honourable Robert Boyle Esq; In the XXXV. Experiment of his Epistolical Discourse touching the Aire. In Confirmation of a former Conjecture

[1] Waller, *Posthumous Works of Robert Hooke . . . with the Author's Life, by Richard Waller, F.R.S.*, f°, London, 1705; J. Ward, *The Lives of the Professors of Gresham College*, f°, London, 1740, 169–93; Anthony à Wood, *Athenæ Oxonienses*, ed. Bliss, London, 1820, iv, 628; Andrade, *Nature*, 1935, cxxxvi, 358–61, 603; *Proc. Roy. Soc.*, 1950, cxxxvii B, 153; M. Boas, *Nature*, 1956, clxxviii, 336; A. M. Clerke, DNB, 1908, ix, 1177; *The Diary of Robert Hooke, 1672–80*, ed. [from the MS. in the Guildhall Library, London] by H. W. Robinson and W. Adams, London, 1935; H. B. Dixon, *B.A. Report*, 1894, 594; Espinasse (Mrs. M.), *Robert Hooke*, 1956; J. C. Fischer, *passim* (see index, viii, 935); Gunther, (1), vi, vii, x, xiii (*Life and Work of Robert Hooke*); *Nature*, 1935, cxxxvi, 603; A. R. Hall, *Isis*, 1951, xlii, 219–30 (2 letters); Harcourt, *Phil. Mag.*, 1846, xxviii, 487; G. Keynes, *A Bibliography of Dr. Robert Hooke*, 1960; Koyré, *Isis*, 1950, xli, 195–6; 1952, xliii, 312–37; Lysaght, *Ambix*, 1937, i, 93; McKie, *Discovery*, 1935, 200; *Ambix*, 1938, i, 161; Middleton, *Ann. Med. Hist.*, 1927, ix, 237; Morgan, *Sci. Progr.*, 1930, xxv, 282; Morhof, (1), 1747, II–III, 284 (Vir maximi ingenii, & in rebus naturalibus tum acutum, quam Aquila, cernens); L. D. Patterson, *Isis*, 1948, xxxviii, 151–6; 1949, xl, 327–41; 1950, xli, 32–45, 304–5; Pelseneer, *Isis*, 1929, xii, 237; 1931, xv, 97, 173; 1935, xxv, 466; *Phil. Trans.*, Abgd., 1809, i, 3; Picton, 1889, 138; Poggendorff, (2), 1883, 344, 358; Rodwell, *Chem. News*, 1865, xi, 38, 74; Rosenberger, 1884, ii, 169; T. Thomson, (3), 1812, 332; Weld, *History of the Royal Society*, 1848, i, 137, 173, 359 f.

[2] 1740, 169 f.; on some Hooke MSS. in the British Museum, S. Ayscough, *A Catalogue of the Manuscripts preserved in the British Museum*, 2 vols. 4°, 1782, i, 452–4.

made by R.H., London, 1661. This was published while Hooke was assistant to Boyle.

II. Micrographia: or some Physiological Descriptions of Minute Bodies made by Magnifying Glasses. With Observations and Inquiries Thereupon, f°, London, Printed by Jo. Martyn, and Jo. Allestry, Printers to the Royal Society, and are to be sold at their Shop at the Bell in S. Paul's Church-yard, 1665; t.p. in red and black, imprimatur signed by Lord Brouncker, President of the Royal Society, xviii ll., 246 pp., v ll., 38 copper plates.

Reissued, 1667, with t.p. in black, printed for James Allestry, and are to be sold at his Shop, at the Rose and Crown in Duck-Lane, 1667. Brewster, Memoirs of Sir Isaac Newton, 1855, i, 156, calls this 'a trick of the printer, to indicate a second edition, which was never printed'. Reprinted in Gunther, (1), xiii; extracts in ACR, 1894, no. 5, and Old Ashmolean Reprints, Oxford, 1926, no. 6. It is dedicated to King Charles II and to the Royal Society. The plates only were published separately as:

Micrographia Restaurata, or the Copperplates of Dr. Hooke's wonderful Discoveries by the Microscope, reprinted and fully explained, f°, London, John Bowles, 1745 (printed from the original plates, for the most part, the work 'being grown extremely scarce').

III. Lampas, or Descriptions of some Mechanical Improvement of Lamps and Water-poises. Together with some other Physical and Mechanical Discoveries. Made by Robert Hooke Fellow of the Royal Society. London. Printed for John Martin, Printer to the Royal Society at the Bell in St. Paul's Churchyard, 4°, 1677.

IV. Lectiones Cutlerianæ, or a Collection of Lectures: Physical, Mechanical, Geographical, & Astronomical. Made before the Royal Society on several Occasions at Gresham Colledge. To which are added divers Miscellaneous Discourses, 6 pts., 4°, London, 1679, repr. in Gunther, (1), 1913, viii.

V. The Posthumous Works of Robert Hooke, M.D. F.R.S. Geom. Prof. Gresham ec., publ. by Richard Waller, R.S. Sec., f°, London, 1705: contains I The present Deficiency in Natural Philosophy. II The Nature, Motion and effects of Light, particularly that of the Sun and Comets. III An Hypothetical Explication of Memory. IV An Hypothesis and Explication of the Cause of Gravitation, Magnetism, etc. V Discourses of Earthquakes. VI Lectures for improving Navigation and Astronomy. With the Author's Life.

VI. Philosophical Experiments and Observations Of the late Eminent Dr Robert Hooke. . . . And Other Eminent Virtuoso's in his Time. . . . Publish'd by W. Derham, 8°, London, 1726.

J. Robison[1] claimed to have 'rediscovered' Hooke from reading his *Lampas* in 1798, and complained that he had fallen into oblivion. In an age which included such a universal genius as Wren, Hooke stands out for his amazing versatility and solid achievement. 'Quick, restless, imaginative, he sprang from discovery to discovery . . . we can hardly name a discovery of this age in which Hooke had not in part participated and claimed as his own.'[2] The dispersion of his effort seems to have been due at least in part to the varying interests of the Royal Society, which set Hooke to perform a bewildering variety of experiments without giving him time to finish any of them. The Society also asked him to repeat the same experiment over and over again, refusing to see the correct interpretation Hooke put upon it. When Hooke was not present at a meeting, no one else seems to have been able to show any experiments, and he was more than once censured by the Council for supposed neglect of his duties. In such circumstances he did a surprising amount of research. Hooke also had poor health and slept badly; his *Diary* is full of

[1] *Ency. Brit. Suppl.*, Edinburgh, 1801, I, ii, 744; ed. of J. Black, *Lectures on the Elements of Chemistry*, Edinburgh, 1803, i, 335, 537.
[2] Dixon, *B.A. Report*, 1894, 594 (599).

references to his ailments and drugs he took for them. He was a constant visitor to coffee-houses and, except late in life, mixed freely with others. For a few years before his death he is said never to have gone to bed or taken off his clothes, and to have developed parsimonious habits.

Sir Godfrey Copley, in a letter written about the time of Hooke's death, said Hooke is 'much concerned for fear he should outlive his estate. He hath starved one old woman already, and I believe he will endanger himself to save sixpence for anything he wants'. In another letter written a few weeks after Hooke's death, Copley says it was a pity that Hooke did not leave his £12,000 for science 'than to have it go to those whom he never saw nor cared for' (Hooke had said he would leave it to the Royal Society to endow a professorship).[1] The picture of Hooke which I have formed after reading his *Diary* and many other sources is unattractive, but others think better of him. Robinson and Adams[2] refer to 'the almost perverse vanity of his character'.

Hooke claimed to have anticipated Newton in 1687 in the suggestion of the inverse-square law in gravitation, and this led to what Koyré called 'bitter hatred' between Hooke and Newton.[3] The law was suggested by Hooke in a letter to Newton in 1680 and again in 1682[4] and his claim was admitted by Newton.[5] Andrade says Newton was in possession of the law before Hooke wrote to him. Newton is said to have kept back the publication of his *Opticks* till after Hooke's death, as several experiments were also claimed by Hooke and some were published in his *Micrographia* (1665), where he accepts the theory that heat is a property 'arising from the motion or agitation' of the parts of a body,[6] and burning bodies, like all hot bodies, have their parts in motion;[7] this theory had been proposed by Francis Bacon (p. 393), with whose writings Hooke was very familiar, and it was also adopted by Newton.[8]

Hooke says: '[The cause of fluidness] I conceive, to be nothing else but a certain pulse or shake of heat; for heat being nothing else but a very brisk and vehement agitation of the parts of the body (as I have elsewhere made probable) the parts of the body are thereby made so loose from one another, that they easily move anyway and become fluid.'[9] 'Heat, as I shall afterwards prove, is nothing but the internal motion of the particles of body; and the hotter a body is, the more violently are the particles moved, and with a quick motion.'[10]

It has been suggested that Hooke had some idea of the conservation of energy,[11] but he did not live long enough to put in a claim for this! Hooke argued, on the Baconian method (of which he made effective use), that light is a pulse in a medium or 'Æther', which also propagated gravity,[12] and he even suggested that 'the motion of light in an uniform medium . . . is propagated by

---

[1] Brande, *Manual of Chemistry*, 1848, I, xxx.   [2] *Diary*, 1935, xix.

[3] Letter of Aubrey to Anthony à Wood, Sept. 1689, in Gunther, (1), 1930, vii, 714; L. D. Patterson, 1948, 1949, 1950; Koyré, 1950, 1952 (letter from Newton to Hooke, supplementing letters in W. W. Rouse Ball, *An Essay on Newton's Principia*, 1893).

[4] V, 93, 113, 185.

[5] *Principia*, Scholium to book i, prop. 4: ut seorsum collegerunt etiam nostrates *Wrennus, Hookius & Hallæus.*

[6] *Micrographia*, 1665, 37.   [7] *Ib.*, 54.

[8] J. C. Fischer, 1802, iii, 134: Hooke 'konnte in keiner Sache, worin er selbst etwas gethan haben wollte, einen Nebenbuhler vertragen'; cf. Hooke's attitude to Mayow, p. 598.

[9] II, 12.   [10] V, 116 (1680).

[11] L. D. Patterson, *Isis*, 1948, xxxviii, 151.   [12] V, 130, 171, 183.

simple and uniform pulses or waves, which are at right angles with the line of direction', i.e. transverse vibrations.[1] Hooke discovered the coloured bands called 'Newton's rings'.[2]

Hooke was elected F.R.S. in 1663; in 1681–2 he published 7 numbers of *Philosophical Collections*, which are usually regarded as part of the *Philosophical Transactions* of the Royal Society, these having been suspended from 1678 to 1783. He was Secretary of the Royal Society in 1677–82. In 1687 Tancred Robinson wrote to Sloane: 'The Royal Society declines apace; not one correspondent in being. The revenue is settled upon Mr. Hooke, and Monsieur Papin goes back next week to settle in Germany'. John Ray had resigned the secretaryship in 1686.[3]

In 1660 Hooke discovered what is now known as Hooke's Law of Elasticity, which in 1676 he put forward in the form of an anagram: c e i i i n o s s s t t u u [= ut tensio sic vis], but published in an intelligible form in 1678.[4] Mariotte gave it independently in 1680, with applications (not given by Hooke). Hooke's experiments on capillary attraction[5] had been anticipated (but not published) by Borelli,[6] whose experiments were shown to the Accademia del Cimento in 1655. Hooke's explanations are wrong and he repeated them later:[7] the rise in the capillary tube was due to the pressure of air being less inside the tube than outside, and the miscibility and non-miscibility of liquids is due to their 'congruity' and 'incongruity'.

Andrade (1950) says 'Hooke was certainly one of the first, if not the first, to draw attention to thermal expansion as a general property of matter. "This property of expansion with heat, and contraction with cold, is not peculiar to liquors only but to all kinds of solid bodies also, especially metals" '; he gives no reference.

Hooke had an idea of the kinetic theory of gases; he says air 'consists of the same particles single and separated, of which water and other fluids do, conjoyned and compounded', and widely spaced; 'its vibrative spaces exceeding large, comparative to the vibrative spaces of other terrestrial bodies.' He mentions a million a second as the kind of frequency he has in mind. He also gave a deduction of Boyle's law.[8] Gassendi had previously had some idea of this (see p. 461).

In his microscopical observations Hooke had been anticipated by the

---

[1] Birch, (1), iii, 12; Wilde, *Ann. Phys.*, 1850, lxxix, 82.

[2] II, 47 f.; Brewster, *Memoirs of Sir Isaac Newton*, Edinburgh, 1855, i, 160: 'Newton has not done justice to Hooke. . . . The results of his experiments are made use of, and his theory partly adopted and altered, without any acknowledgment of the one, or notice of the other.' On Newton's similar treatment of Grimaldi, etc., see Brewster, *ib.*, 198, 215, 241; on Hooke's criticism (uninformed) of Huygens, see A. R. Hall, *Isis*, 1951, xlii, 219.

[3] Gunther, (1), vii, 710.

[4] Hooke, *De Potentia restitutiva, or of Spring*, London, 1678, 1; Love, *Theory of Elasticity*, Cambridge, 1906, 2; Partington, *Advanced Physical Chemistry*, 1952, iii, 168.

[5] I, 1661.

[6] *De Motionibus Naturalibus a Gravitate Pendentibus*, 4°, Reggio, 1670, 366 f.; Leyden, 1686, 232 f., 384; Partington, *Advanced Physical Chemistry*, 1951, ii, 134.

[7] II, 10; of small glass canes.

[8] *Potentia Restitutiva*, 1678, 9, 15–16; Jeans, *Kinetic Theory of Gases*, 1940, 3; Tait, Hooke's anticipation of the kinetic theory, *Proc. Roy. Soc. Edin.*, 1885, xiii, 118 (note); *id.*, *Properties of Matter*, 1899, 295.

publication of Henry Power (1623–New Hale, nr. Ealand, Yorks., 23 December 1688), one of the first two elected members of the Royal Society (1663), correspondent of Sir Thomas Browne[1] and Hooke.[2] The second part deals with the Torricellian vacuum and the third with magnetism, with an appendix on the damp (gas) in coal-mines. Power left some manuscripts, including a course of chemistry.[3] From his experiment on the Torricellian vacuum, Power concluded that the apparently empty space is not a vacuum, nor does it contain mercury vapour, light, or air. He mentions a perpetual motion experiment of Charles Townley, some tricks on vomiting various liquids after drinking 'an infusion of brasil' by Floram Marchand the 'water-drinker' (depending on colour changes of Brazil wood extract by acids and alkalis), and suggested that in after-life the animal spirits might form the pneumatic body, uniting from the circumambient ether with the separating soul, etc. In the preface to the *Micrographia* Hooke mentions that he had been informed 'that the Ingenious Physitian Dr. Henry Power had made several microscopical observations'.[4]

The readable long preface to the *Micrographia* says the understanding 'must watch the irregularities of the senses, but it must not go before them or prevent their information'. It develops the Baconian idea that by observation and the experimental method everything can be discovered, perhaps before very long. The five senses, which furnish the materials of science, might be artificially sharpened in ways specified or suggested. The 'real, the mechanical, the experimental philosophy' is contrasted with 'the fine dreams of universal metaphysical natures' (he means the philosophy of Descartes), and an ordinary man with its aid would get further than a cleverer one relying only on acute speculations (Bacon's idea). The Royal Society is praised and defended on lines anticipating Thomas Sprat's *History of the Royal Society* (1667). Hooke mentions his own achieved or projected contributions to experimental science.

Although ultimately permitted to dedicate his *Micrographia* to the Royal Society, Hooke was informed that 'the several hypotheses and theories laid down by him therein, are not delivered as certainties, but as conjectures; and that he intends not at all to obtrude or expose them to the world as the opinion of the Society'. Hooke's preface was framed accordingly,[5] and his 'hypotheses and theories' are, therefore, certified for all time as Hooke's personal property.

Hooke thought 'there is no necessity to suppose atoms',[6] and hence there is more matter (of ether) in a vacuum (which is continuous) than in an equal bulk of gold (which has ether mixed with it). 'The essence of body is only determinate extension' — pure Descartes.

In 1661 Hooke said:[7] 'Flame (which what it is, and how it consumes bodies, I shall on some other occasion by many luciferous Experiments manifestly prove.'

In January–February, 1665, Hooke described to the Royal Society[8] some experiments 'tending to show, as he conceived, that air is the universal dis-

---

[1] *Letters*, ed. Keynes, 1946, 277.

[2] Power, *Experimental Philosophy in, three books: containing New Experiments — Microscopical, Mercurial, Magnetical — with some deductions and probable Hypotheses raised from them, in Avouchment and Illustration of the now famous Atomical Hypothesis*, 4°, London, T. Roycroft for John Martin, 1664 (xiii ll., 193 pp., plates, BM 537. h. 1, sep. t.ps. dated 1663).

[3] Sloane 496, 1352, etc.; Cooper, DNB, 1896, xlvi, 256; Thorndike, viii, 211.

[4] Partly repr. in ACR, no. 5.   [5] Gunther, (1), vi, 219; Boyle, *Works*, 1744, v, 542.

[6] V, 172.   [7] I, 45.   [8] Gunther, (1), vi, 233 f.; Harcourt, *Phil. Mag.*, 1846, xxviii, 487.

solvent of all sulphureous bodies, and that this dissolution is fire; adding that this was done by a nitrous substance inherent and mixed with the air'. These consisted in shewing that a live coal went out in a [closed] glass vessel, that a burning body would be extinguished even if agitated, if it had not a free access of fresh air, that 'a combustible substance heated red-hot, yea even in a fire as hot as to melt copper, would not waste, but as soon as fresh air was admitted, did burn away and consume'; that sulphur heated red hot in a hermetically sealed pipe 'yet burned not, but as soon as the air was admitted, burned away'; that charcoal heated in such a pipe did not consume or burn, and was scarcely diminished when strongly heated for 2 hours in a crucible when covered with sand.[1] He 'desired, that some experiments might be suggested, that were thought not solvable by the hypothesis of fire proposed by him'. He 'was of the opinion, that as air much rarefied, wherein the parts are enlarged, was found to make burning bodies go out, so condensed air would keep them alive longer'. 'In order to see, whether the compression of the air caused the extinction of fire, there was put a lamp into the condensing engine; and a great quantity of air being crowded into it, it was found, that the lamp burnt in that compressed air about 15 minutes; whereas in the uncompressed air in the same engine, it burnt not above 3 minutes.'[2]

On 15 March 1665, a bladder was (at Wren's suggestion on 8 March) blown up with 'air' from powdered oyster-shells and aqua fortis by Wilkins; the shells were put into a bottle with two pipes, the bladder being tied to one and aqua fortis was poured through the other pipe, which was then closed with hard cement. On 22 March, 'the bladder was found evidently shrunk.'[3] On 29 March an experiment was made of collecting the 'air' from aqua fortis and powdered oyster-shells in a small glass phial under water, 'and whelming a large glass filled with water over it to receive the steam to be generated by the corrosion: the success whereof was that the whelmed glass was filled about ¼th full with an aërial substance.' On 12 April it was reported that 'the greatest part of it was returned into liquor and air was to be collected from ale, but on 19 April it was reported that the experiment was unsuccessful'.[4] On 23 April air was collected from oyster-shells and aqua fortis.[5] In a note to a paper by Huygens[6] attention was directed to the above experiments, in which a bladder tied over a bottle of strong ale 'was almost half-filled with an aërial spirit generated by the working liquor'.

In experiments on 22 March, 1665, a bird dying in an exhausted receiver was expected to revive when 'a new kind of air fit for respiration' generated from vinegar and pounded oyster-shells was admitted, but the bird 'recovered not'. In a similar experiment with a kitten, the air was drawn out 'till the animal had done struggling, and was upon the point of expiration', when air from distilled vinegar and oyster-shells was admitted, when the animal 'soon began to recover'.[7]

On 12 April 1665 Boyle suggested 'trying whether seeds would germinate

[1] See also II, 104 for this experiment.   [2] Birch, (1), ii, 8, 10.   [3] Birch, (1), ii, 20–2.
[4] Birch, (1), ii, 27–32; Harcourt, *Phil. Mag.*, 1846, xxviii, 478 (492–5).
[5] Birch, (1), ii, 84; for further experiments in May and June, *ib.*, 85–91.
[6] *Phil. Trans.*, 1675–6, x, no. 119, p. 443.   [7] Birch, (1), ii, 25; Harcourt, 493–4.

and thrive in an exhausted receiver, and Dr. Goddard affirmed that plants live
as much upon air as the earth'. On 14 June an account was given of an experiment of the growth of water-cresses in a receiver. When kept a week in an
exhausted receiver they showed no growth, but after air was admitted 'they
grew in the same time two or three inches'.[1] This was probably suggested by
the observations of Kenelm Digby (p. 425). Homberg[2] reported that seeds
grew in a vacuum, which was probably imperfect.

Experiments on collecting the 'air' from aqua fortis and powdered oyster-
shells and its effect on a burning candle and respiration were made again in
April–May 1673, with a suggestion that the change in weight should be
found.[3] The air from bottled ale was tried in June and Hooke found that a
candle would not burn in it:[4] he said he would 'try, whether it might be
corrected by precipitation'.

John Locke records in his diary on 12 May 1678 the frothing of a bottle of
Muscat wine when uncorked: 'Fermentation. I saw by chance an experiment
which confirmed me in an opinion I have long had, that in fermentation a new
air is generated. . . . Q. whether this be air new generated, or whether the
springy particles of air in the fruits out of which these fermenting liquors are
drawn, have by the artifices of Nature been pressed close together, and
thereby other particles fastened and held so: and whether fermentation does
not loosen these bonds, and give them liberty to expand themselves again.
Take a bottle of fermenting liquor, and tie a bladder on the mouth. Q. How
much new air will it produce? Whether this has the quality of common air?'
Locke was associated with Boyle in making observations of the temperature of
the air, etc., and in 1666–83 'was much engaged in chemical as well as physical
studies'.[5]

In February 1665 Hooke had 'made an experiment with charcoal enclosed
in a glass, to which nitre being put and the hole suddenly stopped again, the
fire revived, though no fresh air could get in'. Boyle affirmed that gunpowder
burns 'very well in a closed receiver out of which the air has been extracted'.
Hooke then made an experiment on gunpowder without air, and casting
sulphur on melted nitre in an earthen crucible, when the sulphur 'gave a very
bright vivid flame', even under an exhausted receiver. He 'was ordered to
devise more experiments to elucidate the nature of fire and burning'.[6] These
experiments are mentioned in his *Micrographia*. Boyle[7] mentions an experiment (described previously by Berigard, see p. 423 and Van Helmont,
see p. 232) in which charcoal strongly heated in a closed retort does not
disappear, but the *caput mortuum* (residue) becomes black on cooling. If, however, air is admitted, the charcoal burns away and did hastily degenerate or
'fall asunder . . . into pure white ashes'. Boyle, therefore, distinguished between
the effects of heating substances in closed vessels and with exposure to air.

[1] Birch, (1), ii, 29, 56; Harcourt, 495.   [2] AdS, 1693, x, m. 348; 1733, ii, 157.
[3] Birch, (1), iii, 84–5, 89.   [4] *Ib.*, 90.
[5] *The Life and Letters of John Locke*, ed. P. K. King, London, 1830, i, 217; 1884, 30, 117;
Paris, *Life of Davy*, 1831, i, 254; Gunther, (1), 1926, iii, 64; Locke took the Oxford M.B. in
1675.
[6] Gunther, (1), vi, 235–7.   [7] *Sceptical Chymist*, 1680, 62; Everyman ed., 43.

This is the basis of Hooke's experiments and theory. He found that a piece of wood put into a crucible and covered completely with sand when made red hot was 'well charr'd and cleans'd of its waterish parts' and when cold could be taken out as charcoal, but if, while still warm, it was exposed to the free air, it would take fire and readily burn away.[1]

The parts of the *Micrographia* of chemical interest deal with observations on charcoal,[2] on the sparks from flint and steel,[3] and Hooke's theory of combustion.[4] The theory of combustion will be dealt with first. Hooke gives no details of any experiments, but on the basis of his unpublished observations he puts forward twelve propositions in which he says, among other things:[5] (1) 'Air is the universal dissolvent of all sulphureous bodies; (2) this action of dissolution produces a very great heat and that which we call fire; (3) this dissolution is made by a substance inherent, and mixt with the air, that is like, if not the very same, with that which is fixt in salt-peter; (4) this action is perform'd with so great a violence, and does so minutely act, and rapidly agitate the smallest parts of the combustible matter, that it produces in the diaphanous medium of the air, the action or pulse of light; (5) in this dissolution of bodies by the air, a certain part is united and mixt, or dissolv'd and turned into the air, and made to fly up and down with it.' Hooke did not succeed in isolating this constituent common to air and nitre. Boyle also speaks vaguely of a 'volatile nitre' in the air.[6]

In June 1667 Hooke mentions 'an experiment long since made before the Society with a chafing-dish of coals set in a close box, wherein was a pair of bellows so contrived as to blow the coals with that air only, that was included in the box: the air so kept had this quality, that after one whole day's time fresh fire would not burn in it, till the grosser parts thereof were precipitated'.[7] In February, 1672, Hooke showed that, besides the flame and smoke of a candle there is a continual 'stream of liquor' ('steam' in a later entry) rising up from the flame, distinct from the air; this was seen because of the different refraction of light; the dissolution of the parts of the candle heated was the flame, and the stream was the composition of the air and the relic of the effluvia of the parts of the candle dissolved, continually ascending and distinct from the air.[8] This was shown again in January 1679.[9] The 'fluid in the form of air', although heavier than air, rises from the flame 'from the extraordinary rarefaction of the same by the nearness and centrality of the flame and heat, whereby it is made much lighter than the ambient air'.

In 1665 Hooke[10] thought (as Boyle did later) that there is only very little of this nitrous component in the air:

The dissolving parts of the Air are but few, that is, it seems of the nature of those Saline menstruums, or spirits, that have very much flegme mixt with the spirits, and

---

[1] II, 102.   [2] II, 100 f.   [3] II, 44.
[4] II, 103 f.; these parts are reprinted in ACR No. 5, and in *Old Ashmolean Reprints*, No. vi, Oxford, 1926.
[5] II, 55, 103 f.; see also V, 47, 56, 164, 169; H. D. Turner, *Centaurus*, 1956, iv, 297–310; a long extract was given by 'R.B.' in *Nicholson's J.*, 1799, iii, 497.
[6] *Suspicions about some hidden Qualities of Air*, 1674; *Works*, ed. Birch, 1744, iii, 467.
[7] Gunther, (1), vi, 309; Hooke, V, 1705, 53.
[8] Harcourt, 1846, 490; Gunther, (1), vi, 393 f.   [9] Gunther, (1), vii, 508.   [10] II, 104.

therefore a small parcel of it is quickly glutted, and will dissolve no more . . . as in other solutions, if a copious and quick supply of mentruum, though but weak, be poured on, or applied to the dissoluble body, it quickly consumes it: So this menstruum of the Air, if by Bellows, or any other such contrivance, it be copiously apply'd to the shining body, is found to dissolve it as soon, and as violently as the more strong menstruum of melted Nitre.

Hooke also suggested that 'the *Air* . . . seems to be but as 'twere a tincture or saline substance, dissolv'd and agitated by the fluid and agil æther', and that it might be possible to strain out the saline part, as Nature precipitates the solution as rain and dew.[1] He does not say that the nitrous part of the air exists in the air as a gas, mixed with another gas which does not support combustion. This was first asserted by Mayow in 1674 (p. 588). The similarity of Hooke's theory to the Phlogiston Theory proposed later[2] was pointed out by R. Watson.[3]

Hooke's theory of the atmosphere is quite fully explained by Morhof, who says he does not think it is true:[4]

Rob. Hookius, qui in Micrographia sua statuit, aerem nihil esse aliud, quam tincturam & solutionem quandam particularum, ex terra & aqua prodeuntium, quæ in æthere exsolvuntur, & continenter moventur, fere ut parum salis aut pigmenti multumquæ inficit. Atque, ut hoc pigmenti arte potest separari, sic aer ab æthere secernitur, atque ita, secundum ejus sententiam, aer nihil aliud esset, quam particulæ aqueo-terreæ diffusæ quarum sustentaculum esset æther. Quæ tamen sententia vera esse non videtur.

A long scheme of 'Queries' on the Atmosphere drawn up by Hooke[5] is on the model of Francis Bacon's method (see p. 393).

Hooke first used the name 'nitrous air' in 1682, long after Mayow's publication (1674):[6] 'all Fires and Flames we know have need either of actual nitre, or of a nitrous air to make them, which being satieted, the fire or flame will no longer continue.'

In 1682[7] Hooke said: 'the air it self is no farther the menstruum that dissolves bodies by fire and flame, than as it hath such a kind of body raised from the earth, as has a power of so dissolving and working upon unctuous, sulphureous or combustible bodies; and this is the aerial or volatile nitrous spirit', as may be shown by combustions with nitre under water or in an exhausted receiver, 'as I have often tried.' In his Cutlerian Lectures on Light (1680–2)[8] Hooke says nitre and sulphur 'burning each other' make a very bright light, and[9] repeats his ideas about 'sulphureous bodies' being 'preyed upon and dissolved by the air'. The name 'aerial or volatile nitrous spirit', and the experiment on combustion with nitre under water, are borrowed from Mayow (1674) (see p. 588). Hooke says[10] the 'nitrous air' does not extend beyond the atmosphere of the earth.

---

[1] II, 13–14.
[2] Juncker, *Conspectus Chemiae*, Halle, 1730, i, 157: Ingens aëris quantitas requiritur ad dissolvendas & recipiendas ignitas illas & ultimo motu attenuatas particulas, unde nisi sat aëris fit, extinguitur ignis.
[3] *Chemical Essays*, 1796, iii, 40.   [4] (1), 1747, ii, 355.   [5] V, 30 f.
[6] Hooke, A Discourse of Comets, read to the Royal Society 'soon after Michaelmas 1682'; V, 164.
[7] A Discourse of Comets; V, 169.   [8] V, 92.   [9] *Ib.*, 220–1.   [10] *Ib.*, 164.

In 1651 John French[1] speaks of the production of 'an acid nitrous salt . . . by condensing the nitrous aire (for indeed as many judicious philosophers are of opinion, the air is wholly nitrous, as it appears by the condensation of it in cold places into Nitre)'; also (from de Rochas) of a:

virgin earth which did attract, and condense the nitrousnesse of the aire, but withall by making it so acid that it might cause an ebullition when it came to be joyned with a sulphur mine. . . . The virgin earth through which the acid nitrous water did run, did condense the nitrous air or vapours into a nitrous salt, and withall it is to be considered that before this nitrous aire or vapour, before it be condensed, even when it is neer unto condensation, is acid . . . if so in spirits that have lost their bodies, why not after some proportion in those that have not yet assumed a body, as vapours of nitre, or nitrous aire being neer to congelation, and bodying, and impregnant with spirits of nitre? . . . nitrous vapours, or nitrous air being a salt embodied, are not so acid as spirits of nitre, because they are more phlegmatick and crude, which flegme they lose by being congealed into a salt.

William Clarke[2] said that when nitre is distilled with potters' earth, the pure spirit comes over 'in form of red vapours which will make the recipient bright, and red as a Ruby, which spirit is called the *Flying Dragon*, which in quality is very corrosive, vaporous, and stinking, like *Aqua-fortis*'.[3] Nitre is 'sublim'd into the Air, in which it is universally dilated, and is therefore called Aer Nitrosus, or Nitrous Air' by 'our Modern Philosophers'.[4] He goes on to explain that it is a cause of meteors, formed from nitrous and sulphureous vapours,[5] as Sennert taught. He quotes Agricola, Digby, and Thibaut, but not Hooke. The name 'nitrous air' for oxygen was used long afterwards by William Cowper, who in his poem[6] says:

> '. . . whilst the nitrous air
> Feeds a blue flame, and makes a cheerful hearth.'

H. Guerlac[7] collected some earlier references to 'nitre in the air', which was a literary commonplace before Hooke and Mayow, as a cause of thunderstorms and earthquakes (Milton, Dryden), snow (from its cooling properties), fertility of the soil (R. South, 1661).[8]

On 13 November 1672 Hooke suggested that it would be 'worth trying, whether air be consumed or increased by burning'. Trials made before the Royal Society on 27 November and 4 December, 1672, and 19 and 26 February, 1673, all 'miscarried'. On 4 December 1672 Hooke said he had found it neither increased nor decreased, and on 19 March 1673 that he had found it decreased by $\frac{1}{20}$th part.[9] The decrease in volume when the combustion was carried out in air confined by water was first established by Mayow (1674).[10]

In January and February, 1679, Hooke showed experiments in which a dish of live coals was put into a tin box and kept alight by blowing upon it with bellows; but in air which had been 'satiated' by coals burning out in the box, a

---

[1] *The Art of Distillation*, London, 1651, 157 f.
[2] *The Natural History of Nitre: or, A Philosophical Discourse of the Nature, Generation, Place, and Artificial Extraction of Nitre, with its Vertues and Uses*, sm. 8°, London, 1670, Printed by E. Okes for Nathaniel Brook (8 ll., 93 pp.); Latin, Hamburg, 1675.
[3] *Ib.*, 9.   [4] *Ib.*, 22.   [5] *Ib.*, 26.   [6] *The Garden*, ll. 32–3; *The Task*, bk. iii, 1785.
[7] *Isis*, 1954, xlv, 243–55.   [8] Watson, *Chemical Essays*, 1793, ii, 77.
[9] Birch, (1), iii, 61, 63, 68, 76–8.   [10] See p. 593; Lysaght, *Ambix*, 1937, i, 93 (102).

candle flame and other live coals ceased to burn. A piece of charcoal sealed up
in a glass tube was not consumed even if the tube was heated so strongly as to
melt the glass; the same happened if the coal were suspended by a wire inside
a glass urinal stopped at the mouth with clay. In another experiment a piece of
charcoal weighing 128 grains was heated in sand in a closed iron box, and after
cooling has lost only $1\frac{1}{2}$ grains, attributed to moisture.

Melted nitre in a crucible did not burn 'till a sulphureous substance was put
into it, such as wood, coal, brimstone or the like, upon the injecting of any
of which there were presently produced a fire and flame, by which those substances were consumed. Mr. Hooke argued, that the nitrous part of the petre
was that, which corroded the sulphureous body, and thereby the alkalizate
part of the petre was left behind, and augmented by parts of the coal taken into
itself.' He also 'mentioned the way of making saltpetre with spirit of nitre and
alkali salt mixed, whereby it appeared, that saltpetre might be compounded of
an alkalizate and an acid salt mixed together, and so coalescing into saltpetre'.
This, of course, was Boyle's experiment (p. 540). In March, 1679, Hooke
thought that nitre 'from its manner of production might be supposed to consist
of two kinds of salts united together into one compositum; the one a very
volatile and aerial salt rarefied and flying in the air; the other an earthy fixed
and alkalizate salt mixed with the earth'. This is long after Mayow's clear
account of 1674, which is curiously not mentioned. Objections were made to
Hooke's hypothesis of combustion, it being supposed 'that the fire went out
when all the pores of the air were filled so, as there was no more space left for
the vapours and smoke to fly out of the coal',[1] to which he replied that a
candle or coal would go out sooner if the air were drawn out and would continue burning longer if more air were compressed into the vessel.[2]

In March 1686 Hooke gave an account of firing gunpowder in vacuo with a
burning glass and found that 'now and then a single corn would go off upon
the whole heap without kindling the next corn';[3] but when it was melted into a
lump, 'it went off after the manner of the pulvis fulminans with a very great
report, and burst his glass into a thousand pieces, and stuck great part therof
into the ceiling.'[4]

In February 1687 some experiments were ordered to be made in the Royal
Society on the 'air' produced by burning gunpowder in an exhausted receiver
'to try whether this air . . . would serve for a pabulum to fire, with design to
examine the hypothesis of the fires feeding upon the nitrous parts of the air;
this medium being wholly made up of the substance of niter dispersed in the
form of air'.[5]

That Hooke was far from clear in his theory of combustion is shown by his
suggestion[6] that combustion may occur in the 'medium' (ether) with which he
supposed space to be filled: 'this indefinitely or exceedingly fluid Body may
be, and is a medium, in which a solid compound body of proper materials may

[1] Van Helmont's idea, see p. 232.
[2] Birch, (1), iii, 460 f., 465, 469, 471, 517; Hooke, V, xxi, 111 (1680); Gunther, (1), vii, 508–14;
Lysaght, *Ambix*, 1937, i, 93.
[3] Cf. Boyle, p. 527.   [4] Gunther, (1), vii, 691.
[5] Letter of Halley, Gunther, (1), 1939, xii, 126.   [6] Of Comets and Gravity; V, 163 f., 171.

be fired and kindled into an actual fire and flame, and may be continued in that state so long as the said materials shall last.' Although he had said (see p. 558) that nitrous air does not extend beyond the atmosphere of the earth, Hooke asserted that the sun is a burning body.[1]

'All metals (excepting gold and silver, which do not so much with the bare fire, unless assisted by other saline bodies) do more or less vitrifie by the strength of the fire, that is, are corroded by a saline substance, which I else-where shew to be the true cause of fire; and are thereby, as by several other menstruums, converted into scoria; and this is called, calcining of them, by chimists . . . most kind of vitrifications or calcinations are made by salts, uniting and incorporating with the metalline particles. Nor do I know any one calcination wherein a saline body may not, with very great probability, be said to be an agent or coadjutor.'[2] Hooke also thought the temper colours of steel 'are produced from nothing else but a certain thin lamina of a vitrum or vitrified part of the metal, which by that degree of heat, and the concurring action of the ambient air, is driven out and fixed on the surface of the steel', i.e. he thought the vitrum of the film came from *inside* the metal. 'Steel is a, substance made out of iron, by means of a certain proportionate vitrification of several parts, which are curiously and proportionately mixed with the more tough and unalter'd parts of the iron.' On heating, the parts of the steel that were before 'streached or set atilt as it were' are loosened and 'some of the more brittle interjacent parts are thrust out and melted into a thin skin on the surface of the steel'. Apart from the confusion of oxidation of the surface and structural changes in the body of the metal, this account,[3] as Andrade said, is a foreshadowing of 'the explanation of the change of properties of metals by heat treatment on strictly physical and structural lines'. Hooke remarks that 'those metals which are not so apt to vitrifie (oxidise) do not aquire any hard-ness by quenching in water, as silver, gold, &c.'[4] That it is 'nothing but the vitrify'd metal that sticks upon the surface of the colour'd body, is evident from this, that if by any means it be scraped and rubb'd off, the metal under-neath it is white and clear'. Also, 'iron or steel will keep longer from rusting which is covered with this vitrify'd case', but on longer heating it increases to a considerable thickness and may, by blows, be beaten off in flakes. The same is found with brass, copper, silver, gold (*sic*) and tin but is most conspicuous in lead in fusion.

Descartes (p. 436) regarded the sparks struck from flint and steel as fire-particles struck from the flint; Hooke criticised this theory and showed that they are incandescent particles of steel which (as he found by microscopic examination) had become fused by the intense heat. The sparks thrown off from steel when struck with flint, received on white paper, were found by the microscope to consist of (i) small round fused globules, (ii) long thin slivers of iron or steel, (iii) the same as (ii) but melted into a globule at one end. The globules were formed by the vitrifying (oxidation) of some 'very combustible sulphureous body in iron or steel, which the air very readily preys upon, as

[1] Lectures on Light, 1680; V, 94, 100.
[2] II, 51.   [3] II, 51-2.   [4] II, 52.

soon as the body is a little violently heated' and 'devoured' by it. Iron filings burn when thrown through a flame.[1]

In 1694 Hooke showed that red-hot iron became hotter and appeared to burn when a blast of air was directed upon it, and said other metals, as copper, brass, lead, tin and silver would also burn 'when they have first been prepared by a proper degree of incallescency'.[2]

Boyle having remarked that 'tin mixed with nitre will kindle it', Hooke added that iron filings will do the same, whereupon the Royal Society ordered the experiment to be tried; it was found that 'filings of tin being cast upon nitre, over a fire, made it flame; though it be not known', says Oldenburg, the writer of the minutes, 'that sulphur was ever extracted out of tin; which seems to infer that there are bodies combustible which are not sulphureous.'[3]

In December 1679 Henshaw said that 'antimony by calcining would increase in weight and Mr. Boyle had found the same thing', whereupon Hooke 'urged that he had several times calcined antimony by the help of a burning glass and had always found it to grow considerably lighter by such calcination'.[4] Goddard in 1664 had found that so far from increasing in weight the antimony showed a decrease from twelve grains to three or four, and Boyle asserted that he had made a similar observation.[5]

In 1661[6] Hooke promised to show 'by many luciferous experiments' that the oil or melted tallow rising through the wick of a lamp or candle 'is dispersed and carried away by the flame', and in 1665 Hooke says:[7]

that shining transient body which we call flame, is nothing else but a mixture of air, and volatile sulphureous parts of dissoluble or combustible bodies, which are acting upon each other whilst they ascend, that is, flame seems to be a mixture of air, and the combustible volatil part of any body, which part of the encompassing air doth dissolve or work upon, which action, as it doth intend the heat of the aerial parts of the dissolvent, so does it thereby further rarefie those parts that are acting, or that are very neer them, whereby they growing much lighter than the heavie parts of that menstruum that are more remote, are thereby protruded and driven upwards.

Hooke also[8] describes the formation of a mushroom-like snuff on the candle wick as due to the 'steamy parts of the filtrated oil issuing out of the sides of this ragg, and being inclos'd with an air that is already satiated and cannot prey upon them or burn them'. Also, 'in the middle of the flame of the candle, neer the top of the snuff, the fire or dissolving principle is nothing neer so strong, as neer the bottom and out edges of the flame, which may be observ'd by the burning asunder of a thread, that will first break in those parts that the edges of the flame touch, and not in the middle.'

In his *Lampas* (1677)[9] Hooke gave a much fuller account of the structure of a candle flame:

The hypothesis of Fire and Flame I did about eleven years since publish in the 16. Observation Pag. 103, 104 and 105 of my Micrographia which hath so far obtained, that many authors have since made use of it, and asserted it; nor have I yet met with

[1] II, 43–7.   [2] Gunther, (1), vii, 748 f.   [3] Birch, (1), ii, 15, 20; Harcourt, 492.
[4] Birch, (1), iii, 512; Gunther, (1), vii, 534 f.   [5] Birch, (1), i, 452.
[6] I, 45.   [7] II, 105.   [8] II, 128–9.
[9] III, 3; cf. Birch, (1), iii, 10, 19, 30 (22 February 1672); Partington, *Ann. Sci.*, 1945, v, 231; Roscoe and Schorlemmer, *Treatise*, 1920, i, 821.

one considerable objection against it. It shall not therefore be my business at present to discourse of, or farther explain that Theory, which any one upon a strict enquiry into, I question not, will find cause sufficient to confirm him in, but rather to mention some pleasant and beneficial uses thereof, and to hint some Mechanical Contrivances for the supplying the *Pabulum* Oyl or Spirit by the same degrees by which it is consumed in the flame of a Lamp, that great dissolvent . . . for the flame, as I formerly proved, being nothing but the parts of the Oyl rarefied and raised by heat into the form of a vapour, smoak or steam, the free Air that encompasseth this steam keepeth it into a Cylindrical form, and by its dissolving property preyeth upon or dissolveth those parts of it that are outwards and next to the Air, so as by the said dissolution it continueth the heat, and produceth the light which we observe; but those parts of the body of steams that rise from the Wick, which are in the middle, and not contiguous to the outward Air, are not dissolved or turned into shining flame by the Air till they rise towards the top of the Cone of flame where the free Air can come to each, and so dissolve them, and thence about the Wick in the Center of the Cone of flame they choak, clog, and quite stifle it that the flame will quickly go out. That this is so, anyone may easily find if he examine the flame of a Lamp or Candle by the help of a piece of glass: For by the transparency thereof he will plainly perceive that all the middle of the Cone of flame neither shines nor burns but only the outward Superficies thereof that is contiguous to the free and unsatiated Air, and that the middle parts may be collected in the form of Soot as very fine powdered coal dust.

Take then a piece of Glass, whether Window Glass, Looking-glass Plate, or the side of a Viol, it matters not, or, which is best of all, a thin plate of *Selenitis* or *Muscovia* Talk, and hold it horizontally in the middle of the flame so as to cut off the top or upper part of the Cone thereof, then presently, before it be choaked with soot, look down upon it and you shall plainly see that all the middle part of the Flame and the Wick have no shining power or light at all; nor are they dissolved by the Air, but remain in the form of Soot, but that only the Superficies or outside of the said cone doth burn, shine and consume into and mix with the ambiant Air.

In the same manner, if you hold the Glass or Selenitis perpendicularly and apply the side of it so as to cut the flame *per axia coni*, that the Air cannot come to one side thereof, you may plainly perceive that the shining part of the flame is only that which is contiguous to, and preyed upon by the free and unsatiated Air, and that where that Air cannot come free without being glutted and satiated in its way, there neither the consumption of the Oyl nor the heat and light of the flame is produced, but only a sooty, choaking and stifling substance.

It is noteworthy that in this later work Hooke does not enlarge his theory of combustion sketched in the *Micrographia* in 1665, nor does he give the experiments on which the latter was based. Hooke in 1663 described some experiments on qualitative analysis with the blowpipe, in which a lamp flame was 'very intensely cast . . . by a blast through a small pipe',[1] and in 1665[2] he describes heating on charcoal before the blowpipe.

Hooke, at the suggestion of the Royal Society two years previously, reported in 1671 that he had made experiments on respiration in rarefied air. The apparatus 'consisted of two tuns, one included in the other; the one to hold a man, the other filled with water to cover the former, thereby to keep it stanch; with tops put on with cement'. There was a gauge and a tap which could be turned by a person sitting in the inner vessel, connected with an air pump. Hooke found that he could sit in the inner vessel when a quarter of the air was evacuated for fifteen minutes with no inconvenience than a pain in the ears and a sensation of deafness, both of which disappeared when he emerged and walked about. A candle in the vessel had gone out before these effects were felt.[3]

---

[1] Gunther, (1), vi, 136.　　　[2] II, 108.　　　[3] Birch, (1), ii, 467, 472.

In January 1663 Hooke shut up 'in an oblong glass a burning lamp and a chick; and the lamp went out within two minutes, the chick remaining alive, and lively enough'.[1] In a 'scheme of inquiries concerning the air', brought to the Royal Society in February, 1663[2] he is concerned only with its physical properties, except 'the use of it in respiration'. In March, 1664, a bird enclosed in a vessel containing air compressed to 2 atm. lived for 10 hours, and in air compressed to 4 atm. lived from 11 a.m. till 10 p.m.[3]

In 1663 Hooke showed that a dog could live with its lungs (exposed and perforated) motionless if blown up fully with a pair of bellows, or if a blast of air were sent through them; this experiment was repeated in 1667 (24 October) and, apparently, the Royal Society wished to see it again and again, but Hooke announced that he had no wish to repeat such a cruel experiment, 'whereupon others were appointed to do it.'[4] The experiment was twice (quite unnecessarily) repeated by the Rev. Stephen Hales,[5] who kept up the process for over an hour, when the dog died, although Hales had not finished his experiment. He drew no conclusion of the slightest value from it.

In January 1665, at the suggestion of Ent, a bird was shut up in a receiver with a chaffer of live coals, when it was noticed that the extinction of the fire was followed by failure of vitality in the bird, which revived on the readmission of air.[6]

Hooke[7] hints that he will further expound his 'hypothesis' when 'I come to shew the use of the Air in respiration, and for the preservation of life'. In April, 1668, Hooke remarked that dark, almost black, blood became florid when exposed to air.[8] In 1678 Hooke reported some experiments on 'factitious air' and asserted that air is the pabulum of animal spirits and the principal cause of animal heat.[9] He says[10] the heat in animals may be caused by

'the uniting of the volatile salt of the air with the blood in the lungs, which is done by a kind of corrosion or fermentation, which to me I confess seems somewhat more than probable', since rapidity of breathing goes with increase of heat; the 'ebullition of steams into the lungs, which are carried out with the breath by expiration, may probably be caused by the ebullition of the blood upon the mixing of the salt of the air, somewhat after the nature, as oyl of tartar will bubble by the affusion of volatile and acid salts'.

In his Cutlerian Lectures on Light (1680–2),[11] long after Mayow (1674), Hooke brings in the part played by air in respiration.

Hooke was apparently the first to speculate in a modern way about crystal structure, saying that the forms in which rock salt and alum (both cubic crystals) appear can be built up of spherical particles: 'all these regular figures . . . arise onely from three or four several positions or postures of globular particles . . . and this I have *ad oculum* demonstrated with a company of bullets, and some few other very simple bodies . . . even almost by shaking them to-

[1] Birch, (1), i, 180; Gunther, (1), vi, 101.　　[2] Gunther, (1), vi, 112–15.
[3] Gunther, (1), vi, 171–2.
[4] Sprat, *History of the Royal Society*, 1667, 232; Birch, (1), iii, 407; *Phil. Trans.*, 1667, i, 539, no. 28; abdg. ed., 1809, i, 194; Gunther, (1), vi, 214 f., 307, 310, 315 f.; Hooke, V, 1705, 111 (1680); Robinson, *Proc. Roy. Soc. Med.*, *Hist. Med.*, 1945, xxxviii, 489.
[5] *Vegetable Staticks*, 1727, 250, 252.　　[6] Birch, (1), ii, 10, 12; Harcourt, 492.
[7] II, 105.　　[8] Gunther, (1), vi, 331 f., 338.
[9] Birch, (1), iii, 89.　　[10] V, 50.　　[11] V, 220–1.

gether.' He gives two-dimensional drawings to illustrate this (Fig. 24, p. 566), suggesting further experiments, e.g. to crystallise several other salts alone and mixed, to observe the specific gravity, refraction, etc., in order to 'enquire the closeness or rarity of the texture', so that 'we shall be the better able to proceed in our next enquiry after the forms of vegetative bodies; and least of all, of animate ones'.[1]

In 1668, 1679, and 1680 Hooke made a number of experiments on the specific gravities of alloys, showing that some of them, e.g. alloys of tin and silver, were 'heavier than the compounding parts'.[2] On 26 March 1673 he showed that 21 measures of water and 3 measures of oil of vitriol on mixing gave only 23 measures.[3] He described in 1678 an apparatus consisting of a counterpoised globe for indicating changes in the density of the air.[4]

In November 1679 Hooke 'alleged, that he had about eight years before shown the society at Arundel House an experiment to prove the penetration of liquors one into another by putting oil of vitriol and water in a bolt-head of glass; whereby it manifestly appeared, that those two liquors put together took up much less room than when they were separated'.[5] In 1686 he compared the densities of mercury and turpentine by measuring the heights in the two limbs of a U-tube.[6]

Hooke mentions the *sealed* thermometer brought from Italy (by Brouncker ?); in 1664 he proposed that the temperature of freezing water (ice point) should be marked o, degrees below being marked minus;[7] in 1684 he proposed the heat of boiling water as another fixed point.[8] The freezing and boiling points of water had been proposed as fixed points by Van Helmont (p. 220) long before Hooke. Dalancé in an anonymous work,[9] suggested two fixed points, but they were badly chosen (melting and solidifying points of butter; a deep cave and a mixture of ice and salt). Boyle used freezing oil of aniseed for a fixed point (p. 508).

The so-called Rupert's drops (*lachrymæ vitreæ*), investigated by Hooke[10] and others, were, apparently, discovered in Holland early in the 17 cent. but were first described by Reyher, who saw them in Leyden in 1656: they were called 'Dutch tears', and were imported into England by Prince Rupert in 1661 and given for investigation to Gresham College by Charles II. They are mentioned by Pepys.[11] Hooke wrongly supposed that the action was due to compressed air contained in them. The correct explanation that it was entirely due to internal stress in the glass was given by Hobbes and by Montanari

---

[1] II, 85–8.
[2] Birch, (1), iii, 511 (1679); Gunther, (1), vi, 325 f.; vii, 540 f.; Lewis, *Commercium-Philosophico-Technicum*, 1763–5, ii, 556; Parkes, *Chemical Essays*, 2 ed., 1823, i, 223.
[3] Birch, (1), iii, 79; Gunther, (1), vii, 410.   [4] Birch, (1), iii, 386–8.
[5] Gunther, (1), vii, 533; experiment shown in 1689, *ib.*, 712 f.
[6] Gunther, (1), vii, 691–2.   [7] II, 38.
[8] V, 556; Robison, in Black, *Elements of Chemistry*, 1803, i, 53–4; Crafts, *J. Chim. Phys.*, 1913, xi, 429, says Huygens (1664–5), Newton (1680), and Renaldini (1694), proposed the ice pt. and b.p. as fixed points; Poggendorff, (1), 1863, ii, 604; *id.*, (2), 1883, 235; for Huygens see Gerland, *Z.f. Instrumentenkunde*, 1893, xiii, 340–3, who says Hooke was not really convinced of the constancy of the freezing-point of water.
[9] *Traité des baromètres, thermomètres et notiomètres*, 12°, 1688, q. by Poggendorff, (2), 316.
[10] II, 33: Obs. VII: Of some Phænomena of Glass drops.
[11] *Diary*, 13 January 1662; ed. 1905, 113.

(1670).[1] The Bologna vial was first described in 1740 by Paolo Baptista Balbi, professor of physics at Bologna.[2]

Hooke apparently first described crystals (gravel) of uric acid deposited from urine[3] and he first used the name 'cell' in describing vegetable structures.[4]

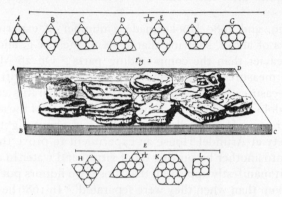

FIG. 24. HOOKE.
FIGURES OF CRYSTALS (OF URIC ACID?) AND SECTIONS OF PACKINGS OF SPHERES IN CRYSTAL STRUCTURES.

The liquefaction of camphor by aqua fortis was shown by Hooke in 1680,[5] although it had been described by Boyle in 1661.[6] In three discourses (displaying much classical lore) upon amber, Hooke concluded that it was the gum of a certain tree petrified and altered.[7] He may be said to have anticipated (in idea) the artificial silk industry by drawing out 'an artificial glutinous composition' as good as, or even better than (the usual industrial cliché!) 'that Excrement, or whatever other substance it be', from which the silk-worm draws its thread. 'This hint' is offered to 'some Ingenious inquisitive Person' for trial,[8] but no one until very recent times was inquisitive enough to notice what Hooke had said in 1665. Lewis[9] describes a process of Hooke's for gilding live fish — 'artificial gold-fish', another hint which does not seem to have been taken up.

Hooke thought that 'fermentation is somewhat analogus, or of the same kind with dissolutions or corrosion', just as 'fire is nothing but the dissolution or corrosion of sulphureous heated bodies, by the air as a menstruum'.[10]

In a description of the book-worm[11] he remarks on 'the excellent contrivance of Nature, in placing in animals such a fire, as is continually nourished and supply'd by the materials convey'd into the stomach, and fomented by the bellows of the lungs', and 'to make the very spending and wasting of that fire, to be instrumental to the procuring and collecting more materials to augment and cherish it self'.

[1] Rosenberger, 1884, ii, 171; Poggendorff, (2), 251.
[2] J. C. Fischer, 1801, i, 287; Poggendorff, (2), 251–2.
[3] II, 81, and plate VII, 2; Middleton, *Ann. Med. Hist.*, 1927, ix, 237.   [4] II, 113.
[5] Gunther, (1), vii, 539.   [6] *Physiological Essays*; *Works*, ed. Birch, 1744, i, 270.
[7] Gunther, (1), vii, 768 f.   [8] II, 7.
[9] *Commercium Philosophico-Technicum*, 1765, i, 64.   [10] V, 47, cf. 59.   [11] II, 210.

GREW

Nehemiah Grew (Coventry, *c.* 1628–London, 25 March 1711) a Presbyterian, was a physician in Coventry and from 1672 in London, and secretary of the Royal Society from 1677. He studied the anatomy of plants from 1664 and in 1670 he gave the manuscript of an essay to his brother-in-law Dr. Henry Sampson, who showed it to Oldenburg, who passed it to Wilkins, who read it to the Royal Society, which ordered it to be printed.[1] The continuation of it, and other lectures read to the Royal Society in 1674–7 were collected and printed in 1682.[2] This contains A Discourse Concerning the Nature, Causes, and Power of Mixture,[3] Experiments in Consort of the Luctation Arising from the Affusion of Several Menstruums Upon all sorts of Bodies,[4] on the Salts of Plants,[5] on Essential and Marine Salts of Plants,[6] on the Colours of Plants by Infusion,[7] and on the Solution of Salts.[8] Grew says the true principles of bodies are atoms of different sizes and figures.[9]

The causes of mixture are congruity, weight, compression, solution, digestion, and agitation,[10] and there are five kinds of 'luctation', bullition, elevation, crepitation, effervescence, and exhalation.[11] Oil forms an emulsion with water if first mixed with egg-yolk.[12] Grew has a confused classification of materials into acid, subacid, alkaline, subalkaline, etc. Mercury is subacid because it dissolves in spirit of nitre (nitric acid), which is a 'subalkaline acid',[13] and osteocolla knits broken bones because it dissolves in 'a Nitrous Acid in the body' and 'is precipitated upon the broken part'.[14]

Spirit of nitre (nitric acid) congeals olive oil owing to its cold, whilst sulphuric acid will not do this;[15] if the 'nitre' could be separated from the air it would be so cold that it would freeze water in summer.[16] Spirit of nitre does not act on steel filings or on tin unless some water is added; it 'will not make the least Bullition: but if hereto you add only a drop or two of water, they presently boil up with very great vehemency', a 'remarkable circumstance'.[17] Alkaline salt is formed as such by the combustion of various plants, in amounts which Grew determined quantitatively, but it is present in another form (*quatenus*) in the plant before combustion.[18] Plants contain both essential salt and common (marine) salt.[19] Grew made many experiments on the colours of flowers, etc., their extraction by infusion, and the effects of reagents on them.[20] He also has an elaborate classification of tastes, simple and compound, their causes, and their production by 'tearing the fibres' of the tongue.[21]

The saturation points of different salts in water are different. There is expansion when the salt dissolves but a more soluble salt may cause a smaller

---

[1] *The Anatomy of Vegetables Begun. With a General Account of Vegetation Founded thereon*, sm. 8°, 1672, 198 pp., 83 plates (with other works).
[2] *The Anatomy of Plants. With an Idea of a Philosophical History of Plants. And several other Lectures Read before the Royal Society*, la. 4°, 1682.
[3] *Ib.*, Book IV, pp. 221 f.   [4] *Ib.*, 238 f.   [5] *Ib.*, 255 f.; read in 1676.
[6] *Ib.*, 261 f.; read in 1676.   [7] *Ib.*, 273 f.   [8] *Ib.*, 296 f.   [9] *Ib.*, 233.
[10] *Ib.*, 229.   [11] *Ib.*, 239.   [12] *Ib.*, 237.   [13] *Ib.*, 244.   [14] *Ib.*, 243.
[15] *Ib.*, 233–5.   [16] *Ib.*, 233.   [17] *Ib.*, 244–5; cf. Boyle, p. 540.
[18] *Ib.*, 233 f., 251 f.   [19] *Ib.*, 261.
[20] *Ib.*, 269 f., 275 f.   [21] *Ib.*, 279 f., 287 f.

expansion, showing that there are vacuities in the water. By measuring the specific gravities of salts by the displacement of oil of turpentine he showed that sal ammoniac is the only one which increases the volume of the water by exactly its own volume.[1]

This part of Grew's book was translated, as 'Experiences dv combat, qui provient de l'affusion & du mélange des corps', in the *Recueil d'Experiences* (1679) (see p. 496). Grew also investigated Epsom salt (see p. 696).

Marcello Malpighi (Crevalcuore, 10 March 1628–Rome, 29 November 1694), then professor of medicine in Bologna, in 1671 and 1674 sent two communications to the Royal Society, which were published by it in 1675.[2] His work was independent of Grew's.

LOWER

Richard Lower (Tremeer, nr. Bodmin, Cornwall, January 1632–London, 17 January 1691), educated at Westminster and Oxford, made in 1666 successful experiments on the transfusion of blood from one animal to another, and in 1667 with Edmund King on the transfusion of blood from one man to another. The experiments are described in his book on the heart.[3] Lower injected dark venous blood into the insufflated lungs and concluded that its consequent bright colour was due to the fact that it had absorbed some air passing through the lungs.[4] Lower's book had a great vogue.[5] Lower left Oxford in 1666 for London, where he lived first in Hatton Garden, and finally, from 1673, near Covent Garden.[6] On account of his political views as a Whig his practice declined after 1675.[7]

Lower, a year after the publication of Mayow's *Tractatus duo* (1668; see p. 583), speaks of 'some kind of nitro-sulphureous fermentation in the ventricle of the heart' (fermentum quoddam nitrosulphureum in Cordis ventriculo)[8] as a known idea, which he rejects,[9] and also the theory that heat

[1] *Ib.*, 296 f.
[2] *Anatome Plantarum*, f°, London, 1675; Ostwald's *Klassiker*, cxx; *Opera Omnia*, 2 vols. f°, London, 1686–7.
[3] *Tractatus de Corde*, 1669, ch. iv: De transfusione sanguinis ex animali alio in aliud; the book also corrects Harvey's theories of circulation.
[4] F. H. Garrison, *An Introduction to the History of Medicine*, 2 ed., Philadelphia, 1917, 267 f.; K. D. Franklin, 'The Work of Richard Lower', *Proc. Roy. Soc. Med.*, 1931, xxv, 113; Fulton, *A Bibliography of Two Oxford Physiologists, Richard Lower and John Mayow*, Oxford Bibliographical Society *Proc. and Papers*, 1935, iv, 1–62; Payne, DNB, 1893, xxxiv, 203; Gunther, (1), 1926, iii, 66, 127 (with earlier experiments of Potter and Wren); Plot, *Natural History of Oxfordshire*, Oxford, 1705, 309; Patterson, *Isis*, 1931, xv, 79; the transfusion from man to man was first carried out by Denis, in Paris; see Maluf, *J. Hist. of Medicine and Allied Sciences*, New Haven, 1954, ix, 59; see also under Libavius.
[5] *Tractatus de Corde. Item De Motu & Colore Sanguinis et Chyli in eum Transitu*, 8°, London, 1669 (the BM copy has Walter Charleton's signature and date 1668 (perhaps early in 1669) and is full of his corrections of Lower's Latin, the word 'prout', which occurs repeatedly, being uniformly struck out); there were 16 eds. (one in Manget, *Bibliotheca Anatomica*, Geneva, 1685) to 1749; facsim. ed. with intr. by K. J. Franklin, in Gunther, (1), 1932, ix; Franklin, *Ann. Sci.*, 1939, iv, 283; French tr., *Traité du Cœur, du Mouvement et de la Couleur du Sang, et du Passage du Chyle dans le Sang*, 8°, Paris, 1679 (from the 1669 Latin ed.) perhaps by Jean Denis, graduate of Montpellier and professor in Paris, who was in London in 1673, and had performed blood transfusion on man before Lower. Fulton does not identify the translator.
[6] Franklin, in Gunther, (1), 1932, IX, pp. xxi, xxv.
[7] M. Foster, 1901, 181 f.   [8] 1669, 61.   [9] *Ib.*, 64.

was produced in the heart.[1] These are Willis's ideas (see p. 307). Lower says the 'spirits' interact by 'explosion' in the muscles (praetera si ab explosione diversae indolis spirituum sibi mutuò in Musculo concurrentium).[2] The fact that an animal can be kept alive by insufflation is ascribed to Hooke (quod experimentum quo pulmones in continuâ distentione, salvâ interim animalis vitâ, diu continentur, Celeberrimo Domino Rob. Hooke deberi, atque inde mihi ansam hujus conficiendi datam esse agnosco).[3]

Lower[4] says that 'where a fire can burn sufficiently well, there we can equally well breathe' — as had been said by Hippokrates (Vol. I). He mentions that dark venous blood becomes florid on exposure to the atmosphere, and suggests that this is due to the absorption of particles of air:[5]

praeterea colorem hunc rutilum particulis aëris sese in sanguinem insinuantibus omnino debere . . . ita sanguinis venosi in vase excepti superficies & pars summa, quatenus aeri exposita est, coccineum quoque colorem aquirit.

But (as Boyle knew, p. 548)[6] that had been shown before 'in Italy by an ingenious man', viz. Fracassati, professor of anatomy at Pisa, who noticed that only the upper part becomes bright red; hence he inferred that the dark colour of blood is not due to the 'melancholy humour' but to want of a mixture of air, since the presence of air at once converts it into red blood.[7] Lower asks if this is not due to the absorption of nitro-aerial spirit (*si per quos pulmonum meatus spiritus aëris nitrosus in sanguinem transit* [transeat], *eumque copiosus imbuit* [imbuat] . . .),[8] and says this spirit passes as cold from the snow used to cool wine in a metal or pottery vessel.

The theory that cold is due to frigorific particles of saltpetre in air, which can penetrate glass, was proposed by Gassendi:[9] (frigoris semina . . . frigorificis Atomis, abire in halinitrum . . . qualitatem Frigoris requirendam esse . . . in natura corpusculorum cuiusmodi, exempli causâ, nitrosa sunt), or as Charleton translates 'a particular species of *Atoms* (of which sort are those whereof Salnitre is for the most part composed) which being introduced into Earth, Water, Aer, or any other mixt Bodie, imprægnate them with cold'.

Hooke's experiment on artificial respiration (p. 564) gave Lower a clue. On examining the lungs of an animal kept alive by artificial respiration Lower found that the blood was florid in the pulmonary veins long before it reached the heart. He then took dark venous blood from the vena cava and injected it through the lungs. So long as insufflation of the lungs was kept up, the blood ran from the pulmonary veins florid in colour, but it ran out dark and unchanged if no fresh air was driven into the lungs.

Although Foster says it was Mayow who brought forward reasons for supposing that in breathing only part of the air, not the whole air, is taken up

[1] *Ib.*, 71.   [2] *Ib.*, 77.   [3] *Ib.*, 167.   [4] 1669, 171.   [5] *Ib.*, 168.
[6] *Works*, 1744, iii, 468.
[7] Signior Fracassati, *Phil. Trans.*, 1667, ii, 492: An Experiment . . . upon Bloud grown cold.
[8] *Ib.*, 169.
[9] *Opera Omnia*, f°, Lyons, 1658, i, 399–401; De Calore et Frigida, *ib.*, ii, 66; the theory is summarised by W. Charleton, *Physiologia Epicuro-Gassendo-Charltoniana*, f°, London, 1654, 310 f., 313; and Boyle, *Works*, ed. Birch, f°, 1744, ii, 311 f., 313 f.

into the blood, Lower seems to have suggested this and he also gave it the name, *spiritus aeris nitrosus*, afterwards used by Mayow as *spiritus nitro-aerei*. Foster[1] speaks of Lower as 'the henchman of the fashionable Willis, whose false fame in large measure rested on Lower's careful, unacknowledged work', and[2] quotes Wood[3] as saying that Lower 'helped or rather instructed [Willis] in some part of anatomy'. Willis[4] gives Lower full and unstinted acknowledgment. Mayow[5] mentions Lower's experiments and gives him full credit for them. Whatever else Lower's *spiritus aeris nitrosus* may have been, it was something of the nature of the matter of cold and could pass through metal or pottery. Mayow said igneous particles could penetrate metal.[6]

Yeats[7] points out that the fourth ed. of Lower's *Tractatus de Corde* appeared above six years (1680) after Mayow's *Tractatus Quinque* and 'it appears extraordinary that Lower should not have quoted Mayow's experiments and observations' confirming his own view, which 'was very much doubted by physiologists of the first respectability'.

SERVETUS

Michael Servetus (Tudela, Navarre, 1511–burned alive at Calvin's instigation, Geneva, 27 October 1553), a Spanish physician and theologian, asserted[8] that the blood in the lungs changes colour and becomes bright red; 'it is prepared and takes a yellow colour, then the arterial vein transmits it to the venal artery, in which it mixes with the inspired air, and by expiration is purified from smoky matters. . . . It is not simply air but a mixture of air and blood that the lungs send to the heart by the venous artery, and thus the mixture is made in the lungs. It is in the lungs and not in the heart that spirituous blood receives that yellow colour (a pulmonibus praeparatur, flavus efficitur, et a vena arteriosa in arteriam venosum transfunditur. Deinde in ipsa arteria venosa inspiratio aëri miscetur, exspiratione fuligine repurgatur. . . . Item a pulmonibus ad cor non simplex aër sed mixtus sanguine mittitur ad arteriam venosum. Ergo in pulmonibus fit mixtio. Flavus ille color a pulmonibus datur sanguini spirituoso, non a carde).'

Servetus has been credited with a knowledge of the circulation of the blood. His book on syrups,[9] published under an assumed name, explains digestion as the source of animal heat; it is what in the natural state corresponds with coction in the unnatural; yellow and black bile are formed from blood and cannot be assimilated.

[1] 1901, 187.   [2] *Ib.*, 269.   [3] *Athenæ Oxonienses*, ed. Bliss, 1820, iv, 297.
[4] *Cerebri anatome*, 1664.   [5] *Tractatus Quinque*, Oxford, 1674, 148.
[6] Mayow, *Tractatus Quinque*, 1674, 27.
[7] *Observations on the Claims of the Moderns, to Some Discoveries in Chemistry and Physiology*, 1798, 124.
[8] *Christianissimi Restitutio* (anon.), *s.l.* [Vienne, Dauphiné], 1553, 170–1 (this part was missing in the copy available to me and I rely on Dutens, *Inquiry into the Origin of the Discoveries attributed to the Moderns*, 1769, 217–20; Daremberg, 1870, ii, 596; and Haeser, (1), 1881, ii, 245); Sprengel, (2), 1827, iii, 167; Thorndike, v, 288.
[9] *Syruporum universa ratio, ad Galeni censuram diligenter exposita . . .* , Michaële Villanovano authore, 8°, Paris, 1537 (BM 778. c. 41 and 540. c. 21. (1.); 70 pp.'); 8°, Venice, 1545 (BM 547. c. 1. (1.)), 8°, Lyon, 1546 (BM 540. c. 21. (2.)).

SCALIGER

J. C. Scaliger says that saltpetre contains moisture, converted by heat into air:[1]

Sal dicit in igne crepitare, quia humoris in se plurimum continent: qui ab igni attenuatus, *spirituosam* induit naturam ... Sal tamen aerem potius, quàm aquam continere, aut saltem plus aeris intelligas: qui ignescat; the explosion of gunpowder is due to a blow on the air; tonitru verò fit ex aeris complosione ... aliquando risum mouet, simulque nares ut occludamus, cogit.

Scaliger also thought respiration had a moistening and cooling effect and generated spirit which repaired the body like food:[2]

Spirando necessitas omnibus nota est. De eius humectatione, præter uulgatam refrigerationem, à nobis alibi dictum est. Quin etiam illud additum. Fortasse ex inuecto aere spiritus generari, quasi transcriptis colonis augeatur ciuitas ... Modus diuersus ad ipsorum spirituum reparationem. ... Quemadmodum à cibo fit corporis instauratio: ita ab aere fit, siue per spirationem, siue per transpirationem, spirituum noua generatio. Quamobrem sicut à cibo conuenienti animans alitur: ita & animantis spiritus à conuenienti materia. Ergo quibus aerei spiritus: iis aer materia est ad reparationem.

THRUSTON

Some statements about the effects of air on the blood in respiration (he thought the most important was the increase of fluidity) were made by Malachi Thruston in a Cambridge M.D. thesis presented in 1664 but not published till 1670.[3] Thruston[4] made four assertions, without proof, the third of which he thought the most important:

(1) By the experiments of Boyle, air has been given an elastic force (aerem vi elasticâ ... donatum esse).

(2) Air of average constitution (aerem mediocritèr constitutum) is laden with nitrous particles (nitrosis particulis), as Gassendi, Ent, Digby, and others have shown by reasoning and experiment. Their properties depend on their figure and motion, which can in different bodies produce opposite effects (planè contrarios effectus producere possint), so that the nitrosity of the air has by some been considered a cause of cold and by others a cause of heat, by some a cause of density and by others a cause of rarity, etc., as explained by Descartes in the fourth part of his *Principia*.

(3) The tenuity and thickness of the air must be in certain limits for it to be fit for animal respiration.

---

[1] *Exotericarum Exercitationum*, Paris, 1557, XXIV, CI, pp. 49 r–v, 153 v.

[2] *Ib.*, CCLXXIII, 1–2, pp. 343 r–347 v.

[3] *De Respirationis Usu primario, Diatriba*, 8°, London, 1670, 34 f., 47 f., 54, 62 f.; repr. in *De Respirationis Usu primario, Diatribe, ut et Johannis Mayow . . . Tractatus duo, Quorum prior agit de Respiratione: Alter de Rachitide*, sm. 8°, Leyden, 1708, pp. 1–136 (Mayow, sep. pag., 1–57); Patterson, *Isis*, 1931, xv, 84, says Thruston's tract was also added to the 1671 Leyden edition of Mayow's *Tractatus duo*, and Yeats, *Observations on the Claims of the Moderns*, 1798, 105 f., 134 f., quoted Thruston copiously from this; the book as printed contains some additions (from p. 119: a Cl. Doctissimoque Viro conscriptae) to the original thesis. Thruston is mentioned by Mayow, *Tractatus Quinque*, 1674, ii, 43.

[4] *Ib.*, 1670, 39–42.

(4) 'It is very probable that as the more pure, more subtle, and more penetrating part of the air is absorbed by the lungs, and is there as it were lost, so the expired air, becoming replete and vitiated with the exhalations and vapours and deprived of its better parts, is in some degree rendered effete and useless: moreover, I believe, it loses very considerably its elasticity, being in a great measure deprived of its more mobile matter':

verisimile etiam esse, puriorem, subtiliorem, magisque penetrabilem aëris partem, dum ille inspirando pulmonibus hauritur, ibidem quasi deperdi; adeóque aerem expiratum, utpote fuliginibus & vaporibus implicitum & inquinatum, orbatúmque potiori parte sui, vappidum quodammodo atque effætum reddi; quinetiam (ut facile crediderim) eidem *elasticitatis* suæ vim magnâ ex parte perire, nempe mobiliori illâ materiâ plurimùm spoliato.[1]

The blood becomes more fluid by a process of coction which separates, as in fermentation and distillation, subtle particles which can be called spirit (ac tandem subtilissimæ evadunt illæ particulæ quæ *spirituum* grandi nomine insigniuntur . . . natura omnes omnium Chymicorum ostentabundas ἐγχειρ-ήσεις longissimo intervallo post se relinquit).[2] The air at some times and in some places is light, hot, nitrous, and spirituous, in others heavy, cold, vapid, and thick.[3] The heart communicates its heat to the blood; the heat of the heart is mostly unknown; some think it is a flame, others a ferment not seen or touched, but these views are not based on experiments or reasons.[4]

Respiration serves not only to keep the blood fluid by ingress of air (de aeris in sanguinem ingressu) but the nitrous particles of the air also conserve the heat of the blood, as could easily be shown by a great variety of experiments if he did not study brevity.[5]

Porro particulæ aëris sanguini commixtæ . . . non ad *fluiditatem* solûm, verum etiam ad *calorem* ejus conservandum non parùm valent. . . . Nitrosus etiam aëris particulas illud ingenium obtinere, jam alicubi supra posuimus, ut conceptum semel calorem adaugeant; id quod ex multis variisque experimentis confirmare liceret nisi brevitate studerem.

The production of animal heat is due to fermentation; the food contains much air (qui tamen aer non se omninò prodit, priusquam illorum compages fermentatione soluta est) which finally passes to be mixed in the lungs. In the part added to the original dissertation, Thruston says:[6]

It is our opinion that the peculiar office of the lungs is to transmit air into the blood, by which it acquires a red and florid colour; whence it happens that it becomes not only more florid but also more fluid; and the more fluid it is, the more easily will it be fitted for the functions of the circulation. Those two celebrated philosophers, Hooke and Lower, seem to have put this beyond doubt by a very ingenious experiment. And I do not a little rejoice, and return them my hearty thanks, that they have produced a complete confirmation of my theory, which has been publicly attacked by several without mentioning my name.

Tandem hoc pulmoni proprium ac peculiari esse volumus, quòd intromissus particulis aeris, colore coccineo, rutilóque sanguinem, in transitu suo per eundem, donet: unde non floridior tantùm, sed etiam fluidior ut sit, necesse est; quo autem fluidior est, eò facilius circuitu etiam suo defungitur . . . celeberrimus Hookius, & Lowerus, jam aliquoties laudatus (Tract. de corde c. 3) nobilissimo experimento, rem hac difficilli-

---

[1] *Ib.*, 41.   [2] *Ib.*, 21.   [3] *Ib.*, 36.   [4] *Ib.*, 48.
[5] *Ib.*, 54, 62-3; q. by Yeats, 1798, 105.   [6] *Ib.*, 157.

mam confecisse videntur, nec sinunt nos diutiùs de eâdem dubitare. Ego verò non parum lætor, illísque gratias ago, quod theoria meæ (a nonnullis publicè, sed suppresso meo nomine impugnatæ) rem ipsam testem dederint.

Thruston says that the inspired air unites with the blood and promotes its fluidity, by means of which its circulation is restored, which had stagnated in the right ventricle and in the lungs (Nimirum ispiratus aer & sanguini commiscebatur, ejúsque fluiditatem promovebat, ac totum ejus flumen, quod jam in dextro cordis ventriculo atque in pulmonibus stagnârat, forti impulsi ad *progressum* & circulationem solicitabat).[1]

Sprengel[2] says Thruston tried to combine Mayow's theory with Malpighi's that the air mixes with the blood in the cells of the lungs, no air as such passing into the surrounding blood-vessels; only the nitrous part of the air, according to Thruston, passed into the blood. The air cools the heart.

Views similar to Thruston's had been criticised previously by Walter Needham (Shavington, Shropshire, 1631–London, 5 April 1691)[3] who refers to Boyle, Lower, Willis, Gassendi, Henshaw, etc.[4] He rejected the vital flame theory of Willis (see p. 307). He did not question that air is received into the mass of the blood but doubted whether there was a 'highway' for air from the lungs to the blood. The function of the lungs is the constant agitation and comminution of the blood to render it fit for due circulation, and this office is performed in fish by the continual motion of the gills, a succedaneum to lungs.

ENT

Thruston's book was criticised by Ent.[5] Pepys[6] records that on 22 January 1666 he went to Gresham College: 'But what, among other fine discourse, pleased me most, was Sir G. Ent, about respiration; that it is not to this day known, or concluded on, among physicians, nor to be done either, how the action is managed by Nature, or for what use it is.'

Ent in his principal work,[7] written to defend Harvey's doctrine of circulation against the attacks of the Italian physician Emilio Parigiano (1567–1643), brought forward a mass of classical and contemporary references. In discussing the respiration of fish[8] he says that air 'in the state we know it' is not contained in water, but 'that nitrous virtue (virtutem illam nitrosam) . . . for which we chiefly breathe the air, is likewise contained in water, and fish live upon that'.

---

[1] *Ib.*, 77.   [2] (2), 1827, iv, 139.

[3] D'Arcy Power, DNB, 1894, xl, 164: Needham was B.A. Cambridge, 1654, M.D. 1664, F.R.S. 1671; in 1660 he was in Oxford attending lectures of Willis, Millington, and Lower.

[4] *Digressio de biolychnio & ingressu aëris in sanguinem item de sanguinificatione*, ch. vi in *Disquisitio Anatomica de Formato Foetu*, sm. 8°, London, 1667, 129–75; Amsterdam, 1668 (BM 957. a. 7); long review in *Phil. Trans.*, 1667, ii, 503, no. 27.

[5] *ANTIΔIATPIBH. Sive Animadversiones in Malachiæ Thrustoni, M.D. Diatribam de Respirationis Usu Primario*, London, 1679 (portr.), 34, 97 (Hooke's experiment); other eds., 1681 and 1685; George Ent, Sandwich, Kent, 6 November 1604–London, 13 October 1689, M.A. Cambridge 1631, M.D. Padua 1636 and Oxford 1638, F.R.C.P. 1639, knighted 1665; friend and disciple of Harvey; Moore, DNB, 1889, xvii, 377.

[6] *Diary*, ed. Braybrook, 1858, ii, 346.

[7] *Apologia Pro Circuitatione Sanguinis: Qua respondetur Æmilio Parisano Medico Veneto*, 8°, London, 1641; 2 ed. 1685.

[8] 1641, 18.

He then[1] explains that blood absorbs air in its passage through the lungs of higher animals and is carried to the left ventricle, where, as in ordinary combustion, it maintains the fire of the heart. Deprived of air, this vital heat is extinguished like any fire when the air is cut off (in quo flamma ardens ære privata extinguitur). It is well known to all how fire is extinguished 'in medical cupping glasses, in a closed furnace, and elsewhere. And this happens because the fire is fostered by the nitre of the air (ab aeris nitro) — I have previously called it dew (rorem). And the more nitre is contained in the air, the more strongly this flame burns. . . . That is the power (virtus) by which we breathe (ob quam spiramus); without it, air would only injure us. Thus, from putrid swamps and caves redolent of mephitis, the pestilential air, deprived of this nitre, breathes forth and brings certain death to living creatures.' Ent does not quote Sendivogius on the 'dew' (see p. 428) but[2] mentions the *Palladium Spagyricum* (1624) of Pierre Jean Fabre (see p. 181).

BATHURST

Ralph Bathurst (Howthorpe, nr. Market Harborough, 1620–Oxford, 14 June 1704), M.A. Oxford 1641, B.M. and M.D. 1654, Dean of Bath and Wells 1670, Vice-Chancellor of Oxford 1673–6 (who may, as Dean, have been consulted by his Bishop, whom he succeeded as Vice-Chancellor, when the latter affixed his imprimatur to Mayow's *Tractatus Quinque* in 1673; see p. 583) has been hailed as a 'discoverer of oxygen'[3] and 'an unknown (!) forerunner of Lavoisier'.[4] In his lectures on respiration,[5] Bathurst[6] refers to Helmont's experiment of heating charcoal in a closed vessel (giving a reference to 'Beregard, p. 135. p. 4' as well as to Helmont; see p. 422): cum in istis angustiis nullos locus sit fuliginibus aliisve particulis inter ardendum dissipandis. Yet the particles of fire can pass through the glass and render the carbon incandescent. In the lungs, similarly, air must ventilate the fuliginous vapours or recrimentitious species from the blood.[7] He refers to a nitrous spirit entering in respiration and tempering the blood, existing in the earth and forming mineral nitre, and present in water and air. Fish die in water excluded from air (he quotes Scaliger for the experiment).[8] This nitrous spirit is the pabulum of respiration, and as a lamp deprived of air is extinguished, so life ceases when deprived of this nutritive breath. The nitrous spirit is present in snow and penetrates a glass or metal vessel containing wine, cooling it, and

[1] *Ib.*, 96–8. [2] *Ib.* 83.
[3] Sprengel, (1), iv, 408: '1654: discovery of oxygen by Henshaw and Bathurst.'
[4] Charlotte Saechtling, *Z. angew. Chem.*, 1933, xlvi, 199; Lippmann, *ib.* 351; an article by Crane on 'Bathurst and oxygen' in *Gentleman's Magazine*, 1800, 48, is given in the index but could not be found in the volume.
[5] *Praelectiones tres de Respiratione*, read in 1654 for the M.D. Oxford, but first published, 8°, London, 1761; T. Warton, *The Life and Literary Remains of Ralph Bathurst, Dean of Wells*, London, 1761 (portr.), says (p. 60) the 'lectures on *Respiration* . . . had remained in his hands for some years, received his repeated corrections, and were highly approved by Mr. Boyle'; this apparently was in 1656, *ib.*, 162 (letter from Boyle). It seems, therefore, that Bathurst's lectures as printed may include materials added until his death in 1704, and we do not know which or when.
[6] 1761, 179. [7] *Ib.*, 180–1.
[8] Scaliger, *Exotericarum Exercitationum*, CCLXXIII, 2; Paris, 1557, 346 *v.*

hence will more easily penetrate the loose structure of the lungs (cf. Lower, p. 569):

Dicimus itaque inspirationem præcipue inservire ad pabulum nitrosum animali subministrandum, quo sanguis ita contemperetur, ut, spiritibus, ad obeunda vitæ munia generandis, idoneus fiat;[1]

quod ubicunque spiritus ille nitrosus intra terram cohibetur, ibi nitri mineralis copia brevi concrescit;[2]

Spiritius hic, ut in terrâ primitus nidulatur, ita exinde in ambientem aerem et aquam sublimatur, et vicissim per aerem aquæ et per utrumque terræ communicatur: atque in circulatione quâdam per omnia diffunditur . . . illum nitrosum appello, non solùm quia, instar nitri . . . sed etiam quia substantiam habet nitro minerali valdè affinem, et tantundem ferè discrepantem, quantùm sal fixum differt à volatili;[3]

Ex his facile constat, quod dixi, spiritum quendam nitrosum, terram, aquam, et aerem permeare: Quid tamen hic ad vitam conducat, restat proxime decendunc;[4]

excluso sc. spiritu hoc nitroso qui ex aere in aquam se insinuare;[5]

spiritus hic nitrosus qui respirationis pabulum est . . . sicut flamma quæ in ellychnio est, nutritio halitu privata, ne momento quidem ardet;[6]

ille spiritus nitrosus qui in nive est, per delicatulorum pocula transit, ut æstiva vina refrigeret: Quòd si vitrum aut metallum spiritui huic non sint impervia; certè laxiaris pulmonis vasa quantò minus?[7]

The idea of a 'nitrous spirit' was probably floating in the Oxford air from the time of Bathurst's lectures, and Lower and Mayow were probably both familiar with it. About the same time Willis, in Oxford, was developing similar ideas (see p. 307). Patterson[8] is certainly in error in giving Lower the sole credit for it.

Walter Charleton[9] refers to fermentation in the stomach by the gastric juice,[10] and to the flame and fermentation in the blood, which he says was first mentioned by Ent.[11] He deals with respiration,[12] and the *Biolychnii flammentae*,[13] saying:[14] inspirari aërem, ad sanguinis subtilitationem, spirituum vitalium ignescentiam flammæque vitalis sufflamen. The motion of the muscles[15] is explained on mechanical principles only.

A book on 'the lamp of life and death' by Johann Ernst Burggrav (or Burggrave), born in Neustadt in the Palatinate, who practised medicine in Simmern and translated Drebbel (see p. 322), is medical and contains superstitious material on lamps burning human blood.[16] Burggrav also wrote alchemical works[17] and is often quoted by other authors, e.g. Boyle.[18]

Nathaniel Hodges (1630–88), who studied in Oxford and is famous for his work as a physician in the Great Plague of London,[19] in his book on the plague[20] speaks of nitrous particles in the air or a nitro-aerial spirit, raised from

---

[1] Bathurst, 1761, 184.   [2] *Ib.*, 186.   [3] *Ib.*, 185–6.   [4] *Ib.*, 188.
[5] *Ib.*, 199–200.   [6] *Ib.*, 203–5.   [7] *Ib.*, 209.   [8] *Isis*, 1931, xv, 81–2.
[9] *Oeconomia animalis, Novis in Medicina Hypothesibus superstructura & Mechanicè explicata*, 4 ed., London, 1669; pref. dated 1659, dedic. to Ent dated 1658.
[10] *Ib.*, 18–19.   [11] *Ib.*, 92, 95.   [12] *Ib.*, 173 f., 182 f.
[13] *Ib.*, 189 f.   [14] *Ib.*, 191.   [15] *Ib.*, 248 f.
[16] Jöcher, i, 1494; Thorndike, vii, 183; viii, 391, 413–14; *Speculum*, 1953, xxviii, 692; Burggrav, *Biolychnium seu Lucerna, cum vita ejus, cui accensa est Mysticæ*, 8°, Leyden, 1610; Franckeræ, 1611; Frankfurt, 1629, 1620; *Lampadem vitæ & mortis, omniumque graviorum . . . παθῶν indicem; hoc est Biolychnium sive Lucernam*, 12°, Leyden, 1678 (CUL U*. 8 161³ (G)).
[17] Ferguson, i, 131.   [18] *Works*, 1744, iv, 200.
[19] D. Guthrie, *A History of Medicine*, London, 1945, 207.
[20] Λοιμολογία *sive pestis nuperæ apud Populum Londinensem Grassantis*, London, 1671, 1672, 2 ed. 1720, 3 ed. 1721 (all in BM).

the interior of the earth, and impaired by rain and winds, is inimical to the balsam of Nature and is the cause of disease:[1]

spiritus nitroaerus; nec non salici eorundem insinuatione; Aerem verò spiritibus admodùm vitalibus conditum ... Ab iisdem insuper spiritibus nitroaeris modo illibatis, sanguinis, succorumque statum optimum ... ab eodem nitro, vigorem, & integram mutari sanitatem, conjecturâ augurari, quid herclè absurditatis?

neque insuper meâ duntaxit opinione nixus assero huic Spiritui coccineum colorem acceptum referre sanguinem.

An anonymous work on fevers[2] attributed to Hodges, deals with fermentation,[3] terrestrial nitre,[4] solar sulphur, and a 'Nitrous Pabulum' in the air;[5] the 'Elastick Niter' in the air favours the movement of the blood by its elasticity, not by its fermentation:

'the attracted, and El⌐stick Niter being on their conjunction [with solar sulphur] so expanded, that from thence the Circulating Blood acquires that activity that facilitates its passage ... and the free motion of the inspired Air communicating it self to its own fuliginous vapours.'[6]

Sir Thomas Browne, who knew Mayow's book on respiration and rickets of 1668, but not, apparently, that of 1674 (see p. 583), said[7] the air in respiration 'serves to preserve the vital flame from extinction by ventilation'; and 'the air so entreth the lungs that by its nitrous spirit doth affect the heart, and several ways qualifie the blood, and though it be also admitted into other parts, even by the meat we chew, yet that it affordeth a proper nourishment alone, is not easily made out'.[8] In a letter (1690) Browne says he 'was put in hope of advantage by change of air, and imbibing the pure aerial nitre of these parts'.[9]

[1] 1671, 45–6, 50–8.   [2] Πυρετολογια, or a History of Feavers, London, 1674 (BM).
[3] Ib., 33.   [4] Ib., 28, 38.   [5] Ib., 41.   [6] Ib., 40.
[7] The Letters of Sir Thomas Browne, ed. Keynes, 1941, 42, 45.
[8] Pseudodoxia Epidemica, 6 ed., 1672, bk. iii, ch. 21, p. 175 (the passage is not in the 5 ed., 1668–9, or earlier ones); Works, ed. Sayle, 1927, ii, 55; later in the section Browne refers to 'Libavius tom. 4 Chym'. On Browne's theories of respiration and combustion see E. S. Merton, Osiris, 1952, x, 206–23.
[9] Works, ed. Sayle, 1927, iii, 371.

CHAPTER XVI

MAYOW

John Mayow (Morval, nr. Looe, Cornwall, baptised 21 December 1641–London, buried 18 October 1679) was born in the Manor House of Brae, Morval.[1] He matriculated (as John Mayouwe) on 2 July 1658 at Wadham College, Oxford, and was admitted scholar on 23 September 1659. In 1660, on the recommendation of Henry Coventry, he was elected a fellow of All Souls College. He studied law, becoming B.C.L. in May 1665 and D.C.L. in July 1670.[2] Wood says he 'studied physic and became noted for his practice

FIG. 25. JOHN MAYOW, 1641–1679.

therein, especially in the summer time in the city of Bath', and that in 1670 'he was now, and after, a profess'd physician'. Mayow's degree was D.C.L. (the Ll.D. was abolished in 1535, although Mayow is described as 'Ll.D. &

[1] R. B. Gardiner, *The Registers of Wadham College Oxford*, London, 1889, 224; J. Foster, *Alumni Oxoniensis*, Oxford, 1892, iii, 997; Anthony à Wood, *Athenæ Oxoniensis*, ed. Bliss, London, 1817, iii, 1119; *id.*, *Fasti Oxoniensis*, ed. Bliss, London, 1820, ii, 281, 320 (b. London, 1645); Hartog, DNB, 1894, xxxvi, 175 (b. London, 1643); *ib.*, 1909, xiii, 175 (b. 1640); McKie, *Nature*, 1941, cxlviii, 728; *id.*, *Phil. Mag.*, 1942, xxxiii, 51; Partington, *Isis*, 1956, xlvii, 217.

[2] Richard Peers, *A Catalogue of all Graduates in Divinity, Law, and Physick: . . . who have regularly Proceeded or been Created, in the University of Oxford*, Oxford, 1689, 100.

'Medici' on the t.p. of his 1674 book) and I can find no record of his having taken a degree in medicine. Although T. Thomson[1] gives 'John Mayow, M.D.', the register of the Royal Society has 'John Mayow, D.', i.e. doctor simply. It has been assumed (e.g. by Dixon) that he studied under Willis and came in contact with Willis's assistant Lower (who came from the same part of Cornwall), who left Oxford in 1666. Mayow mentions Willis several times in his book but always critically (once at least very severely, see p. 603) and it is possible that Mayow really studied under (Sir) Thomas Millington (Newbury, Berks., 1628–London, 1704; Trinity College, Cambridge, A.B. 1649, M.A. 1657), who went to Oxford in 1659, was a fellow of All Souls College, and in 1675 followed Willis (1660) as Sedleian Professor of Natural Philosophy, but practised medicine in London; he was knighted in 1680.[2]

Mayow in 1674 refers to Dr. Thomas Millington as having 'not long since' given him details of a case which Mayow himself confirmed, of 'a young man of good position'.[3]

Mayow became F.R.S. in 1678 on Hooke's proposal (proposed 7 February 1678, elected 30 November 1678, 27 votes, one negative) but he does not seem to have been formally admitted.[4]

Hooke[5] reports meeting 'Dr. Mayow' in coffee-houses in London (not at Boyle's house or at the Royal Society) in October–December, 1674, February 1675, and November 1677; in an entry of 8 November 1679[6] he says: 'Mayow Dead a month since.' Wood says he died in September (?) 1679 in 'an apothecary's house bearing the sign of the Anchor, in York Street, Covent Garden (having a little before been married, not altogether to his content) and was buried in the Church of St. Paul in Covent Garden'. The register of burials of St. Paul's, Covent Garden, has 'John Mayo: Docter of Phisick. In the Church', on 10 October 1679.

His death at an early age suggests that, soon after his book was published in 1674, he became ill, since otherwise, as Foster[7] says, we should expect to have heard something from him in the five years he had still to live. He may, however, have had no time or opportunity for doing any more research; we do not know. The entries in Hooke's diary suggest that Mayow did not move in Royal Society circles and did not visit Boyle; Hooke frequently called on and had meals with Boyle.

Gunther[8] thinks Mayow carried out his experimental work in All Souls College, Oxford. Dixon[9] says: 'the ideas, the names, proposed by Hooke and Mayow are so exactly similar that it is impossible to imagine that the work was done independently'; he thought that Hooke and Mayow 'worked together under Boyle between 1660 and 1662' and 'in Boyle's laboratory they saw and assisted in the experiments which led them jointly to their theory', Hooke

[1] (3), 1812, Append. IV, xxvii.
[2] Boulger, DNB, 1894, xxxvii, 442, says he took part in meetings with Boyle, etc., leading to the foundation of the Royal Society, but Millington was never F.R.S.
[3] Mayow, *De Motu musculari*, 1674, 96; ACR, xvii, 295.
[4] Birch, (1), iii, 384, 442; Gunther, (1), 1930, vii, 501.
[5] *The Diary of Robert Hooke*, ed. H. W. Robinson and W. Adams, 1935, 128, 130, 133, 135, 146, 219, 325.
[6] *Ib.*, 430.   [7] 1901, 199.   [8] (1), 1923, i, 31 f.   [9] *B.A. Report*, 1894, 594 f.

publishing his hypothesis in London in 1665 without experiments, whilst 'Mayow in Oxford systematically worked through the experiments on which he based his conclusions'. Hooke's experiments were probably made in London in 1664–5; the use of an air-pump by Mayow (see p. 604) may indicate that he had the use of the one in Boyle's laboratory.

Boyle left Oxford for London in 1668, and since Mayow's experiments seem to have been made after that date they were probably not made in Boyle's laboratory in Oxford. Mayow began his medical practice in London and Bath in 1670, and it is possible that the experiments were made in All Souls College in 1669–70, or after 1670 in London; we do not really know where or when they were made, but since the experiments are not described in his first publication of 1668 they were very probably made between 1670 and 1673.[1]

[1] A. and C. R. Aikin, *A Dictionary of Chemistry and Mineralogy*, London, 1807, i, 120; W. M. Bayliss, *Principles of General Physiology*, 1915, 606; T. Beddoes, *Chemical Experiments and Opinions. Extracted from a Work published in the last century*, Oxford, 1790; J. F. Blumenbach, *Institvtiones Physiologicae*, Göttingen, 1787, § 145, p. 114 (Magna iam pars memorabilium horum phaenomenorum quibus nuperis lustris et physica de aëribus factitiis disciplina et physiologia negotii respirationis tam egregie ditata et illustrata est, iam ante centum et quod excurrit annos innotuit acutissimi ingenii medico Jo. Mayow, cuius *de sal-nitro et spiritu nitro-aëreo* (quod nempe nomine dephlogisticatum aërem insigniuit) tractatus Oxon. 1674. 8. editum magna cum voluptate legi et relegi); in *The Institutions of Physiology*, tr. J. Elliotson, London, 1817, § 150, p. 79, the passage is replaced by a reference to A. N. Scherer (see below).
H. Boruttau, Versuch einer kritischen Geschichte der Atmungs-theorien, in *A. Med.*, 1909, ii, 301–50 (326–33) (based on Foster); J. Bostock, *An Essay on Respiration*, Liverpool, 1804, 71, 194–5, 198, 200 (far excelling any of his contemporaries, and at least equal to any chemist before the time of Scheele and Priestley); W. T. Brande, *Manual of Chemistry*, 6 ed., London, 1848, I, xxxiii–viii; A. Crum Brown, *Edinburgh Med. J.*, 1899, vi, 116–29 (points out some of Mayow's weaknesses); *id.*, pref. to ACR no. 17; J. C. Brown, *History of Chemistry*, 1913, 443 (Mayow and Lower); W. Brownrigg, *Phil. Trans.*, 1765, lv, 218 (232); abdg. ed., 1809, xii, 243; L. C. Cadet, tr. of Juncker, *Élémens de Chymie*, Paris, 1757, iii, 386 (Mayow's book 'très rare'); J. F. Cartheuser, *Dissertationes Physico-Chymico-Medicæ*, Frankfurt on the Oder, 1775, 296 (dissertation by Wolff, 1772, mentions Mayow's book (1674) *De Respiratione*); T. Cavallo, *A Treatise on the Nature and Properties of Air and other Permanently Elastic Fluids*, 4°, London, 1781, 42, 402; J. B. Cohen, *Chemical World*, 1914, iii, 247; T. Cooper, in *Memoirs of Dr. Joseph Priestley*, London, 1805, 226 f., 246 (Haller did not understand Mayow, who clearly states the combination of oxygen with the blood in respiration, the theory of animal heat of Crawford, on muscular stimulus of Goodwyn, and the succedaneum for respiration in the fœtus by Beddoes); L. Crell, *Ann.*, 1793, ii, 269–72; G. Cuvier, *Histoire des Progrès des Sciences Naturelles*, Brussels, 1837, i, 30; H. Davy, *Elements of Chemical Philosophy*, 1812, 26–7 (Mayow's experiments 'original', but his hypotheses vague); J. C. Delametherie, *Obs. Phys.*, 1790, xxxvii, 154–6; H. B. Dixon, *B.A. Rep.*, 1894, 594; A. Findlay, *The Spirit of Chemistry*, 1930, 140; Sir M. Foster, 1901, 187, 196, 198 (Mayow more of a chemist than Hooke, Lower, or even Boyle; Foster wrote art. 'Respiration' in H. Watts, *Dictionary of Chemistry*, London, 1874, v, 82–97); A. F. de Fourcroy, *Ency. Méthod., Chimie*, 1796, iii, 390–400; repr. in *Ann. Chim.*, 1799, xxix, 42–90 (Considerations sur les Expériences de Mayow, faites à la fin du 17ᵉ siècle, extraites du Dictionnaire encyclopédique); J. F. Fulton, *A Bibliography of Two Oxford Physiologists. Richard Lower and John Mayow*, Oxford Bibliographical Society Proceedings and Papers, 1934–5 (1936), iv, 1–62 (leans too heavily on Patterson; to some extent corrected in *id.*, *Aviation Medicine in its Preventive Aspects*, Heath Clark Lectures, University of London, 1947, London, 1948, 7–9, 22–3); A. Gamgee, *Text-Book of the Physiological Chemistry of the Animal Body*, London, 1880, i, 407–9 (Mayow's views on muscular contraction); J. F. Gmelin, (1), 1798, ii, 112; F. Gotch, *Two Oxford Physiologists, Richard Lower* (1631–91) *and John Mayow* (1643–79), Oxford, 1908 (40 pp.); H. Guerlac, *Actes du 7ᵉ Congrès Internat. d'Histoire des Sciences*, Jerusalem, 1953, 332–49; *id.*, *Isis*, 1954, xlv, 243; R. T. Gunther, (1), 1923, i, 31 f., 196; 1926, iii, 136 f.; W. V. Harcourt, *Phil. Mag.*, 1846, xxviii, 495 f., 503 f. (Mayow 'made more of a few facts than the greater part of the next generation did of many', *ib.*, 505); A. von Haller, *Bibliotheca Anatomica*, 4°, Zürich, 1774, i, 560 (Juventis, ut ex pictura videtur, vir ingeniosus neque mathematum ignarus, cæterum in hypotheses pronior, quod fere ejus ætatis vitium fuit); P. J. Hartog, DNB, 1894, xxxvi, 175; 1909, xiii, 175 (Mayow had the genius to perceive exactly the problems which must be solved before any great advance in chemistry or physiology could be made, and to guess at and partly to discover their solution); F. Hoefer, (1), ii, 252–63; (2), ii, 260–70 (the *Tractatus Quinque* 'sans contredit l'un des plus remarquables du dix-septième

Mayow's first publication was of two tracts, one on respiration and one on rickets, which appeared at Oxford in 1668:

I. Tractatvs Dvo Quorum prior agit De Respiratione: Alter De Rachitide. A Joh: Mayow, Coll: Omn: An: Socio. Oxon 1668 (Roy. Coll. Surgeons Library, London, and University College Library, London); reissued with new t.p., Oxon, 1669 (Bodleian; CUL, 2 copies, one with inscription 'ē ex' on t.p., both with folding plates); Leyden, 1671 and 1708, all 8°, two engraved copperplates; sep. t.p. of De Rachititide dated 1668: Tractatvs Secundus. De Rachitide. A Joh: Mayow, Oxon. Coll: Omn: An: Soc. Oxon: 1668, but the pagination (1–61, 65–108) of the two tracts is continuous; original price bound, 1s; De Respirationis tr. (for private circulation), 'the work of several hands', ed. Dobbin, Edinburgh, 1946, 24 pp., 1 plate.

A revised issue of the two tracts, with three new tracts, making five in all, appeared in 1674:

-----

siècle'; Mayow cultivated science 'avec un esprit indépendant et avec une supériorité incontestable'); J. Ingen Housz, *Miscellanea physico-medica*, Vienna, 1795, 145 etc.; R. Jagnaux, 1891, i, 105–11; A. Jörgensen, Die Entdeckung des Sauerstoffes, in *Samml. chem.-u. chem. techn. Vorträge*, ed. Herz, 1909, xiv, 111–72 (dates *Tract. Quinque* 1669); K. in NBG, 1860, xxxiv, 555–6; J. Keir, *A Treatise on the Various Kinds of Permanently Elastic Fluids, or Gases*, 2 ed., London, 1779, 9 (q. Mayow, probably from Hales, that air is diminished $\frac{1}{30}$th by combustion); H. Kopp, (1), 1844, ii, 294, 347; 1845, iii, 14, 15, 131, 134–5, 171, 173, 181, 186, 191–9, 206, 214, 224–5, 230–2, 244, 260, 309–10; 1847, iv, 22, 148, 290 (good summary of *Tractatus Quinque*, erroneously dated 1669 throughout; probably based on Scherer).

Richard Lubbock, *Medical and Physical Journal, containing the Earliest Information on the Subjects of Medicine, Surgery, Pharmacy, Chemistry, and Natural History*, ed. Bradley and Willich, London, 1799–1820; 1799, i, 220, 417 (German ed., *Physisch-Medizinisches Journal*, Leipzig, 1800, quoted by Speter, 1910, 205, etc.: Mayow was 'the Kepler, perhaps the Newton of chemical science'; Mayow's chemical opinions were neglected on account of the rise of Stahl's phlogiston theory; Thruston's dissertation very generally known before its publication — Ent criticised it in 1670).

D. McKie, *Ambix*, 1938, i, 162; *Nature*, 1941, cxlviii, 728; *Phil. Mag.*, 1942, xxxiii, 51; in Singer, (1), 1953, i, 469; S. L. Mitchill (New York), *Med. and Phys. J.*, 1799, i, 298 (letter to Haworth; Mayow unknown to Franklin in relation to water-spouts, to Scheele in relation to fire air, and to Girtanner in relation to muscular action); J. J. Manget, *Bibliotheca Scriptorum Medicorum*, 2 vols. f°, Geneva, 1731, II, i, 283 (*Tract. Quinque* dated 1669); J. W. Mellor, *Treatise on Inorganic and Theoretical Chemistry*, 1922, i, 62 (concisely anticipating Patterson); E. von Meyer, in *Kultur der Gegenwart*, Theil III, Abteil. ii, Bd. 2, 1913, 5; *id.*, *History of Chemistry*, 1906, 113, 137, 142, 173 (Mayow came pretty near the right interpretation of respiration, combustion, and calcination; he surmised that oxygen is present in saltpetre); F. J. Moore, *A History of Chemistry*, 3 ed. (prepared by Prof. W. T. Hall), New York and London, 1939, 48; *Neues allgemeines Journal der Chemie* (Gehlen), 1804, iii (portrait of Mayow); W. Nicholson, Art. 'Air' in *A Dictionary of Chemistry*, 1795, i, 79–80; H. C. Oersted, *Observations on the History of Chemistry*, (1807), tr. in *The Soul in Nature*, 1852, 300–24 (319); W. Ogle, *Aristotle on Youth & Old Age, Life & Death and Respiration*, 1897, 19, 23, 48, 54, 56–7 (q. 1669 and 1674 eds. of Mayow); S. Parkes, *Chemical Catechism*, 5 ed., London, 1812, 353 (the 'undecompounded nature' of metals first suspected by Mayow); J. R. Partington, *Text-Book of Inorganic Chemistry*, London, 1921, 37–8 (and later eds.); *Nature*, 1954, clxxiv, 291; *Isis*, 1956, xlvii, 217, 405; 1959, l, 211; T. S. Patterson, *Isis*, 1931, xv, 47, 504 (crit. by Partington); R. Plot, *Natural History of Oxfordshire*, 1677; Oxford, 1705, 310 (brief summary of the *Tractatus Quinque*, published in Mayow's lifetime; in full in Patterson, 534); J. C. Poggendorff, (1), 1863, ii, 95 (*Tract. quinque* 1669); W. Ramsay, *Gases of the Atmosphere*, 4 ed., 1915, vii, 16; G. F. Rodwell, *Chem. News*, 1865, xiv, 51; *id.*, *The Birth of Chemistry*, London, 1874, 117 f. (portr.); J. Robison, in Black, *Lectures on the Elements of Chemistry*, Edinburgh, 1803, i, 536 (unfavourable).

A. N. Scherer, *Grundzüge der neuern chemischen Theorie*, Jena, 1795, 299 f. (bibl., giving *Tractatus quinque* as 1669); *id.*, *Eudiometria sive methodus aeris atmospherici puritatem examinandi*, Vienna, 1782, 5 (not seen); *id.*, *Geschichte der Luftgüteprüfungslehre*, Vienna, 1785, i, 3; ii, 147 (not seen); *id.*, *Allgem. Journ. der Chemie*, 1798, i, Heft 2, Intelligenz-blatt Nr. 1, p. 5; 1803, x, 571; *id.*, *Beweis, dass Johann Mayow vor hundert Jahren den Grund zur antiphlogistischen Chemie und Physiologie gelegt hat*, Vienna, 1793, pp. 188, 1 errata; medallion portr. of Mayow on t.p., tr. of Mayow with original Latin below, pp. 1–123; notes, 124–88; Lower is copiously quoted, full Latin text, pp. 161–6; Scherer used the 1681 Hague ed. of the *Tractatus Quinque*

II. Tractatus Quinque Medico-Physici. Quorum primus agit de Sal-Nitro, et Spiritu Nitro-Aereo. Secundus de Respiratione. Tertius de Respiratione Foetus in Utero, et Ovo. Quartus de Motu Musculari, et Spiritibus Animalibus. Ultimus de Rhachitide. Studio Joh. Mayow Ll.D. & Medici: Necnon Coll. Omn. Anim. in Univ. Oxon. Socii. Oxonii, e Theatro Sheldoniano. An Dom. M.DC.LXXIV. 8°. Reverse of t.p.: Imprimatur. Petrvs Bathon, & Wellen. Episc. Vice-Cancellarius. Oxon. Jul. 17. 1673. Dedication to Henry Coventry (pp. iii–vii); Blank; Portrait of Mayow (unsigned); ix–x, Authori In ejus quinque Tractatus Carmen, signed C.T. Coll. Omn. An. Soc.; Elenchus Rerum Pars. I. xi–xxx; Elenchus Rerum Pars II. xxxi–xxxix, xl blank, pp. 1–335 (v blank).

Pars II has two t.ps.:

(1) Tractatus Quartus. De Motu Musculari Et Spiritibus Animalibus. Obiter De Motu Cerebri: Nec Non De Usu Lienis & Pancreatis. Pars Secunda. Pp. 1 (t.p.), 2 blank, 3–106;

(2) Sep. t.p. (p. 107): Tractatus Quintus De Rachitide. Cui Methodus medendi annectitur. Secunda Editio. P. 108 blank, pp. 109–52.

---

and says, p. viii: 'Die erste Ausgabe zu Oxford von 1674. konnte ich, aller Mühe ungeachtet, nicht eigen erhalten'; mentions *Tractatus duo*, 1668; says Mayow confused oxygen with heat or fire. Speter, 1910, 177 says Scherer in his *Eudiometria* mentioned Mayow as the discoverer of nitrous gas (NO) (it was really first prepared by Boyle) but did not understand his text. For a letter from Scherer to Yeats, see Yeats, 1798, 402–3.

M. Speter, Lavoisier und seine Vorläufer, in *Sammlung chem. und chem.-techn. Vorträge*, ed. Herz, Stuttgart, 1910, xv, 109–218, see especially 204–16; a 'separate' with a different pagination appeared; *id., Chem. Ztg.*, 1910, xxxiv, 946, 953, 962 (Lavoisier borrowed from Mayow, and since we now know that Lavoisier had a copy of the *Tractatus Quinque* this view cannot be waved aside); Sprengel, (2), iv, 137–8; W. Stirling, *Some Apostles of Physiology. Being an Account of their Lives and Labours*, sm. f°, London, 1902 (privately printed, 32 plates, pp. iv, 129), 44 (confuses 1668 and 1674 books; many good portraits).

Jonathan Stokes, *Dissertatio Inaugurales, De Aere Dephlogisticato*, Edinburgh, 1782, 11, 28, 31, 34, 38: says the increase in weight of metals on calcination was first demonstrated by Rey and Mayow; used *spiritus nitro-aereus* as a synonym for oxygen; *id., Med. and Phys. J.*, 1800, iii, 335: he had then read Mayow and had changed his mind; criticised Yeats (see below), quoting the *Tractatus Quinque*; goes over a good deal of ground covered by Patterson, who does not mention Stokes; Mayow's theory of acids does not imply a combination with oxygen; Mayow's views on light show that *spiritus nitro-aereus* is more like caloric than oxygen; in Mayow's account of respiration, 'how he gets rid of the remaining particles of air I do not know'; Lower, adopting the opinions and language of Bathurst, deposited it in the solids and finally carried it off from the pores.

T. Thomson, (3), 1812, 467 (Mayow's essay 'contains some happy experiments on respiration and air, and some fortunate conjectures respecting the combustion of the metals; but the most valuable part of the whole, is the chapter on affinities'); *id.*, (1), ii, 98 (Mayow 'proved by actual experiment that air was absorbed during combustion and altered during respiration . . . It would be wrong . . . to deprive Mayow of the reputation to which he is entitled for his ingeniously-contrived and well executed experiments'.); *id., Ency. Brit. Suppl.*, Edinburgh, 1801, II, i, 180; *id.*, (2), 1802, i, 18; *ib.*, 1817, i, 135 (method of obtaining and confining air invented by Mayow), 81 (Mayow 'ascribed the increase in weight to the combination of metals with oxygen', quoting the antimony experiment from *Tract. Quinq.*, pp. 28, 29), 347 (Hooke's theory adopted by Mayow; from Robison); *id.*, (6), 1843, 606–7 ('My copy of Mayow is the second edition, printed (I believe, for the title-page is wanting) in 1674', the 'first editon' was published in 1668).

L. Thorndike, viii, 423–9 (Mayow a 'path-finder, not a road-builder'; he erected a sign-post pointing to the discovery of oxygen); C. E. Weigel, *Beiträge zur Geschichte der Luftarten in Auszugen als ein Nachtrag zu dem historischen kurzen Begriffe elastischer Ausflüsse* in *Herrn Lavoisiers physikalische chemischen Schriften*, Greifswald, 1784, I, i, 12 f. (q. by Speter, 212; I have not seen it); G. D. Yeats (of Bedford), *Observations on the Claims of the Moderns, to Some Discoveries in Chemistry and Physiology*, London, 1798, with fine portrait of Mayow; quotes original texts of Mayow, Lower, and Thruston; finds traces of Mayow's views in Hippokrates, Vergil, etc. (as did Lippmann, *Z. angew. Chem.*, 1933, xlvi, 351); the book is dedicated to Dr. Mayo, Dr. Vaughn, and Dr. P. Mayo, physicians to the Middlesex Hospital; an anonymous review of Yeats's book in *The British Critic*, 1798, xii, 345–8, says that Mayow described 'many well-imagined experiments and real discoveries. But . . . a considerable proportion of the chimerical notions of his times' can be found in his book, examples are given; Yeats, *Med. and Phys. Journ.*, 1799, i, 326; 1799, ii, 98 (reply to Stokes, *op. cit.*; says there is still a Mayow family in Cornwall).

Six plates (Tab. 1–Tab. 5; in some copies bound with blank portions and folding, in some copies cut and bound without margins). Original price 5s. bound. Madan, Oxford Books, 1931, iii, 298, 493.

The quotations in the refs. are to this edition, with misprints corrected from IIA. Capital letters and italics are usually disregarded. The two parts are denoted by II (pp. 1–335) and II, ii (pp. 1–152).

IIA. Johannis Mayow Londinensis Doctoris & Medici, nec non Coll. Omn. Anim. in Universitate Oxoniensi Socii, Opera Omnia Medico-Physica, Tractatibus quinque comprehensa. Quorum Catalogum Pagina post Epistolam Dedicatoriam exhibet. Editio novissima, Figuris æneis adornata. Hagæ-Comitum, Apud Arnoldum Leers, 8°, 1681 (iv ll., portr., 416 pp., xii ll. contents; 7 plates; some misprints in II corrected). Parts reprinted in Manget, Bibliotheca Anatomica, Geneva, 1685, ii, 224–31 (De respiratione), 231–36 (De resp. in fœt.), 564–83 (De motu musc. et spirit. animal.) with part of Thruston's book (p. 571) (166–85), and Ent's Diatribe (p. 573) (186–223).

IIB. Dutch tr. by Steven Blankaart (author of Lexicon Novum Medicum): Medicinale en Natuurkundige Werken, van Johannes Mayow, Doctor en Medicyn, 8°, Amsterdam, 1683, 1684 (neither seen).

IIC. German tr. with introd. (by Scherer), made by J. Koellner: Johann Mayow's chemisch physiologische Schriften. Aus dem Lateinischen [1674 ed.] übersetzt . . . Nebst einer Vorrede von D. Alex. Nicol Scherer, Jena, 1799; complete text, 6 plates (the figures rearranged).

IID. Partial German tr. with notes by F. G. Donnan, in Ostwald's Klassiker, 1901, No. 125.

IIE. Partial French tr. (first chapter almost in full, rest summarised) Traduction des œuvres chimiques et physiologiques de Jean Mayow, Doct.-Med. de Londres (sic) par L. Ledru and H. C. Gaubert, Paris, 1840 (not seen).

IIF. English tr. (complete) by A. Crum Brown and L. Dobbin, Alembic Club Reprint No. 17, Edinburgh, 1907; reissued, Chicago, 1908, and (by Gunther), Oxford, 1926 (Old Ashmolean Reprints No. V: this seems to be made up of the sheets of the Alembic Club Reprint); this translation is fair but is not always accurate.

It will be noticed from the remarks in the references in the footnote on pp. 579–81 that many writers have confused the two works, I of 1668 or 1669 and II of 1674, which were apparently rare on the Continent. The second (1674) was mostly quoted from the edition IIA (1681) and it was then assumed that the date of the original was 1669. Kopp, who quotes II many times carefully and accurately, seems to have used the German translation IIC but he always gives the incorrect date 1669 and this led him to attribute to Mayow some things which are contained in an earlier work of Willis, III, p. 305, of 1670, which he dates 1671. Since he did not correct the date 1669 in his Beiträge (1875) the error passed into some modern works. Kopp also gave the date 1675 to material from Lemery's Cours de Chymie, although much of it is from later editions and is not found in that of 1675; and similarly in other cases.

The correct date for II had been given before Kopp wrote by Blumenbach, Yeats, Lubbock and others, and I and II were clearly distinguished by Ogle before Patterson. The literature quoted on pp. 613–31, which otherwise has an interest of its own, is little known; it shows that a lively and sustained interest was taken in Mayow's writings and corrects an opinion that these soon fell into oblivion. It also shows that Boyle's failure to mention Mayow was an isolated idiosyncrasy rather than typical of the general attitude of the time. Mayow's two books were widely read and quoted both by contemporary and by later writers.

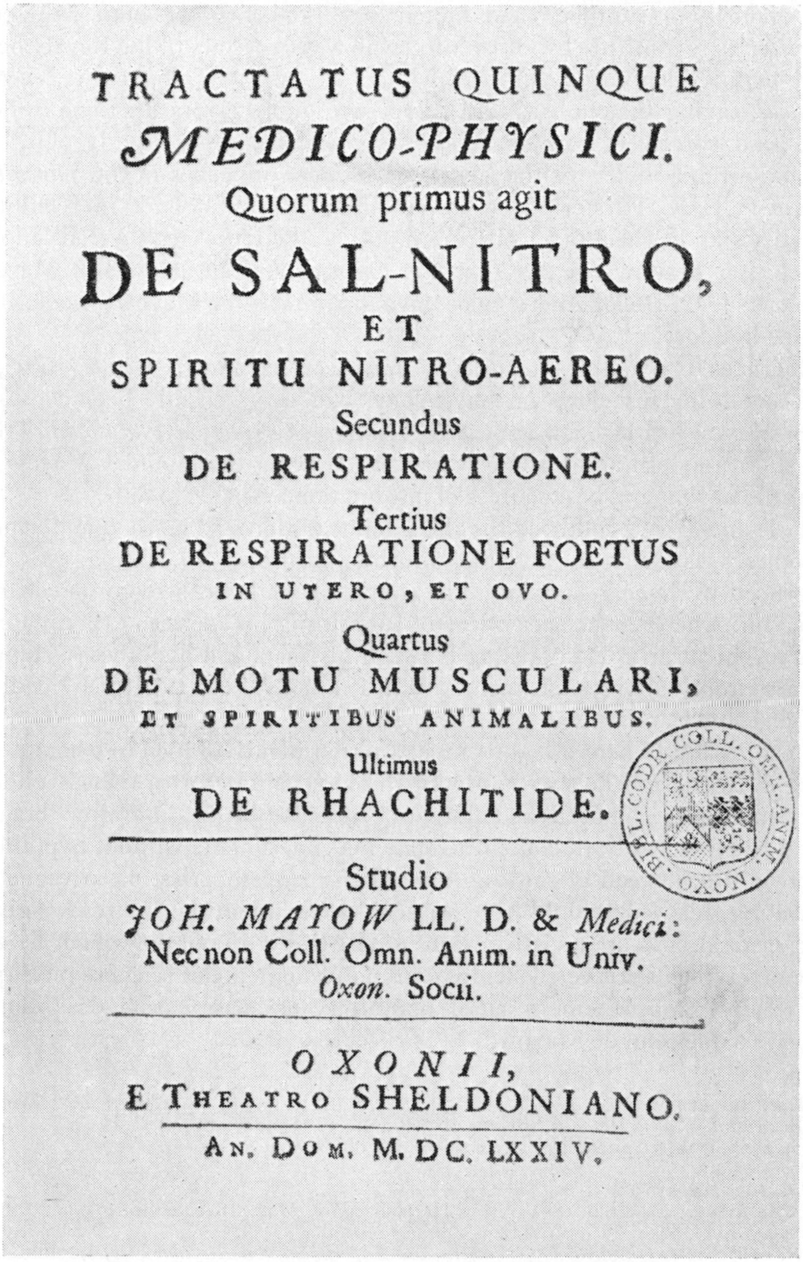

TRACTATUS QUINQUE
MEDICO-PHYSICI.
Quorum primus agit
DE SAL-NITRO,
ET
SPIRITU NITRO-AEREO.
Secundus
DE RESPIRATIONE.
Tertius
DE RESPIRATIONE FOETUS
IN UTERO, ET OVO.
Quartus
DE MOTU MUSCULARI,
ET SPIRITIBUS ANIMALIBUS.
Ultimus
DE RHACHITIDE.

Studio
JOH. MAYOW LL. D. & *Medici:*
Necnon Coll. Omn. Anim. in Univ.
Oxon. Socii.

OXONII,
E THEATRO SHELDONIANO.
AN. DOM. M.DC.LXXIV.

FIG. 26. TITLE-PAGE OF MAYOW'S *Tractatus Quinque* (1674).
(From the copy presented by Mayow to All Souls College, Oxford. By permission of All Souls College.)

Anonymous reviews of both books in the *Philosophical Transactions*[1] are fair but colourless. Gunther,[2] and Gotch[3] say that they are both by Hooke; Patterson[4] says both are by Oldenburg, who was Secretary of the Royal Society until 1677. Oldenburg wrote to Boyle on 10 July 1674 about the *Tractatus Quinque*, saying that he was told there were 'more errors than one in every page', and 'some very learned and knowing men speak very slightly' of it.[5]

A favourable review of the *Tractatus Quinque* appeared in the *Journal des Sçavans*.[6] J. R. Forster[7] drew attention to Mayow's work in relation to Priestley's and Scheele's as 'obscure hints'. T. Beddoes[8] gave a translation of the chapter headings in the *Tractatus Quinque* and an analysis of Mayow's opinions. J. C. Delametherie[9] also gave a summary of Mayow's book, mentioning Beddoes.

Descartes' two important works, *L'Homme* (1662) and *Le Monde* (1664), the first containing his views on physiology, had very recently been published when Mayow's first book appeared; Descartes' *Principia Philosophia* (1644) was still a modern and leading work. In following these guides Mayow was using the newest and best sources of information available to him.

Boyle and Hooke followed the Baconian tradition and method and avoided hypotheses as much as possible, Mayow, according to Hartog, was most influenced by Descartes, who is the source of his hypotheses on mechanical lines; 'but whenever he sees a way of submitting his ideas to experiment, he does so;' he clearly distinguishes between his facts and hypotheses, standing 'immeasurably above such men as Willis and Sylvius, with their medly of half-digested Cartesianism and iatrochemistry.'

Steno[10] said: 'There abounds indeed a rich plenty of men to whom everything is clear', and he was no doubt thinking of Descartes (whose philosophical merit he recognised) and his followers, and of Willis. Fourcroy[11] believed that if Mayow had been content to state his experiments without hypotheses, as Boyle did, instead of putting forward so many theories, often vague and vacillating, his book would have attracted more attention. Fourcroy[12] gives a long, critical, and appreciative analysis of Mayow's book, of which he says: 'Aucun ouvrage, écrit vers le temps du renouvellement des sciences physiques, n'offre des rapprochemens aussi nombreux et aussi exacts des opinions modernes que celui de Mayow.'

---

[1] *Tractatus duo* in *Phil. Trans.*, 1668, iii, 833, no. 41; abdgd. ed. 1809, i, 295; *Tractatus quinque* in *Phil. Trans.*, 1674, ix, 101, no. 105; abdgd. ed. 1809, ii, 142–8.
[2] (1), 1923, i, 31, 33; 1926, iii, 138.
[3] 1908, 35.
[4] *Isis*, 1931, xv, 47 (90).
[5] Boyle, *Works*, ed. Birch, 1744, v, 395; Harcourt, *Phil. Mag.*, 1846, xxviii, 495–6.
[6] 1676, 3 Feb., 30–4, fig. 3 on Mayow's plate 5 reprod.
[7] Tr. of Scheele, *Chemical Observations and Experiments on Air and Fire*, London, 1780, p. xiii.
[8] *Chemical Experiments and Opinions. Extracted from a Work published in the last century*, Oxford, 1790 (plate redrawn from Mayow's 5; pp. xli, 63).
[9] Extrait d'un ouvrage de Mayow sur les airs; *Obs. Phys.*, 1790, xxxvii, 154–6 (from *Tractatus Quinque*, 'à la bibliothèque publique').
[10] *Discours sur l'anatomie du cerveau*, 12°, Paris, 1669; q. by Foster, 1901, 280.
[11] (2), iii, 395–6.
[12] (2), iii, 390–401; *Ann. Chim.*, 1790, xxix, 42–90.

Fourcroy mentions the article by Delametherie on Mayow[1] and says Beddoes 'faisoit sonner la trompette de la résurrection sur Mayow, et le rappeloit à la vie tout rayonnant d'une partie de la gloire qui forme l'auréole de quelques-uns des chimistes modernes'; but 'il est juste de rendre à la mémoire de ce médecin ce qui lui est dû'. Beddoes[2] made a suitable reply. Fourcroy's account of Mayow is much better informed than that of Patterson, who seems to have been ignorant of its existence.

THE TRACTATUS DUO

In the tract on Respiration in the *Tractatus Duo* Mayow says the entry of air into the lungs had been explained by a vacuum, or an imaginary attraction, or that when the chest expands it propels the air about it and this the next and so the propulsion goes on till at last the air near the mouth is driven into the lungs.[3] Boyle[4] had given the last as the view of 'the best of the moderns', saying that Bartholinus had objected that a man can breathe from a large glass vessel with a narrow neck, when the expansion of the chest could not propel the air in the vessel into his lungs. But, says Mayow, it could still be objected (nonnulli respondunt) that some more subtle matter could pass through glass and, propelled by the compressed air outside, pass into the vessel and drive the air into the thorax. But if this be so, how is it that a bird or other animal shut in a glass vessel from which the air is extracted [by an air pump] is unable to breathe (Boyle's experiments)? Ogle[5] says Mayow thus put an end to the old theory of Plato (Vol. I), 'at any rate I have been unable to find any further appearance of the doctrine in later writers.'

Mayow mentions Boyle's (see p. 523) explanation of the pressure of the air in terms of the compressed fleece and uses it to explain the mechanism of inspiration, contradicting Highmore's view of the expansion of the lungs.[6] He gives a correct account of the action of the intercostal muscles and ribs and of the diaphragm.[7] He says that some suppose that respiration chiefly serves for cooling the heart (Harvey did), but it seems that heating rather than such cooling would better suit the circulation of the blood and its fermentation.[8] Others, most recently, thought respiration is necessary in order that the blood may be able to pass through the lungs from the right ventricle of the heart to the left; in that case there would be no need for it to pass through the lungs, since it could (as in the foetus) pass by a shorter path, and it also (as he showed by injection in a dead animal) passes through the lungs without respiration.[9] Others think respiration churns the venous and thicker blood into very minute particles, but any air, even impure, would do this. Hence 'already we do not hesitate to assert that air serves not only for the motion of the lungs, but also to communicate something to the blood (ut jam asserere non dubitemus *aerem non tam pulmonum motui inservire, sed etiam sanguini nonnihil communicare*)'.[10]

---

[1] *Obs. Phys.*, 1790, xxxvii, 154.   [2] *Nicholson's J.*, 1799, iii, 108.
[3] I, 1668, 3.
[4] *New Experiments Physico-Mechanical*, 1660; *Works*, 1744, i, 64-5.
[5] *Aristotle On Youth and Old Age*, etc., 1897, 23.
[6] I, 1668, 5-10.   [7] *Ib.*, 12-36.   [8] *Ib.*, 37-8.   [9] *Ib.*, 38-9.   [10] *Ib.*, 39-40.

Mayow (without naming Hooke) then[1] describes the experiment with the dissected dog, 'lately made before the Royal Society', and says that 'by the inspired air something directly necessary to life is communicated to the blood', and when the air is exhausted of this it becomes useless and unfit for respiration (Quin ergo affirmimus, *ex aere inspirato nonnihi vitæ prorsus necessarium, sanguini communicari; quo, quicquid sit, exhausto, inutilis factus est aer, neque amplius respirationi idoneus)'*. The use of the following expiration is that the vapours exhaled from the blood shall be breathed out with the air. What it is in the air which is necessary for life is not easy to say; 'let me, however, in such an obscure matter make a guess' (Habet etiam *expiratio* ulteriorem usum, viz.: *ut cum aere expulso, etiam vapores à sanguine exhalantes, simul exsufflentur. Quid sit autem illud in aere tam vitæ necessarium, non facile est assignare. Liceat tamen in re obscurâ conjecturam facere)*. It is probable that it is the more subtle and nitrous particles with which the air abounds that are communicated to the blood by way of the lungs; that this aerial nitre (*nitrum hoc aereum*) is so necessary to life that even plants do not grow in earth deprived of it:[2]

Et verisimile est, *tenuiores esse, & nitrosas particulas*, quibus abundat aer, quæ quæ per pulmones sanguini communicantur. Adeo enim ad vitam quamcunque *nitrum hoc aereum* necessarium est; ut ne plantæ quidem in terrâ eodem privatâ crescant, quæ tamen si aeri exposita, sal hoc fœcundante denuò impregnetur, plantis demum alendis rursus idonea evadit: planè ut vel *ipsæ plantæ qualemcumque respirationem, aerisque necessitatem* habere videantur.

In enquiring what part it plays in animal life, it is seen that this aerial nitre, mixed with the sulphureous parts of the blood, causes a due fermentation not only in the heart but also in the pulmonary vessels and the arteries. The motion of the heart and of all other muscles requires this aerial nitre. The nitrous particles from the air lodge between the fibres of the muscles and by interaction with the vital spirits produce the sudden explosion of muscular motion, to which ebullition the blood may contribute something, inasmuch as its sulphureous particles, joined with the inspired nitre, render that liquor nitro-sulphureous and yet more explosive:

Quas autem in *vita animali* partes habet *nitrum hoc aereum* proximè inquirendum est. Et videtur *nitrum hoc*, partibus sanguinis sulphureis commixtum, fermentationem quandam debitam efficere, hujusmodi tamen accensionem in *corde solo* fieri haud existimo, sed statim in vasis pulmonalibus, & postea in arteriis non minus, quam in corde.[3]

There is no explosion in the left ventricle, for 'the heart seems to be nothing but a muscle . . . whose function indeed consists in contraction alone and the expulsion of the blood'.[4] 'It is probable that this aerial nitre is altogether necessary for every movement of the muscles' (Enimvero verisimile est ad *quemvis* musculorum *motum nitrum hoc aereum* omnino necessarium esse . . .).[5]

'Nitro-saline particles proceeding from the inspired air flow everywhere into the fibres of the muscles by the afflux of the arterial blood and inhabit them; but others, the animal spirits namely, consisting of an exceedingly volatile

---

[1] *Ib.*, 41.   [2] *Ib.*, 43–4.   [3] *Ib.*, 44–5.   [4] *Ib.*, 45.   [5] *Ib.*, 49.

salt not differing much from spirit of blood distilled and rectified to the highest degree, . . . as often as they are removed from the nervous supply, in order to cause motion, meet those aforesaid nitro-saline particles and particles of a different kind, and . . . by their mixture, as if from a volatile spirit of blood and a saline liquor united, that sudden explosion is made . . . and by chance the blood somewhat conduces to this ebullition, whose sulphureous particles, joined with the inspired nitre, make the nitro-sulphureous liquor much more explosive.' So the movement of the heart is produced in its muscular substance. In exercises and violent movements a greater expenditure of that explosive nitre (nitrum illud explosivum) is made in the muscles, and the respiration is increased.[1]

Spiritus hi, inquam, quoties motûs obeundi gratiâ à nervoso genere amandati, prioribus illis *nitro salinis*, & diversi generis, particulis occurrunt, ex eorum mixturâ veluti *ex spiritu sanguinis volatili*, & *liquore salino* unitis subitam illam explosionem, & per consequens musculorum inflationem simul & contractionem fieri verisimile est. Et forte etiam *sanguis* ad ebullitionem hanc nonnihil conducit; cujus particulæ sulphureæ, nitro inspirato conjunctæ, liquorem *nitro-sulphureum* & magis adhuc explosivum efficiunt.

'The principal use of respiration seems to be that it may serve for the movements of the muscles and especially of the heart . . . nor does it much matter (nec multum quâ ratione) in what manner air is driven to the blood, whether by the lungs or by any other way (utrum per pulmones, an aliâ quâcunque vitâ).'[2] 'That air which is transferred to the fœtus by the arterial maternal blood seems to supply the want of respiration in the fœtus',[3] and in blood transfusion there is no need for respiration.[4]

This theory (which is not supported by any described experiments and is not extended to combustion and calcination) is practically the same as that of Willis (p. 307), who is specifically mentioned by Mayow in connection with it.[5] Mayow, it will be noticed, uses the names 'this nitre (nitrum hoc)',[6] 'this aerial nitre (nitrum hoc aereum)',[7] and 'nitro-saline particles (particulas alias nitro-salinas)'.[8] In the *Tractatus Quinque* (1674) he uses the name 'nitro-aerial spirit'.

THE TRACTATUS QUINQUE

In the first tract, on *Nitre* (de sal nitro), Mayow says air is impregnated with a nitro-saline, vital, igneous, highly fermentative spirit. Nitre, a salt which makes no less noise in philosophy than in war, is shown by analysis and synthesis (non tantum Analyse, sed etiam Generatione) to contain an acid and an alkaline part; when deflagrated with sulphur the acid spirit flies off and may be collected by means of a tubulated retort and receiver, and the residue in deflagration with tartar is equal in weight to the latter, hence part must have come from the nitre. Nitre is produced from acid spirit of nitre and alkali, with mutual strife. The formation of nitre from potash (potassium carbonate) was described by Boyle, but earlier by Glauber (p. 540). The fixed part of

[1] *Ib.*, 51–2.　　[2] *Ib.*, 54–5; the vitâ is a misprint for viâ.　　[3] *Ib.*, 57.
[4] *Ib.*, 42.　　[5] *Ib.*, 50: uti à Cl. & Doctiss. Willisio loculenter demonstratur.
[6] *Ib.*, 44.　　[7] *Ib.*, 44, 49.　　[8] *Ib.*, 51.

nitre, says Mayow, comes from the earth, its volatile part from the air, which, however, does not contain a volatile nitre.[1]

The formation of a nitre from nitric acid and carbonate of ammonia (ammonium nitrate, previously discovered by Glauber, p. 353) is described (spiritus nitri . . . sali volatili, puro salso affundatur, ex mutua amborum congredientium lucta, insignique æstu sal nitrum generatur).[2]

Spirit of nitre (nitric acid) is composed partly from air and partly from earth. That the air contains an acid is shown by the regeneration of vitriol after calcination on exposure to air and the rusting of steel filings in moist air. The nitro-aërial spirit is fixed in the acid component of nitre:[3]

Jam vero cum pars nitri aerea in spiritu ejus acido existat, non vero in sale fixo, quod reliquam nitri partem constituit, uti supra ostendimus; concludere licet, *Particulas Igneo-aereas Nitri*, quæ cum parte ejus aereâ idem sunt, in *Spiritu nitri reconditas esse, partemque ejus Aeream* constituere.

Thomas Henshaw,[4] who collected saltpetre from icicles hanging in vaults and cellars, thought the air was full of 'volatile nitre', and in the formation of saltpetre in the earth 'the freer ingress the air hath into a place, is still more of advantage'.

It is remarkable that Mayow[5] says that when nitre is heated, nitric acid passes into the receiver and alkali remains in the retort (Si nitri *Analysis* per distillationem instituatur, Spiritus Acidus in receptaculum prodibit, relicto in retorta Nitro Fixo, Sali Alcali simillimo); if he had actually tried the experiment he could have discovered oxygen. Mayow says[6] that there are not particles of actual nitre in the air (as he thought in 1668), since these would be seen flashing in a flame, which does not happen (ob particulas nitrosas, ei intermixtis subinde strepitus ederet: quod tamen fieri non contingit). Borelli[7] in 1681 gave the same reason (si particulæ aeris verè essent nitrosæ, accenderentur à contactu flammæ candelæ, & crepitus efficerent, quod est falsum), without mentioning Mayow.

Mayow says Boyle's experiments have shown that something aerial is necessary for the production of flame; he had shown that a flame goes out much sooner in a glass that contains no air than in one containing air, which proves that the enclosed flame goes out not because it is choked by its own soot, as some have supposed, but because it is deprived of its aerial food.[8]

It must not be thought that the igneo-aerial pabulum is air itself; it is only a more active and subtle part of it. For a candle enclosed in a flask (vitrum) goes out although there is still contained in the flask an ample abundance of air (copia aeris satis ampla). Now we cannot suppose that the particles of air which existed in the flask were destroyed by the burning of the candle, or that they escaped, for we deny that they are able to pass through glass.

Only some part of the air, its more active and subtle part, is the igneo-aerial pabulum, since much air is left when a confined candle is extinguished, and these igneous particles reside also in nitre, since nitre mixed with sulphur will

---

[1] II, 4.   [2] II, 3.   [3] II, 18.
[4] *Phil. Trans.*, 1665, i, 33, no. 3; in T. Sprat, *The History of the Royal Society*, 1667, 260–76.
[5] II, 2.   [6] II, 6.   [7] *De Motu Animalium*, 4°, Rome, 1681, ii, 223.   [8] II, 11.

burn without air. Moist gunpowder rammed into a tube closed at one end, will burn under water or in a vacuum.[1]

At non est existimandum, pabulum Igneo-aereum ipsum aerem esse, sed tantum partem ejus magis activam, subtilemque: quippe lucerna, vitro inclusa expirat, cum tamen copia aeris satis ampla in eodem continentur . . . neque probabile est, particulas istas igneo-aereas nitrum perfectum esse . . . non ipsum nitrum totale, sed tantum partem ejus aliquam in aere residere . . .

nitrum sulphuris admixtum, in vitro aere vacuo, item subter aquas, satis promptè deflagrare . . .

pulvis pyrius . . . cum aquæ tantillo in massam duriusculum redigatur, quâ tubulus quivis, cujus altera extremitas obturata est . . . dein pulvis iste pyrius in extremitate tubuli apertâ accendatur, tubusque inversus aquæ immergatur . . . ita pulvis pyrius ad totalem sui absumptionem subter aquas deflagrabit.

Willis wrongly supposed nitre to contain sulphur, for this is found in neither of its constituents. For the production of flame both sulphureous and igneo-aerial particles are necessary; nitre does not flame when thrown alone into a red-hot crucible, but deflagrates when previously mixed with sulphur, or when thrown on charcoal, when the sulphureous particles of the charcoal ignite it. The aerial parts of nitre are its igneo-aerial particles, which are hidden in the spirit of nitre and constitute its aerial part. Mayow calls these the nitro-aerial particles or spirit. They give causticity to spirit of nitre. They cause the red fumes, rivalling flame, produced in its distillation, but in the spirit they are enveloped with moisture and so put out flame, but when dry, as in nitre, they will produce flame.[2] 'To kindle any sulphureous matter, igneo-aerial particles must be supplied, either from the air or from nitre previously added. . . . Sulphureous matter burns when igneo-aerial particles are supplied from the air, but with nitre from igneo-aerial particles closely packed in itself (nitrum autem particulis igneo-aereis in ipso confertim agglomeratis).'[3]

Mayow explains Boyle's discovery (p. 527) that gunpowder heated in a vacuum burns only in the place where the rays fall on it, by saying that in vacuo the nitro-aerial particles of the saltpetre can burn only those parts of the sulphur in contact with them, whilst in air the nitro-aerial particles communicate the flame. In vacuo they are interrupted (ob particularum igneo-nitrosarum seriem interruptam mox extinguatur).[4] This is correct, and Speter says it is the first correct explanation of the mode of burning of gunpowder in a vacuum.

Mayow says Boyle's *New Experiments touching the relation betwixt Flame and Air* had only just come into his hands; Boyle's book was published in 1673, although it is dated 1672 (see p. 493) and the imprimatur of Mayow's book is dated 17 July 1673. His experiment with gunpowder in the tube was, therefore, made before he saw Boyle's book, and his explanation of Boyle's experiment on gunpowder in a vacuum must have been added just before Mayow's book was sent for approbation.

The view of the moderns (Neoterici, i.e. Boyle) that all natural effects proceed from the same matter in different states of motion or rest, so that any one thing can be made of any other, is rejected: 'certain particles of matter . . . differ so much that they can by no natural power be changed one into another, and the elements consist of primary and in this way peculiar particles (ut

[1] II, 12.   [2] II, 14 f.   [3] II, 15–16.   [4] II, 16–17.

hae in illas nullâ vi naturali commutari possint: atque à particulis istiumodi peculiaribus, primariisque Elementa constitua esse).'[1]

Fire consists of nitro-aerial particles thrown into violent motion by sulphureous particles, as in culinary fires but also in other ways, as in the solar rays collected by a burning glass and in celestial fires. The corrosive and caustic natures of flame and spirit of nitre are akin and proceed from the nitro-aerial spirit in both, and flame is due to their rapid motion. Nitre will not take fire in a hot crucible through which fire particles are penetrating, but oil will burn in it. If a polished metal plate is held over a candle flame the igneous particles penetrate it but the sulphureous particles stick to the underside in the form of soot.[2]

The nitro-aerial particles of the atmosphere (particulis nitro-aereis Atmosphæræ) are agitated by the solar rays concentrated by a burning glass and will calcine antimony to the same *bezoardicum minerale* (antimony oxide) as is produced by the action of spirit of nitre or by the flame of nitre. 'Nor should it be overlooked that antimony, calcined by the solar rays, is considerably increased in weight, as has been ascertained by experiment, and we can hardly conceive that the increase in weight of the antimony arises from anything else than from the igneo-aerial particles inserted into it during the calcination': Neque illud prætereundum est, quod antimonium, radiis solaribus calcinatum, haud parum in pondere augetur . . . quippe vix concipi potest, unde augmentum illud antimonii, nisi à particulis nitro-aereis, igneisque, ei inter calcinandum infixis procedat.[3]

The increase in weight of antimony on calcination by the solar rays had been described by Hamerus Poppius (1618; see p. 635), Rey[4] and Le Févre (see Vol. III).

Although it was commonly believed that an acid salt of a vitriolic nature is concealed in sulphur and exhales in combustion under a bell, the flame of burning sulphur consists of sulphureous particles and nitro-aerial particles in rapid motion, and the saline particles of the sulphur are thus struck into fluid, flexible, attentuated particles like small swords and constitute the common spirit of sulphur; and the blue colour of the flame (like that of an expiring lamp) and its small potency show that the motion is somewhat retarded by the interposition of something, the saline particles, between the sulphureous and nitro-aerial particles.[5] Oil of vitriol distilled from vitriol, and acids distilled from wood, sugar and honey, are probably produced in a similar way. The acid oil of vitriol is not due to any acid already existing in the sulphur, of which there are no signs, sulphur resembling rather an alkali than an acid:[6]

Hactenus obtinuit opinio salem acidum, indolis vitriolicæ, in sulphuris compage reconditum jacere, à quo in sulphuris deflagratione exhalante, & à campana vitreâ superincumbente collecta, spiritus acidus sulphuris componitur: at vero vix probabile

---

[1] II, 23.   [2] II, ch. iii, 21 f., 27.

[3] II, 28; Mayow says elsewhere, II, ii, 41–2; IIF, 256, that 'light depends on the motion of nitro-aerial particles disseminated through the air'.

[4] *Essay*, 1630; ACR No. 11, 49; in Gobet's edit., 1777, 95, Hamerus Poppius is dated 1625.

[5] II, ch. iv, 35 f.; Beddoes, 18, says: 'The *mechanical* part of this theory is only an awkward dress which Truth borrowed from the fashion of the times.' See Boyle, p. 504.

[6] II, 32.

videtur spiritum adeo corrosivum in sulphure communi hospitari; utpote quod saporem subdulcem, neutiquam vero acidum obtinet. Imo sulphur potius naturam salis alcali, quàm acidi fortiri videtur.

Marcasite on distillation produces sulphur, but when exposed to air it forms vitriol by 'the nitro-aerial spirit effervescing with the mineral sulphur, converting the more fixed part into an acid liquid which, as soon as it is produced, attacks the metallic parts of the stone and draws them out, and at last coalesces with them to form vitriol':

Nimirum spiritus nitro-aereus cum sulphure Metallico Marchisitarum istarum effervescens, partem earum fixiorem in liquorem acidum convertit, qui mox ab ortu suo particulas metallicas lapidis dicti adoritur, evocatque; tandemque cum iisdem in vitriolum coalescit.[1]

So also acids are formed in fermentation, and nitre in the earth; the nitro-aerial particles descending into the earth attack the terrestrial sulphur and sharpen the saline particles firmly clasped in its bosom so that they become highly acrid, all acid salts being produced from saline particles brought into a fluid state by the nitro-aerial spirit (salia quæcunque acida à particulis salinis, spiritus nitro-aerei ope, ad fluorem, sive fusionem evectis).[2] 'There is a great affinity and likeness among all acid salts, and in them all, as in an appropriate medium, nitro-aerial and igneous particles reside (inque iis omnibus particulæ nitro-aereæ, igneæque veluti in subjecto idoneo, hospitantur).[3] The acid particles so produced in the earth seek out the seeds of the fixed salts and combine with them in closest alliance, with evolution of heat, to form nitre.[4]

In his chapter (Ch. V)[5] on fermentation, Mayow explains this as arising from the conflict of nitro-aerial particles, which occupy the first place among the principles of Nature and are worthy of being called Mercury (Inter Principia rerum naturalium principem locum obtinet Spiritus nitro-aereus, qui merito Mercurius nuncupetor).[6] This is in a section in which the three alchemical principles, salt, sulphur, and mercury, are parodied in a humorous and sophisticated way; Hales, who borrowed the name without understanding it, clumsily calls it 'the volatile Hermes'.[7]

The nitro-aerial spirit and sulphur are the only two active elements; they are engaged in perpetual hostilities with each other and from their mutual struggle when they meet, and from their diverse states when they succumb in turn, all the changes of things seem to arise:[8]

In principiorum censu proximum locum sibi vendicat sulphur; quod principium, post mercurium nitro-aereum, maxime fermentativum est. Et utique non nisi duo hæc principia activa esse videntur. . . . Spiritus nitro-aereus & sulphur perpetuas inimicitas invicem exercent. Et utique ab eorum mutuâ congredientium luctâ, varioque vicissim succumbentium statu, rerum mutationes quæcunque oriri videntur.

Salt, water and *terra damnata* constitute the passive elements.

Mayow gives[9] a picturesque account of his view of the origin of vegetable matter and the action of manures, which contain nitre: 'thus the much talked

---

[1] II, 39. [2] II, 43. [3] II, 44; an anticipation of Lavoisier's oxygen theory of acids.
[4] II, 44. [5] II, 47–65. [6] II, 47.
[7] Hales, *Vegetable Staticks*, 1727, 316. [8] II, 48–9. [9] II, 52–3.

of fermentation by which . . . plants are produced . . . appears to be nothing else but the internal motion of nitro-aerial particles when they meet with the sulphur and salt of the earth, in virtue of which terrestrial nitre is produced and the sulphur brought to a suitable volatility'. Nitre consists of salts of three kinds. One, the most active, of an ethereal and fiery nature, is derived from the air [=oxygen]. This forges from earthy matter [=nitrogen in the soil] a saline vehicle in which it resides [=nitrogenous matter], which with the fiery salt forms spirit of nitre [=nitric acid], which as soon as it is formed meets the fixed salts of the earth which have attained to proper maturity [=potash] and coalesces with them to form nitre. Just a century later, Lavoisier[1] (who had Mayow's book in his library), restated Mayow's theory, and in the meantime very incorrect views had been held on the nature of nitrification.

Stahl[2] supposed that it is formed from the universal acid (sulphuric acid) and the phlogiston of fermenting substances, and this theory was often accepted until it was disproved by the brothers Thouvenel in 1780,[3] who showed that sulphuric acid is never produced in decaying organic matter. Thomas Henshaw[4] had said that the air is full of 'volatile nitre' and that in the formation of nitre in the earth 'the freer ingress the Air hath into a place, is still more of advantage'. Evelyn[5] speculated on the formation of nitre in the earth from 'pregnant and subtle particles' and 'nitrous spirits' in the air, fermenting with the sulphur and less volatile salts; nitre is 'an indispensable principle in . . . vegetation, and perhaps the first rudiment of life in all things'. A plentiful supply of saltpetre would replace 'other composts to meliorate our ground'.

Heat is the result of a violent conflict between nitro-aerial and sulphureous particles (ignis, qui nihil aliud est, quàm particularum nitro-aerearum sulphureorumque, mutuò se commoventium, fermentatio maxime impetuosa).[6]

Mayow thought the suffocating effect of the fumes of burning charcoal was due to a nitrous spirit, as also the pungent property of fermented liquors kept in closed bottles. Ordinary fermentation, accompanied by effervescence, is caused by internal movement of nitro-aerial spirit and sulphur highly exalted and not fixed: it is one of the many ways in which things rush to destruction. Although liquors are improved for use by man in this fermentation, yet the structure of the compound is impaired, hence effervescence is rightly called destructive. If the entry of nitro-aerial particles is prevented by excluding air, putrefaction and corrosion are prevented (hinc ea, quae spiritum nitroaereum excludunt, res à corruptione vindicant).[7]

Mayow's explanation of rigidity and elasticity (ch. vi) (in which he mentions Hooke's *Micrographia* on the sparks from flint and steel) is on the basis of the idea that the nitro-aërial particles in a state of rest are fixed like wedges or pegs in the pores or between the particles of the body and is not very satisfying. He

---

[1] *Obs. Phys.*, 1775, vi, 339.
[2] *Fragmenta quaedam ad Historiam Naturalem Nitri*, 1698; in *Opusculum*, 1715, 535.
[3] AdS, *Mém. div. Sav.*, 1786, 55.
[4] In T. Sprat, *The History of the Royal Society*, 1667, 260–76.
[5] *Sylva . . . together with . . . Terra . . . Pomona*, f°, London, 1729, 9, 25, 27.
[6] II, 59.   [7] II, 62.

tries to explain why water which has been boiled freezes sooner (see p. 509), and the effect of breaking the tip of a Rupert's drop (guttæ vitreæ vulgo dictæ, quæ ex portiunculâ vitri liquefacti fiunt, aquæ frigidæ instillati).[1]

The chapter on the elastic power of the air as due to the nitro-aerial spirit (ch. vii)[2] describes the experiments with the candle, etc., and with mice.[3] Mayow says Boyle's experiments have proved that air is eminently elastic; it contains nitro-aerial particles which are removed by the burning of flame and at the same time the air loses its elastic force, which therefore seems to be due to the same aerial particles as those by which a flame is supported. It is probable that air is largely mixed with the flame, since it supplies it with nutriment, so that not even the smallest part of the flame is destitute of some portion of air (etenim probabile est, aerem flammæ confertim immisceri; utpote cui in pabulum cedit; ita ut ne minima quidem flammæ pars sit, in qua aeris aliquantulum non existit).[4] Davy[5] said: 'whenever combustible gaseous matter burns in the atmosphere, it must first mix with a certain quantity of air', and he had read Mayow (p. 579).

'The air is quickly deprived of its nitro-aerial and elastic particles, so that it not only becomes unfit for sustaining fire but also loses part of its elasticity.' (Mayow often uses the word 'elasticity' as an alternative to 'pressure'.) 'In the first place, then, I take it for granted that the air contains particles termed by us elsewhere nitro-aerial which are absolutely indispensable for the production of fire, and that these in the burning of flame are drawn from the air and removed, so that the latter when deprived of these particles ceases to be fit for supporting fire:'[6]

Nempe imprimis pro concesso habeo, aerem particulas quasdam, quas alibi nitro-aereas nuncupavimus, ad ignem conflandum omnino necessarias continere; atque eas per flammæ deflagrationem ab aere exhauriri, et absumi; ita ut idem particulis istis deprivatus, in futurum ad ignem sustinendum prorsus inidoneus evadat.

'Let a burning candle be placed in water so that the burning wick may stand about six finger-breadths above the water, and then let a glass flask (cucurbita vitrea)[7] of sufficient height be put over the light and plunged at once into the water surrounding the light, as is shown (Fig. 27). Care must be taken that the water levels within and without are equalised, which may be done, as also in what follows, if one leg of an inverted siphon be enclosed within the cavity of the glass before it is put into the water, while the other leg projects outside, yet so that the end of each leg may be above the surface of the water, as is seen in the figure. The use of the siphon is that the air enclosed in the alembic (in alembico) and compressed by immersion in the water, may escape through the hollow siphon. When the air ceases to issue, the siphon is immediately

---

[1] II, 66–95.   [2] II, 96–134.   [3] II, 100 f.   [4] II, 97.
[5] *Researches on Flame*, 1818; *Works*, 1840, vi, 16.   [6] II, 96; IIF, 67.
[7] H. Guerlac, *Isis*, 1954, xiv, 51, pointed out that *cucurbita vitrea* here means a round-bottomed glass flask, as Mayow's figure shows; it is different in shape from the cupping-glass used in other experiments and called *cucurbitula*, which was the technical name for a cupping glass (R. James, *Medicinal Dictionary*, 1745, ii, *s.v.* Cucurbitula, 'A Cupping-glass'), which is shown in Mayow's other figures. In one figure a small bell-jar is called a 'glass (*vitrum*)'.

withdrawn so that no air can afterwards get into the glass. When these arrangements are made, let the flask (cucurbita vitrea) be firmly fixed so that it may
descend no further in the water, and you will presently see, while the candle

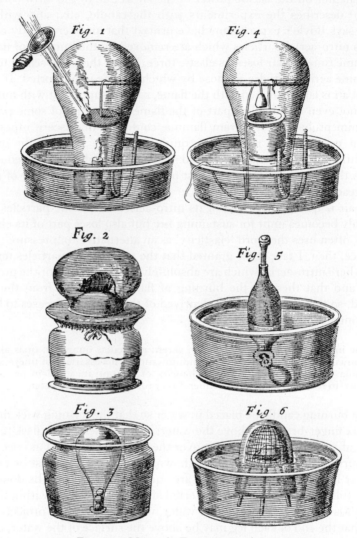

FIG. 27.   MAYOW'S EXPERIMENTS (1674).

The illustrations depict the Experiments on Combustion and on the Respiration of a Mouse described
in the text; also the Contraction of Air confined over Water by the Respiration of a Mouse, and the
collection of Nitric Oxide from Iron Balls and dilute Nitric Acid in an Inverted Flask.
    Fig. 4 shows the generation of Nitric Oxide from Iron and Nitric Acid, Fig. 5 the transference of gas to
a tube at the top for measurement of its compressibility.

yet burns (cum adhuc lucerna deflagrat), the water rising gradually into the
cavity of the flask (gradatim assurgentem percipies).'
    This rise is partly because the air enclosed, when the flame is about to
expire, is less rarefied by the igneous particles than formerly, but partly because
the candle enclosed is by its own burning deprived of nitro-aerial and elastic

particles, so that the air there is not able as before to resist the pressure of the atmosphere (quod lucerna vitro inclusa, per deflagrationem suam particulas nitro-aereas, & elasticas deprædata est; ita ut aer ibidem atmosphæræ pressuræ non, veluti prius, resistendæ valeat).[1]

Hales[2] mentions Mayow twice and says that in this experiment he had not given the size of the glass vessel, Hales having found that the contraction depends on this, as well as on the size of the flame in the same vessel. Fourcroy[3] said it was remarkable that Hales, his countryman and almost his contemporary, had only barely mentioned Mayow's experiments and his apparatus, which was much more ingenious than Hales's.

A form of the candle experiment had been described by Philo of Byzantium and Heron of Alexandria (Vol. I), Van Helmont (p. 232), Flud (p. 326), Francis Bacon (p. 407), and Otto von Guericke (p. 516); according to Bacon it was 'common', but none had equalised the water levels, and without this some air bubbles out and the contraction on cooling may be due to this. When Scheele performed the experiment he closed the narrow neck of the flask with a plug of soft wax. McKie[4] was surprised to find that this experiment had not been made in meetings of the Royal Society before Mayow; it is, in fact, an experiment first performed in this way by him and the use of the siphon is an ingenious device of his.

John Tabor[5] described a modification of Mayow's apparatus in which he carried out experiments on combustion, etc. and respiration.[6] Lavoisier[7] appreciated the source of error in the usual experiment; he worked over mercury, used a siphon like Mayow (who is not mentioned), and ignited the candle by a bit of phosphorus on the wick kindled by a hot iron passed through the mercury.

A piece of camphor to which a bit of linen tinder dipped in sulphur is attached, was suspended from a shelf in the glass, and the height of the water marked by papers pasted on the glass with a paste of barley meal boiled with water. The water outside could be drawn off until the level inside could be distinctly seen, or the flask (cucurbita) could be taken up in a saucer under its mouth and transferred to a suitable vessel almost full of water; it must remain until the air heated by the hands of the operator has been condensed (by cooling) into its original state. Then the combustible was kindled by a burning glass, and when the light had gone out the water rose and the air was reduced by about $\frac{1}{30}$th in volume. The camphor could not be rekindled in the residual air, so that 'the air had been, by the burning of the candle (lucerna), deprived of its igneo-aerial particles, so as to be quite unfit for sustaining flame anew (aerem istum per lucernæ deflagrationem particulis igneo-aereis deprivatum esse, ita ut idem ad flammam denouo sustinendam prorsus inidoneus fit)'.[8] The possibility that the inside of the glass had been so

---

[1] II, 98–9; IIF, 68 f.
[2] *Vegetable Staticks*, 1727, 230, 232, referring to 'De Sp. Nitro-aereo. p. 101', i.e. the 1674 ed.
[3] *Ency. Méthod.*, *Chimie*, 1796, iii, 391, 399, 414.　　　　[4] In Singer, (1), i, 468 (486).
[5] *Exercitationes Medicæ, quæ tam Morborum quam Symptomatum in plerisque Morbis rationem illustrant*, 8°, London, 1724, Tract. II. Cap. II, pp. 156–69; see p. 623.
[6] *Id.*, Tract. III. Cap. III, 170 f.
[7] AdS 1777 (1780), h 29, m 195; *Œuvres*, 1862, ii, 184.　　　　[8] II, 100–1.

dimmed by the smoke of the first candle that the rays of light could not be transmitted with sufficient intensity to kindle the matter again, was negatived by fastening, with a ring of paste round its margin, a piece of paper on the inside of the glass and, after the combustion, pulling this off by an attached thread.[1]

Dixon[2] said: 'I believe this to be the first distinct statement founded on experiment that air is composed of two distinct gases'; Patterson[3] says Mayow never asserted this, that he did not regard the nitro-aerial spirit as a gas, and that he thought the residual air was the same as the original air. This is incorrect. Mayow says: 'Though the air particles are very minute, and are vulgarly taken for a most simple element, it seems to me necessary to judge them to be a compound (easdem quid compositum statuere).'[4] What is left after the nitro-aerial particles are withdrawn is something quite different from ordinary air; it extinguishes a flame, will not support the combustion of camphor, and does not sustain life.

The air given out from the lungs of animals has its elastic force diminished in consequence of the loss of its nitro-aerial particles, as is proved by the following experiments. A mouse is placed on a moist bladder stretched over a jar and tied to it, which is tightly covered with a cupping glass (cucurbitula), which adheres to the bladder. The bladder presently bulges into the glass, which is because the animal acts like a flame in the cupping glass. Hence 'the elastic power of the air enclosed in the cupping glass has been diminished by the breathing of the animal, so that it is no longer able to resist the pressure (pressurae) of the surrounding air'.[5] A mouse in a small cage under a glass flask (cucurbita vitrea) over water (it should be near the surface of the water) causes the water level gradually to rise. Mayow says:[6] 'I have ascertained from experiments with various animals (cum animalibus variis) that the air is reduced in volume by about $\frac{1}{14}$th by the breathing of animals', i.e. by rather more than double the contraction caused by combustion. Haller[7] gives Mayow the credit for first making this observation (Primus id observavit Johannes Mayow,[8] & decimam quartem partem aeris a muris consumtum fuisse observavit, qui per pulmones transiisset).

If an animal and a burning candle are enclosed together in the vessel over water, the candle will soon go out, 'and the animal will not long survive the funeral torch (neque Animalculum diu tedæ ferali superestes erit).' An animal enclosed in a glass vessel (in vitro) with a candle will not breathe much longer than half the time it would otherwise have lived. The animal is not suffocated by the smoke, since the same result is found with a spirit lamp, which does not smoke,[9] and indeed the animal will live in the glass some time after the extinction of the lamp.[10]

'Hence it is manifest that air is deprived of its elastic force by the breathing of animals very much in the same way as by the burning of flame. And indeed

[1] II, 101–2.   [2] 1894, 601.   [3] 1931, 93, 507.
[4] II, 114.   [5] II, 103.   [6] II, 105.
[7] Elementa Physiologiæ, 1761, iii, 206.
[8] De nitro aereo, pp. 102, 103.
[9] This had been shown by Boyle.   [10] II, 108; also shown by Boyle; p. 533.

we must believe that animals and fire draw particles of the same kind from the air, as is further confirmed by the experiment.'[1]

Ex quibus manifestum est, aerem per animalium respirationem, haud multò secus, ac per flammæ deflagrationem vi suâ elasticâ deprivari; et utique credendum est, animalia, ignemque particulas ejusdem generis ex aere exhaurire; id quod sequenti experimento majus adhuc confirmatur.

Mayow says very clearly that these particles from the air enter the blood in some way in the lungs. 'There should be no doubt at all now that an aerial something absolutely necessary to life enters the blood of animals by respiration (aereum aliquid, ad vitam prorsus necessarium, sanguinem animalium respirationis ope ingredi).'[2] The candle goes out before the animal dies 'because a smaller ration of aerial nourishment, and that introduced at intervals, will suffice for animals, so that an animal can be sustained by the aerial particles remaining after the extinction of the flame . . . hence it is that the air in which an animal is suffocated is contracted in volume by more than twice as much [as that in which a candle goes out]: et vero animalibus pabuli aerei penus minutior, isque per vices ingestus, sufficiet: ita ut animal particulis aereis post flammæ extinctionem residuis, sustentari possit . . . unde fit, ut animal haud prius moriturum sit, quàm particulæ aereæ penitus exhaustæ sint. Atque hinc est, quòd aer, in quo animal suffocatur, plus quàm duplo magis quoad extensionem contrahitur'.[3]

This important observation is correct. Combustible matter could not be kindled with a burning glass in air in which an animal had died — although the wintry weather with its clouded sky prevented a repetition of the experiment. Since Mayow's text was approved in the summer of 1673, this suggests that the experiments were made not later than the autumn of 1672.

Mayow points out the difficulty that a good deal of air is left after combustion and respiration. Why, again, does it lose its elastic force, since aerial particles are not annihilated by flame or breathing, nor do they pass through the glass? He concentrated on the *elasticity* rather than the *volume* of the air under Boyle's influence, although in the passage just quoted he speaks of volume. Mayow *seems* to contradict himself by saying[4] that elastic particles pass out of the blood at the same rate as others enter in (although this is strictly correct from the modern standpoint).

Mayow, a young man, adopted the modern view of Descartes and Boyle that air particles are like little springs or fleeces of wool (p. 523), but (and this is Mayow's contribution) they are not all alike; some are branched and hooked together, while others (the nitro-aerial particles) are very subtle, solid, smooth, agile, fiery and truly elementary (et revera elementares esse), and when firmly fixed among the other particles make them rigid, 'the elastic force of the air consisting in this rigidity of the particles, which when compressed and bent by the weight of the incumbent atmosphere, strive to spread themselves out.'[5]

Mayow's own experiments had shown that there are *two kinds* of particles in the air, and the Descartes-Boyle theory that air contained only *one kind* of particle could not explain them. His explanation, based on this theory, is not

[1] II, 107; IIF, 75.   [2] II, 106; IIF, 74.   [3] II, 109; IIF, 76.   [4] II, 112.   [5] II, 114.

good. The simple modern explanation, that on withdrawing one kind of particles from a mixture the volume contracts at constant pressure, or the pressure decreases at constant volume, is based on the kinetic theory of gases. It was beyond Boyle and Mayow (but see p. 601); Hooke could have given it (see p. 553) but did not. Mayow was too much under Boyle's influence to take this step.

The sulphureous particles in a flame, when thrown into violent agitation, impinge on the nitro-aerial particles of the air and by their collision the latter are forcibly driven out (excussas), producing fire. (Lavoisier also thought the heat of combustion came from fire combined with the oxygen.) The aerial particles thus deprived of the nitro-aerial particles lose their elasticity and rigidity and become flexible, and in consequence the air becomes quite effete and destitute of elastic force (aerem prorsus effœtum, et vi elastica destitutum evadere).[1]

The impact of the sulphureous and nitro-aerial particles produces fire; 'in fact, fire seems to be nothing but a collection of very minute sparks very copiously struck out from aerial particles by the collision of sulphureous particles (et quidem ignis nihil aliud esse videtur, quàm scintillularum minutissimarum congeriem ex particulis aereis particularum sulphurearum allisione densissime excussarum).'[2]

Dixon, and Patterson, thought that Hooke's and Mayow's theories of combustion are essentially the same, but Koellner[3] and Donnan[4] more carefully distinguished them. Hooke regarded combustion as a dissolving of a combustible by the air acting as a solvent, a static phenomenon in which the air plays only a semi-passive role. Hooke also supposed that the combustible exhales into the air, much as phlogiston was later thought of as doing, and the heat produced was (as Hooke says) like that set free when a salt dissolves in water or metal dissolves in an acid.

Hooke does indeed say[5] 'this action [of dissolution] is performed with so great a violence, and does so minutely act, and rapidly agitate the smallest parts of the *combustible* matter, that it produces in the diaphanous medium of the air, the action or pulse of light', but here it is only the particles of the combustible, 'the sulphureous body', which are agitated and there is no suggestion of a collision with the particles of the 'substance inherent, and mixt with the air, that is like, if not the very same, with that which is fixt in salt-peter'. Mayow's theory was a dynamical one, the heat being the result of violent collisions between sulphureous and nitro-aerial particles, some aspects of Bacon's theory of heat being present.

Hooke and Mayow remained on friendly terms (p. 578) and Hooke was always watchful of what he thought to be plagiarism and complained of this in no uncertain terms, but he never suggested that Mayow had borrowed from him without acknowledgment. Dixon says: 'knowing what we do of Hooke's

---

[1] II, 114 f., 118; Harcourt, *Phil. Mag.*, 1846, xxviii, 497, quoted this passage to show that Mayow regarded air as made up of compound particles, and the idea is quite different from any Boyle ever entertained.
[2] II, 117.   [3] IIC.   [4] IID, 50.   [5] *Micrographia*, 1665, 103.

jealousy, it seems exceedingly unlikely that Mayow was merely working out Hooke's ideas.'

In the explosion of gunpowder the fixed salt (potash) of the nitre is vola-tilised and flies off as smoke, for the intense motion of the ignited sulphur-eous particles with the nitro-aerial particles breaks up the alkaline particles most finely and probably makes them volatile:[1]

dum nitrum, et sulphur commixta, veluti in pulvere pyrio accenduntur, probabile est, sal fixum, quo nitrum ex parte constat, inter deflagrandum volatilizatum esse, inque auras avolasse . . . nempe in nitri deflagratione particulæ, quibus idem constat, nitro-aereæ, sulphurearum accensarum ope in motum pernicissimum concitæ, particulas salinas, quibus antea strictim combinatæ fuerunt, minutissimè perfringunt, et uti verisimile est volatiles reddunt.

Sir Thomas Browne[2] said the explosion of gunpowder is due to the genera-tion of a large bulk of air; thunder is due to nitrous and sulphureous exhala-tions set on fire in the clouds, and earthquakes are caused by a similar process in the earth. There is an antipathy or contention between saltpetre and sulphur, and in the deflagration of antimony [sulphide] with nitre the sulphur of the antimony reacts. The effervescence and fumes when iron is dissolved in aqua fortis are 'caused from this combat of the sulphur of iron with the acid and nitrous spirits of the *aqua fortis*'. This was said many years before Mayow's book was published.

The theory that earthquakes are due to the ignition of nitre, sulphur, and bitumen in the earth was given by Cardan,[3] who compares the effect with mines (*cuniculi*) and cannon (*machinæ*), quoting Biringuccio,[4] It was adopted by Kircher.[5]

N. Cabeo[6] said the tides were caused by the moon's virtue in exciting sulphureous and 'salnitrous' spirits from the bottom of the sea.

Who can imagine that air as such resides in nitre in such abundance as is required for its production of deflagration in a place void of air (quanta ad illius deflagrationem in loco aere vacuo).[7] If solutions of nitric acid and salt of tartar (potassium carbonate) are mixed in an exhausted receiver (per ant-liam aeream exhauriatur), air (carbon dioxide) is copiously evolved, yet nitre is formed, from the solution of which, after evaporation, hardly any air escapes in a vacuum, 'a clear enough proof that air (as such) is not so densely enclosed in nitre (indicio satis manifesto aerem in nitro adeò confertim colli-gatum non esse).'[8] Thus, it is evident that 'the igneo-aerial particles common to nitre and air are not air itself (ipsum aerem non esse), but particles more subtle than air (particulas quasdam subtiliores, quæ aeri), which fixed in air and in nitre constitute their more active and fiery part (partem eorum magis activam, igneamque constituunt)'.[9]

The difficulty that the residual air is still as elastic as common air, as Mayow *proved* by experiment (see p. 604), was explained by saying that as the particles became less rigid they were also more bent by the pressure of the atmosphere

[1] II, ii, 71; incorrect in IIF, 277.
[2] *Pseudodoxia Epidemica*, ii, 5; 3 ed., 1658, 69; *Works*, ed. Sayle, i, 271.
[3] *De Subtilitate*, 8°, 1560, 202.   [4] *De la Pirotechnia*, Venice, 1540, 149 f.
[5] *Mundus Subterraneus*, 1664, i, 220 f.
[6] *Commentarius in Meteorologica Aristotelis*, Rome, 1646, ii, 42–70; Thorndike, vii, 61.
[7] II, 118–19; incorrect in IIF, 82.   [8] II, 119–20.   [9] II, 120–1.

(ab atmosphæræ pressurâ magis inflectuntur), and recovered the same elastic force; and also the air deprived of elastic particles is reduced to a smaller space and the particles are aggregated in greater abundance and more densely than in common air (majori copiâ, densiusque quàm in aere vulgari colliguntur).[1]

Animals die, and flames are extinguished, sooner in the upper part of a closed vessel of air. If two birds, or mice, are enclosed, one at the top and the other in the lower part of a glass, the one in the lower part survives longer. A mouse shut up in a glass first turns its mouth hither and thither upwards in search of breath, but when it finds that it suffers more there it pushes its mouth as far down as it can and keeps it there. This is probably because the air particles, after deprivation of the extremely dense (maximè solidas) nitro-aerial particles by a flame or breathing, lose not only their elasticity but also their former weight, and are driven upwards by the unchanged air particles pressing upon them (ob particulas nitro-aereas maximè solidas ex iis excussas, etiam pondere pristino destitutas, sursum cogunt).[2] Mayow thus thought that nitrogen is lighter than air. The air expelled from the lungs has become lighter for this reason, and a candle goes out in an inverted bell-jar (cucurbita vitrea inversa) even when the bottom of the jar is open to the air. If this lightness of effete air were not ordained, 'there would be perpetual strife among mortals about the acquisition and determination of the boundaries not so much of fields as of tracts of air (tractibus aereis)', whereas the nitro-aerial spirit, 'the most necessary elixir of life (elixir vitæ summè necessarium)' comes of its own accord and will 'rush uninvited into our very mouths and inmost vitals'.[3]

Mayow thought the effete particles were reimpregnated with nitro-aerial particles floating in the upper atmosphere and derived ultimately from the sun, which seems to be 'an immense chaos of nitro-aerial particles in a whirl (qui nihil aliud esse videtur, quàm particularum nitro-aerearum gyro perpetuo)'.[4] He has forgotten that the nitro-aerial particles would be less rich in the upper atmosphere, where the particles are lighter. Particles of cold (which is something positive) consist of these particles which have a pointed form and move straight like arrows and do not rotate. This part of his book shows the influence of the modern views of Descartes, who is mentioned in it (ut à Cl. Cartesio annotatum est). The blue colour of the sky is due to nitro-aerial particles at rest. (It *is*, actually, due to absorption by the oxygen.)

In his chapter on the nitro-aerial spirit as breathed by animals (ch. viii),[5] Mayow refers to 'our treatise on Respiration published some time ago' (1668), in which it was stated that the chief use of respiration 'is that particles of a certain kind, absolutely necessary for the support of animal life, may be separated from the air by means of the lungs and mixed most intimately with the mass of the blood'. Formerly, he thought the nitro-aerial particles were struck out from the aerial particles by the special structure of the lungs, but he now prefers the view that the aerial particles enter the mass of the blood and are there deprived of their nitro-aerial particles and in consequence lose part of their elastic force (particulas aereas in sanguinis massam facessere; easque

---

[1] II, 123.   [2] II, 124.   [3] II, 126–7.
[4] II, 128–9.   [5] II, 135–61.

ibidem particulis nitro-aereis orbari, et proinde vim elasticam ex parte amittere). Particles absorbed are not air itself 'but only its more subtle parts (summè subtiles), which exist in nitre and constitute its fiery and aerial part (in nitro existunt, partemque ejus igneam, aeremque constituunt).[1]

Mayow's new theory that the air particles entering the mass of the blood are deprived of their nitro-aerial particles, and so lose their elastic force, he tried to prove by experiment.[1] A small glazed pot (vasculum factile intus vitrefactum) was hung by a hook from a rod inside a glass flask over water and was a quarter filled with nitric acid (Fig. 27, no. 4). Some pieces of iron were hung over the pot by a string passing over the rod and outside the flask. The water levels were equalised by a siphon and then the outer water drawn off about 3 finger-breadths, the level inside, after the original temperature was restored, being marked by papers pasted on. The iron was lowered into the acid, when a very intense action occurred, the water inside being at once depressed by the vapours (ab halitus inde ortis statim deprimetur). When the water had been depressed about 3 finger-breadths, after an hour or so, the iron was lifted out. The water had risen in the glass so that about $\frac{1}{4}$ of the space occupied by the air was now filled with water. (This is a reasonably accurate result, and is the figure used later by Lavoisier.) Thus the air has its elastic force diminished by about $\frac{1}{4}$ part by the action produced by the acid encountering the iron. The position of the water level was marked and the iron again put into the acid, and again taken out. The water again rose but not so quickly nor so far as the original level, and similarly if the action be repeated a third time. Nearly the whole air was, therefore, impaired by the first action. This was confirmed by repeating the experiment. This seemed extraordinary but Mayow explained it as follows:[2]

I say that not only the air which was contained in that part of the glass in which the water rose after the first action, but nearly all the air in the glass was impaired.

It is to be noted that the air in the glass is impaired by the vapours dispersed through it even if the iron has been taken out of the spirit of nitre and the fermentation in the pot has ceased. For otherwise if the air had been consumed only while the action lasted, then the space left after the air was impaired would not have been filled by the vapours emitted, and the water would not have risen in the glass except by so far as these underwent condensation . . . so that we must believe that it rose not only into the space of the condensed vapours but also into that [part] of the air impaired at the same time.

probabile est, aerem, non tantum, qui in spatio eo vitri continebatur, in quo aqua post primum elevata est, sed etiam totum ferè, qui in vitro extitit, per æstum primò excitatum deperditum esse. . . .

Etenim annotandum est, aerem in vitro prædicto etiam postquam ferrum è spiritu nitri exemptum est, et fermentatio in vasculo cessavit, ab halitibus per eundem dispersis deperditum esse; alioquin enim si aer non nisi durante æstu absumptus esset, tunc spatium ab aere deperdito relictum, ab halitibus excitatis fuisset impletum, et consequentèr, aqua in vitrum non ascenderet, nisi quatenus isti condensationem paterentur . . . èoque credendum est, eam non tantum in locum halitum condensatorum, sed etiam aeris tunc temporis deperditi elevatam esse.

Donnan[3] pointed out that the 'vapours (halitus)' were mainly nitric oxide. The 'condensation' was partly due to the solution in the water of the nitrogen peroxide formed and partly to the solution of the nitric oxide in the liquid

[1] II, 136.   [2] II, 140–4.   [3] IID, 54.

containing a ferrous salt: 'With magnificent acuteness Mayow perceived the correct nature of the reaction.' Mayow goes on to show that the effervescence of iron with oil of vitriol and of spirit of nitre with fixed salt (potassium carbonate), producing hydrogen and carbon dioxide, do not produce such diminution in volume of air. Mayow said the gas formed by the action of nitric acid on iron, etc., is not air (aura â fermentescentibus excitata non videtur esse aer).[1]

Beddoes,[2] who points out that Mayow's *aura* is a gas and his *halitus* an exhalation or fume, says: 'I wish the passage were out of the book, or at least, that someone would explain it to me.' He was probably thinking of Mayow's statement that 'the aerial particles . . . are rubbed and broken by the fermenting particles (particulæ effervescentes; halitibus) . . . so that the nitro-aerial and elastic particles struck are out of them'. Yeats[3] had noticed that Mayow 'makes a distinction between the diminution of the air's elasticity by the gas, and the condensation of the gas itself. In the first instance, therefore, the water would rise from two causes, *viz*. the loss of elasticity in the air, and the condensation of the gas; but in the second case, when the elasticity had been already destroyed by the gas previously generated, the rise of the water could only be attributed to the condensation of the nitrous air'.

Since the mass of the blood is assumed also to be a liquid in a state of fermentation, the aerial particles in the blood have their nitro-aerial particles struck out. The nitro-aerial particles and the sulphureous particles of the blood produce a fermentation which is necessary to animal life, the dark purple colour being due to the sulphureous particles (as in liver of sulphur). Mayow said Lower (see p. 569) had shown that this changes to bright scarlet when mixed with the air,[4] and Mayow found that when fresh arterial blood is put in a vacuum 'it will expand in a remarkable way and will rise in an almost infinite number of bubbles (idem mirum in modum expandetur, et in bullulas penè infinitas elevabitur)', whilst blood kept for some time in a vessel effervesced only slightly on the florid surface.[5]

Boyle had made this experiment with animal blood in 1670,[6] but did not specify arterial blood, and found the same result with warm milk, so that it was probably due to boiling under reduced pressure. Pitcairne[7] criticised Mayow's experiment; he seems to have thought the results depended on the different viscosities of arterial and venous blood. Beddoes[8] thought the arterial blood in Mayow's experiment was warm and hence evaporated faster. Erasmus Darwin[9] found that fresh arterial blood effervesced in a vacuum and swelled to ten times its bulk, although he doubted if it contained dissolved air; he does not mention Mayow. Magnus[10] was the first to give an accurate account of the composition of the gases dissolved in blood.

Mayow says the fermentation arising from this mixture of nitro-aerial particles with the blood is the cause of animal heat;[11] the increased heat of the body during strong exercise is due to more frequent inspirations,[12] and the heat of fevers to too exalted saline-sulphureous particles in the blood.[13]

Just as the fermentation of the blood, so also its heat arises I think from the effervescence of nitro-aerial particles with salino-sulphureous particles of the blood.

[1] II, 145.   [2] 1790, 35, 52.   [3] 1798, 53.   [4] II, 148.   [5] II, 149.
[6] *Phil. Trans.*, 1670, v, 2035, no. 63; *Works*, ed. Birch, 1744, iii, 127.
[7] Dissertatio De Caussis diversæ molis qua fluct sanguis per pulmonem natis & non natis; *Dissert. Medicæ*, 4°, Rotterdam, 1701, 44–6; *Opera Omnia*, 4°, Leyden, 1737, 231–2.
[8] 1790, 55.   [9] *Phil. Trans.*, 1774, lxiv, 344.   [10] *Ann. Phys.*, 1837, xl, 583.
[11] II, 150 f.   [12] II, 306.   [13] II, 159.

Quemadmodum sanguinis fermentationem, ita etiam illius Incalescentiam à particulis nitro-aereis cum particulis cruoris salino-sulphureis exæstuantibus, oriri existimo.

For the same reason freshly-dug marcasite (iron sulphide) becomes hot on exposure to moist air.[1]

A most important statement by Mayow was that the heat developed is produced in the muscular parts:

'Nevertheless, the heat excited in animals by violent exercise is in part also due to the effervescence, originating in the motor parts themselves, between the nitro-aerial particles and the salino-sulphureous particles.'
Quanquam calor iste in animalibus, per exercitia violenta excitatus, etiam ab effervescentiâ particularum nitro-aerearum & salino-sulphurearum in partibus motricibus ortâ, partim provenit.[2]

The translation is by W. M. Bayliss,[3] who points out that 'Mayow rightly held that combustion went on in the muscles themselves, although he was incorrect in his statement that it took place in the blood also', and corrects the Alembic Club translation,[4] since *effervescentia* agrees with *ortâ*. This point is important, since Lavoisier thought that the combustions take place in the lungs, and thus Mayow was in advance of his successors.

Willis in his treatise on the *Heat of the Blood* (p. 305) stated that liquids never acquire heat on fermenting, but Mayow says this is contradicted by the common experience of fermentation, although there is no similarity between other liquids and the mass of the blood. Willis's theory of the vital flame (p. 307) is criticised; fire is fitter for the destruction of things than for sustaining life: 'fires of this sort and new lights, no less in Anatomy and Religion, have always seemed to me vain and fanatical (non minus in Anatome quàm in Religione mihi usque vana, & fanatica visa sunt).' In Willis's theory 'the vital flame, if there is any such thing, is for the first time kindled in the viscera of animals, so that we all now burn like Ucalegon, and there is no reason why we should wonder any more at a salamander living in the midst of flames'.[5]

Mayow seems to have had an obscure idea that the product of the effervescence of the sulphureous and nitro-aerial particles was a gaseous substance:[6]

Etenim dum particulae nitro-aereæ modo prædicto cum sanguinis massa effervescunt, particulæ ejus salino-sulphureæ ad justam volatilitatem perducuntur; haud secus ac particulæ sulphureæ è terrestri materiâ spiritus nitro-aerei ope ad justam maturitatem evehuntur, prout alibi ostensum est.

Foster[7] suggests that Mayow's mention of 'effervescence' shows that he had read Sylvius (p. 284).

In his chapter 'Whether air can be generated anew' (Utrum Aer de novo generari possit)[8] Mayow describes an experiment which he says is not very unlike one of Boyles (see p. 525; the apparatus was slightly different). Equal volumes of nitric acid and water are mixed, and filled into a small bottle (vitrum parvulum) which is inverted in a glass vessel of the same liquid. (Fig. 27, no. 3.) Two or three iron balls are put in the neck, and the exhalation (*halitus*) rises in bubbles in the bottle. If the balls are allowed to fall

[1] II, 151   [2] II, 152.   [3] *Principles of General Physiology*, London, 1915, 606.
[4] IIF, 105.   [5] II, 152–9.   [6] II, 160–1; the ref. is probably to II, 15 f.
[7] 1901, 196.   [8] II, ch. ix, 161–71.

out, the gas (*aura*) will condense [NO dissolving in the acid ferrous salt solution] but not wholly dissolve. The gas from dilute oil of vitriol [hydrogen] will not condense, and the same is found if the iron is left in contact with the nitric acid for a day or two [when the acid is practically spent]: Mayow's excellent observational skill is evident here. It is not easy to say whether gas of this kind (*aura istiusmodi*) is really common air, but it is certain that it expands and contracts on heating like common air and has the same elastic force, as he showed by an experiment, the first ever made which proved Boyle's law for gases other than common air.[1] A small graduated glass tube closed at one end was cemented to a funnel-shaped tube and the whole filled with water and inverted in a jar of water (Fig. 27, no. 5). The vessel containing the *aura* is transferred by a small dish placed under its mouth to the jar containing the funnel-shaped tube, its mouth brought under the orifice of the glass tube, and some of the *aura* transferred to the tube by tilting the vessel, when it bubbled up through the water. The tube inverted in a vessel of water was then put into a glass vessel from which the air was exhausted by a Boyle's air-pump (ex quo aer per Antliam *Boylianum* postea exhauriatur), when the gas (*aura*) in the tube expanded and bubbled out. On letting in the air, the gas was compressed into a small space, and so it was found that it had expanded to more than 200 times its volume, and if it had been relieved of the pressure of the surrounding water would have expanded to 400 times; 'nor will common air, when treated in the same manner, expand more.'

Another way of taking a sample of gas was to draw up an inverted glass filed with water into the jar containing the gas by means of a string passing over a rod, when the water falls out and gas enters the glass. The jar filled with gas is then drawn out in its inverted position by another string fastened to its mouth. This kind of manipulation is completely ignored by Patterson and later writers, who mistakenly say that Mayow's apparatus is the same as Boyle's. Yet Fourcroy had emphasised the true position.

An animal will not live much longer in a given volume of air mixed with two or three times its volume of this gas (*aura*) than in the common air alone; that it lived a little longer was because the diluted air could be less copiously breathed. (He must have used hydrogen in this experiment, not nitric oxide.) Yet on the whole, Mayow thinks there is perhaps not much difference between gas of this kind and common air (verisimile est, auræ istiusmodi cum aere vulgari affinitatem magnam intercedere),[2] for a reason which he gives.

In the chapter on the propagation of fire and why flame rises to a point (ch. x),[3] Mayow introduces some speculations on the 'subtle matter', i.e. ether of Descartes, and compares the production of flame with the breaking of a Rupert's drop. All natural movements, such as the generation and destruction of things and the internal motion of opposed liquids (liquorum contrariorum

---

[1] II, 163 f., 165 f.: utrum aura istiusmodi revera aer fit necne, non ideo facile est intellectu: illud autem certum est, quod eadem à calore leni ei admoto, instar æris expanditur, denoque refrigerata contractionem patietur. Quinimo aura prædicta, haud minori vi elastica quàm aer vulgaris donatur, prout sequenti experimento mihi compertum est. It is curious that Boyle never mentions Mayow's experiment.
[2] II, 170–1.   [3] II, 172–81.

motus intestinos) are to some extent due to the pulsation of the subtle matter. It is not enough to say, with Willis, that in them the more active particles expand, ascend, and at last fly away (the reference is to Willis's *Diatribe de Fermentatione*), for what is at rest will remain so unless some perpetually moving matter gives it an impulse; the nitro-aerial particles penetrating a sulphureous mass enter the region of the subtle matter which is in violent agitation and are driven off.[1]

The lower part of a flame is blue since it is produced only by the kindling of sulphureous particles, but the upper part burns more brightly. The sulphureous particles passing up the flame are rendered more subtle by their own burning and become at last so fine that they are incapable of constituting the grosser structure of soot or of producing flame. If a polished plate is held in the flame of a candle it is covered with soot but if held a little distance over the flame no soot gathers on it. Mayow mentions[2] the flame rising from the wick before it is extinguished (cf. Boyle, p. 526). This was written before the publication of Hooke's *Lampas* in 1677.

The chapters on the water spout (Ch. xi),[3] which is due to the whirling motion of the air; on light and colours (Ch. xii),[4] in which Mayow adopts Descartes' theory that light is a pulse in the ether, and assumes that it consists of nitro-aerial particles,[5] and on thunder (Ch. xiii)[6] (again quoting Descartes), contain little of importance, but the latter is better than the old theory,[7] which was adopted by Newton,[8] that lightning is due to the kindling of 'sulphureous steams and nitrous acids' in the atmosphere.

Mayow's chapter on the heat of quicklime and on the combination of opposite salts (acids and bases) (Ch. xiv)[9] is very interesting. In it he opposes Willis's theory of the production of heat on slaking quicklime, that it is due to the expulsion of particles of fire fixed in limestone on burning (see p. 306), and supposes that some fixed salt of an alkaline nature exists in the lime (sal fixum in calce vivâ contineri), since lime neutralises an acid with generation of heat (due to the reaction of acid and alkali), dissolves sulphur on boiling with it and water, and expels volatile ammonia from sal ammoniac, all of which are properties of an alkali. There is also an acid salt in lime (an anticipation of Meyer's *acidum pingue*), since lime water is precipitated by a solution of any fixed salt (calcium carbonate from the potassium carbonate), it fixes a volatile salt as Zwelfer says (calcium carbonate from ammonium carbonate) and it coagulates boiled milk. These two contrary salts (acid and alkali) are united in slaked lime (calx extincta) with a stony earth (terrâ lapideâ), and the heat of slaking is due to the liberation and effervescence of the acid and alkaline salts; lime does not become hot with highly rectified spirit of wine or turpentine, which do not dissolve salts.[10] The fixed salt comes from the earth, the acid salt

[1] II, 175-6.   [2] II, 178.
[3] II, 181-95: De Vortice Aereo. Anglice A Spout.   [4] II, 195-213.
[5] Newton's letter on his new theory of colours had appeared in *Phil. Trans.*, 1672, vi, no. 80, p. 3075.
[6] II, 214-22.   [7] Guerlac, *Isis*, 1954, xlv, 243.
[8] *Opticks*, Qu. 31; 1730, 355; it was taught by Charles Morton (B.A. Wadham Coll., Oxford, 1649) at Harvard from 1687, Cohen, *Chymia*, 1950, iii, 17 (27).
[9] II, 222-46.   [10] II, 226-7.

is made by the action of the nitro-aerial and igneous particles during the long calcination sharpening the particles of fixed sulphur in the limestone and at last converting them into an acid salt.[1] This is wrong but ingenious.

In this chapter Mayow also sets out very clear ideas on affinity, to which Thomson had drawn attention (see p. 582), and Brande[2] remarked that the sketch of a theory of chemical attraction given by Newton[3] 'is nearly in the language, and quite in the spirit and meaning, of his predecessor Mayow'. Very similar views were put forward, simultaneously with Mayow, by Willis (see p. 310). Mayow says[4]

When the acid spirit of salt (HCl) is coagulated with a volatile salt (ammonia) . . . although the mixed salts (acid and base) seem to be destroyed, yet they may be separated from each other with their forces unimpaired, as takes place when sal ammoniac . . . is distilled with salt of tartar (K_2CO_3). . . . And the reason of this is, that the acid spirit of salt is capable of entering into closer union (strictiori unioni) with any fixed salt than it is with a volatile salt, so that it immediately leaves the volatile salt that it may be combined more intimately (intimius combinetur) with the fixed salt.

He gives a very clear account of the displacement of the more volatile nitric acid from nitre by sulphuric acid, on lines long afterwards elaborated by Berthollet (see Vol. III).

If oil of vitriol is poured upon nitre, which consists of an alkaline and of a volatile acid salt . . . the fixed salt of the nitre will soon leave its own acid and will enter into union with the acid of vitriol, which is more concordant with it (sibi magis congruo unionem inibit) . . . if nitre mixed with oil of vitriol is distilled, the spirit or acid salt of the nitre will pass under a gentle heat into the receiver, while yet in other circumstances that spirit will not be carried up except by a very violent fire. No doubt it is because the volatile acid salt of nitre has been expelled from the society of the alkaline salt (è salis alcali consortio protrusum est) by the more fixed vitriolic acid that the nitric acid (acidum nitri), now liberated from the union with the alkaline salt, ascends under a heat no greater than is required for the rectification of spirit of nitre. . . . It is a proof of this (huc etiam facit) that the mass left in the retort after a distillation of this kind closely resembles vitriolated tartar (K_2SO_4) and can be properly substituted for it.

Although Mayow does not use the name 'attraction' afterwards employed by Newton, his language clearly implies the idea. According to Rodwell[5] Mayow uses the name *affinitas* for the cause of union of an acid and earth and in discussing the *congressus* of different substances he speaks of *combinatur* and *combinentur*.

Mayow explains the precipitation of lime water by fixed alkali as due to the union (conjunctum) of the acid of the quicklime with the alkali, 'so that the limestone can now no longer be dissolved by the destroyed acid of the lime, but is precipitated to the bottom along with these combined salts (ita ut lapis calcineus non amplius jam ab acido calcis destructo dissolvi queat; sed unà cum salibus iis combinatis ad fundum præceps ruat).'[6] In causticising alkali, the latter combines with the acid of the quicklime, and the alkaline salt of the latter is extracted by the water with its forces unimpaired and shows its caustic nature (which is again the same as Meyer's later theory).

The chapter (xv) on Bath waters[7] describes experiments to prove that they

[1] II, 228–9. [2] *Manual of Chemistry*, 6 ed., 1848, I, xxxviii. [3] *Opticks*, Qu. 31.
[4] II, 232. [5] *Chem. News*, 1865, xiv, 51. [6] II, 239–40. [7] II, 246–65.

do not contain nitre, sulphur, sal ammoniac or vitriol; e.g. the residue on evaporation does not deflagrate on burning charcoal, no smell of ammonia is formed on adding potash, and powdered galls give no colour (except a little with the King's Bath). The sand of the springs (mostly calcium carbonate) effervesces with acid and the solution is coloured by galls, indicating the presence of iron. Potash (K_2CO_3) or saline volatile salt (ammonium carbonate) gives a white precipitate with the water, showing the presence of 'a certain stony or aluminous matter', and lime water gives the same precipitate. If an inverted flask filled with the water is put in a vessel of the water which is boiled, air collects in the top of the flask; this was proved to have the same compressibility as air. There is a good deal of material in this chapter which long afterwards appeared in the publication of Black (Vol. III), who does not seem to have read Mayow's book.

Air dissolved in water (which can be driven out in a vacuum or by heat) is drawn in for respiration by the gills of fish and passes into their blood (aereum aliquod vitale ab aqua, veluti aliàs ab aurâ secretum, in cruoris massam trajiciatur).[1] The air bladder in a fish, Mayow thought, was a receptacle for atmospheric air to be inspired. Priestley incorrectly thought it contained 'perfectly or not quite noxious air'[2] and Fourcroy[3] that it contained nitrogen. It is actually common air. Although in prehistoric fish the air-bladder probably had a respiratory function, in modern fish its use is hydrostatic.

The springs have their origin in rain water, which has acted on saline-sulphureous particles in the earth by means of aerial particles in the water, so becoming warm and dissolving mineral salts.

Thomas Guidott[4] criticised Mayow as 'a Novel Writer', who 'hath ploughed with my Heifer' (1725, 14), yet he accepted most of Mayow's results, maintaining, however, his previous view that the Bath water contains nitre and sulphur. An earlier work by Guidott was printed with one by Edward Jorden.[5] Jorden's work was first printed in 1631[6] and in it he says[7] that fire cannot be the cause of the heat of mineral waters, since fire requires air; the heat was generated by the fermentation of minerals in the earth.

William Simpson (1636–7—1680) (see p. 484)[8] assumed that all mineral salts are formed from an essurine (hungry) spirit or sulphurous acid, water, and mineral glebe, in the bowels of the earth, the salt formed depending on the glebe in the particular place. He also believed in a universal salt, which gave mineral waters their properties, and speaks of 'nitrous particles' in the air. Simpson, a 'Helmontian', had a long controversy with Robert Wittie (1613–84).[9] Simpson[10] explained the heat of mineral springs

[1] II, 259.   [2] E. & O., 1790, ii, 462–3.   [3] Ann. Chim., 1789, i, 47.
[4] A Discourse of Bath, 1676; 2 ed., A Collection of Treatises Relating to the City and the Waters of Bath, London, 1725, ch. ii, pp. 7 f.; id., De Thermis Britannicis, 4°, London, 1691, f. a4x, pp. 43 f.
[5] A Discourse of Natural Bathes . . . An Appendix concerning Bathe . . . by Tho. Guidott, 1673 (pref. dated 1668).
[6] A Discovrse of Natvrall Bathes, and Minerall Waters . . . , 1631 (92 pp.); enlarged ed. 1733.
[7] 1631, 59 f., 68 f.
[8] Hydrologia Chymica; or, the Chymical Anatomy of the Scarbrough, And other Spaws in York-Shire, London, 1669 (BM 1171. e. 8. (1.)), with motto on t.p. ex aqua omnia, recalling Van Helmont; Simpson also publ. Philosophical Dialogues concerning the Principles of Natural Bodies, 12°, London, 1677 (BM 536. a. 22).
[9] Pyrologia Mimica, Or, An Answer to Hydrologia Chymica of William Sympson Phylo-Chymico-Medicus; In Defence of Scarborough-Spaw, London, 1669, 312 pp.; Poynter, in Singer, (1), ii, 72.
[10] Zymologia Physica, Or a brief Philosophical Discourse of Fermentation, 8°, London, 1675 with Appendix, A Discourse of the Sulphur-Bath at Knarsbrough in York-Shire, 8°, London, 1675.

as due to the 'intestine duellings and inward collisions' of 'acidum and sulphur' derived from the earth, which is like Mayow's theory.

Mayow[1] criticises Hooke's theory that springs are due to denser sea-water forcing spring-water to the tops of mountains, and correctly says that 'at least the majority of springs have their origin in rain-water', not stored in underground caverns but soaked up by the surface of the earth, which is like a sponge or filter and can absorb sufficient rain-water to form springs that will endure for a long time.

The second tract, *On Respiration*, a revision and enlargement of the book of 1668,[2] is largely anatomical, and correctly explains the expansion and contraction of the lungs as due to the movements of the ribs by the attached muscles, this being illustrated by diagrams, and by the movements of the diaphragm. No one has seen the lungs performing their functions; 'they alone of all the parts of the body collapse at once when they are shown the light, hence such an ignorance of respiration and a holy wonder (sancta quædam admiratio). Still, let me draw near to the inmost vitals and, concerning so obscure a matter, make at least a guess (de re tam obscura saltem conjecturam facere).'[3] Willis is again criticised.

The experiment of a bladder enclosed in a pair of bellows with a glass window, illustrating the theory of the mechanism of breathing,[4] is a great improvement on the experiment imagined, but not tried, in 1667 by Swammerdam, viz. enclosing *lungs* in bellows.[5] Swammerdam says:

> Quae jam enumerata sunt experimenta, ope follis è vitro confecti, ac Pulmones alicujus animalis intra se continentis, extra corpus ad oculum demonstraturos Curiosis, aliquando, si Deus volet, pollicemur.

Pierre Sylvain Regis (1632–1707) in his Cartesian encyclopædia[6] gives Mayow's explanation of the action of the ribs in respiration without naming him. Mayow's explanation (1668) of the anatomy of respiration is clearer, more exact (it is worked out in detail), and truer than that given later by Borelli (1680–1): 'the whole account . . . might almost have been written at the present day.'[7]

The swelling of a flaccid lamb's bladder tied at the neck when in a partly exhausted receiver is described by Boyle[8] and probably suggested Mayow's

---

[1] II, 255.   [2] II, 267–308; secunda editio, Auctior, & Emendatior.
[3] II, 269.
[4] II, 274, plate II, fig. 6 — figs. 1–4 of this plate were printed in the *De Respiratione*, 1668, as well as plate IV of the 1674 edit.
[5] J. Swammerdam, *Tractatus Physico-Anatomico-Medicus de Respiratione usuque Pulmonem*, sm. 8°, Leyden (7 ll., 121 pp., 11 ll.), 1667, frontispiece and cap. v, § 5, p. 39; 2 edit., 4°, Leyden, 1738; F. J. Cole, *Nature*, 1937, cxxxix, 219. The microscopical observations of Jan Swammerdam (Amsterdam; 12 February 1637–15 February 1680) were made mostly before those of Leeuwenhoek, but published later. The work on respiration was his inaugural dissertation for the M.D. Swammerdam's important *Biblia Naturæ* was first published by Boerhaave in 1737–8 (see p. 745); Foster, 1901, 99.
[6] *Systême de Philosophie*, 3 vols. 4°, Paris, 1690, Bk. VII, pt. i; Vol. ii, p. 551.
[7] Foster, 1901, 192–3.
[8] *New Experiments Physico-Mechanical* (1660); *Works*, 1744, i, 12.

experiment,[1] but Boyle says his experiment is only a repetition of an earlier one by Roberval, who used a carp's swimming-bladder.

In the section dealing with the purpose of respiration, Mayow denies that its purpose is to cool the blood, since it produces the opposite effect. Nor is it intended to transmit blood from the right to the left side of the heart, for the blood can pass through the lungs without their motion, as he proved by injecting blood or any other fluid by a syringe into the pulmonary artery of a dead animal, when it readily passed into the left ventricle of the heart.[2] This experiment is already mentioned in the *Tractatus Duo*.[3] Isbrand de Diemerbroeck[4] gives this theory as proposed by Maurocordatus of Constantinople in *De Motu et Usu Pulmonum* and says it was 'refuted by a celebrated experiment of John Mayow':

hanc opinionem etiam egregio experimento refutat Joh. Majow, *tract. de respir*. mihi p. 21, apud ipsum auctorem vivendo.
which opinion John Mayow refutes by producing an admirable Experiment, in his Treatise of Respiration.

Yeats[5] says this is the only mention of Mayow in Diemerbroeck. Alexander Mavrocordatus, M.D. Bologna, dragoman at the Ottoman Porte in Constantinople, published a work[6] which contributed to making known Harvey's recent discovery; translated into German, French, and Spanish.[7]

Mayow then gives his own theory of respiration:[8]

With respect, then, to the use of respiration, it may be affirmed that an aerial something, whatever it may be, essential to life, passes into the mass of the blood. And thus air, driven out of the lungs, these vital particles having been drained from it, is no longer fit for breathing again.

Circa respirationis ergo usum affirmare fas sit, nonnihil, quicquid sit, Aereum ad vitam sustinendam necessarium, in sanguinis massam transire. Hinc aer è pulmonibus egestus, è quo particulae istae vitales exhauriuntur, non amplius ad respirationem idoneus est.

This, he says, will be made clear by an experiment which he mentions very briefly of insufflating the lungs of an animal, a dog for example, by bellows. This is Hooke's experiment of 1663 (p. 564). Hooke is not named but Mayow does not claim the experiment as his own; he had previously[9] said it was 'lately made before the Royal Society'.

'It is probable that certain particles of a nitro-saline nature, and these very subtle, agile, and in the highest degree fermentative, are separated from the air by the action of the lungs and conveyed into the mass of the blood . . . it is probable that nitro-aerial spirit, mixed with the saline-sulphureous particles of the blood, excites in it the necessary fermentation.'

Plants also seem to have a kind of respiration and are under the necessity

---

[1] Bostock, *An Essay on Respiration*, Liverpool, 1804, 199.   [2] II, 298.   [3] I, 1668, 39.
[4] *Anatome Corporis Humani*, 4°, Utrecht, 1672, bk. ii, ch. 13, p. 527; *The Anatomy of Human Bodies . . . by Isbrand de Diemerbroek . . . Translated . . . by William Salmon, Professor of Physick*, la. 4°, London, 1689, 360.
[5] 1798, 118.
[6] *Pneumaticum Instrumentum, sive de Usu Pulmonem et Respiratione ex Sanguinis Circulatione*, 12°, Bologna, 1664; Frankfurt, 1665; Leipzig, 1682.
[7] Fustel de Coulanges, NBG, 1861, xxxviii, 457.   [8] II, 299; IIF, 204.   [9] I, 41.

of absorbing air (ipsæ plantæ aliqualem respirationem, aerisque hauriendi necessitatem habere).[1]

Thorndike[2] points out that Arnald of Villanova[3] said air through the arteries reaches every member of the body and alters it and whatever is contained in it (aer etenim per arterias universas omnia membra pertingens suis qualitatibus actualibus alterat ea et quecumque etiam continentur in eis), but in his time the arteries were thought to contain only air.

The motion of the heart does not depend on the rarefaction of the blood, for hearts cut from animals pulsate even if all the blood is squeezed out of them, and Mayow found by repeated experiments that if a solution of opium or cold water is injected into the jugular vein the motion of the heart becomes quicker (statim crebrior erit).[4]

The aerial salt is necessary for movement of the muscles, including the heart, which is nothing but a muscle. The fermentation produced in the blood commences in the lungs but continues in the muscles, the venous blood, after a great expenditure of nitro-aerial salt (maxima fit salis nitro-aerei impensa), returns to the lungs. Respiration conduces to the motion of the heart as of all other muscles, for which this aerial salt (sal hoc aereum) is altogether necessary. The effervescence requires also the presence of sulphureous particles, 'and in fact motion is produced in the heart in no different way than in other muscles; but I do not think that the motive effervescence takes place in its ventricles but in its muscular substance, not otherwise than in other muscles.'[5]

Stokes (1800) pointed out that Mayow had two theories of respiration: (1) the 'saline theory' in 1668, which he compares with the views of Sylvius de le Boë,[6] and (2) the 'igneous theory' of 1674, when Mayow, however, still spoke of sal aereum[7] or sal nitro-aereum[8] or particulæ nitro-salinæ[9] in the tract on Respiration, as well as spiritus nitro-aereus, as though the old names had been carried over in the revision of the tract of 1668.

Although Mayow owed much to Descartes he was no blind follower; he criticises Descartes for supposing, against Harvey's arguments, that the beat of the heart is an expansion due to the rarefaction of the ventricular contents, whilst Harvey and Lower had proved that it is due to the contraction of the muscular walls. Of the ultimate fate of the nitro-aerial corpuscles absorbed into the blood, Mayow was able to say only: 'As to expiration, it should be noted that it serves a further purpose, namely that together with the air driven out of the lungs, the fume raised by the fermentation of the blood is also blown away (halitus à sanguinis æstu excitati, exsufflentur).[10] Stokes[11] said: 'how he got rid of the remaining particles of air I do not know'; Lower (adopting the opinions and language of Bathurst), deposited them in the solids and finally carried them off from the pores of the skin.

In his third tract, On the Respiration of the Fœtus in the Uterus and of the Chick in the Egg,[12] Mayow suggests that the fœtus is supplied with arterial

[1] II, 300-1.   [2] viii, 424.   [3] Opera, 1504, 31a.
[4] II, 303.   [5] II, 303 f.; IIF, 208 f.
[6] Disput. Med., vii, no. 77; Opera, 1698, 19; Praxis Med., i, 21; Opera, 1698, 151.
[7] II, 301, 304, 305.   [8] II, 306.   [9] II, 305.   [10] II, 300.
[11] Med. and Phys. J., 1800, iii, 335.   [12] II, 309-35.

blood from the umbilical arteries, and the required stimulus of the nitro-aerial particles is provided without respiration. A 'well-known experiment' in which arterial blood from a dog is transfused to another, which 'although previously panting and breathing violently, yet, after receiving the arterial blood, scarcely seems to breath at all', shows that 'if arterial blood, which is imbued with the nitro-aerial spirit, came to the heart instead of venous, there would be no need at all for respiration. . . . We may hold with divine old Hippocrates that in the embryo the umbilicus supplies the place of respiration, which is also the opinion of the learned Everard',[1] although Everard wrongly thought the function of the long circuit of the umbilical vessels was to cool the blood. A similar theory is applied by Mayow to the respiration of the chick in the egg, the air not being enclosed in the cavity in the egg, as this would not be enough, but is somehow mixed up with the egg itself; egg white or yolk in a vacuum froths from emission of air.

The air stored in the egg is not common air but 'that aerial something which is separated from common air by the action of the lungs', the rest being expelled, 'but what there is of air pure and vital (such as we are to suppose contained in the egg), may be compared and held to be equal to a great quantity of common air (non esse vulgarem, sed aerum illud, quod ab aere vulgari pulmonum ministerio secernitur . . . aeris autem puri, vitalisque (qualem in ovo contineri putandum est) cum magnâ aeris vulgaris quantitate conferri, & æquari potest).'[2] Laurent Bellini (Florence; 3 September 1643–8 January 1704), a disciple of Borelli, suggested that the air-sac (folliculis aeris) of the egg supplied the respiration of the fœtus.[3]

It is noteworthy that Mayow[4] speaks of particles of vital air (particulæ aeris vitales indolis nitro-salinæ esse videntur), and of the pure and vital part of the air (aeris autem puri, vitalisque),[5] equal in effect to a great quantity of common air, as synonymous with nitro-aerial spirit.

The fourth tract, *On Muscular Motion and Animal Spirits*[6] again criticises Willis and mentions Lower. It describes the anatomy of muscle. Mayow says that he did not doubt that an influx of 'animal spirits' through the nerves is necessary, since if a nerve be cut or obstructed, the muscle to which the nerve is distributed cannot contract. But this is not sufficient, and the arterial blood passing to the muscles probably deposits something necessary to muscular contraction, since Steno had found that if an artery is tied, the muscle to which it is distributed was unable to undergo contraction.[7] The motive particles secreted from the mass of the blood are salino-sulphureous, since in animals at rest fat is deposited on the muscles. The animal spirits also necessary to the motion are, Mayow suggests, formed from nitro-aerial particles which, descending from the brain, meet the salino-sulphureous particles,

---

[1] Beddoes, p. 56, says Mayow totally rejects Everard's premises, whilst adopting his conclusion.
[2] II, 322; IIF, 219.
[3] *Opuscula ad Archibaldum Pitcairn*, 4°, Leyden, 1714, prop. ix, xii; Daremberg, (1), 1870, ii, 768.
[4] II, 300.   [5] II, 322.   [6] II, ii, 1–106.
[7] II, ii, 12, 15 f.; Steno's assertion is erroneous.

effervesce with them, and being thrown into agitation produce the contraction of all muscles, including the heart. The inspired air tends rather to the heating than to the cooling of the blood. The nitro-aerial particles are separated from the mass of the blood in violent movements, are spent in the contraction of the muscles, and are lost. A mixture of most highly rectified spirit of wine and spirit of nitre deprived of its moisture produces a conspicuous heat, for the nitro-aerial particles of the acid, and the very volatile salino-sulphureous particles of which the spirit of wine consists, excite one another to motion. In the production of animal spirits the salino-sulphureous particles are more exalted than those producing animal heat, and are put in a condition of the highest vigour. Mayow illustrates his theory by a feeble experiment, the twisting of a violin string heated by a candle flame, which he thought imparted nitro-aerial particles to it.[1] Yeats[2] said: 'The æther of Sir I. Newton, the fire-air particles of Mayow, with the oxygen and nervous electricity of modern times, have perplexed, divided, and confounded the medical world' in the explanation of muscular action, and the subject is even now only beginning to be elucidated. A recent theory is that muscular motion is produced by acetylcholine liberated from the nerves.

The 'so-called ferment' of the stomach is chiefly composed of nitro-aerial particles deposited through the medium of the nerves or the membranes of the stomach, there mixed with a proper fluid (liquori idoneo) secreted from the blood by glandular membranes and carried into the stomach, to compose its fermenting liquid (liquor ejus fermentativus componitur). If the stomach is empty, its inner membranes are irritated by the nitro-aerial particles and hunger is produced.[3] The 'so-called ferment' of the pancreas is also composed of nitro-aerial particles and the spleen serves as a reservoir for these. Mayow thus rejects Van Helmont's theory of ferments, and his theory is retrograde.

Mayow mentions that, after he had written, de Graaf's De Succo Pancreatico (Leyden, 1663) had come into his hands, in which the same use was assigned to the pancreatic juice as by himself, viz. to form by its union with bile a proper digestive for the chyme, but he disagreed with de Graaf's view that the juice was acid (it is, in fact, feebly alkaline).[4] Mayow's theory of the function of the spleen as a reservoir of arterial blood which, in certain circumstances, passes to the stomach and bowels to assist digestion, was adopted (mentioning Mayow) by W. Stukely.[5]

The fifth tract 'On Rickets'[6] is a revised form of that published in 1668 (p. 583), the first part being identical apart from a few variations to improve the style. A hypothesis in which an 'explosive matter' in the muscles concurs with a 'locomotive spirit' from the nerves[7] is omitted; this assumed that animal spirit and blood unite and the ebullition is carried off in fumes (etenim spiritus animales & sanguis simul uniti, ebullitione suâ in halitus absumuntur).[8] The treatment is also changed and numerous prescriptions are added. The disease is said to be caused by a deficiency of nervous juices or animal spirits (causa ulterior . . . nihil aliud esse potest praeter spirituum

[1] II, ii, 78.   [2] 1798, 174.   [3] II, ii, 55–7.   [4] II, ii, 58.
[5] Of the Spleen, 1723.   [6] II, ii, 107–52.   [7] I, 96.   [8] I 98.

animaliam defectum . . . non tantum ad nutritionem, sed etiam ad motum omnino requiruntur).[1]

According to Fulton, Mayow is the second English writer (the first being Glisson) to publish a tract on rickets; 'not only does he give a clear description of the clinical symptoms . . . but his suggestions concerning orthopaedic management are novel and praiseworthy.' Mayow says that he will 'with apologies to so eminent a man [Glisson] repeat some things he has said before, as this cannot be avoided'.

Glisson's work,[2] which was based on an earlier small one by Arnold de Boot,[3] assumed that rickets is due to imperfect nutrition (ἀλογοτροφία) and has its seat in the spinal marrow, as Mayow also supposed. He also laid stress on diet.

Francis Glisson (1597–1677), professor of medicine in Cambridge (in absentia) and London, in his book on the nature of substance,[4] assumed that every substance has a fundamental substance in virtue of which it exists, an 'energetic' in virtue of which it acts, and an 'additional' which gives it its accidental qualities; he attributed feeling to all matter and has always been regarded as having anticipated Leibniz.[5] In another work[6] Glisson anticipated Haller in attributing 'irritability' to muscular fibre. Walter Charleton[7] had similar but vaguer ideas.[8]

Mayow's treatise on rickets was translated into English[9] by the otherwise unknown William Sury.

Mayow's medicine is notably rational. He has nothing of the superstititous practice still found in Boyle and long after Mayow, and he seems to have tried to base his theories on mechanical principles yet without bringing in Iatro-mechanics (p. 442). His remedies, although perhaps ineffective, are not disfigured by 'sympathetic' components, and he completely avoided the use of amulets, still approved by Boyle.

APPRECIATION AND CRITICISM OF MAYOW

Nicolas Lemery in his famous text-book[10] explains that nitre is impregnated with abundance of spirits from the air; it is not at all inflammable, as most chemists believe, but where it finds sulphur it unites with it and promotes its combustion by its volatile part. If it is thrown into a red-hot crucible it will not burn, but if thrown on coals, which contain sulphur, it is kindled. This is practically what Mayow says.[11]

John Nicholas Pechlin (Leyden, 1646–Stockholm, 1706), for a time professor of medicine in Kiel (1673–80), referred to the participation of nitrous

[1] I, 95–6; II, ii, 126–7.
[2] De rachitide sive morbo puerili qui vulgò The Rickets dicitur, London, 1650, 2 ed. 1660, 3 ed. Leyden, 1671; A Treatise of the Rickets, transl. by Armin. Enlarged [and] Corrected by N. Culpeper, 8°, London, 1651 (two printings with different t.ps., one omitting Culpeper's name).
[3] Observationes medicæ de affectibus omissis, London, 1649, Helmstädt, 1664.
[4] De Naturâ Substantiæ Energeticâ, 4°, London, 1672.
[5] Sprengel, (1), v, 272, 277; Foster, 1901, 111, 287; Pagel, in Singer, (1), i, 503 (portr.).
[6] De Ventriculo et Intestinis, 12°, Amsterdam, 1677.
[7] Oeconomia Animalis, 12°, Hague, 1681.
[8] Sprengel, (1), v, 274–6.
[9] Ραχιτιδολογια or a Tract of the Disease Rhacitis Commonly called the Rickets . . . , 12°, Oxford, 1685; The Mothers Family Physician . . . Being a Discourse of the Disease in Children, commonly called the Rickets, . . . , 12°, Oxford, 1687 (reissue with new t.p.); Fulton, 1936, 52.
[10] Cours de Chymie, 1675; tr. W. Harris, A Course of Chymistry, 1677, 171.   [11] II, 1–8.

particles (particulæ nitrosæ) in respiration, mentioning Drebbel and Thruston but not Mayow.[1]

Mariotte[2] said 'some anatomists' think air mixes with the blood in the lungs during respiration, but this is not at all necessary since there is plenty of aerial matter in that of the veins, although experiments with the air pump show that arterial blood gives a larger quantity of air bubbles than venous blood. The change of colour of the blood is due to filtration in the membranes of the lungs, when it is purified and made more subtle. Some chemists speak of a nitro-aerial spirit (esprit nitro-aerièn) in the air, but alkali solution exposed to air does not form saltpetre, which rises from the interior of the earth to its surface in caves; with inflammable exhalations it is the cause of thunder. Air does not furnish a nitro-aerial matter to flame, which is extinguished in air because it is too compressed; when it is insufficiently compressed, as in an air-pump receiver, it is also extinguished, except gunpowder, when the spirit of the saltpetre blows the flame.

BARBERIUS

Gmelin[3] and Hoefer[4] mention a book by 'L. M. Barbieri' which they date 1681; the correct date, 1680, was given by N. Scherer.[5] This book was re-issued with notes by Luigi Angeli in 1828:

I. Spiritvs / Nitro-Aerei / Operationes / in Microcosmo. / Illvstriss. et Ampliss. / Senatvi / Imolensi. / Ludouicus Maria Barberius / Imolensis, Philosophiæ / & Medicinæ Doctor / D.D.D. / Bononiæ, M.DC.LXXX. / Typis Iosephi Longi. Super. permissu. 12°, vi ll., 156 pp.; dedication, preface, and imprimatur given by Brother Thomas Mazza, Inquisitor-General of Bologna (BM 780. a. 19).

II. Osservazioní e Rilievi fatti sull' Opera di Lodovico M. Barbieri Medico Imolese stampata in Bologna l'anno 1680 la quale sendo di sommo pregio, e l'Edizione Rarissima ha determinato a procurarne la ristampa il suo concittadino Cavaliere Luigi Angeli. . . . (Imola: dai Tipi d'Ignazio Galeati, 1828.) Portrait of Barberius, pp. (10), vi, 64, 30, (4), with notes by Angeli (14 pp.); extract of a letter from Professor G. Carradori to Professor L. Brugnatelli, 'Prove dell' Antichità dei Principj della Moderna Chimica Pneumatica in Italia' (pp. 15–30); note by Angeli, 1 p.; approbation, 1 p. (Historical Library, Yale Medical Library).

The book is mentioned by Manget[6] and Mazzuchelli[7] and a short analysis of it appeared in 1782[8] which was probably the source of Gmelin's reference. Attention was drawn to it by Carradori[9] and Gaspare Brugnatelli[10] who attempted to show that Barberius anticipated Lavoisier, but Carradori in the supplement to II (1828) pointed out that most of the material was borrowed from Mayow, as Barberius himself admits. The book by Barberius has five essays and a dissertation:

[1] Pechlin, De Aeris et Alimenti defectu ac Vita sub Aqvis Meditatio, 8°, Kiel, 1676 (BM 784. a. 27), 87 (Thruston), 127 (Drebbel), 140–2 (particulæ nitrosæ).
[2] Discours de la Nature de l'Air, 1676; Oeuvres, 1717, i, 179–82.
[3] (1), ii, 113.   [4] (1), ii, 262.
[5] Allgem. Journ. Chemie, 1803, x, 571; B. Boni, Isis, 1955, xlvi, 279; Partington, ib., 1959, l, 211.
[6] Bibliotheca Scripta Medicorum, f°, Geneva, 1731, i, 229.
[7] Gli Scrittori d'Italia, Brescia, 1763, II, ii, 302.   [8] Acta Eruditorum, 1782, i, 304–5.
[9] Giornale di Fisica, Chimica, Storia Naturale, Pavia, 1813, vi, 153–7; G. Cervetto, Di Giambatista da Monte, Verona, 1839, 116.
[10] Guida allo Studio della Chimica Generale, Pavia, 1819, i, 26.

Exercitatio Prima. De ingressu aeris in sanguinem. De aeris parte, quæ sanguinem ingreditur. De modo respirationis. I, 1–31.
Exercitatio II. Concoctio à spiritu nitro-aereo. I, 32–74.
Exercitatio III. À Spiritu nitro-aereo nutritio. I, 75–101.
Exercitatio IIII. À Spiritu nitro-aereo sanguinis depurationes. I, 103–14.
Exercitatio V. À Spiritu nitro-aereo sanguificatio. I, 115–33 (p. 134 blank).
Dissertatio Epistolica Ad Illustriss. ac Sapientiss. Virum Comitem Scipionem Saxatellvm de Pororum Bilisiorum vsu. I, 135–56.

Authorities quoted include Highmore, Thruston, de le Boë Sylvius, Lower, Malpighi, Boyle, Mayow, Harvey, Swammerdam, Severinus, Deusing, Willis, Descartes, Diemerbroeck, Fracassatus, Graaf, Wharton, Bartholinus, Needham, Steno, Cole, Dodoens, and Apinus. Mayow is named and quoted at the beginning (I, pp. 12, 19 and 27); his experiments on burning sulphur, on a candle and a mouse in a receiver, on the burning of gunpowder under water, on the calcination of antimony, and on the effervescence of arterial blood in a vacuum are described and attributed to him. Before this Barberius says that *spiritus nitro-aereus* is the elastic part of the air (*pars namque nitro-aerea, à qua aeris elastica habetur*), and wrongly suggests that he originated the name (*spiritus nitro-aerei nomine per me*). In the first essay he says (before mentioning Mayow) that this spirit passes from the air in the lungs into the blood, that it causes the motion of the muscles, effervesces with sulphur in the blood, and produces a flame (*flammula*) which maintains life. In his second essay he identifies the nitro-aerial spirit with the subtle matter of Descartes (*est enim materia subtilis Cartesiana*), which is also the same as animal spirits. The salino-sulphureous particles of Mayow are also called a spirit, which is like spirit of wine (*spiritus salino-sulphurei, vti Vini spiritus*). Thus the cause of inebriation is the presence of sulphur in the blood. The nitro-aerial spirit vitalises the ovum and is the cause of the development of the embryo. In the third essay the presence of nitro-aerial spirit (or vital spirits) in the blood is said to be the cause of nutrition. It effervesces with the sulphur of the blood and this drives the nutriment into pores (*in partis nutriendæ poros impellere*). This process differs from lapidification, which forms tartar. The fourth essay says that the nitro-aerial spirit causes the separation from the blood of salts, which are carried off by the lymphatic ducts and excreted in the urine. The fifth essay explains that, just as spirit of wine diffuses through water to form a spirituous liquid, so the nitro-aerial spirit mixing with the chyle forms blood.

MUNDY

Henry Mundy (Henley-on-Thames, bapt. 21 September 1623–nr. Hurley, 28 June 1682), B.A.Oxon. 1647, headmaster of Henley grammar school and practitioner of medicine (apparently without a medical degree)[1] in his book[2]

---

[1] Porter, DNB, 1909, xiii, 1194.
[2] Βιοχρηστολογία seu Commentarii De Aere Vitale De Esculentis De Potulentis. Cum Corollario de parergis in Victu. Authore Hen. Hundy Med: Oxford Impensis Jo: Crosley, sm. 8°, 1680, xii ll., 362 pp. i l. ('Libb: impressi Joh: Crosley', including 'Mayow Tractatus quinque Medico-Physic'.); repr., Henr. Mundii Medic. Doct. Londinens. Opera Omnia Medico-Physica, Tractatibus tribus comprehensa. De Aere Vitale De Esculentis De Potulentis. Una cum appendice

gives (pp. 4–7) without mentioning Mayow's name, a summary of the *Tractatus Quinque*, speaking of *aer vitale, particulæ nitrosis, spiritus nitro-aerëi*, and *nitrum aereum*, and even the water spout. He quotes (p. 32) 'D. Jo: Mayow, quid de his rebus ingeniose commentatus est', with the passage 'nulla omnino foret hominum . . . amplus, unique suppetert'.[1] He quotes a great number of other authors throughout the book, including Monardes (pp. 97, 360 on tobacco). The part on air deals largely with its impurities, including metallic exhalations (as in Boyle). Solar heat is regarded as due to sulphur and nitro aereo (*sic*) (p. 7) and there is mention of a 'nitrosulphureorum furor' (p. 80). The 'Commentarii de Aere Vitali' (pp. 1–89), a section on mineral waters (pp. 315 f.) and very brief accounts 'de coffâ' and 'de thea' (pp. 351–2), occupy the rest of the book. J. Bohn[2] gives Mayow's theory of combustion without naming him.

KÖNIG

Emanuel König, professor in Basel (pp. 318, 713), in widely-read books, mentions Mayow often. In his book on the animal kingdom he refers at least eleven times to Mayow by name.[3] In the preface, in a list of English authors following Harvey, he puts Mayow before Willis and Lower:

post Harvæum ex Anglis clarent imprimis Mayovv egregiis de Nitro sale illo catholico hypothesibus, ac Willisius Cerebri & Nervorum Anatome . . . ; Lovverus item qui ea, quæ Harvæo circa motum sanguinis & Cordi accuratius posthac ex multis observationibus palàm facienda restabant, addidit.

König[4] attributes to Willis the idea that the blood is crowded with nitro-aerial particles breathed from the air (in quâ sanguis particulis nitro-aëris ex aëre haustus stipatus appellens), which pass to the brain and nerves and produce muscular motion:

spirituum nitro-aërorum non tantum aëris mollitio ad impressiones recipiendas, sed & ignis vigores ad actiones vibrandas dotetur, dum enim hi spiritus è cerebro in nervos jam ab ortu spiritus inflatos, influunt, musculus cum sanguine contrahant.

He quotes[5] Mayow's experiment[6] on the twisting of a violin-string on heating, and on the causes of epilepsy, melancholia, etc., by the effervescence of nitro-aerial particles from the nerves with salino-sulphureous particles in the blood, as Mayow ingeniously deduced from his hypothesis:[7]

in musculum motui determinato inservientem determinat fibrísque ejus ex particularum nitro-aërearum à nervis & sulphureo-salinarum ex vasis hæmagogis (ut Mayovv Op. Med. Phys. p. 363 ingeniosè è suis hypothesibus deducit) concursu velut classicum canit, ut ex suâ contortione facillimæ sint. . . .

de Parergis in Victu ut Chocolata, Coffe, Thea, Tabaco &c, sm. 8°, Leyden, 1685, 362 pp.; eds. of London 1681, Frankfurt 1685, Leipzig 1685, and Leyden 1715, are mentioned in DNB; the BM has only the 1680 ed. and one other, imperfect, ? 1685.

[1] *Tract. Quinque*, 1674, 127.

[2] *Dissertationes Chymico-Physicæ*, 4°, Leipzig, 1685, Dissert. iv, § 20.

[3] *Regnum Animale*, 4°, Basel, 1682 (full title see p. 713), pref. 4 *v*, 19, 25, 31, 47, 68, 72, 75· 85, 98.

[4] *Ib.*, 22–3.   [5] *Ib.*, 31.   [6] IIA, 359.   [7] Mayow, IIA, 353.

In his book on the mineral kingdom, König mentions Mayow on rickets,[1] on the action of heat on nitre,[2] on the formation of acid from sulphureous and nitro-aerial particles,[3] and on the hot-springs of Bath.[4]

Mayow is quoted in Vigani's text-book,[5] and Henricus Gerardus Herfeld[6] quoted Mayow 'de sale nitri, p. 4,' for nitro-aerial particles in the air.

ETTMULLER

Michael Ettmuller (d. 1683), professor of medicine in Leipzig, mentioned Mayow and Boyle in his lectures as having shown that air is necessary for combustion and respiration,[7] also Mayow's theory of the nitro-aerial spirit mixing in the blood with salino-sulphureous particles and exciting a vital fermentation which is requisite for animal life.[8]

NEUKRANZ

Zacharia Neukranz, of Hamburg, later a physician and inspector of schools in Torgau, presented under Ettmuller's presidency an elaborate thesis on respiration in which Mayow's theories are fully and critically discussed.[9] It quotes a large number of authors, including Guericke, Torricelli, Boyle, Lower, Thruston, Mayow, and Pechlin, and Mayow's *Tractatus Quinque* (1674) repeatedly by page. Chapter V explains Mayow's theory of the action of the diaphragm and the intercostal muscles in the mechanism of respiration.[10] Chapter VII deals with the mechanical properties of air, Guericke, Torricelli, and especially Boyle, being quoted.[11] Chapter VIII, entitled 'Loca ad quae aër in Respirantibus Hominibus pertingit, diligenter investigiat', repeatedly quotes Mayow,[12] e.g. on the effervescence of arterial blood in an air-pump receiver, the bulging in of a bladder closing the mouth of a vessel containing a mouse, and Mayow's refutation of Highmore by an experiment showing that the lungs do not protrude through an opening in the chest unless the thorax is contracted. (Much of this material is also in Mayow's book on Respiration of 1668.)

Chapter X ('Respirationis Humanæ Usus')[13] deals with Mayow's nitro-aerial

---

[1] *Regnum Minerale*, 4°, Basel, 1686, 40.   [2] *Ib.*, 133.   [3] *Ib.*, 162.   [4] *Ib.*, 183.
[5] *Medulla Chemiæ*, 8°, London, 1683, 8; 1693, 28.
[6] *Philosophicum hominis de corporis humani machina deque centro nobili, sede mentis tractatum, observationibus anatomicis confirmatum*, 8°, Amsterdam, 1685; enlarged, Leyden, 1687, 28.
[7] *De aëris inspiratione læsa*, in *Doctrinæ Practicæ*, c. xiii; *Opera*, Lyons, 1685, 174: Jam vero experimentis *Majovv. Tr. de spirit. nitri aëreo, & Boylei in sua machina* constat, parilem aëris ad ignem & vitam animalium esse necessitatem, & ut aëris alteratio aut defectus subitò ignem extinguit, ita etiam vitam tollit.
[8] *Opera Medica*, Frankfurt, 1696. i, 113 (*De Respirationis Usu*), quoting Mayow 'Tr. de Nitro, p. 147', i.e. II.
[9] *De Abtruso Respirationis Humanæ Negotio, Exulante famosa Vacui Fuga, ab Autore Zacharia Neukranz, Hamburgensi, hactenus Medicinæ Doctore, Physico Torgaviensi, & Scholæ ibidem Inspector*; in Ettmuller, *Opera Omnia: Nempe Institutiones Medicinæ . . . Chymia Rationalis; cum Collegio Causali, et variis curiosisue Dissertationibus*, 3 parts, la. 4°, Frankfurt, 1688, Pt. III, *Dissertationes Academicæ*, Dissert. V, pp. 12–53 (refs. are to this ed.); also in Ettmuller, *Operum Medicorum Theoretico-Practicum*, ed. J. C. Westphal, Frankfurt, 1697, la. 4°, Tomi Secundi Pars II, pp. 1846–86.
[10] 1688, 17–22.   [11] *Ib.*, 25 f.   [12] *Ib.*, 31 f.   [13] *Ib.*, 39 f., 42–3; 1697, 1874 f.

spirit, asks the attention of the reader for a careful discussion of the solid parts of Mayow's opinions, and gives ten arguments against them.

(i) It is improbable that the contraction of muscles can be caused by effervescences in them, since effervescences cause expansion and no closed vessel can withstand them.

(ii) Boyle has shown that the density of air, including factitious air, is only about a thousandth that of water. Let us grant that one part of liquid aerial spirit (*spiritus aerei*) can be condensed from 906 of air, and that one drachm of this liquid will furnish one grain of nitro-aerial salt (*salis istius nitro-aerei*). In one inspiration a volume of air equal to two ounces of river water is taken in, which will contain one grain of aerial liquor, and $\frac{1}{60}$ part of this is aerial salt. For one inspiration and expiration the heart beats four times and for each beat $\frac{1}{240}$ grain of salt is taken in. This tiny amount effervesces with a sufficient quantity of salino-sulphureous particles of the blood in the dense substance of the heart, and according to Mayow is enough to produce one systole or beat of the heart. The heart must beat 240 times to obtain one grain of nitrous salt from the air (*priusquam vel unicum granum salis istius nitrosi ex aere lucrari poterit*). In each beat, nevertheless, at least fifteen pounds of blood are moved, not to speak of that in the vessels of the body and the tissue around them. Therefore, during an hour the heart, by its incessant motion, can drag out no more than $14\frac{144}{240}$ grains of nitro-aerial salt from the reluctant lungs, according to Mayow's hypothesis.

(iii) How can the nitro-aerial salt penetrate the compact substance of the heart with its multitude of fibres (*quomodo sola Ispiratione in ipsam cordis compactam substantiam sal istud nitro-aereum . . . penetrare possit*)?

(iv) How is the salt separated from the air in the lungs? Surely, so many absurd conclusions encompass this hypothesis that it is surprising that such an otherwise clever man as Mayow had not foreseen them (*certe tam ridiculis consectariis tantisque difficultatibus angitur hæc hypothesis, ut mirer, ingeniosum alioquin Mayovvium hæc non prævidisse*).

(v) Frogs and leeches can live all winter under ice without air, and frogs breathe in mud and in small holes in the earth, as Van Helmont[1] had pointed out.

(vi) How does the fœtus respire, and its heart beat, in the uterus without air? (Mayow had actually explained this.)

(vii) Four criticisms are given of Mayow's explanation of Hooke's experiment with the dog.[2] Hooke, Mayow, and Thruston ascribed the death of the dog to a deficiency of nitro-aerial salt, but the true function of respiration is the removal of a fume (*halitus*) from the lungs. About two drachms of liquor like phlegm are separated in one or two inspirations, and if the nose is closed this passes into the blood. The air is also expanded by the heat of the lungs, and unless this air is let out by expiration it impedes the circulation. Again, why does an animal, with its lungs inflated by inspired air, soon die if its mouth and nose are closed?

---

[1] *Ortus Medicinæ*, 1652, 149.   [2] Ettmuller, *Operum*, 1688, 44.

(viii) Neukranz mentions the experiment of Drebbel reported by Boyle[1] in which a vial of liquor unstopped in a submarine enabled people to live in the enclosed space, but says the effect was due to the cold water outside condensing moisture in the breath, the liquor assisting this rather than supplying anything to the air.

(ix) The function of respiration is to maintain the circulation by keeping the lungs distended (*respirationis Usus est sanguinis haud interrupta circulatio*). In a Boyle's vacuum, the blood vessels in the lungs are damaged, the lungs collapse, the circulation is so impeded, and the death of an animal is due to this effect rather than to deprivation of nitro-aerial spirit in the air (see p. 448). Mayow's statement that if, after the heart has ceased to beat when respiration is stopped, air is blown through a tube fitted to the vena cava the heart beats again,[2] is discussed in considerable detail, Malpighi, Thruston, and Van Helmont being also quoted.

(x) Neukranz concluded that the nitro-aerial salt, the pabulum of life, and the universal spirit (*Mundi Spiritus*) are so many splendid words (*solo verborum splendore*).[3] For good measure he adds an epimetron on alchemy.

Gmelin and Hoefer mention a book by A. Littre[4] as referring to Mayow, but I have not been able to see it. John Viridet (b. 1655), mentions Mayow on animal spirits and nitro-aerial particles.[5]

MISCELLANEOUS AUTHORS

Stanford Wolferstan[6] postulated the absorption of an 'aereal salt' or 'nitrous salt' by the blood from the air in the lungs, which causes the motion of the heart by irritating its muscles, causes hunger by entering the stomach (with food) and lungs, prevents the coagulation of the blood, and facilitates secretion and the separation and expulsion of humours. Wolferstan[7] quotes a 'learned Author'[8] that air driven from the lungs is unsuitable for respiration or to support life, that an aerial something passes into the blood, and that air driven out of the lungs (these vital particles having been drained out of it) is no longer fit for breathing again.

Daniel Georg Morhof (Wismar, 6 February 1639–Lübeck, 30 July 1691) in a book which was widely read,[9] says of nitre: 'John Mayow has very learnedly and with much perseverance enquired into its composition in a whole treatise

---

[1] *Works*, 1744, i, 69. [2] Mayow, II, 307.
[3] 1688, 51. [4] *Ergo aer hominem nutrit*, Paris, 1689.
[5] *Tractatus Novus Medico-Physicus de Prima Concoctione Praecipuéque de Ventriculi Fermento . . .* , 8°, Geneva, 1691, 7 (Mayow on *particulis*, or *Spiritus, Nitro-aëreus*), 16–17 (nitro-aerial particles), 148 (*aëris nitrum*, Mayow not mentioned), 159 f. (*Frigoris natura in acidis & Nitrosi particulis*, only Boyle mentioned.) He distinguished, 120, three kinds of fermentation.
[6] *An Enquiry into the Causes of Diseases in general, and the Disturbances of the Humours in Man's Body: wherein the Nature of the Blood, of the Air, and of a Pestilential Constitution, are briefly considered. Together with some Observations, shewing wherein the Venom of Vipers, particularly that of the English Adder, does consist*, 12°, London, 1692, 9, 15, 22 f., 28, 33 f.
[7] *Ib.*, 71 f. [8] Mayow, II, 299.
[9] *Polyhistor Literarius, Philosophicus et Practicus*, 3 vols., Lübeck, 1688–92; 4 ed. (reprint), Lübeck, 1747 (the ed. quoted here); the second volume containing the material quoted was published posthumously in 1692.

on the subject, and has shown that there is a certain spirit, which he calls nitro-aerial, dispersed through the earth and air, whence air derived the production and permutation of all things.'[1] He gives a long summary of Mayow's theory of combustion as the collision of nitro-aerial and sulphureous particles, and of the nitro-aerial spirit;[2] of the origin of cold;[3] of an artificial spring;[4] the heat of Bath water;[5] the theory (which he does not accept) that light is constituted of nitro-aerial particles;[6] on the water-spout;[7] and Descartes' theory of the cause of thunder.[8]

Philip Verheyen (1648–1710), professor of anatomy and surgery at Louvain, mentions Mayow only in passing in the first edition of his text-book on anatomy,[9] but a supplement to the second edition[10] has a long section on respiration which mentions Mayow's tract on respiration with approbation (*quem ego in multis admodum ingeniòse & doctè conscriptum judicio*) and quotes from it. He also quotes Mayow's views on animal spirits. In his section on the use of respiration he gives long extracts from Mayow on nitrous particles in the air, and for further details refers readers to Mayow's tract (*legere poterit tractatem quem prælaudatus D. Mayow de sal nitro, & spiritu nitro-aëreo conscripsit*). He quotes Mayow's theory of muscular contraction but regards it as unsatisfactory (*non placet*), and he will not discuss how the air in the upper regions of the atmosphere becomes re-impregnated with nitrous material (*de novo imprægnetur materiâ nitrosâ*).

William Coward M.D. (Winchester, 1656–London, 1725), Fellow of Merton College, Oxford, mentions 'the most ingenious Mayow' five times.[11] Bernard Connor, M.D. (d. 1698), who lectured in Oxford about 1695 (when he became F.R.S.) dealt in great detail with Mayow's experiments and theories.[12] He says it had been assumed that a coalescence and fermentation of sulphureous and nitrous particles (*salino-volatilia*) occurs in the blood (*ad perennem sanguinis fermentationem fovendam sponte conspirent*); mentions the 'detonation' of particles of nitre in the air in a candle flame (*ut creditur*), and Boyle's experiments with a candle and animals in a vacuum. He begins his discussion of nitre and air (*sale nitrosam indolem, æmulante ita ut similac nitrosum aeris symbolum*; Boyle's idea) by mentioning Mayow's experiment with a candle and an animal in a closed vessel, and the detonation of nitrous particles with sulphur in gunpowder. Up to now he has not mentioned Mayow by name. He gives Mayow's older theory of nitre (as such) present in air (*Cl. D. Mayow quòd aeris nitrum*

---

[1] *Ib.*, ii, 422.   [2] *Ib.*, ii, 349.   [3] *Ib.*, ii, 351.   [4] *Ib.*, ii, 370.
[5] *Ib.*, ii, 371.   [6] *Ib.*, ii, 379.   [7] *Ib.*, ii, 382.   [8] *Ib.*, ii, 384.
[9] *Corporis Humani Anatomia*, 4°, Louvain, 1693, 125 (Cl. D. Mayow on the motion of the diaphragm), 256 (D. Mayow Doctori Londinensi visum fuit ratione, of the intercostal muscles).
[10] *Corporis Humani Anatomia*, 2 ed., 4°, Brussels, 1710; *Supplementum Anatomicum sive Anatomiæ Corporis Humani Liber Secundus*, sep. pag., 164–84.
[11] *De Fermento Volatili Nutritio Conjectura Rationalis. Quâ ostenditur Spiritum Volatilem Oleosum, è Sanguine suffusum, esse Verum ac Genuinum Concoctionis ac Nutritionis Instrumentum*, 8°, London, 1695 (BM 784. m. 20), 2 (animal spirits in nerves), 5 (*in Aere spiritus quidam Heterogenus, è fonte Nitroso*), 14 (*spiritu Nitro-aereo per pulmones sanguini communicato*), 30 (*Nervosi spiritûs affluxu (prout Mayovius*)), 47 (*acidum in Ventriculo . . . negant*), 129 (*subtiliores particulas, in Vesiculas pulmones haustas, massæ sanguineæ communicari si . . . Mayovio credamus*).
[12] *Dissertationes Medico-Physicæ*, sm. 8°, Oxford, 1695; I. *De Antris Lethiferis*, 50–77; Cooper, DNB, 1908, iv, 946.

in sanguinem introducitur per pulmones, quòd fermentat & attenuat ipsique fluorem & rubédinem conciliat, & quod spiritibus animalibus gigendis materiam suppeditat). He presumes to differ from such a distinguished man (*præclaros viros*) as Mayow only in the interests of truth. He says that nitre is not volatile when heated alone in a retort, and that neither air nor aerial nitre is necessary for the generation of flame (*sentiret quod neque aer neque nitrum aereum generandæ flammæ necessaria sunt*). In a second dissertation on the theories of the causes of volcanic fires (the ignition of antimony and nitre, iron and sulphur, etc.), Connor does not mention Mayow.

Lorenzo Bellini (1643–1704) adopted (without mentioning him) Mayow's views on the respiration of the fœtus, the air-sac in the egg, and the admixture of air in the lungs with the blood (*admiscetur aeri, vel illi rei, quæ ab aere secernitur per respirationem*).[1]

Pitcairne, an Iatromathematician (p. 442), criticised Mayow's experiment[2] on the effervescence of arterial blood in an air-pump receiver, and denied that nitro-aerial particles are a cause of elasticity. Pitcairne thought Mayow's experiment could be convincing only if the following proposition was shown to be untrue. Take two equal portions of the same liquid, which have absorbed equal parts of air by weight, thoroughly mixed with them; then a greater portion of air can be withdrawn by the air-pump from the portion of liquid that is thoroughly mixed and thin than from that which is not thin, provided that the pumping is done in the same time and equally for each liquid. For arterial blood is thinner than venous blood.[3]

John Conrad Barchusen, of Utrecht (see p. 700), goes through Mayow's book (1674) in great detail and points out its contradictions. According to Mayow, nitro-aerial particles are sometimes solid and sometimes liquid, sometimes hot and sometimes cold, 'and I do not know what else besides.' They change their form like Proteus. The true causes would be obvious to all who were not blockheads (*plane plumbeus*) in chemistry. But in a mention of Mayow's experiment with the gas from nitric acid and iron causing a contraction of a volume of air, Barchusen stupidly says that if the fumes contain nitro-aerial particles it would have been expected that these would increase the volume.[4]

Georgio Baglivi (Ragusa, 1668–Rome, 1708), professor of medicine in Rome, quoted Mayow's system of aerial nitre along with the chemical philosophers, Gilbert on the magnet, the practical system of acid and alkali, and the triumvirate of humours, as new medical and philosophical theories of which he disapproved because they were based on too few experiments. Baglivi found that saliva on evaporation leaves a whitish saline residue, hence it contains a

---

[1] *Opuscula Aliquot, ad Archibaldum Pitcarnium . . . , Digressio de Ovo, Oviaere, et Respiratione in Genere*, 4°, Leyden, 1696, 45 f., 55 f., 77 f., 85 (respiration); the passages are contained in the editions of Leyden, 1714 and 1731, pp. 48 f., 83 f. [2] II, 149.

[3] Pitcairne, *Dissertatio De Caussis diversæ molis qua fluit sanguis per pulmonem natis & non natis; Dissertationes Medicæ*, 4°, Rotterdam, 1701, 44–6; 4°, Edinburgh, 1713, 53 f.; *Opera Omnia*, 4°, Leyden, 1737, 231–2.

[4] *Acroamata, In quibus complura ad Iatro-Chemiam atque Physicam Spectantia, Jocunda rerum varietate, explicantur*, 8°, Utrecht, 1703, Dissertatio IV–V, *Confutatio Spiritus Nitroaerei*, 63–83.

nitrous saline salt analogous to the universal salt (*sal nitro-salinum universali sali analogum*) to which it owes its virtue, and a similar but black salt is obtained on evaporating snow.[1]

In his essay on blood and respiration[2] Baglivi mentions a theory that aerial nitre is filtered off by the lungs and mixes with the blood. He thought part of some aerial salt (*salem aëris*) is so used but it is not all nitre (*sed totam nitri quantitatem omnino nego*). It is more likely that the aerial salt is dissolved in the saliva and passes into the blood by way of the stomach. Baglivi quotes Duhamel and Sendivogius for a nitrous spirit infused in all nature (*imo spiritum illum nitrosum infusum esse in omni natura*).[3] In discussing the nervous fluid Baglivi says no one can with prudence assert it to be in some way fiery, sulphureous, nitrous, and impetuous like gunpowder; those physicians are wanting in wisdom who continually ascribe great force, activity, and power to spirits and the nervous fluid. If the motion of the body was produced with such a great impetus and continual explosion which the spirit excites in the parts, as nitre makes in gunpowder, then men, instead of moving naturally, would be continually and vehemently subject to convulsions.[4]

Gunther Christoph Schelhamer distinguished clearly the 1668 and 1674 works of Mayow. He says Mayow audaciously thought that air is full of nitre, that spirit of nitre forms air, and that nitre can be formed artificially from alkali and nitric acid, all of which he denies.[5]

Martin Lister[6] says nitre is not sufficiently volatile to exist in air, and (as Borrichius had shown) it is not itself inflammable. Lister denied that there is a fermentation in the blood. Louis Lemery in a memoir on the origin of nitre mentions 'Mayou, Auteur Anglois et grand defenseur du Nitre-Aèrien', and gives a brief summary of his experiments and theories.[7] Charles Malouin (1694–1717), an Iatromathematician and a follower of Borelli, dealt with fermentation and held a theory of 'oscillations' based on Borelli's. Animal spirits, he says, were regarded by Willis as igneous and urinous, by Borelli as sulphureous and like spirit of wine, by Paschal as acid, by Wirdigius as sweet, Vieussens as volatile and spirituous, whilst 'Monsieur Majovv les admet Nitro-aëriens'. The elasticity of bodies comes from air in their fibres, and air is the cause of the elasticity of other bodies, which consist of corpuscles or atoms capable of being set in motion by irritation.[8]

---

[1] *Praxeos Medicæ*, bk. ii, ch. 1; *De fibra motrice specimen*, bk. i, ch. 1; *De Salivæ natura*; *Opera*, 2 vols. 12°, Leipzig, 1827–8; i, 206, 314, 328–9; ii, 79.

[2] *De Sanguine et respiratione, de statice aëris et liquidorum*; *Opera*, 4°, Lyons, 1704, 459–60; *Opera*, 1828, ii, 120.

[3] *De vegetatione lapidum*; *Opera*, 1828, ii, 174.

[4] *De fibra motrice specimen*, i, 7; *Opera*, 1827, i, 375.

[5] *De Nitro Cum Veterum, tum Nostro Commentatio. Qua Utriusque ortus & natura excutiuntur, multa de eo veterum Græcorum, Latinorum, Arabum loca currupta emendantur, & explicantur, virtutesque ejus & utilites ad rectæ rationis leges expenduntur*, sm. 8°, Amsterdam, 1709, 68, 99 f., 237.

[6] *Dissertatio de Humoribus*, 1709, 72 f., 88, 278; the ref. to Borrichius is to *Nitrum non inflammari*, in his *Acta Medica et Philosophica Hafniensia*, Copenhagen, 1680, v, 213–16; he had obtained oxygen gas by heating nitre without identifying it.

[7] AdS 1717, h 29, m. 31.

[8] *Traité des Corps Solides et des Fluides, ou Examen du Mouvement du Sang, de celui du Cœur, des Artéres, & des autres vaisseaux du Corps Humain, Selon les Loix de la Mécanique, de la*

Giambattista Mazini (d. 1743), a follower of Borelli and professor of medicine in Padua, thought particles of light enter the blood in the lungs and give it its red colour, rather than Mayow's nitro-aerial spirit. Chemists had found that volatile salts mixed with sulphureous spirits gave a red tincture, which may be formed in the blood in the lungs from such materials.[1] Mazini speculated on sulphureous particles in the blood and chyle; he says air as such cannot mix with the blood but Lana had found that water is condensed from air on a cooled vessel, and in some such way it might enter the blood (*hæ necessariò unitæ sero supra caetera elementa naturaliter frigidiori*). Malignant fevers are due to the mixture of spirit of nitre and a spirit of vitriol; these are innocuous by themselves but when mixed they form a third substance which acts like water of Styx in dissolving all bodies.[2]

TABOR

John Tabor, of Lewes, in an iatromathematical work[3] in which Borelli is largely drawn upon, has several references to Mayow. In Tract. I, Cap. II (*Quod Aer in Pulmones inspiratus, Sanguini admisceatur*, pp. 86–92) he refers to Boyle's experiment on the effervescence of blood in a vacuum; this shows that there is much air in the blood, which was received in the lungs. He refers to Mayow's experiments on the respiration of a mouse in a confined volume of air and to Pitcairne's criticism of them, in which he said that air in which an animal has died is, soon after, of the same density and elasticity as it was when the animal was shut up in it. But several experiments of Mayow[4] had shown that air by the respiration of animals is always diminished in dimensions or extension, which is called by Mayow a diminution of elater (*Aeris dimensionem seu extensionem, ab Animali respirante semper imminui; quæ Aeris alteratio à Mayovio nuncupatur, Imminutio Elaterii*). In Tract. II, Cap. I (*De Respirationis usu primario*) Tabor,[5] after quoting Boyle and saying that the air particles are compressible like springs, and that air can be loaded or entangled with foreign particles (*aer alienigenis corpusculis onerari vel implicari possit*), proceeds to dilate on the opinion of 'our Mayow',[6] which is prevalent but is trifling and futile. His aerial nitre which, if he is to be believed, is involved in the kindling of fires, the growth of plants, and the origination of animal motion, is a jumble of everything (*totam Rem confecisse credita sunt*).

Physique & de la Médecine . . . mis en lumière par M. Jacques-Laurent Malouin, sm. 8°, Paris: chez Jouenne, 1718, 70, 90 f., 99 f., 115 f.

[1] *Mechanices Morborum desumptæ a Motu Sanguinis, Auctore Joanne Baptista Mazino*, 4°, Brescia, 1723, 83–4; 2 ed., 4°, Paris and Leyden, 1731, i, 53–4; Daremberg, (1), i, 839.

[2] *Op. cit.*, 1731, iii, 4, 16, 25, 44, 50; q. Boyle, etc., but not Mayow.

[3] *Exercitationes Medicæ, quæ tam Morborum quam Symptomatum in plerisque Morbis rationem illustrant*, 8°, London, 1724 (imprimatur dated February 1711). John Tabor, born 1667 at Faccombe, Hampshire, son of John Tabor, Rector of Faccombe (1656), matriculated at Merton College, Oxford, on 30 March 1684, graduated B.A. in 1687, M.A. 1690, M.B. 1694; the above is his M.D. thesis; see J. Foster, *Alumni Oxonienses*, Oxford, 1892, iv, 1453; A. Portal, *Histoire de l'Anatomie et de la Chirurgie*, 1770, iii, 390; iv, 622; Sprengel, (2), 1828, V, i, 233, 349; Partington, *Isis*, 1959, l, 211.

[4] II, 102–3.   [5] *Ib.*, 139–55.

[6] *Ib.*, 147: the marginal title is: De Nitro Aereo, Popularis, nugatoria tamen & futilis, percrebuit Opinio.

Tabor's next paragraph, entitled in the margin 'the hallucinations of Mayow on aerial nitre', quotes several passages from the *Tractatus Quinque*[1] which Tabor thinks are self-contradictory; he has quoted to show the wavering and vacillation of the author's meaning and notions and the vanity and uncertainty of his hypothesis.

FIG. XXII.

FIG. XXIII.

FIG. 28. TABOR'S APPARATUS.

In Tract. II, Cap. II, on the use of air in sustaining flame (*De Aeris usu ad Flammam Sustentandam*)[2] Tabor refers to Mayow's experiment with the candle as insufficiently careful for his purpose, since when the receiver is brought over the candle flame, some of the air in it is expanded by the heat of the flame and escapes, and the air is much expanded in a sphere or cone surrounding the flame.

Tabor used a tallow candle giving a cone of flame which, inclusive of the wick, occupied $\frac{3}{10}$th cu. in. The region in which the air was heated by the combustion was not less than 4 to 5 in. wide and 8 in. high. The apparatus is shown in Fig. 28. A glass globe with a cylindrical neck $2\frac{5}{10}$ in. diam. on which was pasted a paper scale, had a total capacity of 75672 grains of water or 295·59 cu. in., each division of the scale containing 125 grains of water. To find the expansion of the air due to the heat of the flame, the candle was fixed to a stand, with its wick just above the surface of water in which it was immersed. The receiver was put over the flame, and at the instant when it entered the water the candle was submerged and extinguished. After two minutes, when the air had cooled again, the water rose in the neck of the receiver 0·7 in., and hence the expansion by the heat of the flame was $7 \times 125 = 875 \div 256$ (the number of grains of water in 1 cu. in.) $= 3·41$ cu. in., or 22 times the volume of the candle flame.

To the neck of the receiver was cemented a glass or brass collar C, to which a bladder D was attached by wire (Tabor's Fig. XXII). The receiver was held by a frame ABCD (Tabor's Fig. XXIII) immersed in water so that the water surface was about 1 in. above the step E on which the lighted candle was fixed. All the air in the bladder was pressed out and the receiver was put over the candle. As soon as the receiver touched the water the bottom of the bladder was gently lifted so that the air expanded by the candle flame passed into it and did not bubble through the water. Then the frame and receiver together were slightly lifted, the air in the bladder passing again into the receiver, and the frame was placed on a stool, so that the mouth of the receiver was fixed motionless two inches below the surface of the water. In 1 min. 30 sec. the candle went out and after 45 mins., when the receiver and the air in it had cooled, the water had risen about $2\frac{1}{10}$ in. in the neck. After 24 hours the water had subsided to $1\frac{6}{10}$ in. The maximum decrease of elater or extension of the air is $\frac{1}{43}$. After 24 hours the air had recovered its former extension to

[1] II, 5–6, 10–11, 18–19, 31.   [2] *Op. cit.*, 156–69.

about $\frac{1}{67}$th of the capacity of the receiver. The candle had lost 2 grains of tallow.

Tabor then repeated the experiment of Mayow (who is not mentioned) of generating nitric oxide in the air of the receiver. He put steel filings mixed with nitre in a pot O, and aqua fortis in a phial P. The receiver was put over, and by means of a thread F the phial was inverted and the acid poured into O. This was followed by a tremendous commotion (*lucta ingens*) and the bladder D swelled. After twenty hours the water had subsided to $\frac{9}{10}$ in.; and after many days had practically reached its original level. Tabor's apparatus evidently leaked.

After several trials it was found that one grain of gunpowder could be burnt by a cotton wick dusted with half a grain more, without air bubbling out. After two days the bladder subsided notably, after three days the water was elevated $\frac{8}{10}$ in.; only after six days was the rise a maximum of $1\frac{5}{10}$ in.; and after that the air began to recover its original volume until in the eighth day the water level was $\frac{8}{10}$ in. After burning gunpowder three times without purging the fumes from the receiver, the water after 24 hours had risen $1\frac{4}{10}$ in., and after 72 hours was only $\frac{8}{10}$ in. A candle was allowed to burn to extinction and then the receiver, without purging the air, was at once brought over another candle, which burnt for 10 or at most 15 seconds. But if the air had stood an hour the candle burnt for 20 seconds, after 12 hours it burnt 45 seconds, and after standing 24 hours, 50, or rarely 60, seconds.

Tabor thought that if the air agitated by the fumes of the burning matter, and contracted by their load, had been allowed to stand long enough it would have recovered its original volume and have become better able to sustain the burning of a flame than when it was first saturated with the fumes. That thick vapour which is naturally raised up by the action of heat is the substance of flame and flame itself. Air contributes in two ways to the burning of a candle. First, by its intimate mixture with the ignited vapour it enlarges its extension; and again by the resulting rapid rushing motion in the lowest part of the flame which comes in contact with the cup of melted tallow, that liquid is sucked up into the wick. The confined volume of air in which the flame burns passes through the flame and is saturated, loaded, and satiated with the particles thrown off by the flame. In this way the aerial particles are compressed and so the extension and spring of the air can be reduced. After no great time the air can shake off its constraining bones and ensnaring connexions and, anew unfolded, can again recover its pristine and absolute purity. Tabor then describes an experiment in which a small animal lived in the receiver for three to four hours, the air being moved about by frequently compressing the bladder. The residual air extinguished a candle, and Tabor refers to Mayow's experiment with the mouse and candle together. He found that after 48 hours the water had risen 6 in., hence the volume of the air had diminished about $\frac{1}{10}$th, while Mayow had found $\frac{1}{14}$th. The nitrous spirit or salt of the air is come upon only in conjectures, the inspired air being the principal instrument in vital processes and animal motion. Tabor's work, published just half a century after Mayow's, represents a retrogression rather than an advance.

ROBINSON

Bryan Robinson (1680–1754), professor of medicine in Dublin,[1] in the chapter on respiration in his book[2] says: 'The Life of Animals is preserved by acid Parts of the Air, mixing with the Blood in the Lungs: Which Parts dissolve or attenuate the Blood, and preserve its Heat; and by both these, keep up the Motion of the Heart.'

A candle goes out in a vacuum or in a small volume of air, in which an animal also dies. Hooke had found that when air is rendered effete, then when it is blown over live coals it has no effect but to blow off the ashes, and animals put into effete air soon die. Robinson mentions the inflaming of essential and other oils by spirit of nitre (nitric acid), an experiment first performed by Borrichius, and the experiment of Boyle and Mayow (without naming them) of burning a mixture of sulphur and nitre under water (they actually used gunpowder). He quotes (without naming him) several pages from Lower on the red colour which the blood acquires in the lungs (Lower is named on page 200 and Thruston on page 197; Mayow is nowhere mentioned), and Hooke's experiment with the dog. Robinson concludes that air 'preserves the Life of Animals, by the Operation of the very same Particles whereby it preserves Fire and Flame'. He refers to the heat evolved by the action of acids on iron as support for his theory that air contains 'acid parts' producing heat in the blood. It is not the elasticity of the air which is concerned with the support of flame and of life; if animals die or candles are extinguished in two different confined quantities of air, there is a greater diminution of elasticity in the smaller quantity than in the greater. The acid in the air dissolves or attenuates the blood; fire burns best in cold air. Robinson's book is full of mathematical calculations on flow through tubes, etc., Harvey and Newton being cited. It suggests to me that he had borrowed freely from Mayow and then suppressed his name.

Jean Pierre Crousaz[3] deals with phosphorescence, coal, subterranean fires, gunpowder, burning glasses, etc., and on nitrous spirits contained in the air, discussing Mayow's book at length.

John Arbuthnot, although freely quoting Boyle, Boerhaave, and (especially) Hales, and dealing with sulphurs, salts, damps, and respiration, does not mention Mayow.[4] Bernard Nieuwentyt (Westgraftdyck, N. Holland; 10 August 1654–30 May 1718)[5] supposed that the change of colour of blood to bright red on exposure to air is probably connected with the taking up of nitre, since meat pickled with saltpetre becomes bright

---

[1] Sprengel, (1), v, 173; Norgate, DNB, 1897, xlix, 4.

[2] *Treatise of the Animal Oeconomy*, 8°, Dublin, 1732; 3 ed. 1738; Prop. XXIV, 1732, 187–203; 1738, 190–206.

[3] *Dissertation sur la Nature, l'Action, et la Propagation du Feu*, sm. 8°, Bordeaux, 1729 (72 pp. BM *Recueil des Dissertations qui ont remporté le prix à l'Académie Royale de Bordeaux*, t. 3), 46.

[4] *An Essay Concerning the Effects of Air on Human Bodies*, 8°, London, 1733, 19 f., 94 f., 119 f.

[5] *The Religious Philosopher: Or, the Right Use of Contemplating the Works of the Creator . . . Throughout which, all the late Discoveries in Anatomy, Philosophy and Astronomy, together with the various Experiments made use of to illustrate the same, are most copiously handled. Translated from the Low-Dutch, by John Chamberlain, F.R.S. To which is prefixed, a Letter to the Translator, by the Reverend J. T. Desaguliers, LL.D., F.R.S.*, 3 ed., 3 vols. London, 1724, i, 50 (Dutch ed. 1720).

red. Thomas Knight[1] thought that the red colour of blood was due to a compound of sulphur and alkali, and the white colour of chyle is the result of the action of an acid on this.

HALLER

Albrecht von Haller (Bern; 18 October 1708–12 December 1777) studied in Tübingen (1723) and at Leyden under Boerhaave (1725; M.D. 1727), visited Belgium, England (where he became the friend of Sir Hans Sloane) and France, and studied under John Bernoulli in Basel (1728), returning to Bern in 1730; he was professor of anatomy, botany, and medicine in a chair in Göttingen created for him by King George II in 1736. Refusing offers from Oxford and Berlin, he returned to Bern in 1753 to spend his remaining years in retirement.[2] His famous and widely read text-book of human physiology[3] shows very wide reading.

Haller, a pupil of Boerhaave, was well acquainted with physical researches on air. He gave a long discussion of respiration in his book on Physiology, Book VIII on that subject (*Respiratio*) in volume iii (1761) occupying pages 1–365. In it he repeatedly quotes Mayow by page in the 1674 edition of the *Tractatus Quinque*, and also, among a multitude of authors, Boyle, Hooke, Lower, Thruston, Perrault, Sylvius, Hales, Boerhaave and Musschenbroek. He also quotes his own experiments on respiration, previously published.[4]

The earlier part of the *Elementa Physiologiæ* has several incidental references to Mayow.[5] Section iii of book VIII (*Aer*)[6] deals mostly with physical properties of air, but[7] quotes Mayow's experiment with the mouse and correctly says that Mayow was the first to observe that air loses its elater as a consequence of respiration, $\frac{1}{14}$th of it being consumed by the respiration of a mouse. In this section, dealing with the causes which destroy the elater of air, Haller says he finds it difficult to understand why the reduction of elater should make air unfit for respiration. He mentions that Mayow had observed a loss of $\frac{1}{30}$th in. air in which a tallow candle had burnt, and had found the factitious air from the solution of metals in acids unfit for respiration.[8]

In Section iv (*Respiratio*) Haller[9] quotes Mayow on the mechanism of respiration, and Hooke and Mayow for the fact that air can be breathed from a phial with a long neck or a bladder, as disproving Plato's theory on the basis of abhorrence of a vacuum. The experiment with the bladder inside a bellows[10] and Mayow's theory of the mechanism of laughter[11] are mentioned.

[1] *An Essay on the Transmutation of Blood; Containing the Ætiology: Or, An Account of the immediate Cause of Putrid-Fevers or Agues* (Anon.), 8°, London, 1725 (BM T. 336. (4.), 52 pp.), 11; Sprengel, (1), 1815, v, 129; on colour of blood see E. Farber, *Isis*, 1954, xlv, 3.

[2] Foster, 1901, 204–12; Hoefer and Jourdan, NBG, 1858, xxiii, 167–80.

[3] *Elementa Physiologiæ Corporis Humani*, 8 vols. 4°, Lausanne, 1757–66 (pref. to vi lists his own discoveries). Foster says if we open its pages 'we feel that we have passed into modern times', although it has 'no small deficiencies in all that relates to the chemical changes in the body'.

[4] *Opuscula Anatomica de Respiratione, de Monstris, aliaque minora*, 8°, Göttingen, 1751; *Opuscula Pathologica . . . Accedunt Experimenta de Respiratione*, 8°, Venice, 1755.

[5] 1761, iii, 24, 44, 92.   [6] *Ib.*, iii, 179–224.

[7] *Ib.*, 206; Mayow, II, 102–3.   [8] *Ib.*, 210.   [9] *Ib.*, 228–30.

[10] *Ib.*, 237: '& experimentum fecit Johannes Mayow l.c. quem alii Cl. viri imitati sunt.'

[11] *Ib.*, 305; Mayow, II, 295.

The long Section v on the use of respiration (*Respirationis Utilitas*)[1] explains Mayow's theory of aerial nitre (*nitrum aëreum*) entering the lungs, and thence reaching the blood, giving this a bright red colour and by fermentation producing heat in it; Haller thought this theory doubtful. In his small text-book[2] Haller says there is nitre in the air but it is of no use in respiration (*non ideo haec utilitas respirationis est*). Mayow gives no mechanism for the removal of the air after its use (*non videntur machinis ad educendum aërem idoneis unquam usi esse*).[3]

Haller's own view of the use of respiration is that the function of the lungs is to expel the poisonous moisture and noxious air contained in them. The suction of the thorax is to facilitate the return of the blood to the heart, and inspired air, like all air in the body, acts as a kind of glue.[4] He concludes by saying that the various explanations of the functions of respiration do not satisfy him completely and he wishes for a better one.[5] As Boruttau[6] says, Haller's uncritical survey of his material presents a dreary picture (*ein recht trostloses Bild*).

BERNOULLI

James Bernoulli (Basel; 25 December 1654–16 August 1705), professor of mathematics in Basel, frequently refers to Boyle's experiments on the compressibility of air.[7] His brother, John Bernoulli (Basel; 27 July 1667–1 January 1748), professor of mathematics in Groningen and later in Basel, F.R.S. 1712, in his dissertation of 19 September 1690, on effervescence and fermentation, refers to Mayow.[8]

Bernoulli defines effervescence and fermentation as more and less violent types of internal motion (chs. iii–iv). He complains that chemists are not clear in their definitions, e.g. of acid and alkali, and use horrible names; he proposes to free the science from its imperfections and reconstitute it on physical principles (nova quoque principia physica constituerentur) or mechanical laws, which would not be difficult (præsens negotium mechanicæ legibus explicare possim; ad quam normam, aliarum operationum Chymicarum causas pervestigare mihi difficile non esset) (ch. viii). He does this on Descartes' model. Bodies which produce effervescence on mixing contain tetrahedral active particles, which break up the eight-rayed passive particles (ch. ix; Plate, Figs. 1–2), liberating the air compressed in them (ch. x). He mentions Boyle and Mayow (chs. xiii–xvii), and agrees with Mayow that the bubbles emitted

[1] *Ib.*, 313–65.
[2] *Primae Linae Physiologiae*, 8°, Göttingen, 1751, 173–80.
[3] *Elem. Physiol.*, iii, 340.
[4] *Ib.*, 329, 354, 360–3.
[5] *Ib.*, 365.
[6] *A. Med.*, 1909, 330.
[7] *De gravitate ætheris*, 8°, Amsterdam, 1683; *Opera*, Geneva, 1744, i, 53–163.
[8] *Dissertatio de Effervescentia et Fermentatione Novâ Hypothesi fundata*, 4°, Basel, 1690 (BM 1179. g. 8. (27.) lacks the part of interest to us); also in *De Motv Musculorum*, 4°, Basel, 1694, §§ viii–xxv (BM 1185. i. 15. (22.)); in Alphonse Borelli, *De Motu Animalium, Pars Prima. Editio Nova, a pluribus mendis repurgata, Ac Dissertationibus Physico-Mechanicis de Motu Musculorum, et de Effervescentia, et Fermentatione. Clarissimi Viri Joh. Bernoulli*, 2 vols. 4°, Hague, 1743 (end of vol. ii with sep. pagin. 1–45, and plate XIX); in Bernoulli, *Opera Omnia*, Lausanne and Geneva, 4 vols. 4°, 1742, i, 1–44 and plate I; quotation in Harcourt, *Phil. Mag.*, 1846, xxviii, 505–6; Hoefer, (1), ii, 262 (misdated 1590); Daremberg, (1), ii, 814; J. C. Fischer, 1802, iii, 416–28.

on heating water are air, since fish will not live in boiled water and respire air through the gills (ch. xiv):

Videmus enim, si aqua vel alius liquor, super igne coquatur, bullulas excitari; manifesto certe aëris intra latentis indicio, qui ope ignis dilatatur, omniaque vincula, quibus retinebatur, solvit, et, ob levitatem, ad superficiem usque fertur, ubi tales bullulas format: hic fit, ut pisces in aqua quae semel ebulliit, vivere non possint, ob defectum nempe aëris, qui in ebullitione omnis exhalavit; aërem enim et pisces haurire aeque necesse est, ac caetera animalia; in hunc finem eorum branchiae conditae sunt, ut, illarum ope, aërem, qui ad vitam sustentandam necessarius est, ab aqua uti de hac recte sensit Cl. Majowius secernant.

He gives a figure of a tube filled with acid (liquore quodam acido) inverted in a basin of the same liquid and says that if a ball of earth or chalk, which contains many particles of alkali (globulus G de luto, vel creta, in quibus nempe multæ particulæ alcali insunt), is put under the tube a great effervescence, lasting about an hour, is produced, and all the air particles in the alkali, set free from their bonds, rise to the top and the earthy matter subsides. The air in the upper part of the tube occupies a large space EH (Fig. 29, 5) and

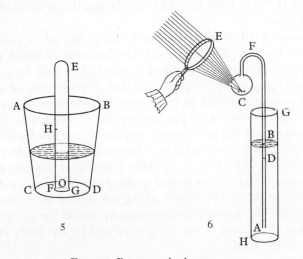

FIG. 29. BERNOULLI'S APPARATUS.

by levelling the liquid inside and outside the tube it is found that the air is from two to four times the volume of the earth, according to the kind of the latter (ch. xv).

Mayow in similar experiments had concluded that the air collected is not true air but an *aura* or *halitus* driven out of the solid, but he had shown that it has the same elasticity as air. Although it would not support life, neither would the atmosphere in plagues, and the aura is air loaded with all sorts of foreign particles. The 'air' which Mayow had collected from iron and nitric acid was nothing but common air 'filled with miasmata' thrown up by the impetuous motion of the acid liquor, or the solid globule, and carried up by the air. Nor can we wonder that such an air, filled with miasmata, if breathed by animals, cannot keep them alive, especially when it is obvious that the spirit of nitre, and the globule of iron, used by the distinguished author, abound in many impure and poisonous particles, which if introduced into the system in breathing, may well corrupt the mass of the blood and induce death. Even the 'air' extricated from chalk by oil of vitriol destroys life only because it 'abounds with particles of a different kind and unfit for the support of life' (ch. xvi).

That the air is simply contained in the pores of the chalk and is not produced from its substance is proved by weighing the dried chalk, acting upon it with acid, and collecting and drying the solid sediment, which 'has lost nothing of its weight, or at most scarcely a hundredth part, which perhaps exhaled with the air during the effervescence'. Mayow would suppose that the air occupying the upper part of the tube had been taken from the substance of the globule, which would then notably diminish in weight, contrary to the experiment (ch. xvii).

This is one of those clever quantitative chemical experiments made by physicists; Bernoulli did not know that the sediment was not chalk but gypsum ($CaCO_3 + H_2SO_4 = CaSO_4 + H_2O + CO_2$), and that it should have weighed *more* than the chalk.

Bernoulli says that the sponginess of bread is due to air produced in the pores of the fermented dough (ch. xx). He describes (without naming him) Van Helmont's experiment of bursting a sealed glass flask by generated 'air' (ch. xxi). The explosion of gunpowder is due to generation of air. Bernoulli proved this by an experiment he had recently made with his brother James. Four grains of gunpowder were put into a globe C which was continued in a curved tube immersed in a jar of water, the tube being filled with water to the level B. The gunpowder was fired by a burning mirror E. After cooling, the water was depressed to D (Fig. 29, 6). After levelling, it was calculated that the air produced was formerly condensed in the gunpowder in a state 100 times denser than atmospheric air. (Some of the gas would have dissolved in the water) (ch. xxii). The strongly compressed air inside the gunpowder comes from the action of the acid of the nitre, separated by the entry of the pointed fire particles, on the alkali:

enim pulveri pyrio ignis admoveatur, idem est, ac si alcali et acidum misceantur invicem; nam statim ac ignis pulverem pyrium attigerit, illius particulæ acidæ, ob motum velocissimum, subito et quasi momento in hujus particulas alcali, easque diffringendo, aëri incluso, qui arctissime compressus est, exitum parant.

A similar experiment had been made before by Huygens and Papin,[1] who concluded that the air was compressed three hundred times. Bernoulli's theory was criticised by Pierre Varignon in 1696,[2] but it was repeated by Euler, another mathematician.[3]

Varignon thought inflammable bodies contain a very condensed air; flame consists of an infinity of very small points, dissolving and rising in flakes of fire

[1] *Phil. Trans.*, 1675–6, x, 544.
[2] AdS, 1733, ii, 274–6; sur le feu et la flamme.
[3] *Lettres à une Princesse d'Allemagne sur divers Sujets de Physique et de Philosophie*, St. Petersburg, 1768–72, Lettre xiii; i, 49.

(s'elever en flamméches). The particles of gunpowder are disrupted by pointed fire-particles, with the liberation of more fire particles 'et ainsi de suite', a sort of chain-reaction.

All these experiments, says Bernoulli, demonstrate the presence in bodies of air which is denser than ordinary air:

Allata experimenta satis, ni fallor, ostendunt existentiam aëris in corporibus, sed et alterum nobis ostendendum est, nimirum quod aër iste sit aër naturalis consistentiæ densior.

The air in the ball of chalk is much denser than the external air (aerem istum, cum omnis adhuc in globo contineabatur, multo densiorem fuisse quam aër externus est). The solid consists partly of pores in which this air is condensed, and by measuring the volume of air extricated by acid and comparing it with the volume of the chalk globe, the density of the air in the latter is easily calculated (ch. xiv):

si vero ponatur spatium materiæ terrestris non esse æquale spatio pororum, sed in alia ratione majoris vel minoris inæqualitatis, densitates aëris in globulo æque facile ad calculum revocari possunt.

In his dissertation on muscular motion[1] Bernoulli refers to Mayow's theory of the contraction of muscular fibrils[2] as 'unsuitable, and contrary to the views of all sober anatomists'.

Daniel Bernoulli, the son of John Bernoulli, said:[3] 'The question has long been agitated whether the factitious elastic *aura* brought out of bodies is ordinary air or not, which question I shall not decide.' He goes on to say:

It is probable that the same *aura* which lies latent in the pores of gunpowder is the cause of the elasticity of elastic bodies and contractile villous (shaggy) materials; for when bodies are reduced by force to an unnatural form, the elastic aura abounding in the little vacuities is compressed, and giving the form of greatest space to those vacuities brings the body back to its original shape and extent.

This type of mathematical-physical rationication reappears in Hales (1727), who was under the influence of Newton.

Mayow is also mentioned by Brownrigg,[4] J. F. Cartheuser,[5] and Black.[6]

REY

We should not leave the path of true discovery opened out by Boyle, Hooke and Mayow for the jungle of the Theory of Phlogiston without a word for Jean Rey, a physician of Perigord, who, long before them, had published some essays on the cause of the increase in weight of tin and lead on calcination.[7]

---

[1] *Dissertatio Physico-Anatomica de Motu Musculorum*, § 2; *Opera*, 1742, i, 99.
[2] Mayow, II, ii, ch. 2, 12 f. [3] *Hydrodynamica*, Strasbourg, 1738, 243.
[4] *Phil. Trans.*, 1765, lv, 232.
[5] *Dissertationes Physico-Chymico-Medicae*, Frankfurt on the Oder, 1775, 296: dissertation by Wolff, 1772.
[6] *Lectures on the Elements of Chemistry*, ed. Robison, 4°, Edinburgh, 1803, i, 428, 553.
[7] *Essays de Iean Rey Doctevr en Medecine. Svr la Recerche de la cause pour laquelle l'Estain & le Plomb augmentent de poids quand on les calcine*, A Bazas, Par Gvillavme Millanges, Imprimeur ordinaire du Roy, 1630; v.sm. 4°, 144 pp.; Nouvelle Edition ... Avec des Notes, par M. Gobet, Paris, chez Ruault, 8°, 1777 (xxxii, 216 pp.); the 1630 ed. was repr. by

The book contains a dedication to the Duc de Bouillon, an ode on its contents by Bereau, some verses by Deschamps, a letter from Brun, Master-Apothecary in Bergerac (proposing the problem of the increase in weight of tin on calcination and the decrease in weight of lead, for Rey's solution), a preface (dated at Bugue, January 1, 1630), 28 essays, and a conclusion.

A copy (now in the British Museum) of the 1630 edition was acquired by J. G. Children, who published an English translation of the text.[1] Another copy was owned by J. Murray,[2] there is a copy which belonged to James Smithson in the Library of the Smithsonian Institution in Washington,[3] and there are several copies in French libraries.[4]

Jean Rey was born about 1582–3 at Le Bugue, a village in Dordogne, took the M.A. at Montaubon, matriculated in 1605 and studied medicine at the University of Montpellier, where he learned much that was unorthodox and not taught in Paris, and graduated M.B. in 1607 and M.D. in 1609. He returned to practise in Le Bogue. The last record of him shows that he was still alive in 1645; the date of his death is unknown. His friends were Jean Brun, apothecary, and Deschamps, physician of Bergerac, and Pierre Trichet, of Bordeaux. The book was printed by Millanges at Bazas, where he had set up a small press when the plague was raging in Bordeaux in 1629–30. The 1630 edition was mentioned by Borel[5] and Lengelt du Fresnoy.[6] A copy of the book was found in 1774 by Pierre Bayen, who gave a long account of it in 1775.[7]

After Bayen's note and Gobet's republication of Rey in 1777, Guyton de Morveau[8] said those who had reproached Lavoisier for not knowing of Rey's publication should remember how much better it is to make experiments than to waste time in thumbing over old and forgotten books; 'an idea is not a theory . . . the work of M. Lavoisier has given a true demonstration of an opinion which, until then, no one had deigned to recall.'

Lavoisier seems to have been annoyed by the republication, since he said:[9]

Sans examiner ici l'authenticité de l'ouvrage dont on s'est empressé de donner, à cette époque, une nouvelle édition, j'ai vu avec quelque plaisir que le public impartial avait jugé qu'une assertion vague et jetée au hasard . . . n'empêchait pas que je pusse être regardé comme l'auteur de la découverte de la cause de l'augmentation de poids des chaux métalliques.

This suggests that Gobet had perhaps forged the book with the object of taking merit from Lavoisier (who was, apparently, ignorant of Borel's and Lenglet du Fresnoy's notices). In a note written about 1792, Lavoisier[10] gives

Grimaux (1896), Petit (1907, with commentary), and McKie, 1951 (facsim. with intr. and notes); tr. of parts in ACR, xi and by Inchenhäuser and Speter, Ostwald's *Klassiker*, 1909, clxxii.

[1] *Quart. J. Sci.*, 1821, xi, 72, 260; 1822, xii, 54, 294; 1822, xiii, 136, 278.
[2] *Phil. Mag.*, 1823, lxii, 93.   [3] Letter from the Secretary, A. Wetmore.
[4] McKie, *Ambix*, 1958, vi, 136.   [5] *Bibliotheca Chimica*, 1654, 196.
[6] 1742, iii, unpaged Addition, no. 31: 'Livre rare'; Gobet, 1779, I, xxxviii, says the price of his ed. (1777) was 3 livres.
[7] *Obs. Phys.*, 1775, v, 47; Crell's *Beyträge*, 1785, iii, 123; Gobet, *Essays de Iean Rey*, Paris, 1777, p. xiii.
[8] *Élémens de Chimie*, Dijon, 1778, iii, 177.   [9] AdS, 1783 (1786), m 505; *Oeuvres*, ii, 629.
[10] *Mémoires de Chimie*, ii, 78; *Oeuvres*, 1862, ii, 97 f.

quite an appreciative account of Rey's book: it 'develops views so profound, so analogous to all that experiment has since confirmed, so conformable with the doctrine of saturation and affinities' that it impressed him at first as a forgery. He then spoils the effect by saying:

I did not know then [in 1772] what Rey had written in 1630, and if I had known I could only have considered his opinion on this matter as a vague assertion . . . which did not excuse chemists from verifying the truth of his opinion by experiments.

Wiegleb[1] says Rey's book: 'enthielt den angeführten grundfalschen Gedanken zum Erstenmale, auf welchen in der neuern Zeit Lavoisier sein neues chemisches System gegründet hat.'

A pencil note on the fly-leaf of the British Museum copy says Lavoisier and his friends bought up all the copies of Gobet's edition of Rey's book they could lay hands on, and it is very scarce.[2]

Since the separate 'essays' are very short, the quotations give the essay numbers, which are easily found in any of the editions.

Nothing is more certain than that a vacuum, which is nothing, can have no place in nature (iv). All things, even air and fire, are heavy, and lightness is never absolute but only relative; 'the weight with which each portion of matter was endued at the cradle will be carried with it to the grave' (vi). Air weighed in air itself is not heavy any more than water weighted in water, for 'an element shows no weight when weighed in itself'. 'The examination of weights by the balance differs from that made by the reason. The latter only is employed by the judicious, whilst the former can be practised by the veriest clown. The latter is always exact, whilst the former is seldom without deception' (viii). An experiment in which the weight of air is proved by compressing

---

[1] (1), 1792, 234.
[2] S. Brown, *Essays*, 1858, i, 196 ('the unwitting herald of Lavoisier'); Dixon, *B.A. Rep.*, 1894, 601; Fourcroy, *Ency. Méthod.*, *Chimie*, 1796, iii, 346; Gmelin, (1), i, 647; Grimaux, *Rev. Scient.*, 1884, vii, 408; Hoefer, (1), ii, 245; Kopp, (1), iii, 119 f., 131, 178; Lippmann, (1), ii, 292 (q. Guareschi, *Storia della Chimica*, Turin, 1909, viii, 88, for the statement that Rey was first mentioned in later times by the Italian physicist Giuseppe Eandi, who sent a copy of Rey's book to Beccaria in 1754; Poggendorff, (1), i, 637, gives a publication of Eandi, *Essai sur l'histoire des théories de la respiration et de la combustion*, in '*Mém. Acad. Turin*, 1801, vi,' but this publication contains only the notice mentioned below. Eandi (Saluces, 12 October 1735–Turin, 1 October 1799) was professor in the theological college of the Provincials in Turin, succeeding Beccaria. In his *Physicæ Experimentalis* (88 pp., 1793, reprinted 1800) he mentioned both Mayow and Rey: Vassali-Eandi, *Mém. Acad. Turin*, 1801, Pt. I, pp. i–lxxv (li, lxvi); summary of a work on physics of 1772, *ib.*, xviii–xxi); McKie, *Lavoisier*, 1935, 195; F. J. Moore, *History of Chemistry*, New York, 1918, 30 (no one can believe Rey capable of making any serious discovery); Parkes, *Chemical Essays*, 2 ed., 1823, i, 608; Rodwell, *Chem. News*, 1864, x, 208; id., *Phil. Mag.*, 1868, xxxv, 20; Speter, Lavoisier und seine Vorläufer, in *Samml. chem. u. chem.-techn. Vorträge*, 1910, xv, 180; Spielmann, *Institutiones Chemiæ*, Strasbourg, 1766, 275 and unpaged *Syllabus Auctorum* at end ('Rey *Essais*'; not in 1 edit. of 1763; perhaps from Lenglet du Fresnoy, mentd. *op. cit.*, 4; Speter, Ostwald's *Klassiker*, clxxii, notes, ments. allusions to Rey's book in Spielmann; in a dissertation by a pupil of Spielmann, Corvin, *Dissertatio sistens historiam aëris factitii*, Strasbourg, 1766, which Gmelin, (1), iii, 317, 358, dates Pt. i, 1776, Pt. ii, 1777; Bordeu, *Analyse Médicinale du Sang*, § 93 in *Oeuvres Complètes*, 1818, ii, 1003–4, who mentions Bayen's ed. of Rey; Speter says a long extract from Rey's book was given by Weigel, *Beiträge zur Geschichte der Luftarten*, Greifswald, 1784, i (all publ.), 1–11. It was also mentioned, probably from Gobet's reprint, by J. Stokes, *De Aëre Dephlogisticato*, Thesis, Edinburgh, 1782; R. A. Vogel, *Experimenta chemicorum de incremento ponderis corporum quorundam igne calcinatorum examinat*, 4°, Göttingen, 1753; id., *Opuscula medica selecta*, Göttingen, 4°, 1768, 51 (both q. by Gmelin, (1), i, 647); a portrait of Rey in the Académie des Sciences is mentioned in *Archives*, 1950, ii, 689.

it into a weighed vessel (x) is, apparently, imaginary;[1] the actual experiment was made by Galileo in 1638.[2]

Rey (x)[3] claimed that he had invented an air-gun some years before David Rivault, Sieur de Fleurance, who published it in 1608; it had been proposed before by Lobsinger in Nürnburg (1550), Bartolomeo Crescentio (1602) and Porta (1606), and the idea probably goes back to Ktesibios ($\dot{a}\epsilon\rho o\tau\acute{o}\nu o\nu$) (Vol. I). Rey also claimed that he had received the royal privilege for another machine, perhaps an air-compressor.

Bodies become heavier when compressed without addition of matter, as when iron is hammered for a long time or feathers are compressed; masses of iron and gold equal when weighed in air are not so really, as they displace unequal weights of air (xv). Air is rendered dense in three ways: (i) by admixture with matter heavier than itself, (ii) by compression, (iii) by separation of its less heavy parts. Fire makes water and air denser; water remaining in a still after part has come over is denser than the distillate (xiii). To prove that 'fire can make air denser' (xiv)[4] Rey says:

Stand a cannon upright and put a red-hot ball into it. You must admit that the air in the gun is so small in quantity that it will be heated to the same temperature as the ball. Nevertheless you can hold your hand in the mouth of the gun at first, but in a short time you cannot do so. Not that the air has got hotter, it is cooling all the time and so is the shot; it is because the air is thickened and made denser by the separation of the more subtle parts. . . . If the air over the muzzle did not become denser it would not blur objects seen through it; this is not due to swaying of the air, since I see distinctly the charms of a lady through the air she agitates with her fan. Now if you drop a fleece of wool into the mouth, it will not descend, and if you push it in, it will come up again, which would not happen if the air were not denser than at a distance from the cannon.

Rey seems to suggest vaguely here that air contains different parts, but whether only when altered by heat or naturally is not clear. He suggests (xiv) that if one could transport the laboratory to the region of fire above the atmosphere, air could be distilled and so separated into light and heavy parts. Various oils are progressively thickened by prolonged heating in a retort, the thickening being due to the absorption of matter of heat, since the substances are homogeneous and do not change of themselves. This is also true of water and even of air (xii–xiv). Apparently the refraction striæ produced on heating water and air suggested a 'thickening' to Rey.[5]

The Sieur Brun, apothecary in Bergerac, had found that 2 lb. 6 oz. of English tin became 2 lb. 13 oz. of calx, but 6 lb. of lead *lost* 6 oz. on calcination (xvi). Rey says he had 'devoted several hours' to the consideration of this increase in weight, and in one crude experiment on the calcination of tin on a pig or ingot of cast-iron, he found an increase in weight (xxii); the experiment was made in the forge of his brother 'Iean Rey sieur de la Perrotasse'. In the calcination, the loss due to the increase in volume (when weighing in air),

---

[1] Kopp, (1), iii, 178.
[2] *Discorsi e Demonstrationi Matematiche, intorno a due nuoue Scienci*, Leyden, 1638, 81; *Opere*, Bologna, 1655, ii, 59; Ostwald's *Klassiker*, 1890, xi, 69.
[3] Gobet, 1777, 37.　　　　　[4] Gobet, 1777, 56.
[5] O. C. de C. Ellis, *A History of Fire and Flame*, 1932, 182.

and that due to the loss of vapours and exhalations must have been compensated (remplacé). Rey says he maintains proudly that the increase:

comes from the air, which in the vessel has been rendered denser, heavier, and in some measure adhesive, by the vehement and long-continued heat of the furnace, which air mixes with the calx (frequent agitation aiding) and becomes attached to its most minute particles (xvi).

This happens as water makes sand heavier by adhering to the grains.

The mistake has often been made,[1] but not by Kopp, of supposing that Rey stated that air attaches itself to the *metal*, and so increases its weight in forming the calx; he says distinctly that it is the calx which takes up the air and gives no explanation of how the calx is formed from the metal.

Rey gives a good summary of the earlier explanations by Cardan, Scaliger, Caesalpinus, and one of Rey's friends (Petit thinks Dr. Deschamps, of Bergerac), all shown to be unsatisfactory (xvii–xxiv), and finally (xxv), since his arguments are like cutting off the Hydra's head, when two more heads grow, he will deliver a mighty blow which will finish off the beast. Hamerus Poppius[2] showed that antimony when calcined by a burning-glass, increased in weight, in spite of the abundant evolution of fumes. The air, thickened by heating by the sun's rays, becomes heavier and mixes with the calx. Thus, 'by a single experiment, all opinions contrary to mine are entirely destroyed' (xxv).

Rey (xxvii)[3] says zinc (le metal Indien, qu'on nomme Calaem) can be calcined but decreases in weight (this was probably taken from Libavius). Rey does not mention that Agricola[4] quotes Galen (see Vol. I) as saying that lead kept in damp places increases in weight, adding that lead roofing on old buildings had become much heavier. This is perhaps the source of the statement by Hallopeau[5] that Galen said that tin increases in weight on calcination.

The calx does not increase in weight indefinitely, 'for when all is saturated with air it can take up no more'; 'Do not continue your calcination with this hope; you will lose your labour. . . . Nature is her inscrutable wisdom has set limits which she never oversteps (s'est ici mises des barres qu'elle ne franchit jamais)' (xxvi). Other calces and ashes do not increase in weight on calcination because they lose so much exhalable and evaporable matter that this loss more than counterbalances the weight of air absorbed (xxvii).

In 'Conclusion' Rey says: 'Behold now this truth, whose brilliance strikes the eye, which I have drawn from the deepest dungeons of obscurity. . . . The labour has been mine; may the profit be to the reader and to God alone the glory.'[6]

Rey argued that air on heating separates into a lighter part and a heavier part which is 'adhesive' and has a viscid grossness (xxvi); this heavier part attaches itself to calces and causes such of them as possess much ash to become heavier after calcination. Vegetable and animal matters do not so increase in weight, as the weight of expelled volatile matter exceeds the weight

---

[1] Humboldt, *Cosmos*, 1849, ii, 729; Lippmann, (1), ii, 304.
[2] *Basilica Antimonii*, Frankfurt, 1618, 21.   [3] Gobet, 1777, 103, and note.
[4] *De Ortu et Causis Subterraneorum*, bk. 5; *De Re Metallica*, Basel, 1657, 519.
[5] *Rev. gén. Sci.*, 1918, xxix, 246.
[6] This was quoted by Bancroft, *Permanent Colours*, 1794, i, 262.

of thickened air taken up (xxvii), but *all* calces, from a vegetable ash to a metallic calx, attract this thickened air.

What is evidently Rey's theory was adopted by Segner,[1] who does not mention Rey. After saying that the increase in weight of lead on calcination had been attributed to the fixation of fire, which had been supposed to have weight, Segner proceeds:

It is, however, more probable that a part of the air, without which such operations cannot be carried out, is that which, so thickened, adheres to the bodies and so increases their weight. We know that air has weight, that it can be combined and exerts no expansive force so long as it is in this state, from which it can again be recovered, and . . . finally much air is either bound or set free by the solution of bodies or their destruction by fire.

Rey sent a copy of his book to Trichet, of Bordeaux, and this copy was used by Gobet, who also published letters of Rey and Mersenne, whose attention was drawn to the book by Trichet. In a letter of 1 September 1631, Mersenne objected to several of Rey's views, particularly that heat makes air heavier; it makes it lighter, as when air expands in a thermoscope. Rey replied in a long letter, 'le premier de l'an 1632',[2] in which he says, among other things, that the 'thermoscope ou thermometre' which he himself used was a small bulb filled with water, with a long thin neck; on warming, the water expanded and rose in the neck.[3] He used it for taking the temperature of the body of a patient. Mersenne replied in April 1632. In a letter to Mersenne of 21 March 1643, Rey says Mersenne had found water 255 times heavier than air by heating a phial, dipping it in water, and measuring how much water was sucked in. But Rey said this gave different results according to the degree of heating.[4] Mersenne mentioned Rey's theory in one of his books,[5] saying that, although not free from difficulties (many of which Rey had resolved in his letters), he preferred it to all others which had been proposed.

Henry de Stanihurst wrote to Mersenne in 1625 about an alchemist Le Febvre of Rouen who had an oil drawn from the dung of a goose fed on lead filings which transmuted mercury into silver, and could turn aqua vitae into hard crystal. Mersenne wrote to Le Febvre, who sent him a long letter giving away very little.[6]

[1] *Einleitung in die Naturlehre*, 2 ed., Göttingen, 1754, 259 (§ 377); Partington and McKie, *Ann. Sci.*, 1938, iii, 1 (39); Johann Andreas von Segner, M.D., Pressburg, 9 October 1704– Halle, 5 October 1777, professor of physics and mathematics in Jena (1733), Göttingen (1735–55), and Halle (from 1755); Poggendorff, (1), ii, 892; this passage is not mentioned by Gmelin, Kopp, or Hoefer.

[2] Gobet, 1777, 117–38.   [3] *Ib.*, 136.

[4] *Correspondance du P. Marin Mersenne, Réligieux Minime*, publ. by Tannery and de Waarde, 3 vols., 1932, 1936, 1946; 1946, iii, 92, 185 (letter to Rey, 1.9.1631) – 198, 232 (letter of Rey to Mersenne, 1.1.1632) – 249, 273 (Mersenne to Rey, 1.4.1632) – 289; Harcourt Brown, *Scientific Organizations in Seventeenth Century France*, Baltimore, 1934, 31, 41.

[5] *Les Questions Theologiqves, Physiqves, Morales, et Mathematiqves*, Paris, 1634, qu. 3, pp. 11–16; reprinted in Gobet, 1777, 176–81.

[6] *Correspondance*, 1932, i, 275–88; 321–3.

CHAPTER XVII

THE PHLOGISTON THEORY. PART I. BECHER

BECHER

Johann Joachim Becher (Speyer, 6 May 1635–London ?, 1682 ?) was the
son of a Protestant pastor, although he himself later became a Catholic.[1] He
was self-taught but became a teacher and was always interested in education.
He then travelled in Germany, Sweden, Holland and Italy, meeting many

FIG. 30. J. J. BECHER, 1635–1682.

famous men. In 1663 he became professor of medicine in the university of
Mainz (where he became M.D. in 1661) and physician to the Elector, but he
left in 1664 to become physician to the Elector at Munich, where he had the
best laboratory in Europe. In December 1665 he left for Vienna, where
Zinzendorf the finance minister was his friend. In Vienna he interested himself in political and economic projects. As a result of some quarrel (he was of a
very restless disposition) he left Vienna and in 1678 was in Holland, where he
persuaded the authorities of Haarlem to buy a process for turning silver into

[1] Thomson, (3), 467, says he 'seems to have been of Jewish extraction'.

gold by means of sand, which he had brought to their notice in 1673. The process was worked on a small scale in 1679 and seemed to give successful results, but it was not pursued. Becher also had a process for making iron from clay by heating it with oil. At the end of 1679 he came to England (it is said at the invitation of Prince Rupert), where he studied mining in Cornwall and (according to some accounts) in Scotland. He is said to have died in London in 1682 and to have been buried in St. James's Church, which was not built until 1685; some accounts say that he died in Germany. Roth-Scholtz says Becher died in London in 1682 and that he attended his funeral. Becher left a family in poor circumstances, one of his daughters going into domestic service.

Becher was one of those restless, inventive, and plausible characters which appear frequently among his countrymen. Besides his chemical works he wrote on theology, mathematics, philosophy, philology, history, and economics, and invented a universal language.[1] Becher was responsible for the building and organisation of a workhouse (Werkhaus) in Vienna on the lines of that afterwards established in Munich by Benjamin Thompson (Count Rumford). It contained a chemical laboratory for the manufacture of pigments but was mostly concerned with textiles (wool and silk) and glass.[2] He was a candidate for F.R.S. in 1680 and presented a book,[3] but Flamsteed reported that there was very little in it, that his proposed clock was not as good as that of Huygens, and that his ideas on the use of the pendulum were not new.[4] Becher says in it that in 1660 he had invented a 'thermoscope' for regulating the temperature of a furnace automatically.[5] Neither Becher nor Stahl, the outstanding chemists in Germany, who profoundly influenced chemistry in England for decades, became F.R.S. Poor Becher sought election and mentioned Boyle and others in his books; Stahl, the physician of the King of Prussia, was indifferent.

Becher is an obscure writer and some practical discoveries which he made he was at some pains to conceal; he was quarrelsome and vain, and was more successful with theories than with experiments. Kopp[6] says Becher put forward more new names than correct ideas. He believed firmly in alchemy, and his 'proof' that Solomon was an alchemist[7] is a good specimen of his mentality.

---

[1] Kopp, (1), i, 177; (2), iii, 202; (4), i, 66; Thomson, (1), i, 246; S. Brown, *Essays*, i, 202; Gmelin, (1), ii, 142; Ferguson, i, 86; NBU, v, 85; J. Hawkins, *Trans. Roy. Geol. Soc. Cornwall*, 1832, iv, 70; pref. to Roth-Scholtz's ed. of Becher's *Opuscula Chymica Rariora*, Nürnberg and Altdorf, 1719, with bibl. of Becher's works, 6–40, and life of Becher, 41; Gibbs, *Ann. Sci.*, 1953, ix, 197 (BM Sloane MSS. on Becher); K. L. Wolf and R. Ramsauer, *Zeitschr. für die gesamte Naturwissenschaften*, 1935, i, 494 (with portr. from Becher's *Mineralisches ABC*, Nürnberg, 1723); Ramsauer, *ib.*, 1936–7, ii, 135; H. Hassinger, J. J. Becher. Ein Beitrag zur Geschichte des Merkantilismus, in *Veröffl. d. Kommission f. neuere Geschichte Österreichs*, Vienna, 1951, xxxviii, 1–272 (full bibl.); Hassinger, 271, says Rostock University Library has three vols. (2000 pp.) of Becher's papers, containing a draft of the *Physica subterranea*; Thorndike, vii, 578–83, 619; viii, 137.

[2] Hassinger, 196.

[3] *De nova temporis dimetiendi ratione et accurata Horologiorum constructione Theoria et Experimenta*, 4°, London, 1680 (Roth-Scholtz, *Opuscula*, 1719, 29); printed in *Physica Subterranea Suppl. III*, 1680; ed. 1738, 489 f.

[4] Birch, (1), iv, 16; Hassinger, 242.

[5] *Phys. Subterr.*, 1738, 500.

[6] (1), i, 179; ii, 277.   [7] *Physica Subterranea, Suppl. II*; 1738, 351 f.

In the laboratories at Munich and Vienna he seems to have worked mainly on alchemy. In the preface to his *Physica Subterranea* Becher calls himself:

one to whom neither a gorgeous home, nor security of occupation, nor fame nor health appeal; for me rather my chemicals amid the smoke, soot and flame of coals blown by the bellows. Stronger than Hercules, I work forever in an Augean stable, blind almost from the furnace glare, my breathing affected by the vapour of mercury. I am another Mithridates, saturated with poison. Deprived of the esteem and company of others, a beggar in things material, in things of the mind I am a Crœsus. Yet among all these evils I seem to live so happily that I would die rather than change places with a Persian king.

Leibniz[1] says he was ingenious but uncritical; Becher had met Leibniz in Hamburg in 1678 in the negotiations with Brand, the discoverer of phosphorus,[2] and they were later enemies. Another example of Becher's outlook is his statement[3] that, since the creation of minerals is not mentioned in *Genesis*, they must have been formed from gross earth after vegetables and animals. His Latin style is simple but lacks elegance; he says: excuso latinitatem in hoc opere . . . sic rebus attentus verba neglexi.[4] He frequently contradicts himself in the same work or in different works, and uses the same word in a variety of meanings, and different words for the same thing (haerent Peripatetici in verbis nos in rebus).[5] He is, however, easier to read than Kunckel or Stahl. Becher had the true German's pride in himself: Ich muss gestehen dass, wie meine Schrifften ausweisen, zumalen der *Tripus Hermeticus Fatidicus* keiner in dieser *Seculo* gelebt, der die Chymie so weit entdekt und entblösset.[6]

Some of the older ideas which had been accepted by Paracelsus were wearing rather thin in Becher's time; he is sceptical about astrology and the relation between planets and metals:

Miror quod non etiam in sole leonem, in Marte Virum, in Venere fœminam, imo lupus et Salamandras viderint, quæ objecta quoque mineralibus tribui solent, sed asinos potius vidisse credo, cum seipsos viderint, et talia simplici, et credulo popello prærudunt.[7]

But his whole outlook shows the influence of the Neoplatonic ideas and confused thinking of Paracelsus, e.g. his belief that minerals as well as plants and animals have a sort of life and grow in the earth from seeds.

Becher in England was protected and befriended by Edmund Dickinson and Prince Rupert, the latter arranging the visit of Becher and the Gotha mines inspector Hayn to Cornwall in 1681; Hayn in 1680 had visited the Scottish mines.[8] Becher frequently quotes Boyle's *Sceptical Chymist*, but disapproved of Boyle's mechanical explanations, being more in sympathy with the views of Sir Kenelm Digby.

Hassinger (1951, 63) says that although Becher criticised Paracelsus and Van Helmont, he owed much to them; he believed he had much advanced from his

---

[1] *Miscellanea Berolinensia*, 1710, i, 95: vir ingeniosus et Germanicis scriptis validus, sed qui nimium indulgibat scripturienti calamo, et comperta incompertaque protrudebant, cum plerumque ex aliorum narrationibus haussiset, quæ scribebat; Peters, *A. Nat.*, 1916, vii, 275 (281).

[2] Hassinger, 238. [3] *Physica Subterranea*, Bk. I, sect. i, ch. 3; 1738, 18.

[4] *Physica Subterranea*, preface. [5] *Ib.*, 1738, 270.

[6] *Chymischen Rosengarten*, pref.; *Opuscula Chymica*, 1719, 215.

[7] *Phys. Subterr.*, Bk. I, sect. iv, ch. 6; 1738, 126. [8] Hassinger, 243.

predecessors, but failed to express his indebtedness to Van Helmont, Digby, and Sennert.

Wolf and Ramsauer thought Becher was much influenced by Digby's *Two Treatises* (p. 424) as well as by Paracelsus. He had the truly German idea of the unity of Nature; Stahl later destroyed the significant arrangement (sinnvollen Ordnung) of this by restricting the theory to unorganised bodies, and making phlogiston a material substance (a new creation of Stahl), under the influence of mechanists like Boyle. He thus fell away from the characteristic German school inaugurated by Paracelsus and continued by Becher.

The bibliography of Becher is rather difficult; the full titles of his works are very long and some appeared in several editions.[1] His publications on political economy cannot be mentioned here although they are of some interest.[2] His most important works of chemical interest are:

I. Actorum Laboratorii Chymici Monacensis, Seu Physicæ Subterraneæ Libri Duo . . . Joannes Joachimus Becherus . . . , 8°, Frankfurt, Joh. David Zumner, 1667; engr. f.p., xix ll. dedic. to the Elector of Bavaria, preface and index, 633, iii ll. errata; *Isis*, 1926, viii, 427; in spite of the title it contains, even in the last ed. (1738), only one book; a second book may have been written but is lost. A second edition of the Actorum with the same title as the first, but including three supplements was published at Frankfurt in 1681: Ferguson, i, 88. The symbolical frontispiece, representing the earth as a matrix, appeared in another form in a frontispiece to the Philosophia Pauperum (attributed to Albertus Magnus), Brescia, Baptista de Farengo, 1493: W. Pagel, Paracelsus, Basel, 1958, 239. The style of the frontispiece is different in the 1669 and 1703 eds.

The book was republ. by Stahl with the title: Physica Subterranea . . . , 8°, Leipzig, 1703 (full title in Ferguson, i, 88-9), with the three supplements (II-IV) and index, and a long introduction by Stahl: Specimen Beccherianum . . . principia mixtionis subterraneae . . . demonstrantur. Lenglet du Fresnoy, iii, 116; Gmelin, (1), ii, 150; Hoefer, (1), i, 207; and Kopp, (1), i, 192; *id.*, (2), iii, 211, mention an ed. of 1702 but none of them appears to have seen it; the older bibliographers: Roth-Scholtz, in XVI, 1719, 19; J. C. Goetz, Scripta D. Georg Ern. Stahlii, 2 ed., 4°, Nürnberg, 1729, 42, 65; and Spielmann-Cadet, Instituts de Chymie, 1770, ii, 318, know nothing of it, and Hassinger does not mention it.

The last ed. (with the three supplements, II-IV): Physica Subterranea profundam subterraneorum genesis, . . . opus sine pari, primum hactenus ac princeps, editio novissima . . . et Specimen Beccherianum . . . subjunxit Georg. Ernestus Stahl . . . , 4°, Leipzig, Weidmann, 1738 (MDCCXXXIIX), engr. f.p., vii ll., 504, ix ll. index, 161 Spec. Becch., iv ll. index, is the one quoted in the text.

The title is reminiscent of Kircher's *Mundus Subterraneus*, published four years previously, and the opening chapters show some resemblance. Despite its title, Becher's work is chemical, not physical, and he differed from Kircher in having a firm belief in the possibility of transmutation.

A German tr. by Becher himself, of I, II and III, also of VII, was published as: Chymisches Laboratorium Oder Unter-erdische Naturkündigung . . . , 8°, Frankfurt, 1680 (xxviii, 732; 175, xv; 192; 156, iv pp.; contents in Bolton, (1), 289; it is often incomplete). An issue 1690, according to Roth-Scholtz, in XVI, 21, is only this with a new t.p., but the arrangement in it is reported in a bookseller's catalogue as different: xv ll. (last blank), 732 pp., i l. blank; 192 pp.; 173 pp. (last mis-numbered 175); viii ll. (last blank), 156 pp., ii ll.: Gurney, *Cat.* 20 (1958), no. 52.

II. First supplement to I: Experimentum Chymicum Novum, quo artificialis &

---

[1] Many titles are given by Gmelin, and Bolton, (1), 289-93; Thomson, (1), ii, 248; complete list in Hassinger, 254-72, who mentions some publications in the British Museum which are not in German libraries.

[2] F. A. Steinhüser, *Johann Joachim Becher und die Einzelwirtschaft*, Nürnberg, 1931; O. Brunner, in R. Meister, Festgabe an das Österreichischer Staatsarchiv, in *Sitzb. Österr. Akad. Wiss., Phil.-hist. Kl.*, Vienna, 1949, ccxxvi, no. 3, 85-91 (sketch of contents of Becher's projected 20 books on 'Oeconomia ruralis et domestica' in Rostock Univ. Libr.; includes a cookery-book, prayer-book (Gebettbuch), and a Curiosa-oder kunstbuch of recipes); Hassinger, 1951, xxxviii.

instantanea Metallorum Generatio & Transmutatio ad oculorum demonstratur, . . . et responsi ad D. Rolfincii, 8°, Frankfurt, 1671, 172 pp. (BM 1034. a. 2). It is a defence of alchemy. There is a MS. of it in Bodleian Miscellenea varia 122. German tr.:

Experimentum chymicum novum: oder neue Chymische Prob, worinnen Die künstliche gleich-darstellige Transmutation, oder Verwandlung derer Metallen augenscheinlich dargethan (*s.l.*) 1680 (pp. 175, xv).

III. Second supplement to I: Supplementum secundum in physicam subterraneam, with sub-title: Theses chymicae veritatem et possibilitatem transmutationis metallorum in aurum evincentes, 8°, Frankfurt, 1675 (pp. xlix, 136); German tr.:

Nochmaliger Zusatz über die Unter-erdische Naturkündigung . . . oder Chymische, die Wahr- und Mögligkeit derer Metallen Verwandelung in Gold bestreitende Lehr-Sätze, (*s.l.*) 1680 (pp. 175, xv); for a MS. in the BM, see S. Ayscough, A Catalogue of the Manuscripts preserved in the British Museum, 2 vols. 4°, 1782, i, 480.

IV. Third supplement to I: Experimentum novum et curiosum de minera arenaria perpetua, sive Prodromus historiæ seu propositionis Præp. D.D. Hollandiæ ordinibus ab authore factæ, circa auri extractionem mediante arena littoralia per modum mineræ perpetuæ. . . . Loco supplementi tertii in physicam subterraneam, 8°, Frankfurt, 1680. Another ed.:

Minera Arenaria Perpetua: Sive Prodromus Historiae, seu Propositionis . . . circa auri Extractionem . . . Londini . . . in viâ Regia vulgo dicta The Strand, 4°, 1680 (pp. 112, viii) (BM 1033. h. 19. (2.)).

Dedic. dated Londini Calend. Martii 1680. As printed in I, 1738, it lacks some parts. German tr. by Roth-Scholtz, Deutsches Theatrum Chemicum, 1730, ii, 619–82, and in XVI, 256–94: Bericht von dem Sande, als einem ewig-währenden Metall- oder Berg-Werck.

V. Naturkündigung der Metallen . . . , frontispiece dated Frankfurt, 1660 with title: Metallurgia Becheri, 11 pts. (pp. xiii, 347, xxxiii), 8°, Frankfurt, 1661 (Chemical Society, London); also (with same frontispiece), 1679 (BM 1034. a. 6; Sotheran *Cat.* 852 (1938) No. 1425), and 1705 (Hassinger, 258). It contains alchemical ideas based on the four element theory, and deals with the generation of metals and testing ores.

VI. Parnassi Illustrati Pars Tertia, Mineralogia, das est: Dess erläuterten Medicin-alischen Parnassi Dritter Theil, nehmlich das Berg-Buch, f°, Ulm, 1662 (88 pp.); the repetition in the title is very characteristic of Becher's mentality; a part was issued as: Parnassus medicinalis illustratus, oder ein neues . . . Thier-, Kräuter- und Berg-Buch, mit zwölff-hundert Figuren gezieret, f°, Ulm, 1663 (so dated on t.p.) (BM 986. g. 13).

VII. Institutiones Chimicae Prodromae i.e. . . . Oedipus Chimicus Obscuriorum Terminorum & Principiorum Chimicorum Mysteria Aperiens et resolvens, 12°, Frankfurt, 1664, also Amsterdam (202 pp.) (Duveen, 55) and 1665; repr. 8°, Frankfurt, 1705, 1716, with suppl.: Supplementa Beccheriana, Elementa Chymiæ Methodo Mathematica conscripta exhibentia subjungit J. J. Rosenstengelius. Roth-Scholtz, in XVI, 20, and Lenglet du Fresnoy, iii, 117, give an Institutiones Chymicæ, 4°, Mainz, 1662. VII is repr. in Manget, 1702, i, 306–36. Opposite the t.p. is a reprod. of the Prague alchemical medal and there is another engraving of Oedipus and the Sphinx; the dedic. is dated 1663. The work is in seven 'titles', German tr.: Oedipus Chymicus oder Chymischer Rätseldeuter, 8°, *s.l.*, 1680 (pp. 156, iv); as Pt. IV of German tr. of I, Chymisches Laboratorium oder unter-erdische Naturkundigung, Frankfurt, 1690 (not in BM or Chem. Soc. London copies); and in Roth-Scholtz, Deutsches Theatrum Chemicum, Nürnberg, 1728, ii, 620 f.; Hassinger gives for the German tr. only Frankfurt, 1680 and 1690.

VIII. Tripus Hermeticus Fatidicus, Pandens Oracula Chymica, seu I. Laboratorium Portatile (pp. 1–63). II. Centrum Mundi concatenatum seu Magnorum duorum Productorum Nitri & Salis Textura & Anatomia (pp. 64–97). III. Alphabetum Minerale (pp. 98–149). His accessit Concordantia Mercurii Lunæ (pp. 150–186). Omnia juxta Authoris Doctrinam & Principia in Physica sua Subterranea ejusque Supplementis conscripta, sm. 8°, Frankfurt, 1689; repr. 1690 (Sotheran *Cat.* 839 (1934), No. 307), and in XVI, with the same pagination. Denoted below by VIII (I), VIII (II) and VIII (III).

The dedication to Edmund Dickinson concludes: 'Truro in Cornubia penes Portum Falmouth ad extrema Anglia ora vulgo Landes Ende', and Pt. III has a separate t.p. dated 'Truro Anno 1682', and a dedication to Robert Boyle. There is a reference to Windsor Castle (p. 79). The t.p. of the whole work has: 'exaratum in Cornubia in extrema Angliæ ora inter ipsa mineralia experimenta & autopsiam.' The book contains information gained by Becher on his visit to Cornwall in 1680. The Treatise I is accompanied by a plate (opp. p. 28) of 64 pieces of apparatus, including three types of balance (Bilanx), a laboratory coat, a tin of tobacco and two pipes (Tabacus; Pipae). The portable furnace described in VIII (I) was copied by Shaw, tr. of Boerhaave, A New Method of Chemistry, 1741, ii, 375, and plates.

Wiegleb, (2), 1790, I, i, 71, gives 'Alphabetum minerale . . . Truro, 1682', as the date of the work, but Roth-Scholtz, XVI, 21, says the 1689 Latin ed. is the first; German tr. by Roth-Scholtz:

Mineralisches ABC. Oder vier und zwantzig chymischer Theses von der Geburt, denen Principiis, Unterschied, Vermischung und Auflösung deren Mineralien, Metallen und übrigen Unterirdischen Dingen, etc., 12°, Nürnberg and Altdorf, 1723.

IX. Trifolium Becherianum Hollandicum of Haer . . . Bechers Drie nieuwe Inventien, 4°, Amsterdam, 1679 (20 pp.) (BM 1033. h. 19. (1.)); German:

Trifolium Becherianum Hollandicum oder . . . Drey Neue Erfindungen, Bestehende in einer Seiden-Wasser-Mühle und Schmeltz-Wercke, in Holland vorgeschlagen und werckstellig gemacht . . . Auss der Niederländischen in die Hochteutsche Sprache übersetzet, 8°, Frankfurt, 1679 (54 pp.) (an ed., 12°, Leipzig, 1691, is mentioned).

X. Chymischer Glücks-Hafen, oder Grosse Chymische Concordanz Und Collection, Von funffzehen hundert Chymischen Processen . . . , 4°, Frankfurt, 1682 (BM 1033. i. 16); new ed. with Stahl's preface and his Bedencken von der Gold-Macherey, 4°, Halle, 1726 (Gmelin, (1), ii, 151; Ferguson, i, 86; Hassinger, 262); 4°, Leipzig, 1755, with different pref. and portr. of Becher (xxvii, 876, xxvi pp.). This gives extracts from other authors and detailed recipes for making the philosophers' stone. The original preface is dated London, 24 March, 1682.

XI. Närrische Weisheit und weisse Narrheit, 12°, Frankfurt, 1683; contains autobiographical matter, a complaint of persecution because he advocated the exclusion of French goods from Germany, and short notices of discoveries and inventions, many by Becher himself and some in collaboration with Prince Rupert, including coke and tar manufacture, weaving and spinning apparatus, mining and metallurgical processes, and Count von Zinzendorff's process for making gold. Gmelin and Hassinger give eds. of 1682 and 1686; republ. (with a life of Becher), 12°, 1706, 1707, and 1725, s.l. (lxxviii, 208 pp.), with different frontispieces and t.ps.; Roth-Scholtz, XVI, 9, 31, gives (incorrectly) the first ed. as 12 mo., Frankfurt, 1672. This small work was obviously very popular. It was probably inspired by the Marquis of Worcester's Century of Inventions.

XII. Psychosophia oder Seelen-Weisheit, Güstrow, 1673; Frankfurt, 1683, 12°, Hamburg, 1705, 1707, 1725; contains details of Becher's life and his opinions on alchemy (on tobacco, 1707, 219 f.; on alchemy, 130 f., 'axioms' on alchemy, 169 f.; Kopp, (4), i, 241).

XIII. Magnalia Naturae; Or, the Philosophers-Stone Lately expos'd to publick Sight and Sale . . . published at the Request . . . especially of Mr. Boyl, &c. By John Joachim Becher, London, T. Dawks, 1680 (31 pp.) (BM 1035. c. 42) apparently spurious, although Hassinger (pp. 242, 261), who had not seen it, regarded it as genuine and also mentions eds. of 1744 and 1808. It gives an account of a transmutation by Wenzel Seiler at Vienna, with circumstantial detail (Duveen, 56).

XIV. Pantaleon Delarvatus, directed against Gassmann and first printed in Johann Michael Faust's Philaletha Illustratus . . . Accessit . . . de Vita et scriptis Starckii, nec non Dn. Doct. Becheri Pantaleon delarvatus, 8°, Frankfurt, 1706 (pp. 106–22); incl. in XVI; Ferguson, i, 266; Duveen, 209; Hassinger, 263; an ed. of Leipzig, 1706, is mentioned.

Three works of 'Pantaleon' in Roth-Scholtz, Deutsches Theatrum Chemicum, Nürnberg, 1728, ii, are: Pantaleonis Tumulus, 197 f.; Pantaleonis Examen Alchymisticum, 259 f.; Pantaleonis Bifolium Metallicum, 513 f.; the author's real name was Franz Gassmann of Silesia, a physician in Passau and Vienna: Ferguson, ii, 166.

XV. Becheri, Lancelotti, etc. Epistolæ quatuor Chemicæ, 4°, Amsterdam and Hamburg, 1673, q. by Lenglet du Fresnoy, iii, 117.

XVI. J. J. Becheri . . . Opvscvla Chymica Rariora, Addita nova Praefatione ac Indice locupletissima multisque Figuris aenis illustrata. Ed. F. Roth-Scholtz, 8°, Nürnburg and Altdorf, Apud hæredes D. Tauber, 1719 (vi ll., 310 pp.); list of contents in Bolton, (1), 291 f.; Kopp, (2), iii, 202, dates it by mistake 1729; it contains, pp. 3–39, a list of 44 of Becher's works, and, pp. 40–50, a life of Becher.

XVII. Chymischer Rosengarten, ed. Roth-Scholtz, 16°, Nürnburg, [1717]; and in XVI, 207 f. An extract from X. Becher complains in it that some of his manuscripts were stolen when he was travelling from Amsterdam to The Hague.

Thomson says that Becher was 'the first person who can with propriety be said to have attempted to construct a theory of Chemistry'; Boyle, who was responsible for hastening the downfall of alchemical and other opinions, did not attempt to set out a theory of chemistry.

Becher[1] taught that all subterranean [inorganic] bodies are of an earthy nature and can be mixed with water. All bodies, including metals, are composed of water and three earthy principles. In his earlier works these are practically the salt, sulphur, and mercury of the alchemists and Paracelsus;[2] he explains the properties of the different metals on the old theory of the different proportions of these principles in varying degrees of colour and purity (stannum multum terrae calcis habet, paucissimum mercurii, sulphur impurum et imperfectum; ferrum constat ex multo sale, pauco sulphure et pauciori mercurio). A tabular classification of bodies[3] illustrates Becher's views (italics in the original are disregarded and the numerous symbols replaced by words):

I. Mineræ: marcasite, orpiment, regulus.

II. Metalla: gold, silver, copper, iron, tin, lead, mercury.

III. Mineralia: antimony, Bismuth, Zinck, Marcasit, Kobolt, Zaffra, Magnesia, Magnes.

IV. Salia: common salt, nitrum, vitriolum, alumen, Salmiak, tartares, Borax, Chrijsocolla.

V. Decomposita: mercurius sublimatis, mercurius præcipitatis, realgar, arsenicum, sulphur, cinabrium.

VI. Terræ: verdigris (viride aeris), crocus of iron, crocus of copper, glass of antimony, glass of lead; minium, Lithargirium; Cadmia, Tutia; Ochra, Schmalta.

VII. Destillata: Aqua fortis and Aqua regis, spirit of vitriol and spirit of sulphur, spirit of salt, spirit of nitrum, spirit of wine, spirit of tartar, acetum destillantur, spirit of urine.

VIII. Olea: oil of vitriol, oil of sulphur, fetid oil of tartar, oil of tartar per deliquium, butter of antimony, Liquor Silicum, Ol. Therebent [turpentine].

IX. Limii: calx viva; arena, cineres; creta Rubrica; Terra Sigillata, Bolus; Haematites, Smiris; Talcum; Granati; Asbestus.

X. Compositiones: Fluxus Niger, Fluxus Albus, Cera Tinctoria, Coloriza, Decoctio, Tirapelle.

The *Physica Subterranea* (I) begins with an account of the Creation of

---

[1] Wiegleb, (2), 1790, I, i, 27; J. C. Brown, 226–8; Kopp, (2), iii, 202.
[2] II, 1738, 334 f.; VII, Titulus III (de principiis qualitatis, nempe mercurio, sulphure et sale), 1675, 53.
[3] VIII (I), 1689, 41; list of symbols, 28.

Heaven (the cause of space and solidity by its moving force) and Earth (consisting of the unmixed elements earth, water, and air, differentiated only by space and solidity). The first Angel then induced *rarefactio* and the elements separated, fire appearing as a 'secondary' element, both a moving principle and a chemical element. All bodies, animals, plants, and subterranean minerals, are mixtures of water and earth, air not being contained in the mixture, but acting only as an agent, along with fire. In the centre all things are mixed to a complete body (integra corpora). There is a curious account of the part played by Angels in the Creation.[1]

Becher criticises the theories of the four elements and three principles, and says the true elements of bodies can be found only by analysis (*anatomia*). He speaks of simple bodies as *mixta simplicia*, and compound as *composita*, *decomposita*, and *superdecomposita* in increasing order of complexity.[2] What he calls *principia*, the components of mineral bodies (*corpora subterranea*), are 'remotely' water and earth, but 'intimately' three earths, the vitreous (*terra prima, terra fusilis, terra lapidea, terra vitrescibile, calx*), the combustible (*terra secunda, terra pinguis, terra sicca*), and the fluid or mercurial (*terra tertia, terra fluida*). These correspond with what were called salt, sulphur, and mercury,[3] but Becher thought improperly since salt, sulphur and mercury are really compounds, e.g. sulphur of acid salt and earthy bitumen:[4]

in secundo metallorum principio valdè errant, qui illud sulphur commune inflammabile esse existimant . . . sed per sulphur intelligitur aliqua *terra pinguis, specifica sui generis*, quam sulphur metallorum vocant, e.g. in sole terra subtilis flava; in luna, terra alba splendens; in Venere rubra; in Marte, Jove et Saturno, fusca, livida.

Common sulphur is a compound of an acid salt and terra pinguis:[5] ex sale acido et nostra hac secunda terra; si [terra pinguis] cum sale acido permiscetur sulphur fit. He even gives the proportions of inflammable principle ($\frac{1}{30}$th) and acid in sulphur as found by burning the sulphur and weighing the spirit of sulphur (sulphuric acid) formed:[6] [sulphur] totum deflagrat, cum interim ejusdem analysis Chymica doceat, vix in eo trigesimam partem inflammabilem, reliquum sal acidum esse, ut spiritus sulphuris docet. This 'analysis' of sulphur was later completed by its 'synthesis' by Stahl (p. 671).

The first earth is the part of a body which is fixed in the fire, making bodies solid and (except with alkalis) almost incapable of alteration; it is vitrifiable and corresponds with body. The second earth is moist and oily, confers odour, colour, taste, and combustibility; it corresponds with soul. The third earth gives metals weight, ductility, fusibility, and volatility; it exists in mercury, arsenic, spirit of salt, etc., and corresponds with spirit. Even fire, air and water are 'earths' for Becher: terra in genere est sicca; aqua est terra fluida; aër terra subtilis, ignis est terra rarefacta.[7]

---

[1] I, 1738, 22 f.; Thorndike, *Speculum*, 1953, xxviii, 692.
[2] I, Bk. I, Sect. vi, ch. 1; sect. vii, ch. 1; 1738, 231, 273.
[3] I; 1738, 19, 53 f., 58 f., 61–89 (de primo metallorum et lapidum principio), 165, 327.
[4] VIII (III), 1689, 111; XVI, 111.   [5] I, 1738, 70 f.
[6] I, Bk. I, sect. v, ch. 2; 1738, 161.
[7] I, Bk. I, sect. vii, ch. 1; 1738, 272; VIII (I, III), 1689, 51 f., 104.

Since Becher says the vitrifiable earth, which fuses to a glassy mass (in igne fluit, et fluens vitrum exhibet), is an unfailing accompaniment of metallic ores (sine quo nulla minera bona est . . . infallibile signum futuri metalli sit),[1] Chaptal[2] thought it was barytes, which generally occurs with ores of metals. Becher's account, however, seems to refer to several kinds of stones occurring in ore veins.

The fatty or oily earth (terra pinguis) is an old idea. ψ-Roger Bacon[3] has: 'Et ex pinguedine terrae per eandem decoctionem & caliditatem generatur sulphur'; H. Khunrath[4] has *terra pinguis unctuosa* as a name for alchemical sulphur, and Sir Thomas Browne[5] remarks that 'the sulphur of bodies . . . is the oylie fat, and unctuous parts wherin consist the principles of flammability . . . containing terrestrious parts, and carrying with it the volatile salt of the body'. This is an idea often expressed by the alchemists and Paracelsus (p. 141). Becher's contribution was to classify it as one of three earths.

As to what happened to the *terra pinguis* on combustion, Becher is not clear. It has generally been assumed[6] that 'when substances were burnt or metals calcined, the *terra pinguis* escaped', leaving behind a metallic calx, but I have nowhere found this clearly asserted by Becher (although it may be); more is said on this matter below. A combustible body is one which is rarefied and dissolved in flame (ustile autem dicitur, quod rarefit, et in flammas dissolvitur).[7]

A succinct account in easy Latin of the three earths is given in the *Alphabetum Minerale*:[8]

Nonnulli credunt, omnia constare ex sale, sulphure et Mercurio; sed ego probabo, omnia, seu potissima mixta, constare ex triplici terra, una vitrescibili, quæ salis vicem præbat, matricem et basin, altera pingui, quæ sulphur est, compagem, tincturam et tenacitatem dat, tertia subtilis est, et materiam supplet, Mercurius vocatur seu potius Arsenicum. . . . *Prima terra* dat corpus ac substantiam et hypostasin mixtis, et est duplicis generis; vel calcinabilis, vel vitrescibilis; unde in animalibus ossa, in vegetabilibus cineris elixati, in mineralibus lapides. . . . *Secunda terra* dat mixtis consistentiam, colorem, saporem etc. et est duplicis generis; consistens vel liquida; unde in animalibus sevum, adeps, axungia; in vegetabilibus oleum, gummi; in mineralibus et metallis sulphur, bitumen. Ejus ideam conspicimus in omni re ardente, in carbonibus ligneis, et possibilibus innumerabilibus. . . . *Tertia terra* dat mixtis formam, penetrantiam, odorem, pondus, splendorem, lucem, etc. Est quoque duplicis generis, vel pura et tùm est terra; vel mixta, et tùm est salina, aut aquea spiritus forma; in animalibus eam cernimus in eorum salibus volatilibus; in vegetabilibus in illorum aquis destillatis, spiritibus et aquis ardentibus in fuligine; in mineralibus conspicimus eam vel fluidam, ut in argento vivo, vel consistentem, ut in arsenico.

From water and the three earths, three kinds of mixtures are formed: water with water, earth with earth, earth with water, the last two being in different proportions and different degrees of fineness in the animal, vegetable, and mineral kingdoms. In the mineral kingdom the formative principle is a kind of spirit, and minerals are formed and grow from seeds. The allegorical frontispiece of the *Physica Subterranea*, with the motto: *circulus aeterni motus,*

---

[1] I, Bk. I, sect. iii, ch. 2; 1738, 61 f.
[2] *Elements of Chemistry*, 1791, ii, 203 f., with long quotation.
[3] *Speculum Alchemiæ*, ch. iv; in *Theatrum Chemicum*, 1659, ii, 382.
[4] *Amphitheatrum Sapientiæ*, Hannover, 1609, unpaged table at end.
[5] *Pseudodoxia Epidemica*, 1646, bk. vi, ch. 12; *Works*, ed. Keynes, 1928, iii, 249.
[6] E. von Meyer, 1906, 116; Mellor, (1), 1922, i, 64.
[7] I, Bk. I, sect. vii, ch. 1; 1738, 278.
[8] VIII (Pt. III), § 6; 1689, 105–7; XVI, 105–7.

expressed Becher's belief in the ceaseless activity of nature, and the transition of substances from one kingdom of nature to another.

Rodwell[1] equated Becher's three earths with the *tria prima*:

> vitrifiable earth = salt = principle of fixity and solidity,
> inflammable earth = sulphur = principle of combustibility,
> mercurial earth = mercury = principle of volatility.

Becher also calls these 'three sulphurs'; the first is sulphureous, volatile and combustible; the second is arsenical, only with difficulty combustible; the third is metallic, fixed and incombustible.[2] He also calls the combustible earth *sulphur adustibile* and *sulphur φλογιστὸν*, the Greek work being used as the neuter of the verbal adjective in the sense of *ardens*:[3]

Mars enim dat suum arsenicum (Mercurium) antimonio, et hoc vicissim retribuit suum sulphur φλόγιστον Marti;
si à scoria liberetur sulphur φλόγιστον;[4]
hinc licèt sulphur φλόγιστον quocunque modo metallis incorporetur, ad combustibilitatem tamen suam reduci potest;[5]
omni sulphure sive phlogiston sive arsenicale, esse Mercurialis naturæ, et procedere ex fonte Mercurii, ac tendere ad eundem;[6]
metalla imperfecta, et mineralia omnia, tria sulphura contineant, unum adustibile commune . . . alterum arsenicale . . . quod etsi sulphure communi phlogisto sit liberatum (title in margin: Sulphur *phlogiston*).[7]

Becher sometimes calls the third earth a 'mercurial *spirit* (spiritum seu substantiam subtilem, volatilem, claram, lucidam, Mercurium vocarunt)'.[8] It is in a sense the radical humidity (humidum radicale) of metals:[9] non immerito ergo humidum radicale metallorum vocatur . . . aqua mineralis sicca . . . metalla resolvit, rursusque cum illiis figitur.

According to Rodwell the following compositions may be found in Becher's writings. Let W = water, S = vitrifiable earth, C = inflammable earth, V = mercurial earth. Then:

(1) $W + S$ = universal acid
(2) $W + C$ = oils
(3) $(W + S) + C$ = bitumen
(4) $\{(W + S) + C\} + (W + S)$ = sulphur
(5) $(W + S) + C$ = saltpetre
(6) $(S + C + V) + (S + V)$ = arsenic
(7) $(S + C + V) + V$ = mercury
(8) $\{(S + C + V) + V\} + \{[(W + S) + C] + (W + S)\}$ = cinnabar.

Becher uses the name 'reaction' in the modern sense and deals with mixtion and separation on the lines of what was later called elective affinity, speaking of substances 'cohering' by connexion (compages) or with force (arctius). He

[1] *Phil. Mag.*, 1868, xxxv, 1 (21–3); *Chem. News*, 1868, xvii, 101.   [2] III; 1738, 391.
[3] VIII (III); XVI, 136.   [4] *Ib.*, 139.   [5] *Ib.*, 147.   [6] III; 1738, 381.
[7] III; 1738, 393.   [8] VIII (III), 1689, 106.   [9] I, Bk. I, sect. v, ch. 3; 1738, 210.

appears to think that the stronger the reacting subjects, the stronger is the reaction. He refers to Descartes' doctrine of the shapes (textures) of corpuscles.[1] Becher does not speak directly of attractive *forces*. One substance '*attrahet*' another, in virtue of its '*affinitas*':

argentum nitrum amat . . . hinc fit, ut singulis solutionibus argenti in spiritu nitri, semper nonnihil auri inveniatur. Quare argentum eadem ratione nitrum quam aurum appetit. Cuprum seu Venus, adultera et amatoria vocatur; quod et nitrum et salem amet.[2]

Some definitions in a 'physical nomenclature' are obscure: sal nitri est terra pinguis, sale volatili, urinoso, acido soluta; while others are clear: cinabrium argentum vivum est, intermixta communis sulphuris terra.[3]

The phlogistic chemists retained all three of Becher's 'earths', and although Stahl made little use of the third or mercurial earth, others always found a place for it. Henckel[4] explained that the first earth is composed of a very hard, heavy, stony and vitrescible solid matter, existing in its purest state in flint and quartz, and is also the matrix of metals, since many of these when deprived of phlogiston by intense heat form glasses. The second earth is fatty and inflammable, soft and moist, found in sulphur and coal, pyrites, amber, bitumens, etc.; but also in quartz and flint, since these emit fire when struck; and also in the imperfect metals, which detonate with nitre or, as zinc, regulus of antimony, and tin, burn of themselves. It adds nothing to the weight of these, since regulus of antimony weighs the same after as before calcination. The third earth was called mercurial because of its volatility but more particularly because it is found in mercury. It is called the 'metallic earth' because it gives lustre to metals, and also the 'essential earth' because it constitutes the metallic essence, distinguishing metals from all other bodies. The other two earths are present in flint but this is not a metal. Henckel thought the mercurial earth might be formed by coction of the two first. Becher claimed to have converted silver into running mercury by distillation by adding more of the third earth, but the reverse process was very difficult.

Eller[5] dealt similarly with the three earths; the third is the metallic principle, a simple, fluid, mercurial earth, uniquely destined for the metals, to which it imparts lustre and malleability. Juncker[6] thought it was easy to demonstrate the identity of the first two earths in the mineral, vegetable, and animal kingdoms, but difficult for the third or mercurial earth. It may, however, be presumed that it does not differ from the other principles, is always found with phlogiston (the second earth) and never abandons it. The tartarous salts of vegetables, soot, and urinous salts, volatilise metals and make them fluid like mercury, and it may be believed that those effects result only from the mercurial principle in them.

[1] I, Bk. I, sect. iv, ch. 3; sect. v, chs. 2, 3; 1738, 102–4, 177–8 (solutio, actio et reactio), 196 f., 200; VIII (I), iii; VIII (III), xxii; XVI, 47–55, 141; Kopp, (2), iii, 203–7; Rodwell, *Phil. Mag.*, 1868, xxxv, 1 (23) who says 'the stronger the "subjecta reagentia, hoc fortior etiam est reactio, et reaction is effectus",' but gives no ref.
[2] I, 1738, 178.   [3] I, Bk. I, sect. vi, ch. 8; 1738, 271–2.
[4] *Flora Saturnisans*, ch. viii; *Oeuvres*, Paris, 1760, ii, 148–51.
[5] *Hist. Acad. Berlin*, 1753 (1755), 3; *Abhandlungen*, 1764, 310.
[6] *Conspectus Chemiae*, Halle, 1730, i, 85, 90; *Élémens de Chymie*, Paris, 1757, i, 146 f.

Becher says the *materia ignis* is well called *salamandra*, because it feeds upon fire,[1] but not common fire. Combustion is decomposition and the only inflammable things are those which can be rarefied or resolved into atoms:

Quodcunque non potest rarefieri, id etiam non potest flagrare. Nihil posse ardere, quod non summe raribile sit; et omne quod ardet, rarescere; et in atomos resolvi. Causam ignificationis seu incensionis omne id esse, quod rarefacit summeque attenuat.[2]

The presence of saline particles (mostly water) is also necessary to combustion:

nihil enim ardet, licet pingue sit, nisi particulæ salinæ interveniant; sълinæ autem magna parte ex aqua constant, quæ ad flagrationem requiritur, ut nempe in aёrem resolvatur atque aёr rarefiat; illa ergo subterranea, quæ pinguia quidem, sed non salina sunt, non ardent. Deinde etiam comburi dicuntur, quæ igne consumuntur; licet proprie ignis nihil consumat, sed potius alteret, atque partes volatiles evaporare faciat, et hoc modo in igne omnia comburantur, quæ non fixa sunt. Nihil autem fixum vocari potest, quod igne alteratur ut in flammas agitur.[3]

Gold and silver contain an 'incombustible philosophical sulphur', quod nihil aliud est, nisi terra pinguis, fixissima, purissima, nullo sale intermixta, sed terra mercuriali imbibita atque incerata.[4]

Every combustible body must contain in itself the cause of combustibility (ignem sustinens corpus, animam quoque ignis patientem disiderabat), and this cause is a principle which he calls fatty earth (*terra pinguis*), which is not common sulphur but is contained in this as well as in other combustible mineral bodies, just as an inflammable material, which the moderns call oil, is contained in animal and vegetable matter.[5] The name *terra pinguis* for bituminous earth had been used by Agricola in 1546,[6] and Becher sometimes used it in the same sense (secunda est terra seu sulphur, unde componitur nitrum, nempè pinguis, calidum innatum, oleosa, unctuosa, inflammabilis).[7] He sometimes even speaks of it as present in saltpetre (primam dixi lapidem esse, et in quovis sal alcali latere; alteram in nitro vel sulphure; tertiam in sale communi).[8] The part taken by the air in combustion is quite secondary; combustion is the elevation, rarefaction and extension of condensed sulphureous particles by the fermentive action of fire, and the air interposes itself in the pores of the burning body (et aёre se in poros interponente).[9]

The effect of calcination upon metals is the expulsion of volatile parts by fire (ignis omnia dissolvit et disunit, quae ex heterogeneis partibus constant . . . In metallis . . . pars volatilior ab igne expellitur).[10]

In the First Supplement to the *Physica Subterranea* Becher enlarges upon the production and perfection of metals in the bowels of the earth. All subterranean bodies tend to assume a metallic nature and metals tend to perfec-

---

[1] I, bk. I, sect. v, ch. 3; 1738, 219.   [2] I, Bk. I, sect. v, chs. 1, 3; 1738, 135, 218 f., 222 f.
[3] I, Bk. I, sect. vii, ch. 1; 1738, 278; cf. VIII (III), 1689, 145 f.; the idea was taken over by Lavoisier, *Opuscules Physiques et Chimiques*, 2 ed., 1801, 347: sans doute, me suis-je dit à moi même, l'eau est nécessaire à l'aliment de la flamme.
[4] I, Bk. I, sect. vii, ch. 1; 1738, 278.   [5] I, Bk. I, sect. iii, ch. 3; 1738, 68, 70.
[6] De ortu et causis subterraneorum, bk. i; *De Re Metallica*, Basel, 1657, 497.
[7] VIII (III), 1689, 108.   [8] I, Bk. I, sect. iii, ch. 5; 1738, 88.
[9] VIII (III), 1689, 145.
[10] I, Bk. I, sect. v, ch. 3; 1738, 223; Agricola and Libavius had held this view.

tion.[1] Becher in his writings repeatedly expresses belief in the possibility of transmutation, e.g.:[2]

Fac ergo ex Luna et Sole Mercurios, quos cum primo Ente sulphuris præcipita, præcipitatum Philosophorum igne attenua, exalta, et cum sale borracis Philosophorum liquefae et fige, donec sine fumo fluat; quæ licet breviter dicta sint, longo tamen labore acquiruntur et itinere: ex arenoso namque terrestri Arabico mari, in mare rubrum aqueum, et ex hoc in bituminosum ardens mare mortuum itinerandum est, non sine scopulorum et voraginum periculo. Nos, Deo sint laudes, jam appulimus ad portum.

He opposed St. Augustine's view that metals were created and do not grow. All sublunary bodies, including metals, are mixed, and must therefore be formed from their components. Many older authors, such as Pliny (Vol. I), believed that metals grew in the earth, and Boyle and Tachenius still assumed this.[3]

Becher[4] gives a recipe of Gerhard Thilenius, a Frankfurt doctor, for making copper by melting on a cupel $\frac{1}{2}$ oz. of lead, a drachm of tin, and two or three grains of silver, scorifying several times, and then fusing the product with two or three parts of potash, 'et habebis grana pura cupri.' He mentions the arsenical ore *mundic* of Cornwall:[5] hic in Anglia in Cornubia abundantissimè circa mineras stanni et ferri reperitur, quam vulgari linguâ Mondyck vocant. Metallic arsenic is obtained by heating white arsenic with soap, oil, etc. in a retort: si smegma, sevum, oleum, vel quodcunque pingue arsenico misceas, et per retortam destilles, urgenti igne sublimabitur in collum, arsenicum insigniter antimonii instar metallisatum.[6]

Becher may have been acquainted with phosphoric acid glass (metaphosphoric acid) obtained by the action of sulphuric acid on bone ash, since he says man is glass and can be reconverted into glass, and similarly other animals (homo vitrum est, et in vitrum redigi potest, sicut et omnia animalia), and that a series of ancestors could be formed in glass by a process which he declines to specify, 'propter varios abusus.'[7] He believed in the alkahest or universal solvent (p. 218), which was capable of resolving a body into atoms (corpora in tenuissimas atomos redigendo).[8]

The formation of nitre from decaying animal matter in the earth depends on the attraction of a spirit from the air:

sed et ipsum nitrum necdum finis ultimus putrefactionis est; nam cum ejusdem partes igneæ separantur, reliquæ in terram convertuntur, prorsus puram et insipidam; sed singulari magnetismo præditam, novum spiritum aëreum attrahendi, rursusque nitrum fiendi.[9]

Becher, who quotes Albertus Magnus, speaks of large iron meteorites which

[1] II; 1738, 284, 288, 330. [2] I, Bk. I, sect. v, ch. 3; 1738, 231.
[3] Kopp, (1), iii, 108 f. [4] I, Bk. I, sect. v, ch. 3; IV; 1738, 227, 461.
[5] VIII (III), 1689, 131.
[6] II, ch. 3; 1738, p. 299; Chaptal, *Elements of Chemistry*, 1791, ii, 221.
[7] I, Bk. I, sect. iii, ch. 3; 1738, 67; Proust, *Obs. Phys.*, 1781, xvii, 145.
[8] I, Bk. I, sect. iii, ch. 4; 1738, 79.
[9] I, Bk. I, sect. v, ch. 1, § 52; 1738, 147; Chaptal, *Elements of Chemistry*, 1791, i, 236, who says 'Becher possessed a considerably accurate knowledge of the formation of nitre'. Chaptal had a great admiration for Becher, whom he frequently quotes.

have fallen on the earth, one of 48,000 lb. weight.[1] He thought that fire alone, entering iron, converts it into steel (solum ignem ex ferro chalybem facere, habet se vero chalybificatio sequenti modo).[2]

The increase in weight of metals, such as tin, lead and antimony, on calcination was quite well known to Becher, who also quotes experiments of his own in which tin and lead are reduced to powder, with increase in weight, when calcined in glass retorts. He explained it as due to the incorporation of ponderable particles of fire, capable of penetrating glass:

Quem notabilem excessum ponderis, a corpusculis retortam vitream penetrantibus profectum esse, vix credibile est;[3]
nam ita cum igne comparatum est, ut seipsum substantiæ, quam coquit et calcinat, incorporet; uti ad oculum patet in antimonii calcinatione per speculum quoddam causticum, quo calcinatur, corpus majus acquirit pondus, etsi ignis per idem tempus, magnam quandam humidarum et volatilium partium quantitatem ex fumante massa expellat;[4]
coloris et gravitatis causam, igneis particulis, subjecto reverberii igne tractato inhærentibus, adscribent;[5]
metalla igne tractata, sine ulla alia additione graviora reddi, id est in gravitate mutare. Hoc vero solo vocabulo coctionis fiere, sine corpusculorum interpositione et interventu, absurdum et durum est. . . . Statuendum ergo, ab igne particulas prodire, quæ in corpora agunt, et in iis, pro subjecti tamen varietate figuntur; unde major gravitas.[6]

This theory had been adopted by Boyle in 1661 and more definitely in 1673 (p. 529). From about 1700, the belief in a *ponderable* fire matter seems to have lost ground, and the increase in weight was either ignored as unimportant or explained in other ways (see p. 675).

Becher prepared butter of antimony (antimony trichloride) by distilling a mixture of stibnite, common salt, and green vitriol or alum.[7] He is said to mention boric acid, prepared by distilling oil of vitriol with borax (cum vitriolo seu spiritu aut oleo vitrioli, & oleo tartari, vel borrace).[8] The red fumes evolved when a metal dissolves in aqua fortis can be condensed to a green volatile spirit (in viridem spiritum valde subtilem),[9] which would be impure nitrous anhydride.

In his section on mineral waters[10] Becher says water in the centre of the earth dissolves a particular earth, from which a universal acid or esurine spirit is formed, of the nature of vinegar, and a universal solvent (acidum universale, spiritum esurinum, acetum naturæ, et solvens Catholicum). This universal acid (acidum primogenium) produced all the other acids in nature. He seems to have regarded it as the acid of common salt (ex præfato acido universali originem trahere).

Becher extended his theory of the three earths to the vegetable and animal kingdoms, but says the materials of these are more complex than minerals.[11] The different kinds of mixtures in the three kingdoms result in three different

---

[1] II, ch. 4; 1738, 303, Chaptal in 1790, *Elements of Chemistry*, 1791, ii, 328, could still call this a 'ridiculous assertion'.
[2] I, Bk. I, sect. v, ch. 3; 1738, 226.   [3] I, Bk. I, sect. iii, ch.5; 1738, 87.
[4] I, Bk. I, sect. iv, ch. 5; 1738, 120.   [5] I, Bk. I, sect. v, ch. 3; 1738, 220.
[6] I, Bk. I, sect. v, ch. 3; 1738, 225.   [7] XVII; in XVI, 238.
[8] III; 1738, 398; Thomson, (1), i, 248.   [9] I, Bk. I, sect. v, ch. 2; 1738, 180.
[10] I, Bk. I, sect. i, ch. 4; 1738, 41 f.
[11] I, Bk. I, sect. iv, ch. 6; VIII (III); Thesis viii, 1689, 105 f.; 1738, 123 f.

types of dissolution, viz. putrefaction (putrefactio) in animals, fermentation (fermentatio) in plants, and fusion (liquefactio) in minerals. These are due to the insinuation of watery, airy, and fiery particles, respectively.[1]

Becher believed in spontaneous generation; he mentions an experiment in which worms were produced in meat under an air-pump receiver but were found to be all dead, so that air is necessary for the production of living beings, and they moved when air was let in.[2]

Becher distinguished putrefaction, in which the mixt is completely broken down and destroyed, from fermentation, which is a process of rarefaction leading to perfection. Putrefaction is in some ways analogous to combustion; fermentation requires the participation of air, the particles of which dilate, extenuate and subtilise the fermenting matter, and it is facilitated by water and heat. Fermentation cannot occur in closed vessels (in which air is shut off) and if too much heat is applied the rare particles are expelled.[3]

Saline and sulphureous particles act upon one another to produce alcohol or vinegar: (spiritus vini et aceti qui duo inter se differunt, quod prior ... plures partes sulphureas, pauciores salinas, posterior plures salinas, pauciores sulphureas contineat).[4] He thought vinegar could be reconverted into alcohol (actually acetone) by distilling sugar of lead (si spiritus aceti cum plumbo, in concluso vase per aliquod tempus digestus, et dulcificatus, destilletur, non amplius spiritus aceti, sed rursus spiritus vini ardens in lucem prodeat).[5]

He distinguishes three kinds of fermentation: (1) intumefactio (effervescence or any kind of evolution of gas); (2) proprie fermentatio (alcoholic fermentation); and (3) acetificatio seu acescentia (acetous fermentation). He gives a concise statement of his views on fermentation (which he compares with combustion) in seven theses in his *Alphabetum Minerale*,[6] e.g. that it does not occur in closed vessels, that only sweet things ferment, and that the final results are fæces (tartar), a middle sub-acid substance (substantia media subacida) and sulphureous intoxicating spirit (spirituosa sulphurea inebrians).

Flame is a kind of fermentation, fire being the ferment which rarefies and kindles the combustible matter, and the subtle parts pass off in flame and cannot be condensed:

ignis quasi fermentum est, quod rarefacit, et incendit comburendum; ... Combustione ergo seu rarefactione partium separatio fit; et quidem omnium primæ et subtilissimæ in flammam abeunt, tanquam Gas in vino ... deinde subtilis spiritus, et sulphureus, et salinus ... fumusque nihilominus capiatur.[7]

The philosophical air (aer philosophicus, artificialis, congelatus) perhaps included hydrogen from metals and acids:[8] philosophorum aër ... item aër corporum, qui in generatione præsertim metallorum inhalat, exhalat et coruscat, hic aër corporum, eorum Mercurius aut Mercuriale principium est.

---

[1] I, Bk. I, sect. v, ch. 1; 1738, 132–92; he often uses the names *gas* and *spiritus sylvestris*, e.g. pp. 152 f.

[2] I, Bk. I, sect. v, ch. 1; 1738, 144, 146.

[3] I, Bk. I, sect. v, chs. 1–2; 1738, 134 f., 156 f.; J. C. Fischer, iii, 372–6 (full account).

[4] I, Bk. I, sect. v, ch. 2; 1738, 189.   [5] I, Bk. I, sect. v, ch. 2; 1738, 183.

[6] VIII (III), ch. 24; 1689, 144; Chaptal, *Elements of Chemistry*, 1791, iii, 240 f., 394; Kopp, (1), iv, 292.

[7] I, Bk. I, sect. v, ch. 2; 1738, 188.   [8] VII, tit. iv, § 4; 1705, 121.

Becher mentions the evolution of an inflammable gas, perhaps ethylene, from a mixture of alcohol and oil of vitriol: evidens demonstratio est, in spiritu vini et oleo Vitrioli, utroque probe rectificatio. Quamprimum enim confunduntur, ignem concipiunt; qui vase obstructo extinguitur, aperto rursus incenditur:[1] he omits to say that a lighted taper must be applied, and it is possible that ether vapour was the cause of the inflammation.

Becher[2] claimed that he had invented a method of converting English coal into smokeless coke for smelting, demonstrating it to Boyle and in Windsor, where it was carried out on the large scale. He also obtained tar from coal as good as the Swedish wood-tar, giving a specimen to the King. He took out a patent for this in conjunction with Henry Serle (19 August, 1681).

[1] I, Bk. I, sect. v, ch. 3; 1738, 223.
[2] XI, 64; B. Faujas Saint-Fond, *Travels in England, Scotland and the Hebrides*, 2 vols., London, 1799, i, 151.

CHAPTER XVIII

THE PHLOGISTON THEORY. PART II. STAHL

STAHL

One of the outstanding chemists of the eighteenth century was Stahl.[1] Georg Ernst Stahl (Anspach, Bavaria, 21 October 1660–Berlin, 14 May 1734) was the son of a Protestant pastor. He studied medicine at Jena under the Iatrochemist Georg Wolfgang Wedel (see p. 315), taking his M.D. at the age of twenty three, when he began to give public lectures. Before going to the university Stahl, at the age of fifteen, had read a MS. copy of the lectures on chemistry given at Padua by Jacob Barner (afterwards published as *Chymia Philosophica perfecte delineata*, Nürnberg, 1689), and Kunckel's *Nützliche Observationes* (1676), and he says he knew these works practically by heart. He had also made experiments and had been taught some practical secrets by an enameller. In 1684 he gave a course of lectures on chemistry in Jena (see item XVII below).[2]

In 1687 he became court physician to Johann Ernst, Duke of Saxe-Weimar. Destined for an academic career, he became in 1694, at the solicitation of Hoffmann (with whom he afterwards quarrelled), the second professor of medicine at the University of Halle, founded in 1693. He taught there for twenty-two years. His duties at Halle included lectures on the theory of medicine, physiology, dietetics, materia medica, chemistry, botany and anatomy, completing the course given by Hoffmann in the first chair (p. 692), and it is noteworthy that he kept his chemistry and medicine entirely separate, teaching that chemistry can throw no light on the vital functions, and is dangerous to medicine. In particular, he violently opposed the Iatrochemical

[1] Chevreul, *Compt. Rend.*, 1864, lix, 973; 1872, lxxiv, 898–913; Choulant, ed. of Stahl's *Theoria Medica* (see I' below; life, list of publications, specimens of Stahl's handwriting); Daremberg, (1), ii, 1020–60 (1057: Stahl est un esprit chagrin, atrabiliare, jaloux; un écrivain obscur; c'est un Van Helmont, moins l'illuminisme et la chimiatrie; c'est un Paracelse, moins la grossièreté du langage et avec un esprit beaucoup plus élevé et mieux cultivé); Ferguson, ii, 399; Formey, *Éloges des Académiciens de Berlin et de divers autres Savans*, 2 vols. 8°, Berlin, 1757, i, 328–33 (Stahl 'joignoit à une lecture immense une pénétration exquise . . . Il était droit & franc dans ses procédés, n'ayant point d'égard à l'apparence des personnes'); Gmelin, (1), ii, 659–80; Haeser, (1), 1881, ii, 519; A. von Haller, *Bibliotheca Medicinae Practicae*, 4 vols., Basel and Bern (1776–88), 1779, iii, 575–94; Hoefer, (1), ii, 395; Koch, *A. Med.*, 1926, xviii, 20; Kopp, (1), i, 187; (2), iii, 211; H. Metzger, *Isis*, 1926, viii, 427; 1927, ix, 294; *id.*, *Newton, Stahl, Boerhaave et la doctrine Chimique*, Paris, 1930; Meyer-Steineg and Sudhoff, 1922, 339; Rodwell, *Phil. Mag.*, 1868, xxxv, 1; *Chem. News*, 1868, xvii, 101; Saverien, 1769, vii, 263 (curious list of Stahl's discoveries); Sprengel, (1), v, 199; T. Thomson, (1), i, 250; Verzeichniss des Naturalien-Cabinets, der Bibliothek, Kupferstiche und Musikalien . . . des seligen . . . Herrn G. E. Stahl, 8°, Berlin, [1773], 182 pp. (BM 657. i. 38); Wiegleb, (2), 1790, I, i, 87; X in NBG, 1865, xliv, 397; a promised life of Stahl by Leporinus never appeared.

[2] Thomson, (1), ii, 251, incorrectly said 'there is no evidence that he ever taught [chemistry] in any public school'; he seems to have lectured on it also in Halle.

theory of acid and alkali. In 1697 he began to publish a journal, *Observationes chymico-physico-medicae mensibus singulis bono cum Deo continuandae*, which ceased in 1698 (see IV in list below).

Stahl in 1716 accepted appointment as body-physician to Frederick I, King of Prussia, in Berlin, and retained this post until his death in 1734. His colleague at Halle, Friedrich Hoffmann, had been called to Berlin in 1709, but the austerity of the court life there did not suit his genial temperament, and he returned to Halle in 1712. Stahl's hard disposition, however, was suited to the

FIG. 31. G. E. STAHL, 1660–1734.

atmosphere of the Berlin Court. He was married four times,[1] losing his first wife through puerperal fever, which he could not cure.

Stahl was proud, morose, atrabilious, a Pietist (the university of Halle, founded in 1694, was a Pietistic centre); he quarrelled with his senior colleague Hoffmann, to whom he owed his appointment in Halle (perhaps Hoffmann's unforgivable offence); he rarely answered letters; he showed contempt for all who differed from his views and reacted violently to criticism. These qualities, as T. Thomson said, greatly enhanced his reputation. J. Thomson[2] says that in his medical writings he studiously avoided every form of expression and thought which he did not believe to be peculiar to himself. In them, Stahl quotes very few authors, among them Campanella, Paracelsus and Van Helmont (whom he criticises) occasionally.

Like Hoffmann (p. 700), Stahl prescribed and sold some nostrums

[1] Choulant, III, vi (correcting *ib.*, I, x).
[2] *Life of Cullen*, Edinburgh and London, 1859, ii, 182.

(balsamic pills and a stomach powder) of his own, and a remedy which Goetz thought was rectified alcohol. His *essentia alexipharmaca* contained angelica root.[1] Stahl seems to have regarded his ideas as at least in part due to divine inspiration, and the common herd could have no inkling of them. Blumenbach[2] says his lectures were dry and intentionally difficult; few of his students understood them and in their dissertations merely repeated his opinions.

Choulant[3] says the Latin style of Stahl's medical works is obscure but copious, with long periods hard to disentangle and often lacking classical purity (usus tamen stilo obscuriori, longissimis periodis et difficulter extricandis impedito, latinitate copiosa quidem et locuplete, sed singulari prorsus et a classica puritate non ita raro aliena). Most of Stahl's medical writings were collected and extended by himself in 1708 as *The True Theory of Medicine*:

I'. Theoria medica vera, physiologiam et pathologiam, tanquam doctrinae medicae partes vere contemplatativas e naturae et artis veris fundamentis, intaminata ratione et inconcussa experientia sistens, 4°, Halle, 1708 (portr., vi, 1434, xxxix pp.; BM 544. g. 12); 2 ed., 4°, Halle, 1708; 3 ed. by Juncker, 4°, Halle, 1737 (rearranged); ed. L. Choulant, editionem reliquis emendatiorem et vita authoris auctam (as vols. xiv–xvi of Scriptorum Classicorum de Praxi Medica nonnullorum Opera collecta), 3 vols. 12°, Leipzig, 1831-2-3; German tr. by Ruf, Halle, 1702, and (abbreviated) by K. W. Ideler, Georg Ernst Stahl's Theorie der Heilkunde, Berlin, 1831-2 (with introduction); French tr. (part only) by T. Blondin, Oeuvres medico-philosophiques et pratiques, vols. 2–6 (all publ.), Sotheran *Cat.* 852 (1938), no. 133; see BN *Catal. Gén.*, 1950, clxxvii, 16). The title is very characteristic; the adjectives 'vera', 'rationalia', and 'fundamenta' occur in the titles of nearly all Stahl's books.

The first vol. of Choulant's ed. (1831) contains:

(a) Disquisitio de mechanismi et organismi diversitae, pp. 5–52;
(b) Paraenesis ad aliena a medica doctrina arcendum (4°, Halle, 1706), pp. 53–80;
(c) Demonstratio de mixti et vivi corporis vera diversitate (De vera diversitate corporis mixti et vivi . . . demonstratio, 4°, Halle, 1707 (BM 549. d. 19. (4.)), pp. 81–158;
(d) Vindiciae et indicia schediasmatibus (4°, Halle, 1707), pp. 159–220;
(e) Physiologia, with a preface, six sections subdivided into membra, and a brief summary, pp. 221–491.

The second vol. (1832) is on:

(f) Pathologia generalis et specialis, the first part (α) divided into five sections subdivided into membra, the second part (β) also divided into five sections subdivided into membra.

The third vol. (1833) is on:

(g) Pathologia specialissima in two sections subdivided into membra, and a copious index (pp. 395–481).

The quotations and refs. are on the above scheme, with the volume and page of Choulant's ed.

Stahl[4] traced the confusion which afflicted medicine to the views of Aristotle and Demokritos and their followers. Aristotle used the purely mathematical concept of the divisibility of bodies to infinity, and regarded mixtion as an act or effect which penetrates the parts of bodies so intimately that every material corpuscle, even infinitely small, is conserved even in all the varieties of organised being, of whatever size in mass or volume (quaecunque corporis talis particula, etiam infinite minima, adhuc retineat illam eandem per omnia

---

[1] Sprengel, (1), v, 226–7.   [2] In Choulant, I, xiv.   [3] 1831, I, xi.   [4] I' c; i, 83–5.

et aequalem penitus mixtionem, quae in corpore tali supponi possit). Demokritos, followed by the moderns, had proposed a rival opinion and assumed that there is a limit of divisibility of simple bodies (sit certae cuidam ultimae magnitudini simpliciorum imo tandem simplicissimorum corporum naturalium). These eminent men had not established their assertions on a solid basis and to-day there are scarcely any who rely so much on experience as on mechanico-geometrical arguments (nisi illi soli, qui chymiae aeque atque mechanico-geometricae tam experientiae quam rationes satis compotes sunt). Although geometry and mechanics can easily convince us that a mere apposition, union, or mutual adhesion could form what are called mixts or compounds (partim mixtiones partim compositiones vocamus), and although things may well happen in this way, it must be recognised that experimental chemistry alone can fully demonstrate the truth, viz. that things do not happen in a way different from those we have explained (dico quod non aliter se habere soleant, adeoque vere probabiliter non possint aliter se habere, sola utique chymia commonstrare valet).

The first to distinguish clearly between mixts, simple bodies, and compounds was Becher:

primus in hoc genere ita ob oculus posuit Becherus, inter corpora mixta simplicius, et composita . . .
Sane vero chymia magno exemplorum numero hoc testatum reddere potest, quod compositiones tales imprimis, imo hinc inde etiam mixtiones subtiles variae, iterum dirimi possint in eadem illa intemerata priora seu principia, e quibus coaluerunt; et subsistant etiam sincere talia, quoad novo illo artificioso interventu dirimantur.[1]

There is a great gulf between non-living and living (however simple) beings. Stahl gives twelve arguments in support of this view.[2] Living beings differ from non-living in possessing a soul (anima). Stahl's animism (vitalism) had its roots in classical antiquity, writers of the Renaissance, Van Helmont (whom he studied carefully), and Leibniz, although Stahl was an original thinker in many ways.[3]

Stahl's vitalism differed from Helmont's since he believed that the 'sensitive soul' worked directly on chemical processes in the body without the intervention of archei; as Foster said, 'it is not a mortal something associated with, and as it were the shell of an immortal mind, but it is itself the immortal principle, spiritual and immaterial, coming from afar, and at the death of the body returning to whence it came.' 'Nature', 'life', and 'soul' were synonymous.[4]

Van Helmont had rejected the distinction between vital and animal spirits. The blood contains vital spirits (arterial blood) and is carried to all the tissues. The sensitive soul (anima sensitiva) belongs to man alone, the Archeus and the archei acting through the ferments, are its servants. The soul dwells in the Archeus of the stomach; 'it is present in a point situated centrally, in an atom as it were, in the middle of the thickness of a mere membrane. Though it is placed in a locality, it is nevertheless not there

---

[1] I' c; i, 84.
[2] I' c, e, sect. IV (de generatione); i, 84 f., 108, 111, 421; Foster, 1901, 169, 225 f.
[3] A. Lemoine, Stahl et l'Animisme, Paris, 1858; id., Le Vitalisme et l'Animisme de Stahl, Paris, 1864 (antagonistic); Foster, 1901, 169; E. Rádl, Geschichte der biologischen Theorien seit dem Ende siebzenten Jahrhunderts, 2 vols., Leipzig, 1905–9, i, 83 f.; Koch, 1926.
[4] Daremberg, (1), ii, 1027; Haeser, (1), ii, 523–4.

in a local manner. For it is a light, and there is nothing in the universe more like it than the light of a candle. It is present in the stomach in some such way as light is present in a burning wick. But I do not mean a burning, heating, light, the cause of the heat of the body, for the heat of the body is merely the product of life, of vital actions, and is not life itself.'[1]

The sensitive soul is mortal and in man in his present state coexists with the immortal mind (mens immortalis). 'The sensitive soul is, as it were, the husk or shell of the mind, and the mind works through it, so that at the bidding of the mind the soul makes use of the Archeus whether it itself will or no.' Before the Fall, man possessed only the immortal mind, which acted directly on the Archeus and man was immortal. 'At the Fall, God introduced into man the sensitive soul, and with it death, the immortal mind retiring within the sensitive soul and becoming as it were its kernel.'[2]

The rational soul of Descartes (p. 440) included Van Helmont's immortal mind, and both are outside and distinct from the animal spirits.[3] Stahl rejected the animal spirits of Wedel, as Bohn had before him.[4]

Stahl supposed that the human body would undergo putrefaction (as it does after death) unless it is preserved by a protective principle, which is the soul:[5]

totum corpus animale, ex universa sua materiali constitutione intima atque penitissima, est expositum corruptioni itidem penitissimae atque praesentissimae, omnibus temporis momentis aequaliter.[6]

The soul thus behaves in some way like the Archeus of Van Helmont or the anima brutorum of Willis (p. 305), the old anima vegetativa (see Vol. I), and a similar view was proposed shortly before Willis by Perrault.[7] It is an old Stoic idea; Chrysippos said life, like salt, prevented putrefaction.[8]

Some criticisms by Leibniz[9] were answered by Stahl.[10] Stahl criticised severely the Iatrochemical theories of Sylvius, etc., which referred coagulation to acids, liquefaction to volatile alkali, stimulation to sulphureo-saline acrimony, fermentation, etc.:[11]

Quod enim tanto promittit hiatu chymicorum nomine sibi placens multitudo, in paucas profecto opiniones fatiscit, dum de coagulatione per aciditatem, de colliquatione per alcaliam volatilitatem, de efficacia stimulante per acrimoniam sulphureosalinam, de fermentescente mutabilitate κράσεων loquendo . . . certe rerum suarum curiosius satagenti persuadebit . . . videri possit tot specialibus fiendi modis. . . .

dum aliud acidum hemicranicum, aliud ophthalmicum, aliud odontalgicum, aliud anginodes, aliud pleuriticum, aliud nephriticum, aliud hystericum, aliud fixum, aliud volatile, aliud vagum comminiscuntur, neque vero ullam specialiorum originem ipsis e tota sua chymia assignare valent, nisi quod per modum fermentationis haec ita fieri loquantur . . . ab omni specialiore usu adeoque verius scientifica perceptione revera alienum.

Stahl regarded anatomy, as well as physics and chemistry,[12] as of little importance in medicine.[13]

---

[1] Van Helmont, *Ortus Medicinæ*, 1652, 229 f., 280.
[2] *Ib.*, 212 f., 230 f., 520 f., 526; Foster, 1901, 142–4.
[3] Foster, 1901, 260.   [4] Sprengel, (1), v, 202.   [5] I' *c, e*; i, 98, 100, 475.
[6] I' *f* α (Pt. I, sect. ii, memb. 1; sect. iii, memb. 1); ii, 25, 41.
[7] *Essays de Physique*, 4 vols., Paris, 1680–88 (not in BM or CUL).
[8] Cicero, *De Nat. Deor.*, ii, 64.
[9] Animadversiones circa assertationes Stahlii; *Opera*, 1768, II, ii, 131.
[10] *Negotium otiosum, seu* σκιαμαχία *adversus positiones aliquas fundamentales theoriae verae medicae*, 4°, Halle, 1720 (Choulant, I, xxxviii, no. 2).
[11] I' *b*; i, 70.   [12] I' *c*; i, 109–12.
[13] Two of his small publications have the titles: *Programma quo vindicias theoriae vere medicae a superfluis, alienis, falsis opinionibus et suppositionibus ex incongruâ Anatomiae, Chymiae*

Stahl denied the existence of the gastric ferment postulated by Van Helmont[1] and thought saliva was sufficient for digestion:

Dicendum potius est de *asservatione* illa ciborum sufficiente in ventriculo, donec fermentativam suam resolutionem assecuti sint . . . Recte utique jam inde post Helmontium in genere statuunt scholae medicae, quod resolutio ciborum in ventriculo fiat per modum fermentationis . . . Sine nova itaque peculiari et plane specifica in ventriculo fermentali materia . . . sufficere utique potest saliva pro fermentali ejusmodi energia.

He thought the heating of the blood is due to friction[2] and is not due to any innate heat and spirits as Caspar Hoffmann supposed:

motu incalescat sanguis . . . dum nempe per fortes agitationes partium corporis . . . quando per pulsum multo vehementius agitatum sanguis fortius circumpellitur, indivisus comines incendit incrementum etiam caloris proportionatum.

Willis's theory of a flame in the blood (see p. 307) is criticised,[3] and the opinion of the moderns that respiration heats the blood and that air insinuates itself into the blood.[4] The heating of the blood is a purely mechanical effect, due to the 'transpulsion through the soft porous tissues (per spongiosas partes transpulsus)'. It is a vital tonic movement, independent of will and consciousness, the porous structures at one time being more constricted and compact and at another time being relaxed.[5] This varying tonicity of the tissues was the corner-stone of much of Stahl's pathology[6] and exerted a powerful influence over medical thought.

The air 'contributes to this whole business of breathing in no other than a formal manner as the phrase is [i.e. mechanically]'. If it adds something, this 'is neither great in quantity nor dense in quality, nor indeed anything different from the true nature of atmospheric air, which it must necessarily be if breathing supplied any kind of spirit to the blood'. If anything, it would be phlogiston, but there is not enough of this in air to add anything of moment to the blood, even in a place where inflammable things are burnt. 'These considerations, interesting perhaps to the curious, add absolutely nothing to medical practice, and it is not meet to waste any more time upon them':[7]

Sicut autem ad hoc negotium universum aër ita satis evidenter non nisi formaliter tantum, uti loquuntur, concurrit atque contribuit . . . certum interim omnino est quolibet intuitu, quod illud, quicquid tandem esset, nec adeo multum, nec adeo crassum esse posset; interim neque etiam a reliqua vera indole aëris atmosphaerici alienum; quale quid necessarium esset, si spiritus suppeditare deberet: sed potius longe simplicius φλογιστὸν quoddam principium; quamvis de hoc etiam non minoris ponderis dubitationes, quam adsertiones, sese offerant. Ut etiam nihil aliud dicam,

et *Physicæ, tractatione et applicatione prognatis,* 4°, Halle, 1694 (in XII, 47–54); and *Programma isagogicum de natura ut subjecto physiologiae et superfluis anatomicis,* 4°, Halle, 1696 (Choulant, I, xix, no. 5).
   [1] I' *e,* sect. iii (de nutritione); i, 399, 402; Foster, 1901, 169 f., 224 f. (Stahl's physiology was retrograde).
   [2] I' *e,* sect. I, memb. iv, art. 1 (de circuitu humorum cum sanguine); sect. II, memb. 1; I' *f β,* memb. 3 (de inflammatione); i, 255, 325 f.; ii, 213 f.
   [3] I' *d, e* (sect. I, memb. iv, art. 1); i, 179, 256 f.
   [4] I' *e,* sect. II, memb. 1 (de rebus non-naturalibus); i, 349.
   [5] I' *e,* sect. I, memb. 8, i, 335–41; publs. of 1695–6, see *ib.* I, xvii.
   [6] I' *f β,* sect. III, memb. 1 (de tonicis variationibus); ii, 248 f.
   [7] I' *e,* sect. II, memb. 1; i, 353–4; Foster, 1901, 225–7.

certe tanta quantitate in aëre non abundat hoc principium. . . . Quicquid tamen omnium harum rerum sit, quamquam curiositate considerationes hae multum velificentur, usui certe medico absolute nihil conferunt: unde etiam tempus illis amplius insumere non convenit.

The beginning of a true theory of respiration made by Mayow was destined to be smothered by the weight of Stahl's authority. We turn now to the chemical work of Stahl, which is of the first importance.

Venel,[1] who had a high opinion of Becher and a poor one of Boyle, is very flattering in his account of Stahl: everything he wrote teemed with genius and imagination, 'qui s'étendent au-delà de l'objet sensible & qui finissent, pour ainsi dire, par un long fillon de lumière qui brille aussi loin que la vue de l'esprit peut le suivre.' He admits that his style is difficult, which may prevent some scribblers and poets [Voltaire] from ornamenting their works with the name of Stahl, as they have done with Newton's. Fourcroy[2] says Stahl, by collecting facts 'en fit véritablement une science nouvelle par la précision de ses idées lumineuses'; but all this is too favourable.

A bibliography of the very numerous writings of Stahl was prepared by Johann Christopher Goetz (Nürnberg; 1688–1733).[3] They include:

I. Fragmentorum Aetiologiae Physiologico-Chymicae ex Indagatione Sensu-Rationali, seu Conaminium ac concipiendam notitiam Mechanicam de Rarefactione Chymica, Prodromus de Indagatione Chymico-Physiologica, 12°, Jena 1683 (xxii, 139, viii pp.; BM 1036. a. 5, incompl. at end; Goetze, 1; repr. in XII, 1–46 ('Fragmentorus' omitted).

II. Programma quo Vindicias Theoriae Vere Medicae, a superfluis, alienis, falsis opinionibus & suppositionibus ex incongruâ Anatomiae, Chymiae, & Physicae, tractione . . . , 4°, Halle, 1694, 1705; repr. in XII, 47–64.

III. Zymotechnia fundamentalis, seu Fermentationis theoria generalis, Qua Nobilissimæ hujus Artis, & Partis Chymiae, utilissimae atq; subtilissimæ, Causæ & effectus in genere, Ex ipsis Mechanico Physicis principiis, summo studio eruuntur, Simulque Experimentum Novum Sulphur verum arte producendi, Et alia utilia Experimenta atque observata, inseruntur, 1697 s.l. [Halle], sm. 8°; pp. viii, 200, last misnumb. 400; BM 1033. a. 20; Goetz, 15; repr. in XII, 65–194. German tr. with notes:

Zymotechnia Fvndamentalis oder Allgemeine Grund-Erkänntnis Der Gährungs-Kunst . . . mit einem neuen Chymischen Experiment, wie ein wahrer Schwefel durch Kunst zum Vorschein zu bringen . . . aus dem Lateinischen ins Teutsche übersetzt, 8°, Frankfurt and Leipzig, 1734 (304 pp.; BN R 51706; Chemical Society, London); 8°, Stettin and Leipzig, 1748 (304 pp., BM 1035. c. 3).

IV. Observationes Chymico-Physico-Medicae curiosae, Mensibus singulis . . . , 8°, publ. separately monthly: i–vi, July–December, Frankfurt and Leipzig, 1697; vii–xi, January–May, Halle, 1698; continuous pagin.; BM 1033. a. 21. (3.); Choulant, I, xlii. All repr. in XII with another part, xii. The separate parts are:

(a) 1697:
   (i) July: Experimentum novum verum Sulphur Arte producendi; XII, 299–333.
   (ii) August: Spiritus Vitrioli Volatilis in copia parandi; XII, 333–61.
   (iii) September: E Bolo communi pigmentario, etc.; XII, 361–97.
   (iv) October: Concentrationem sive Dephlegmationem Vini; XII, 398–429.
   (v) November: Anchiater, seu Venenum pro Remedio Venditum, Febrifugum nequissimum; XII, 430–80.
   (vi) December: Reguli Antimonii Stellati Enchirises; XII, 481–508.

[1] Art. 'Chymie', Diderot's Encycl., repr. in Ency. Méthod. sect. Chimie, iii, 301.
[2] Ency. Méthod., Chimie, iii, 332.
[3] Scripta D. Georg. Ern. Stahlii . . . aliorumque ad ejus mentem disserentium, serie chronologica Recensit D. Joh. Christoph. Goetzio, 4°, Nürnberg, 1726; 2 ed. 1729 (BM 1179. c. 12, the ed. quoted); Jöcher spells the name Goetze, BM Cat. has Goetz; see also the lists in Spielmann-Cadet, ii, 424 f.; Gmelin, (1), ii, 661 f., and Choulant, I, xvi–xlvi (255 items). The BM and BN have large collections of Stahl's works, the BM also of dissertations publ. under him.

(b) 1698:

   (vii) January: Crocus Martis Aperitivum Singularem; XII, 509–31.
  (viii) February: Fragmenta quaedam ad Historiam Naturalem Nitri; XII, 532–564.
   (ix) March: De Usu Nitri Medico Polychresto; XII, 564–85.
   (x) April: Vitulus Aureus Igne combustus; XII, 585–607.
   (xi) May: Historiam Febris Epidemicae Petechizantis. [Not in BM copy]; XII, 608–59.
  (xii) June: De Alvi Libero Successu; XII, 660–87.
        The BN Catal. Gén., 1950, clxxvii, 22, incorrectly dates this work 1797–8.

V. Observationes Physico-Chymico-Medicae Curiosae, 8°, Halle, 1709; Collect. of works previously publ. in the *Observationes Hallensis* (all anonymous) various dates, and later repr. in XII:

   (i) Aristotelis error circa Definitionem Naturae correctus (1700); XII, 197–204.
   (ii) De Verosimillima causa motus Mercurii in tubo Torricelliano seü Barometro (1700); XII, 205–15.
  (iii) Brevis Explicatio Observationis praecedentis (1700); XII, 215–18.
  (iv) Meteorologiae Cokio-Sluterianae commendatio (1700); XII, 218–26.
   (v) De Differentia Mixti, Texti, Aggregati, Individui (1700); XII, 226–36.
  (vi) De Divisionis et Diffissionis differentia (1703); XII, 237–45.
  (vii) De Copiosa . . . collectione Spiritus Acidus summe volatilis (1700); XII, 246–58.
 (viii) De Arcani Duplicati et Tartari Vitriolati Genealogia (1700); XII, 258–68.
  (ix) De Metallorum Emendatione Fructu profutura (1703); XII, 268–76.
   (x) De Sollicita Diaeta (1700); XII, 276–85.
  (xi) Suspiciones Defectuum Judicii Historici; XII, 285–98.

VI. De Ortu Venarum Metalliferarum, 4°, Halle, 1700. In XII, 851–6; English tr. in Pyrotechnical Discourses. Containing I. An Experimental Confirmation of Chymical Philosophy . . . II. A Short Discourse on the Origin of Metallic Veins, by George Ernest Stahl, M.D., III. The Grounds of Pyrotechnical Metallurgy . . . by John Christian Fritschius, 8°, London, 1705, 1730 (with new t.p.); the first work is by Kunckel (see p. 364); contains interesting geological material (see also XXIII, 395 f.).

VII. Metallurgiae Pyrotechnicae & Docimasiae Metallicae Fundamenta, 4°, Halle, 1700. In XII, 765–850. German tr.: Anweisung zur Metallurgie, Oder der metallischen Schmeltz- und Probier-Kunst. Nebst dessen Einleitung zur Grund-Mixtion Derer unterirrdischen mineralischen und metallischen Cörper . . . (see IX), 8°, Leipzig, 1720 (pp. xvi, 407, xvii; BM 1034. a. 17). Stahl had an excellent knowledge of German metallurgical processes.

VIII. Ars Tinctoria fundamentalis oder Anweisung zur Färbekunst, 8°, Frankfurt and Leipzig, 1703, said by Juncker, Conspectus Chemiae, 1730, i, 31, and Wallerius, Der Physischen Chemie, Gotha, 1761, i, 41, to be a German tr. from the French with a preface by Stahl; Latin, 8°, Jena, 1703; Choulant, I, xliv (who had not seen it).

IX. Specimen Beccherianum sistens Fundamenta, Documenta, Experimenta, quibus Principia Mixtionis Subterraneae, & Instrumenta Naturali atque Artificialia demonstrantur. Ex Autoris Scriptis, colligendo, corrigendo, connectendo, supplendo, concinnatum, exhibet Georg. Ernestus Stahl . . . , appended to Stahl's edition of Becher's Physica Subterranea, 8°, Leipzig, 1703; also 4°, 1733 and 1738 (see p. 640). German tr.: Einleitung zur Grund-Mixtion Derer Unterirrdischen mineralischen und metallischen Cörper. Alles. Mit gründlichen Rationibus, Demonstrationibus, und Experimentis nach denen Beccherischen Principiis ausgeführet, 8°, Leipzig, 1720 (see VII; Choulant, I, xxxv) and 1744 (pp. 407, xvii; BM 7106. aa. 16). Summary in Goetz, 42, 56; Bolton, (2), Suppl. I, 393, mentions an ed. of 1698.

X. De Vera Diversitate Corporis Mixti et Vivi et vtrivsqve pecvliarivm conditionvm atqve proprietatvm necessaria discretione, demonstratio, 4°, Halle, 1707 (pp. 90; BM 549. d. 19); repr. in I', i, 81–158 (see p. 655).

XI. Dissertatio de Solutio Martis in puro alcali & Anatomia Sulphuris Communis, Halle, 1712 (with a letter to the candidate annexed); XII, 706–8 (letter), 729–64.

XII. Opusculum Chymico-Physico-Medicum, seu Schediasmatum a pluribus annis variis occasionibus in publicum emissorum nunc quadantenus etiam auctorum et deficientibus passim exemplaribus in unum volumen jam collectorum, . . . Præfationis loco Authoris Epistola Ad Tit. Dn. Michaelem Alberti . . . , 4°, Halle, 1715 (pp. vi, 856, xxxviii index), with new t.p. 1740 (Sotheran *Cat.* 832 (1932), no. 5743; Choulant, I, xli: novus forsan huic operi additus est titulus); repr. of several smaller works; portr. of Stahl.

XIII. A. Zufällige Gedancken und nützliche Bedencken über den Streit von dem sogenannten Sulphure, und zwar sowohl dem gemeinen verbrennlichen oder flüchtigen als unverbrennlichen oder fixen, sm. 8°, Halle, 1718 (no index). (BM 1033. a. 23. (2.); BN R 51701); Hoefer, (1), ii, 397, gives: 'Halle, 1717, in 12°, opuscula rarissime, que nous avons sous les yeux', but all copies I have seen (including my own) are dated 1718, which is the only edition mentioned by Goetz, 92 f.; 2 ed., 1747;

B. French tr. (by Baron d'Holbach):

Traité du Soufre, Remarques sur la Dispute Qui s'est élevée entre les Chymistes, ou sujet du Soufre, tant commun, combustible ou volatil, que fixe, &c. Traduit de l'Allemand de Stahl, 12°, Paris, 1766 (with good index; BM 233. b. 15; pp. iv, 392).

XIV. Chymia rationalis et experimentalis; oder Gründliche der Natur und Vernunfft gemässe und mit Experimenten erwiesene Einleitung zur Chymie . . . , 8°, Leipzig, 1720 (pp. xvi, 520, xxix; BM 1033. a. 22); 2 ed., 1729 (Chem. Soc. Library); 3 ed., 1746, la. 12°, (Sotheran *Cat.* 832 (1932) No. 5734). Said in the preface to be tr. from Latin; it is entirely in German and the text is the same as the Latin XVII (1723), the preface of which is dated 1720. There is a slight difference in the arrangement of paragraphs at the end (p. 234 Latin, p. 514 German). It is quite different from XVII and XXIII. (Summary in Gerding, 103–6.)

XV. Fundamenta Chymico-Pharmaceutia Generalia. Accessit manductio ad enchireses artis pharmaceuticae specialis. Cura Benjamin Rothscholzii, 8°, Herren-stadii, 1721; q. by Goetz, 97, and Choulant, I, xxxvi (who says it is a mediocre work partly compiled from Stahl's notes, partly written by a pupil, and it really appeared complete in 1725: prodit omnis liber, qui tribus solummodo plagulis constat, anno MDCCXXV, quamvis MDCCXXI jam inceperat impressio); contains a short list of Stahl's works.

XVI. Billig Bedencken, Erinnerung und Erläuterung uber D. J. Bechers Natur-Kündigung der Metallen, 8°, Frankfurt and Leipzig, 1723 (BM). The most specifically metallurgical work by Stahl (Goetz, 99).

XVII. Fundamenta Chymiae Dogmaticae & experimentalis, & quidem tum communioris physicae mechanicae pharmaceuticae ac medicae tum sublimioris sic dictae hermeticae atque alchymicae. Olim in privatos Auditorum usus posita, jam vero Indultu Autoris publicae luci exposita . . . , 4°, Nürnberg (Sumptibus Wolfgangi Mauritii . . . Typis Johannis Ernesti Adelbulneri), 1723, title in red and black (viii, 255, xxiv; Goetz, 105; BM copy (44. f. 12) bound with Fundamenta Chymiae Rationalis, 76 pp., contained in XXII. The work was prepared for the press by Johann Samuel Carl (J.S.C. in the pref., dated 1720) (1675/6–1757), of Oehringen in Würtemberg, regarded by Stahl as his best pupil, from Stahl's lecture notes, and was published with Stahl's approval; Kopp, (1), ii, 16; (4), i, 69. It is important as giving Stahl's *early* views (e.g. on the composition of metals, p. 9), since the lectures go back to 1684 in Jena: Stahl, pref. to his edit. of Becher's Physica Subterranea (IX): Quod huic rei jam a multis annis animum applicauerim; Quod testatur Collegium, anno 1684 a me Jenæ habitum; quod sicut a me calamum dictatum fuerat . . . in multorum pervenit manus.

The book is full of chemical symbols with Latin case-endings and is very difficult to read.

Second ed. as part of XXIII, 1746, with same title (differently printed), concluding: Editio secunda, emendatior et Auctior. Pars I . . . , Nürnberg, 1746 (BM 1033. i. 25); the pagination and contents are identical with those of the 1723 ed., but some misprints are corrected and some symbols replaced by words. Choulant, I, xxxvi, gives also 4°, 1749. English tr. of the first 234 (out of 236) pages:

Philosophical Principles of Universal Chemistry: Or, The Foundation of a scientifical Manner of Inquiring into and Preparing The Natural and Artificial Bodies for the Uses of Life . . . Design'd as a General Introduction To the Knowledge and Practice of Artificial Philosophy: Or, Genuine Chemistry in all its Branches. Drawn from the

Collegium Jenense of Dr. George Ernest Stahl. By Peter Shaw M.D., 8°, London (Osborn and Longman, Paternoster-Row), 1730 (xxvii, 424, xxiv index, iv list of books).

The translator omitted the last section (alchemical) of the original and also the appendix, containing the work of Isaac Hollandus, interpolated several references to Boyle, etc., not in the original, and varied the order somewhat in a few places.

XVIII. A. Ausführliche Betrachtung und zulänglicher Beweiss von den Saltzen, dass dieselbe aus einer Zarten Erde, mit Wasser innig verbunden bestehen, 8°, Halle, 1723 (xvi, 432 pp.; the ed. quoted; BM 1033. a. 23. (1.)); repr. 1738; 2 ed. by J. J. Langen, Halle, 1765 (Goetz, 102, Gmelin, (1), ii, 664).

B. French tr. (by Baron d'Holbach):

Traité des Sels, Dans lequel on démontre qu'ils sont composés d'une terre subtile, intimément combinée avec de l'eau, 12°, Paris, 1771 (Goetz, 102), 1783 (the ed. quoted), good index; approbation dated October, 1770. The translator is anonymous but the 'Avertissement du traducteur' (also anonymous) in the Traité du Soufre (XIII) says the Traité des Sels, 'dont nous venons d'achever la traduction, suivra de près celui-ci'; Cadet-Spielmann, 1770, ii, 428, says the two were tr. in 1766.

XIX. Elementa Chirurgiae Medicae ex mente, manu, methodoque Stahliana pro-flua, jamque communis usus reddita, 8°, Budingae, 1727 (BM copy bound with XX).

XX. Fundamenta Pharmaciae Chymicae manu methodoque Stahliana posita, 8°, Budingae, 1728 (pp. 288; BM 782. d. 22), three parts, dealing with Operations, Pharmaceutical Products, and Chemical Potions, respectively.

XXI. Experimenta, Observationes, Animadversiones, CCC Numero, Chymicae et Physicae, 8°, Berlin, 1731 (pp. 420, xvi index).

XXII. Fundamenta Chymiae Dogmatico-Rationalis & Experimentalis, quae planam ac plenam viam ad Theoriam & Praxin Artis hujus tam Vulgatioris quam Sublimioris per Solida Ratiocinia & dextras Enchireses sternunt, 4°, Nürnberg, 1732 (viii, 199, xxxiii pp.; BM 44. f. 12; parts of title in red), 2 ed., 4°, Nürnberg, 1746 (with the addition 'Pars II' to title now printed in black; contents and pagination the same; followed by Fundamenta Chymiæ Rationalis. Pars II. Tractatus I, 76 pp., viz. XVII).

XXIII. Fundamenta Chymiae Dogmatico-Rationalis et Experimentalis, quæ planam ac plenam viam ad Theoriam et Praxin Artis hvivs tam vulgatioris qvam sublimioris per solida ratiocina et dextras Encheireses sternvnt. Pars III, 4°, Nürn-berg, 1747 (viii, 508, xviii pp.) BM 1033. i. 25; Spielmann-Cadet, ii, 430; Goetz, 96. The anonymous preface says it was printed from a MS. in Goetz's library. It is in four sections: prolegomena (pp. 1–50), zymotechnia (50–123), halotechnia (123–343), and pyrotechnia (343–508), without breaks in the text, and appears to be based on lecture notes. It refers to experiments made 'twenty years ago', and contains anecdotes, some humorous, mostly in German. The information is mostly summarised in Latin, per-haps dictated. A French tr. of XXII–XXIII by Demachy, 6 vols. 12°, Paris, 1757, ment. in NBG, 1865, xliv, 401, is really a tr. of Juncker (see p. 688).

XXIV. Grundliche und nützliche Schriften von der Natur, Erzeugung, Bereitung und Nützbarkeit des Salpeters. Mit denen hieher gehörigen Kupfern und vielen diensamen Anmerkungen vermehret ... aus dem Latein ins Teutsche übersetzt, 8°, Frankfurt and Leipzig, 1734 (Choulant, I, xxxvii: praefationem et notas addidit anonymus); a tr. of items viii–ix in IV, or XII, 532–85; Bolton, (1), 847, gives 12°, pp. x, 206 and 'another ed. Stettin and Leipzig, 1748'; and BN S 20677, is 8°, Berlin, 1764.

XXV. Materia Medica, d. i. Zubereitung, Kraft und Wirkung (Würckung) derer sonderlich durch chymische Kunst erfundenen Arzneien ..., 8°, Dresden, 1728 (Choulant, I, xlv), and 1744 (2 pts.) (BN 8° Te^{128}. 121).

The *Fundamente Chymiae Dogmatico-Rationalis et Experimentalis* is in three parts (XXII and XXIII), Part II divided into two Tracts, the first (Tractatus I) usually bound up after the second (Tractatus II).

Tractatus I (76 pp.) is divided into three sections: (1) solids and fluids, solution and menstrua, the effects of heat and fire, effervescence and boiling, fermentation and putrefaction, volatilisation, fusion and liquefaction, distilla-tion, precipitation, calcination and incineration, detonation, amalgamation, crystallisation and inspissation, and fixity and firmness of bodies; (ii) salts (including acids and alkalis), sulphur and inflammability, phosphorus, colours, metals and minerals; (iii) reduction of calces and scoriae, artificial gems, colouring copper yellow to make sophisticated gold (with zinc).

Tractatus II (199 pp.) is divided into two parts, the first subdivided into four sections: (i) instruments of chemical motion (fire, air, water, subtle earth or salt); (ii) dissolving aggregates, trituration and solution, calcination and combustion; (iii) chemical corruption, separation of solids and fluids, mixts, the solution of compounds from solids (including cupellation, etc.); (iv) fermentation. The second part, on chemical generation, is subdivided into (i) the collection of aggregates into fluids and solids, (ii) compositions of (a) volatile and (b) of solid bodies, Becher being frequently quoted, and (iii) the combination of mixts.

The third part of the *Fundamenta Chymiae* (XIII) is an interesting work and is based on Stahl's chemical lectures. The text is a mixture of Latin and German. Two specimens (otherwise interesting) are:

1. Nihilominus tamen vvenn dieses häufige acidum vitriolicum mit dem Bissgen φλογιστοῦ seu inflammabilis portionis miscirt oder imbibirt ist im Schvvefel, und kömmt ein alcali dann dazu, so greifft das alcali den Schvvefel an, non ex parte acida, sed ex parte pingui inflammabili; quod inde patet, quando sulphur hoc modo cum alcali solutum & combinatum est, das ist, vvenn das alcali mit den corpusculis sulphuris sich an einer Seiten verhänget hat, und man giesst nur auch das schvvächste acidum, Essig, vinum säuerlichen Wein &c dazu, so stösst es den Schvvefel ab alcali in forma pulveris loss.[1]

2. Praeterea accuratius attendi et notari meretur phaenomenon (sequens) transumtionis materiae inflammabilis et ejus quasi transitus de uno metallo in aliud, dass wenn man Glett-Glass mit Eisenfeilig schmelzt und ihm Zeit zu fliessen lässt, so reducirt sich die Glette in Bley, und nimmt aus dem Eisen so viel φλογιστὸν heraus, als sie nöthig hat ad reductionem sui in Bley, so viel nöthig ist zur Revivication.[2]

Hoefer[3] says: 'l'auteur pousse à l'extrême ce pédantisme littéraire, alors fort à la mode, qui consistait à entremêler l'idiome ancien d'expressions allemandes', but Kopp[4] suggests that this was the result of printing the work from the notes of a student who attended Stahl's lectures, given in Latin, who took down what he could in Latin and scribbled the sense of the rest in German. The anecdotes, however, seem to have been presented originally in the vernacular.

This Part III (508 pp.) begins with a list of authors quoted (including John Mayovv) and after an introduction deals with fermentation or zymotechnia, the production and properties of salts or halotechnia, and pyrotechnia. The last part deals with the phlogiston theory (the name φλογιστὸν is always in Greek). From the point of view of Stahl's ideas this volume is of considerable interest. It is said that chemistry depends first on a knowledge of facts, which are discovered only by experiment and not by speculation (Diese Laboranten nun haben das Ding am ersten hervor gebracht . . . denn aus speculieren lassen sich solche Sachen nicht, wenn man nicht selbst Hand anleget). In Thuringia, the peasants and schoolmasters know how to make oil of vitriol better than the university professors, but this is not chemistry, which implies an understanding of the processes (aber Chymia erfordert Verstand, und heist

[1] XIII, 309.   [2] XIII, 453.   [3] (1), ii, 396.   [4] (2), iii, 212.

eine Wissenschaft, scientia causarum, darbey die Operationes das wenigste sind: Denn Sudlerly gehöret für Taglöhner und nicht Chymicos, sonde rn dass man jedes Dinges Natur und Eigenshafft erkennen lerne . . . das gehöret in die Chymie und ist für Chymicos).[1] Becher was the first to give a real chemical theory (da Becherus der erste gewesen, der von der Chymie conceptus theoricos reales zu formieren gesucht hat).[2] Stahl had a high opinion of physical chemistry, which he regarded as a separate branch of chemistry and distinct from common physics:[3]

und endlich ists ein anders ein Physico-Chymicus zu seyn, der die connexionem Naturæ & Artis recht versteht, und nicht allein chymische, sondern auch physische rationes weiss und versteht. Ich meyne aber nicht die gemeine Physic, sondern die so auf einem bessern fundament stehet.

Stahl's definition of chemistry[4] is the art of resolving compound bodies into their principles and of recombining these again:

Chymia, alias Alchymia & Spagirica, est ars corpora vel mixta vel composita, vel aggregata etiam in principia sua resolvendi, aut ex principiis in talia combinandi.

which is much better than Boerhaave's (p. 746).

The 'physical' principles of a mixt are uncertain, since the four Peripatetic elements do not deserve this title. The 'chemical' principles into which all bodies are resolvable by chemical operations, are called salt, sulphur and mercury, taken by analogy from minerals or dry earth, inflammable volatiles, and fluid volatiles; and are also called salt, oil, and spirit, to which Willis added phlegm and earth, but with little advantage. The chemical principles have no more significance than the physical, since no one has hitherto pretended to show that they are specifically the same in all bodies (statuantur in omnibus corporibus eadem esse specie, hoc demonstrare hactenus nemo sustinet).[5]

Although Stahl[6] and his followers[7] taught that 'a body is composed of the materials from which it is formed and into which it is resolved,' their theory of composition,[8] which is a systematic form of Becher's nomenclature,[9] is complicated and rather puzzling.

A *mixt* is formed from very subtle elementary particles (*molecula*) or principles coming together to form a new body composed of insensibly small particles called *principiatum* or *principium secundum*, only a few of which are known, such as gold, silver and the universal acid. Two or more particles of this kind unite to form an insensibly fine particle called a *compositum* or *mixtum secundum*, such as regulus of antimony (metallic antimony), formed of an arsenical vitrefiable substance and inflammable earth; or sulphur, formed of the universal acid and the simple principle, phlogiston. Two or more particles of this kind of different natures combine to form a *decompositum* such as antimony (stibnite, antimony sulphide) formed from the regulus and sul-

---

[1] XXIII, 169, 171, 218.   [2] XXIII, 113.   [3] XXIII, 219.
[4] XVII, 1; XII, 37; as motto on t.p. of Roscoe and Schorlemmer, *Treatise on Chemistry*.
[5] XVII, 4.   [6] XII, 758, XVIIIB, 131, 140, 153, 392.   [7] Juncker, (2), i, 246.
[8] Stahl, IX, 1738, 1 f.; XVII, 3 f.; Juncker, (1), i, 102: de syncrisi et diacrisi naturali et artificiali.
[9] Becher, *Physica Subterranea*, 1738, 85, 91, 103, 123 f., 256, 263 f., 269, 273 f.

phur, or a *superdecompositio* such as an amalgam of metal and adhering mercury. The invisible particles of mixts form visible aggregates.

Stahl was not impressed by the mechanical type of explanation dear to Descartes, Boyle and Lemery: 'Mechanical Philosophy,' he says, 'though it vaunts itself as capable of explaining everything most clearly, has applied itself rather presumptuously to the consideration of chemico-physical matters . . . it scratches the shell and surface of things and leaves the kernel untouched.'[1] The 'corpuscles' are mere occult qualities (hæc enim omnia . . . figuræ incertæ, & specie absolute occultæ).[2] He rejected a mechanical interpretation of chemical action, which is not a result of 'wedges' or the incursion of several separate particles into one, but of an 'apprehension' or strong 'application' of such corpuscles, and this is the reason for the powerful action of solvent on solute by reason of similarity:[3]

resolutio velut ordinariae peragatur non per modum cunei; neque per modum incursus in unam particulam separandam seorsim: sed potius per modum apprehensionis seu arctæ applicationis, ad illud ipsum corpusculum . . . Est inde ratione quam maxime consentaneum, quod effectus tales potius arctiori unione solventis cum solvente contingant, quam nuda & simplici formali instrumentali divisione.

He assumed that similar bodies unite; Zimmermann[4] gives as Stahl's doctrine: 'qu'il faut, pour que deux corpes puissent se combiner ensemble, qu'ils se rensemblent par quelques-unes de leur parties'; water dissolves bodies containing water, alcohol dissolves bodies containing spirits, mercury dissolves metals, etc. Stahl also discussed some applications of Descartes' theories to chemical processes.[5]

The anonymous translator (Baron d'Holbach) of the *Traité du Soufre* (XIII B) says in his preface that although Becher had shown that the sulphureous principle is not common sulphur but 'a simple being of an earthy nature', Stahl 'has made known to us the different states in which this principle occurs in the three kingdoms of nature, its passage from each of these reigns into the others; . . . that it is the principle of colours and odours, that it gives to metals their malleability, and finally that it is the colouring principle, the fixed sulphur, etc., of the old chemists'. Stahl, in fact, deals with these matters in the treatise.

Stahl says Becher (quem virum studii Physici magnae illustrationi natum arbitramur) taught that the constituents of bodies were water and three earths,[6] the vitrefiable, the inflammable, and the liquefiable or mercurial. He gives full credit to Becher (Beccheriana sunt quæ profero)[7] but criticises him on some points. After a lumbering panegyric of Becher he concludes 'Audite hoc, manes Beccheriani! DIXI'.[8] Opinions differ as to the extent of Stahl's indebtedness to Becher; Rodwell[9] says: 'we give too much credit to Stahl, or at least too little to Becher', whilst White[10] improbably concluded that 'Stahl's theory owed little to Becher'. The truth is probably to be sought in Stahl's own

---

[1] XVII, pref. sign. 2 v.   [2] IX, 1738, 18.   [3] IX, Pt. I, sect. i, § 10; 1738, 7.
[4] Note on Henckel's *De l'Appropriation*, ch. ii, § 88; Henckel, *Oeuvres*, Paris, 1760, ii, 303.
[5] XXIII, 15, 43.   [6] XVII, 4–5.   [7] IX, pref., 1738, Vvv 3 r.
[8] IX, 1738, 52.
[9] *Phil. Mag.*, 1868, xxxv, 1 (31).   [10] *The Phlogiston Theory*, 1932, 183.

attitude; he took the foundation of his theory from Becher and developed it into a system of chemical doctrine, leaving out some parts of Becher's theory which were unsatisfactory. He says[1] that, although Becher taught that metals contain a mercurial spirit, this is uncertain. He disagrees with Becher's ideas that metals grow in the earth and that common metals become noble with lapse of time; the tin of the British Cassiterides is the same as was extracted 2000 years ago,[2] 'a peculiar kind of addled egg which will not be hard-boiled (eine eigene Art Wind-Eyer sie wollen nicht hart werden).' Stahl found in the views of Becher, then little regarded, 'a collection of enigmas which he had the talent to solve';[3] Becher gives practically no experimental support for his theories and this was largely supplied by Stahl, who must be regarded as the real originator of the Phlogiston Theory. Rodwell says Becher, very well read and thoroughly versed in chemical literature, had attempted to introduce order among the vast number of chemical facts known in his time; he 'did not accomplish this; but the more comprehensive (and less original) mind of his disciple Stahl, taking his design as the starting-point, did accomplish it', and the phlogiston theory was the first real chemical theory. Stahl's main contribution was to elaborate from Becher's 'second earth' a new chemical principle, phlogiston. He deals with this in a rather unsystematic way, and a clearer account of the phlogiston theory is given by Juncker[4] and particularly by Richard Watson.[5]

Stahl says[6] that he began to think on the theory of phlogiston in 1679 on reading Kunckel's *Chymische Anmerkungen de principiis chymicis* (1677) on the composition of metals. He criticises Kunckel (Stahl never lost an opportunity of doing this in his works) for having postulated that metals contain a mercurial, a saline, and an earthy principle, quite neglecting a sulphureous material (ein sulphurisches Zeug), and for stating that common metals contain also an acid salt, a volatile salt, heat (calido oder vielleicht calore), viscous, unctuous and spermatic principles, etc. Becher was the first to give a satisfactory theory of combustion and calcination.[7] Stahl always ignores the work of Boyle (except his theory of ponderable fire), Hooke, and Mayow (who is occasionally mentioned[8] on minor matters) and quotes mostly German authors. Actually, says Stahl, in calcination something is expelled, the expeller (der Treiber) is actual fire or fiery motion (das würckliche Feuer, oder die feurige Bewegung), and there is no conflict of heat and cold (calidum and frigidum) as Kunckel supposed. It is the sulphureous principle or fundamental principle (Sulphurischen oder Schwefelischten Principio, oder Grund-Wesen),[9] or the first real fundamental combustible thing[10] (das erste, eigentliche, gründliche, brennliche Wesen), or fire and sulphur fundamental principle (Feuer- und Schwefel-Grund-Wesen),[11] an unthought-of secret till Becher's time,[12] which is a link between sulphur and combustibles, metals and vegetable and animal

---

[1] IX, 1738, 45; XIIIA, 299; XIIIB, 254.   [2] IX, 1738, 82 f.
[3] Formey, 1757, 330.   [4] (1), i, 73–102, 121, and *passim*.
[5] Of Fire, Sulphur and Phlogiston, in *Chemical Essays*, 1781; 6 ed., 1793, i, 149–80.
[6] XIIIA, pref., 55 f., 64, 115.   [7] XIIIA, 69 f.
[8] XXI, 217, etc.   [9] XIIIA, 77, 153.
[10] XIIIA, 79.   [11] XIIIA, 101.   [12] XIIIA, 120.

beings.[1] Whereas Aristotle thought a burning body absorbed fire, Sebastian Basso[2] had supposed that the body lost most of its particles of heat:

putat Aristoteles, res adustione partes calidas acquirent; quin contra longè plurimas deperdunt, paucissimasque retinent, cum aliis paratas avolare.

Stahl's phlogiston, although introduced mainly to explain combustion, became the centre of his whole system of chemistry. He taught (with Sennert, p. 275) that it is the cause of solidity[3] and particularly of colour.[4] This was extended by Juncker.

As evidence for the production of colour by phlogiston, Stahl could point to the dark colour of soot, liver of sulphur, etc.; the blackening of lead glass by combustibles and of lead salts by sulphides; and the colour of Prussian blue.[5] In his last work, however, Stahl says colour is not a certain principle present in bodies but (as Kunckel had maintained)[6] merely the reflexions and refractions of light, and it exists mainly in the mind, as is shown by the experiments with the glass prism.[7]

The general principle of inflammability required a name. To it, says Stahl, 'I have given the Greek name of phlogiston, in German, combustible (habe ich es mit dem Griechischen-Namen Phlogiston, zu Teutsch brennlich, beleget).'[8]

Rodwell[9] says 'φλογιστὸς is an adjective derived from φλογίζω, to inflame, which is related to φλέγω, to burn, and to φλὸξ, flame. The word φλογιστός is rarely used by ancient writers', but 'in the very extensive Lexicon Græco-Latinum of Robert Constantinus, published in 1592 the word is given with only two meanings, thus: φλογιστὸς — ardens, splendidus'. Φλογιστὸν is a neuter adjective; its meaning is 'burnt' rather than 'combustible', but it is used by Aristotle[10] in the sense of 'inflammable', and in the same place he says: 'combustible bodies are those which dissolve into ash (καυστὰ ... εἶνα ὅσα εἰς τέφραν διαλύεται)'; whilst inflammable bodies (φλογιστὰ) are those which produce flame (φλόγα), which is burning wind or smoke (φλὸξ πνεῦμα ἢ καπνὸς καόμενός ἐστιν).

Phlogiston is a descendant of a very old idea of the dismembering escape of fire, whether fire itself or its equivalent in a sulphureous, oily, or combustible principle.[11] It is also a descendant of the alchemical principle sulphur.[12] S. Brown[13] thought it was a lineal descendant of the old *pneuma*.

The name φλογιστὸν had been used before Stahl as an adjective by Hamerus Poppius (1618),[14] by Van Helmont,[15] and by Becher (see p. 646). Stahl often writes the word φλογιστὸν in Greek letters. In his earlier works he uses it as

[1] XIIIA, 152, 372; XX, 18: 'substantia immediate inflammabilis, resinosa in vegetabilibus, sulphurea in mineralibus' — the name phlogiston does not seem to be mentioned.
[2] *Philosophia naturalis*, etc., 1621; edit. Amsterdam, 1649, 69–70.
[3] XIIIA, 82; XXI, 25.   [4] XIIIA, 80 f., 93 f.   [5] XIIIA, 93 f.; XXI, 281f.
[6] XIIIA, 97.   [7] XXII, II, i, 58.   [8] XIIIA, 80; cf. IX, 1738, 19, 96.
[9] *Phil. Mag.*, 1868, xxxv, 22; *Chem. News*, 1868, xvii, 101.
[10] *Meteorologica*, iv, 9, 387 b.
[11] T. Thomson, (2), 1817, i, 134 (fire 'devours' a combustible); O. C. de C. Ellis, *A History of Fire and Flame*, 1932; J. C. Gregory, *Combustion from Heracleitos to Lavoisier*, 1934; Langhans, *Z. für das gesamte Schiess-u. Sprengstoffwesen*, 1937, xxxii.
[12] Hallopeau, *Rev. Gén. Sci.*, 1918, xxix, 246.
[13] 1858, i, 186; T. C. Allbutt, *Greek Medicine in Rome*, 1921, 262 f.
[14] *Basilica Antimonii, sive expositio naturæ Antimonii*, 4°, Frankfurt, 1618; in Hartmann, *Praxis Chymiatrica*, 8°, Geneva, 1648, 600: sulphur impurum, crudum inflammabile sive φλογιστὸν.
[15] *Ortus Medicinæ*, 1652, 550: sulphur totum sit pingue et φλογιστὸν; 672: saxa autem, quæ sulfur phlogiston habent.

an adjective, e.g. φλογέστατον[1] The word was used much earlier, perhaps first (1606), by 'Nicolaus Niger Hapelius' (Raphael Eglinus Iconius, or Raphael Eglin), a Swiss (Goetz in Münchhof, 1559–Marburg, 1622),[2] who says:

sulphure nihil ad flammam concipiendam est: et metalla non sunt φλογιστὰ . . . sciendum est, τὸ φλογιστὸν esse quidem proprium omnis sulphuris, adde et solius sulphuris in omnibus rebus . . . quippe fixari potest, etc.

The name φλογιστὸν is also used by Sennert[3] for the principle of inflammability, colour, odour, and taste, present in minerals, animals, plants, spirit of wine, sulphur, etc., and is quoted from him by Boyle.[4] In his *Specimen Beccherianum* (1703)[5] Stahl says:

Briefly, in the act of composition, as an instrument there intervenes and is most potent, fire, flaming, fervid, hot; but in the very substance of the compound there intervenes, as an ingredient, as it is commonly called, as a material principle and as a constituent of the whole compound the material and principle of fire, not fire itself. This I was the first to call phlogiston.

Breviter, ad actum mixtionis, ut instrumentum concurrit, et plurimum valet, ignis flammeus, fervidus, calidus; Ad substantiam ipsam mixti, ut ingrediens (vulgata voce) ut materiale principium, et pars totius compositi constitutiva, concurrit, materia et principium ignis, non ipse ignis: Ego Phlogiston appellare cœpi; Nempe primum ignescibile, inflammabile, directe atque eminenter ad Calorem suscipiendum atque fovendum habile Principium.

Flame is inflammable matter brought to its highest degree of subtlety and homogeneity; passing through cracks in a distilling flask it converts oil of vitriol into the volatile acid of sulphur.[6] Although he repeatedly says that phlogiston is material,[7] he regarded heat in a body as a violent motion of the molecules (de gradu etiam Motus hujusmodi intensiore aut remissiore, pro caloris ambientis diversitate).[8]

---

[1] III, 1697, 112.

[2] *Disquisitio de Helia Artium ad illustrissimum principem Mauritium, Hassiæ Landgravium, &c.*, τριαρχία, 8°, Leipzig, 1606; repr. as *Nova disquisitio de Helia Artista Theoph(r)asteo super metallorum transformatione*, etc., auctore Heliophilo a Percis Philochemico in *Theatrum Chemicum*, 1659, iv, 220, 223; see T. L. Davis, 'Neglected evidence in the History of Phlogiston', *Ann. of Medical History*, 1924, vi, 280; *id.*, *J. Soc. Chem. Ind.*, 1925, xliv, 725 R; *id.*, *Isis*, 1927, ix, 161; Ferguson, i, 232, where the confusing bibliography is sorted out, and i, 364, for another work by Nicolaus Niger Hapelius (Eglin), *Cheiragogia Heliana de Auro Philosophico*, 8°, Marburg, 1612; tr. as *Cheiragogia Heliana. A Manduction to the Philosopher's Magical Gold . . . To which is added . . . Zoroaster's Cave: Or, an Intellectual Echo . . .*, by George Thor, Astromagus, 12°, London, 1659 (Duveen, 189); it is printed in *Theatrum Chemicum*, 1659, iv, 261–88, and is mystical. Eglin was for a time associated with Giordano Bruno and had a chequered career; in 1595 he published a volume of excerpts from Bruno's *Summa Terminorum Metaphysicorum* (1591); D. W. Singer, *Giordano Bruno*, 1950, 153.

[3] *De chymicorum cum Aristotelicis et Galenicis consensu et dissensu*, 1619, 283; in *Operum*, Lyon, 1656, i, 214, 215, 223: colores, odores, sapores, esse φλογιστὸν et similia alia, mineralibus, metallis, gemmis, lapidibus, plantis, animalibus insunt; sulphuris autem proprium est, esse φλογιστὸν, et nil sine sulphur inflammatur.

[4] *Sceptical Chymist*, 1680, 313; ed. Muir (Everyman ed.), 1911, 167; Kopp, (1), iii, 112; (2), iii, 218; Rodwell says φλογιστὸν as a *substantive* was first used by Stahl.

[5] IX, 1738, 19.

[6] XVIIIA, 1723, 212: zu seiner höchsten Zartheit, und gleichsam homogeneität gekommene, allereigentlichste Brand-Wesen.

[7] E.g. XIIIA, 174: Womit dann also hoffentlich hinlängliche Zeugnisse gegeben seyn werden, dass das sulphurische Wesen in allerley Verstand darinnen es jemals vernünftig und vernehmlich allegiret wird, für ein cörperliches wahres und würckliches *Wesen zu erkennen* (the words italicised are in black type in the original); XIIIB, 144; XXI, 326: quod sit aliquid corporeum.

[8] III, 1697, 84.

He sometimes speaks of the fiery motion as a gyratory motion of incandescent particles — whirling sparks (ignis ... est congeries corpusculorum vehementissimo verticillari motu affectorum).[1] Preston[2] pointed out the relation between this *motus verticillaris* and the later hypothesis of molecular vortices of Rankine,[3] but the idea seems to have come from Descartes.

As a proof that violent motion can produce fire Stahl mentions a 'little known' experiment of Borellus in which an iron rod exposed to repeated blows of a hammer becomes not only hot but incandescent.[4]

Phlogiston is the material principle which, by its escape from the burning body, alone stirs up this said motion (ipsa vera Ignis ... materia quam solo citatissimo motu in formam ignis deducatur).[5] Phlogiston is never found in a perfectly pure state: the purest form is the soot from burning oil.[6] It is a dry substance of an earthy nature, as Becher had correctly recognised, and capable of being set into violent motion[7] (ein erdisches ... trockenes wesen; siccam ... qua cum terreis aliis; siccissima, terrea consistentia). So it appears in charcoal, and in the soot from burning turpentine, etc.

The idea that fire is a kind of vortex motion is a very old one,[8] also taught by Descartes (p. 434); Rodwell,[9] in fact, thought Stahl's phlogiston is the same as the *materia coelestis* of Descartes, who regarded fire as a result of the rapid motion of this in ordinary matter.

The meaning of phlogiston as used by Stahl and his followers often approached that of potential energy[10] or ether.[11] Odling[12] also pointed out the relation of phlogiston to energy, saying 'the phlogistic and antiphlogistic theories are in reality complementary and not ... antagonistic to one another'.

Juncker[13] pointed out that phlogiston had been given very varying properties. It had been described as earthy, aqueous, or elastic in nature, or if of any nature as a fatty substance, or a sulphureous, inflammable, oily, unctuous, viscous, etc., matter. Thus very obscure ideas had been held on this principle, which, in the way it has been explained is rather a compound than a simple substance.

Ignoble metals (*not* silver and mercury)[14] contain an inflammable substance and 'ash' (*cinis*): on heating in the fire or with nitre, the inflammable substance escapes in fumes and leaves the ash:

ignobilia quatuor metalla, continent substantiam inflammabilem; quae partim nudo igne aperto in auras abiens, metallum in cinerem fatiscens relinquit: Partim nitro ita exuri potest, ut flammam cum ipso formet.[15]

---

[1] IX, 1738, 15, 63; XII, 354; XXI, 117, 315, 388.   [2] *Theory of Heat*, 1894, 75.
[3] *Trans. Roy. Soc. Edin.*, 1850, xx, 147; *Phil. Mag.*, 1851, ii, 61, 509.
[4] XXI, 202; the experiment is often mentioned by Boyle.
[5] XXI, 11, 388; there is a resemblance with the ether vortex theory of Descartes here.
[6] XII, 310; IX, 1738, 160.   [7] XIIIA, 82; XXI, 3, 42, 316; XVI, 74 f.
[8] Aristotle, *De Cœlo*, bk. i, ch. 2; Seneca, *Quæst. Nat.*, bk. ii, ch. 24: Ignis enim natura in verticem surgit, et, si nihil illum prohibit, ascendit.
[9] *Phil. Mag.*, 1868, xxxv, 27.
[10] Crum Brown, *Proc. Roy. Soc. Edin.*, 1866, v, 328; Deville, *Compt. Rend.*, 1860, l, 538, compared it with latent heat.
[11] Chevreul, *J. de Sav.*, 1851, 160; 1856, 97; *Compt. Rend.*, 1864, lix, 977.
[12] On the revived Theory of Phlogiston, *Proc. Roy. Inst.*, 1871, vi, 315; *Chem. News*, 1871, xxiii, 243, 256; *Ber.*, 1871, iv, 421 (ment. R. Watson).
[13] (2), i, 167.   [14] IX, 1738, 14.   [15] IX, 1738, 156; cf. XX, 62.

Reduction of ash to metal occurs only by again adding this inflammable substance (nisi quod materiam talem inflammabilem illis iterum communicare atque insinuare possit).[1] This takes place when the ash or calx is heated with carbon, oil, pitch, tallow, etc., which are all materials rich in the inflammable principle:[2]

φλογιστὸν ex pinguedinibus, carbonibus, in ipsa metalla promptissime ingrediatur, eaque regeneret, ex calcibus exustis, in fusilem suam . . . consistentiam.

Thus neither iron itself nor tin is convertible by any art whatever into a dense, solid, shining, ductile, fusible metallic mass unless the phlogistic substance (which it had lost for the most part in the previous calcination) is again added to them.[3]

Stahl generally uses the name ash (*cinis*) for the earthy residue after calcination of a metal; the name *calx*, used by later phlogistic chemists, is derived from the Latin *calx*, quicklime (made by burning limestone), extended to the 'earths' formed on heating metals.[4] Ettmuller[5] says:

calcinatio est corporis compacti in minutissimas sui partes corrosio et solutio, qua metalla in calces et vegetabilia in cineres rediguntur.

Stahl found it impossible to convert any earth proper into a metal by adding phlogiston, and acids do not easily dissolve perfectly calcined metals;[6] hence he thought the mercurial spirit of Becher (p. 647) is also necessary in the formation of a metal, which then consisted of the primitive earth, the mercurial spirit, and phlogiston.[7] The difficulty of this theory was that when a metal is calcined the mercurial spirit presumably escapes, yet the calx is now easily reduced to metal by adding phlogiston only. Henckel[8] tried to get over this difficulty by supposing that a metal consists of an earth and phlogiston only, but on calcination some of the phlogiston remains in the calx, which then attracts more phlogiston on reduction, whilst common earth is free from phlogiston and will not absorb more phlogiston to form a metal. According to Thomson[9] it was Bergman who first taught that each metal consists of a *peculiar* earthy substance combined with phlogiston, and 'for this great improvement in accuracy' chemistry is chiefly indebted to him.

As an example of the 'proof' that phlogiston enters into the composition of metals, Stahl[10] remarks that when tin is melted it becomes covered with dross, but if a little oil, pitch, resin or tallow is thrown on the surface and the mass stirred, 'the cinder melts anew and unites itself with the rest of the tin in such a way that not the least particle of it can be seen.' Again, if lead is heated, the dross formed can be collected and heated on a cupel, when it becomes whiter, then yellow and finally red. One of these calces when heated in a small hole in a piece of charcoal before the blowpipe melts to a glass: 'when this drop of glass touches the edge of the charcoal a slight hissing is heard and instantly it returns to the state of lead.' As a 'proof' that a limpid volatile liquid like oil of

[1] IX, 1738, 158.   [2] III; XII, 144.
[3] III, (Experim. novum verum Sulphur arte producendi); XII, 330.
[4] R. Watson, *Chemical Essays*, 1793, ii, 175.
[5] *Collegium Chymicum, Opera*, London, 1701, 83.
[6] XVIIIA, 291.   [7] XVII, 9.   [8] *Flora Saturnisans*, Paris, 4°, 1760, 150 f.
[9] *Ency. Brit. Suppl.*, 1801, I, i, 222; *id.*, (2), 1802, i, 79.
[10] XIIIA, 118 f.; XIIIB, 93 f.

turpentine contains an opaque fixed solid, he cites an experiment made thirty years before [i.e. in 1688]: 'when I had presented the problem I found no one able to answer it . . . I simply put oil of turpentine in a spoon, kindled it with a candle, and received the soot on another spoon placed over the first. Thus I demonstrated the possibility of my problem and showed that the truth is always simple.'[1]

Some bodies on burning lose phlogiston wholly as fire, others partially: the latter, such as turpentine, give it off also as soot, which is the purest form of phlogiston, since it burns away without residue.[2] Stahl especially emphasises that the inflammable substance or phlogiston is the same in all the three kingdoms of Nature and can be transferred from one substance to another:

Freylich so wohl in dem Fett / da man die Schuhe mit schmieret / als in dem Schwefel auss den Bergwercken / und allen verbrennlichen halben und gantzen Metallen / in der wahren That / einerley / und eben dasselbige / Wesen sey / was die Verbrennlichkeit eigentlich giebt und machet.[3]

Sulphur is a compound of a volatile and combustible part with a fixed and incombustible part, the latter being an acid.[4] In his earliest writings Stahl adopts Becher's theory that sulphur, instead of being an element or principle as the alchemists taught, contains the same inflammable principle (terra pinguis, phlogiston) as metals, its other principle, corresponding with the calx of a metal, being oil of vitriol (acidum vitriolicum). This is proved by a new experiment (novum experimentum), which Stahl claims as his own (hujus rei uspiam mihi Autor fuisse credi velit) and always considered as very important. It appeared in his earliest work, *Zymotechnia fundamentalis* (1697) and in later works.[5] In 1697 he says sulphuric (vitriolic) acid is 'fixed' by combining with potash to form vitriolated tartar (tartarum vitriolatum; potassium sulphate). This is fused with salt of tartar in a crucible and some charcoal dust thrown in, when sulphur is generated and forms with the potash a liver of sulphur (hepar sulphuris). The vitriolic acid takes phlogiston from the charcoal and becomes true sulphur (so engreifft das Vitriol-Sauer das brennliche Wesen in den Kohlen, und wird mit selbigen wieder zu einem wahren Schwefel). When a melt of potash and sulphur, giving liver of sulphur, was kept (exposed to air, a condition not mentioned, as unimportant) for a quarter of an hour, it lost its red colour and became white vitriolated tartar such as is made from salt of tartar and oil of vitriol (ein solches Saltz als aus dem unter der Glocken gemachten Schwefel Oel und dem Weinstein Saltz entstehet). By heating this with charcoal, liver of sulphur is again formed, from which sulphur is at once precipitated by acids.

[1] XIIIA, 38, 87; XIIIB, 24, 64 f.: the prestigiatory style is very typical of Stahl; XXIII, iii, 310: Womit ich würcklich viel Chymicos vexiret habe; for another example see XVIIIA, 423.
[2] IX, 1738, 160; XIIIA, 89 f., 172; XXI, 15, 59, 314, 334.
[3] XIIIA, 36, 82; XXI, 3, 18: materia haec igniscens, in omnibus tribus regnis, una eademque existit.
[4] Anatomia sulphuris communis (1712); in XII, 749 f.
[5] III, 1697, 118; German tr., 1748, 176 f.; XII, 142 (Experimentum novum verum sulphur arte producendi, 1697), 299 f., 312, 315; XIIIA, 76; IX, 1738, 54; XXI, 34; XXIII, 163 (he complains that the experiment had been much criticised and misunderstood); Henckel, *Flora Saturnisans*, *Oeuvres*, Paris, 1760, ii, 185 f.

... wenn; man dieses Alcali schmelzet und eine Kohle darzu thut, und hernach ausgeust, so ist ein hochroth Wesen, wie ein Stücke Leber . . . : solviret man diess im Wasser, so giebts eine goldgelbe Solution, præcipirit diese mit einem acido, so fällt ein weisslich subtil Pulver zu Boden, welches, wenns davon geschieden, veritabler Schwefel ist.[1]

Stahl admits that a similar experiment with sodium sulphate had been made by Glauber,[2] but Glauber supposed that the sulphur came from the charcoal, which he calls a sulphur. He made this mistake because he had not weighed the materials.[3] Stahl also says that Boyle had made an experiment in the wet way (in via humida) with oil of vitriol and oil of turpentine.[4]

Stahl's famous experiment was regarded as a proof that sulphuric acid (oil of vitriol) was an element and sulphur a compound of sulphuric acid and phlogiston (ϕ). Liver of sulphur can be made by heating potash with sulphur *or* by heating vitriolated tartar (oil of vitriol + potash) with charcoal, rich in phlogiston (ϕ). Hence:

$$(\text{sulphur} + \text{potash}) = (\text{oil of vitriol} + \text{potash}) + \phi$$
$$\therefore \text{sulphur} = (\text{oil of vitriol} + \phi).$$

Johann Christoph Kühnst (Ronneburg (Altenburg), 7 August 1702–Zeittz, 2 May 1762), a physician, tried to prove the presence of phlogiston in metals by heating their filings with vitriolated tartar in a retort, extracting with water, and adding distilled vinegar, when he found that a true sulphur was precipitated.[5] He also tried to prove that nitric acid is a compound of phlogiston and hydrochloric acid,[6] wrote on analogues of sulphur[7] and on the volatilisation of silver as a butter.[8]

Stahl mentions that phosphorus deliquesces to an acid liquid when exposed to air in a porcelain dish[9] and he thought phosphorus was a kind of sulphur, analogous to common sulphur except that its acid was more subtle and volatile, which is the reason why phosphorus consumes in air. Phosphorus is a compound of the acid of common salt (hydrochloric acid) and phlogiston (ex acido salis communis et $\phi\lambda o\gamma\iota\sigma\tau\tilde{\omega}$).[10] Macquer[11] was surprised that Stahl could have made this assertion.

The ancients believed that in combustion the element fire ascended into the empyrean, the region of pure fire enclosing the atmosphere (Vol. I), but the phlogistians taught that it combined with the surrounding atmosphere: 'fire was the momentaneous glance of phlogiston in its passage from one engagement to another.'[12] Stahl says the air contained in a closed space ten feet square is sufficient to receive the phlogistic particles from half an ounce of wax candle (vix tantum corpusculorum phlogistorum recipere valeret, quantum e portione candelae cerae dimidiam unciam pendente, procedere posset).[13] He thus

---

[1] XXIII, 163.
[2] *Von den dreien Anfängen der Metallen*, 1666; *Works*, tr. Packe, Pt. III, 4.   [3] XII, 311.
[4] *Sceptical Chymist*, 1661; 1680, 222; *Works*, ed. Shaw, 1725, i, 544; a similar experiment is attributed to Kunckel by Metzger, 1930, 172, who gives no reference.
[5] *Acta Phys.-Med. Acad. Nat. Curios.*, Nürnberg, 1740, v, Obs. XCVII, 345–8: $\phi\lambda o\gamma\iota\sigma\tau\grave{o}\nu$ quod metallis inest sulphurificatione demonstrare.
[6] *Ib.*, 1742, vi, Obs. CXXVIII, 464–8: Nitri acidum ex acido salis & phlogisto concretum.
[7] *Ib.*, 1742, vi, Obs. CXXXIX, 469–71: Sulphuri analogon.
[8] *Ib.*, 1742, vi, Obs. CXL, 471–3: Volatisatio Argenti.
[9] XXI, 139.   [10] XXI, 401; cf. Juncker, (1), ii, 135; *id.*, (2), iv, 377.   [11] (1), ii, 230.
[12] S. Brown, 1858, i, 187 f., 195.   [13] IX, 1738, 40.

adopted Becher's theory (p. 648) that the atmosphere is a mere receptacle for phlogiston emitted by burning bodies, and he mentions (without naming him) Van Helmont's experiment showing that charcoal does not change when heated in a closed vessel. Although Stahl knew that metals and carbon would not burn or calcine in closed vessels, he said this was because the phlogiston could not escape, and he denied that air combines with the body: it could be replaced by steam, which supports flame (ita . . . ad flammam formandam, absolute opus est aëre, aut ad minimum, aëris instar, elastice expanso halitu atque flatu aqueo).[1] He seems to have thought sometimes that only a small part of the weight of some combustibles (charcoal, sulphur, etc.) was phlogiston.[2]

Flame is only the whirling motion due to escape of phlogiston (see p. 669) and air is necessary only for the productionof this motion (aer excitat motum aetheris seu flammam).[3] This was also Boerhaave's opinion.[4]

Stahl adopted Becher's view[5] that the production of flame requires the presence of water; almost pure phlogiston as soot does not flame, but when it is combined with water in thin oils or ardent spirits it flames; expressed oils and sulphur, containing less water, flame less easily. Again, salt (containing water — actually it does not) thrown on glowing coals produces a flame:

Indem nemlich das brennliche Principium, an und vor sich selbst, gar keine eigene Aufblähung oder Ausdähnung erweiset: Wie sowohl an dem allersubtilesten Russ . . . zu sehen. Dahingegen, so lange dergleichen Materie in denen zarten Oelen mit viel Wässerigkeit verbunden: oder gar in einem brennenden Geist, mit noch mehrerem Wasser ausgedähnet ist, aus solcher Vermischungen Anzündung auch eine solche weit ausschlagende Flamme entstehet.[6]

Water thrown on a fire strongly increases flame.[7]

Stahl was acquainted with Van Helmont's views on gas and (some years before the publication of Hales' *Vegetable Staticks*, 1727) he describes some experiments on effervescences of acids with metals, chalk, etc., in which vessels were broken. In one he attempts a crude measure of the 'air' evolved in bladders, without mentioning Boyle or Mayow.[8] At that time, he says, the phenomena were explained by Descartes' system, some attributing them to air lodged in the substances, others by the Cartesian ether, but neither is possible. The inflammable principle, as it is found for example in soot, is incapable of such expansion, and this is really due to water, which is disposed to such expansion in vapour by heat, much more even than strongly compressed air: zu solcherley Luft ähnlicher Aufblähung geschickt ist; dass es auch unmässig mehr, als die allerdickste eigentliche Luft, durch die Hitze sich auseinander dehnen lasset. This occurs especially when the water is joined to phlogiston. Thus, the effervescences are due to the water contained in the substances, and the more watery parts there are in them, the stronger is the effervescence.[9]

Air cannot be condensed by itself or with other mixtures to a solid (elastica illa expansio, aeri ita, per essentiam suam propria sit, ut nunquam ad vere

[1] IX, 1738, 20; XIIIA, 186; XXI, 346.   [2] XXI, 17, 53.   [3] XVII, 28, 36 f.
[4] (2), i, 426.   [5] *Phys. Subterr.*, 1738, 278, see p. 648.
[6] XIIIA, 233 f.; XIIIB, 198.   [7] XIIIA, 179.
[8] XVIIIA, 362 ff.: Von dem blästigen Brausen, oder Aufwallen, bey den solutionibus chymicis.
[9] XIIIA, 374.

densam aggregationem, nec ipse in se, nec in ullis mixtionibus, coire sentiri possit).[1] In another place, however, Stahl says 'nitre is an aerial salt where elastic air is, as it were, concentrated,'[2] and in his *Natural History of Nitre*[3] he says plenty of air is necessary for the production of flame, except that nitre can supply this:

> Et cum nihil aliud, quantumlibet summopere & flagrantissime, flammare aptum, sine sufficiente aeris commercio, in talem ardorem erumpere possit, solum quasi Nitrum prærogativam hanc obtinuit, ut veluti domesticum aëreum vaporem contineat, eumque ad flammam efformandam, & constituandam, contribuat atque subministret.

Juncker[4] said that air cannot enter into compounds, its true nature is unknown, and in combustion it merely serves to carry off phlogiston but does not enter into the combination of fire. When a space is saturated with phlogiston combustion ceases. Calcination also involves the expulsion of the inflammable parts of a body, and for this it is necessary to have contact with the air to carry them off, since 'no metallic substance is entirely calcined in vessels exactly closed'.[5]

Stahl evidently thought that some explanation was needed as to why the atmosphere does not gradually become loaded with phlogiston. The reason is that this principle is removed from the air by plants (höchstglaublich und wahrscheinlichst selbsten auss der Luft / in dergleichen Wachsthum mit eingeflochten zu werden / bemercket werden kan). The resinous pine tree and other trees not only grow in pure sand but even spread their roots above the surface of the earth into the air, and no one can believe that so much fatty resin can come from sand. It must come from the atmosphere (viel glaublicher ist / dass sie selbsten aus der vermischten Luft / oder Atmosphæra, darin gezogen werde).[6]

The incandescence resulting when sulphur is heated with certain metals, such as iron (which had been described by Kunckel):

> Wenn ich Eisen-Feil mit Schwefel vermenge / und Setze es über das Feuer / so schmeltzt der Schwefel / und fängt an zu brennen; So bald er das Eisen berühret / so entzündet es sich heftig,[7]

or copper, tin, or lead, was a difficulty which Stahl explained by the theory[8] that the combustible particles of the sulphur combine with similar particles in the metal:

> dass es sein Theilchen Verbrennliches, mit gleichmässigen Theilchen in solchen Metallen haftenden brennlichen Wesens vergesellschaftet / fahren lasse,

and also that the watery particles of the acid of sulphur, which is entirely destroyed, break out in a state of expansion and produce a flame:

> etwas von seinem brennlichen Wesen / durch dasjenige / so auch in dem Metall ihm gleich stecket / vermehret und verstärcket / in eine solche Flamme aussbreche: Wobey

---

[1] XXI, 312, § 247.   [2] XXII, Pars II, Tract. I, 3.
[3] Historiam Naturalem Nitri, ch. i; XII, 538; see also XIV.
[4] (2), i, 157 f., 252 f.   [5] *Ib.*, ii, 532.   [6] XIIIA, 84–5.
[7] Kunckel, *Laboratorium Chymicum*, 1716, 355; Kopp, (1), iii, 326, says this is the first description.
[8] XIIIA, 130.

auch würcklich derselbe Theil des acidi Sulphuris eben dieselbe Zerreisung seines
Saltz-Wesens erleidet / und mit Losbrechung seiner Wässerigkeit solche Entzündung
in eine würckliche Flamme ausbläset.[1]

Stahl was thus of the opinion that metals combine with sulphur because
they themselves contain phlogiston, since calces do not combine with sulphur.
Strongly ignited calces (e.g. crocus martis) do not even combine with acids, so
that the presence of phlogiston is also necessary for the union of acids and
calces, and the phlogiston in metals 'opens the way' for attack by acids.[2]

Acids do not attack metals in their entirety, each acting in its own way,
nitric acid attacking the phlogiston in the metal, vitriolic acid the earthy part,
and the acid of salt the mercurial part.[3] Stahl seems to have noticed the
passivity of iron in concentrated nitric acid:

man kan es auf gewisse Weise versehen, und mit dem Aquafort in wenigen Minuten
das Eeise so alteriren, dass ob es zwar ganz bleibt, dennoch aber von dem Aquafort
nicht mehr angegriffen werde.[4]

Stahl, who paid little attention to changes of weight,[5] was quite well aware of
the increase in weight of metals on calcination; he did not accept Boyle's explanation that it was due to the fixation of igneous corpuscles:

Ex adverso bonis speculationibus meriti Boylei aliquid condonandum est, denn er
hat die Chymie nicht ex professo studirt, dass er in seinem Tr. de Ponderabilitate
Partium flammæ dafür gehalten, es ziehe sich oder krieche durch ein Glass, per poros
vitri, von einem Lampen-Feuer so viel von der materia flammæ in das Glass, und in
die darinn enthaltene Materie hinein, dass sie (z.e. Zinn-Kalch den 10. 12 ten Theil)
schwerer vvird; da er doch hier vielmehr auf den (modum mechanicum) motum
materiæ ankommt, indem vielmehr was weggegangen, als das was dazu gekommen seyn
solte: Und ist hier von der arctiore combinatione particularum zu reden, da die lucker-
und also auch leichte-machende Materie weg ist . . . daher also calcinirt Bley auch
leichter werden solte, welches aber nicht geschieht, sondern es wird schvverer: Sed
hæc phænomena non possunt judicari, nisi (ut jam dictum est) ab experientia &
ratione bene experta.[6]

The entrance of phlogiston into a body such as a metal calx, which it reduces
to the metal, makes the body actually lighter:

. . . . circa hoc principium inflammabilitatis . . . de tam nullo quasi ipsius pondere, da
die corpora, nempe metallica, quæ ingreditur, numero multum [of corpuscles of
phlogiston], licet non pauca, sed certe magna quantitate & copiosissime eadem intret,
doch nicht nur gar nicht schwerer davon vverden, sondern vielmehr leichter, vvelches
man am Bley, Zinn, regulo antimonii siehet; denn wenn man gemeine Bley-Glette
recht reducirt, dass nichts davon verlohren geht, vviegts nach der Reduction $\frac{1}{8}$
weniger als vorher, obgleich nichts davon verlohren gangen; calcinirt man aber
vvieder, so erhält es vvieder sein vorig Gevvicht. . . . Per accessionem enim partium
inflammabilium levius fit concretum;
with regard to this principle of inflammability . . . concerning its weight as being as
nothing, then those bodies, namely metallic ones, that it enters in great number [of
corpuscles of phlogiston], granted that it enters them, not in small but certainly in
great amount and most copiously, yet become scarcely any heavier thereby, but much
lighter, which we see with lead, tin and regulus of antimony; then when we properly
reduce common litharge, that nothing thereby gets lost, it thus weighs after the
reduction $\frac{1}{8}$ less than before, although nothing has thereby been lost; but [when] we

[1] XIIIA, 236 f.   [2] XIIIA, 195; XVIIIA, 196 f., 296 f.
[3] XVIIIA, 1723, 296, 309, 313: das Salpetrische an dem brennlichen; das Vitriolische an
dem Erdischen; das Koch-Saltzige, an dem Mercurialischen.
[4] XXIII, 237.   [5] Odling, Proc. Roy. Inst., 1871, vi, 318.   [6] XXIII, 507.

calcine anew, it thus again gets its former weight. . . . By accession of inflammable parts, the concrete becomes lighter.[1]

In earlier publications Stahl had pointed out that the escape of phlogiston from metals made their calces heavier, and calces when reduced to metals become lighter (in dem deren Calces, oder Gläser, schwerer, durch dessen Beytritt aber wieder leichter werden), and there is no doubt that he means absolute weight, not specific gravity.[2] When regulus of antimony is calcined it loses its volatility without anything going from it, in fact it becomes noticeably heavier, so that 1 oz. of regulus increases by 1 dr. although phlogiston leaves it, as is seen by the reduction to metal in contact with a glowing coal:[3]

so verliehret er durch das Glüen seine Flüchtigkeit, dass man im grossen Feuer hernach glüen kan, ohne dass ihm etwas abgienge, ja er wird noch merklich schwerer, also dass ℥ j reguli wohl bis ℈ j mehr wiegt, wenn es recht lange geglüet wird, die Hitze aber nimmt ihme nichts ab (als das φλογιστὸν), daher zu sehen, dass das φλογιστὸν ihm entgehe: . . . das es sich von einer hinein gefallenen Kohle reduciret.

Stahl[4] emphasised that the original weight of metal is not recovered on reducing the calx:

quamvis enim lithargyrium, minium, cineres plumbi, sub ipsa sui calcinatione, majus pondus acquirant, quam ipsa prima assumta quantitas plumbi exhibuerat. Nihilosecius in reductione perit non sola illa portio quasi supernumeraria: sed interit notabile pondus de tota quoque prima assumta gravitate,

a statement often made by later authors.[5]

In another place Stahl says phlogiston retains its very subtle nature when combined in mixts, 'so much so that it is not capable of being measured, not to say weighed, by any degree of acuteness of the senses or of subsidiary apparatus.'[6]

He says[7] the entry of phlogiston makes nearly all bodies from which it is easily separated lighter in texture. In dicussing the increase in weight of metals on calcination,[8] he says Kunckel had explained it as due to an increase in density, as bricks become heavier when baked or, as Stahl says, as eiderdown when compressed. Kunckel,[9] in fact, had said in 1677 that metallic antimony on calcination diminishes in bulk and increases in weight, since porous bodies are buoyed up by the air, but when they become compact the air presses upon them and thence the increase in weight results: so hat sich mein Maass verringert, und mein Gewicht gemehret.

The same account is given by Juncker,[10] who says: 'it is found that the calx

[1] XIII, 374; Hoefer, (1), ii, 399; (2), ii, 406; Partington and McKie, Ann. Sci., 1937, ii, 368 f.
[2] XIIIA, 329; XIIIB, 277.   [3] XXIII, 454.   [4] IX, 1738, 70.
[5] Macquer, (1), i, 258; (2), i, 346: cette reduction se fait toujours avec perte.
[6] XXI, 361: 'as dust in the balance.'
[7] XVI, 70: durch seiner Beytritt, fast alle Cörper, darinnen es noch leichtlich scheidbar hanget, etwas leichter oder lockerer mache.
[8] XXI, 346 f.: Eyder-Dunen . . . densa compressione in saccos compactæ, tantum incrementum ponderis inde sortiantur.
[9] Chymischen Anmerckungen . . . von denen Principiis Chymicis, Wittenberg, 1677; in V Curiose Chymische Tractätlein, Frankfurt, 1721, 29; the passage is mentioned by de Morveau, Digressions Académiques, Dijon, 1772, 92 f.
[10] (1), i, 185 f.; cf. ib. 461, 579, 834. Juncker adds that bricks become heavier on baking, and quotes Kunckel by name, thus following Stahl.

occupies less space in the crucible than the regulus and becomes heavier'; when reduced the calx takes up phlogiston, 'the resulting metal regains its former lightness and it cannot be supposed that any heavy particles escaped during reduction, as can be shown by calcining it again, when it shows its increase in weight':

tum manifesto residuus hic cinis in eodem vasculo minus spatium occupabit, quam assumtus regulus & simul gravior reperietur. Hoc cinis si immixtione φλογιστοῦ reducatur in metallum, hoc rursum levius erit; ac ne forte putes, corpuscula ponderosa sub reductionis actu in auras abiisse, reductum metallum denouo calcina, & idem ponderis incrementum senties.

(The fact that the calx is actually less dense than the metal was, of course, well known to Boyle.)[1] Juncker's statement[2] that phlogiston (Becher's *terra secunda*) makes bodies lighter and more volatile apparently does not mean that it confers on them a negative weight:

Quippe durissima & crassiora aggregata sui immixtione protinus mollia, fusilia, leviora, volatilia efficit, uti e.g. cerussa seu calx reguli antimonii, item vitrum plumbi per inflammabile hoc proprium non modo fluidiora & vere metallica fiunt, sed etiam largiore carbonum additione volatilisantur & in auras florum forma effumant.

Stahl in one place, after declining to accept Boyle's view that the increase in weight of calcined metals is due to fixation of igneous corpuscles, says[3] the cause cannot be decided; in another,[4] he says phlogiston is the lightest of all corporeal bodies; in others, he tries to give some idea of the small proportion which phlogiston makes of the weight of an inflammable body.[5] In such cases he seems to attribute a small but definite weight to phlogiston. Stahl says very little on the weight of phlogiston, although the passages quoted show that he had given the matter some thought.

Georg Friedrich Stabel of Halle, 'Medic. D. & Civitat. Halensis Physici adj.' as he is described on the title-page of a book[6] with a title similar to Stahl's, in which he said that, since metals increase in weight on calcination, the process cannot be due to their losing anything, and a calx loses weight when it is reduced to the metal and so cannot have gained anything.

Stahl[7] tried to determine the amount of phlogiston in sulphur by gently roasting 1½ oz. of liver of sulphur until it was converted into a white residue; he does not say what happened to the weight (it should have increased) but concluded that only a small weight of phlogiston was present:

---

[1] A Discovery of the Perviousness of Glass to Ponderable Parts of Flame, 66–7, in *Essays of Effluviums*, London, 1673.
[2] (1), i, 74–5.
[3] XXIII, 507 f.: Sed hæc phœnomena non possunt judicari, nisi (ut jam dictum est) ab experientia & ratione bene experta.
[4] XVI, 70: Hingegen aber eben dieses Wesen, unter allen Cörperlich begreifflichen Wesen, nicht allein das allerleichteste seye; Nehmlich, an Maasse viel, an Gewicht aber aus der massen klein und Wenig, betrage.
[5] XI, in XII, 756; XIIIA, 329; XXI, 17, 53.
[6] *Chymiæ Dogmatico-Experimentalis Tomus Prior Complectens Doctrinæ Chymicæ Fundamenta* (126 pp.); *Fundamentorum Chymicorum Tomus II. De productis Chymicis Medicamentosis* (pp. 127–324), 8°, Halle, 1728; BM 1034. f. 16; Ferguson, ii, 397; Gmelin, (1), ii, 683; Kopp, (3), 53.
[7] XXI, 53.

Hoc residuum, iterum pondere examinatum, ostendet, quam parva quantitas Igniscentis illius substantiæ, in illa circiter dimidia uncia Sulphuris hæresit, quæ in massæ rubicundæ uncia una & dimidia, comprehensa fuerat.

Macquer[1] says Brandt found by a careful experiment that the proportion of the inflammable principle to vitriolic acid in sulphur is 3 to 50, or sulphur contains only $\frac{1}{16}$ its weight of inflammable principle.

Stahl's work on salts (1723), the purpose of which is explained by its title (see XVIII, p. 662), was less convincing than that on sulphur; d'Holbach, the French translator, in fact, says:[2]

We are forced to admit that his demonstration is not rigorous. He shows, it is true, that the earthy element and the aqueous element enter into saline combinations, but nothing proves that they enter alone. It could be wished that he had been able to reproduce a saline substance by recombining anew these two elements, as in recombining the principle of inflammability with the vitriolic acid he was able to reproduce sulphur. This complement would have put the seal to the evidence of his demonstration.

Still, the empirical knowledge of salts had made little progress since Stahl's time, and his work was worth translating after the lapse of half a century. The style is worse than usual and Stahl says in the preface he had been obliged, through lack of time, to throw his ideas on paper (auf das Papier zu werffen) as they occurred to him.[3] The experimental evidence is also weaker than usual; as an example, Stahl says that borax (Borrax) on heating gives off water and leaves a soft glass (which he took for an earth), and this is 'the simplest and most obvious proof that a salt consists of water and a fusible or subtle earth' (i.e. Becher's *terra vitrescibilis*).[4] He gives experimental evidence for the pre-existence of acids in plants.[5] The vegetable acids, containing much oily (combustible) matter, entered the plants in solution from the air and soil.[6]

The work is comprehensible only when it is remembered that the acids (vitriolic acid, spirit of salt, and nitric acid) and alkalis (potash, soda, and ammonia) are still classed as 'salts'. There is an interesting section on the varying strengths of acids as demonstrated by their varying power of dissolving metals, which however, depends on dilution and temperature.[7] He points out that although vitriolic acid does not dissolve silver in the cold, it does so when heated, and that the compound formed is also precipitated by vitriolic acid from a solution of silver in nitric acid.[8] There is a long section, describing many experiments, on the precipitation of a metal in solution by another metal, i.e. an affinity series.

Stahl[9] extended the affinity series of metals described by Boyle[10] (p. 535). He describes experiments with zinc, iron, copper, lead, tin, mercury, and

---

[1] (1), ii, 506.   [2] XVIIIB, pref., iv.
[3] XVIIIA, Vorrede, 5 v.–6 r.   [4] XVIIIA, 25–6; 30 f.
[5] *Ib.*, 39 f., 48 f. — where he seems to have obtained tartaric acid; cf. IX, 1738, 132, no. cxcviii.
[6] XVIIIA, 47 f.
[7] *Ib.*, 214; XVIIIB, 213; ch. xxii: von der unterschiedenen Stärcke der Salium acidorum; Des différens degrés de force des Acides.
[8] XVIIIA, 221.
[9] XVII, 26; XVIIIA, 223, 244; XVIIIB, 222, 241 (chs. xxiii–iv); XXIII, 245, 256, 376.
[10] *Physiological Essays, Hist. of Fluidity and Firmness*, 1661, sect. 23; *Works*, ed. Birch, 1744, i, 250; ed. Shaw, i, 315, 522.

silver, each metal precipitating from solution one following it in the series. He says clearly that the precipitating metal takes the acid from the salt of the metal precipitated. He also says that sulphuric acid displaces nitric acid in warm copper nitrate solution, and he recognised affinity series for acids and bases[1] after Mayow's manner (see p. 606). Stahl also clearly recognised affinity series in the dry way.[2] When metallic antimony is distilled with cinnabar (mercury sulphide), mercury is displaced. The antimony sulphide when fused with silver forms silver sulphide (Silberschlacke), which when fused with lead forms lead sulphide; this when fused with copper forms copper sulphide, and copper sulphide when fused with antimony and iron forms iron sulphide and a copper-antimony alloy. From iron sulphide and nitric acid the sulphur is finally precipitated. Stahl says: 'By this experiment the gradation of sulphur from one metal to another is demonstrated (Durch diese experiment erweiset sich des Schwefels Abfall, von einem Metall in das andere; le Soufre quitte un métal pour s'unir avec un autre).'

Stahl was clear that the course of a reaction is different in solution and when dry substances are heated together. Calomel (mercurous chloride) precipitates horn-silver (silver chloride) from a solution of a silver salt, but when horn-silver is heated with mercury the process is reversed and calomel sublimes: so kehret sich das gantze Blatt herum (la médaille se retourne).[3]

In the work on salts the process of fractional crystallisation is fully described, with a mixture of common salt and nitre as an example.[4] Water of crystallisation Stahl calls additional or superfluous (überflüssig).[5] He was wrong in supposing that alum contained vitriolic acid with a calcareous earth as a base:[6] es giebt auch die Kreide mit diesem acido vermenget, eine gleichmässige Alaunichte Art; wie aus Kreide und Vitriol-Spiritu, ein rechter Alaun erwächset. He also confused magnesia (present in the mother-liquor of nitre) with lime:[7]

was vor Redens und theurer Preis von den so genanndten *magnesia alba* einige Jahr hero, gemacht worden, ist biss zum Verdruss bekanndt; was ist sie aber doch anders, als eben der in der Mutter-Lauge noch solvirt gesteckte Kalch.

Stahl believed that sulphuric acid was the 'universal acid'; nitric acid was a compound of this with phlogiston; and spirit of salt a compound of the universal acid with Becher's mercurial earth.[8] He recognised the formation of a peculiar acid, different from sulphuric acid, formed by burning sulphur, and he obtained a salt (sulphite) of a peculiar crystalline form by absorbing the fumes in rags dipped in alkali solution, extracting with water, and evaporating; and on adding a strong acid to the salt so formed, the 'volatile spirit of sulphur' is expelled:

imbuimus nempe linteamina aliquot saturarissimo quodam lixivio alcalino ... hæc distribuimus in aliquot vasa sublimatoria seu Aludel, ita disponendo, ut fumus exhalens sulphureus, ipsa quantum potest undique perreptare queat ... spiritus qui

[1] XVIIIA, chs. ix, xxiii, 75, 227, etc.
[2] XIIIA, 348 f.; XIIIB, 290 f.; XXIII, 419, 453; see p. 357.
[3] XVIIIA, 425; B, 405.   [4] XVIIIA, 278 f.   [5] *Ib.*, 287 f.
[6] *Ib.*, 121, 305; cf. XVII, 55.   [7] XVIIIA, 132–3.
[8] XVII, 10; Juncker, (2), v, 62 f., 181, 237.

ta fumi forma ab illis exit, insinuat se in alcali illud quod inde saturatum siccescit . . . dum itaque fortiora hæc acida, sali nostro affusa, alcali ejusdem invadunt, excutitur eo ipso debilius nostrum volatile acidum.[1]

He also obtained a salt with ammonia and (long before William Higgins, 1789) a solution of iron in sulphurous acid:

Leget man in den recipienten . . . hinlängliches von einem flüchtigen urinosischen Saltz, so giebt es ein sehr subtiles Salmiac-Geschlecht;

si in apto vase volatile alcali . . . apponitur; in hoc denuo statim invadens, novum cum eo volatile sal medium, velut ammonialis indolis, repræsentat;

solviret man Metall / als Eisen / damit / so giebt es abermalen / so wohl an der Farbe / als Geschmack / consistenz, præcipitationen etc. gute Anmerckungen. Nimmt man aber die damit gemachte roth-gelbe Eisen-Solution. . . .[2]

By the action of cold he obtained liquid sulphur dioxide:[3]

si in arctum collectus, frigori hyberno exponatur, totus congelatur. In vitro autem firmiter obturato, non adeo forti calore agitatus, elastica forti expansione, vitrum diffringat.

Boerhaave[4] apparently doubted whether there was any real difference between ordinary sulphuric acid and the 'volatile spirit of sulphur'. Stahl points out that phlogistication weakens the strength of an acid.[5]

Ephraim Rinhold Seehl, of whom nothing seems to be known,[6] 'improved' Stahl's process by adding oil of vitriol to an impure alkali sulphite made by boiling sulphur with a solution of alkaline salt (K_2CO_3) and evaporating to dryness. The acidified mixture was then distilled and a liquid collected with a pungent 'gassy' smell, 'almost like the gas sulphuris.'

Stahl gives the weights of nitric acid required to dissolve equal weights of various metals (1 lb. acid dissolved $\frac{3}{4}$ lb. mercury, $\frac{1}{2}$ lb. silver, zinc not quite $\frac{1}{2}$ lb., copper not quite $\frac{1}{4}$ lb., iron less than $\frac{1}{4}$ lb.); and by dissolving silver in nitric acid, evaporating, and weighing the silver nitrate, he found that the silver took up only a fifth of its weight of acid.[7]

Stahl,[8] mentioning Kunckel's experiment,[9] says more water is produced when a volatile oil is heated with vitriolic acid than is contained in the acid (so viel Wassers, als das dazu genommene Vitriol-Sauer auf keine weise nicht ausmachet). Sand displaces the acids of nitre and common salt at a red heat, and hence seems to have an acidic nature.[10]

Stahl believed that nitric and muriatic acids are the same (nicht unfüglich ein gleiches erachtet werden).[11] He explains the liberation of hydrochloric and nitric acids from their salts by sulphuric acid in the same way as Mayow (p. 606), but seems to think it is his own theory.[12] Stahl says that sulphuric

[1] IV, *a*, ii (1697); V, vii (1700); quotation is from: Observatio VII. De copiosa, facili, et concentrata collectionis spiritus acidi summe volatilis sulphureo-vitriolici, et theoretico-practica Αποδειξει generationis eiusdem, in XII, 246 f., 252 f., 254 f., 333; IX, 1738, 136; XIIIA, 190; XVIIIA, 110; XXIII, 175 f.; XXI, 72, 77.
[2] XIIIA, 192; XXI, 79.   [3] XXI, 80.   [4] (2), i, 324, 810.   [5] XVIIIA, 297.
[6] *Phil. Trans.*, 1744, xliii, 1; *id.*, *A New Improvement in the Art of Making the True Volatile Spirit of Sulphur*, London, 1744 (60 pp.) (BM); Gmelin, ii, 557, gives his name wrongly as 'E. Reinhardt Seehl'.
[7] XVIIIA, 170 f., 303; XVIIIB, 168 f., 300.   [8] XVIIIA, 10 f.
[9] *Chym. Anmerckungen*; *V Curiose Chym. Tractätl.*, 1721, 93.
[10] XVIIIA, 71.   [11] XVIIIA, 357.
[12] XXIII, 169 f.; he quotes Mayow in other parts of the book and had certainly read him.

acid is stronger than nitric acid, which is stronger than hydrochloric acid; when nitric acid is heated with common salt, hydrochloric acid is expelled and nitre remains:[1]

spiritus nitri, ob er gleich ex hoc gradu geringer und schwächer als spiritus vitrioli, ist er doch stärcker als salis acidum . . . kehrt sich die κράσις des trockenen eingelegten Salzes also dass man nitrum an des Salis communis Stätte bekommt . . . Ratio hæc est; der spiritus nitri ist stärcker als das acidum salis communis.

He supposed that alkalis, which are subtle earths, are actually produced in the combustion of plants.[2]

He mentions the blue flame seen when common salt is thrown on glowing coals.[3] Common salt is of unknown origin, but it is present in the urine of animals which eat no salt.[4] Stahl, however, seems to have been the first to state[5] that the basis of common salt is an alkali (vulgo vocant hanc substantiam, quae *corpus* praebet sali communi . . . alcalinam): if common salt is heated with sulphuric or nitric acid, and the acid is then removed from the residue (ab hoc corpore iterum avellatur) — he does not say how, an alkali remains (remanet alcalinum salinum corpus). This 'previously little-considered salt of an alkaline nature (ein bisher wenig bedachte saltzigte Art alkalischen Geschlechtes)'[6] is soda, first clearly described by Duhamel (Vol. III). Boerhaave[7] denied that common salt contains any alkali at all: when it is heated with bole (clay), spirit of salt is formed, but water extracts no alkali from the residue (the complex silicate is insoluble).

Sea-water or salt brine can be concentrated by freezing, since when saturated with salt it freezes only at a very low temperature (ohne die äusserste Kälte nicht gantz hart frieret).[8]

The action of quicklime in causticising an alkali is due to the combination of the lime with the sulphureous and volatile acid part of the alkali salt, which when so freed from its acid constituent, shows a much more caustic nature[9] (accrevit alcalici Salis parti Sulphureæ, exterminata ejusdem acido-salina volatiliori, & hoc ipso fixius & penetrantius in actionibus suis hoc Alcali fecit); the approach to Black's theory is striking.

Nitre, formed by putrefaction,[10] as Becher[11] said, contains phlogiston and the acid part is inflammable; nitre is the only substance which takes fire in a closed space:[12] solum nitrum non tamen expetat aërem, quam suppeditat atque præbet. Its acid removes phlogiston from metals and hence contains phlogiston itself, since chemical reactions occur between similar substances.[13] Stahl later recognised that nitre is not inflammable of itself but only in presence of combustible substances and metals, the phlogiston of the latter giving that imprisoned in the nitre the force to break its bonds with the aid of fire.[14] He thought, however, that its capacity for causing flame is due to the water it contains (see p. 673) which acts as a blast on the flame:[15] das Wasser in dem nitro-

---

[1] XXIII, 257. [2] IX, 1738, 121; XVII, 84 f. [3] XIIIB, 198, 265.
[4] XVIIIA, 144. [5] IX, 1738, 111, 123; Kopp, (1), i, 191. [6] XVIIIA, 51.
[7] (2), i, 794. [8] XVIIIA, 146. [9] XVII, 88. [10] IVb, viii; XII, 536.
[11] *Physica Subterranea*, 1738, 144: hæc enim putrefacta, in terra abeunt prorsus nitrosam, ex qua etiam communi modo nitrum copiosum parari potest, sola elixatione cum aqua communi.
[12] XII, 555–8. [13] *Ib.*, 562. [14] XIIIA, 27, 180, 186. [15] XVIIIA, 95.

sischen Saltz- (als Saltz) Wesen losgerissen, in einem schnellen Blast ausgedeh-
net, die Feuer-Bewegung in eine Flamme aufbläset. Since it is formed from excrements and urine, which contain much common salt, he thought the acid of
nitre was very like muriatic acid;[1] earlier (1698),[2] he said nitric acid was
formed from the universal acid (vitriolic acid) and the phlogiston of fermenting substances (Nitrum revera subnasci possit, dum sulphurea illa portio, quae
vegetabilibus & animalibus inest, putrefactione resoluta atque attenuata cum
acido universali . . . intimus coalescit. In another place he says that nitre and
common salt contain no water of crystallisation as such:[3] Salpeter aber, gar
nichts empfindliches: wie auch das Koch-Saltz, wann es in feste Crystallen
gebracht. He obtained crystals of cubic nitre (sodium nitrate) by distilling to
dryness a solution of common salt in nitric acid, and showed that the crystals
deflagrate like nitre with burning coals:[4] so setzet sich . . . viele viereckigen
crystallen . . . Massen sie auf Kohlen, wie ein ander nitrum verpuffen.

Stahl's writings are rich in observations on metals. Although it was previously thought that steel is very pure iron, it is iron which has taken up more
phlogiston but contains less crude earth than iron.[5] He gives a long account of
the solution of iron in nitric acid in various conditions, and the formation of
a blood-red solution which deposits a red coagulum very difficult to filter,
after which the liquid will dissolve more iron;[6] when iron filings are strongly
heated with nitre a substance (potassium ferrate) is formed which gives a
purple alkaline solution:

combustione ferri dextra cum *nitro*; unde sal alcali nitri causticum remanens, aliquam
portionem ferri ita solvit, ut *amethystino-purpureo* colore limpido, etiam per filtram
secum ducat.[7]

This in four hours deposited a brick-coloured powder and became colourless:
interim vix horæ quadrantis spatio, secedit iterum . . . portio illa martialis, in
forma pulveris . . . lateritii coloris et ad fundum subsidet, alcalino illo lixivio
limpido iterum relicto.[8]

The formation of metallic zinc (Zinc) in the furnaces at Goslar is described.[9]
Stahl's essay on zinc[10] is very confused and inaccurate, although he gives a
good description of the process of extraction in Goslar.

In his dissertation on the stellate regulus of antimony (1697)[11] Stahl concluded that it often contained a little of the other metal (iron, copper, tin) used
in its preparation, since if evaporated on charcoal before the blowpipe (diffla-
tione super carbone) it sometimes left a bead of other metal; calx of antimony
prepared with nitre could be reduced when heated on charcoal by the blowpipe (per tubulum, quali aurifabri ad ferruminandum utuntur).[12] Lemery[13]
thought the star was formed by the iron hardening the regulus, the parts of
non-stellar or common antimony not having the requisite tension. Becher[14]
thought the star was produced by the 'sulphur' of the iron. Stahl, however,

[1] XVIIIA, 129, 133.   [2] IV, viii; XII, 535.   [3] XVIIIA, 288.   [4] XVIIIA, 281.
[5] IVa, vii; XII, 520; XXIII, 451.   [6] XVIIIA, 173 f., 338 f., 365 f.; XXIII, 249.
[7] IX, 1738, 127; XXIII, 248.   [8] XII, 743.   [9] XIIIA, 201 f.; XIIIB, 169.
[10] XII, 791–3, 837.   [11] IVa, vi; XII, 481 f.
[12] *Ib.*, 497; XVII, 206.   [13] *Cours de Chymie*, 1690, 272 f.
[14] *Phys. subterr.*, *Suppl.* II; 1738, 410.

showed that a stellate regulus could be formed by merely melting ordinary antimony, without using any iron at all, and allowing it to cool slowly and regularly, say when covered with scoria.[1]

The account of the golden calf of the Israelites which Moses burnt, ground to powder, and strewed upon water for them to drink, had been supposed[2] to prove that chemistry was practised in the time of Moses.[3] Stahl, in a special treatise,[4] supposed that the gold was fused with liver of sulphur, when it became a soluble salt.

Stahl obtained white cuprous chloride by the slow action of spirit of salt on copper filings or wire, although he did not understand the nature of the precipitate (formed in presence of a little air).[5] He thought red precipitate of mercury (oxide) has the same weight as the mercury from which it is made.[6]

When common salt, calcined vitriol, and metallic mercury are mixed and sublimed, corrosive sublimate is formed, which is only the acid of common salt combined with mercury (vvelcher nichts, als acidum salis communis corrosivum cum mercurio soluto combinatum). But more acid is combined with the mercury than is necessary to dissolve it, the surplus acid remaining corrosive. If 4 oz. of corrosive sublimate is ground with 4 oz. of mercury and the mixture sublimed, the acid takes all the mercury, dissolves it, saturates itself with it, and becomes sweet mercury, i.e. calomel (so nimmt das acidum noch den mercurium alle an, solvirt ihn, saturirt sich mit ihm, und vvird also mercurius dulcis).[7] Juncker[8] says that in the second process: 'cet acide peut dissoudre le double de son poids de mercure' as compared with that in corrosive sublimate, a recognition of multiple proportions (Hg_2Cl_2 and $HgCl_2$). This superabundance of acid can only be explained by having recourse to 'l'identité des principes mercuriels que contiennent l'acide marin & le mercure; identité qui fait que ces deux substances se réunissent abondamment'.

Stahl's contributions to Organic Chemistry are also of interest. Like Becher, he devoted much attention to fermentation, on which he wrote a special treatise (*Zymotechnia fundamentalis*, 1697). He defines fermentation[9] as the resolution of a body by internal agitation of its molecules into its loosely-combined constituents, and the recombination of these into their former and also into new combinations. Here he seems to have been influenced by Bernoulli (1690) (p. 628).[10] No motion originates *de novo* but is transferred from one body to another; the addition of a ferment increases and accelerates the motion and directs the process into the production of that kind of fermentation which otherwise, in very heterogeneous material, would occur merely promiscuously and irregularly.[11]

A fermentable body contains molecules (*moleculæ*) composed of salt, oil, and earth, which are violently agitated by the water molecules, accelerated by the

[1] IV*a*, vi; XII, 484, 504.
[2] Borrichius, *Hermetis, Aegyptiorum et Chymicorum Sapientia*, Copenhagen, 1674, 226.
[3] Partington, (1), 485.
[4] *Vitulus Aureus igne combustus: Arcanum simplex, sed Arcanum*; IV*b*, x; XII, 585.
[5] XVIII*A*, 194 f.   [6] XVII, 128.   [7] XXIII, 233.   [8] (2), iii, 445.
[9] III, 1697, 6 f.   [10] J. C. Fischer, 1802, iii, 377–416.
[11] III, 1697, 49 f., 200; XXI, 385 f.; fermentation = combustion.

ferment, and driven against one another, so that they fall apart into their components, which then rearrange themselves by 'confermentation' into other groupings, the spirit containing mostly the oily particles. The ferment acts by communicating the motion of its particles to the particles of the fermenting body. The 'oily particles' were then identified with phlogiston.[1] This idea of the transmission of molecular motion is an early theory of catalysis,[2] and was much later developed by Liebig.[3] It really goes back to Willis (p. 306).[4]

Boerhaave[5] also believed that fermentation involves motion of the particles (fermentationis nomine intellegam motum intestinam), but Kunckel[6] said no one had understood or would understand the nature of fermentation (bishero keiner gelebet, und noch zur Zeit nicht lebet, auch nimmer kommen wird, der das Punctum Fermentationis recht accurat treffen solte).

Stahl regarded fermentation as a variety of putrefaction — although he sometimes includes putrefaction as a kind of fermentation[7] — and hence he did not regard effervescence as characteristic of fermentation; this is the exception rather than the rule, since it does not occur in putrefaction or acetification. Certain changes of inorganic bodies are fermentations, e.g. combustion, which differs from fermentation only in the intensity and velocity of the change:[8] Cum quo plurimum concidit, est Combustio; Differt tamen ab hâc etiam, energiâ & velocitate actionis. Unlike Becher (p. 651) he did not think air necessary for fermentation.[9] In neglecting the gas sylvestre (carbon dioxide) evolved in fermentation, Stahl is decidedly behind Van Helmont.[10]

Kunckel[11] found that on adding sulphuric acid or alcohol, fermentation stops (so steht die Fermentation stille), and Stahl knew that a sulphite arrested fermentation and putrefaction:[12] Solviret man in diesem reinen flüchtigen spiritu [sulphurous acid] eine subtile Erde, und bringet es unter ein fermentirendes oder faulendes Werck, so giebt es wieder vernünftige Anmerckungen.

Inflammable spirits are constituted of aqueous and oily particles of equal mobility not combined but in proximity:[13]

combinationem ejus non in Continuitate partium, sed in proxime æquali utrarumque Mobilitate, sitam esse, qua ipsa non tam singula hujus Liquoris individua ex duabus istis partibus, atomo oleosa et aquosa, connexis constent, quam totum Aggregatum ex his actu coagitatis.

Stahl showed that wine, beer, and vinegar are concentrated by freezing.[14] He describes in some detail an experiment of distilling good oil of vitriol and alcohol and obtaining an ardent spirit or oil of pleasant burning odour and very volatile and inflammable, and this would be ether:[15]

---

[1] XVII, 31; XX, 77 f.   [2] Chevreul, Compt. Rend., 1864, lix, 979; 1872, lxxiv, 898–913.
[3] Ann., 1839, xxx, 250 (262); Letters on Chemistry, 1851, 180 f.
[4] Diatribe duae . . . , 1659; Opera, Venice, 1720, i, 5, 9.
[5] (2), ii, 166.   [6] Laboratorium Chymicum, 1716, 697.
[7] XVIIIA, 151: Putredo . . . das wahre genus aller fermentation ist.
[8] III, 1697, 6 f., 173 f., 176.
[9] Ib., 73 f.   [10] J. C. Fischer, 1802, iii, 387.
[11] Laboratorium Chymicum, 1716, 714.   [12] XIIIA, 192.
[13] XVII, 31.   [14] IVa, iv; XII, 410 f.   [15] XVIIIA, 421; XXI, 104 f.

Consistit Experimentum, in eo, ut bonum oleum Vitrioli, cum optimo Spiritu ardente mixtum, provide conjungendo, et modeste tractando, destillationi submittatur. Ita Spiritus prodit, primo loco, certe summe volatilis; ardens, et grati odoris, sed ita penetrans, ut vesica obligatus, tam odore acuto, quam ipsa sua substantia, intra tempus non ita longum, ad sensum imminuatur et exhalet.

Many women know more than the chemists: when making vinegar they add from time to time a small quantity of brandy which contributes to the goodness of the vinegar, whilst the chemists, who imagined that spirit of wine prevents fermentation, removed it by boiling before trying to make vinegar.[1] The ardent spirit of wine, which during the formation of vinegar is not very strongly attached to a coarse fatty principle (gröberer Fettigkeit), then combines more strongly with the acid principle, and cannot then be separated from it by distillation or by means of an earth, whilst at the same time the coarseness of the acid is ameliorated and also rendered more subtle and penetrating.[2] The vinegar can be concentrated by freezing out the water,[3] or by adding dried copper sulphate and crystallising out blue vitriol.[4]

Stahl describes the preparation of glacial acetic acid by distilling an alkali acetate with sulphuric acid:[5]

Acetum, si sale alcali saturetur, aquositatis bona pars potior leniter exhalare, permittatur, tandem spiritus aut oleum vitrioli instilletur, regeneratur acetum, fortificatum seu concentratum.

It can also be obtained by distilling sugar of lead or of iron (the acetates) alone or with sulphuric acid, or by the dry distillation of verdigris (basic copper acetate) and is inflammable (wie ein Wein-Geist Flamme fanget und brennet).[6]

Johann Christoph Westendorf (Wismar, 25 March 1740–Güstrow, 26 May 1803)[7] suggested using soda instead of potash, and distilling the sodium acetate with sulphuric acid, so that concentrated acetic acid was sometimes called Westendorf's acid.[8] In the same dissertation Westendorf described the formation of an essential oil by the repeated distillation of pure spirit of wine, but this was disproved by Westrumb.[9]

Stahl believed that plants extracted phlogiston from the air, which is what happened in Van Helmont's tree experiment, and that it passed into animal bodies with the vegetable food. Plants produce oily substance in places where water is scarce. When phlogiston is separated from water by the combustion of vegetable matter, the latter can be formed again only with great difficulty.[10] From plants, phlogiston passes to animals, and finally returns to the atmosphere.[11]

Alchemy, which came to Europe from China[12] or Egypt,[13] was not wholly to be condemned and the processes merited careful examination, although it was

[1] XVIIIA, 152.   [2] Ib., 154.   [3] Ib., 158.   [4] Ib., 290.
[5] IX, 1738, 132; XVIIIA, 159.   [6] XVIIIA, 156 f.
[7] Disputatio Inauguralis Chemico-Medica De Optima Acetum Concentratum ejusdemque Naphtham Conficiciendi (sic) Ratione utriusque Affectionibus ac Vsu medico . . . , 4°, Göttingen, [1772] (iii ll., 75 pp., i l.); BM T. 613. (2.); Ferguson, ii, 545; Duveen, 617.
[8] Gren, i, 577.
[9] Chemische Versuche die Entstehung der Zuckersäure . . . betreffend, in Kleine Phys.-chem. Abhl., Leipzig, 1785, i, 76: ich fand von jenem nichts.
[10] IVa, ii, XII, 339 f.; XIIIA, 82 f.; XXI, 44, 161–2; Juncker, (2), i, 199, iv, 343.
[11] XXI, 263.   [12] V, ix; XII, 269.   [13] XVII, 219.

not free from imposture. Silver can be obtained by the cupellation of lead[1] and copper can be converted into iron and vice versa.[2] The followers of Paracelsus worked on vitriol, those of Sendivogius on nitre, whilst most adepts, influenced by 'Philalethes', hoped to succeed with mercury: 'some advise one thing and some another.'[3] Stahl frankly admits that the art was not known to him (ich eine solche Kunst selbst nicht wisse),[4] although some believed he did, convinced that he possessed the secret because he showed no apparent interest in it. The preparation of philosophical gold is not impossible and might be of inestimable moral value when well employed, although Stahl held out little hope of success.[5] Gmelin[6] prints a letter from Stahl to Juncker saying that whilst he freely admitted the possibility of transmutation in his old lectures in 1684 as printed by Carl,[7] he had become more cautious:

wiewohl auch nicht ganz vergebens oder falsch seyn dürfte, wenn es bloss *ad veritatem physicam inveniendam* untersuchet, nicht aber auf die thörichte *transcendental-* Hoffnung oder Einbildung der Goldmacherey angewendet würde.

His later works contain clear warnings against its pursuit,[8] although they often quote old or recent alchemical books.

VIGANI

John Francis Vigani (Verona, 1650 ?–Newark-on-Trent, February, 1713) who worked in Paris, came to Newark-on-Trent about 1682 and went in 1683 to Cambridge, where he lectured privately until 1703, when he was appointed professor of chemistry in the university, holding this purely honorary position till about 1708; he was succeeded by J. Waller, B.D. in 1713. His collection of materia medica is in Queens' College, Cambridge.[9]

Vigani wrote a small text-book:

Medulla Chemiæ, sm. 8°, Dantzig, 1682 (29 pp.); Medulla Chymiæ, Variis Experimentis aucta, multisq; Figuris illustrata, sm. 8°, London, 1683 (xvi, 71 pp., last blank, 3 copper plates of furnaces and distillation apparatus); Medulla Chymiae . . . Notis illustrata observationibusque practicis . . . aucta a D[avid] Stam, 8°, Leyden, 1693 (xii ll., 96 pp., iv ll., 3 folding plates); 8°, Nürnberg, 1718, with A. Q. Rivinus's Manvdvctio ad Chemiam Pharmacevticam, and at end, Chymia Curiosa variis (cura F. Roth-Scholz), and 3 plates now in 6, and with extracts of recipes (by Bohn) in E. König, *ΚΕΡΑΣ ΑΜΑΛΘΕΙΑΣ* seu Thesaurus Remediorum è Triplicè Regno, 4°, Basel, 1693; Coleby ments. an ed. of the Medulla, London, 1685.

The book contains fairly long extracts from several chemical authors. It quotes Van Helmont's *Daegeraad* (1660)[10] and Mayow's *Tractatus Quinque* (1674) for

---

[1] IX, 1738, 69; Hellot, Tillet and Macquer, AdS, 1763, m 1, showed that no transmutation occurred.
[2] XVII, 185.   [3] *Ib.*, 220–2.
[4] XIIIA, 139 f.; XIIIB, 113 f.: j'avoue ingénuement que cette grand arcarne m'est absolument inconnu.
[5] XVII, 234.   [6] (1), ii, 676.   [7] XVII, 219 f.
[8] IX, 1738, 68; XIIIA, 336 f.; XVIIIA, 332 f.
[9] Wiegleb, (2), 1790, I, i, 74; Kopp, (1), iv, 106; Hoefer, (1), ii, 235; E. S. Peck, *Proc. Cambridge Antiquar. Soc.*, 1934, xxxiv, 34; Coleby, *Ann. Sci.*, 1951, viii, 46; Gunther, (1), 1923, i, 51; *id.*, (2), 1937, 221–4, 238, 333; Ferguson, DNB, 1899, lviii, 305; MS. in English of his lectures, CUL Dd. 12. 53 (57 pp. and index).
[10] Vigani, 1693, 14.

the statement that on distilling nitre the residue is similar to a fixed alkaline salt, which Vigani did not confirm:[1] nihil est præter nitrum, non alcali, ut quidam putant. It describes the purification of green vitriol (ferrous sulphate) from copper by putting iron into the solution;[2] says that on distilling verdigris the quantity of acetic acid collected is the same as that required to dissolve the calx of copper remaining in the retort (tantum aceti esse absorptum, quantum collectum fuit sub formâ spiritus);[3] and that antimony when calcined by a burning glass descreases in weight, those who assert that it increases being wrong.[4] From vinegar and soot Vigani obtained crystals of the compound of fixed alkali and vinegar (potassium acetate ?).[5] He mentions the preparation of ammonium sulphate,[6] describes tobacco,[7] the distillation of vipers[8] and human skull,[9] and describes and illustrates a portable furnace.[10] Vigani is commended by Stahl[11] for his experiments on the preparation of aqua fortis and spirit of salt; Stahl says Vigani worked more with his hands than his head, and criticised some of his theoretical conclusions.

ROTHE

Gottfried Rothe (or Rothen) (Lissa, 14 October 1679–Leipzig, 18 May 1710), a practising physician in Leipzig, was a diligent pupil of Stahl,[12] graduating with a dissertation De Salibus Metallicis (4°, Halle, 1708, 28 pp.).[13] He wrote a small posthumously published work on pharmaceutical chemistry which went through many editions (according to Gmelin to 1750):

Gründliche Einleitung zur Chemie . . . , sm. 8°, Leipzig, 1717 (pp. xii, 216, xii); Leipzig, 1721 (pp. xii, 240, iv), 1727 (same pagin.); and Anhang, handlend von denen Metallischen Saltzen . . . , 8°, Leipzig, 1723 (96 pp., BM 1035. f. 32).

French tr. by Meuder, Introduction à la Chymie, 12°, Paris, 1741 (Nourry-Thiebaud Cat. 66 (1938), no. 917), incl. a tr. of De salibus metallicis.

English tr. by A. Macbean, A Synopsis, or, Short Analytical View of Chemistry, 8°, London, 1743 (pp. viii, 131, xii; Ferguson).

It begins with a 7-page Chymiæ Brevis Sciagraphia in Latin, and an historical introduction and bibliography, and then deals with operations (solution, precipitation, etc.) and a section on lutes, and in the second part with chemical products (alkalis, acids, salts, sulphurs, and earths). It says: 'aus der Vereinigung der acidorum mit den alcalicis entstehen die Salsa', which are divided into 'plena saturata oder parte 1. alcalina 1. acida excedentia'.[14] The second half of the second part deals with chemical processes and contains recipes for sixty preparations. The book is very clear and practical. It does not use the phlogiston theory explicitly, speaking usually of the principium sulphureum,[15] or substantia inflammabili,[16] although volatile spirit of sulphur, made by distilling oil of vitriol in an earthen retort with a crack in the bottom, is said to owe its penetrating sulphureous smell to the 'particulas φλογιστὰς s. flammam

---

[1] Ib., 1683, 8; 1693, 28. [2] 1683, 6. [3] 1683, 13. [4] 1683, 51. [5] 1683, 30.
[6] 1683, 17. [7] 1683, 28. [8] 1683, 39. [9] 1683, 44. [10] 1683, 60.
[11] Beweiss von den Saltzen, Halle, 1723, 65, 283.
[12] Stahl, Chymia Rationalis et Experimentalis, Leipzig, 1720, preface; Gmelin, (1), ii, 682; Ferguson, ii, 296.
[13] Ferguson, ii, 398. [14] 1717, 123 f. [15] 1717, 79. [16] 1717, 127.

constituentes'.[1] It mentions[2] the Magisterii Antepileptici Michaëlis, due to Johann Michaelis (Soest, Westphalia, 1606/7–Leipzig, 29 November 1667), professor of medicine in Leipzig who edited Hartmann's *Praxis Chymiatrica* (1647),[3] which was precipitated calcium sulphate.

JUNCKER

A systematic account of Stahl's medical and chemical doctrines was given by his pupil Johann Juncker (Lehndorf, nr. Giessen, 23 December 1679 (var. other dates are given)–Halle, 25 October 1759), who studied at Giessen, Marburg and Halle. He taught at Halle in 1701–2 and then studied medicine in Erfurt; M.D. 1717. He practised medicine for a short time, then returned to Halle in 1716 as physician to the Royal Pædagogy and Orphanage, then became professor of medicine in the university, subsequently Prussian Hofrath. He published a large number of dissertations and medical works (with the general title *Conspectus*) and an excellent text-book of chemistry,[4] which is almost a primary source for the phlogiston theory:

   I. Conspectus Chemiae theoretico-practicae in forma Tabvlarvm repracsentatvs . . .
      e Dogmatibvs Becheri et Stahlii potissimvm explicantvr, eorvndemqve et
      aliorvm celebrivm Chemicorvm experimentis stabilivntvr, 2 vols. 4°, Halle,
      1730–38; 2 ed. 1742–4 (BN R 7734–5; BM has vol. i of 2 ed., 1744; Bolton, (1),
      565, incorrectly gives 1730 for both vols. of 1 ed.; Gmelin gives revised ed. 1749,
      1750); portr. by Bernigeroth.
  II. French tr. by Demachy: Élémens de Chymie, suivant les principes de Becker (*sic*)
      et de Stahl, 6 vols. 12°, Paris, 1657.
 III. German tr. by Johann Joachim Lange: Conspectus Chemiae theoretico-practica.
      Vollständige Abhandlung der Chemie nach ihrem Lehr-Begriff und der Aus-
      übung . . . vornehmlich nach Bechers und Stahls Grundlehren ausgeführt . . . ,
      3 vols. 4°, Halle, 1749–50–53 (Bolton, 566; BM).

Juncker[5] says an ounce of phosphorus, 'a new rarity (rara Chemiæ sobolcs)' then cost $10\frac{1}{2}$ ducats in England and 16 in Amsterdam. He collects several processes for extracting mercury from metals;[6] e.g. by repeated sublimation with sal ammoniac, treating the residue with vinegar, and salt of tartar, precipitating the distillate with spirit of salt and reducing with salt of tartar. He thought the detonation of fulminating gold was due to the sudden expansion of the watery parts of salt particles (distensione salium humidorum seu aquam in sua mixtione tenentium . . . ab igne velociter expanduntur).[7] His class of 'sulphurs or inflammables in general'[8] includes sulphur, bitumens, turf, resins, oils and fats, camphor, coals, soot, and phosphorus. He says water is easily formed by burning spirit of wine in a tubulated retort and collecting the vapour in a receiver (in aqueum humorem, ab aqua simplici communi nulla in re differentem).[9] The constituents of spirit of wine are acid, phlogiston, and water, without specifying any binary combination of these in it.[10] Sugar, consisting of salino-acid and oily principles, is made from sugar-cane juice[11] but also separates from raisins and honey.

[1] 1717, 111.   [2] 1717, 38.   [3] Ferguson, ii, 94.
[4] Gmelin, (1), ii, 681; NBG, 1858, xxvii, 238; Ferguson, i, 443.   [5] I, ii, 137.
[6] I, i, 396, 981, 1001.   [7] I, i, 873.   [8] I, ii, 1–145.   [9] I, ii, 536.
[10] I, ii, 532: constans ex aqua et phlogisto, per subtilem acidum connexis.   [11] I, ii, 545.

Juncker begins his book by a history of chemistry, praising Boyle, Becher and Stahl; Kunckel was an accurate experimenter but destitute of philosophical theory. He deals with the definitions, aims, and divisions of chemistry, symbols, instruments and vessels. The active and passive principles (salt, sulphur, mercury, earth and phlegm) are criticised, and Becher's three earths and phlogiston are adopted.[1] Syncrisis and diacrisis are the separation of corpuscles and the union of bodies.[2] The section on instruments[3] deals with the four elements, the matter of fire being phlogiston φλογιστὸν).[4] The function of air in combustion is to facilitate escape of phlogiston.[5] It is doubtful if there is a nitro-aerial spirit in the atmosphere.[6] The section on menstruums[7] deals with the alkahest, acids, alkalis, sulphurs (spirit of wine and oils), liver of sulphur. After a section on the subjects of chemistry in general, he deals with water, solution, extraction, amalgamation, mercurification, coagulation, vitrification, reduction, sublimation, distillation, digestion, secretion and clarification, crystallisation, precipitation, calcination and cementation, the transmutation of metals,[8] metallurgy, assaying, the metals in general, and particular metals. The second volume deals with inflammables, salts, fermentation, and putrefaction (which is a kind of fermentation).

Spielmann

Jacob Reinbold Spielmann (Strasbourg; 31 March 1722–9 September 1783), M.D. 1748, professor of chemistry at Strasbourg from 1749, of Greek and Latin poetry from 1754, and of medicine from 1759, was a pupil of Pott, Marggraf, Henckel and Geoffroy and the chemical teacher of Goethe (who had an elementary knowledge of chemistry).[9]

Spielmann's chemical lectures were published as an excellent concise textbook, giving copious references to the literature:

I. Institutiones Chemiæ prælectionibus academicis adcommodatæ, 8°, Strasbourg, 1763 (309 pp. and unpaged Syllabus Auctorum, and index); 2 ed., revisa, aucta, potita, 8°, Strasbourg, 1766 (pp. xii, 350, xxxii syllabus auctorum, xxxix index).

II. French tr. by Cadet, with notes and extended bibliography: Instituts de Chymie, 2 vols. 12°, Paris, 1770. (German trs. of 1783 and 1787 are ment.; see p. 768).

He also published some medical and pharmaceutical works:

Delectus Dissertationum Medicarum Argentoratensium, 4 vols., Nürnberg, 1777–81 (collected by Johann Conrad Wittwer); Kleine praktische medizinische und chemische Schriften, 8°, Leipzig, 1786 (473 pp., 1 fold. plate); Pharmacopoea Generalis edita a D. Jacobo Reinboldo Spielmann, 4°, Strasbourg, 1783 (with portr. dated 1881).[10]

Spielmann's publications on soap,[11] and elastic mineral resin,[12] in which he describes the distillation of the mineral oil of Alsace, comparing the lighter fraction (sp. gr. 0·808) with ethereal oils and points out the fluorescence of the heavier fractions of the distillate, are of interest. He found[13] that milk can undergo vinous fermentation provided casein ('cheese') is present; the Tartars prepare an intoxicating drink from milk. Albrecht von Haller[14] mentions that

[1] I, i, 66 f.   [2] I, i, 102.   [3] I, i, 151–99.   [4] I, i, 152.
[5] I, i, 156.   [6] I, i, 163.   [7] I, i, 199–232.   [8] I, i, 604–56.
[9] Wittwer, Crell's Ann., 1784, I, 545; Vicq-d'Azyr, Éloges historiques, Paris, 1805, ii, 48; Cap, Études biographiques, 1857, i, 264; Gmelin, (1), ii, 535, 689, 701, 733; iii, 754; Lippmann, (1), ii, 445; Meyerson, De l'explication dans les sciences, Paris, 1921, i, 293; Ferguson, ii, 393; Poggendorff, (1), ii, 971: Schelenz, in Diergart, 1909, 161.
[10] A Venice ed., 3 pts., 1786, is mentioned.
[11] Nova Acta Acad. Curios., 1767, iii, 442–59 (Spicilegium circa Saponum historiam); Crell's Neues chemischen Archiven, 1786, v, 297–316.
[12] Hist. Acad. Berlin, 1758 (1765), 105–28.
[13] Mém. Soc. Roy. de Médec., 1776 (1779), 330; letter of August 1777.
[14] Bibliotheca Anatomica, 2 vols., Zürich, 1774–7; 1777, ii, 492.

the famous chemist Spielmann had made a chemical study of the milk of several animals. Spielmann's dissertations on neutral salts (1748), tartar (1780), phosphoric acid (1781) and *acidum pingue*,[1] may be mentioned.

Gottfried August Hoffmann (Leissnig, Saxony, 1700–Halle, 1775) was the author of one of the first text-books on chemical technology.[2] Johann Christopher Ebel wrote on woad.[3]

---

[1] *Dissert. inaug. resp. M. Fr. Boehm sistens examen acidi pinguis*, 4°, Strasbourg, 1769.

[2] *Chymie zu Gebrauch des Haus-, Land- und Stadtwirthes, des Künstlers, Manufacturiers, Fabrikanten und Handwerkers*, 8°, Leipzig, 1757; *Einleitung zur Chemie für Künstler und Fabrikanten*, 2 ed. with notes by J. C. Wiegleb, 8°, Gotha and Langensalza, 1779.

[3] *De Indo Germanico sive Colore coervleo solido ex glasto*, Dissert., Halle, 1756 (46 pp.); German tr., Brunswick, 1757.

CHAPTER XIX

HOFFMANN AND OTHER 18TH CENTURY CHEMISTS

HOFFMANN

Friedrich Hoffmann (Halle; 19 February 1660–12 November 1742; 4 October 1742 is also given), the son of a physician of the same name (p. 320), lost both his parents and his elder sister from typhus in 1675. From 1678 he was a pupil of Wedel in Jena, then of Caspar Cramer in Erfurt, and he graduated M.D. at Jena in 1681 with a thesis on cinnabar of antimony (I below),

FIG. 32. FRIEDRICH HOFFMANN, 1660–1742.
(From his *Opera Omnia Physico-Medica*)

containing several quantitative chemical experiments. He lectured on chemistry for a short time at Jena (exciting, it is said, the jealousy of the professors), then visited Holland and (in 1683, or 1684–5) England, where he became acquainted with Boyle. He then practised as a physician at Minden and Halberstadt, but was appointed to the first chair of medicine at Halle in 1694 (Gmelin says 1693), teaching physics, chemistry, anatomy, practical medicine, and surgery. He taught there for 48 years, interrupted by a period in 1709–12 as physician in Berlin to the king of Prussia. He became F.R.S. in 1719. Hoffmann was a man of high moral qualities and great learning, and his style is clear, elegant, and precise. Sprengel says, however, that although Hoffmann's conclusions follow his propositions clearly, the fundamental axioms are either missing or, if they are indicated, their truth is not incontestable.[1]

Like his colleague Stahl (p. 653), he kept his medicine and chemistry quite separate and criticised the Iatrochemical theories of Sylvius. He still believed in the influence of the planets on the atmosphere, and thence on the human body.[2] He ascribed bodily activity to the sensitive soul, which is a very tenuous and volatile material substance, identical with the ether, which is contained both in plants and animals.[3]

Hoffmann's inaugural dissertation (*De Cinnabari Antimonii*, 1681) was presented under Wedel, from whom he learnt the Iatrochemical theories of Sylvius. After his visit to England, when he met Boyle and Sydenham, Hoffmann repudiated these views in his *Exercitatio de acidi et viscidi . . . debellandis insufficientia* (1689), giving his views on the composition of body fluids.

I. Exercitatio Medico-Chymica de Cinnabari Antimonii, Ejusque Viribus, usuque in morbis secretori, quo ipso via ex illa veram panaceam conficiendi aperitur.[4]

II. Exercitatio acroamatica de acidi et viscidi pro stabiliendis omnium morborum causis et alcali fluidi pro iisdem debellandis insufficientia, 8°, Frankfurt, 1689 (72 pp.; BM 1034. e. 24. (1.)); German tr., 8°, Halle, 1696; Töpley, 362 f.

III. Dissertationes physico-medica curiosae selectiores, ad sanitatem tuenda maxime pertinentes, Pars I & II (2 t.p.), 8°, Leyden, 1708, (the ed. quoted); Dissertationum physico-medicarum selectiorum, Leyden, Decas I, 1713, Decas II, 1719; another ed. 1733–5 is mentioned.

IV. Observationum physico-chymicarvm selectiorvm libri III, in quibus multa curiosa Experimenta et lectissimae Virtutio Medicamenta exhibentur, 4°, Halle, 1722, 1729, 1736; French tr. by de Puisieux, Observationes Physico-Chimiques, 2 vols. 12°, Paris, 1754 [BN].

V. Opuscula physico-medica antehac deorsim edita de elementis, viribus, utilitate et usu medicatorum fontium, 2 vols. 8°, Ulm 1725–6, and with new t.p., 1736; Sotheran, *Medic. Cat.* 889 (1951), no. 44, has Opuscula Medico-Practica, 4°, Halle, 1736.

I–V printed (with somewhat varying text from originals) in Vol. iv of

---

[1] Life by Schulze in Hoffmann, *Opera Omnia*, f°, Geneva, 1740, i, prelim.; J. G. Francke, *Ein christlicher Medicus . . . D. Friedrich Hoffmann. Trauer-Rede, Gedächtniss-Predigt*, etc., 4°, Halle, 1743 (BM T 508); *Catalogus scriptorum omnium B. DN. Friderici Hoffmanni Ab Anno 1681 usque ad Annum 1742 editorum, continuatus Opera* I. G. K. G. C. Q. (*), 4°, Halle, 1743 (BM T 508); Gmelin, (1), ii, 170 (with a list of 122 chemical works); Sprengel, (1), v, 117, 282–306; Thomson, (1), i, 218; Kopp, (1), i, 193; Hoefer, (1), ii, 224; Saucerotte, in NBG, 1858, xxiv, 884–90; Daremberg, 1870, ii, 905; Haeser, 1881, ii, 509; Meyer-Steineg and Sudhoff, 1922, 341; Ferguson, i, 409; R. von Töply, in Diergart, 1909, 360; Thorndike, viii, 83, 399.

[2] *Opera*, Geneva, 1740, v, 70.   [3] *Opera*, 1740, i, 83 f.

[4] 4°, Jena, 1681; 12°, Leyden, Van der Aa, 1685 (engr. t.p., t.p., iii ll., 11–64., ii ll.); *Opera*, Geneva, 1749, Suppl. I, pt. ii, 126 f.

the Geneva *Opera* (vi); other chemical works are in Vol. v (on mineral waters) and in the first and second supplements. The chemical symbols are freely used, e.g.:[1]

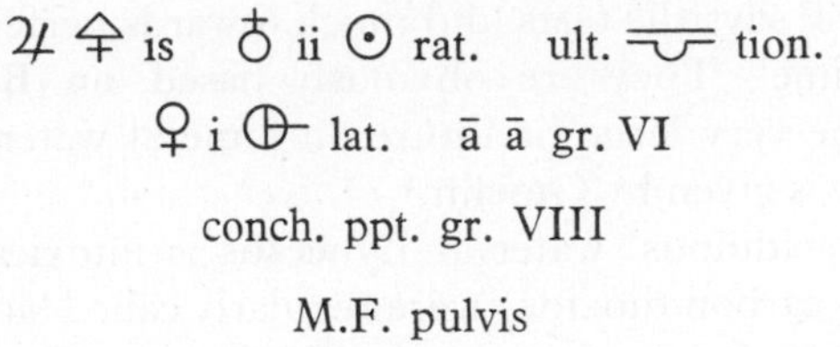

♃ ♀ is ☿ ii ☉ rat. ult. ℥ tion.

♀ i ⊕ lat. ā ā gr. VI

conch. ppt. gr. VIII

M.F. pulvis

Fig. 33.

VI. Opera Omnia Physico-Medica Denuò revisa, correcta & aucta, in sex tomos distributa; Quibus continentur Doctrinæ solidis Principiis Physico-Mechanicis, & anatomicis, atque etiam observationibus chimico-practicis superstructæ. . . . Cum Vita Auctoris, Et ejus Præfatione de differente medicinæ & medicorum atque conditione, & criteriis boni ad periti medici, 6 vols. f°, Geneva, des Tournes, 1740 (portr.); VIA Operum Omnium Physico-Medicorum Supplementum, Pars I–II, 2 vols. f°, Geneva, 1749 (conts. sev. pts. with sep. pagin.); VIB Second Supplement, 3 vols. f°, 1753–60.

Besides the above ed. (the one used and quoted), eds. of Venice, 17 vols. 4°, 1745, and Naples, 25 (or 27) vols. 4°, 1753, and 17 vols. 4°, 1763, are mentioned.

VII. Chymia Rationalis et Experimentalis, ment. by Gren, 1794, i, 14 (8° Leyden 1748); Gmelin, (1), ii, 179 (12° Leyden 1748, 8° Halle 1749); Bolton, (1), 1894, 537 (8° Leyden 1748); Fourcroy, (1), i, 27 (8° 1756); Kopp, (1), i, 196 (1784); Hirsch, Allgemeine Deutsche Biographie, Leipzig, 1880, xii, 584 (1784, prob. from Kopp); Mielke, Ostwald's Klassiker No. 187 (1913 — label pasted over date 1912 on t.p.), p. 45, who actually quotes from it, says it was published at Leyden, in 1748 and was 'eine Art Katechismus der Chemie, der als Leitfaden bei Vorlesungen gebraucht wurde'. Erxleben, Anfangsgründe der Chemie, mit neuen Zusätzen vermehrt von J. C. Wiegleb, Göttingen, 1784, 17, gives 8°, Leyden, 1748, and 8°, Hamburg, 1756.

Hoffmann's experiments on mineral waters are important:

Examen aquarum mineralium, in IV, ii, 32; VI, iv, 515; De methodo examinandi aquas salubres, 4°, Halle, 1703, in III, ii, 161, and (with somewhat varying text) in VI, v, 131–40. Other treatises, Opuscula de Aquis Mineralibus in the 1743 Catalogue, are: no. 220, De Aquæ Naturâ ac virtute in medendo (1716); no. 222, Examen chym.-med. fontium Sedlicensis in Bohemia (1724); no. 227, De Fonte Medicato Lignicensi (1729); no. 233, De Acidulis Veteraquensibus in Silesiâ (1731); no. 270, De fontis Spadani (1730); no. 305, De Sale medicinali Carolinarum (1734): these are repr. in Opera, 1740, VI, v, 131 f., and V, 1725. Works on artificial mineral waters are: (1) De Balneorum artificialium ex scoriis Metallicis usu Medico (Halle, 4°, 1722), Catalogue no. 239, repr. in VI, 1753, Suppl. II, pt. i, 1 f.; and (2) Observationes de acidulis, thermis et aliis fontibus salubrius ad imitationem naturalium per artificium parandis, in V, 1725, no. x; (3) Gründlicher Bericht von dem Selter-Brunnen, 4°, Halle, 1724 (Cat. 1743, p. xxv); New Experiments and Observations upon Mineral Waters, . . . extracted From his several Essays upon this Subject and illustrated with Notes, tr. by Peter Shaw, 8°, London, 1731 (BN); 2 ed., 8°, London, 1743, with Shaw's An Enquiry into the Contents, Vitrues, and Uses of the Scarborough Spaw Waters: with the Method of examining any other Mineral Water, which had been publ. separately, 8°, London, 1734; French tr., Nouvelles Expériences et Observations sur les Eaux Minerales de l'Allmagne, by Coste junr., 8°, Berlin, 1752 (BN).

He points out that the favourite test with the hydrometer is vitiated by the evolution of bubbles and the varying temperature of the waters, and recommends

---

[1] *Opera*, Geneva, 1749, Suppl. II, 33.

the examination by chemical reagents (per mixturam reagentium).[1] Kopp, who does not seem to have read the originals, says the tests were not very good, but Hoefer (whose accurate quotations are from the originals) gives a good account of the work. Moore[2] says the tests 'did much towards perfecting the analytical methods of his time'. They are obviously based on Boyle's (p. 533). A bibliography of the very large literature on mineral waters published in the eighteenth century is given by Gmelin.[3]

Pliny[4] says an 'acidulous' water at Lyncestis is intoxicating. Effervescent waters (containing carbon dioxide) were regularly called 'acidulous' (acidulæ). Peter Le Givre (1618–84), a physician in Charly, near Chateau-Thierry[5], was apparently, the first to notice that they had an alkaline reaction towards indicators, and ascribed the acid taste to 'spirits'. Ab Heer[6] noticed that acidulæ effervesce with sharp (acid) wines, and he mentions the reaction of a vitriolic spirit with tincture of roses.[7] Hoffmann,[8] who mentions Ab Heer and Givre, noticed the alkaline reaction of acidulæ with indicators, and said they should really be called 'alkalinæ'.

Hoffmann followed Van Helmont (p. 230) in recognising the presence of carbon dioxide in some mineral waters. This volatile spirit (spiritus mineralis, spiritus aëreus-aethereus) escapes in bubbles in vacuo; on pouring the water, especially acidulous, from one glass to another; or on adding sugar. It escapes on standing or on boiling, when the water deposits an ochry sediment (tunc exhalante spirituoso elemento, ad ima defertur levissimus et tenuissimus croceus pulvis), and no longer gives a colour with galls (aut aqua igne incaluit, omnem tincturam recusant: manifesto indicio, abripi simul cum spiritu, minerale quoddam volatile principium).[9] He recognised that the 'spirit' is a weak acid (rationis hujus phænomeni si inquirimus, procul dubio hæc suggerenda erit, quod spiritus mineralis indolis fuerit acidusculæ), which reddens litmus solution (aqua torna solis),[10] and says mineral waters contain this spirit (aqua composita est ex elemento fluidissimo videlicet spiritu æthereo), water proper, and salts,[11] but speaks of the iron as dissolved in the form of a 'volatile vitriol' (vitriolum illud quod aquæ in sinu fovet, sit duplex, volatile nempe et fixum . . . sed in acidulis et thermis aliisque celebrius medicatis aquis, fixum tale vitriolum non hospitatur).[12] The ochry sediment when strongly heated becomes magnetic, which proves that it contains iron (igne tosta magneti prompte accedit, manifesto documento martialis esse naturæ).[13] The gas evolved from effervescent waters can burst closed bottles (vasa vigrea ad fontem repleta facillime cum impetu disrumpantur).[14]

As a test for iron Hoffmann also used powdered galls or other materials con-

---

[1] De fontis Spadani; VI, v, 230.   [2] History of Chemistry, 1939, 55.
[3] (1), ii, 740–90; iii, 718–53.   [4] HN, ii, 103 (106).
[5] Arcanum Acidularum principiorum chimicorum, Paris, 1670; Amsterdam, 1682.
[6] Spadacrene, Leyden, 1685, 13; not in 1614 ed.
[7] Spadacrene, 1614, sign. C2 r: aut spiritu, quo nihil acidius, dicto citius tincturam rosarum.
[8] VI, v, 134, 156, 162, 177, 217.
[9] De methodo examinandi aquarum; De conveniantia elementorum in thermis et acidulis; in VI, vi, 134, 138, 155.
[10] III, ii, 183.   [11] Ib., 168.   [12] VI, v, 138.   [13] Ib., 138; III, ii, 196.
[14] VI, v, 133, 143; III, ii, 172: si nimis accurate claudantur, saepius soleant frangi.

taining tannin, which give a purple colour with small quantities and a black with larger amounts (nasciuntur purpureum si minor copia inest, si vero major, atrum colorem).[1] The presence of common salt is indicated by the formation of cubic crystals on evaporation which decrepitate on heating, give a white precipitate with a solution of silver, give white acid fumes with oil of vitriol, and when dissolved in aqua fortis form a liquid (aqua regia) which dissolves gold. The presence of fixed alkali in some waters (Carlsbad) is detected in the residue on evaporation by the green colour given to syrup of violets, the evolution of ammonia from sal ammoniac, the yellow colour with corrosive sublimate solution, the formation of liver of sulphur when heated with sulphur, the effervescence and formation of vitriolated tartar with sulphuric acid, and the sharp explosion on heating with sulphur and saltpetre (quando tres partes nitri, cum parte una sulphuris, et hujus salis partibus duabus, miscentur, pulvis emergit, qui in cochleari impositus carbonibus vivis, horrendum fragorem instar sclopeti edit),[2] a test which he had mentioned in a dissertation on nitre in 1694.[3] Sulphureous waters are not very common: they have an odour of rotten eggs, blacken silver, and on standing deposit sulphur.[4]

The presence of sulphate (sal quod ab acido sulphureo suam originem ducit) is detected by fusing the residue with salt of tartar and charcoal, when liver of sulphur is formed, turning silver black and giving a yellow solution in alcohol.[5] The opinion that gold, lead, arsenic, saltpetre, etc., exist in mineral waters is pure rubbish (plane furfuris).[6]

Hoffmann was the first to distinguish magnesia from lime. Magnesia alba was sold by the Count di Palma as a secret remedy in Rome about 1700; the preparation, by evaporating and calcining the mother-liquor of nitre, was disclosed by the Giessen professor Michael Bernhard Valentini (1657–1729; F.R.S. 1717, he also edited Van Helmont).[7] Slevogt[8] obtained it by precipitating saltpetre mother-liquor with fixed alkali (potassium carbonate).

Johann Adrian Slevogt (Jena; 1653–29 April 1726) lectured on chemistry at Jena from 1698, was professor of anatomy, surgery and botany from 1695, of chemistry from 1722; he gave practical instruction in his laboratory and taught many chemical preparations (including acids, many salts, mercury compounds, ether, and cane sugar). Most of his writings are medical.[9]

J. M. Lancisi (Rome; 26 October 1654–21 January 1720), Papal physician in Rome,[10] in his notes to Mercati's posthumous work (see p. 92)[11] also

[1] III, ii, 197; VI, v, 139.   [2] VI, iv, 515; v, 139, 174; III, ii, 199.
[3] VIB, 1753, Suppl. II, part i, 682; cf. Baumé, *Chymie expérimentale et raisonnée*, Paris, 1773, i, 479; Wallerius, *Elementa metallurgiæ speciatim Chemicæ*, Stockholm, 1768, 129, calls the detonating composition *Fulmen Paracelsi*; see p. 354.
[4] VI, v, 140; in I, 1685, 127, he speaks of: 'Gas illud sive effluvia Sulphurea,' i.e. hydrogen sulphide.
[5] VI, iv, 515.   [6] VI, v, 138.
[7] *Relatio de magnesia alba, novo genuino et polychresto et innoxa pharmaco purgante*, Giessen, 1705; q. by Gmelin, (1), ii, 262; Bergman, *Opuscula*, i, 365, dates it 1707 and says Valentini in his *Praxis Medica* calls the substance *laxativum polychrestum*; Kopp, (1), iv, 53 (dates 1707); Hoefer, (1), ii, 241, gives the title differently.
[8] *Dissertatio de Magnesia alba*, Jena, 1709, q. by Bergman, who spells the name Slevoght.
[9] Chemnitius, *Die Chemie in Jena von Rolfinck bis Knorr*, Jena, 1929, 14, 49 (portr.), 53, 65 f.
[10] Jöcher, ii, 2235.   [11] *Metallotheca*, f°, Rome, 1717, 50.

described the preparation of magnesia by evaporating and calcining the salt-peter mother-liquor.

Hoffmann clearly distinguished magnesia from lime.[1] He showed that it is precipitated as a white powder (magnesia alba) without effervescence on adding salt of tartar to the mother-liquor from salt brine (containing magnesium chloride and nitrate). The filtrate deposits on evaporation a salt (potassium chloride) similar to common salt. The mother-liquor gave red nitrous fumes when heated with oil of vitriol. Magnesia alba dissolves in acid of vitriol to give a soluble bitter salt (Epsom salt), whilst shells, etc., and quicklime give an almost tasteless sparingly soluble salt (gypsum) (miscetur cum spiritu vitrioli ad saturationis usque punctum, nec amarities, nec ingratus salsus vel calcarius sapor percipitur). He had previously shown[2] that several mineral waters (Eger, Elster, Schwalbach, Wildung, Hornhausen) contain a neutral salt formerly unnamed and hardly known (sal quoddam innominatum et ferme etiam incognitum). Although salts from mineral waters had been called nitre (nitrum) this had none of the properties of saltpetre but is a neutral salt similar to Glauber's salt or to arcanum duplicatum (potassium sulphate) not producing aqua fortis, not effervescing with acids or alkalis, with a bitter taste producing a sensation of cold on the tongue, and not easily fusible:

non est inflammabile, non in crystallisatione figuram pyramidalem assumit, neque aquam fortem dat; sed est sal neutrum instar arcani duplicati saporis amaricantis, et frigus quoddam relinquit in lingua, neque cum acido vel alcali effervescit, nec fluit in igne facile.

He thought then that it was a compound of sulphuric acid with a weakly alkaline calcareous earth (hoc sal originem suam trahere videtur ex combinatione acidi sulphurei et calcaria terra indolisque est alcalinae).[3]

He recognised that it was the same salt as had been very accurately depictcd (Fig. 34) and described by Martin Lister[4] as a 'calcareous salt' or 'wall nitre' (nitrum murale), obtained from several mineral springs, e.g. of Scarborough:

FIG 34. EPSOM SALT CRYSTAL.

hujus salis Calcarii crystalli tenues, longaeque sunt; iisque mediis quatuor latera parallelogramma [sic in London ed.] sunt, at ferè inæqualia; ex altera verò parte, ipse mucro ex binis planis lateribus triangularibus formatur.

The 'Epsome waters' are mentioned about 1657 by Henry More,[5] and Bergman[6] says 'the sal catharticus amarus had been in high esteem at Epsom

[1] Animadversiones et experimenta circa magnesiam albam; Observat. phys.-chym., Bk. II, obs. ii; De lixivio à coctione salis communis relicto et ex eo prodeunte terra laxante sive magnesia, et sale sic dicto Ebsoniensi, ib., Bk. II, obs. xviii; IV, 1722, 107, 177; VI, 1740, iv, 479, 500, 514.

[2] III, 1708, ii, 200; VI, v, 139, 190.

[3] III, 1708, ii, 200 f.; somewhat different text in VI, v, 139.

[4] De Fontibus medicatis Angliæ, 8°, York, 1682; sm. 8°, London, 1684, 8, 43; 8°, Frankfurt and Leipzig, 1684, 13 (ch. i), 27 (ch. iv; a twin crystal); also q. in Hoffmann, III, 1708, ii, 201; the crystals shown in the plate, including a twin, are of the correct rhombic form of Epsom salt; a figure of a crystal similar to Lister's was given later by Benjamin Allen, The Natural History of the Chalybeat and Purging Waters of England, sm. 8°, London, 1699, 184.

[5] Nicolson, Conway Letters, 1930, 144.   [6] Opuscula, i, 75.

from the year 1610'. The existence of another (deliquescent) salt (magnesium chloride) in sea water was suspected by John Brown.[1] Nehemiah Grew (1695)[2] described the crystalline form of Epsom salt and many chemical tests, and emphasised that it differs from alum, common salt, calcareous and nitrous salts. A translation of Grew's pamphlet[3] was distributed by the brothers Moult, who extracted the salt from a spring at Shooter's Hill.[4]

Hoffmann clearly distinguished by several tests between vitriol and alum.[5] Vitriol is a compound of a metallic base, iron or copper, whilst the base of alum is a true absorbent earth (nam vitrioli caput mortuum metallicae, martialis nempe et venereae, indolis est: aluminis vero terra valde spongiosa, subtilis, bolaris sui generis videtur). Alum does not precipitate solutions of gold or silver, or blacken infusion of galls, etc., and good crystals are obtained only when an alkali is added (ex ejus lixivio, sine additione cinereum clavellatorum vel salis cujusdam alcali, alumen non in solidescentem formam redigi), but he thought this served only to neutralise excess of acid. Although mineral waters had been supposed to contain alum (p. 228), Hoffmann never found it in medicinal waters, although it can be present in drainage waters from aluminous deposits (nos nunquam in aquis soteriis alumen deprehendisse).[6]

In explaining the formation of hot springs, e.g. of Carlsbad,[7] Hoffmann mentions the heat evolved from a moist mixture of iron filings and sulphur described by Lemery (Vol. III) and the inflammation of essential oils, e.g. oil of cloves, by concentrated fuming nitric acid (quo lucidissima flamma in momento producitur, dum spiritus concentratissimus fumans debita enchiresi oleo caryophyllorum confunditur).[8] He thought the hot springs were heated in the same way as volcanoes, which are near the sea, have access to air through the cone, and eject sulphur (primo sulphur commune inflammabile, secundo terram porosam, tertio aërem et quarto mare). He also explained the formation of winds[9] and pointed out the utility of barometric observations to the physician, at the suggestion of Leibniz. He described the salt works at Halle.[10]

The phosphorescent product from a kind of talc found in Germany which imitated the Bologna phosphorus (barium sulphide, see p. 334) may have been calcium sulphide[11].

Hoffmann seems to have been acquainted with microcosmic salt. Spielmann[12]

---

[1] *Phil. Trans.*, 1723, xxxii, 348, 372: 'a third salt produced from the sea-water.'

[2] *Tractatus de salis cathartici amari in Aquis Ebshamensibus, et hujusmodi aliis contenti Natura & Usu*, 12°, London, 1695 (vi ll., 96 pp.); in Baccio, *De Thermis*, f°, Padua, 1711, 298.

[3] *A Treatise of the Nature and Use of the Bitter Purging Salt contain'd in Epsom and such other Waters*, sm. 8°, London, 1697; an 'Advertisement' pasted on the reverse of the t.p. of BM copy (BM 7470 aaa 25) says the salt is made and sold by Francis Moult, at the Sign of Glaubers-Head in Watling-Street, 'and this translation at no other place.'

[4] Roscoe and Schorlemmer, *Treatise on Chemistry*, 1923, ii, 643.

[5] IV, Bk. III, obs. viii (*De alumine ejusque genesi ac natura*), 1722, 171; VI, iv, 527.

[6] III, 1708, ii, 202; VI, v, 140.

[7] *De Thermis Carolinis*, Halle, 1704; III, 1708, ii, 206; VI, v, 170.

[8] III, 1708, ii, 211; VI, v, 170; cf. IV, i, 10; VI, iv, 459.

[9] *De ventorum causam, vires et operationes*, III, 1708, i, 140; VI, v, 15.

[10] *Kurtze doch gründliche Beschreibung des Salz-Wercks in Halle*, 4°, Halle, 1708 (Cat. 1743, p. xxii); *Dissertatio Physico-Medica sistens Oryctographiam Halensem* (1730); VIB, 1753, Suppl. II, part i, 1 f.

[11] *Demonstrationes physicæ curiosae*, X, iii; VI, v, 5.

[12] *Institutiones Chemiæ*, 1766, 78.

says this was described by Schockwitz in a dissertation[1] at Halle under the presidency of Hoffmann, and also by Le Mort.[2] Pott[3] said he had found it described in manuscripts of Thurneisser and even in a manuscript of another Swiss chemist fifty years earlier.

As a result of an accident in Jena in 1715, Hoffmann in 1716 published a history and description of poisoning by the fumes of burning charcoal[4], in which he mentions that the characteristic bright-red colour of the face in carbon monoxide poisoning had been pointed out by Marcellus Donato (1588): this was emphasised again by Wepfer in 1727.[5]

Sulphur dissolves in alkali solution: on adding an acid it is precipitated, with a smell of rotten eggs (solvitur facile in lixivio, et cum acido summo cum foetore *wie faule Eyer* in pulverem lividum praecipitatur).[6] Ammonium polysulphide (tinctura sulphuris volatilis), obtained by distilling 3 pts. of quicklime, 2 pts. of sal ammoniac and 1 pt. of sulphur, is a yellow fuming liquid, used medicinally in a dose of 30 to 40 drops mixed with spirit of wine: when agitated with mercury it converts it into red cinnabar. It is 'a solution of common sulphur in the strongest spirit of sal ammoniac'.[7]

Hoffmann noticed that when oil of vitriol is dropped on red-hot coals a strong smell of burning sulphur is produced;[8] when orpiment (containing sulphur) is distilled with oil of vitriol, a substance like butter of antimony is left behind, whilst large quantities of volatile spirit of sulphur are emitted: 'that very acid and corrosive liquid, by combination with the insipid phlogistic earth (cum terra nempe phlogista) can be converted into an insipid substance itself, which seems very remarkable.'[9]

Potassium carbonate (cineres clavellati) on exposure to air forms a neutral salt (potassium bicarbonate) of bitter taste, in hexagonal crystals (sal neutrum ... amaricantis est saporis, figuræ sexangularis).[10] Hoffmann gives a clear definition of a neutral salt as one in which the acid and alkali dominate and qualify one another in due proportions (Sal neutrum dicitur illud, in quo sal acidum et alcali dominantur, et ita sese contemperant).[11]

Hoffmann mentions a pink solution extracted from a bismuth ore, used as a sympathetic ink, becoming green on heating: this would contain cobalt.[12] On adding a tin solution (stannous chloride) to a very dilute solution of gold (gold chloride), a red colour instantly appears diffused through the mass of liquid (in momento exsurgit color rubineus, dispersus per totam corpus aquae) — colloidal gold.[13] When silver free from copper is dissolved in aqua fortis, the

---

[1] *De mirabili Sulphuris antimoniati fixati efficacia in Medicina*, 1699.
[2] *Chymiæ facie purificata*, [1712], 344.   [3] *Dissertations Chymiques*, 1759, iii, 4.
[4] *Gründliches Bedencken und physikalische Anmerckungen von dem tödlichen Dampf der Holtz-Kohlen*, 8°, Halle, 1716 (q. in Catalogue, 1743, p. xxiii); repr. in Neuburger, *Friedrich Hoffmann ueber das Kohlenoxydgas*, Leipzig, 1912; tr. as *Dissertatio de fumo carbonum noxio et quandoque lethali*; VIA, 1749, Suppl. ii, 62 f.; cf. *Experimenta circa mirabilem carbonum virtutem*, IV, iii, 13, VI, iv, 535.
[5] Lewin, *A. Med.*, 1910, iii, 1 f., 25 f.   [6] IV, Bk. iii, Obs. ix; VI, iv, 529.
[7] IV, Bk. ii, obs. xxxi; VI, iv, 514.   [8] IV, Bk. iii, xiii; VI, iv, 536.
[9] IV, Bk. ii, xii; VI, iv, 494.
[10] *Demonstrationes physicæ curiosæ*, XXIX, 3; III; VI, v, 10.   [11] III, Bk. i, § vii; VI, iv, 560.
[12] *Dissertatio de acido vitrioli vinoso* [=ether], 1732; VIA, 1749, Suppl. I, pt. ii, 228.
[13] *Demonstrationes physicæ curiosæ*, ii, § 6; VI, v, 3.

precipitate dispersed through the liquid solution poured on chalk and again dissolved (eaque solvitur), the liquid becomes an amethyst colour, especially (praesertim) when exposed to the open air and the rays of the sun.[1] This would be an action of light on the silver salt.

Hoffmann's theoretical views approached those of his colleague Stahl, but he declined to accept the presence of phlogiston in metals, believing that a calx is a compound of the metal with an acid principle (sal acidum) which he thought was sulphuric acid, which it lost on reduction:[2]

inhaerescit mineris metallicis sulphuris acidum, quia per leniorem calcinationem pars oleosa et inflammabilis avolat; metallorum quoque ac mineralium calces ac vitra identidem acido, quod intime poros penetrat et particularum figuram et situm immutat, debentur: hoc acido sale, tanquam causa, sublato, reditus fit in pristinum corpus. Indicantur itaque ea, quæ intime penetrant et quæ acidum absorbendi potentia pollent, quo spectant maxime carbones, qui in flammam redacti, corporibus reducendis non modo immediatem ignem subministrant, sed et simul oleoso et rarefactivo alcalino-volatili suo principio intimos poros, ubi acidum occultum est, ingrediuntur, illud absorbent, et sic metallum restituunt.[3]

Calces are also formed by the action of acids on metals as well as by heating, e.g. oil of vitriol or aqua fortis evaporated with mercury form a yellow or red powder; oil of vitriol evaporated with antimony sulphide or regulus leaves a fixed calx (calx paulo fixioris naturæ relinquitur). The acid in sulphur calcines metals, e.g. forms cinnabar with mercury, and a solution of silver in aqua fortis gives a white calx with common salt or spirit of salt or oil of tartar (potassium carbonate) — he confused chlorides and carbonates with oxides.[4]

In his Inaugural Dissertation of 1681[5] Hoffmann mentions the increase in weight of metals on calcination, which he says was observed by Tachenius, whose explanation as a fixation of acid from the wood fire he rejects, since the increase occurs on calcination by solar light or by solution in acid and precipitation. He thought it was due to fixation of igneous corpuscles:

non tam in sale acido ignis materiali, quam subtili æthereo penetrantissimo, quod corpore menstruali suâ virtute dissolvere ac transmutare, illorum poros radicaliter permeare, ac particulas quasdam menstruales ipsis affricare aptum natum est: non aliter ac omnia menstrua solutis gravitatem quandam fœnerant.

He mentions experiments of Kunckel on calcining lead, and of Boyle on calcining tin and lead.

Hoffmann[6] followed Becher in supposing that running mercury can be extracted from all metals, particularly gold, silver, lead, and antimony, and he explained the high density of mercury as due to compression by the atmosphere.

Hoffmann regarded phosphorus, made by distilling evaporated urine, charcoal, and alum, as a compound of phlogiston, sulphuric acid and spirit of salt:[7]

materiam hujus sulphureæ sublucidæ substantiæ præbet acidum aluminis et salis in urina humana communis, quod cum oleosa et phlogiston urinæ et carbonum

---

[1] IV, bk. iii, obs. 17; VI, iv, 541.

[2] *De calcinationis ac reductionis fundamento ac causis; Experimenta circa mirabilem carbonum virtutum*; IV iii, obs. xii, xiii; VI, iv, 534 f.; Kopp, (1), iii, 115 f.; J. C. Brown, 233.

[3] VI, iv, 536–7. [4] VI, iv, 534. [5] I, 1685, 60; VIA, pt. ii, 133–4.

[6] I; in VIA, pt. ii, 126 f.; IV, iii; VI, iv, 578–9; tr. in James, 1745, art. Mercurius.

[7] *Experimenta circa Phosphorum Anglicanum*; IV, Bk. iii, obs. iv; VI, iv, 537.

substantia intime permixtum efformat corpus sulphureum, quod . . . volatile evadit et perpetuo fumos eructat.

Hoffmann describes the preparation of ether, which he calls *acidum vitrioli vinosum* as a better name than *spiritum vini vitriolatum*, and gives a history of the substance.[1] He regarded alcohol as mainly a compound of water and oil, with some acid. Sulphuric acid removes the water and leaves the oil in the form of ether,[2] although the latter might contain some vitriolic particles (ab omni partium vitriolicarum immixtione non sit penitus immune).[3] A mixture of alcohol and ether was long used in medicine as *liquor anodynus minerali Hoffmanni*, or 'Hoffmann's drops'. Since Hoffmann was writing to Leibniz in 1701 about the *oleum vitrioli dulce*, *spiritum aromaticum*, made with oil of vitriol, he must have made his preparation then, and he perhaps knew of the work of Valerius Cordus published by Gesner in 1561 (see p. 166).[4] Hoffmann described as new the dehydration of alcohol by salt of tartar (which was described by ψ-Lull, Vol. I).[5]

Other publications by Hoffmann[6] are on chemical subjects. In his work on materia medica[7] the materials are divided into Regnum minerale, Regnum animale, and Regnum vegetabile: it mentions cobalt (p. 137), bismuth (p. 137) and zinc (p. 138), which collects on the fore-walls of the Goslar furnaces and is used to make Printz-Metall (brass); nitrum a Græcis vocatur $\phi\lambda o\gamma\iota\sigma\tau\grave{o}\nu$ (p. 134) is an unusual identification.

In his medical theories Hoffmann assumed that a vital fluid acted through the nervous system on the muscles, keeping them in a state of partial tonic contraction, and also kept the humours of the body in motion. The four causes of disease (spasm, atony, humoral changes, and faulty excretions) were relieved by sedatives, tonics, alteratives, and evacuants, respectively. He used only a few remedies, including his own 'drops', from the sale of which, Haller said, he made considerable sums of money.[8] Blood consists of phlegm, spirit, oil, volatile salt, and fetid oil, and gives a caput mortuum containing a soluble salt. Urine contains a great number of constituents, including phosphorus.[9]

BARCHUSEN

Johann Conrad Barchusen (or Barckhausen) (Horn, Lippe, 16 May 1666– Leyden, 2 October 1723),[10] who taught chemistry at Utrecht from 1694, was M.D. and lector in 1698, and extra-ordinary professor of chemistry in 1703.

[1] *Dissertatio de acido vitrioli vinoso*, Halle, 4°, 1733, BM 1033. h. 21. (4); VIA, Suppl. I, pt. ii, 224; in Catalogue, 1743, No. 283 (1732) this is given as a dissertation of Carl Hoffmann; it is also printed in Pott's *Exercitationes Chymicæ*, Berlin, 4°, 1738, 159; Demachy, in his translation of Pott's *Dissertations chimiques*, Paris, 1759, i, 388, says the very incomplete work had been 'retouched' by Pott.
[2] *De vero oleo vitrioli dulci*; IV, ii, 13; VI, iv, 494, 513.
[3] *De acido vitrioli vinoso*; VIA, Suppl. I, pt. ii, 229.
[4] VIA, pt. i, 55; Peters, *A. Nat.*, 1916, vii, 275 (279); J. Ince, *Pharm. J.*, 1858, xviii, 263 (Hanckewitz).
[5] IV, i, 27; VI, iv, 473.
[6] *Dissertatio chymica de experimentorum quorundam Chymicorum perversâ explicatione*, 1697, VIB, 1753, Suppl. II, part i, 19; *Dissertatio medica de salis volatilis*, 1697, VIB, 1753, Suppl. II, part i, 24; on opium, *ib.*, 648; sugar, *ib.*, 685 (publ. in 1701); etc.
[7] *Opusculum de Materiâ Medicâ*, VIB, 1753, Suppl. II, part iii, 125–94.
[8] Haeser, (1), ii, 511–17.   [9] II; Sprengel, (1), v, 117.
[10] Poggendorff, (1), i, 100; Kopp, (1), ii, 286 (dates 1666–1732); Jöcher, i, 780; Sprengel, (2), iv, 400; Ferguson, i, 71.

He wrote a text-book of pharmacy[1] and a text-book of chemistry.[2] The text of the latter is full of symbols and is very difficult to read. A folding plate (opposite p. 62) shows the interior of the Utrecht laboratory, with stills and Barchusen (?) seated at a table holding a pair of apothecary's scales. At the end is a syllabus of courses for 1695–7 emphasising that practical demonstrations as well as lectures were given.

FACIES INTERIOR OFFICINAE CHEMICAE ULTRAIECTINAE

FIG. 35. BARCHUSEN'S LABORATORY IN UTRECHT.

An enlarged edition, published in 1718, has at the end a number of mystical alchemical plates which Barchusen says were from a manuscript in a Benedictine monastery in Swabia.[3] Barchusen also published a collection of discourses, including his address on his appointment as professor in Utrecht (De antiquitate et utilitate Chemiæ), defences of chemical principles against the peripatetic and mathematical, explanations of some chemical fables, and on acids, salts, precipitation, fermentation, etc.;[4] a compendium of chemical rules treated geometrically;[5] and a not very good history of medicine[6] in the form of

---

[1] *Pharmacopoeus synopticus, plerasque medicinarum compositiones ac formulas* . . . , 12°, Frankfurt, 1690; 2 ed., 8°, Utrecht, 1696; 4°, Leyden, 1698 (BN Te[131]. 140).

[2] *Pyrosophia, Succincte atque breviter Iatro-Chemiam, Rem Metallicam et Chrysopoeiam Pervestigans*, 4°, Leyden, 1698 (pref. dated December 1697); Gmelin, (1), ii, 690, incorrectly dates the book 1696; viii ll., 469 pp., 1 p. errata, 5 plates).

[3] *Elementa Chemiæ, quibus Subjuncta est Confectura Lapidis Philosophici Imaginibus Repræsentata*, 4°, Leyden, 1718 (vi ll., 532 pp., x ll., 5 plates, and 19 mystical alchemical plates).

[4] *Acroamata, In quibus complura ad Iatro-Chemiam atque Physicam Spectantia, Jocunda rerum varietate, explicantur*, 8°, Utrecht, 1703 (xii ll., 376 pp., xi ll.); my ed. has not the portr. on reverse of t.p. ment. in Ferguson.

[5] *Compendium Ratiocinii Chemici More Geometrarum Concinnatum*, 8°, Leyden, 1712 (70 pp.; Ferguson, i, 71).

[6] J. Conrad Barckhausen (*sic*), *Historia Medicinæ*, 8°, Amsterdam, 1710; *Dissertationes de Medicinæ Origine et Progressu*, 4°, Utrecht, 1723.

dialogues with Le Mort, etc. He wrote a long 'Confutatio Spiritus Nitro-aerei' attacking Mayow,[1] and criticised the acid-alkali theory of Sylvius.[2] In his dissertations on fermentation[3] he uses the name auctificum instead of ferment.

Barchusen[4] said corrosive sublimate and calomel are both compounds of mercury and spirit of salt; in calomel the corrosive properties of sublimate, which are due to spirit of salt and not to arsenic as had been assumed, were mitigated by the excess of mercury (intricata sit atque obruta). He recognised that the volatile salt of amber (succinic acid) is an acid, effervescing with alkali.[5] Barchusen[6] speaks of the difficulty of separating the elements of bodies because of their affinities for one another (arctam autem atque reciprocam inter se habent affinitatem), and of the effervescence of acids and alkalis as due to their attraction (ab amicis quam arctissime sibi cognatis . . . ut eo citius ad invicem congredi, combinandi sc. caussa, possent).[7]

NEUMANN

Caspar Neumann (Züllichau, Silesia, 11 July 1683–Berlin, 20 October 1737) at first worked for several apothecaries. In Berlin in 1704 he met visitors from Holland, Hannover, Schwerin, etc. and found time for study. His musical talent interested King Frederick I, who in 1711 sent him to study technology, mining, pharmacy and chemistry in various parts of Germany, Holland, and England. On the death of Frederick I in 1713 Neumann was again in poor circumstances and took a post as laboratory assistant to a Dr. Cyprian for five years. In 1716 he followed King George I to Hannover and was later in Berlin, where Stahl obtained for him a royal stipendium, with which he visited England and France, where he worked with the Geoffroys. In 1719 he returned to Berlin as court apothecary to King Frederick William I and greatly improved the laboratory, installing a water service. In 1721 he was elected to the Berlin Academy and in 1723 he became professor of practical chemistry in the newly founded Collegium Medico-Chirurgicum in Berlin, in 1724 a member of the Higher College of Medicine, and Hofrat in 1733. He became F.R.S. in 1725.[8]

Neumann's papers are not very important. He showed that the coloration of French brandy by iron salts is not a specific test but due to matter from the oak casks.[9] He gives a description of a camphor[10] which he obtained from thyme, which was really thymol. He believed that the alkali in wood ash is formed from an acid, an earth, and phlogiston, by the action of fire and that

[1] Acroamata, 63–83.   [2] Varia de Salibus, Acroamata, 125–46.
[3] Acroamata, 230–69 (259).   [4] Pyrosophia, 1698, 192–6.
[5] Ib., 265.   [6] Ib., 9.   [7] Ib., 17.
[8] Formey, Éloges des Academiciens de Berlin, Berlin, 1757, ii, 42; Gmelin, (1), ii, 603; Thomson, (1), i, 263; Kopp, (1), i, 202; Hoefer, (1), ii, 406; Poggendorff, (1), ii, 273; Ferguson, ii, 137; Schelenz, 1904, 548; J. Graetzer, Edmund Halley und Caspar Neumann, Breslau, 1883 (BM 8226. eee. 17).
[9] Phil. Trans., 1725, xxxiii, 398.
[10] Phil. Trans., 1725, xxxiii, 321; Brown, ib., 361.

caustic alkalis are formed only from materials which have been subjected to fire.[1] His other published papers need only be mentioned.[2]

Neumann's collected works were mostly published posthumously: one of his text-books (probably I) was used by Scheele:

I. Praelectiones Chemicæ seu Chemia Medico-Pharmacevtica Experimentalis & Rationalis, Oder Gründlicher Unterricht der Chemie . . . herausgegeben von D. Johann Christian Zimmermann, 4°, Berlin, 1740, portr., t.p. red and black (pp. xxviii, 1872, lxii index, i errata), is said in the preface of III to 'consist of notes taken down by one of [Neumann's] pupils, intermixed with a number of incoherent compilations from different authors'. The text is in German and is so full of chemical symbols that it is almost impossible to read it.

II. Allgemeine Grundsätze der theoretisch-practischen Chemie, das ist, gründlicher und vollständiger Unterricht der Chemie . . . Herausgegeben von D. Johann Christian Zimmermann, 2 vols. 4°, Dresden, 1755 (1604 pp.; said in the preface of III to be 'not materially different' from I but Neumann's name is omitted from the t.p.; not seen). Johann Christian Zimmermann of Schneeberg tr. Lemery's Cours de Chymie into German (Vol. III); he is different from the Carl Friedrich Zimmermann who edited Henckel (p. 707).

III. The Chemical Works of Caspar Neumann . . . Abridged and Methodized. With large Additions . . . By William Lewis, 4°, London, 1759 (pp. xvi, 586, xxxviii), the ed. quoted; 2 ed. 2 vols. 8°, 1773. Thomson says the translation is by Lewis's assistant, Chisholm. The preface contains a list of Neumann's publications. The additions, 'from the writings of others and not a little from the diaries of my own elaboratory', are by Lewis. The book is divided into three approximately equal parts: Chemical History of the Mineral Kingdom, Chemical History of the Vegetable Kingdom, and Chemical History of the Animal Kingdom. Lewis says 'the Zullichau edition has been followed', presumably the two-volume ed. mentioned in IX.

IV. Lectiones chymicæ von Salibus alkalino-fixis und vom Camphora, etc., 4°, Berlin, 1727

V. Lectiones Publicæ von Vier subjectis Chemicis, nehmlich vom Saltpeter, Schwefel, Spiess-Glass und Eisen, 4°, Berlin, 1732.

VI. Lectiones Publicæ von Vier subjectis Dieteticis, nehmlich von dem viererley Geträncken, vom Thee, Caffée, Bier, und Wein, 4°, Leipzig, 1735.

VII. Lectiones Publicæ von Vier subjectis Pharmaceutico-Chemicis, nehmlich vom Gemeinem Saltze, Weinstein, Salmiac. Und Der Ameise, 4°, Leipzig, 1737 (Duveen, 429).

VIII. Lectiones Publicæ von vier subjectis Pharmaceuticis, nehmlich vom Succino, Opio, Caryophyllis aromaticis und Castoreo, 4°, Berlin, 1730.

IX. Editions of Neumann's chemical lectures (alternative to I and II) which I have not seen are:

A. Chemiae medicae dogmatico-experimentalis, das ist, gründliche und mit Experimenten erwiesene medicinischen Chemie, Herausgegeben von Christoph. Heinrich Kessel, 4°, Züllichau, J. J. Dendeler (BN 4° Te[146]. 123; 4 tomes in 10 vols.); Gren, 1794, i, 14, gives: Bd. I, Theil 1 and 2, 1749, Theil 3, 1750; Bd. II, Theil 1 and 2, 1751, Theil 3 and 4, 1752; Bd. 1753; Bd. IV Theil 1, 1754, Theil 2, 1755; Bolton, (1), 699, gives 4 vols.; pref. to III gives 7 vols. (incomplete ?),

---

[1] Phil. Trans., 1726, xxxiv, 1: de salibus alcalino fixis.

[2] In Acta physico-medica Academiæ Caesaræ Naturæ Curiosorum, Nürnberg; 1730, ii, 304 (de oleo destillato formicarum æthereo); 1740, v, 220 (de albumine ovi succino simili). In Miscellanea Berolinensia; 1727, iii, 55 (Meditationes in binas observationes de aqua, per putrefactionem rubra, vulgo pro tali in sanguinem versa habita), 60 (Succincta Relatio ex Actis Pomeranicis de Prodigio Sanguinis, in Palude circa pagum Stargardiensem Sarow, viso, anno 1724: on the miraculous liquefaction of blood), 62 (De Prodigio Sanguinis ex Pomeranio nunciato Observatio), 70 (Disquisitio de Camphora); 1727, iii, 79 (De Experimento probandi Spiritum Vini Gallici perquam usitato, sed revera falso & falacii), 87 (De Spiritu Urinoso caustico); 1734, iv, 310 (Syrupi violarum commixtionem ad probanda liquida non esse sufficere), 321 (Correctionem olei seminis raparum examinat); 1737, v, 74 (de vi causticâ et Conversione salium alcalino-fixorum aëri expositorum in Salia neutra: the conversion of potassium carbonate into bicarbonate by absorption of carbon dioxide from the atmosphere).

upwards of 7000 pp., 'printed by the booksellers of the orphan hospital of Zullichau.'
B. Same title as A but 2 vols. 4°, Züllichau, 1756, 2560 pp. (BN 4° Te[146]. 124); ment. in the pref. of III as an abridgement of A but 'an account of the apparatus of the tea-table, and the manner of making tea' still fills $1\frac{1}{2}$ pp. Both A and B have portrs.

A French tr. by Roux, 4°, Paris, 1781, ment. by Bolton is not in the BM or BN.

Neumann in 1720 communicated to the French chemists a problem from Stahl, viz. to decompose vitriolated tartar (potassium sulphate) in an instant in the palm of the hand; as Stahl[1] says: also kalt, in der hohlen Hand, in wenig Augenblicken, zu Ende bringen . . . einem solchen vernünftigen Mann . . . in seinem Sinn auf sich selbsten böse seyn wird, dass er nicht daran gedacht. This baffled E. F. Geoffroy, but in 1724 Stahl's son communicated the solution to Boulduc. It was the addition of silver nitrate, when silver sulphate was precipitated.[2] Neumann's theoretical views are mostly incorrect, e.g. he thought that *magnesia alba* was a form of lime, and stated that he had precipitated it from a solution of lime in aqua regia.[3] He thought that the imperfect metals contain 'an inflammable principle which is burnt out in the calcination and extracted from them by acids',[4] which is essentially the phlogiston theory. He held the same view as Becher (p. 648) in saying:[5] 'without water there can be no flame, this fluid being the very basis of the flame.' Coals, wood, etc., when freed from all humidity or reduced to charcoal no longer flame; a little water increases conflagrations and when thrown on burning pitch, oil, etc., increases the flame.

Neumann investigated the nature of osteocolla.[6] This drug, used for consolidating broken bones (hence its name) and supposed to consist of fossil bones, he showed was the petrified root of a tree.[7] He seems to be the first to mention that calomel blackens on exposure to sunlight (an der Sonnen schwartz wird).[8]

The following details are taken from III, the page references being given. He gives a detailed account, from his own experience ('I have several times been at this work, and kept at it two days and a night without leaving the furnace'), of the extraction of zinc at Goslar and the properties of zinc (also called contrefait, tutenag, spiauter, and spelter) (115 f., 122) and of its ore calamine, used to make brass, and really an ore of zinc although not then worked for it (123). White vitriol is principally zinc and when calcined it can be used to make brass (183). Neumann gives a long account of bismuth or tin-glass, 1 lb. of which on calcination gains nearly $\frac{1}{2}$ oz.; the magistery of bismuth (basic nitrate or chloride) slowly darkens the hair to black (106). Bismuth is extracted from its ore near Schneeberg in Saxony and is also counterfeited from tin and arsenic (113). Cobalt (cadmia metallica, Blaufarben kobold) is found near Schneeberg and also St. Andreasberg (upper Harz); the

---

[1] *Beweiss von den Saltzen*, 1723, 198.
[2] Neumann, III, 172, 475; Bergman, *Scheffers Chemiske Föreläsningar*, Upsala, 1775, § 52, n. 2, p. 73; *ib.*, German tr. by Weigel, 1779, 115; Kopp, (1), iv, 20.
[3] Neumann, III, 1759, 204.   [4] III, 53.   [5] III, 255.
[6] See also Marggraf, *Hist. Acad. Berlin*, 1748 (1750), 52; J. G. Gleditsch, *ib.*, 1748, 32–51 (Observations sur la véritable osteocolle de la Marche de Brandebourg).
[7] III, 11.   [8] I, 1612.

manufacture of smalt in Saxony is kept secret (the process is described fully) and raw cobalt is never exported (148 f.). The Spanish mines at Almaden supplied 3,000,000 lb. of mercury in 1717, the metal being exported to Mexico for gold and silver extraction; the Friuli mines in Carinthia sent all their mercury to Holland (104). Corrosive sublimate is made in Venice, London, and Amsterdam, and in smaller amount in France (98). Calomel prepared by sublimation is the same as that precipitated by spirit of salt or common salt from a solution of mercury in aqua fortis (101). *Mercurius praecipitatus per se* is a calx of mercury, and air is necessary for its production by heating mercury; the change of the mercury is slight since 'on a bare increase of the heat it puts off its disguise and resumes its original running form' (102). On the explosion of fulminating gold, which acts equally in all directions, the gold is revived into little granules which may be caught in proper vessels, as he showed to the Royal Society (36).

A description of alum manufacture (including that near York) is given (185). Chalk does not form alum with oil of vitriol, as had been said, the crystals formed being quite different (9). Epsom salt is a particular species (189). Nitre is never found native but is always manufactured (197). The acids and alkalis are classed among the mineral salts (159). The manufacture of sal ammoniac in Egypt is described; horse, ass, or camel urine, common salt, and soot from cow-dung, are some ingredients used but Neumann thought there were others, and Geoffroy (Vol. III) had not given all the details; it is surprising that it is not made in Europe, since its constituent parts are perfectly known to be ammonia and spirit of salt (216, 225).

Sea water can be made fresh by filtering it through porous stones, sand, and insipid earth, but on board ship best by distillation: 'I saw, in the French academy, a drawing of a curious machine of this kind invented by M. Gautier' (250–1). Neumann determined the solubilities of many salts and of sugar in water, and mentions that water saturated with one salt (alum) will dissolve another (nitre), and the resulting solution will further dissolve green vitriol, common salt, soluble tartar, sugar, and fixed alkali, in succession (256–7); numerical values are given but no temperature.

Oils owe their liquidity to water, which nevertheless forms part of many hard crystalline salts such as green vitriol and alum (247). Amber is formed by the action of vitriolic acid vapour on petroleum (this is incorrect), since it is found in Italy where there is no fossil wood (as in Prussia) 'but plenty of mineral oil or petroleum' and sulphur (233); it is distilled in Prussia to form a peculiar acid salt (actually succinic acid) which approaches nearest to the vitriolic acid but is nearly always adulterated (236). Pit coal is a kind of bitumen and there are many kinds; jet is a black amber; small coal is powdered and briquetted with loam in Belgium; coal is unsuitable for smelting iron, and it cracks the crucible in glass-making (244).

Gum resins include gamboge, used as a pigment and a strong purgative, euphorbium, scammony, aloes, opium, gum hederæ, sarcocolla, assafœtida, bdellium, galbanum, olibanum, opoponax, sagapenum, myrrh and terra japonica (catechu) (300–318). Camphor from Japan is the only kind brought to

Europe, especially Holland, where it is refined, the Venice trade being abandoned. The process is carried out by women and is sublimation but is kept secret as to detail, although Gronovius had given a good account of it (318). Neumann thought he had obtained a true camphor from thyme (277), but this would be thymol. His analyses of 27 kinds of wine (447) giving the alcohol contents, are said to be good.[1] Neumann criticised some beliefs of his time:

'The ant, noted by the naturalist for its agility and industry, affords likewise some remarkable phaenomena to the chemical observer. On searching the ant-hill, we commonly find pieces of a resinous substance. This was supposed formerly to possess peculiar virtues, and distinguished by the names of wild Frankincense, *Suffimentum sylvestre, thus Germanicum, mastix & electrum formicarum*. It looks, tastes, and smells, like the common Resin of the Fir-tree, and in effect it is no other. It is about the roots of old Fir-trees that Ants principally lodge; and it is in such lodgments that the Resin is principally met with. For what purpose they collect it, I do not pretend to know.'[2]

'It is said that the Elk is subject to epileptic fits; and that he effectually cures them by scratching behind his right ear with his left hinder hoof, or behind his left ear with the hinder hoof of the right side; for the hoof of the same side, or the hoof of the fore foot will not do: From hence Elk's hoof has been celebrated as a specific in epilepsies, being taken internally, or worn as an amulet. . . . We might ask, how it comes that the Elk should ever be troubled with an epilepsy, when he carries the Amulet constantly about him, . . . and whether it is anywise possible for the Elk to get his hinder hoof up to his ears; and if it was, whether the scratching might not be more rationally attributed to another cause.'[3]

Such remedies had been criticised by Robert Pitt (1653–1713), teacher of anatomy at Oxford, and then serving (1698–1707) at St. Bartholomew's Hospital. He also says that of a multitude of chemical remedies, those which had destroyed the greatest number of patients had been weeded out by trial and the remainder 'reserv'd as the most innocent or the most useful'.[4]

HENCKEL

Johann Friedrich Henckel (as usual, sometimes Henkel) (Merseburg, 11 August 1679–Freiberg, 26 January 1744), physician and director of mines (Bergrat) in Freiberg (Erzgebirge), had an extensive knowledge of mineralogy, on which he wrote some important works:

I. Flora saturnizans, / Die Verwandtschafft / Des Pflanzen mit dem Mineral- / Reich, . . . Nebst einem Anhang / vom / Kali Geniculato Germanorum / oder Gegliederten Saltz-Kraut. . . . Von einer. . . . Blauen Farbe . . . , 8°, Leipzig, 1722 (f.p., pp. x, 671, xvi); another edit., 1755.

II. Pyritologia, Oder Kiess-Historie, Als des vornehmsten Minerals, Nach dessen Nahmen, Arten, Lagerstätten, Ursprung . . . , 8°, Leipzig, 1725 (f.p., pp. xliv, 1008, xxxii, xii plates); IIA, another ed., Leipzig, 1754.

IIB. English tr.: Pyritologia: or, a History of the Pyrites, The Principal Body in the Mineral Kingdom . . . , 8°, London, 1757 (f.p., pp. xviii, 376, vi), in which Henckel's 'strain of low pleasantry and affectation of learning have been entirely dropt'.

IIC. French tr. (with other works): Pyritologie, ou Histoire Naturelle de la Pyrite, . . . on y joint le Flora Saturnisans . . . et les Opuscules Minéralogiques . . . (with sep. t.p.,

---

[1] J. and W. Thomson and D. Craigie, *Life of Cullen*, 1859, ii, 561, 576.
[2] III, 497.   [3] III, 514.
[4] *The Craft and Frauds of Physick expos'd*, 1702 (BM 1038. e. 38; and 1703), 106; Thorndike, viii, 102.

Œuvres de M. Henckel, traduites de l'Allemand), 4°, Paris, 1760, (f.p., pp. xvj, 404, 524 (incl. sep. t.p.); v plates); the tr. is by Baron d'Holbach.

IIIA. D. Johann Friedrich Henkels . . . Kleine Minerologische und Chymische Schrifften . . . herausgegeben von Carl Friedrich Zimmermann, 8°, Dresden and Leipzig, 1744 (pp. xlviii, 619, xliv, ii plates; contains (1) Appropration, 1–312, (2) Ursprung der Steine, 313–528; (3) Besondere Untersuchungen, in 8 sects. (tr. from Latin), 529–619. An ed. of 1747, Dresden and Leipzig, is ment. The work is tr. in IIC.

IIIB. 2 ed. 8°, Vienna and Leipzig, 1769, same pagin. as A, one (?) plate (missing in BM Copy).

Carl Friedrich Zimmermann (Dresden; 1713–47), an expert on mining and mineralogy, also wrote on alchemy: Ferguson, ii, 568.

IV. Henckelivs in mineralogia redivivvs, Das ist; Hencklischer aufrichtig und gründlicher Unterricht von der Mineralogie oder Wissenschaft von Wassern, Erdsäfften, Saltzen, Erden, Steinen und Ertzten, Nebst angefügtem Unterricht von der Chymia Metallurgica . . . ed. J. E. Stephanus, 8°, Dressden [sic], 1747 (f.p., pp. xiv, 327).

IVA. another edit., Dressden [sic], 1759 (pp. xiv + 344).

IVB. French tr.: Introduction a la Mineralogie; ou Connoissance des eaux, des sucs terrestres, des sels, des terres, des pierres, des mineraux, et des métaux . . ., 2 vols., sm. 8°, Paris, 1756 (I, pp. lxxij, 204, iv, 1 blank; II, pp. 371) with life of Henckel and list of works.

V. Bethesda Portvosa, Das Hülffreiche Wasser zum Langen Leben Insonderheit In dem Lauchstädter Brunnen bey Merseburg, Und in dem Schlacken-Bade zu Freyberg . . . , 8°, Freiberg and Leipzig, 1726; the ed. quoted (Leipzig and Halle, 8°, 1746, BN) (examination of Lauchstadt water in 1718 and Schlacken-Bad in 1720).

VI. Giesshübelium Redivivum, Der Wiederlebende Berg-Giesshübel, In den allda Neuerfundenen Friedrichs-Brunnen Und dem Joh. Georgen Bade . . . , Freiberg, 1729, with Fortsetzungen 1–3, Dresden, 1730–1–2.

VII. Idea Generalis de Lapidum Origine per Observationes Experimenta & Consectaria succincte adumbrata, Dresden and Leipzig, 1734, 108 pp. (tr. in IIC and III).

VIII. Mediorum Chymicorum non ultimum, Conjunctionis primum, Appropriatio, iam in Argenti cum Acido salis communis combinatione, Experimento novo . . . , Dresden and Leipzig, 1727 (pp. 126, ii; tr. in IIC, and III).

IX. Medicinischer Ufstand und Schmeltz-Bogen Insonderheit Von der Bergsucht und Hütten-Katze, und einigen andern, Denen Bergleuthen und Hütten-Arbeitern zustossenden Kranckheiten, . . . , Freiberg, 1728; IXA, 2 ed., Dresden and Leipzig, 1745. (Berg-Sucht is Peripneumonia montana, silicosis; Hütten Katze is colic, as though a cat were scratching in the viscera, due to poisonous smelting-furnace smokes) (tr. in IIC).

X. Mineralogische chemische und alchymistische Briefe von reisenden und andern Gelehrten, 3 pts., Dresden, 1792–5 (not seen; the BN has pt. 3 only).

XI. Dissertations in Acta Physico-Med. Acad. Nat. Curiosæ, Nürnberg, on:

(i) an arsenical clay (Schwaben-gift), 1730, ii, Obs. CLVI, pp. 364–6 (tr. in IIC, 1760, ii, 491–3); (ii) on zinc, 1737, iv, Obs. LXXX, pp. 308–12 (IIC, ii, 494–7); (iii) fossil amber in Saxony, 1737, iv, Obs. LXXXI, pp. 313–16 (IIC, ii, 497–9); (iv) true Saxon topaz, not inferior to the Oriental, 1737, iv, Obs. LXXXII, pp. 316–20 (IIC, ii, 500–3); (v) the volatilisation of silver, 1740, v, Obs. XCI, pp. 321–2 (IIC, ii, 504; (vi) a blue colour from iron (caerulium martis), 1740, v, Obs. XCII, pp. 322–3 (IIC, ii, 505–6); (vii) volatile mineral alkali, 1740, v, Obs. XCIII, pp. 325–32 (IIC, ii, 508–13); (viii) phosphorescent perspiration, 1740, v, Obs. XCIV, 332–6 (IIC, ii, 513–15); (ix) butter of antimony (butyrum antimonii ægro per errorem propinatum lethiferum), 1740, v, Obs. XCV, 336–8.

Henckel accepts Becher's theory of three earths: on the calcination of lead one part vitrifies (vitreous earth), part inflames (terra pinguis) and part sublimes (mercurial earth).[1] He also accepts Stahl's phlogiston theory.[2] The increase in weight of antimony on calcination is due to fixation of particles of fire.[3]

In his analyses of the mineral waters of Lauchstadt (1718), Schlacken-Bad

---

[1] IVB, i, 36.   [2] IVB, ii, 278 f.; IIB, ch. ix, 1561.   [3] IIB, ch. xii, 226 cf. IVB, ii, 235.

(1720) and Giesshübel (1729), Henckel used as reagents infusions of violets, tea, and galls, ammonia, and corrosive sublimate; he concluded that the waters contain vitriol (the origin of which he discusses at length), sulphur, bitter salt ($MgSO_4$?) and an earth like lime;[1] the gas bubbles he thought were only air.[2]

Henckel gives a rather full description of metallic arsenic, which he obtained by sublimation in closed retorts, subliming vessels, etc., 'out of contact with the fire' (otherwise its metallicity or reguline state is destroyed). It is a brittle 'semi-metal', brilliant but rapidly becoming black in air because it contains a fatty inflammable principle; on heating it turns into a calx, which is 'the ash or calx of a metallic body, whose metallicity may be destroyed and again restored'. This calx is white arsenic, the vitreous form of which he calls *arsenicum crystallinum album*.[3] The red silver ore *Rothgültigerz* (already mentioned by Agricola and 'Basil Valentine') contains arsenic.[4]

Henckel gives a description of metallic zinc (*zink, spelter, contrefait*), but was not clear as to its nature, regarding it as an alloy containing lead.[5] He seems to think that zinc oxide (furnace calamine) is phosphorescent.[6] He says:[7]

From some universal earths, which neither are, nor were actual ore of metal, metals may be made; for instance, from fossil calamy, iron, indeed in no considerable, and zink, in a large quantity . . . even without the addition of metal [copper], barely upon the application of the metallising, fatty matter [phlogiston], with proper care and attention, that the matters be not burnt out and reduced to ashes,

so that he must have known how to make metallic zinc but concealed the method.[8] He later[9] gave the method, viz. strongly heating calamine with plumbago or charcoal in a closed earthen vessel, and he implies that this was the method used in Bristol.

A vitriol is a compound of a metal with sulphuric acid. Henckel describes blue, green and white vitriols and related substances (sory, misy, etc.). In the formation of vitriol from roasted pyrites air is necessary, and it perhaps supplies moisture and acid or saline particles. The bases of blue and green vitriols are copper and iron, respectively.[10] White vitriol might contain copper and iron; its principal basis was perhaps alumina although its origin was utterly unknown. That its basis was zinc, as a friend had suggested, or calamine (with iron, tin, and lead) as Geoffroy (1707, see Vol. III) thought, was improbable, and it would be very difficult to combine zinc with sulphuric acid to make white vitriol — it seems as if Henckel was trying to mislead here.[11] Copper and iron vitriols are difficult to separate if crystallised together.[12]

The purple or blood-red 'vitriol' obtained by Henckel from a bismuth ore[13] must have been a cobalt salt. He says the miners give the name 'cobalt' to every poisonous or unfamiliar mineral.[14] He distinguished two kinds of cobalt

---

[1] V, 21 f., 31 f., 145 f.; VI, 30 f.   [2] V, 45.   [3] IIB,ch. x; 169 f.
[4] IIB, 200; it is proustite, Ag_3AsS_3: Proust, *J. de Phys.*, 1804, lix, 404.
[5] IIB, ch. x; 187 f.; IVB, ii, 257.   [6] IX, ch. ii; IIC, 481.   [7] IIB, ch. xiii, 248.
[8] Bergman, *Essays*, 1788, ii, 316; R. Watson, *Chemical Essays*, 1796, iv, 29.
[9] *Acta Phys.-Med. Acad. Nat. Curios.*, 1737, iv, Obs. lxxx, p. 308; IIC, ii, 494–7.
[10] IIB, ch. xiv; 283, 289, 295.   [11] IIB, 275, 284, 312, 315, 319.
[12] IIB, ch. viii, 114.   [13] IIB, ch. xii; 291.   [14] IIB, ch. x; 200.

yielding smalt; although he sometimes distinguishes cobalt from mispickel (arsenical pyrites) he also says the latter is a kind of cobalt.[1]

Henckel says *kupfer-nickel* is a sort of cobalt; he sometimes says it contains copper,[2] at other times that it does not contain 'the least atom of copper'.[3] Sometimes he says the blue colour from smalt is due to bismuth,[4] sometimes to iron, since he obtained a blue glass from iron,[5] and sometimes to a 'crude, vague, and undetermined' non-metallic earth.[6] This is typical of his lack of precision.

Henckel distinguishes yellow (copper), yellowish (iron) and white (arsenical) pyrites, and several varieties of each;[7] pyrites sometimes contain gold and silver.[8] He says Martin Lister[9] was perhaps the first to mention iron as the main constituent of pyrites.[10] Henckel clearly says that sulphur has a greater affinity for copper than for iron.[11]

Wolfram or *lupus Jovis* is 'a kind of mock-tin, or an irony-tin mineral' found with tinstone and hard to separate from it. It does not 'devour' tin but spoils it in smelting;[12] this was the tungsten ore.

Henckel thought minerals were formed on the third day of Creation and have increased and improved since.[13] Rock-crystal has been deposited from water.[14] He described an Egyptian amulet of green jasper.[15]

Alkali pre-exists to some extent in plants but some more is produced on burning them; the soda-plant (*kali*) is described in detail.[16] Henckel reports that Meuder, of Dresden, had obtained Glauber salt (he says Epsom salt by mistake) from borax and sulphuric acid.[17]

Henckel translated a French book on the mineral spirit by P. M. de Respour, of Flanders.[18]

GELLERT

Christlieb Ehregott Gellert (Haynichen, nr. Freiberg, 11 August 1713–Freiberg, 13 or 18 May 1795), the brother of the poet, studied at Meissen and in 1734 at Leipzig. He was professor (1736–7) in a school in St. Petersburg, becoming (1746–7) associate of the Academy of Sciences there, where he met Euler. Returning to Germany (1747) he settled in Freiberg, where he studied mining and metallurgy, gave a course of metallurgical chemistry, and (1753 or 1755) became inspector of mines and smelting in Saxony; in 1762 he became chief administrator of the foundries and forges of Freiberg. He became professor of metallurgical chemistry in the famous Freiberg Bergakademie on its

[1] IIB, 32, 99, 191, 341. [2] IIB, 129, 203. [3] III; in IIC, ii, 505.
[4] IVB, i, 187; ii, 254. [5] III; in IIC, ii, 505. [6] IIB, 129.
[7] IIB, chs. ii, xiii; 17 f., 347, etc. [8] lIB, chs. xi, xii; 212 ff.
[9] *De fontibus medicatis Angliae*, sm. 8°, London, 1684, 25, 41 f.: idque purum putum Ferri metallum est.
[10] IIB, ch. vi, 103. [11] IIB, ch. vi, 101.
[12] IIB, ch. ix; 132; IVB, i, 130. [13] IIB, ch. v, 64. [14] IIB, 92.
[15] *Acta Phys.-Med. Acad. Nat. Curios.*, 1740, v, Obs. xcvi, 339–44.
[16] I, ch. viii, and Suppl. i; in IIC, 132 f., 263 f. [17] I, in IIC, 109.
[18] *Rares Experiences sur l'Esprit Mineral, pour la Preparation et Transmutation des Corps Metalliques*, Paris, 1668; new ed. by C. F. Keller, Leipzig, 1777; tr. Henckel, Dresden and Leipzig, 1743, with notes, and re-ed. by J. G. Lehmann, *P. M. von Respurs besondere Versuche vom Mineralgeist*, 8°, Leipzig, 1772 (Ferguson, ii, 256). Both Keller and Lehmann were puzzled by the name 'Zink' used by Respour.

foundation in 1765. He introduced the process of cold extraction of precious metals by mercury, a works (the largest in Europe) being established at Halsbruck in 1790.[1] Besides translating Cramer's book (p. 711) Gellert wrote a very popular work on metallurgical chemistry:

Anfangsgründe zur metallurgischen Chymie, Leipzig, 1751 (Poggendorff, (1), i, 870, gives 1750), 2 ed. (with portr.) 1776 (BM 972. g. 16. (1.)); Anfangsgründe zur Probierkunst als der zweyte Theil der praktischen metallurgischen Chymie, 8°, Leipzig, 1755. Both tr. by Baron d'Holbach as:

Chimie Métallurgique, dans laquelle on trouvera la Théorie & la Pratique de cet Art. Avec des Expériences sur la Densité des Alliages des Métaux, & des demi-Métaux, & un Abrégé de Docimastique. Avec Figures, 2 vols. 12°, Paris, 1758 (4 folding plates and 2 folding tables).

English tr.: Metallurgic Chymistry. Being a System of Mineralogy in General, and of all the Arts arising from this Science. To the great Improvement of Manufactures, and the most capital Branches of Trade and Commerce. Theoretical and Practical. Translated from the original German by I[ohn]. S[eiferth]., 8°, London, 1776, xii ll., 416 pp., folding table and 4 (Duveen, 242–3, gives 3) folding plates.

In this he modified Geoffroy's affinity table (see Vol. III) by having a table of 28 columns of symbols in which substances having the *least* affinity with the substance at the head of a column are put at the top, i.e. the reverse of Geoffroy's order. Gellert uses letter symbols in the table: cobalt = K, bismuth = W, zinc = X, and a calx (oxide) is shown by prefixing C, e.g. C. X (calx of zinc), C. W (calx of bismuth).[2] Gellert also published some separate papers.[3]

In prismatic capillary tubes he found the height which water rose was inversely proportional to the square-root of the area of section. He found that melted lead, like mercury, was depressed in a capillary tube, the depression being inversely proportional to the diameter, and he correctly interpreted the result as due to the greater attraction between the particles of the metal as compared with the attraction of these to the glass or pottery wall of the tube (particulae plumbi liquefacta sese inuicem fortius attrahunt, quam cum vitro aut argilla cohaerent).

In his work on the density of alloys he showed that this may be greater or less than that calculated by the mixture rule; it was mostly greater. He assumed the existence of pores in metals. He also investigated the magnetism of alloys of iron.

CRAMER

Johann Andreas Cramer (Quedlinburg, 14 December 1710–Berggiesshübel, nr. Dresden, 6 December 1777) first studied law, then (from 1734) mining and chemistry. He composed his book on assaying in Leyden, visited England in 1738 and 1739, then the Erzgebirge (Saxony), becoming in 1743 Kammerrath

---

[1] NBG, 1857, xix, 831.　　[2] *Anfangsgründe*, 1751; 2 ed. 1776, i, 172 (opp.), 231.
[3] De phaenominis plumbi fusi in tubis capillaribus, *Comment. Acad. Petropol.*, 1750, xii, 293–301 (misnumb. 243–51); De tubis capillaribus prismaticis, *ib.*, 1750, xii, 302–11 (misnumb. 243–51); De densitate mixtorum ex metallis et semi-metallis factorum, *ib.*, 1751, xiii, 382–99; Vom Abstrichbleitreiben, *Bergmännisches Journal*, 1789, ii, I, 207; Über ein künstliches rothes Kupferglas, *ib.*, 1790, iii, II, 146; Von Verfertigung einer guten dauerhaften Farbe aus Galmey (green zinc-cobalt oxides), *ib.*, 1791, iv, II, 402; Crell's *Ann.*, 1787, ii, 502; 1789, i, 117 (silver amalgamation process in Freiberg).

of mines and smelteries for Brunswick at Blankenburg, a post which he lost in 1773 by the actions of his enemies. In 1775 he visited the Hungarian mines, returning to Germany in 1777.[1] He was the best assayer of his time and his books are very practical:

Elementa Artis Docimasticae. Duobus tomis comprehensa, quorum prior Theoricam posterior Praxim, et vera Fossilium indole continet, 2 vols. 8°, Leyden, 1739 (I, 311 pp., II, 345 pp., 6 plates); 2 ed. 2 vols. 8°, Leyden, 1744 (BN S 20585); tr. by Gellert: Anfangsgründe der Probierkunst, 8°, Stockholm, 1746 (682 pp.); new ed. by J. F. A. Göttling, Leipzig, 1794; English tr.: Elements of the Art of Assaying Metals, In two Parts. The First Containing the Theory, the Second the Practice of the said Art. The whole deduced from the true Properties and Nature of Fossils. Confirmed by the most accurate and unquestionable Experiments, explained in a natural order, and with the utmost clearness by J. A. C., with several Notes and Observations not in the original, particularly useful to the English reader. With an Appendix, containing a List of the Chief Authors that have been published in English upon Metals and Minerals, 8°, London, 1741 (Chem. Soc. London); 2 ed., 1746 (xxiv, 471 pp., 6 plates); French tr.: Élémens de Docimastique ou de l'art des essais divisés en deux parties la première théorique et la seconde pratique, traduit du Latin [by J.-F. de Villiers], 4 vols. 12°, Paris, 1755 (BN Cat. Gén., 1908, xxxiii, 925).

He recommended the use of small quantities of ores in assaying, using the blowpipe and melting the material on charcoal, borax being used as a flux. His blowpipe was of copper, with a ball an inch in diameter to condense moisture in the breath. Bellows for use with the blowpipe were recommended in 1739 by Carl Friedrich Zimmermann, a Saxon mining official. In his book on metallurgy

Anfangsgründe der Metallurgie. Darinnen die Operationen so wohl in kleinen als grossen Feuer ausführlich beschrieben, und mit Erläuterungen begleitet sind; f°, Blankenburg and Quedlinburg, 3 pts. 1774–7; only the first Abschnitt of Theil 3 was published.

Cramer mentions the segregation of silver in alloy bars. He also wrote on charcoal burning.[2]

LEHMANN

Johann Gottlob Lehmann (place and date of birth unknown — St. Petersburg, 22 January or 20 February 1767, poisoned in an experiment with arsenic) was physician and councillor of mines in Berlin, where he also lectured, until 1761, when he went as professor of chemistry and director of the Imperial Museum at St. Petersburg.[3] His works are mostly concerned with mineralogy, geology, and mining:[4]

I. Abhandlung von Phosphoris . . . , 4°, Dresden and Leipzig, 1750.
II. Einleitung in einige Theile der Bergwercks-Wissenschaft, 8°, Berlin, 1751;
III. Le Secret Des Nouvelles Teintures De Saxe, Avec Quelques Réflexions sur la Theorie, & sur les Avantages de ces nouvelles Teintures. Traduit de l'Allemand sur l'Original imprimé à Vienne 1751, 8°, Paris, 1752 (Duveen, 314);

---

[1] Claus, Crell's Ann., 1786, II, 376.
[2] Anleitung zum Forstwesen. Nebst einer ausführlichen Beschreibung von Verkohlen des Holzes, Nutzung der Torfbrüche etc., f°, Brunswick, 1766 (200 pp. and plate; BM 425. f. 5); Neue Auflage. Mit vielen Kupfern, 4°, Brunswick, 1798 (304 pp., 60 plates).
[3] Gmelin, (1), ii, 579 (periodical publs.); Ferguson, ii, 19.
[4] BN Cat. Gén., 1928, xciii, 656.

   IV. Abhandlung von den Metall-Müttern und der Erzeugung der Metalle, 8°,
       Berlin, 1753 (also 1752 ?);
    V. Versuch einer Geschichte von Flötz-Gebürgen, 8°, Berlin, 1756; II, IV and V
       were tr. as vols. one to three of:
   VI. Traités de physique, d'histoire naturelle, de mineralogie et de métallurgie,
       3 vols. 12°, Paris, 1759;
  VII. Cadmiologia oder Geschichte des Farben-Kobolds, 2 vols. 4°, Berlin, 1760
       (BN); 4°, Königsberg and Leipzig, 1761-6;
 VIII. Entwurf einer Mineralogie zum Dienst allhier in Berlin studierenden, Berlin,
       1759, enlarged 1760 (150 pp.);
   IX. Probier-Kunst, 8°, Berlin, 1761 (pp. lxxxvi, [iv], 318, xiv, iv copper pls.);
    X. Physikalisch-chymische Schriften, als eine Fortsetzung der Probier-Kunst, 8°,
       Berlin, 1761 (portr.; pp. xiv, 412, iv).

   The last work (X) contains chapters on: (1) asbestos from Bergriechenstein
(1–52), (2) artificial asbestos (Amianth) (53–72), (3) copal (73–105), (4)
chrysoprase from Kosemitz (106–125), (5) green fat earth found with this
(126–150), (6) sulphur earth of Tarnowitz (151–185), (7) Clausthal 'Blatter-
erde' (186–204), (8) *sandaracha* of the ancients (205–220), (9) malachite of the
ancients (221–245), (10) Pliny's *asteria* (246–258), (11) *Floribus asteris* in schiefer
(259–274), (12) the wolfram of Zinnwalck (275–357), (13) earth from Baumann's cave (358–386), (14) argentiferous ears of corn from Frankenberg (387–
412).

   Lehmann first described native lead chromate from Siberia[1] in a letter to
Buffon in 1766. He concluded that wolfram (ferrous tungstate) contained a
vitreous or refractory earth, iron, and a little tin.[2] In his *Cadmiologia* he
describes a large number of experiments with cobalt minerals without arriving
at a very definite conclusion, but he proved that the arsenic contained in them
was not the cause of the blue colour of smalt, the manufacture of which he
describes in detail. He thought that metallic cobalt (regulum Cobaldi;
Kobold-König) is a compound of copper, iron, and arsenic, which might contain other impurities. Kupfer-nickel he regarded as a copper mineral containing iron and arsenic.[3] Blende and calamine are the two minerals of zinc.[4]

   Lehmann accepted the Phlogiston Theory, regarding phlogiston as a compound of a fatty substance, saline particles and a little subtle earth.[5] He refers
to the increase in weight of metals on calcination but gives no explanation, and
mentions the phosphorescence of zinc oxide.[6]

   His annotated translation of a work on poisonous mine gases by Zacharias
Theobald[7] regarded them as arsenical.

   Johann Christian Lehmann (Bautzen, Ober-Lausnitz, 16 June 1675–Leipzig, 19
January 1739), professor of medicine in Leipzig, published on an earth-borer (1714),
experimental physics, salt-working, a mineral water, and a dissertation on balsam of
Peru (*Disputatio de Balsamo Peruviano nigro*, Leipzig, 1707), which he showed gave a
sublimate of benzoic acid.[8]

   [1] *De Nova Minerae Plvmbi specie crystallina rubra, Epistola ad dominum de Buffon*, 4°, St.
Petersburg, 1766 (12 pp.); tr. in Sage, *Examen Chymique de Différentes Substances Minèrales*,
12°, Paris, 1769, 170–92.
   [2] VI, 1759, i, 133; ii, 294; IX, 1761, p. xi f.   [3] VI, i, 123; iii, 386.
   [4] VI, i, 137.   [5] IV; VI, ii, 75 f.   [6] VI, ii, 306.
   [7] *De Halitu Minerali quem Metallici vocant den Schwaden*, 1683, in a work by Bruschius
(Ferguson, ii, 442); Lehmann, German tr., 4°, Leipzig, 1750; French tr. in VI, i, 227–300.
   [8] Gmelin, (1), ii, 777; iii, 27; Ferguson, ii, 18.

KÖNIG

Emanuel König (Basel; 1 November 1658–30 July 1731), M.D., professor of Greek (1695–1703), physics (1703–11), and theoretical medicine (1711) in Basel, published at his own press books on the three kingdoms of nature which show wide reading of books (e.g. Mayow's, see p. 616) and recent periodical literature. They contain a great amount of information in small compass, and went through several editions:

I. Regnvm Animale, Sectionibus III. Physicè, Medicè, Anatomicè, Harmonicè, Mechanicè, Theoreticè, Practicè evisceratvm, enumeratum & emedullatum. Hominis scilicet & Brutorum Machinam hydraulico-pneumatiam comparatè, item V. Classes universales, ac Usum Cibarium & Medicinalem Curiosis quibusvis proponens, 4°, Basel, 1682 (xii, 176 pp.); editio altera priore duplo auctior, 4°, Basel, 1698 (355 pp., BM 462. a. 11; BN S 5591); 4°, Basel, 1703, portr. (BM; BN S 5595).

II. Regnum Minerale, Physicè, Medicè, Anatomicè, Chymicè, Alchymicè, Analogicè, Theoreticè & Practicè Investigatum, perscrutatum & erutum. Metallorum nimirum, Lapidum, Salium, Sulphurum, Terrarum, quin & Acidularum, Thermarum Naturam, Ortum, Differentias, Præparationes selectissimas Usúque multiplices candidè sistens, 4°, Basel, 1686 (viii, 192, iv pp.; BM 724. g. 1. (3.)); with rather diff. title, 4°, Basel, 1687 (192 pp.; BM 457. c. 16; BN S 5594); Regnum Minerale, generale et speciale, quorum illud naturalem et artificialem mineralium productionem cum parallelismo alchymico verorum philosophorum . . . hoc vero metalla, lapides, salia, sulphura, terras, quin et acidulas, thermas, physice, chymice, practice recludit, 4°, Basel, 1703 (portr.; BM 457. c. 11; BN S 5595).

III. Regnum Vegetabile, Physicè, Medicè, Anatomicè, Chymicè, Theoreticè, Practicè enucleatum, Vegetabilium nimirum Naturam, Ortum, Propagandi modum, Differentias, Partes varias, Collectionis & Præparationis modum, Saporem, Odorem, Colorem, Figuram, Signaturam, Usus multiplices aliáque curiosa proponens. Accessit Selectus Remediorum e Triplici Regno Juxta normam & ductum Pharmaciæ Ludovicianæ Cum Appendix Compositionis Artificiosæ eorundem secundùm Celeberr. D. Georg. Wolfg. Wedelium, 4°, Basel, 1688 (xvi, 186, ii index pp.; Select. Remed. sep. pp. 1–166, xiv index); 2 pts. (sep. t.ps. and index), 4°, Basel, 1688 (BN S 5593 (1)); Regni Vegetabilis . . . , 4°, Basel, 1696 (271 pp. and index; BM 968. k. 7, 988. 1. 29; BN S 5592 and 5593 (2)); Regnum Vegetabile Quadripartitum . . . , 4°, Basel, 1708 (1112 pp., index, portr.; BN S 5596; BM 447. a. 5, 2 pts. 1708–3). A Regnum Vegetabile tam physice quam medice, 4°, Basel, 1680 (BM B. 134. (2.)) is a different work.

IV. ΚΕΡΑΣ ΑΜΑΛΘΕΙΑΣ seu Thesaurus Remediorum è Triplicè Regno . . . , 4°, Basel, 1693.

A Chymia physica circa corporum naturalem et artificialem statum, 4°, Basel, 1693, q. by Poggendorff, (1), i, 1293, is not in the BM or the BN. König also contributed some papers to the Academia Curiosorum Leopoldina (Nürnberg) of which he was a member with the name Avicenna.[1]

The *Regnum Minerale* deals first with the names, differences, generation, nutrition and augmentation of metals and whether they have organs.[2] Part II deals with the separate metals: gold (including fulminating gold),[3] silver, iron, copper, tin, lead, mercury,[4] and antimony. Cinnabar is natural and artificial.[5] The section on bismuth, orpiment, cadmia, realgar, and zinc[6] is brief.

---

[1] De vitrificatione metallorum, *Ephem. Nat. Curios.*, 1689, 115; de elixir sophorum, *ib.*, 1691, 260; vera et philosophica auri diaphoretici Poteriani praeparatio, *ib.*, 1715, iii, 113.
[2] *Reg. Min.*, 1686, pp. 12–16.
[3] *Ib.*, 28.   [4] *Ib.*, 51.   [5] *Ib.*, 74.   [6] *Ib.*, 80–8.

Section III on stones includes gems, the magnet (including the magnetic plaster),[1] lapis lazuli, pyrites, gypsum, the Bologna stone,[2] coral, etc. Section IV on the middle salts[3] includes also the preparation of acids, etc.; it deals with common salt, nitre, vitriols, alums, sal armoniac,[4] etc. The other sections are on sulphurs, amber, asphalt, ambergris, and camphor, concluding with the medicinal earths and an appendix on mineral waters.

The *Regnum Vegetabile* first discusses the constituents of plants, whether those, according to Dodart, consist of spirit, oil, salt, water, and earth, or whether they consist of mercury, sulphur, salt, phlegm, and caput mortuum.[5] The opinion of Van Helmont, Boyle, and Borellus that they consist only of pure water (ex hisce verò patere potest, puram putat Aquam, ut volant Helmontius, Rob. Boyle, Borellus)[6] is rejected, and it is supposed that nitrous particles from the air, impregnating the water, may play a part:[7]

nisi non tantùm particulæ aqueæ, sed & igneæ, aëreæ, terreæ, sulphureæ, salinæ, nitrosæ aquam imbuerent ac velut imprægnarent, quamvis conjecturæ sint haud adeò spernendæ ipsam Aquam Nitro quodammodo abundare ... dum Aqua Plantis affunditur & per mediam terram percolatur, multa corpuscula devehat.

Rain water may contain nitrous salt cherished in its bosom[8] (aqua pluvialis ... sed unde hoc? nisi ex sale nitroso quod in sinu suo fovet), and nitre may come from the air, which is impregnated with it (nitrum ex ea extrahet, Aëríque, quem Nitro imprægnari meritò statuit).[9] The book also contains discussions on signatures,[10] magnetism,[11] the transplanting (transferring) of diseases to plants,[12] incantations,[13] and medical astrology.[14] König's *Regnum Animale* was noticed on p. 318.

JUSTI

Johann Heinrich Gottlob von Justi (Brücken, Thuringia, unknown date–Küstrin, 20 July 1771, in prison), who was an overseer of mines in Prussia. His writings on metallurgy, etc., were collected as:

I. Gesammlete Chymische Schriften, worinnen das Wesen der Metalle und die wichtigsten chymischen Arbeiten vor dem Nahrungsstand und das Bergwesen, ausführlich behandelt werden, 3 vols. 8°, Berlin and Leipzig, 1760, 1761, 1771; Gmelin, (1), ii, 644; Duveen, 314 (vols. 1 and 2 only).

He described some experiments on transmutation made in Vienna[15] and gave an account (purely on hearsay) of an adept, Sehfeld, who was living in his time and claimed to have transmuted tin into gold.[16] Justi himself was imprisoned for fraud. His papers are mostly superficial and polemical, especially against Pott, who replied to Justi in a special work (see p. 718). The contents of I are:

vol. i: constituents of bismuth, antimony, and Kupfernickel which he thought mostly copper, with some cobalt and arsenic (p. 65); proof that iron is not contained in its ores, on tinplate, tin alloys, hardening of steel, tombak (which must contain zinc) (p. 156); the separation of gold and silver, saltpetre from common salt, salammoniac,

[1] *Ib.*, 109. [2] *Ib.*, 118. [3] *Ib.*, 125 f. [4] *Ib.*, 154. [5] *Reg. Veget.*, 1688, 9–12.
[6] *Ib.*, 12. [7] *Ib.*, 13. [8] *Ib.*, 15. [9] *Ib.*, 17. [10] *Ib.*, 128–33.
[11] *Ib.*, 169–72. [12] *Ib.*, 172–7. [13] *Ib.*, 180–4. [14] *Ib.*, 81–9.
[15] I, ii, 419, 427; Schmieder, 16, 510, 532. [16] I, ii, 435–55.

saltpetre, smalt, Prussian blue, Saxon colours, the imitation porcelain, heavy spar, talc, mica, a new silver ore, black cobalt, the classification of copper ores, the age of fossils, carneol, and working copper ores;

vol. ii ('zweyter und letzter Band' on t.p.): the nature of arsenic, a new system of minerals, whether mercury is an element, brass, silvering and gilding, tinning of copper, the use of copper in domestic vessels, glaze for copper vessels, the nature of borax (which he thought came from alum and urine, or the decay of animal fat), salt-petre, a universal acid, verdigris, sap colours, copper glazes, cinnabar, working stones and earth in the fire, heavy spar, semi-gem stones, Hungarian silver ore, testing gold by the touchstone (p. 383), iron smelting, alchemy (Abhandlungen, so zur curieusen Chymie gehören) (pp. 419–55);

vol. iii: the solution of metals (including gold and silver) in vinegar, vitriolising of metals (including gold and silver), resistance of noble metals to fire, refining silver, iron smelting, sea-salt and bay-salt, salt pans, red lead, colours, fernambuco wood, faïence, infusible clay, if agat or amber is a fossil or marine product, origin of veins and minerals, iron smelting, tin plate, and English cupola furnaces.

SCHLÜTER

Christoph Andreas Schlüter, of whom nothing seems to be known except that he was an official in British pay at Brunswick and dedicated his book on smelting to King George II:

A. Gründlicher Unterricht von Hütte-Werken, Worin man Hütten-Werke auch alle dazu gehörige Gebäude und Oefen aus dem Fundament recht angelegen solle, auch wie sie am Hartz und andern Ortem angeleget sind. Und wie darauf die Arbeit bey Gold-Silber-Kupfer- und Bley-Ertzen, auch Schwefel-Vitriol- und Aschen-Werken geführet werden müsse. Nebst einem vollständigem Probier-Buch, darin enthalten wie allerley Ertze auf alle Metalle zu probieren, die Silber auf unterschiedene Art fein zu brennen, Gold und Silber mit Vortheil zu scheiden und alles, so dazu gehöret, zu verrichten ... Von Christoph Andreas Schlüter, Konigl. Gross-Britan-nischen, auch Chur- und Fürstl. Braunschweig-Lüneburgischen Zehndner am Unter-Hartz, 2 pts. f°, Brunswick, F. W. Meyer, 1738 (xll., 612 pp., xxxiv ll., 198 pp., xii ll., engraved f.p. and 58 plates).

B. Modified French tr. by Hellot, De la Font des Mines, des Fonderies, etc., 2 vols., 4°, Paris, 1750–3, 55 plates; 2 ed. 1764; Thomson, (1), i, 224, calls it 'a very valuable book'.

Schlüter deals fully with the liquation process for separating silver from copper by lead, and by antimony sulphide; the desilverising of argentiferous regulus; the separation of gold and silver by sulphur; the old amalgamation process used with silver ores at Kongsberg, Norway; cupellation; refining copper by oxidation and poling; and gives a detailed description of the rever-beratory furnace. The first part in B, or the second in A, deals with docimacy or the art of assaying. He says that artificial zinc vitriol was first made at Rammelsberg about 1570, and gives the preparation of aqua fortis but says nothing of the manufacture of fuming sulphuric acid, which is said to have been made at Goslar in the Harz.

ELLER

Johann Theodor Eller (Plötzkau, Anhalt-Bernburg, 29 November 1689–Berlin, 13 September 1760) came of a wealthy family (von Brockhausen), had an excellent education in law at Quedlinburg and Jena, and in medicine and science (especially chemistry) at Halle, Leyden, Amsterdam, Paris (where he associated with Lemery and Homberg), and London. On returning to Germany he was appointed in 1721 physician to the prince of Anhalt-Bernburg; in 1724 he was called by the King of Prussia to Berlin, where he became professor of anatomy, dean of the medical college and physician to the army and, from 1735, to Frederick the Great, who made him privy-councillor and director of the Collegium medico-chirurgicum and the Royal Berlin Academy of Sciences in 1755.[1]

Eller's publications in the *Histoire de l'Académie Royale des Sciences et Belles Lettres* of Berlin (the volumes including *Mámoires*), denoted in the references by HAB, are collected in German translations as:

I. J. T. Eller's *Physikalisch-Chymisch-Medicinische Abhandlungen, aus den Gedenkschriften der königl. Akademie der Wissenschaften herausgegeben und übersetzt durch D (r.) Carl Abraham Gerhard*, 8°, Berlin, Stettin and Leipzig, 1764, zwei Theile mit Kupfern: (pagin. contin., pp. 419 (1 errata), 10 plates (BM 740. a. 1)).

They deal with a variety of subjects, many of medical interest only, and in general are of small importance.

In memoirs on the elements, the composition of bodies, and the origin and production of metals,[2] he gives an historical review of chemical theories from the Greek period, with special emphasis on the views of Becher and Stahl and the theory of phlogiston (he uses the Greek work $\phi\lambda o\gamma\iota\sigma\tau\grave{o}\nu$),[3] of which he gives a good summary:[4] He investigated the effervescence of acids with iron filings, tartar, coral, and 'crabs' eyes' under an air-pump receiver,[5] measured the rate of evaporation of water at different temperatures,[6] repeated Boyle's experiments on growing plants in water, and thought he had converted water into earth by grinding it in a glass mortar (which was really abraded in the process).[7] He published on the separation of gold and silver in the dry way by precipitation,[8] on sound and voice,[9] the fruitfulness of the earth,[10] the vegetation of seeds[11] and the preservation of blood for several years in a vacuum.[12] His paper on first principles[13] includes an obscure allusion to what seems to be the spheroidal state of water. In his memoir on human blood[14] he describes the effects of several reagents (copper and iron vitriols, common salt, salt ammoniac, sal volatile, alum, salt of tartar, corrosive sublimate, etc.) on the colour and on the shape and size of the corpuscles, which he examined by means of a microscope obtained from London. He examined human calculi[15] and wrote on the danger of using copper utensils in the kitchen.[16]

A really important investigation is Eller's on the solubility of salts in

---

[1] Formey, *Hist. Acad. Berlin*, 1761, 498; Gmelin, (1), ii, 610; Thomson, (1), i, 269; Kopp, (1), i, 204; Hoefer, (1), ii, 405; Poggendorff, (1), i, 658.
[2] HAB, 1746 (1748), 3, 25; 1748 (1750), 3; 1753 (1755), 3; I, 197, 220, 310.
[3] I, 230 f., 316 f., 328 f.   [4] I, 230 f., 316 f., 328 f.   [5] HAB, 1745, 15.
[6] HAB, 1746 (1748), 25; I, 237.   [7] HAB, 1746 (1748), 25; I, 241.
[8] HAB, 1747 (1749), 3; I, 1.   [9] I, 104.   [10] I, 37.
[11] HAB, 1752 (1754), 17; I, 60.   [12] HAB, 1757 (1759), 20; I, 140.
[13] HAB, 1746 (1748), 42.   [14] HAB, 1751 (1753), 3; I, 178.
[15] I, 243, 388.   [16] HAB, 1754 (1756), 3; I, 398.

water.[1] He found that most salts cause a fall in temperature when dissolved in water but some (e.g. dry Glauber's salt) cause a rise in temperature. He considered that the solvent action of water is due to fire particles mixed with it: at the boiling point the heat passed through the water in the form of bubbles of steam (die übrige Wärme geht durch das Wasser hindurch und verlieret sich in der Luft). The expansion of water between the freezing and boiling points he found to be $\frac{1}{24}$. He discusses the theories of solution — the interposition of salt particles between water particles, attraction, etc.[2] Since 8 oz. of water dissolved at 33° F. only $\frac{1}{64}$ of its weight of kitchen salt, which it lost on freezing, but 2 oz. at 43–45° F. and almost 8 oz. (fast so viel als es wiegt) at the boiling point, Eller concluded that the solution was caused by heat (nicht das Wasser, sondern einzig und allein das Feuer die Auflösung der Körper bewerkstelliget).[3] He measured the solubility of nineteen salts in 8 oz. of water at 40–42° F. (although the temperature could vary 2° F., he gives also the pressure reading as 27 in. 10 lines in Paris measure), e.g.: $9\frac{1}{2}$ oz. green vitriol, 9 oz. blue vitriol, $4\frac{1}{2}$ oz. alum, 4 oz. saltpetre, $3\frac{1}{2}$ oz. rock salt, $\frac{1}{2}$ oz. cream of tartar, $4\frac{1}{2}$ drachms 10 grains borax. Water saturated with one salt can dissolve other salts,[4] e.g. in 8 oz. water at 11–12° R. 9 oz. blue vitriol, 1 oz. saltpetre, 3 drachms common salt, and 1 oz. sugar.

Eller's figures for the effect of temperature on the solubility of common salt are very inaccurate, and Petit in 1729 had shown that: 'le sel marin ne peut se dissoudre dans l'eau très-chaude en plus grande quantité que cette même eau n'en peut tenir en dissolution, lorsqu'elle est tout-à-fait froide.'[5] Eller refers to the 'very remarkable' fact that the volume of water is not increased when a salt is dissolved in it (man eine gewisse Menge Salz in dem Wasser auflösen kann, ohne dass sich sein körperlicher Raum dadurch vermehret).[6] This was also known before. Mercury also dissolves metals without change of volume. Eller concluded that the particles of salt enter the interstices of the water. It is clear from his results, however, that he used only dilute solutions (2–3 drachms of salt in 8 oz. of water), for which the volume changes would be very small.

POTT

Johann Heinrich Pott (Halberstadt, 1692–Berlin, 29 March 1777) studied at Halle under Hoffmann and Stahl and became professor of theoretical, and on Neumann's death in 1737 of practical, chemistry in the Collegium medico-chirurgicum in Berlin, and Director of the Royal Hofapothek. He was a man of great practical industry and also learned and widely read. The very complete

---

[1] Von der Natur und den Eigenschaften des gemeinen Wassers, in so fern es als Auflösungs-mittel betrachtet wird; 2. Von den Begebenheiten, welche sich ereignen, wenn man alle Arten der Salze, jewede besonders, in gemeinem Wasser auflöset; HAB, 1750 (1752), 67, 83; I, 254–73, 364–81.
[2] Cf. Hoffmann, Animadversio physica-chymica, qua demonstratur, corporum solutionem non fieri per receptionem in poros menstrui; in Observat. phys.-chym., ii, 8; Opera, 1740, iv, 486.
[3] I, 268.   [4] I, 378: long table of results; see Gassendi, p. 463.
[5] AdS, 1729 (1731), h 19–22; m 225–334 (De la precipitation du sel marin dans la fabrique du salpêtre).
[6] I, 373.

historical introductions to his dissertations were often used by Bergman for his own memoirs. Pott refers to some authors very little known, such as Jungius and Isaac Lawson.[1]

When Frederick the Great made Marggraf director of the Chemical Laboratory (1754) and director of the Physical Class (1761) of the Berlin Academy, Pott (who was much older, and was elected in 1720) was greatly annoyed: he ceased his chemical work, severed his relations with the Academy in 1754, and (in order that the Academy could not make any use of them after his death) burnt all his unpublished papers, including a detailed history of chemistry on which he had been engaged for many years.[2] He also fell out with Brandes, Eller, Lehmann, and Justi, replying at length to some of Justi's criticisms:

D. Johann Heinrich Potts Chym. Prof. Reg. neue wichtige und mit vielen über-führenden nützlichen Experimenten erläuterte und ausgeführte Physicalisch-Chymische Materien, in einer chymischen Zerlegung derer Vorwürfe und Beschuldi-gungen die ihm der Herr Bergrath von Justi in den zweyten Theil seiner chymischen Schriften so übermüthig, unbescheiden und anzüglich, ja mit so schlechten Grunde zur Last gelegt hat, 4°, Berlin, 1762 (x, 86 pp.).

His disputes with Eller were especially virulent on both sides.[3]

Pott was commissioned by the King of Prussia to discover the secret of porcelain as made at Meissen, in Saxony, and he is said to have made over 30,000 experiments with all kinds of materials subjected to fire: his observa-tions are recorded in his *Lithogeognosia* (1746):

I. Chymische Untersuchungen welche fürnehmlich von der Lithogeognosia oder Erkäntniss und Bearbeitung der gemeinen einfacheren Steine und Erden in-gleichen von Feuer und Licht handeln, 4°, Potsdamm, 1746; 2 ed., Berlin, 1757; IA. Fortsetzung, 4°, Berlin and Potsdam, 1751; IB. Zweiter Fortsetzung, 4°, Berlin, 1754;
II. French tr., 2 vols., 12°, Paris, 1753: i, Lithogéognosie ou examen chymiques des Pierres et des Terres en général; ii Continuation de la Lithogéognosie Pyro-technique (the BM copy is autographed: 'Presented by the Translator Baron de Olbatch May 23 1766', i.e. Baron d'Holbach).

Thomson[4] says they 'must have been the result of immense labour.' A note on the history of porcelain is given on p. 722.

Pott recognises four kinds of earth: (1) *terra alcalina* or *calcaria* (limestone), (2) *terra gypsea* (gypsum), (3) *terra argillacea* (clay), and (4) *terra vitrescibilis* (silica). He differentiates them by various reactions and was perhaps the first to characterise silica clearly.[5] He reckons fluorspar (Flusspaat) among the vitrescible earths but says it is better known to miners than chemists.[6] He says oil of vitriol converts *liquor silicum* (potassium silicate solution) to a jelly, but there is no precipitate with nitric acid, acid of salt and acetic acid (colloidal

[1] Formey, HAB, 1777, 55; Spielmann-Cadet, ii, 409–17 (complete bibl.); Gmelin, (1), ii, 605; Thomson, (1), i, 267; Hoefer, (1), ii, 401; Poggendorff, (1), ii, 509; Ferguson, ii, 221.
[2] Thiébault, *Mes Souvenirs de Vingt Ans Séjour à Berlin, ou Fréderic le Grand*, 3 ed., 4 vols., 1813, iv, 16.
[3] Hoefer, (1), ii, 405, and refs.: il [Eller] parle des intrigues amoureuses fort compromettantes pour la réputation de mademoiselle Pott.
[4] (2), 1807, ii, 472.   [5] I, 1757, 3.   [6] *Ib.*, 46; IA, 1751, 33.

silica). Since the precipitate with ammonia is soluble in acid, Pott thought the vitrescible had been converted into the alkaline earth.[1]

His usual method of investigation was to heat the various materials in a crucible and he thus ascertained the reactions of a number of substances in the dry way: his tables of such reactions[2] are an early example of analysis tables. He found that pure white clay, alone or mixed with quartz sand, would not fuse at the highest temperature he could produce, but clay mixed with lime, iron oxide, or fluorspar, fused. With half its weight of borax it formed a compact mass but did not give a hard body with one-third its weight; it fused with twice its weight of litharge or its own weight of gypsum, but not with other proportions. Thomson says such reactions were afterwards applied in blowpipe analysis.

Pott's numerous separate dissertations were collected in Latin and translated into French:

III. Exercitationes Chymicae, 4°, Berlin, 1738, 'sparsim hactenus edita, jam vero collectae . . .', pp. viii (2 bl.), 220, containing 1. De sulphuribus metallorum (Halle, 1716) p. 1 f. (also printed in Hoffmann, Opera, Geneva, 1753, Suppl. II, part i, 32 f.: given as a dissertation by Pott in the Catalogue of Hoffmann's works, 1743, No. 163); 2. Anatomia auripigmenti (Halle, 1720), p. 46 f.; 3. De solutione corporum particulari (Marburg, 1729), p. 113 f.; 4. De terra foliata tartari (Leyden, 1732), p. 137 f.; De acido vitrioli vinoso (Halle, 1732), p. 159 f.; 5. De acido nitri vinoso (Erfurt, 1735), p. 195 f.

IIIA. French tr. by Demachy (who gives the dates of the first publication in vol. i, p. xix f.), with extracts from II and a number of smaller papers: Dissertations Chymiques de M. Pott, . . . Recueillies & traduites, tant du Latin que de l'Allemand, par M. Demachy, 4 vols. 12°, Paris, 1759 The contents are summarised in the text below. Vol. iv contains Extraits des Disputes de M. Pott avec M. Eller (by Demachy; see p. 718), 422–46; a bibliography of works cited by Pott, 447–82; a list of authors cited by Pott without specification of their works, and of works without author's name, 483–4; index, 485–531; errata, 531–2; approbation by Macquer dated 13 October 1757, and privilege du roi, 533–6.

IV. Observationum et Animadversionum Chymicarum, 2 vols. 4°, Berlin: (i) Præcipue circa Sal Commune, Acidum Salis Vinosum et Wismuthum Versantium Collectio prima, 1739; (ii) Præcipue Zincum, Boracem et Pseudogalenam, 1741: contents: i (dedicated to Eller and Henckel), De sale communi 1 f.; De acido salis vinoso 109 f.; De Wismutho 134 f.; ii, De zinco 1 f.; De borace 54 f.; De pseudogalena (zinc blende) 105 f.

IIIA. vol. i: Dissertation sur les soufres des métaux, 1 (1716) — dates of first publication are in brackets; l'analyse d'orpiment, 133 (1720); l'histoire de la dissolution particulière de différents corps, 319 (1729); l'acide vitriolique vineux, 388 (1732); l'acide nitreux vineux, 489 (1735); la cause de la rougeur des vapeurs de l'acide nitreux, 557 (1743) (the cause is phlogiston).

vol. ii: Le sel commun, 1–248 (1739);[3] l'esprit de sel vineux, 249 (1739) — a mixture of spirit of salt and alcohol, used as a solvent for fulminating gold; la nature de la base du sel commun, 297 (1743); le borax, 319 (1741); alkali

---

[1] I, 1757, 49; IA, 1751, 74.

[2] II, ii, end (first publication); IB, 1754, 33–148: Tabellen von denen Würckungen der verschiedenen Mischungen derer Erden aus der Lithogeognosie. Aus dem Französischen übersetzt und . . . vermehret.

[3] In this long dissertation Pott refers to the curious work of Georg von Welling, *Opus Mago-Cabbalisticum et theosophicum, darinnen der Ursprung, Natur, Eigenschaften und Gebrauch, des Saltzes, Schwefels und Mercurii*, 4°, Homberg von der Höhe, 1735.

naturel de l'Inde et le borax, 459 (1743); expériences chymiques sur l'existence de l'acide dans les animaux, 469 (1740); l'analyse du vitriol blanc, 507
(1743); la terre feuillée du tartre, 527 (1732) — potassium acetate.

vol. iii: Le sel fusible microcosmique, 1 (1757); recherches sur l'union de
l'acide du vitriol avec l'acide du tartre, 159 (1757) — indications of the existence of tartaric acid crystals, which he thought contained sulphuric acid; la
dissolution de la chaux vive dans l'acide nitreux, 178 (1727); la décomposition
du tartre vitriolé, 219 (1737); la distillation par la chaleur du soleil, 251 (1743);[1]
le bismuth, 267 (1739); le zinc, 392 (1741); la manganise, 523 (1740);[2] la
pseudogalène, 559 (1741) — zinc blende.

vol. iv: Examen chymique du crayon noir appellé en Latin plombago, 1
(1740)[3] — he confused graphite with molybdenite; examen pyrotechnique du
talc, 28 (1746) — he did not find magnesia; expériences pyrotechnique sur la
topaz de Saxe, 66 (1747); examen pyrotechnique des stéatites, 90 (1747) — he
did not find magnesia; la natur et les propriétés du Fiel de Verre, 139 (1748)
— glass 'gall', can be used as a flux; essai sur la manière de préparer des
vaisseaux qui puissent supporter le feu le plus violent, 167 (1750) — clay
crucibles; those of Ypse and Passau contain plumbago; recherches sur le
mélange de l'acide du vitriol avec le salmiac, 265 (1752) — ammonium sulphate, 'le sel ammoniac secret,' see p. 353; examen chymique de la nature du
sel acide volatil du succin, 326 (1753); réflexions pratique sur une Dissertation
de M. Hundertmarck intitulé: De l'espece de Soufre anodin qui résulte du
mélange des huiles de vin et de vitriol, 371; recherches sur un Traité de
M. Ludolf: La Chymie Victorieuse, 382.

Pott[4] thought he had proved that the basis of common salt is an alkaline
calcareous earth (une terre alkaline calcaire), but not truly calcareous, since
common salt cannot be prepared from hydrochloric acid (acide marin) with
lime or chalk. He thought he had precipitated an earth with fixed alkali
(potassium carbonate) from Glauber's salt, but must have used Epsom salt
by mistake. In 1743 he criticised Duhamel, who had demonstrated the
difference between potash and soda in 1736 (Vol. III) but Duhamel's results
were later confirmed by Marggraf (see p. 727).

In his experiments on the existence of acid in animals[5] Pott obtained an
impure acid by the destructive distillation of blood and other animal matters.

The dissertation on zinc (1741) is an advance on anything published before,
since the metal was then on the market, and Pott showed conclusively that it
was a peculiar metal. He obtained butter of zinc (anhydrous zinc chloride) by
distilling zinc with corrosive sublimate (transire mercurium sublimatum cum
zinco in forma crystallorum seu butyri).[6] In his dissertation on white vitriol[7]
he showed that it contains zinc and sulphuric acid and prepared it by dissolving zinc in dilute sulphuric acid.

Pott also gives a full account of bismuth (he derives the name from bis Muth,

[1] Miscell. Berolin., 1743, vii, 275.   [2] Miscell. Berolin., 1740, vi, 40.
[3] Miscell. Berolin., 1740, vi, 29.
[4] IIIA, ii, 1 (6), 297; Miscell. Berolin., 1743, vii, 285.
[5] Miscell. Berolin., 1740, vi, 16; IIIA, ii, 469.   [6] IV, ii, 18; IIIA, ii, 175; iii, 479.
[7] Miscell. Berolin., 1743, vii, 306; IIIA, ii, 507.

gedoppeltem Muth!), with a history of the metal.[1] He prepared the 'butter' ($BiCl_3$) by distilling 1 pt. of the metal with 2 pts. of corrosive sublimate, as Boyle had done (p. 537), and showed that the solution of bismuth in nitric acid is precipitated as Spanish white by water only, without the addition of common salt (cf. Lemery, Vol. III).[2] Although he distinguished iron from manganese, Pott regarded the latter (he did not obtain the metal) as a compound of an alkaline earth like alumina with a subtle inflammable principle.[3] He seems to have been the first to repeat Glauber's experiments with manganates (see p. 357).[4]

In his dissertation on borax (1740)[5] Pott showed that sulphuric acid gives a white precipitate from the solution and the remaining liquid deposits Glauber's salt. The white precipitate (boric acid, obtained by Homberg in 1702, see Vol. III) Pott considered to be a neutral salt composed of 'the most subtle part of vitriolic acid' and 'the alkaline earth' of borax, since (like copper vitriol) it colours a spirit flame green.[6] He showed that the product of distillation of amber (succinic acid) is a peculiar acid similar to the vegetable acids[7] and mentions a salt (*alkali citronné*), viz. potassium citrate, obtained from alkali and lemon juice (and other fruit juices).[8]

Pott[9] reports that the Dutch exported white arsenic to the East Indies for use as a fertiliser (as a weed-killer ?), and recalls the statement of Kircher[10] that it was exported from Carinthia to Egypt to kill serpents found after an inundation of the Nile.

In his dissertation on the sulphur of metals[11] Pott identifies this with a fatty earth (Becher's *terra pinguis*), only partly combustible and imparting colour and ductility. It is composed of flexible particles and differs in purity and fixity in various metals. The principle of fire and light exists in greatest abundance and in greatest purity in the mineral kingdom. Very close combination renders it more intimate and compact, but when it is separated by chemical processes from the bonds which retain it, and obtained sufficiently pure, its great and powerful qualities are recognised.[12]

In his essay on 'the properties and effects of light and fire'[13] Pott says phlogiston or the principle of fire is different from light, although many take light and fire for one. The matter of light cannot be separated or enclosed in vessels; when it is combined with a fine combustible earth (and perhaps saline or acid particles) and set in motion with it, fire is produced. The 'motus verticillaris gyratorius immanens' is pure fire; so long as no water or earth enters it is not volatile or elastic but fixed and permanent in the fire. Fire cannot be compressed or condensed, when pure it cannot be measured or weighed. In 1 lb. of sulphur there is less than 1 drachm of it, and the rest is all acid. Metallic calces, when phlogiston is removed, weigh more rather than less,

---

[1] IV, i, 134 f.; IIIA, iii, 267. [2] IIIA, ii, 167, 171. [3] IIIA, iii, 523.
[4] IIIA, iii, 538. [5] IIIA, ii, 319. [6] IIIA, ii, 362, 365.
[7] IIIA, iv, 326. [8] IIIA, ii, 553. [9] IIIA, i, 239.
[10] *Mundus Subterraneus*, f°, Amsterdam, 1665, ii, 227 (serpentem . . . arsenico per agros sparso enecant; cf. *ib.*, ii, 148: plantæ suffitu arsenico tinctæ pereunt.
[11] IIIA, i, 8 f. [12] *Ib.*, 4 f.
[13] Versuch Chymisch Physicalischer Betrachtungen über die Eigenshaften und Würckungen des Lichts und Feuers; in I, 1746, 60–84; *ib.*, 2 ed., 1757, sep. pag., same as 1746 ed.

and it is less than 1 per cent. of the weight of charcoal. Phosphorus, when it loses phlogiston, weighs more than before.[1] Water is necessary for the production of flame; air is helpful in increasing the motion. Phlogiston is present in light from the sun and stars, in lightning, rain, plants (especially in seeds, juices, sugar, oils, etc.), spirit of wine, charcoal and soot, animals, inflammable minerals, sulphur and metals. Metals contain it in varying amounts, there is most in zinc and very little in lead, and those metals which contain most phlogiston evolve most heat on solution in acids; with the same metal nitric acid evolves more heat than sulphuric and this more than muriatic.[2]

Phlogiston expands most bodies according to their texture and mixture; it does not increase the weight of a body, as is seen in red-hot iron, but by long calcination the weight may increase, when the particles fall together and make the body more compact, as in the case of lead; or when heavy air particles enter, as in the case of flowers of zinc (theils weil sie compacter in einander fallen und mole kleiner werden wie beym Blei, oder von den eingetretenen schwerern Luft Theilgen wie bey den Floribus Zinci). Air attracts phlogiston from bodies, as in rusting iron, decaying animals and vegetables, and phosphorus.[3] When set in motion, phlogiston is the active principle of inanimate and in part of animate bodies, the basis of colours, odours and tastes, of manures, and the principal agent of fermentation and putrefaction.[4] In the mineral kingdom it is the cause of metallic lustre, malleability, and fusibility, and plays a part in the separation of metals.[5] It is the Salvator Naturæ,[6] and perhaps the greatest Clarificator naturæ.[7]

Porcelain

An account of the Chinese porcelain manufacture (without detail or mention of the glazing) was given by Juan Gonzales Mendoza (Toledo, c. 1540–Mexico, 1617), a Spanish Augustinian missionary who visited China in 1580.[8] Chinese porcelain is mentioned by van Linschoten, Boetius de Boodt, Albinus, and Sir Thomas Browne.[9] The Jesuit missionary Dentrecolles (1664–1741) visited the Chinese porcelain factory at Ching-te-Chen and gave a detailed description of the process, mentioning the use of kaolin (kao ling) and 'petunse' (pai tun tzu, felspar), and the preparation of the blue cobalt glaze from a mineral ch'ing shih. The factories at Ching-te-Chen were established fairly early and were supported by the Ming emperors; the district, in S.E. China, is still the chief pottery locality.[10]

Small specimens of the materials sent to Paris by Dentrecolles were identified by Reaumur in 1729, but he did not succeed in making true porcelain, which was first made at Sèvres in 1769 as a consequence of finding a deposit

[1] Ib., 66–8.   [2] Ib., 70–3 f.   [3] Ib., 77.   [4] Ib., 78 f.
[5] Ib., 80 f.   [6] Ib., 83.   [7] Ib., 84.
[8] Historia de las cosas mas notables, ritos y costrumbres del gran reino de la China, 8°, Madrid, 1586; French tr., 8°, Paris, 1589; q. in Salmuth's notes to Panciroli, Rerum Memorabilium, Amberg, 1608, 141f.
[9] Pseudodoxia Epidemica, 1646, bk. ii, ch. 5; Works, ed. Keynes, 1928, ii, 154.
[10] Dentrecolles, in Duhalde, Description de la Chine, 4 vols. f°, Paris, 1735, i, 144; ii, 177 f.; Davis, The Chinese, 1836, ii, 257; Hoefer, (1), i, 14–16.

of kaolin at St. Yrieix.[1] Meanwhile, the secret of porcelain manufacture was independently discovered in Germany. The white clay of Waldenburg in Saxony had been mentioned by Agricola, Cardan, and others, and fire-resistant and non-absorbent white vessels are mentioned by Albinus,[2] who quotes from Agricola (see p. 52). The Kürfurst August of Saxony (1670–1733) collected Chinese porcelain.[3]

Johann Friedrich Böttger (or Böttiger) (Schleiz, 4 or 5 February 1682 (1685 also given)–Meissen, 1719) was (aged 12) assistant to Zorn, an apothecary in Berlin, and worked at alchemy, having received some of the philosophers' stone from an adept Laskaris, who represented himself as a Greek archiman-drite.[4] Frederick I of Prussia was given a piece of Böttiger's artificial gold and ordered an enquiry; fearing the consequences, Böttiger fled from Berlin and in 1701 was confined in the laboratory of the Kurfürst August in Dresden, with the task of making gold. Tschirnhaus (or Tschirnhausen), who travelled extensively, heard in 1675 in Paris of the attempts to make Chinese porcelain, including the use of large burning mirrors. In 1679 he began to make a large copper mirror and also large lenses, and in 1696–7 he melted asbestos with a large lens. In 1693–4 he had been trying to make porcelain, in 1702 he saw the so-called 'porcelain' works at Delft, and in 1709 he communicated to Homberg in Paris a secret process for making porcelain, realising that a special Chinese earth was not essential. He is said to have supervised Böttiger's work but in 1707 the two were working independently. Tschirnhaus died in 1708. In 1709 Böttiger discovered the process of making red porcelain and a patent was taken out on 23 January 1710. This porcelain was made in Meissen but did not come on the market till 1713, when white porcelain was on sale in small pieces. The secret was taken to Berlin in 1715 by Samuel Kempe, one of Böttiger's workmen.[5]

MARGGRAF

Andreas Sigismund Marggraf (Berlin; 3 March 1709–7 August 1782), the son of a court apothecary, was a pupil of Neumann about 1725 and then studied in Frankfurt on the Oder, Strasbourg (with Spielmann), Halle, and in 1734 with Henckel at Freiberg. On his return to Berlin in 1735 he worked with his father in the Royal Hofapothek: in February 1738 he became a member of the Berlin Academy (which gave him a house and laboratory in

---

[1] See Macquer, (2), iii, 215; E. Bucher et al., Geschichte der technischen Kunst, Berlin and Leipzig, 1893, iii, 556.

[2] Meissnische Bergk-Chronica, Dresden, 1590, 173.   [3] Prandtl, Chymia, 1953, iv, 115.

[4] On Laskaris, see Schmieder, 470; Kopp, (4), i, 201; Waite, The Secret Tradition in Alchemy, 1926, 320.

[5] C. A. Engelhardt, J. F. Böttiger, Erfinder der Sächsischen Porzellans, Leipzig, 1837 (portr.); Bucher, 1893, iii, 533; Peters, in Diergart, 1909, 378; Strunz, (2), 162 (portr. of Böttger); Feldhaus, (1), 810; Dannemann, 1921, ii, 342; Fester, 1923, 179; Peters, A. Nat., 1910, ii, 399–424; Heintze, ib., 183–200; Diergart, ib., 1930, xiii, 167–87; Reinhardt, Tschirnhaus oder Böttger, Görlitz, 1912, q. by Fester (name is Böttiger, not Böttger); E. Kalkschmidt, Der Gold-macher Joh. Fr. Böttger und die Erfindung des europäischen Porzellans, Stuttgart, 1926, 18 f., 22 f., 31 f.; Prandtl, Chymia, 1953, iv, 115. For Böttiger as alchemist, Schmieder, 471 f.; Kopp, (4), i, 130; for the Meissen porcelain factory, J. Hanway, An Historical Account of the British Trade over the Caspian Sea; with a Journal of Travels, 4°, 1753, ii, 228 (700 workmen practically prisoners; porcelain sold by King of Saxony for private use only, but some seen in London shops).

1754) and in 1760–1 he succeeded Eller as director of the mathematical-physical section. In spite of his weak health, Marggraf carried through a large number of most important researches. He divided his life between his laboratory and the Academy of Berlin. Hoefer says Marggraf 'compte avec raison au nombre des plus grands chimistes du dix-huitième siècle . . . expérimenteur habile, ingénieux et réservé dans ses vues théoriques'. He became a corresponding member (associé étranger) of the Paris Academy in 1777, but he divided with Scheele the distinction of never being an F.R.S., and in many ways he resembled Scheele both in his personal character and in his work. He was conscientious, modest and sincere, and kept himself quite apart from the quarrels of the Berlin chemists. For some years before his death he was unable to write because of a stroke. He was a follower of the phlogiston theory but more distinguished as a practical discoverer than as a theoretician; a certain natural timidty often prevented him from drawing theoretical conclusions from his results.[1]

Marggraf's papers were written in German and translated by himself into Latin for the *Miscellanea Berolinensia* of the Berlin Academy, then (again by Marggraf) from Latin (later, from German) into French for the *Histoires* of the Berlin and Paris Academies. A few later ones were published in German.[2] They were collected by Marggraf at the instance of J. G. Lehmann and published in two volumes in 1761–7:

I. Chymischer Schriften, 2 vols., 8°, Berlin, I (ed. Lehmann), 1761 (pp. xxiv, 358, plate, errata sheet); II (ed. Beausobre), 1767 (pp. xiv, 206, plate and errata in one); revised ed., I, 1768 (pp. xxii, 330, vi, 2 plates, folding table), II, 1767 (pp. xiv, 206, 1 (1 blank), plate);
II. French tr. by Formey (Secretary of the Berlin Academy), publ. by Demachy, Opuscules Chimiques, 2 vols. 12°, Paris, 1712 (I, pp. li, 402, vi; II, pp. vi (2 blank), 456).

Distinctive features of Marggraf's work are (i) his very sparing use of hypotheses; (ii) his use of several reagents in analysis in the wet way (he also used the blowpipe); and (iii) his use of quite small amounts of materials: whereas many of his contemporaries worked with pounds, he rarely used so much as an ounce, and often obtained excellent results with a drachm or less, a sure sign of the highly skilled manipulator. Thomson says he was 'in some measure the beginner of chemical analysis; for before his time the chemical analysis of bodies had hardly been attempted'. Marggraf made use of the microscope in his chemical work.[3] Condorcet says Marggraf used the phlogiston theory so sparingly and with so much reserve that he seems to have suspected that it would soon lose its validity (cette doctrine serait bientôt

---

[1] *Allgem. J. Chem.*, 1804, ii (portr.); Condorcet, éloge, in *Oeuvres*, 1847, ii, 598–610; Crell, *Ann.*, 1786, I, 181–92; Formey, HAB, 1783 (1785), 63; Gmelin, (1), ii, 612 f. (bibl. of 52 papers); Hoefer, (1), ii, 407; A. W. Hofmann, (1), 1882, 64; Kopp, (1), i, 208; A. de L. in NBG, 1860, xxxiii, 549; Ladenburg in *Allgemeine Deutsche Biographie*, Leipzig, 1884, xx, 334; Lehmann, pref. to Marggraf, *Chymischer Schriften*, Berlin, 1761, i; Lippmann, (1), i, 275; Lockemann, *Chem. Ztg.*, 1932, lvi, 621; id., *Geschichte der Chemie*, 1950, i, 97 (says he signed his name 'Marggrafe'); Scheele, *Nachgelassene Briefe*, Stockholm, 1892; 332; Thomson, (1), i, 271.

[2] List of papers, Köhncke, in Harnack's *Geschichte der Kgl. Preuss. Akad. d. Wiss. zu Berlin*, Berlin, 1900, iii, 179.

[3] Lippmann, Ostwald's *Klassiker*, clix, 69, says for the first time, but cf. Eller, p. 716.

ébraulée). According to Klaproth and Wolff[1] Marggraf assumed that phlogiston has a negative weight.

Marggraf's earliest publications are on phosphorus and its compounds. In 1740 he investigated the preparation of solid phosphorus and its action on metals, obtaining phosphides of copper and zinc, on sulphur, and on acids.[2] The compound with sulphur gave 'a strong odour of sulphur' (hydrogen sulphide) with water. On heating phosphorus he noticed the 'serpentine motion' of the luminous points before inflammation: when the phosphorus burnt, white 'flowers' (P_2O_5) were formed, 1 oz. $3\frac{1}{2}$ drachms from 1 oz. (8 dr.) of phosphorus, which liquefied in air to an oily acid. The increase in weight of phosphorus on combustion (8 dr. gave 10 dr.) had been observed previously by Boyle's assistant, Ambrose Godfrey Hanckewitz.[3] On evaporation of the solution in water, Marggraf observed the flashes of light (phosphine from the decomposition of phosphorous acid) already noticed by Boyle (see p. 544), and finally a glassy residue (metaphosphoric acid) was obtained.

On heating phosphorus with concentrated nitric acid, copious red fumes were evolved and there was a violent explosion. In 1743[4] Marggraf showed that phosphorus is more easily obtained from evaporated urine if lead chloride (Bleykalk) and charcoal are added and the mixture strongly heated in an earthenware retort. He says he obtained the process from Henckel, who in his *Pyritologia* (1725) says:[5] 'calx of lead digested with sal ammoniac, salt of tartar, and stale urine, and at length distilled, yields an arsenical odour, nay, at last a beautiful phosphorus.'

Marggraf points out that Stahl regarded phosphorus as a compound of spirit of salt (hydrochloric acid) and phlogiston (see p. 672), but all attempts to prepare it from common salt and combustible materials failed. Marggraf did not feel able to assert that Stahl is wrong: 'I hope, if God gives me life and health, that I may reach more precise knowledge of this subject, not by simple conjectures, but by real experiments.'[6] He obtained by evaporation a 'fusible salt of urine' (microcosmic salt), which he says was not quite unknown but little investigated;[7] the residual urine was 'much less proper for the production of phosphorus'. By heating a mixture of this salt, white earth and soot, Marggraf obtained first a 'spirit of urine' (ammonia), then phosphorus. He mentions that the acid of phosphorus, mixed with soot and distilled, regenerates phosphorus.

He gave a fuller account of this 'very remarkable salt of urine', or 'microcosmic salt', in 1746.[8] It is obtained in larger amount from putrefied than from fresh urine; 120 pints of urine gave 3 oz. of purified (recrystallised) salt. On heating to redness it loses ammonia and leaves a clear glass, which Marggraf thought was phosphoric acid (it is really sodium metaphosphate). It gave a

[1] 1809, iv, 25.   [2] *Miscell. Berolin.*, 1740, vi, 54; I, i, 42; II, i, 1.
[3] *Phil. Trans.*, 1733, xxviii, 58; Abdg. ed., vii, 596; Crell, *N. chem. Archiv*, 1783, iii, 6.
[4] *Miscell. Berolin.*, 1743, vii, 324 (plate); I, i, 57 (2 plates); II, i, 30 (no plate); Mielcke, Ostwald's *Klassiker*, 1913, clxxxvii, figs. from original.
[5] *Pyritologia: or, a History of the Pyrites*, 1757, 373: Miscellaneous Observations, xiv: Marggraf gives the reference 'Spicilegium p. 1004, § 14'.
[6] II, i, 62.   [7] Boerhaave, (2), ii, 317: sal nativus urinae; this may have been urea.
[8] HAB, 1746 (1748), 84; I, i, 80; II, i, 123.

white precipitate with silver nitrate (Marggraf describes a large number of other reactions). When 'mixed with the phlogiston of soot and distilled it gives phosphorus': from the residue water extracts another salt which does not give phosphorus with soot (Na_3PO_4 or $Na_4P_2O_7$); this melts before the flame of a candle urged by the blowpipe into a clear bead which (unlike the one from microcosmic salt) becomes opaque on cooling. The origin of the salt in the urine was probably vegetable food, since it is more abundant in summer (when more vegetables are eaten) than in winter.

In 1745 Marggraf showed that the precipitates (oxides) formed from solutions of gold and silver salts by ammonia are soluble in excess of this reagent;[1] the same is true of the precipitates formed with 'fixed alkali which had been calcined with dry ox-blood for the preparation of Berlin blue'. This would contain potassium cyanide, in which the precipitated carbonate, oxide, or cyanide of silver or gold would dissolve. In 1746 Marggraf obtained salts of gold and silver with vegetable acids (vinegar, lemon juice) by dissolving the precipitated oxides in the acids.[2]

In 1746 Marggraf showed that calamine ('Gallmey-Stein', native zinc carbonate) can be reduced to metallic zinc by distilling with charcoal in absence of air: the reaction is the same as in 'other reductions of metallic earths by the phlogiston of charcoal.[3] Welsh ore from Holywell (in Flintshire) gave the best yield, whilst some reputed German calamines gave no zinc. The precipitate from white vitriol (zinc sulphate) by alkali also furnished zinc. By boiling calamine with alum solution, the aluminous earth was precipitated and its acid joined to the earth (oxide) of zinc to form white vitriol.

A method used by Marggraf to obtain pure silver (1749) was to mix a solution of horn silver (AgCl) in ammonia with mercury, and drive off the mercury from the resulting solid amalgam by heat.[4] From 2 oz. of silver he obtained, by dissolving in nitric acid and precipitation, 2 oz. 5 drachms 4 grains, which is only slightly less than the correct amount. Marggraf's observation (1747) that commercial tin contains considerable amounts of arsenic[5] was erroneous and caused much trouble until refuted by Bayen (see Vol. III).

In an examination of the Bologna stone (heavy spar; barium sulphate; see p. 334) Marggraf concluded that its base is different from lime; it is heavier and more soluble. In the same work he found that a phosphorescent material (calcium sulphide) is formed by heating gypsum with charcoal.[6] Canton later[7] obtained the same material by heating calcined oyster-shells with sulphur in a crucible, hence it was called 'Canton's phosphorus'. By boiling finely powdered Bologna stone or gypsum with a solution of potash (potassium carbonate) Marggraf obtained crystals of vitriolated tartar (potassium sulphate) from the solution. He showed that gypsum contains water, lime and vitriolic acid.

---

[1] HAB, 1745 (1746), 61; I, i, 122; II, i, 72.
[2] HAB, 1746 (1748), 58; I, i, 112; II, i, 106; cf. Boerhaave, p. 755.
[3] HAB, 1746 (1748), 49–57; I, i, 263; II, i, 86 f.
[4] HAB, 1749 (1751), 16; I, i, 275; II, i, 265.
[5] HAB, 1747 (1749), 33; I, ii, 87, 106; II, i, 177.
[6] HAB, 1749 (1751), 56; 1750 (1752), 144; I, ii, 133, 135; II, i, 312, 351.
[7] Phil. Trans., 1768, lviii, 337.

Although taking precautions against the entry of dust (see p. 752), Marggraf thought he had proved that water, when distilled in glass retorts, is converted into an earth containing lime and silica.[1] In the experiments in 1751 he made use as a reagent of the lye (containing potassium ferrocyanide) used for making Prussian blue (Vol. III), which gave a blue colour with Berlin waters containing iron. He showed that nitrate is present in Berlin waters. Although Kopp[2] says that Benjamin Allen[3] had found selenite in natural water and stated, before Marggraf, that it consists of lime and sulphuric acid, Allen's statements did not seem to me as clear as this would suggest.

Stahl regarded alum as a compound of vitriolic acid and lime. Marggraf (1754) found that these substances produce only selenite (gypsum), which is a salt, not an earth. To obtain alum he treated clay with sulphuric acid, but found that crystals were formed only when potash or ammonia was added, so that alum contains these alkalis.[4] The 'earth of alum' (Alaun-Erde) is a peculiar one, present in combination with silica in clay.[5] It is precipitated by alkali from alum solution and, after drying in air, is soluble in acids, and is hence an 'alkaline earth'. Marggraf prepared salts of alumina, e.g. the crystalline nitrate and chloride and the non-crystalline acetate. By strongly heating a mixture of sand, earth of alum, steatite, and selenite, he obtained a white, compact mass striking sparks with steel.

Marggraf distinguished clearly (1758–9) between potash and the 'fixed mineral alkali' (soda) or alkali of common salt.[6] He mentions Duhamel's memoir of 1736 (see Vol. III) and says: 'Salze sind bekanntermassen schmackhafte im Wasser ganz auflösliche Körper.'[7] Duhamel's correct conclusions had been criticised by Pott,[8] so that Marggraf's experiments were necessary, although they did not add very much to Duhamel's.

To prepare 'the alkali of the mineral kingdom' (soda crystals, Na_2CO_3, 10 H_2O) Marggraf recrystallised common salt, heated $\frac{1}{2}$ oz. of the latter with 2 oz. of very strong spirit of nitre (nitric acid) in a retort, and evaporated to dryness, obtaining cubic nitre (sodium nitrate) which deflagrated with charcoal with a yellow flame (ordinary nitre with a bluish flame).[9] By distilling the cubic nitre with strong spirit of salt, common salt was regenerated. To obtain the alkali from cubic nitre he 'employed phlogiston'. He mixed 4 oz. of cubic nitre with 5 drachms of powdered willow charcoal, deflagrated the mixture in a crucible, dissolved the residue, filtered and evaporated. The crystals were like Glauber's salt, had a milder taste than vegetable alkali (potash), could be causticised with lime, and gave Glauber's salt with sulphuric acid. Glauber's salt fused with charcoal gave a liver of sulphur (sodium sulphide): 'macht mit

---

[1] HAB, 1751 (1753), 131; 1756 (1758), 20; I, i, 291, 325; II, ii, 176.   [2] (1), iv, 51.
[3] *Natural History of the Chalybeat and Purging Waters of England. With their Particular Essays and Uses*, sm. 8°, London, 1699, 96 f., 105 f., 114 f., 122 f.
[4] HAB, 1754 (1756), 31; I, i, 199; II, ii, 86.
[5] HAB, 1754 (1756), 41; I, i, 212, 226; II, ii, 111, 136.
[6] Von den besten Art das alcalische Wesen des gemeinen Salzes zu scheiden, I, i, 144; II, ii, 331; Erweis, dass der aus dem Koch-Salz geschiedene alcalischen Theil ein würkliches Sal alcali und keine Terra alcalina sey, I, i, 167; II, ii, 375 (from a MS.).
[7] I, i, 169.   [8] *Dissertations Chymiques*, 1759, ii, 297.
[9] Scheele remarked on this in 1767: Nordenskiöld, Scheele, *Nachgelassene Briefe*, Stockholm, 1892, 7.

dem Phlogisto carbonum im Feuer geschmolzen, eine eben so gute Schwefel-Leber als der Tartarus Vitriolatus mit besagten Phlogisto.'[1] The nitrate, acetate and formate were different from the potash salts: with cream of tartar 'ad saturationem' he obtained Seignette's salt.

Marggraf also showed in 1757[2] that a solution of platinum in aqua regia (which deposited red crystals on evaporation) gave a yellow precipitate with a potash salt (da fiel ein Pomeranzen-farbenes Pulver nieder) but no precipitate with a salt of soda. He particularly emphasises that the solution does not precipitate a solution of lead in nitric acid, which is peculiar 'since the acid of common salt exists in the aqua regia, which otherwise at once precipitates lead in the form of horn-lead (lead chloride)'.[3] In 1764 Marggraf showed by several experiments that the vegetable alkali (potash) is not generated *de novo* by combustion but is present (as salts) in the plant. Thus, from tartar (a natural product) by the action of nitric acid he obtained nitre, which is a salt of the vegetable alkali.[4]

By distilling fluorspar and sulphuric acid in a glass retort, he thought in 1768 that he had obtained a 'volatile earth' — actually silica, deposited by water in the receiver from the gaseous silicon fluoride.[5] By precipitating the mother liquor of salt brine with salt of tartar (potassium carbonate) he obtained a white precipitate which gave Epsom salt with sulphuric acid, and he thus again distinguished magnesia from lime,[6] confirming the work of Hoffmann (see p. 695), whom he mentions; he was apparently ignorant of Black's publication of 1756.[7] Marggraf also showed that the earth (Erdart), i.e. magnesia, is the base of the serpentine of Saxony, which is not aluminous; his experiments were confirmed by Bayen (1775).[8] Marggraf showed that a piece of paper dipped in a solution of magnesium nitrate and dried burns with a green flame.[9]

In his memoir on beet sugar[10] Marggraf showed that sugar exactly like that of the cane exists in many plants (*Beta alba; Sisarum Dodonaei*-now *Sium Sisarum, Beta radice Rapæ Seu rubra*), particularly the beet and carrot. It can be extracted from the dried roots by boiling alcohol, from which it crystallises on cooling. He also obtained it from beet juice by purification with milk of lime and crystallising. Although Marggraf pointed out the economic importance of his discovery, its technical exploitation was begun by Achard in 1796 (see Vol. III).

Marggraf in 1747 (before Proust, Vol. III) also pointed out that dried grapes (raisins) contain a peculiar sugar. In 1749 Marggraf investigated oil of ants and

---

[1] I, i, 171; II, ii, 331.
[2] Versuche mit dem neuen mineralischen Körper Platina del Pinto genannt; HAB, 1757 (1759), 31; I, i, 1; II, ii, 226 (253).
[3] II, ii, 240.　　　　　　[4] I, ii, 49; II, ii, 414.
[5] HAB, 1768 (1770), 3; Partington, *Manchester Mem.*, 1923, lxvii, No. 6, 73.
[6] HAB, 1760 (1767), 75; I, i, 183; ii, 1, 20, 32; II, ii, 406.
[7] Bergman, *Opusc.*, 1779, i, 366.
[8] Bayen, *Opuscules Chimiques*, An VI, ii, 108.　　　　　[9] II, ii, 412.
[10] Chemical experiments made with the object of obtaining a true sugar from various plants which grow in our countries; HAB, 1747 (1749), 79; I, ii, 70; II, i, 213; Ostwald's *Klassiker*, 1907, clix (ed. Lippmann); R. Pique, *Compt. Rend. du VIe Congrès de Chimie industr.*, 1927, 625, q. in *Isis*, 1938, xxviii, 264, says beet sugar was discovered by Olivier de Serres, chief gardener to Henri IV. Jöcher, iv, 528, calls him a physician and ments. his *Théâtre d'Agriculture*, f°, 1600; NBG, 1864, xliii, 792–5.

acid of ants (formic acid). He showed that the acid reduces mercuric oxide to mercury. He prepared several metallic formates,[1] including the beautiful green crystals of the copper salt, and those of lead formate (like lead acetate). He heated potassium formate with concentrated sulphuric acid but missed the inflammable carbon monoxide evolved.

Minor researches by Marggraf dealt with potassium tartrate (1770), pyrolusite (1773),[2] lapis lazuli,[3] the action of alkali of common salt on regulus of antimony,[4] cedar wood,[5] and a product smelling of musk from oil of amber and concentrated nitric acid.[6] He says camphor is purified commercially by subliming it from slaked lime.[7] He investigated the action of sulphuric acid on several stones and earths,[8] the solution of tin in vegetable acids and on arsenic contained in tin,[9] osteocolla,[10] fixed alkali from the rhinoceros,[11] the action of sulphuric acid on several stones and earths,[12] Carlsbad water,[13] and an insect feeding on the leaves of the woad plant and therefrom becoming blue.[14] He published a letter from Model refuting Buchholtz.[15]

His paper on the preparation of fixed alkali from tartar by means of acids, without employing a violent fire,[16] may have suggested the preparation of tartaric acid to Scheele. Papers in the *Nouveaux Mémoires* of the Berlin Academy deal with tortoises (tortuës d'aigue),[17] a red vegetable lake (dye),[18] the parts of the lime tree,[19] the composition of metals and semi-metals,[20] an analysis of a calculus,[21] the topaz from Schneckenberg,[22] the fusibility of earths with the earth (magnesia) of bitter salt,[23] the presence of arsenic in gold ruby glass,[24] the production of copper from the ore,[25] the imitation of gems by fused pastes,[26] and the calcination of cobalt.[27]

DELIUS

Heinrich Friedrich von Delius (Wernigerode, 8 July 1720–Erlangen, 22 October 1791), professor of medicine in Erlangen[28] published on chemistry, botany, and medicine. His numerous dissertations and publications, rather inaccessible, listed by Gmelin, are now unimportant.

He recommended the use of porcelain crucibles (1778), showed that the so-called Würtemberg wine test for lead, a solution prepared from orpiment and slaked lime by Johann Zeller, a physician of Tübingen, gave a black precipitate (ferrous sulphide) in the absence of lead (1779). He converted Glauber's salt into sodium sulphide by reduction and converted this into sodium nitrate (1783). His dissertation on forensic chemistry[29] is rudimentary, the first detailed work on this subject being by Wilhelm Hermann Remer.[30]

[1] HAB, 1749 (1751), 38; I, i, 340; II, i, 291.   [2] *Nouv. Mém. Acad. Berlin,* 1773 (1775), 3.
[3] I, i, 131; II, ii, 305.   [4] I, i, 190; II, ii, 421.   [5] I, i, 247; II, ii, 72.
[6] Nachricht von einigen merkwürdigen chymischen Observationen, Von Vitriolo martiali, etc.; I, i, 255; II, ii, 438 f., 450.
[7] II, ii, 454.   [8] I, ii, 11.
[9] HAB, 1747 (1749), 33; 1756 (1758), 122; II, i, 177; ii, 204.
[10] HAB, 1748 (1750), 52; I, ii, 163; II, i, 245.
[11] HAB, 1756 (1758), 145; I, ii, 174; II, ii, 216.   [12] I, ii, 11.   [13] I, ii, 191.
[14] *Nouv. Mém. Acad. Berlin,* 1764 (1766), 18; I, ii, 180.   [15] I, ii, 197.
[16] HAB, 1764 (1766), 3.   [17] 1770 (1772), 3.   [18] 1771 (1773), 3.
[19] 1772 (1774), 3.   [20] 1774 (1776), 108.   [21] 1775 (1777), 3.
[22] 1776 (1779), 73.   [23] 1778 (1780), 3.   [24] 1779 (1781), 3.
[25] 1779 (1781), 7.   [26] 1780 (1782), 3.   [27] 1781 (1783), 3.
[28] Gmelin, (1), ii, 406, 625–33; Kopp, (1), ii, 29, 62 (dates him 1725–88); iv, 38, 135; Poggendorff, (1), i, 544.
[29] *Dissertatio sistens primas lineas chemiae forensis,* 4°, Erlangen, 1771.
[30] *Lehrbuch der polizeilich-gerichtlichen Chemie,* 8°, Helmstädt, 1803; 3 ed., 2 vols. 1827.

BERNHARDT

Johann Christian Bernhardt (no particulars of whom are available to me)[1] first described the formation of solid sulphur trioxide (*sal volatile olei vitrioli*) by distilling fuming sulphuric acid and distinguished it from hydrated oil of vitriol solid above 0°, whilst others called them both *oleum glaciale*.[2]

CARTHEUSER

Johann Friedrich Cartheuser (Hayne, Stolberg, 29 September 1704–Frankfurt on the Oder, 22 June 1777) was professor of chemistry, pharmacy, and materia medica (1740–59), then of therapeutics and pathology in the university of Frankfurt on the Oder.[3]

His writings, which are of interest from the point of view of botany and phytochemistry, are very numerous and only the following were available to me:

I. Specimen Amoenitatvm Natvrae & Artis Oder Kurtze Probe von Der . . . Abhandlung Aller Merckwürdigkeiten Der Natur und Kunst, 4°, Halle, 1733 (BM 435. b. 2. (1.)): deals with amber (p. 51), mineral water (Sauerbrunnen) (p. 83), and phosphorus (Von Den Phosphoro Brandii, pp. 106–16).

II. Amoenitatvm Natvrae, sive Historiæ Naturalis Pars Prima, Oder . . . Abhandlung Aller Merckwürdigkeiten Der Natur Erster Theil, 4°, Halle, 1735 (BM 435. b. 2. (2.)): deals with air (Lufft, p. 89), minerals (p. 280), plants (p. 337) and animals.

III. Elementa chemiae medicae dogmatico-experimentalis, una cum synposi materiae medicae selectioris. In usum tyronum edita, Halle, 1736 (360 pp.); Frankfurt on the Oder, 1753, 3 ed. 1766.

IV. Dissertatio Chymico-Physica de Genericis Plantarvm Principiis, hactenvs plervmque neglectis, Frankfurt a.M., 1754; describes camphor, waxes (including Chinese tree wax), lac, cocoa butter, soap, dry volatile oils, flowers of benzoin, sugar, and balsamic acidulous spirit.

V. Dissertationes physico-chymico-medicae, annis nuperis de quibusdam materiae medicae subjectis exaratae ac publice habitae. Nunc iterum recusae, Frankfurt on the Oder:

(a) 1774 (BM B. 188. (1.)) describes Mungo root (p. 1; 1769), opobalsam (p. 51; 1770), millepedes (p. 80; 1771), Ceylon cassia (p. 109; 1773), and Colombo root (p. 136; 1773).

(b) 1775 (BM B. 188. (2.)) deals with cinnabar (de cinnabaris inertia medica, p. 1; 1743), myrrh (de eximia myrrhae genuinae virtute, p. 28; 1746), cajeput oil (p. 87; 1754), crocus of iron (de crocis martialibus, p. 133; 1759), starch (p. 187; 1767), respiration (Wolff, 1772, p. 296, mentioning Mayow), and oily volatile salts (de sale volatili oleoso solido in oleis æthereis reperto) (p. 327; 1774).

In his text-book he says spirit of wine (spiritus sulphurei ardentes ut plurimum vinosi) is a compound of water and oil or sulphur,[4] mentions Dippel's animal oils,[5] says that calcination is the expulsion of sulphur or volatile

---

[1] *Chymische Versuche und Erfahrungen, aus Vitriole, Salpeter, Ofenruss, Quecksilber, Arsenik, Galbano, Myrrhen, der Peruvianer Fieberrinde und Fliegenschwämmen kräftige Arzneyen zu machen*, 8°, Leipzig, 1755 (pp. xxx, 328, viii; 3 plates), 3, 45 (BN Te¹⁴⁷. 62).
[2] Gmelin, (1), ii, 473, 587; Kopp, (1), ii, 131; iii, 305, 312; Duveen, 70.
[3] Gmelin, (1), ii, 387, 621, 683; Poggendorff, (1), i, 384.
[4] III, 59; Thomson, *Ency. Brit. Suppl.*, 1801, I, i, 294, and Kopp, (1), iv, 284, say that Cartheuser regarded alcohol as a compound of pure phlogiston and the element water, but in the 1736 ed. he does not mention phlogiston.
[5] III, 118.

salt from bodies,[1] and defines a clyssus as the result of the deflagration of a body with saltpetre.[2] He described lac gum.[3]

The son of Johann Friedrich, Friedrich August Cartheuser (Halle, 1734–Schierstein, 12 December 1796), was privatdocent in mineralogy, botany, and chemistry at Frankfurt on the Oder (1754–66), professor of natural history in Giessen, then a Bergrath.[4] He showed that silica cannot be converted into lime or alumina.[5] In attempting to crystallise vegetable alkali (potassium carbonate) he distilled carbonate of ammonia from it and found that the residual solution deposited crystals. These were potassium bicarbonate but he did not recognise this.[6]

METALLURGY AND ASSAYING

During the eighteenth century great numbers of books on metallurgy and assaying appeared in Germany, some of them anonymous; a few titles are collected below:[7]

Christian Carl Schindler, Metallische Probier-Kunst das ist eigentlicher Bericht von dem Ursprung und Erkäntnüs derer metallischen Ertzen . . ., Dresden, 8°, 1697 (BN); id., Der geheimbde Münz-Guardein und Bergprobirer, 8°, Frankfurt, 1705; tr. by C. J. Geoffroy, L'Art d'Essayer les Mines et les Métaux, 12°, Paris, 1759; Die aufrichtig entdeckte Probier- und Scheidekunst der Venetianer, 8°, Saalfeld, 1717; Probierkunst, mit einer Erklärung aller chymischen Wörter und Zeichen, auch Bericht vom Salpetersieden, 12°, Nürnberg, 1718; David Kellner, Ars separatoria reformata et renovata, oder erneuerte und sehr nüzliche Scheidekunst, 12°, Leipzig, 1693; 8°, Chemniz, 1727; Ars fusoria fundamentalis et experimentalis, oder gründliche aus Erfarenheit stammende Schmelzkunst, wie auch Unterricht vom Rohschmelzen, Rösten und Saigern, 12°, Cassel, 1735; J. G. Kiessling, Relatio practica de arte probatoria, mineralium et metallorum, d.i. Erzehlung, wie alle Mineralien probirt und geschieden werden, 8°, Leipzig, 2 ed., 1752; J. E. Claus, Kurzgefasste Anleitung zum Probiren und Müntzen, 8°, Stollberg, 1753; Der wohlerfahrne Scheidekünstler, 8°, Frankfurt and Leipzig, 1755; Eröffnetes Geheimniss der Probierkunst, des Münzwesens und Feuerleinsverrichtung, 8°, Leipzig, 1756; J. G. Lehmann, Probirkunst, 8°, Berlin, 1761; M. Krapp, Dissertation pref. J. G. Wallerius, Proberkonsten, 4°, Uppsala, 1760; J. G. Jugel, Gründlicher Naturbericht des ganzen mineralischen Reichs, oder naturliche Berg- Schmelz- und Figirkunst, Th. I, 8°, Vienna, 1765, and Vollkommene Bergwerkskunst, Th. II, der Bergmann vom Feuer, 8°, Berlin, 1773; Kurze und deutliche Vorstellung der edlen Probierkunst, 8°, Nürnberg, 1766 (perhaps the same as Deutlicher Vorstellung der edlen Probierkunst nebst einem Bericht vom Salpeter, 8°, Nürnberg, 1770).

BORN

The amalgamation process for the extraction of gold and silver, practised in Mexico about 1590 (see p. 39), was improved and introduced in Schemnitz by Baron Ignaz Edler von Born (Carlsburg, Transylvania, 26 December 1742–

---

[1] III, 165.   [2] III, 178.

[3] IV; *Acta Acad. Mogunt.*, 1776, i, 56; *ib.*, 58, on the water plant Bardiage.

[4] Poggendorff, (1), i, 385; Elwert, *Nachrichten von dem Leben und dem Schriften jetzlebenden teutscher Aerzte, Wundaerzte und Natuforscher*, Hildesheim, 1799 i (all publ.), 109; F. A. Cartheuser, *Elementa Mineralogiæ systematice disposita*, 8°, Frankfurt on the Oder, 1755; *Vermischte Schriften*, 8°, Leipzig and Magdeburg, 1759 (Gmelin gives Frankfurt on the Oder, 1756–7); *Mineralogische Abhandlungen*, 2 vols. 8°, Giessen, 1771–3 (BM 990. c. 20).

[5] *Miner. Abhl.*, ii, 220.

[6] *Acta Acad. Mogunt.*, 1757, i, 149: Observatio chemico-physica de crystallisatione salium alcalium fixorum (BM 963. a. 34).

[7] From Gmelin, (1), iii, 55–6; and Bolton, (1); I have not seen many of them.

Vienna, 28 April (or 24 July) 1791). He was educated by Jesuits in Vienna (he joined the order but left it after 16 mònths) and in law in Prague, travelled in Germany, Holland, the Low Countries and France, studying mining, and after being nearly killed by suffocation in a mine, was called in 1776 to Vienna to catalogue the imperial natural history collection for Maria Theresa, and became Aulic Councillor in the Department of Mines and the Mint in Vienna.

In 1769 Born founded a Privatgesellschaft in Böhmen, which later published six volumes of *Abhandlungen* (Prague, 1775–84), containing papers by him.[1] This later became the Böhmische Gesellschaft der Wissenschaften (1785), and in 1791 the Königlich Böhmische Gesellschaft. An account of his travels, of mineralogical interest, in the form of letters to Ferber was published:

Ignaz von Born Briefe über mineralogische Gegenstände auf seiner Reise durch den Temeswarer Bannat, Siebenbürgen, Ober- und Niederhungarn, an den Herausgeber derselben, J. J. Ferber, geschrieben, 8°, Frankfurt and Leipzig, 1774; Engl. tr. by R. E. Raspe, Travels through the Bannat of Temeswar, etc., To which is added, J. J. Ferber's mineralogical History of Bohemia, 8°, 1777; French tr. by A. G. Monnet, Voyage Minéralologique faite en Hongrie et en Transylvanie, 12°, 1780 (Sotheran *Cat.* 837 (1933), 38, no. 571), also Italian, Venice, 1778.

He issued *Physikalische Arbeiten der einträchtigen Freunde in Wien*, 6 pts. in 2 vols., Vienna, 1783–8.[2] With Friedrich Wilhelm Heinrich von Trebra he published a work on mining.[3] Born also published works on mineralogy,[4] but his most famous book is on the amalgamation process:

Ueber das Anquicken der gold- und silberhältige Erze, Rohsteine, Schwarzkupfer und Hüttenspeise, 4°, Vienna, 1786 (viii ll., 227 pp., frontispiece, bust of Joseph II), vignette on t.p. and 2 in text on amalgamation process in Chile; 21 folding plates; gives excerpts from Alonso Barba, Joseph Acosta, Don Juan de Corduba, Francisco Xavier de Gamboa, Juan Ordonnez Montalvo, etc., and an account of Born's own amalgamation process for gold and silver;
French tr.: Méthode d'extraire les métaux parfait des minerais et autres substances métallique par le mercure, 4°, Vienna, 1788 (iv, 198 pp., 21 plates); also 8° (iv, 295 pp., 21 plates); another ed., Métallurgie, ou l'Amalgamation des Minéraux, Méthode d'extraire par le Mercure, 8°, Bern, 1787, with supplement, Lettres de M. Rubin de Celis à MM. Duhamel et de Born, avec une répouse de M. Born sur l'Amalgamation des Métaux en Allemagne, 8°, 1789;
English tr.: Baron Inigo Born's new Process of Amalgamation of Gold and Silver Ores, and other Metallic Mixtures, tr. R. E. Raspe, 4°, 1791, 22 plates, with Supplement, or comparative View of the former Method of Melting and Refining; and an address to the Subscribers, giving an Account of its Latest Improvements, and of the Quicksilver Trade (London Chem. Soc.).

The amalgamation process consisted in first roasting the ore, which must contain some pyrites, with common salt, when silver chloride is formed. This was reduced by mercury in rotating horizontal barrels, and the silver amalgam produced was separated and the mercury removed by distillation per descen-

---

[1] Gmelin, (1), iii, 609.   [2] Gmelin, iii, 610.
[3] *Bergbaukunde*, 2 vols. 4°, Leipzig, 1789–90, with 11 folding copperplates; Gmelin, (1), iii, 611, says this was published by a Gesellschaft der Bergbaukunde; vol. ii, 200–96, contains a paper by Fausto d'Elhuyar on the theory of the amalgamation process.
[4] *Index Fossilium quæ collegit, et in classes ac Ordines disposuit*, 2 vols., Prague, 1772, 1775 (with plates); *Catalogue Méthodique et Raisonné de la Collection des Fossiles de M*[lle] *Éléonore de Raab*, 2 vols., Vienna, 1790.

sum. The process required a supply of mercury which was obtained from cinnabar at Almaden in Spain (worked by the Romans) and Idria (Yugoslavia, former Austria Hungary, worked since 1508). There is a description, with illustrations, of the process of extraction of mercury used at Almaden by Antoine de Jussieu[1] and an account of the mines and extraction of mercury in the Palatinate and Zweibrücken by an anonymous author.[2]

Born found native metallic antimony in Siebenbürgen (1777).[3] He characterised the Hungarian red schörl in which Klaproth later discovered titanium,[4] described the preparation of tombac by amalgamation,[5] and invented a laboratory bellows-blowpipe.[6] In collaboration with Anton von Ruprecht, at first a teacher of chemistry in the School of Mines at Schemnitz, then Hofrath for mines and coinage in the Hofkammer in Vienna, Born described the supposed isolation of molybdenum, tungsten, and metals from baryta, magnesia, lime, and silica.[7]

An apothecary, Capell of Copenhagen, reported that some gold is produced when silver is heated with arsenic[8] and Guyton de Morveau[9] confirmed this. Born showed that the result is obtained with arsenic from Salzburg, the kind commonly sold, which contains traces of gold, but not with Bohemian arsenic, which is free from gold.[10]

RASPE

A colourful personality was the translator of Born's book, the German scholar-vagabond Rudolf Erich Raspe (Hannover, 1737–Muckross, Ireland, end of 1794), at first professor of archaeology and conservator of the Museum in Cassel. He published a book on geology which drew attention to Hooke's work[11] and edited the works of Leibniz from manuscripts in Cassel.[12]

In Latin papers to the Royal Society he concluded that elephants (mammoths) of which fossil teeth and bones were found in America were originally natives of the northern regions and that the bones were not those of true elephants,[13] and that white marble had been deposited from water like tufa of hot-springs;[14] and in a letter to the Secretary 'containing a Short Account of some Basalt Hills in Hessia', with two plates, he described some basalts near Cassel, concluding (with Desmarest, 1771, who is mentioned) that basalt is of volcanic origin.[15] He was made F.R.S. in 1769.

[1] AdS, 1719, m 346–62, 2 plates.   [2] *J. des Mines*, An III, No. VI, 69–78, No. VII, 3–24.
[3] Gmelin, (1), iii, 693; native antimony was discovered in 1748 in Sweden by Swab, KAH, 1748, ix, 99–106.
[4] Born, *Catal. de la Collect. de Mlle Raab*, 1790, i, 168; Klaproth, *Analytical Essays*, 1801, i, 200.
[5] Crell's *Ann.*, 1787, II, 517.   [6] Köstler, Crell's *N. Entdeck.*, 1782, iv, 3–8, plate.
[7] Crell's *Ann.*, 1790, I, 483; 1790, II, 5, 91, 195, 291, 483; 1791, I, 3 (on Ruprecht and Tondi), 99, 387.
[8] Report by Kratzenstein, Crell's *N. Entdeck.*, 1783, x, 136–7.
[9] Crell's *Ann.*, 1786, II, 427.   [10] Klaproth, Crell's *Ann.*, 1787, I, 337 (report).
[11] *Specimen Historiæ Naturalis Globi Terraquei, præcipue de novis e mari natis insulis, et ex his exactius descriptis et observatis ulterius confirmanda Hookiana telluris hypothesi, de origine montium et corporum petrefactorum*, 8°, Amsterdam and Leipzig, 1763 (BM 987. i. 9; BN 21677; xxii, 191 pp).
[12] *Oeuvres philosophiques latines et françoises*, 4°, Amsterdam and Leipzig, 1765.
[13] *Phil. Trans.*, 1769, lix, 126–37.
[14] *Phil. Trans.*, 1770, lx, 47–53.   [15] *Phil. Trans.*, 1771, lxi, 580–3.

Having purloined medals from the collection in Cassel of which he was curator, he departed for England in 1775 and was expelled from the Royal Society. He made his paper on basalts into a small book[1] and published a history of oil painting[2] and a catalogue of gems (he was associated with James Tassie, who modelled in a white vitreous paste),[3] but his most famous work was the anonymous collection of tall stories, *Baron Munchausen's Narrative of his Marvellous Travels and Campaigns in Russia* (Oxford, 1785, later enlarged eds.). He acted as a spy for Boulton and Watt in Cornwall and had the post of assay master with a laboratory at Entral, from which he communicated a paper on analyses of two tungsten minerals (scheelite, calcium tungstate), from which he alleged he had extracted the metal 'im Schmelzfeuer'.[4] In 1791 in a tour in the North of Scotland he professed to discover signs of great mineral wealth and induced Sir John Sinclair to part with a substantial sum of money (Raspe is the original of Dousterswivel in Sir Walter Scott's *The Antiquary*). He absconded to Ireland, where he died.[5]

PALLAS

Much information on the mines and industries in Asiatic Russia, the Crimea, and Siberia, collected in travels by Peter Simon Pallas (1741–1811), in large part reflects earlier techniques, including that of the Chudes (Estonians):

    A. *Voyages* [1768–74] en differentes provinces de l'empire de Russie et dans l'Asie septentrionale, tr. from German by Gaulthier de la Peyronie, 6 vols. 4°, Paris, 1788–93 (Vol. vi plates).

    B. *Voyages enterpris dans les gouvernemens méridionaux de l'empire de Russie dans les années 1793 et 1794*, tr. from German by Delaboulaye and Tonnelier, 2 vols. 4°, Paris, 1805 (vol. ii plates).

He describes the primitive industries of the Chudes (A i, 425; ii, 160, 212; iii, 331 f.) using copper picks and tools and stone hammers; the sack bellows open at one end, also used by the Kalmuks (Tartars) (A i, 520), the mining of native gold, silver, electrum and copper (A ii, 207; iii, 323), the silver mine at Kuchuk (A ii, 153), the mines and metallurgy of the Urals (A ii, 91–403, 453) and Siberia (A iii, 217 f., 293 f., 310 f., 321 f., including much zinc at Schlangenberg), lacquering at Névianskoi (A ii, 260), dyeing (A i, 95 f.), the distillation of brandy in Siberia by a very crude method (A iii, 75), a forge (A iii, 352),

[1] *Account of some German Volcanos, with a New Hypothesis of the Prismatical Basalts, established upon facts*, 8°, London, 1776, 136 [140] pp.

[2] *A Critical Essay on Oil-Painting; Proving that the Art of Painting in Oil was known before the pretended discovery of John and Hubert Van Eyck; To which are added, Theophilus De Arte Pingendi Eraclius De Artibus Romanorum. And a Review of Farinator's Lumen Animæ*, 4°, London, 1781, 148 pp., with extracts from Cambridge MSS. of Theophilus and Heraclius (see Vol. I).

[3] *A Descriptive Catalogue of a General Collection of Ancient and Modern Engraved Gems . . . Taken from the Most Celebrated Cabinets in Europe and Cast . . . by J. Tassie . . .*, 2 vols. 4°, London, 1791; a *Reise nach England in Rücksicht auf Manufakturen, bildende Künste, Industries* etc., Berlin, 1785, was probably never published; see Carswell, 263.

[4] *Sur l'analyse chimique le quelques minéraux remarquables; Nova Acta Acad. Petropol.*, 1785, iii, 63–7 (in German), dated 'Entral bey Mamborn [i.e. Camborne] in Cornwall 5 März 1785'.

[5] Seccombe, DNB, 1896, xlvii, 301; J. Carswell, *The Prospector. Being the Life and Times of Rudolf Erich Raspe (1737–1794)*, 1950.

compressed dung fuel used by the Crimean Tartars (B i, 58, 542), crusts of Glauber salt and sylvine (KCl) on sand near Astrakhan (B i, 107), saltpetre in an old cemetery (B i, 111), the magnesium sulphate and common salt of Lake Krasnoijarsk (B i, 118), saltpetre manufacture (B i, 160, 163) and a hill of salt-petre at Scharenoi Bugor (B i, 205), Turkey-red dyeing with madder at Astrakhan (B i, 235), where there were Brahmins painted with cinnabar (B i, 260), coal mines north of Taganrog (B i, 543), wolfram mines in Tar-sak (B i, 569), and the Siberian meteorite found with 'natural glass' (B i, 164). The inhabitants of Tibet had anticipated Darwin by claiming descent from aboriginal monkeys (B i, 602).

CHAPTER XX

BOERHAAVE

MAETS

Before Boerhaave there were some notable teachers of chemistry in Leyden. The first chemical laboratory in the University was opened in 1665.[1] Charles Louis (Carolus Ludovicus) van Maets (de Maets) (Utrecht, *c.* 1640–Leyden, 29 January 1690) lecturer in chemistry at Utrecht from 1668, went to Leyden in 1669, was acting professor of medicine in Leyden from 1670, full professor from 1679,[2] compiled an introduction to rational chemistry and published anonymously a rational philosophical chemistry.[3]

MORLEY

In 1684 an Englishman, Christopher Love Morley, M.D. (Leyden 1679), F.R.C.P.,[4] b. *c.* 1646, who practised in London from 1684, published a collection of notes of the Leyden courses by de Maets, Marggrav, and Le Mort.[5] The *Collectanea* contains recipes arranged topically in alphabetical order, the name of the author (de Maets, Margravius, and Le Mort) responsible for each being given in the margin. De Maets attacked this book in the *Animadversiones* in his *Prodromus* (1684), saying it was published without his knowledge, and Morley's knowledge or consent (as the printer admits in the preface), from his lecture notes lent to a friend, and he had never had Morley as a private auditor. After the death of de Maets, a disciple of his, Theodore Muykens, published a corrected and enlarged edition.[6] An edition of 1696 had Le Mort's name omitted.[7]

[1] Jorissen, *Chem. Weekbl.*, 1919, xvi, 1054.

[2] Poggendorff, (1), ii, 10 (says d. after 1700); Thorndike, vii, 145; Van der Aa, *Biographisch Woordenboek der Nederlanden*, Haarlem, 1869, xii, 66.

[3] *Prodromus Chemiæ Rationalis . . .*, Leyden, 1684 (Animadversiones, pp. 3–16; Prodromus, pp. 17–77, BM 1165. c. 23. (2.); *Chemia Rationalis Rationibus Philosophicis*, 4°, Leyden, 1687, 1690; BM Sloane MSS. 1235, 1286, contain his private lectures in Leyden, 1675–6, Sloane MS. 1278 a medical *Collegium practicum* held at Leyden in 1680, and Sloane MS. 3287 *Chemical Experiments*, both in Latin, an English tr. of 1676 being in Sloane MS. 1292. The MSS. deal with embalming, cosmetics, and chemical and secret recipes taken from named authors.

[4] Payne, DNB, 1894, xxxix, 73.

[5] *Collectanea Chymica Leydensia, id est, Maëtsiana, Margraviana, Le Mortiana. Scilicet trium in Academia Lugduno-Batavâ Facultatis Chimicæ . . . Professorum*, 4°, Leyden, 1684 (BM 1033. k. 17); Ferguson, i, 153; ii, 110; Duveen, 378; German tr., 8°, Jena, 1696; extensive notes of Morley's medical and chemical lectures at Leyden in 1677–9 are contained in BM Sloane MSS. 1259–80, 1282–94, 1297–9; Thorndike, viii, 152.

[6] *Collectanea*, 8°, Leyden, 1693; Ferguson, ii, 110; Sotheran *Cat.* 889 (1951), no. 1009; engr. f.p., t.p., 22 ll. (incl. unpaged Prolegomena), 587 pp., 18 ll. index.

[7] Thorndike, viii, 165.

LE MORT

Jacobus Le Mort (Haarlem, 13 October 1650–Leyden, 1 April 1718), son of a chemist, at first worked with de Maets but in 1672 opened a laboratory in Leyden, starting a pharmacy in 1675, also giving private instruction in chemistry, pharmacy, and medicine. In 1676 he became M.D. of Utrecht. In 1694 (or 1696) he received permission to teach chemistry publicly in Leyden, and in 1702 was made a professor in the faculty.[1] He was familiar with Boyle's writings, imbued with the atomic theory, and followed Descartes in paying special attention to the shapes of the particles; drugs are saline, watery, or earthy, the first giving acridity, the second attentuation, and the third viscosity to the humours. He opposed the theory of ferments.[2] He wrote several chemical works:

Compendium Chymicum, 12°, Leyden, 1682; Chymia Medico-Physica, Rationibus et Experimentis Instructa, Brevi et facili via, Processus Spagyricos rite et Artificiose ad finem perducendi, normans exhibens. Cui annexa est, metallurgia Contracta, Succinctam Metallorum tractionem demonstrans, 8°, Leyden, Van der Aa, 1684 (Duveen, 350); Chymia Rationibus et Experimentis auctoribus usque demonstrativis superstructa . . . , 8°, Leyden, 1688 (Thorndike, viii, 163); Pharmacia Medico-Physica Rationibus & Experimentis Instructa, 8°, London, Abel Swalle, 1684 (Duveen, 350); Chymiæ Veræ Nobilitas & Utilitas, in Physica Corpusculari, Theoria Medica . . . Quibus seorsim excusa Collectanea, Maetsiana & Marcgraviana, Bibliopolæ subjunxerunt, 4°, Leyden, 1696 (Ferguson, ii, 24; CUL L. 4. 28).

These use Cartesian ideas of shapes of particles, theories of atoms and pores, etc., combined with practical recipes.[3]

Le Mort published an attack on Marggraf.[4] The Leyden chemists seem to have been unusually touchy and quarrelsome, since in addition to de Maets' attack on Morley, and this of Le Mort on Marggrav, Marggrav published an attack on Le Mort.[5]

Christiaan Marggrav is said[6] to have been a professor of medicine in Leyden,[7] where he died in 1687. He wrote medical and pharmaceutical works.[8]

Steven Blanckaert (Middelburg, 24 October 1650–Amsterdam, 23 February 1702)

---

[1] Thorndike, viii, 163.

[2] Sprengel, (1), 1815, v, 104.

[3] Fourcroy, Ency. Méthod., Chimie, 1796, iii, 748, 751, also quotes as by Le Mort: Facies & pulchritudo chemiæ ab affectis maculis purificata, atque ad veras naturæ suæ leges exornata, 8°, Leyden, 1712; Idiæ actionis corporum motum intestinam præsertim fermentationis delineans, 8°, Leyden, 1693.

[4] Ignorantia circa chemiam et universam scientiam naturalem detecta a C. Marggravio, Leyden, 1687 (BM); Chymia ab insidiis erroribus et calumniis Philosophorum et Galenicorum . . . vindicata, Leyden, 1700 (BM).

[5] Jacobi Le Mort, Pseudochemici et Ratiocinatoris Dupondiarii, Ignorantia circa Chemiam et Universam Scientiam Naturalem detecta, 12°, Leyden, 1687 (Sotheran Cat. 800 (1926), no. 11515).

[6] Jöcher, iii, 165; Gmelin, (1), ii, 238, 248.

[7] Poggendorff, (1), ii, 50, remarks that he is not mentioned in Siegenbeek, Geschiedenis der Leid'sche Hoogeshool, Leiden, 1832.

[8] Prodromus Medicinæ Practicæ Dogmaticæ & verè Rationalis. Superstructæ circulari sanguinis motui, nec non Principiis Chemicis ac Hypothesi Helmontianæ & Sylvianæ, Leyden, 1674 (112 pp.), 2 ed. 4°, Leyden, 1685 (xii ll., with life, 173 pp., vii pp. index); Materia Medica Contracta, exhibens Simplicia et Composita Medicamenta Officinalia, 4°, Leyden, 1674 (BM 547. f. 10); 2 ed. Amsterdam, 1682 (280 pp.).

was the author of a book on practical chemistry,[1] and a dictionary of medical terms.[2]

Most of the Dutch physicians at the end of the 17 and beginning of the 18 cents. were Iatrochemical and many also Cartesian. Benjamin Broekhuysen wrote a treatise on physiology on Cartesian principles.[3] Cornelis Bontekoë (Alkmaar, 1647–Berlin, 14 January 1685), whose real name was Dekker, took the name Bontekoë, 'bunte Kuh' in German, because his father kept an inn at the sign of the Spotted Cow. He was later professor at Frankfurt on the Oder. He recommended the use of opium, the incessant smoking of tobacco, and the continual drinking of tea (forty or fifty cups in succession), or sometimes coffee, for illness and prolonging life. This was to encourage Dutch trade. Bontekoë supported Sylvius's theory of acid and alkali.[4]

LEYDEN PHYSICISTS

There was also a notable school of physics in Leyden. Wolferd Senguerd (1646–1724), professor of philosophy in Leyden,[5] invented an air-pump with double perforated stopcocks. He was eclectic, trying to reconcile the Aristotelian with the new corpuscular philosophy, and was an admirer of Boyle. In his book on natural philosophy and the species of bodies[6] he defined fermentation as an irregular intestine motion in a body, produced by the impeded translation of the most subtle particles, facilitated by heat, and tending to divide bodies, in which they are aided by the coarser particles. In it, the pores in the body must be impervious, so that the colliding particles cannot escape; if they pass through the pores, fermentation ceases. He admits that a vacuum is possible and explained the barometer in terms of the pressure of the air, and he recognised the elastic force of air. In another work[7] he explains that the corpuscles of elastic bodies are rigid, oblong, and branching. In later life Senguerd turned to law as a profession.

Burchard (Burcherus) de Volder (Amsterdam, 20 July 1643–Leyden, 28 March 1709), M.D., professor of natural philosophy and of mathematics (1681) in Leyden, an enthusiastic follower of Boyle, published on the weight of air and improved the air-pump. He visited England in 1674 and probably met

---

[1] *De Nieuwe Hedendaagsche Stof-Scheiding, ofte Chymia*, 8°, Amsterdam, 1678, 1685; tr. *Die neue Heutiges Tages gebräuchliche Scheide-Kunst, oder Chimia nach den Gründen des fürtreflichen Cartesii und des Alcali und Acidi eingerichtet*, 8°, Hannover and Wolfenbüttel, 1697 (BN R 29154); Hannover 1708, Wolfenbüttel, 1718.

[2] *Lexicon Medicum Graeco-latinum*, 8°, Amsterdam, 1679 and later eds., e.g. Leyden, 1702 (portr.), tr. *The Physical Dictionary*, 8°, London, 1684, 2 ed. 1693, 3 ed. 1697, 4 ed. 1702; Hoefer, (1), ii, 275; Ferguson, i, 111.

[3] *Œconomia Corporis Animalis*, 8°, Noviomagus (Nijmegen), 1672; Sprengel, (1), 1815, v, 105.

[4] Bontekoë, *Fragmenta . . . van het Acidum met het Alkali*, 8°, Hague, 1683 (BM 774. b. 28. (6.)); tr. as *Fundamenta Medica, sive de acidi et alkali effectibus, per modum fermentationis et effervescentiæ*, 8°, Amsterdam, 1688 (BM 544. d. 17); *Alle de Philosophische, Medicinale en Chymische Werken*, 5 pts., 4°, Amsterdam, 1689 (BM 7305. c. 8); tr. (with life of Bontekoë) by Devaux, *Nouveaux Élémens de Médecine*, 2 vols. 12°, 1698 (BM 774. e. 11–12); Sprengel, (1), v, 107–8.

[5] Poggendorff, (2), 290; Lasswitz, (1), ii, 495; Thorndike, vii, 690; viii, 228.

[6] *Philosophia Naturalis, quatuor Partibus, primarias Corporum Species, Affectiones, Vicissitudines Differentias, exhibens*, 4°, Leyden, 1680 (CUL M. 16. 69); 2 ed. 1685 (Sotheran *Cat.* 908 (1955), 84, no. 1020).

[7] *Inquisitiones Experimentales, quibus naturæ operandi ratio in nonnullis detegitur et mechanice proponitur*, 4°, Leyden, 1690 (not in BM or BN; rev. in *Acta Eruditorum*, 1690, ix, 137–8); 2 ed. (priore plusquam altera parte auctior) *Inquisitiones experimentales quibus præter particularis nonnulla phænomena atmosphærici aeris natura explicatius traditus . . . Adjectæ sunt Ephemerides nostri æris . . .*, 4°, Leyden, 1699 (BM 538. e. 2), Inquis. 93–4; Thorndike, viii, 228.

Boyle. He set up the first physical laboratory in Leyden, visiting France in 1681 to purchase apparatus, and was made Rector of Leyden by William of Orange, then King of England, in 1697.[1] Senguerd and de Volder were Cartesians but in a modified form. De Volder later saw the weakness of Cartesianism and favoured Newtonianism. His lectures were published without his permission.[2]

Willem Jacob Storm van 's Gravesand (Bois-le-Duc, 27 September 1688– Leyden, 28 February 1742), first studied and practised law. In 1715 he was secretary to the two ambassadors of Holland who felicitated George I on his accession to the English throne and was made F.R.S. He remained a year in London, a friend of Newton. In 1717 he became professor of mathematics and astronomy in Leyden and in 1734 became also professor of philosophy. His text-book of physics based on experiment[3] is in four books (bodies and motion, fluids, light, astronomy). It was translated by Desaguliers.[4] An abridged edition[5] was a popular text-book.

A pupil of Boerhaave and s' Gravesand was the renowned Petrus Van Musschenbroek (Leyden; 14 March 1692–19 September 1761), M.D. 1715, who heard Desaguliers' lectures in London, D.Phil. 1719, professor of mathematics in Duisburg and Utrecht, F.R.S. 1734. Declining offers from Copenhagen, Göttingen, and Spain (in absentia, with an enormous salary), he succeeded Wittich as professor of philosophy in Leyden in 1740. His lectures and books on experimental physics, and his invention of the Leyden jar (Vol. III) were very famous.[6] The *Introductio* contains in vol. i bodies in general, mechanics, electricity, magnetism, and the attraction of bodies, in vol. ii water, fire (including thermometry), light, air, and sound. Boerhaave, 's Gravesand, and Musschenbroek influenced Nollet, Voltaire, Senebier, and the Encyclopédistes.[7]

[1] J. Le Clerc, *Bibliothèque Choisie* (29 vols., Amsterdam, 1703–18), 1709, xviii; W. R. Scott, *M.A. Essay*, Johns Hopkins, Baltimore, 1955.
[2] *Disputationes philosophicæ sive cogitationes rationales de rerum naturalium principiis*, 8°, Middelburg, 1681 (BM 1134. b. 4. (1.)); *Quæstiones Academicæ de aëris gravitate*, 8°, Middelburg, 1681 (BM 1134. b. 4. (2.)); *Exercitationes Academicæ, quibus R. Cartesii philosophia, defenditur, adversus P. D. Huetii censuram philosophiæ Cartesianæ*, 8°, Amsterdam, 1695 (BM 536. a. 7).
[3] *Physices elementa mathematica, experimentis confirmata, sive Introductio ad Philosophiam Newtonianam*, 2 vols. 4°, Leyden, 1720–1; 1725, 1742.
[4] *Mathematical Elements of Natural Philosophy, confirmed by Experiments, or an Introduction to Sir Isaac Newton's Philosophy*, 8°, London, 1720 (BN R 10684), 5 ed. 2 vols. 8°, 1737; 6 ed. 2 vols. 4°, 1747; tr. de Virloys, *Élémens de Physique*, 2 vols. 8°, Paris, 1747; Jean Théophile Des Aguliers (Desaguliers) (La Rochelle, 13 March 1683–London, 29 February 1744) exiled at the age of two to England, studied in Oxford, M.A. 1712, F.R.S. 1714, chaplain to the Prince of Wales, a Freemason, held a course of experimental physics in London, then in Holland, populariser of Newton; he wrote himself *A Course of Mechanical and Experimental Philosophy*, 8°, London, 1724; 2 ed. 1725; *A Course of Experimental Philosophy*, 2 vols. 4°, 1734, 2 ed. 1745, 3 ed. 1763; and other works; Hunt, DNB, 1888, xiv, 400.
[5] *Philosophiæ Newtonianæ Institutiones, in usus Academicos*, 2 vols. 8°, Leyden, 1723, 1728, 1744.
[6] *Epitome Elementorum physico-mathematicorum in usus academicos*, 8°, Leyden, 1726 (BM 536. b. 21), and often reprinted and translated; *The Elements of Natural Philosophy*, tr. J. Colson, 2 vols. 8°, London, 1744; last ed., *Introductio ad Philosophiam Naturalem*, 2 vols. 4°, Leyden, 1762; he also wrote *Physicæ experimentales et geometricæ . . . dissertationes* (incl. capillarity), 4°, Leyden, 1729 and 1753 (BM); Van der Aa, *Biographisch Woordenboek der Nederlanden*, Haarlem, 1869, xii, 1181–4; *Nouv. Biog. Univ.*, new ed., Paris, xxix, 637–40.
[7] P. Brunet, *Les physiciens hollandais et la méthode expérimentale en France au XVIII⁰ Siècle*, Paris, 1926; review in *J. Chim. Phys.*, 1927, xxiv, 660.

BOERHAAVE

Herman (or Hermann) Boerhaave (Voorhout, a village nr. Leyden, 31 December 1668 'about one in the morning'–Leyden, 23 September 1738) was one of the thirteen children of James Boerhaave, a pastor of Flemish family, and was destined for the ministry, but in addition to his theological studies he read mathematics and philosophy. His father died when he was fifteen and left

FIG. 36. HERMAN BOERHAAVE, 1668–1738.
(From a mezzotint by George White)

him without resources. He gave lessons on mathematics to pupils. It is related that he happened to take part in a conversation on Spinoza (of whom he had written a refutation) on a public ferry, was accused of atheism, and abandoned theology for medicine as a profession. His brother Jacobus (James) who assisted him in chemical experiments, was destined for a medical career by his father but became a pastor.

In 1684 Boerhaave began a three-year course in natural philosophy at Leyden under the professor of physics Wolferd Senguerd, who was greatly influenced by Boyle, and during this period Boerhaave submitted five dissertations (disputations) under the auspices of Senguerd. He also attended courses on Greek and Latin by Gronovius, on Latin, rhetoric, chronology and geography under Rychius, and Hebrew and Chaldee under Trigland and Scaaf. He then spent three years under de Volder, professor of philosophy and mathematics, another enthusiastic supporter of Boyle. Under Senguerd Boerhaave published a disputation on cohesion[1] in which he used Boyle's *History of Fluidity and Firmness* (1661), but denied Boyle's theory that cohesion is due to atmospheric pressure. In 1688 he catalogued the library of Isaac Voss, brought from England to Leyden. In 1690 Boerhaave became doctor of philosophy, with a thesis 'on the distinction between body and mind'. He began theological studies with a view to ordination, but also studied medicine and graduated M.D. at the university of Harderwyk in July 1693 with a dissertation *De Utilitate explorandorum in Ægris Excrementorum ut Signorum*,[2] which contains some chemical material (analysis of urine) and refers to Paracelsus, Van Helmont, Boyle, Tachenius and Sylvius. One of his teachers in Leyden was Pitcairne and he took lessons in chemistry from a Leyden chemist David Stam (who edited Vigani's text-book, p. 686); 'chemiam dies nocteque exercuit', he says in his autobiography.[3]

He began medical practice in Leyden, also teaching mathematics privately and, from about 1703, chemistry. In 1701 he was placed as lecturer in the chair on the institutes of medicine left vacant by the death of Drelincourt in 1697. His lectures were very successful and attracted flocks of students, so that the university on the death of Hotton made him ordinary professor of medicine and of botany (1709), of practical medicine (1714), succeeding Bidloo, and of chemistry (1718), succeeding Le Mort. He resigned the chairs of botany and chemistry in 1729, owing to illness, Gaubius succeeding him in the chair of chemistry.

He was elected correspondent (1725) and associate (1728) of the Paris Academy, and F.R.S. (1730). From his marriage, his practice and his three chairs, he accumulated a fortune of two million florins, which he left to his daughter. He cared for his pupils like a father, treating them in illness without fees. Although Boerhaave did not make any outstanding discovery in chemistry, his fame as a teacher was immense: he had many foreign students, especially German, English and Scottish; through his pupils he may be said to have founded the Edinburgh system of concentrating all medical teaching, clinical and subsidiary, in one university school.[4]

---

[1] *De Cohæsione Corporum*, in *Disputationum Physicarum Selectorum*, Leyden, 1687, xxiv, Theses lxviii–lxxv (in Library of Royal College of Surgeons); analysed by W. L. Scott, Johns Hopkins *M.A. Essay*, 1955, 18 f.

[2] Printed in Burton, 1746, 185–202.   [3] Burton, 1746, 208.

[4] Atkinson, *J. Chem. Educ.*, 1942, xix, 103 (Johnson's *Life* of B.); William Burton, *An Account of the Life and Writings of Herman Boerhaave*, 8°, London, 1743 (anonymous), 2 ed., 1746; E. Cohen, *Janus*, 1918, xxiii, 223–78 (193–369, papers by 8 authors on 250 anniv. of B's birth); Daremberg, (1), ii, 888; T. L. Davis, *Isis*, 1927, ix, 165; 1928, x, 33; 1929, xii, 372; 1931, xv, 424; *id.*, *Nucleus*, March, 1930; *id.*, *Medical Life*, 1926, xxxiii, 260; Diergart, *Z.*

Boerhaave's papers were acquired by C. F. Kruse, physician to the Emperor of Russia,[1] and are still in Russia.[2] His library was sold by auction.[3] Boerhaave's separate publications are numerous and mostly of medical interest.[4]

Dr. Samuel Johnson was a great admirer of Boerhaave (of whom he wrote a life); he was also interested in chemistry. Boswell records that in 1763 he had chemical apparatus in his garret; in 1772 he sent Mr. Peyton to a chemist's shop in Temple-Bar to buy an ounce of oil of vitriol for a penny; in 1781 in a journey to Bedfordshire he read the second volume of Watson's *Chemical Essays*, and in 1783 he attended some experiments on the new kinds of air made by a physician of Salisbury. Johnson also wrote the dedication (to Dr. Mead) and part of the (valuable) historical introduction to the *Medicinal Dictionary* (3 vols. f°, 1745) of Robert James (Kilverston, Staffs., 1703–London, 23 March 1776), inventor of 'James's powder', from which he made a fortune;[5] Pearson showed that it was a mixture of bone-ash and antimony oxide.[6]

Boerhaave regarded chemistry as an independent science. In a lecture in 1718[7] he showed how the Iatrochemical school had abused chemistry in medicine and also criticised the alchemists. Since, however, he says[8] he had been able to repeat many of the chemical experiments described in books of the alchemists he could not deny the possibility of transmutation: sapientes est omnia explorare, retinere probata (cf. Zosimos, Vol. I).[9]

Some of their experiments, however, he could not repeat: the supposed fixation of mercury did not succeed. He kept mercury gently heated in an open vessel for 15 years and found the only change was the formation of a little black powder which turned into mercury on rubbing. It did not change when strongly heated in a closed vessel for six months, nor when shaken in bottles on a windmill, nor when distilled 500 times.

angew. Chem., 1919, xxxii, 1, 58; Ferguson, i, 112; Fontenelle, Éloge, in *Oeuvres*, 1792, vii, 481–99; *Éloge, written by Fontenelle and translated from the French by W. Burton*, London, sm. 8°, 1749; Foster, 200; Gibbs, Ph.D. Thesis, London, 1949; *Ambix*, 1957, vi, 117; *Ann. Sci.*, 1957 (1958), xiii, 47; Gmelin, (1), ii, 552, 692; Haeser, (1), ii, 496 (important details); Hoefer, (1), ii, 367–8; Jöcher, i, 1178; Samuel Johnson, *Gentleman's Mag.*, 1739, ix, 37, 72, 114, 172; id., *Works*, ed. Lynam, London, 1825, iv, 417; J. L. Kesteloot, *Lofrede op Hermannus Boerhaave*, Leyden, 1825 (unusual portr.); Kopp, (1), i, 197; ii, 14; iv, 419 (96 refs. to B.); Lippmann, (3), ii, 274; Macquer, *Dictionnaire de Chymie*, 1766, I, xxiv ('c'est à coté de Stahl, quoique dans un genre différent, qu'on doit placer l'immorrel Boerhaave); Maty, *Essai sur le caractère du grand médecin, ou éloge critique de M. H. Boerhaave*, Cologne, 1747 (German tr., *Versuch über den Character des Grossen Arztes, oder kritische Lebensbeschreibung Herrn D. Hermann Boerhaaves*, 8°, Leipzig and Freyberg, 1748); Matthew Maty (nr. Leyden, 1718–London, 1776), M.D. Leyden, came to England in 1740, F.R.S. 1758, succeeded Birch as Sec. Roy. Soc. in 1765; Metzger, (1), 191 f.; NBU, 1853, vi, 352–7; Pettigrew, *Medical Portrait Gallery*, 1844, iii (youthful portr.; specimen of handwriting); Read, *Humour and Humanism in Chemistry*, 1947, 128; Saverien, 1769, vii, 259 (portr.); A Schulten(s), *Oratio Academica in memoriam H. Boerhaave*, 4°, Leyden, 1738 (BM 541. f. 9. (9.)); Thomson, (1), i, 209 (with analysis of B.'s *Elementa Chemiae*).

[1] Magellan in Cronstedt, *System of Mineralogy*, London, 1788, ii, 614; Burton, 1746, 49, says he left his *Adversaria* or common-place book to his nephews Herman and Abraham Kaau, and to the latter his anatomical and chemical preparations, many of which were purchased of Ruysch, and 'these gentlemen are willing to dispose of the said Legacies on reasonable terms.'

[2] Maty, 1748, 97, says they included a chronological list of alchemical authors and some experiments with mercury.

[3] *Bibliotheca Boerhaaviana, sive Catalogus librorum instructissimae bibliothecae viri summi H. Boerhaave, Auctio in officina Luchtmanniana*, 8 Junii, 1739, Leyden, 1739.

[4] Burton, 1746, 222–6; M. Hertzberger, *Short-Title Catalogue of Books written and edited by Hermann Boerhaave*, Amsterdam, 1927.

[5] *Notes and Queries*, 1950, cxcv, 378.   [6] *Phil. Trans.*, 1791, lxxxi, 317.

[7] *Sermo Academicus de Chemia suos errores expurgante*, 4°, Leyden, 1718 (42 pp.); repr. in his *Opuscula omnia*, The Hague, 4°, 1738, 36.

[8] *Elementa Chemiae*, Leyden, 1732, i, 124; cf. *ib.*, 661, 669, 751, 868.   [9] Maty, 1748, 68 f.

Processes for extracting mercury from lead according to Isaac Hollandus (see p. 203) also failed; it was said that mercury could be made from sugar of lead, but Boerhaave calcined this, treated the residue with strong alkaline lixivium, kept the mixture for months, adding water to replace that evaporated, and distilled it at a red heat, but not a particle of mercury was obtained.[1] According to Schmieder[2] Boerhaave published a Latin translation of the work of the English adept Mundanus,[3] which is really by Dickinson (see p. 327), and Kopp[4] says this was first published in Oxford in 1686. Boerhaave admits that he had a high veneration for the ancient alchemists, who taught that gold and silver proceed from pure mercury and a condensing sulphur (solo sincero argento vivo per sulphur densans stipato) and the other metals are formed of less pure mercury and less pure sulphur, differently combined.[5]

Boerhaave's chemical lectures were published (like some of his earlier medical works) by some of his students, without his consent, in 1724:

I. Institutiones et experimenta chemiae, 2 vols. 12°, 'Paris' (really Leyden), 1724 (I: pp. xvi (1 blank), 375, 1 fold. plate; II, pp. iv (1 blank), 290 (my copy has only one t.p.); repr. 1724 ('Paris') and 1726 (Amsterdam, and Venice) apud Sebastianus Colei Superiorum Permissa, 350 pp. (Wellcome Hist. Library). Burton, 1746, 148, says the book was published from incorrect copies of lecture notes in Leyden 'under the name of Paris'; he also, *ib.*, 225, gives '4to Angl. 1725' perhaps a mistake for 1727; see II.

An English translation with notes and two plates, prepared by Peter Shaw, M.D., and Edmond Chambers appeared in 1727:

II. A New Method of Chemistry; Including the Theory and Practice of that Art: Laid down on Mechanical Principles, and accommodated to the Uses of Life. The whole making a clear and rational System of Chemical Philosophy. To which is prefix'd A Critical History of Chemistry and Chemists, From the Origin of the Art to the present Time. Written by . . . H. Boerhaave . . . Translated from the Printed Edition, Collated with the best Manuscript Copies, 4°, London, Printed for J. Osborn and T. Longman, 1727 (pp. xvi (1 blank), 1–383 (v. blank), 1–335 (v. blank), xxxix index; 2 plates of apparatus).

II was perhaps in circulation soon after May 1726, since it is quoted in Hales's Vegetable Staticks (1727, 288: 'Process 77', on fermentation), which was available early in 1727, the imprimatur (signed by Newton) being dated 16 February 1727.

The publication of this book (I) annoyed Boerhaave intensely, and as it was brought into his lectures by students, he became disgusted with his professorship of chemistry. On the urgent representation of his friends, he brought out in 1732 a text-book which is an enlarged and revised version of his lectures, with some interesting personal details omitted, viz. the famous:

III. Elementa Chemiae, quae anniversario labore docuit, in publicis, privatisque, scholis, Hermannus Boerhaave, 2 vols. 4°, Leyden, 1732; I, pp. xii (1 blank), 896, 16 plates, xl; pp. 423–4 (no gap in text) and plate VI are always wanting; II, pp. viii (2 blank), 538, xliv; each copy signed by Boerhaave on verso of t.p. of vol. i: Ut certus sit Lector, hunc librum a me editum prodire, propria manu nomen adscribendum putavi: nec pro meo agnosco, ubi haec adscriptio abest. H. Boerhaave (sign.). Vol. ii is often bound up with the Opuscula (1738), see IX. Copies of this ed. were apparently

---

[1] *Phil. Trans.*, 1733, xxxviii, 145–67; 1736, xxxix, 343, 368; AdS, 1734, m 539–52; *Opuscula omnia*, 4°, The Hague, 1738, 129; letters in Maty, 1748, 144; extract from Boerhaave's diary in Magellan, Cronstedt's *Mineralogy*, 1788, ii, 614; summary in Burton, 1746, 149.
[2] 1832, 460.   [3] *De Quinta Essentia Philosophorum*, 8°, Leiden, 1732.
[4] (4), ii, 344.   [5] *Elementa Chemiae*, 1732, i, 662.

circulating in the Autumn of 1731, and two eds. were published, one by Severinus (my copy) and one by Imhoff (Patent Office Library). Second (authorised) edition, corrected (with the Opuscula, IX) 2 vols., 4°, Paris, 1733: editio altera, Leydensis multo correctior et accuratior; I, pp. xii (2 blank), 476, 17 plates and descriptions, xlv index; II, pp. viii, 346, xlviii index, 1 blank; Opuscula, pp. iv, 231, 1 leaf.

Lenglet du Fresnoy, iii, 8, refers to a Leyden ed. of 1731; Hoefer, (1), ii, 368, and Lippmann, (1), ii, 349, to a London ed., 2 vols., 1732; spurious Latin eds. quoted are Paris, 1729; Leyden, 1732; London, 1732; Leipzig, 1732; Basel, 1745; Venice, 1746, 1759, 1777; Davis, Isis, 1928, x, 33; Gibbs, Ambix, 1958, vi, 117; Duveen, 84 (2 vols. 8°, Leipzig, Caspar Frisch, 1732, I: viii, 32 ll., 36–374 pp., 36 ll., 17 plates; II: 5 ll., 3–470 pp., 45 ll. index); Bolton, (1), 322 (2 vols. 8°, The Hague, 1746); Gildemeister and Hoffmann, Ätherischen Öle, 1928, i, 72 (Paris, 1732, 1753; London, 1735; Venice, 1746, 1759); Hoefer, (i), ii, 368, gives London, 1732, 1735; Paris, 1732, 1733, 1753; Basel, 1745; Venice, 1745, 1759; Leipzig, 1732.

IV. English tr. of authorised Latin ed.: Elements of Chemistry In two Volumes . . . Englished by a Gentleman of the University of Oxford [? T. Dallowe], 4°, London (1735 ?), 'No. 1' (56 pp., no preface), 'price 1/6' (all published) (BM 719. k. 36); Elements of Chemistry, being the Annual Lectures of Herman Boerhaave, tr. by Timothy Dallowe, 2 vols. 4°, London, 1735 (BM 719. k. 38; I pp. 528, index; II pp. 376, index); Dallowe says he abridged somewhat, with Boerhaave's consent, and Burton, 1746, 149, that this tr. is more correct than the Latin original.

V. A New Method of Chemistry; including the History, Theory and Practice of the Art: Translated from the original Latin of Dr. Boerhaave's Elementa Chemiæ, as Published by Himself, to which are added, Notes; and an Appendix, Shewing The Necessity and Utility of Enlarging the Bounds of Chemistry. With Sculptures. By Peter Shaw, M.D. The Second Edition.[1] 2 vols. 4°, London, Printed for T. Longman, at the Ship in Paternoster Row, 1741, 1753 (The Third Edition; unchanged reprint); I, pp. xxx, 593 (594 list of books), 17 plates; II, t.p. (v. blank), pp. 410, xxxviii index; 8 plates. This ed. includes parts of II, with copious notes and appendices by Shaw.

VI. Abridged English tr. (by Edward Strother): Dr. Boerhaave's Elements of Chemistry faithfully abridg'd from the late genuine edition . . . To which are added . . . notes rectifying several opinions etc. of the learned author, by a physician (anonymous), London, 8°, 1733, 2 pts., pp. vi, 210, viii, 208 (Bolton gives a rather different title and 'second edition' 1734); 2 ed. (with Strother's name), 2 vols. 8°, 1737; criticism of Strother's work in Burton, 1743, 146; Maty, 1748, 143; J. Rogers, 'Some Observations on the Translation and Abridgment of Dr Boerhaave's Chymistry', London, 1733, 72 pp. (BM); it is really not at all bad. Another condensed version was by Robt. Poole, The Chemical Vade Mecum or a Compendium of Chymistry . . . principally from the late celebrated Boerhaave, London, 1748.

VII. French tr.: Elémens de Chimie par Hermann Boerhaave traduits du Latin par J. N. S. Allamand, Membre de la Société Royale de Londres [F.R.S. 1746], 2 vols. 8°, The Hague, 1748; 2 ed. Leyden (C. Haak), 1752 (x ll., 560 pp., t.p., 561–914 pp., x ll. index, 17 pl.) (Sotheran Cat. 851 (1937), no. 1102 A). A third ed., published in three states, printed by Briasson, Chardon, and Jarin, 6 vols. 12°, Paris, 1754 (BN R 29390–5) was in Fourcroy's library, Catalogue des livres de la bibliothèque de Fourcroy, 1810, no. 1614, p. 173. The only French ed. I have seen is the abridged: Abrégé de la Théorie Chymique. Tiré des propres écrits de M. Boerhaave par M. [J. Offray] de la Metrie, 12°, Paris, 1741 (pp. vi, 159, followed by a Traité de Vertige by de la Metrie; this abridgement deals only with the four elements: BM copy bound with Leçons de Chymie de l'Université de Montpellier (anon.), Paris, 1750 (191 pp.) (BM 1034. f. 12. (1.)).

VIII. German tr.: Elementa Chemiae, oder: Anfangsgründe der Chemie, 12°, Leipzig, 1753 (Sotheran Cat. 894 (1951) 9, no. 119); 3 Th., 8°, Berlin, 1762 (BM 1035. d. 5); ed. Wiegleb, Berlin, 1782, 1791; these were much abridged, the theory being omitted and practically only Vol. 2 translated.

A Russian translation of III is mentioned by Walden.[2] Several of Boerhaave's smaller publications were collected as:

---

[1] The First was Shaw and Chambers, II.
[2] In Diergart, 1909, 375.

IX. Opuscula Omnia, quæ hactenus in lucem prodierunt. Ea quidem prius sparsim edita, nunc vero in unum collecta atque digesta, 4°, The Hague, J. Neaulme, 1738, ii ll., 139 pp., fig. p. 97 (the ed. quoted); 8°, Naples, 1739, iv ll., 224 pp., fold. pl.; contains Orationes Academicæ:

(a) De Commendando studio Hippocratico.
(b) De usu Ratiocinii Mechanici in Medicina (1702).
(c) Repurgatæ Medicinæ facilis asseritur simplicitat (1709).
(d) De Comparando Certo in Physicis (1715).
(e) De Chemia suos errores expurgante (1718).
(f) De Vita et Obitu Bernhardi Albini (1721).
(g) De Honore Medici, servitute.

Also:

(h) Epistola Anatomica ad Fredericum Ruysch and Ruysch's reply.
(i) Atrocis, non descripti prius, Morbi Historia, 2 pts., to Jacob de Bye and Jacob Kaau (1724–8).
(j) Tractatus Medicus de Lue Aphrodisiaca (preface).
(k) De Mercurio experimenta.
(l) Dissertatio II De Mercurio.

For the use of his students he published a list of the plants in the Leyden University Botanic Garden:

X. Index Plantarum, quæ in Horto Academico Lugduno-Batavo reperdiuntur, 8°, Leyden, 1710; enlarged, Index alter Plantarum quæ in Horto Academico Lugduno-Batavo aluuntur, 2 vols. 4°, Leyden, 1720.

His medical works, which were celebrated, were often printed:

XI. (a) Institutiones Medica in usus annuæ Exercitationis domesticos, 12°, Leyden, 1708, and many later eds., e.g. Edinburgh, 1752, at least as late as 1796-7 (Madrid); tr. Institutions in Physick, by J. Browne, London, 1714, and in many other languages, incl. Arabic.

(b) Aphorismi de cognoscendis et curandis Morbis in usum doctrinae domesticæ digesta, 12°, Leyden, 1709, and many later eds., at least to 1834 (Paris); tr. Aphorisms concerning the Knowledge and Cure of Diseases, by J. Delacoste, London, 1715, and in many other languages, incl. Arabic; and numerous eds. of a commentary by Van Swieten.

(c) Libellus de Materia Medica & Remediorum Formulis, quæ serviunt Aphorismis, 8°, Leyden, 1719 (BM 547. d. 22) and numerous other eds. and trs. (pirated, London, 1714, 1717, 1718).

(d) Boerhaave's medical lectures edited by his pupil Albrecht von Haller as: Praelectiones Academicae, in proprias Institutiones Rei Medicae, 6 vols. 4° in 7, Göttingen, 1739–44 (BN T³⁰. 112); 5 vols. 4°, Turin, 1742–5 (BN T³⁰. 112A).

XII. Boerhaave, Opera Omnia Medica, 4°, Venice, 1771 (incl. Institutiones Medicæ, Aphorismi, De Materia Medica, De Lue Aphrodisiaca, a number of smaller tracts not often found with Boerhaave's works, and copious indexes; not in BM or BN).

Boerhaave edited the anatomical and surgical works of Vesalius (2 vols., 1725, with Albinus) and produced an elaborate edition of Aretaeus (1731). He first published the *Bible of Nature* of Swammerdam, the MS. of which, after Swammerdam's death in 1680, had passed through the hands of Thevenot and Duverney.[1]

In theory Boerhaave was an independent thinker: 'a learned scholar, and a sound scientific thinker, he was too all-round a man to be led away by any one idea, however tempting; essentially eclectic in nature, he gathered truth from

---

[1] *Biblia Naturæ sive Historia Insectorum . . . accedit Praefatio in quia vitam auctoris descripsit Hermannus Boerhaave*, 2 vols. f°, Leyden, 1737–8.

every source.'[1] Johnson says 'he took care never to provoke enemies by severity of censure' but 'was not overawed or depressed by the presence, frowns or insolence of great men'. His chemical lectures were illustrated by experiments which he performed rapidly and successfully, and were enlivened by touches of humour.[2]

Boerhaave's favourite author was Van Helmont, whom he read seven times and could repeat in parts by heart,[3] although he did not agree with his medical views. In his text-book[4] Boerhaave has a long section on the alkahest, which he himself never possessed, although he tried innumerable tedious experiments (cum poenitentia detestatus).

In his inaugural lecture Sermo Academicus De Chemia suos Errores Expurganti[5] given on 21 September 1718, he says chemists always clear up the errors of an earlier generation, such as the weight of fire, and the acid-alkali theory in physiology and medicine (which Pitcairne had opposed). It is necessary to check the flight of the imagination by the weight of experiments (sed coërcenda est velocitas nimia disputantis mentis pondere Experimentorum).[6] He disliked generalisations: it should not be said that 'acids dissolve metals' but 'certain acids dissolve these or those particular metals'.[7] He seems, following Boyle and Newton, to admit the atomic hypothesis. Atoms are elements of constant figure and dimension (erunt ergo constantis figuræ et mensuræ elementa).[8] In his text-book he often makes use of corpuscles (moleculæ) and he mentions the atoms of Demokritos, the monads of some other philosophers, and the hylarchies (hylarchia) of others.[9]

Boerhaave's text-book III is dedicated to his brother Jacobus (James), 'in memory of the many days and nights we have spent together in the chemical examination of natural bodies, at the time when your chief view was to Medicine and mine to Theology.' It begins in Part I with a good history of Chemistry; Part II is on the Theory of Chemistry (metals, salts, the universal acid, sulphur, bitumens, stones, earths, semi-metals, vegetables, and animals), the use of chemistry in physics, medicine, and the mechanical arts, the instruments of chemistry, on fire, on fuel or the pabulum of fire, on air, water, and earth, on menstruums, and chemical apparatus. Part III, filling the second volume, is on chemical operations, containing detailed descriptions of chemical experiments, with uses of the preparations.

Boerhaave[10] defines chemistry as:

an art which teaches the manner of performing certain physical operations, whereby bodies cognizable to the senses, or capable of being rendered cognizable, and of being contained in vessels, are so changed by means of proper instruments, as to produce certain determinate effects, and at the same time discover the causes thereof, for the service of various arts.

This would apply equally well to cookery or organic chemistry. It was, however, the one adopted in Johnson's *Dictionary* (1755).

The sections on Fire, Air, Water, and Earth (delivered as separate annual

[1] Foster, 1901, 202.   [2] Burton, 1743, 57; Maty, 1748, 22.
[3] Burton, 1743, 67, 158.   [4] III, i, 848–68; this appears, in less detail, in I.
[5] 4°, Leyden, 1718; IX (e), 36; paraphrase in R. James, 1745, art. Chemia.
[6] III, i, 344.   [7] III, i, 843.   [8] IX (d); 29.   [9] III, i, 149.   [10] III, i, 30.

lectures), and on Menstruums, are really comprehensive monographs, the first and second incorporating much recent work in physics.[1] Boerhaave's textbook is distinguished from that of Stahl by its greater common sense, its sparing use of hypotheses, its greater clarity, and above all by its extensive use of the newer results of physics and a bias to what may be called the outlook of physical chemistry. His treatises on Fire, on Menstruums, and on Fermentation exhibit in a striking way the new spirit which he infused into chemistry. Thomson[2] says Boerhaave collected his material from 'a thousand different sources, and from writings equally disgusting from their obscurity and their mysticism', stripping them of their mysticism and producing 'the most learned and luminous treatise on chemistry that the world had yet seen'. In it 'chemistry is shown as a science and an art of the first importance, not merely to medicine, but to mankind in general'.

The second volume, on Chemical Operations, is a collection of preparations from vegetables, animals, and minerals in this order, as of increasing difficulty.[3] The simple chemical operations (solution, coagulation, precipitation, effervescence, etc.) thus come at the end[4] and, as Burton[5] said, the course ends where others usually begin. In this part there are some references to Boyle's publications on tastes, odours, colours, etc., and a criticism of the Iatrochemical doctrine of acid and alkali. Temperatures according to Fahrenheit's scale,[6] instead of vague specifications, are used throughout the book. A small thermometer enclosed in a glass tube for taking body temperatures (pyranthropometrum) is a clinical thermometer.[7] Boerhaave's lecture experiments on the rise in temperature on mixing vegetable, animal, and mineral bodies,[8] must be the earliest in chemical calorimetry.

Daniel Gabriel Fahrenheit (Danzig, 14 May 1686–in Holland, 16 September 1736) was the first to produce consistently reading thermometers, first filled with spirit of wine, later with mercury (1714–15), and introduced a temperature scale. In 1724 he gave the freezing-point of water as 32°, the boiling-point at 28 in. mercury pressure 212°, the body temperature 96°, and 0° the temperature of a mixture of ice, water, and sal ammoniac or common salt.[9] He described very accurately the supercooling of water (to 15° F.),[10] determined specific gravities by Archimedes' method[11] and by a hydrometer,[12] and constructed a thermometer with a large bulb and with a bulb in the capillary part, which would measure the barometric pressure by the variation of the boiling-point of water with the atmospheric pressure.[13]

The Centigrade scale was proposed by Celsius (Uppsala; 1670–1756),[14] but he took

[1] Burton, 1746, 226: 1718–19 (on fire), 1720–1 (on air), 1722 (on water); 1723 Chemica hora nona in Laboratorio Chemico tradid; 1724 to 1728 Idem proponit.

[2] (1), i, 213.

[3] Burton, 1743, 139 f.; Maty, 1748, 52 f.

[4] III, ii, 529: Pars III. Recapitulatio.   [5] 1743, 145.

[6] Phil. Trans., 1724, xxxiii, 1, 78.

[7] III, i, 366; plate V, fig. iv; Sarton, (1), ii, 64, says Anton van Haen (1758) and James Currie (1797) used thermometers in medicine; the modern clinical thermometer was introduced by Clifford Allbutt in 1868.

[8] III, i, 364 f.

[9] Phil. Trans., 1724, xxxiii, 1, 78, 179; Gamgee, Proc. Cambr. Phil. Soc., 1890, vii, 95; Brown, J. Chem. Educ., 1934, xi, 448; Cohen and Cohen-de-Meester, q. in Ann. Sci., 1937, ii, 133; Wolf, Relatio de novo barometrorum et thermometrorum concordantium genere, Acta Erudit., 1714, 380 (early F. scale); Cajori, 1929, 114; Heathcote, Ambix, 1958, vi, 155.

[10] Phil. Trans., 1724, xxxiii, 78.   [11] Phil. Trans., 1724, xxxiii, 114.

[12] Phil. Trans., 1724, xxxiii, 140.   [13] Phil. Trans., 1724, xxxiii, 179.

[14] KAH, 1742, iii, 171; Wargentin, ib., 1749, x, 161.

the f.p. of water as 100° and the b.p. as 0°. The present scale (f.p. 0°, b.p. 100°) is due to Linnaeus[1] or to Prof. Christin of Lyon.[2]

Reaumur[3] used a spirit of wine thermometer and found that the volume increased from 1000 at the freezing point of water to 1080 at the boiling point of the spirit. He divided the interval into 80 degrees, and on this scale the boiling point of water would be 100°. The present Reaumur scale (f.p. 0°, b.p. 80°) was proposed by De Luc.[4]

Boerhaave gives brief accounts of the six metals, gold, silver, copper, iron, tin, and lead, mercury not being a metal but the chief basis or matter of all the metals,[5] and he explains the supposed origin of the planetary symbols of the metals. Still, he includes mercury in the descriptions. His account of salts[6] includes common salt, saltpetre, borax, sal ammoniac, alum, and 'the vague acid of mines' (acidum vagum fodinarum) which, mixing with petroleum forms sulphurs, with metals vitriols, with calcareous earths alums, and with pyrites, sulphur. The sulphurs[7] include common sulphur, orpiment, white arsenic ('unknown 200 years ago'), and bituminous sulphurs: petroleum, naphtha, asphaltum, pissasphaltum, jet (gagates), mineral coal (lithranthrax), amber (succinum, carabe, electrum, formed from a subterraneous bitumen trickling into the sea and being congealed by vitriolic salts there), and 'earth oil' (oleum terrae) found in India but not exported. Stones[8] are divided into transparent (gems), semi-transparent (lapis lazuli, selenite, etc.), and opaque (eagle stone, belemnites, gypsum, osteocolla, etc.). Under earths[9] he gives various clays, chalk, ochre, and marl, but he does not mention the preparation of lime anywhere in the book. Semi-metals[10] are vitriols of iron or copper (he does not mention zinc-vitriol), which are composed of true metal combined with an acid, also cinnabar or minium, antimony (stibium, στίμμι, recentiorum antimonium), bismuth (bismuthum, bisemutum), like antimony but harder, zinc (zincq, zinetum), of which he knows nothing, lapis Armenus or lapis lazuli, haematite or aroph or 'philosophical aroma', magnet, and perhaps ochre. The following sections on vegetables and animals deal mostly with natural history.

Boerhaave next deals with the chemical operations, all of which are due to union and separation brought about by the motions of the particles of bodies under the action of mechanical forces,[11] thus following Boyle. Yet he still taught that metals are compounds of mercury and sulphur, those except gold also containing an admixture of earth and perhaps 'crude sulphur'. Transmutation is possible but difficult, the amount of gold obtainable from another metal being in proportion to the quantity of mercury it contains.[12] That minerals, like plants and animals, grow from seeds is established by adepts (chemicos . . . sane mystæ testantur, universalem hanc fœturæ rationem, ut in aliis, ita et per ipsis fossilibus, inveniri).[13]

He does not refer by name to Stahl's phlogiston theory, which must have

---

[1] Linnaeus, *Hortus Cliffortianus*, Amsterdam, 1737, plate opp. t.p.; Arago, *Oeuvres*, 1858, viii, 608; Nordenmark, *Ann. Sci.*, 1937, ii, 474.

[2] Poggendorff, *Ann. Phys.*, 1876, clvii, 352; Cajori, 1929, 118; J. C. Fischer, 1804, v, 15 (no ref.).

[3] AdS, 1730, m 452.

[4] *Recherches sur les Modifications de l'Atmosphère*, Geneva, 1772, i, 352; G. Martine, *Essays and Observations on the Construction and Graduation of Thermometers*, 4 ed., Edinburgh, 1787, 25.

[5] III, i, 31.   [6] *Ib.*, i, 43 f.   [7] *Ib.*, i, 46 f.   [8] *Ib.*, i, 50 f.   [9] *Ib.*, i, 52.
[10] *Ib.*, i, 53.   [11] *Ib.*, i, 70 f.   [12] *Ib.*, i, 32 f., 41 f., 116 f.   [13] IX (d); 31.

been known to him.[1] He gives the experiment of heating Glauber's salt with charcoal, which he attributes to Becher, and says the oil of vitriol in the salt seizes the inflammable matter of the charcoal and becomes sulphur.[2] Combustible bodies contain a 'food of fire' (*pabulum ignis*),[3] which in sulphur he calls 'oil' (*oleum*):[4] on burning sulphur, the combustible part is burnt in the fire and the acid, saline, incombustible part separates (sulphuris oleosa, combustibilis pars dum in igne deflagrat, pars salina interim acidissima . . . nascitur).[5]

Sulphur is composed of the acid of vitriol, alum or pyrites, and a vegetable or mineral oil: on combustion the oil serves as the pabulum of fire and the acid flies unchanged from the flame (acidum immutatum de ipsa hac flamma dissipari fumi specie),[6] and when joined with fatty oil, sulphur is formed from oil of vitriol (pingui jungitur oleo, dat sulphur).[7] Dry sulphur also contains water, since on burning it yields an acid spirit (flammam dat et acidum spiritum) which may be separated into water and oil of vitriol.[8] Boerhaave clearly describes the solidification of fuming sulphuric acid on cooling:[9] oleum vitrioli meracissimum, frigore hyberno in crystallos solidos coactum. He thought sulphuric acid is also formed on burning phosphorus (in flagrantissimas flammas accenditur, consumitur, relinquit oleum vitrioli, aut simillium acedine, & pondere, liquorem),[10] but the acid formed from phosphorus exposed to air, although not much different from oil of vitriol, is of unknown nature (Unde vero hoc acidum ? ignoro).[11]

When alcohol, which is the purest pabulum of fire, is burnt it leaves only water, the food of fire being dissipated into the chaos of air and so eluding the senses (pabulum ignis, igne consumtum, aquam relinquit, evadit vero ipsum adeo tenue, ut in chaos aërium dilapsum, haud appareat ultra sensibus).[12] It seems as if matter completely combustible by fire consists of a great proportion of water and a little pabulum of fire, and on burning this is separated from the water and vanishes into air (penitus igne combustibilis constaret aqua plurisma . . . unde comburendo ignis hic, ab aqua separaretur . . . iterum elementum ipsum igneum sic constitueret . . . solutus omni alio corpore adhaerescente evanesceret penitus in auras).[13]

The only sure sign of the presence of fire is the expansion it causes in bodies; Boerhaave thought the expansions of air and liquids produced by the same heat are in the ratios of the rarities or inversely as the densities of the bodies (expansionis ab eodem igne spatia esse inter se ut raritates expansorum corporum; vel in ratione reciproce densitatem).[14]

The atoms of bodies tend to draw nearer one another and cohere faster together; fire perpetually agitates them.[15] The particles of fire distributed through a mass act everywhere with the same force on the molecules (particulis Ignis per massam distributas, ubique in moleculas, quas occupant, eadem

---

[1] The anonymous *Leçons de Chymie de l'Université de Montpellier*, 8°, Paris, 1750, 159, states that Boerhaave did not use the 'modern' theory of phlogiston.
[2] III, ii, 435: oleum Vitrioli in Sale mirabili prehendit inflammabile carbonis, fit Sulphur.
[3] III, i, 285 f.   [4] *Ib.*, 357.   [5] *Ib.*, 357; cf. ii, 423.   [6] *Ib.*, 295.   [7] *Ib.*, 811.
[8] *Ib.*, 588.   [9] *Ib.*, 574; Chaptal, *Elements of Chemistry*, 1791, i, 215.
[10] *Ib.*, 380.   [11] *Ib.*, ii, 327.
[12] III, i, 320 f., 325; Van Helmont had made this experiment, *Ortus Medicinæ*, 1652, 86, § 9.
[13] III, i, 329.   [14] III, i, 135–7.   [15] III, i, 147.

vi agere).[1] 'Henceforward I shall call that unknown thing which has this property of penetrating all solid and fluid bodies, and dilating them so as to take up more space, by the name of fire (Ignem).'[2] Fire is present in all space and is equally distributed in all bodies (ipse Ignis, hactenus nobis innotescens, semper praesens existit in omni loco . . . et in omni quoque corpore, etiam rarissimo, vel solidissimo, aequaliter distributus haeret).[3] This fire is at once perceptible in percussion and friction. It was not generated but existed previously in the bodies.[4] It is continually in motion, even in a vacuum, and is striving to separate the particles of bodies.[5]

In some ways this view coincides with the subtle matter of Descartes, and fire is neither uniquely a body nor a movement of any body but the movement communicated to the rest of matter by the atoms of a specific element which the chemists have called fire.[6] A higher temperature corresponds with a more vigorous motion.

Fire is a material though weightless element, an igneous fluid composed of very minute hard spherical particles with polished surfaces, which penetrate matter but not the material atoms (ignem verum elementalem corporeum esse . . . videntur esse omnium, quae nota habentur, corporum minima . . . quae sint omnium corporum maxime solida . . . superficiem habere quam aequabillissime laevam, seu politissimam).[7] Fire is not simply a solvent of bodies but produces profound changes in many of them, e.g. mercury heated in a phial with a long neck forms red precipitate, but some bodies are not changed, such as gold, silver, osteocolla and glass.[8] Boerhaave describes the experiments of Boyle, Du Clos, and Homberg on the increase in weight of metals on calcination,[9] and he proved that the matter of fire has no weight by showing that a bar of 5 lb. 8 oz. of iron weighed the same red hot and cold, and a similar result was found with a large piece of copper.[10] He gives no adequate explanation of the increase in weight on calcination, merely throwing out a suggestion that it is due to the corrosion and attrition of the sulphureous particles and their admixture with particles of other bodies separated in the fusion (adquiritur rodendo, terendo, miscendo; tandem in liquefactione inde separatur).[11]

Is earth contained in the calces of metals? These calces are all true metals (sane omnes hae vera metalla manent), since, although they are all insipid, fine, odourless and sometimes pulverisable, yet they recover their pristine form by the action of fire and some reducing powders, or other ingredients. Thus, whoever feels that these calces are elementary earth will have to admit that it may, at will and with little trouble, be converted into a metal.

sane omnes hae vera metalla manent . . . sit tamen igne, apposito pulverum, quos reducentes vocant, aliisve artificiis, pristinam formam recipiunt. Qui ergo calces hasce pro elementali accepisset terra, ille, eodem jure, levibus hisce artibus terram posset in metalla, quoties vellet, convertere.[12]

He seems here to be following Freind (p. 480) in regarding the calx as a mere physical modification of the metal in which its particles are driven further apart by the interposition of particles of fire, but whereas Freind followed

[1] Ib., 142–3.   [2] Ib., 175.   [3] Ib., 187.   [4] Ib., 186–7.   [5] Ib., 189.
[6] Metzger, (1), 221.   [7] Ib., 386 f., 390, 394 f.   [8] Ib., 405–6.
[9] Ib., 360 f.   [10] Ib., 259.   [11] III, i, 362; V, i, 340.   [12] Ib., 660.

Boyle in supposing that the particles of fire were ponderable and caused the increase in weight, Boerhaave proved experimentally that heat is weightless.

In the section on air[1] Boerhaave describes Boyle's law[2] and says air is rarefied by nearly $\frac{1}{2}$ by a rise in temperature of 252° F.[3] Water is 850 times as dense as air. The atmosphere contains fire, water (making up most of its weight), vegetable and animal matters, oils, salts, earths, sulphurs and metals.[4] He describes the formation of factitious airs from crabs' eyes or chalk and vinegar, oil of tartar and vitriolic acid, nitric acid and iron, nitric acid and oil of caraway, etc., measuring the air by a barometer in a previously exhausted receiver.[5]

He does not distinguish other gases from air, but he mentions gas sylvestre, says it differs from air in not supporting respiration,[6] and doubts whether it is true air. He does not speak of 'fixed air' but says the air may insinuate itself into the pores of bodies, and there, meeting with particles to which it is peculiarly attracted, it unites with them, loses its fluidity and elasticity and remains united till set free again by effervescence, fermentation, putrefaction or heat:[7]

gravitate sua determinatus ad illa corpora, divisibilis interim fluiditate sua, dum simul ita se per minima insinuat . . . cum iisdem elementa sua minima conjungit, fluiditatem amittit; elasticitatem suam fluidam perdit, diu ibidem innexus manet, donec inde effervescentia, fermentatione, putrefactione, igne, iterum liberatur.

The suffocating vapours in mines consist of arsenic, orpiment, cobalt, sulphurs of antimony, bismuth, zinc, etc.[8]

Lavoisier[9] suggested that parts of Boerhaave's chapter on air are in contradiction because part was composed before, and part after, the appearance of Hales's *Vegetable Staticks* in 1727, and that he adopted to a certain extent the doctrine of the fixation of air in bodies, but (perhaps because he did not think it sufficiently proved) did not retract what he had previously said to the contrary.

The action of air in combustion Boerhaave regarded as mechanical, by its streaming into the flame or burning body and so causing a vortex motion of the particles: the flickering of a fire is due to the rise and fall of the heavy column of air above it.[10] Hugh Hamilton[11] and Guyton de Morveau (see Vol. III) held a similar theory.

In a section with the title 'There is in air a wholly special virtue (In Aëre virtus est penitus singularis)' Boerhaave says:[12]

All these things prove that air possesses a certain occult virtue which cannot be explained by any of those properties of air previously investigated. That in this virtue the secret food of life lies hidden, as Sendivogius clearly said, some chemists have asserted. But what it really is, how it acts, and what exactly brings it about (quid proprie efficiat)

[1] III, i, 423 f.   [2] *Ib.*, 447.   [3] *Ib.*, 459.   [4] *Ib.*, 461 f., 484 f.
[5] *Ib.*, 517 f., 526 f., mentioning Hales.   [6] *Ib.*, i, 534; ii, 183.
[7] *Ib.*, i, 537.   [8] *Ib.*, 492.
[9] *Opuscules*, 2 ed., 1801, 26; *Œuvres*, 1864, i, 461; Metzger, (1), 246; M. Kerker, *Isis*, 1955, xlvi, 36–49.
[10] III, i, 349 f.   [11] *Phil. Trans.*, 1765, lv, 146.   [12] III, i, 500.

is still obscure. Happy the man who will discover it! I do not know if it be enough to suggest that it is only its elastic part (an sola pars elastica).

In the section on water, in spite of Helmont's and Boyle's experiments, Boerhaave denied the conversion of water into earth; the small residue which he found on distilling water in glass retorts he thought was dust from the air:[1] 'men often overlook things which mix themselves unexpectedly in chemical operations.'

He attributes to Galileo the discovery that water expands on freezing and he thought this was due to the extrication of bubbles of air, the pressure of which breaks vessels in which water freezes:[2]

aqua gelu constricta ubi fuerit in glaciem, rarescens observata primo ab eximio Galileo, rarior ideo et levior, quam eadem aquae fluidae adhuc quantitas fuerat . . . quando autem frigore concrescit aqua . . . hinc mox bullas elasticas se expandentes, hinc leviores, format. . . . quae tandem majores redditae vim se dilatandi acquirunt adeo ingentem, ut omnia fere vasa, licet fortissima, coërcentia rumpat.

Boerhaave measured the solubilities of some salts in water at 38° F.:[3] 1 pt. of each of the following salts required the pts. by weight of water stated; sea salt $3\frac{1}{2}$, rock salt $3\frac{1}{2}$, sal ammoniac $3\frac{1}{4}$, nitre $5\frac{1}{3}$, borax 20, alum 14, Epsom salt $1\frac{1}{4}$, salt of tartar $1\frac{1}{2}$, vitriolated tartar 6 (after long shaking), green vitriol 16. Water saturated with sea salt would dissolve nitre, and vice versa. Alcohol precipitates the salts.

In Boerhaave's treatise on earth[4] he presents it both as one of the traditional four elements, when it is a mineral body, hard, friable, fixed in the fire, and insoluble in water, alcohol, oil, and air, which cannot be obtained perfectly pure; and also as one of a member of special earths obtained in chemical operations with animal, vegetable, and mineral bodies. Some recent chemists [Becher] regard it as a constituent of metals, but Boerhaave thought, on the basis of his own experiments, that a true earth cannot be obtained from them (enimvero laboravi ipse quam plurimum hac in re, neque talem ibi terram detexi hactenus).[5] Common sand is not elementary earth, since it consists of crystals and when heated with fixed alkali it turns into glass (esse crystallos pellucidas, exiguas, polyedras . . . in vitrum cum alcali fixo coïre facile dudum constitit).[6]

Boerhaave distinguished between mechanical mixtures and chemical compounds: a compound is homogeneous in its smallest parts, cannot be separated by gravity, and is formed with evolution of heat and the disappearance of the properties of the constituents and the formation of a new body.[7]

The section on Menstruums contains accounts of a very large number of chemical facts and experiments.[8] They are divided into four classes: (1) those acting purely mechanically (e.g. the granulation of fused metals by pouring into water), (2) those still partly mechanical but mainly acting by repulsion (as

[1] III, i, 592, 627.   [2] III, i, 621–2.   [3] *Ib.*, 574 f.
[4] *Ib.*, 630 f.   [5] *Ib.*, 658.   [6] *Ib.*, 668.
[7] III, i, 669 f., 699 f.; De menstruis.
[8] De menstruis dictis in Chemia; III, i, 669–868; Dumas, *Leçons sur la Philosophie Chimique*, 1878, 394.

when molten copper explodes in contact with water), (3) those acting by mutual attraction between solvent and solute (mutua attractione partium solventium, & solvendarum; particulae solventis inter partes divisas soluti) (as the combination of sulphur and mercury to form cinnabar), (4) those acting by a concurrence of all the above properties (as when sulphur is melted with potash).[1]

Chemical action, such as the solution of iron in aqua fortis, is not due to a mechanical action or violent propulsions but 'rather to attraction than repulsion (magis ex amore quam odio)', or to 'an appetite of union (amicitia, si amor dicendus copulae cupido)'. Boerhaave emphasises the superior attraction between bodies of different natures, indicating the existence of a special force of chemical attraction, and pointing out that the products of chemical changes usually differ entirely in their properties from the interacting substances.

Boerhaave[2] showed an experiment in which a piece of iron is put into some aqua fortis in a jar. There is a great commotion with evolution of bubbles, great heat, fiery fumes, and frothing, until the acid has combined with force with the iron and dissolved it all, when everything is again at rest:

particulae solventes, & solutae, denuo se affinitate suae naturae colligant in corpora homogenea. Oro Vos, Auditores cum cura perpendite id quod dico: dignissima est cognitione, & memoria, observatio. . . . Non igitur hic etiam actiones mechanicae, non propulsiones violentae, non inimicitiae, cogitandae, sed amicitia; si amor dicendus copulae cupido. . . . En rem spectate: spiritum nitri dilutum vase hoc contineo. Quiescit ille, neque signum ullum motus nobis exhibet. Frustulum jam ferri immitto huic liquido. Quam valida nunc bullarum rarefactarum usque ad margines tam ampli vasis usque expansio? quis motus? aestus quantus, strepitus, & igneus fere fumus! Sed quandiu haec omnia perdurant? sane non diutius, nisi dum salina pars nitri quaedam adhuc adest, quae nondum arcte unita est ferri particulae . . . simul ac vero omnes partes acidi illius combinatae sunt cum omnibus ferri particulis, statim cuncta requiescunt.

The action of all known menstruums depends upon motion. . . . But it is not easy to understand the physical manner in which this motion is excited by the menstruum . . . we cannot fairly attribute the origin of this to the common causes of motion, such as impulse, gravity, elasticity, magnetism, etc., but there is here a particular cause, not common to all bodies, exerted between the solvent and solute. This subject should be carefully enquired into, for he who can learn the power of menstruums will understand the whole nature of chemistry. . . . We are the more incited to this enquiry by the authority of those great men who believe that all the actions of bodies must be accounted for by the laws of mechanics. We shall see.

omnia menstrua cognita, dum actionem suam exercent, solo tantum motu agere . . . attamen non ita facile est modum intelligere physicum, quo excitatur ille motus a menstruo. . . . Non possumus serio meditati, et candide loquentes, causam hanc tribuere communibus motus gignendi originibus. Frustra enim in propulsione, gravitate, elasticitate, vi magnetica, aliave, si quae sit, generali causa, ortum hujus agitationis quaerimus: singularis enim est inter solvens, et solvendum, non communis omnibus corporibus. Verum omnia haec jam accuratissime excutienda nobis veniunt: quia menstruorum potestates bene intellexissi qui potuit, ille totius Chemiae naturam percepit. . . . Id autem ut nos perquiramus flagrantissime cogit omnium maxime autoritas summorum virorum, qui putant: scilicet omnes actiones quorumcunque corporum, per solas mechanices leges intellige et posse, et debere. Ergo videamus.[3]

It is clear from the whole section, comprising Cartesian and Newtonian ideas, that Boerhaave did not think gravitational attraction between particles could account even remotely for the specific chemical actions of substances.

[1] *Ib.*, 688; Partington, *Nature*, 1936, cxxxviii, 646.
[2] *Ib.*, 677–8; omitted in V, i, 493.   [3] *Ib.*, 683–4.

Boerhaave follows Lemery (see Vol. III) in supposing that there must be some relation between the size of the pores of the body dissolved and of the particles of the menstruum. Also, the particles of the menstruum must not adhere too closely to one another; strong oil of vitriol will not dissolve iron, but if the adhesion of its particles is enfeebled by their separation on dilution with water, the acid rapidly dissolves the metal.[1]

In speaking of the action of acids on bases he says a point is reached when the reaction is neither acidic nor alkaline and is called saturation. The compound formed is neither acid nor alkali but is composed of both (atque tum hoc punctum Saturationis vocatur. . . . Tumque illud compositum nec alcali est, nec acidum, sed ex his simul concretis conflatum).[2] Alkalis attract all known acids but some more strongly than others; e.g. oil of vitriol, spirit of salt, or nitric acid expels vinegar from its combination with potash.[3] The effervescence produced on mixing acid and alkali is due to the escape of numerous air bubbles which form elastic air (sicque elasticum valde aëra generantium, productio). It may be due to the acid and alkali rushing together by attraction and expelling what is between them.[4]

Boerhaave speaks of *sales dictos neutros, hermaphroditos, compositos, vel enixos*, and has a section *De salibus neutris*. These neutral salts are sal ammoniac, different forms of common salt, 'modern nitre (nitrum hodiernum)' or saltpetre (sal petrae), borax, alum and 'the vague acid of mines (acidum vagum fodinarum)', which with mineral oil (oleum terrae or petroleum) probably forms native sulphur.[5] A salt is defined as a concrete juice (succus concretus) or body (corpus), soluble in water, fusible (if it does not volatilise), and having a characteristic taste (quem saporem appellant).[6] Saline menstruums[7] are divided into:

I. Fixed alkali (potas) in various forms, kali or soda vel zoda, and volatile alkali.[8]

II. Acid menstruums, comprising: (*a*) native vegetable acids (in acid plants such as sorrel), (*b*) fermented vegetable acids both liquid (sour wine) and solid (tartar), (*c*) acetous vegetable acid (vinegar), (*d*) fermenting acid, viz. gas sylvestre, 'an explosive acid spirit (spiritus acidus et explosivus)', (*e*) vegetable acids formed by burning (wood smoke and liquid from burning wood), (*f*) distilled acid from various woods, smelling of red herrings, (*g*) fossil (mineral) acids, viz. (α) from sulphur, alum and vitriol (sulphuric acid), (β) from nitre (nitric acid), (γ) from sea salt (hydrochloric acid), and the mixture of the two last, aqua regia.[9]

Boerhaave has a further class of salts, compound salts (salia composita), formed from acids and alkalis.[10] These are always somewhat different from the natural salts, e.g. the sal mirabile Glauberi (sodium sulphate) made by distilling sea salt and oil of vitriol is different from that made by mixing oil of vitriol and the alkali (the first would contain much sodium bisulphate). The

---

[1] *Ib.*, 710; Regnier de Graaf had said this, Foster, 1901, 157.   [2] *Ib.*, 788.
[3] *Ib.*, 790.   [4] *Ib.*, 788.   [5] *Ib.*, 43 f., 821 f.   [6] *Ib.*, 43, 762.   [7] *Ib.*, 760 f.
[8] *Ib.*, 764 f., 771.   [9] *Ib.*, 804 f.   [10] *Ib.*, 792 f.

distinction between neutral salts and compound salts is noteworthy and peculiar. He says natural salts do not appear to have been formed from pre-existing acid and alkali, and he thinks the definition of Tachenius (p. 293) is too general, since no alkali can be separated from common salt;[1] and, again, when vinegar is made into sugar of lead the acid is destroyed and cannot be separated again from the compound by heating, a peculiar inflammable liquid (liquorem singularem, in igne inflammabilem; acetone) being obtained, although it is separated from copper by distilling verdigris.[2] He calls potassium acetate, made by dissolving salt of tartar (potassium carbonate) in acetic acid, tartarus regeneratus.[3] It had been called terra foliata secretissima by Philipp Müller.[4]

The difference between vegetable acids and mineral acids (acida fossilia) is that the latter alone dissolve gold, silver and mercury: lemon or orange juice (a vegetable acid) dissolves lead, tin, copper and iron.[5] Boerhaave discusses Homberg's experiments (Vol. III) on neutralisation and concludes that all acids have equal powers of saturation.[6]

An alkali is a substance which effervesces with all acids (quod cum omni acido, cui immiscetur, ilico ebulliat ferveatque).[7] The fixed alkali (potas) is not present in vegetables but is formed by the action of fire.[8] Boerhaave describes the preparation of caustic potash (sal acerrimus, Alcalinus, igneus, cum Calce viva) by causticising potash with quicklime, evaporating and fusing in an iron ladle, pouring on a copper plate, and while still soft cutting up into small sticks for use by surgeons as a cautery.[9] It must be kept in a closely corked bottle. The causticity of an alkali is acquired from the fire (ab igne acquirit acrimoniam) and when causticised with lime, the alkali attracts the fiery virtue of the lime (ex calcis virtute ignea attracta).[10] Acids have been called masculine, alkalis feminine, and the compound of the two (compositum ex hisce binis) hermaphrodite.[11]

Sea salt distilled with spirit of nitre (nitric acid) gives aqua regia and leaves nitre (Boerhaave does not distinguish sodium and potassium nitrates), whilst nitre distilled with spirit of salt (hydrochloric acid) gives sea salt (he says nitre by mistake)[12] and aqua regia:

adhibetur sal marinus ad unciam spiritus nitri, vel aqua fortis ad duas uncias, calore moderato expulsus liquor erit aqua regia, ... sed sal in fundo restitans erit nitrum ... ita quoque si nitri purissimi parti uni, affusae sunt spiritus salis marini partes duae, dabunt in destillatione puram aquam regiam ... in fundo retortae verum iterum nitrum.

The residue from the deflagration of nitre and tartar is a fixed alkali but differs from common fixed alkali (potassium carbonate) in giving with oil of vitriol 'a certain acid spirit, that plainly appears from its smell to be spirit of nitre:[13] emergunt spiritum quidam acidi adhuc, & odore spiritus Nitri satis manifesto distinguendi'; this would result from the potassium nitrite in the product.

[1] Ib., 793 f.   [2] III, i, 681, 819, 820; ii, 220.   [3] Ib., ii, 266.
[4] Miracula Chymica et Misteria Medica, 1611; Ferguson, ii, 115; see 203.
[5] III, i, 804, 809, 817.   [6] Ib., 786, 819.   [7] Ib., 766.
[8] III, i, 768; ii, 62: alcali fixum ignis filium esse.   [9] III, ii, 60.
[10] Ib., 61 f.   [11] III, i, 788.   [12] Ib., 827.   [13] III, ii, 386.

Boerhaave describes the preparation of fuming nitric acid (nitri spiritus Glauberi) by distilling nitre with oil of vitriol; it contains no oil of vitriol. Glauber first discovered the process, which he kept secret 'but at length divulged the method'.[1] The distillation of common salt with oil of vitriol gives Glauber's spirit of salt (spiritus salis Glauberi).[2] The acid spirit of sulphur made by burning sulphur under a glass bell, oleum sulphuris per campanam, is the same as oil of vitriol.[3] He describes the preparation of oil of vitriol by distilling green vitriol and says it boils above 600° F.[4]

Boerhaave describes sal ammoniac, which he thought was made in Egypt by subliming camel's urine, salt, and soot from wood; the fiery spirit (spiritum igneum) obtained from it by distilling with quicklime, 'the most pungent and violent vapour hitherto known' (ammonia gas), is the same as that obtained from urine and quicklime;[5] the saline spirit (ammonium acetate solution) formed from ammonia and distilled vinegar is 'not easily reducible to a solid salt.'[6]

Although Boerhaave classes vitriols with cinnabar, stibium, antimony, arsenic, bismuth, zinc, etc. (mercury is a metal) as semi-metals, he recognised their similarity to salts on account of their solubility in water (ad salina haec genera corporum, referimus hic, respectu Menstrui aquei) and says they are formed from metals and acids.[7] There are five kinds: green (iron), blue (much iron and a little copper), white (little different from the green), red (chalcanthum), and Cyprian (blue, from Hungary); the base (basis) is iron and copper, the acid is sulphuric. He thought the base of alum was lime:[8] quando idem acidum saxa calcaria rodit, cumque iis concrescit alumina.

Mercuric nitrate, made by dissolving mercury in hot aqua fortis, is called 'vitriol of quicksilver (argenti vivi vitriolum)'[9] and the same name is also given to corrosive sublimate,[10] the base of which is quicksilver and the other part the spirit of salt (basis argentum vivum . . . altera pars est spiritus salis marini). Silver nitrate is 'vitriol of silver (argenti vitriolum)', which when fused is lunar caustic or lapis infernalis.[11] A fused mixture of silver and potassium nitrates he called the 'hydragogum argentum' of Boyle or Angelus Sala.[12] Boerhaave condemned the internal administration of sugar of lead, which acts as a slow but sure poison.[13]

Purified metallic antimony crystallises in needles on the surface, which 'form a star, which the alchemical Magi adore'; it is not quite pure, since on fusion again with alkali it affords more sulphureous scoria and, as the metal is always brittle, it is perhaps never free from sulphur, which always destroys the ductility of metals.[14] The 'alchemical regulus of animony', obtained by fusion with iron and then with nitre, is beautifully starred (mire stellata); Boerhaave had spent much time on the process, as he blushed to say (datam fere erubesco).[15] When stibnite (antimony sulphide) is distilled with corrosive sublimate it gives an icy butter (butyrum glaciale) and cinnabar in the neck of the retort; the acid (aqua regia) in the sublimate unites with the reguline part of

---

[1] Ib., 392.　　[2] Ib., 408.　　[3] Ib., 421.　　[4] Ib., 499.　　[5] Ib., 333.　　[6] Ib., 338.
[7] III, i, 53 f., 572, 733, 811.　　[8] Ib., 811.　　[9] III, ii, 481.　　[10] Ib., 487.　　[11] Ib., 464 f.
[12] Ib., 467.　　[13] Ib., 456; Burton, 1743, 183.　　[14] III, ii, 509.　　[15] Ib., 512-13.

the stibnite, forsaking the mercury, and the regulus sublimes with spirit of salt, the sulphur of the stibnite uniting with the mercury and subliming as cinnabar.[1]

Sublimatur regulus cum spiritu illo salis, et fit vitriolum volatile antimonii, dictum butyrum, constans purissimo stibii regulo, et spiritu salis marini, in vitriolum adunatis. Haec ubi separata, et sublimata sunt, restat sulphur stibii in retorta, excusso regulo, et aestat mercurius purus, acido liber, quae bina calore coëunt, et sublimantur in cinnabarium.

As principles of vegetables, Boerhaave recognised: aroma (spiritus rector), oil (seat of the aroma), acid salt, neutral salt, fixed and volatile alkaline salts, oil mixed with alkali like soap, a saponaceous juice, oil adhering to earth, and earth itself.[2] The account of the practice of fermentation[3] is very full and practical; the description of the manufacture of vinegar[4] was praised by Parkes.[5] Boerhaave's theory of fermentation was similar to Stahl's: fermentation is an internal motion (motus intestinus), and Boerhaave distinguished vinous fermentation (producing wine) from acetous fermentation (producing vinegar). Gas sylvestre, a highly expansive and incoercible acid spirit produced in great quantity in fermentation, when received in the nostrils from a small hole in the cask, kills instantly or at least produces apoplexy, paralysis, or vertigo:[6]

Si enim sylvestris hic, nec coërcendus, spiritus, acidus, et explosivus, de ingenti copia fermentatis vegetabilis per exiguum in vase spiramenum ferit nares hominis fortissimi, uno eum ictu exanimat. Si minus fortiter afficit, tum apoplexiam creat subitaneam, si levius amentiam, cum paraplegia, si levissime vertigenem.

In the section on vegetables[7] Boerhaave mentions plant juices, honey, balsam, oil, resin, and gums; also *spiritus rector*, the odoriferous principle, to which the smell of essential oils was supposed to be due, a very subtle and scarcely ponderable body mixed with them.[8] Chemical operations bring about changes in the particular texture of each body and its medicinal virtues, so that caution must be used before the cause of their action can be assigned.

In the section on animals he says plants and animals are sustained by the same food, which is changed in the animal body into various other forms. He mentions only briefly animal salts and oils, and such humours as milk, fat, lymph, serum, saliva, blood, and urine, with no hint of their chemical nature.[9]

He distinguished fermentation from effervescence and from the putrefaction of animal substances, which are not truly fermentable; all these processes, however, are due to internal motions. He recognised that vegetable substances may undergo putrefaction as well as animal.[10] He distinguished acetone, from the distillation of lead acetate, from alcohol and called it liquor singulare in igne inflammabile:[11]

Si acetum stillatitium fortissumum ebulliendo calcem plumbi eroserit, hincque fuerit factum saccharum dictum Saturni. Constabit quidem acido aceti attracto in elementa plumbi, verum quoties sal hic plumbi de retorta igne destillat violento, non reddet aceti spiritum, sed liquorem singularem, in igne inflammabilem. . . . Fallitur

---

[1] *Ib.*, 519–21. [2] III, i, 57 f., 63. [3] III, ii, 166 f.: Fermentationis Historia.
[4] *Ib.*, 107 f. [5] *Chemical Essays*, 1823, i, 33. [6] III, i, 806; ii, 178.
[7] III i, 57–63. [8] *Ib.*, 74. [9] *Ib.*, 63–70. [10] III, ii, 289. [11] III, i, 681; ii, 222.

itaque, qui putaret, acidum aceti attactu plumbi ita fuisse conversum in novum liquoris inflammabilis genus.

He describes the neutralisation of salt of tartar by distilled vinegar, forming regenerated tartar (potassium acetate) and the dry distillation of the product, yielding an oil, as a very instructive experiment, teaching, e.g., what proportion of water and what proportion of acid are contained in an acid liquor, and what proportion of acid is required exactly to saturate an alkali (quaenam proportionalis pars acidi requiratur ratione alcali, ut saturatio justa obtineat).[1]

A crystalline 'salt' (sal nativus urinae) obtained from fresh urine evaporated to a syrup and allowed to stand for a year in a glass cylinder closed with parchment, then recrystallised from warm water,[2] was perhaps urea, since it is described as 'very volatile',[3] but may have been microcosmic salt. Ammonia is obtained as a fiery spirit not effervescing with acids, from *fresh* urine and quicklime.[4] The preparation of soap from olive oil and potash is described.[5] Soap renders oils, etc., soluble in water and hence easily washed away.[6]

Boerhaave thought the function of respiration is to cool the blood:[7]

verum aër, respirando ductus in pulmonem, est semper frigidior longe, quam hic sanguis . . . unde sanguis, ex se, in nulla iterum totius corporis plaga refrigeratur plus, hoc respectu, quam in pulmone nostro.

In his medical works he explained organic phenomena as due to the motions of solid and fluid bodies according to mechanical laws. All parts of the body are composed of an elastic substance mixed with fat and salt. Digestion is largely a mechanical process, facilitated by the heat of the parts around the stomach, although the solvent action of the juices, and a nervous fluid, play a part. Movements of the parts are due to a nervous fluid, a sort of refined water, formed in the brain and communicated by the nerves, the central point of animal motions being the heart. He had the curious idea that the more fluid and nutritive part of the food was expressed by trituration in the stomach, the more solid parts of animal and vegetable foods are not digested at all. Diseases of the fluids arise from kakochymie, not due to chemical processes but to changes of the shapes of atoms, e.g. from spherical to angular, and there are seven kinds of acridity: acid, bitter, aromatic, fatty, saline, alkaline, and glutinous, which can exist in combinations, as in the dilution of some juices and the thickening of others. He shows evidence of having made microscopical observations.[8] Experiments had made him change the opinion he had obtained by reading the books of Sylvius that blood contains acid and alkaline principles.[9] He denied the acidity of the gastric and pancreatic juices.[10]

In his oration on the plain simplicity of medicine when divested of what is foreign to it (1709)[11] he says the additions to medicine since Harvey (except anatomy and mechanics) are due to the Cartesians and the chemists. The first encumbered it with fictions, the second were more useful both to philosophy and medicine by discovering the operations of bodies on one another and their

[1] III, ii, 266, 269.   [2] *Ib.*, 317.
[3] Kurzer and Sanderson, *J. Chem. Educ.*, 1956, xxxiii, 452.   [4] III, ii, 315.
[5] *Ib.*, 262.   [6] III, i, 583.   [7] *Ib.*, 273–4.   [8] Haeser, 1881, ii, 504–8; Foster, 204.
[9] III, ii, 347.   [10] Foster, 203.   [11] IX, (c), 22–3.

powers and effects (nempe applicando corpora corporibus, natos hinc effectus dum observant seduli, proprias quibusdem vires, harumque actiones). But their cant of elements, inane ferments, fictitious heated effervescences, antagonistic salts, and the idea that all chemical preparations are medicinal (cuncta Chemiæ producta salutifera) are to be rejected. Take away all these from the works of Paracelsus, Helmont, Tachenius, and the older chemists and what remains but the few plain discoveries collected with great labour and prudence by the worthy Boyle (arte bonus Boylæus). Harvey and Malpighi dispersed the cells of Archeus, the myriads of ferments, and the strainers and efficacious faculties. The constituent parts of the body separable by art are only water, volatile salt, oil, and earth, and these are produced by the operations on the humours (namque in eo sola materies adest, quæ labore Chemico ita est mutabilis, ut inde demum natas partes exhibeat).

Pitcairne had clearly explained the virtues of mercury simply by its division and weight (minutam divisæ hujus materiæ pondus), and Homberg's explanations are equally good. Boerhaave seems to criticise Willis in particular:

Disparuere . . . de mirâ causâ caloris vitalis; de abdita humoris radicalis natura; de variato fermentorum munere; de tot intestinis fluidorum motibus; de productis Chemicis in sanguine præsentibus; de salibus cruoris accerime oppositis; de conflictu horum explodente scintillas lucentis vitæ; de balsamo quo viger et vita; de sulphure ut causa purpurascentis sanguinis; de sale condiente, ne putrescant, liquida.

Gaubius

Hieronymus David Gaubius (or Gaub) (Heidelberg, 24 February 1705–Leyden, 29 November 1780) studied in Halle, Amsterdam, Harderwyk, and Leyden (M.D. 1726) under Boerhaave, and Paris, then became town physician at Deventer; in 1729 he succeeded Boerhaave as professor of chemistry in Leyden. Manuscripts of his lectures were in circulation. In 1731 he also took the chair of medicine. He assisted Allamand in producing the French translation of Boerhaave's *Elementa Chemiae* (VII).[1]

Another pupil of Boerhaave was John Huxham (Halberton, Devonshire,?–London, 10 or 12 August 1768), F.R.S. 1739, Copley medallist 1755 for observations on antimony, and a remedy made by infusing metallic antimony or glass of antimony in white wine.[2] His prescriptions sometimes contained hundreds of ingredients. He also used tincture of Peruvian bark.[3]

Shaw

Peter Shaw (Lichfield, March 1694–London, 15 March 1763) was a well-educated quack who from 1752 was physician to George II and George III, becoming M.D. of Cambridge by royal mandate, F.R.S. 1752, translated

[1] Crell, *Ann.*, 1784, II, 472; Gmelin, (1), ii, 711 (*Oratio inauguralis qua ostenditur, Chemiam artibus academicis jure esse, inserendam*, 4°, Leyden, 1731 (BN 4° Te⁶. 410; NBG, 1857, xix, 634–5, gives *Oratio de Chemia, artibus, academicis rite inferenda*, 4°, Leyden, 1732); *Lectures on Pharmacy . . . given at the Close of the Annual Course of Chemistry* (on the desire of the late Dr. Boerhaave), 8°, London, 1744 (xvi, 432 pp., xviii ll.); *Adversariorum Varii Argumenti Liber Unus*, 4°, Leyden, 1771 (146 pp.; incl. camphor, sal ammoniac, sulphuric acid, etc.); Vicq-d'Azyr, *Éloges Historiques*, Paris, 1805, ii, 262; J. Thomson, *Life of Cullen*, 1859, i, 38.
[2] *Medical and Chemical Observations upon Antimony*, 8°, London, 1756, BM 546. d. 25. (5.); 2 ed. 1757; *Phil. Trans.*, 1754, xlviii, 832.
[3] *An Essay on Fevers*, 2 ed., 8°, London, 1750 (BM 7561. b. 20).

works of Hoffmann, Stahl, and Boerhaave, edited the works of Boyle (1725, p. 495) and Francis Bacon[1] and delivered courses of lectures on chemistry.[2] Shaw's first publication was his edition of John Quincy's lectures on pharmacy.[3] Other publications are on wine,[4] on concentrating wines and other fermented liquors and on distillation,[5] proposals for a course of chemical experiments,[6] and with F. Hauksbee an account of a portable laboratory (mostly purloined from Becher, p. 642).[7] His lectures of 1731–3 were published in 1733.[8] The book contains a glossary of chemical terms, chapters on fermentation and putrefaction, doctoring wines and the use of sugar in brewing;[9] analytical and synthetical chemistry; distillation; oils, salts and soap; colours; pharmacy; mineralogy; metallurgy; pyrotechny; and a chapter (headed 'of enlarging Chemistry') of suggestions, including a recipe for a borosilicate glass.[10] This book is, in a way, an expansion of the long appendix to Shaw's translation of Boerhaave.[11]

WILSON

George Wilson (London ?; 1631–15 August 1711) had a laboratory where he prepared and sold medicines and gave lectures.[12] He published a successful text-book.[13] The Appendix 'Of Transmutation of Metals' gives experiments from 1661 to 1704, and thus must have been added to the later editions. Wilson gives the processes quite clearly but says: 'I . . . always fell short of, or was entirely baffled in my Expectations.' The book is similar to Lemery's *Cours de Chymie* and is very clear and practical, but Wilson says he omitted 'Mons. Lemery's pompous way of philosophizing upon the processes'. It has eight plates of symbols, furnaces, and apparatus.

[1] *The Philosophical Works of Francis Bacon, methodized, and made English*, 4°, 1733; the tr. of the *Novum Organum* was republ. in 1802 and 1812.
[2] Webb, DNB, 1897, li, 442; Gibbs, *Ann. Sci.*, 1951, vii, 211.
[3] *Praelectiones Pharmaceuticæ; or a Course of Lectures in Pharmacy, Chymical and Galenical . . . from his Original MSS.*, 4°, London, 1723, with a preface by Shaw (who, as in his other earlier books, already calls himself M.D.) on adulterations and superstitious remedies (Sotheran *Cat.* 852 (1938), no. 1356). John Quincy, M.D., d. 1722, wrote *Pharmacopœia Officinalis et extemporanea, or, A compleat English Dispensatory*, 8°, 1718, 1719, 1722 (4 ed.), 1742 (12 ed.), 1769 (14 ed.); Moore, DNB, 1896, xlvii, 112.
[4] *The Juice of the Grape: or, Wine preferable to Water . . . By a Fellow of the College*, 1724.
[5] *Three Essays in Artificial Philosophy, or Universal Chemistry: viz. I. An Essay for the further application and advancement of Chemistry in England. II. An Essay for the improvement of Distillation in the hands of the Malt-Stiller, Rectifier, Compounder and Apothecary. III. An Essay for Concentrating Wines and other Fermented Liquors*, 1731 (pp. xv, 192); 2 ed. *Essays for the Improvement of Arts, Manufactures, and Commerce, by means of Chemistry . . .*, 8°, 1761 (pp. xix, 258).
[6] *Proposals for a Course of Chemical Experiments: with a View to Practical Philosophy, Arts, Trades and Business*, 8° [London, 1731].
[7] *An Essay for Introducing a Portable Laboratory by Means whereof all the Chemical Operations are Commodiously Perform'd, with Sculptures*, 8°, London, 1731; most of the above are in BM 1035. k. 7.
[8] *Chemical Lectures, publickly read at London, in the Years 1731, and 1732; and at Scarborough, in 1733; for the Improvement of Arts, Trades, and Natural Philosophy*, 8°, London [1734] (Sotheran *Cat.* 852 (1938), no. 1373); *The Second Edition, corrected*, 8°, London, 1755 (quoted here).
[9] 1755, 200 f.   [10] 1755, 454.   [11] *New Method of Chemistry*, 1741, ii, 345–410.
[12] Gibbs, *Endeavour*, 1953, xii, 182; Thorndike, viii, 166; not in DNB.
[13] *A Compleat Course of Chymistry: Containing not only the Best Chymical Medicines, But Also Great Variety of Useful Observations. To which are added, The Author's Experiments upon Metals by Way of Appendix*, 8°, London, 1691, 2 ed. 1699 or 1700, 3 ed. 1709 (portr. 413 pp.), 4 ed. 1721 (383 pp.), 5 ed. 1736 (383 pp.), ed. by W. Lewis, 1746 (see below).

Wilson[1] says he could not be expected to theorise, 'who want the great Blessings of Academical Education, and have no more Philosophy than I have fetched out of the Fire'; and after describing the preparation of a Universal Anodyne from opium, French brandy, the 'Secret Corrector' (the preparation of which he clearly describes), etc., he adds: 'Those Gentlemen who have not Conveniency to prepare it, may for twenty shillings the Pound have it of me.'[2]

GODFREY

Boyle Godfrey, one of the sons of Ambrose Godfrey Hanckewitz, Boyle's operator, published a book dealing with foods and diet, materia medica, and 'divers useful discoveries'.[3] Ambrose Godfrey, a brother (?), issued in 1740 a prospectus of a *Compleat Course of Chemistry*, part of the MS. of which is in the Pharmaceutical Society Library. He and his brother John Godfrey Hanckwitz described[4] experiments on the supposed conversion of distilled water into earth by grinding it in a glass mortar (Eller's process, see p. 716) or heating it in a flint glass phial for several months. In the first case, glass ('earth') was abraded from the mortar, in the second the glass was attacked.

GRAVENHORST

The brothers Johann Heinrich (1719–1781/2) and Christoph Julius (1731–1794) Gravenhorst, of Brunswick, manufactured sal ammoniac, Glauber's salt, red alum, and Brunswick green (copper oxychloride), a pigment invented by Johann Heinrich about 1771,[5] and described a method of tinning copper (1774). In a pamphlet[6] containing a section 'Aus dem Glauberschen Wundersalz wahren Schwefel hervorzubringen, ohne Beihülfe des Feuers', they reported that when wormwood was allowed to putrefy in a solution of Glauber's salt, sulphur was formed from the phlogiston lost from the plant.[7]

DOSSIE

Robert Dossie (Sheffield, September 1717–London, 20 February 1777) was at first a consulting chemist in Sheffield, and from about 1757 in London, where he was active in the Society of Arts, particularly in relation to the manufacture of potash, the purification of train oil, and agriculture, and also translated medical works from Latin and French.[8] His best-known work was published anonymously.[9] It deals with furnaces and distillation apparatus

[1] 1721, 356.   [2] *Ib.*, 291.
[3] *Miscellanea vere Utilia: or Miscellaneous Experiments and Observations on Various Subjects*, 8°, London, n.d. (c. 1735); 2 ed. 1737 (v ll., 152 pp.) with additions; Ince, *Pharm. J.*, 1858, xviii, 263–7.
[4] *A Curious Research into the Elements of Water* . . . , 1747.
[5] Gmelin, (1), iii, 24, 52, 891; Ferguson, i, 343.
[6] *Einige Nachrichten an das Publikum, die Gravenhorstische Fabrikprodukte betreffend*, 8°, Brunswick, 1769.
[7] Gmelin, (1), ii, 588.   [8] Gibbs, *Ann. Sci.*, 1948, vi, 33; 1951, vii, 149; 1953, ix, 191.
[9] *The Elaboratory laid open, or, the Secrets of Modern Chemistry and Pharmacy revealed*, 8°, London, 1758, 2 ed. 1768; French tr. 1759, German tr. by Konigsdörfer, 1760, and by

(retorts and receivers), alembics, making oil of vitriol from sulphur,[1] various chemical operations, alkalis, various preparations: spirit of hartshorn and its 'sophistication' with quicklime, sal volatile, 'selle de Seignette'[2] or 'sal Rupiliense', the preparation of imitation Glauber's salt from Epsom salt,[3] corrosive sublimate and calomel,[4] red precipitate by heating mercury 'in a proper glass, for several months',[5] Mosaic gold (stannic sulphide),[6] distilled spirits,[7] and adulterations and their detection.[8]

Other books dealing specifically with distillation were published.[9]

LEWIS

William Lewis (Richmond, Surrey; 1708–19 (or 21) January 1781), educated at Christ Church, Oxford, 'Bachelor of Physick', physician at Kingston-on-Thames, F.R.S. 1745, lectured to the Prince of Wales at Kew.[10] Besides the translation of Neumann (1759, see p. 703) Lewis published several works of merit:

I. A Course of Practical Chemistry. In which are contained All the Operations Described in Wilson's Complete Course of Chemistry. With many new, and several uncommon Processes, 8°, London, 1746.

II. The Pharmacopoeia of the Royal College of Physicians at Edinburgh. Faithfully translated from the Fourth Edition, 8°, London, 1748.

III. Oratio in Theatro Sheldoniano . . . die dedicationis Bibliothecae Radclivianae, 2 eds. Oxford, 1749.

IV. An Experimental History of the Materia Medica, or of the Natural and Artificial Substances made use of in Medicine, 4°, London, 1761 (591 pp.), 1768, and later eds., 1770, Dublin, 1778; London, 1781, 1785; ed. Duncan, Edinburgh and London, 1786, London, 1799; tr. Lebégue de Presle, 3 vols. 8°, Paris, 1771.

V. Commercium Philosophico-Technicum, or the Philosophical Commerce of the Arts, designed as an Attempt to Improve the Arts, Trade and Manufacture, 2 vols. 4°, vol. i, 1766, vol. ii, 1763, with Royal privilege for 14 years;

French tr. by de Rusieux, Expériences physiques et Chymiques sur plusieurs matières relatives au commerce et aux arts, 3 vols., Paris, 1768–9;

German trs. of separate parts by J. H. Ziegler: Historie des Goldes, Zürich, 1764; Historie der Färben, Zürich, 1766 (BM); these works may be parts of Ziegler's tr.: Zusammenhang der Künste, philosophisch-praktisch abgehandelt, 2 vols. Zürich, 1764–6; tr. J. G. Krunitz, Phys.-chem. Abhandlungen und Versuche zur Beförderung der Künste, Handwerke und Manufakturen, 2 vols. Berlin, 1764–6; Geschichte des Goldes, Gräz, 1786 (of which I have seen only the Historie der Färben).

VI. Experiments and Observations on American Potashes, with an easy method of determining their respective qualities, 8°, London, 1767.

VII. Eds. of Quincy's The New Dispensatory . . . Intended as a Correction and

Wiegleb, 1783; Ferguson, i, 222; the book was known in 1757. Dossie also wrote *Handmaid to the Arts*, 1758; *Institutes of Experimental Chemistry . . . By the Author of the Elaboratory laid open, &c.*, 2 vols., 1759, German tr. 1762; *Theory and Practice of Chirurgical Pharmacy*, 1761; *Observations on the Pot-Ash brought from America*, 1767; *Memoirs of Agriculture*, 3 vols., 1768–77–82.

[1] *Elaboratory*, 1758, 44, 158: in glass globes, see Vol. III.   [2] *Ib.*, 132.   [3] *Ib.*, 189.
[4] *Ib.*, 210 f.   [5] *Ib.*, 243.   [6] *Ib.*, 265.   [7] *Ib.*, 331.   [8] *Ib.*, 351.
[9] Ambrose Cooper, *The Complete Distiller, containing the method of performing the various processes of Distillation with descriptions of the several instruments, the whole doctrine of fermentation . .* , 8°, London, 1757 (Gmelin, (1), iii, 17, mentioning the 2 ed., 1761). J. Dujardin, *Recherches Rétrospectives sur l'Art de la Distillation. Historique de l'Alcool de l'Alambic et de l'Alcoometrie*, Paris, 1900 (236 pp.), gives a history and bibliography of distillation.
[10] Thomson, (1), i, 266; Kremers, *William Lewis*, 1931 (BM 010822. i. 11; a bibliography); Gibbs, *Ann. Sci.*, 1952, viii, 122, 202; Archbold, DNB, 1893, xxxiii, 199.

Improvement of Quincy, 1753, 4 ed. 1781, 5 ed. 1785, 6 ed. 1799, and Edinburgh eds., with A. Duncan and Charles Elliot (with a New Table of Elective Attractions), 1789, 1791, 1797.

FIG. 37. A CHEMICAL LABORATORY IN 1765.

(From W. Lewis, *Commercium Philosophico-Technicum: or the Philosophical Commerce of the Arts*, London, 1765.)

Lewis's assistant, Alexander Chisholm, knew classical languages, German and Swedish, and no doubt translated Neumann for him. Chisholm translated foreign publications for Lewis's use and prepared extensive reports and summaries. Chisholm later became Wedgwood's scientific assistant and his copious notes from scientific literature, prepared for Lewis, are still extant in several volumes in the Wedgwood Museum, Stoke, and in the British Museum.[1]

At a time when English chemists were dominated by the mechanical outlook promulgated by Newton (see p. 482), Lewis was quite clear that chemistry is a distinct science, in which such speculations are of very little relevance or value. He says:[2]

'The properties of bodies make the object of two sciences, *natural philosophy* and *chemistry*; which, though in many cases so closely interwoven, and so nearly allied, that perhaps no boundaries can be established between them, appear in others to have essential and important differences. . . . natural or mechanical philosophy seems to consider bodies chiefly as being entire aggregates or masses . . . subject to mechanic laws, and reducible to mathematical calculation. . . . Chemistry considers bodies as being composed of such a particular species of matter', with properties which are 'not

[1] Thomson, (1), i, 266; Gibbs, *Ann. Sci.*, 1952, viii, 202; Schofield, *Chymia*, 1959, v, 180.
[2] V, I, pref., iii.

subject to any known mechanism, and seem to be governed by laws of another kind'. The other branches of knowledge are concerned with attraction in mechanical philosophy and affinity in chemistry, in which the 'effects can be regarded no otherwise than as simple facts, not reducible to any known mechanism, nor investigable from any principles, and each discoverable by observation only. . . . It seems of importance, that these two orders of the affections of bodies be kept distinct, as many errors have arisen from applying to one such laws as obtain only in the other'.

He described a fusible metal bath (2 lead, 3 tin, 5 bismuth)[1] and experimented on the conversion of glass into porcelain on heating (devitrification), which he thought was due to loss of alkali by exudation.[2] Ether extracts gold from its solution in aqua regia, becoming yellow; he found that gold is the only metal behaving in this way.[3] Lewis[4] investigated nut galls from the point of view of the preparation of ink, and says in relation to the black colour produced with iron salts:

The power by which they produce this blackness, and their astringency, or that by which they contract an animal fibre, and by which they contribute to the tanning of leather, seem to depend upon one and the same principle, and to be proportional to one another. Of the other properties of this astringent and colouring matter, little more is known, than that it is dissolved and extracted from the subject both by water and spirit of wine, and that it does not exhale in the evaporation of the liquors by heat.

Although he did not isolate gallotannin he certainly seems to have recognised its existence.[5] He published important papers on platinum.[6]

Several minor contributions of Lewis are announced in his notes to Neumann's *Chemical Works*, 1759 (page refs. are to this). He pointed out that alum reacts with indicators like an acid (p. 187); connected the 'strength' or 'powerfulness' and the velocity of action ('activity') of acids (p. 162); pointed out that waters distilled from bitter almonds and bitter fruit kernels contain a poisonous principle (hydrocyanic acid) (p. 389); described fustic, nephritic wood, logwood, brazil wood, and madder dyes (p. 384), the preparation of glucose (concrete honey) from honey (p. 331), and the fact that borax increases the solubility of tartar, the acid of which is quite different from vinegar (p. 457). He found that bismuth amalgam dissolves lead very easily (p. 93).

PEMBERTON

Henry Pemberton (London; 1694–9 April 1771), who studied at Leyden (M.D.) and Paris, was (1728) professor of Physic at Gresham College, where he also lectured on chemistry.[7] He says that alkali is used in making alum since it precipitates it and without alkali the alum 'would contain too much of this stony part'.[8] The air contains an acid, as its action on metals shows, and 'the acid of the air nearer resembles that of nitre, than any other known to us';

---

[1] V, i, 32.   [2] V, i, 230, 253; see Reaumur, Vol. III.
[3] V, i, 101; ferric chloride is also extracted.   [4] V, ii, 344–50.
[5] Jagnaux, ii, 714; cf. Nierenstein, *Incunabula of Tannin Chemistry*, 1932, 161; id., *The Natural Organic Tannins*, 1934, 105.
[6] *Phil. Trans.*, 1754, xlviii, 638–89; 1757, l, 148–55, 156–66; see also his tr. of Neumann, *Chemical Works*, 1759, 43; *Commercium Philosophico-Technicum*, 1763, ii, 443.
[7] Pemberton, *A Scheme for a Course of Chymistry to be performed at Gresham College . . . to begin Monday, Jan. 18, 1730/1*, 11 pp., BM; life of Pemberton by Jas. Wilson in Pemberton, *Course of Chemistry*, 1771.
[8] *Course*, 1771, 192.

combustion is caused by the action of this acid, just as nitric acid inflames oil of turpentine.[1] Metals when calcined give a calx specifically lighter than the metal, but 'there is besides an accession of new matter', since lead, for example, gains $\frac{1}{20}$th in weight on conversion into minium.[2] On heating calces with 'charcoal, tartar, sea-coal or any other inflammable substance', the metals are restored to their form, 'as if the coal supplied the metal again with what the great heat . . . had deprived them of.'[3] Pemberton[4] says of the increase in weight on calcination, 'I think we may safely answer, that it is from the air.' When a body burns in a closed vessel till extinguished 'a considerable quantity of air is found to have lost its elasticity', and 'without doubt, while the air by acting on the inflammable substance either in metals or other bodies expels it from them, it unites itself (in part at least) to the remains of the body'. This is really the same as Rey's theory (see p. 635).

WATSON

Richard Watson (Heversham, nr. Kendal, August 1737–Windermere, 9 July 1816), perhaps of Scottish ancestry, went in 1753 as Exhibitioner to Trinity College, Cambridge. In 1757 he was private tutor and in 1767 head tutor in the College, having become second Wrangler in 1759 (the first being unfairly preferred). In 1760 he became Fellow. On the death of the professor of chemistry John Hadley (1731–64),[5] Watson in 1764 was unanimously elected by the Senate as professor of chemistry, a subject of which he was then completely ignorant. After 14 months of study with an 'operator' brought over from Paris, Watson became a very competent chemist. He became F.R.S. in 1769, and in 1771 he became D.D. and Regius Professor of Divinity. In 1782 he became Bishop of Llandaff, but he went to live at Calgarth Park on the shore of Lake Windermere, where he later died.[6] Watson is buried in the churchyard of the old church at Windermere; a marble tablet (with a crozier and mitre) being opposite his tomb inside. His wife, who died in April, 1831, aged 81, is buried in the same tomb.

Watson's numerous theological and political writings do not concern us. He defended Christianity against Gibbon's oblique attacks in the *Decline and Fall of the Roman Empire*, in which Gibbon praises Watson's *Chemical Essays* as 'a classic book, the best adapted to infuse the taste and knowledge of chemistry'.[7] Watson's books of chemical interest are: *An Essay on the Subjects of Chemistry and their General Divisions* (Cambridge, 1771, 43 pp.), *Institutiones Metallurgicae* (Cambridge, 1768), and his famous *Chemical Essays*[8] He says he burnt a

---

[1] *Ib.*, 196 f.; some of this is from Mayow.   [2] *Ib.*, 232–3.   [3] *Ib.*, 243.
[4] *Ib.*, 245 f.   [5] Coleby, *Ann. Sci.*, 1952, viii, 293.
[6] *Anecdotes of the Life of Richard Watson*, 4°, 1817 (by himself, with portrait); 2nd. ed., 2 vols. 8°, 1818; Anon., *Critical Examination of the Bishop of Llandaff's Anecdotes of his Life*, 1818 (bound with BM copy); De Quincy, *Reminiscences of the English Lake Poets*, Everyman ed., 54 f., 253; Thomson, *Ann. Phil.*, 1817, ix, 257; Gordon [and Hartog], DNB, 1899, lx, 24; Walker, *Memoirs of the Distinguished Men of Science*, etc., 1862, 205; Partington, *Chem. and Ind.*, 1937, lvi, 819 (portr.); 1960, 146; de Castro, *ib.*, 1937, lvi, 846; V. Bartow, *J. Chem. Educ.*, 1938, xv, 103–11 (bibl.).
[7] *Decline and Fall*, ch. 52.
[8] 2 vols. 12°, Cambridge, 1781, vol. 3 1782, vol. 4 1786, vol. 5 1787; and later eds., with the same pagination, e.g. 6 ed., 5 vols. 8°, London, 1793–6.

large number of his manuscripts on chemistry, as it was not considered becoming in a bishop to have meddled with such subjects. The burnt papers consisted of dissertations on blood, milk, urine, fermentation, wine, ale, vinegar, putrefaction, sugar, balsams, resins, glass, precious stones, metals, etc., all containing the natural and commercial history, and chemical analysis,

FIG. 38. RICHARD WATSON, 1737–1814.
(From *Anecdotes of the Life of Richard Watson*)

of the substances, and all the ancients knew on the subjects.[1] These are, in fact, topics in his *Essay on the Subjects of Chemistry* (1771), and must have formed part of his lectures. The loss must be regretted.

The experiments which Watson made, at the request of the Government, on the manufacture of gunpowder are said to have saved £100,000 a year for some years,[2] but he received no reward. Watson suggested that air might be solidified by sufficient cold.[3] He classed diamond with flint.[4]

Watson's most important published essays (which include his contributions

[1] *Anecdotes*, 1818, i, 236.   [2] *Anecdotes*, 1818, i, 240.
[3] *Essay on the Subjects of Chemistry*, 1771, 3.   [4] *Ib.*, 10.

to the *Philosophical Transactions, Memoirs of the Manchester Literary and Philosophical Society*, etc.) are on the degrees of heat at which water boils (1782); on pit-coal (1781), suggesting the condensation of volatile products on coking; on the smelting of lead ore (1781), suggesting the condensation of lead fume and sulphur dioxide evolved on roasting; on zinc (1786); and especially his 'Experiments and observations on various phenomena attending the solution of salts'[1] and 'Some Remarks on the Effects of the Great Cold in February',[2] in which he anticipated Blagden (Vol. III) in showing that 'in salt of the same kind, the resistance to congelation is in direct simple proportion to the quantity of salt dissolved'; he found that the times taken for solutions of various salts to freeze when exposed to cold air, reckoned from the time when water begins to freeze, are proportional to the quantities of dissolved salt, different salts behaving differently.

Daniel Bernoulli[3] had said that sugar and salts lower the freezing-point of water, perhaps because the foreign particles interposed between the aqueous particles diminish their attraction and tendency to unite (particulis aqueis interpositæ, harum attractionem diminuant, neque hæ conjungi possint), and on freezing they are expelled (tempore congelationis fit quædam partium ex poris expulsio, seu secretio atque præcipitatio).

Watson in his essay on the degrees of heat at which water boils[4] described the well-known experiment in which hot water in a corked flask boils when the vapour space is cooled by cold water, owing to the reduction of pressure. Franklin[5] had noticed a similar phenomenon. Watson also invented a black-bulb thermometer.[6] Some of Watson's *Chemical Essays* were translated into German[7] by Friedrich Andreas Gallisch, who himself wrote on hydrochloric acid and chlorine.[8] The experiment of making coal gas from coal heated in a clay tobacco pipe was ascribed by H. B. Dixon to Watson.[9]

Watson gave an excellent account of the phlogiston theory, based on Stahl's *Zymotechnia Fundamentalis* (p. 659).[10]

WALL

Martin Wall, M.D., 'Public Reader in Chemistry' in Oxford, published two books,[11] and papers on the origin of the fixed vegetable alkali, discussing the old problem as to whether it existed in the plant or was formed by fire, and

[1] *Phil. Trans.*, 1770, lx, 325; *Essays*, 1796, v, 43.
[2] *Phil. Trans.*, 1771, lxi, 213; *Essays*, v, 177.
[3] *Hydrodynamica*, 4°, Strassbourg, 1738, 15.   [4] *Essays*, 1782 (1796), iii, 143 (159).
[5] *Experiments and Observations on Electricity*, London, 1769, 489.
[6] *Phil. Trans.*, 1773, lxiii, 40; *Essays*, v, 193.
[7] *Dr. Watson's chemische Versuche*, Theil I, II (all publ.) Leipzig, 1782 (BM 1035. d. 21).
[8] *Programma de acido salis ejusque dephlogisticatione*, Leipzig, 1782.
[9] It is described in J. J. Griffin, *Chemical Recreations*, Glasgow, 1826 (dedic. dated 18 Sept. 1823), 154.
[10] Of Fire, Sulphur and Phlogiston, *Essays*, 1793, i, 149; Odling, *Proc. Roy. Inst.*, 1871, vi, 315; *Chem. News*, 1871, xxiii, 243, 256; *Ber.*, 1871, iv, 421; Philbrick and Holmyard, *Text-Book of Theoretical and Inorganic Chemistry*, 1956, 20.
[11] *A Syllabus of a Course of Lectures in Chemistry*, Oxford, 1782 (ii ll., 63 pp.); *Dissertations on Select Subjects in Chemistry and Medicine*, Oxford, 1783 (17 + 166 pp.), dealing with 'the study of chemistry,' 'on the origin and use of symbols in astronomy and chemistry', and 'on the diseases prevalent in the South Sea Islands'; Duveen, 608.

concluding that it is 'formed by some transmutation of the native acid of plants, or by a particular combination of it with the earthy and inflammable principles'.[1] He also wrote on the phenomena of oil and water, calling attention to Plutarch's remark on the stilling of waves by oil (anticipating Franklin), with some interesting suggestions on the formation of films,[2] and on attraction and repulsion, criticising Percival for explaining the latter phenomenon as due to repulsion between the particles of oil and water and suggesting that they are due to the relative attractions of oil and water particles — an early discussion of surface chemistry.[3]

NICOLAI

Ernst Anton Nicolai (Sondershausen, 7 September 1722–Jena, 28 August 1802), professor of medicine and (1759) and also of chemistry in Jena, published a *Programm de caussa, cur ferrum per cuprum praecipitetur*, 4°, Jena, 1776 (finding that iron is precipitated by copper in certain conditions), *Progr. I II de affinitate corporum chemica*, 4°, Jena, 1775–6, *Diss. de putredine*, 4°, Jena, 1769,[4] and medical works.

FUCHS

Georg Friedrich Christian Fuchs (Jena, 20 August 1760–Bürgel, 22 August 1813), lecturer in, and later professor of, medicine in Jena, published a translation of Spielmann's *Institutiones Chemiae* (p. 689),[5] many minor researches,[6] and three publications (1794–7) on the action of acids on lead glaze and the preparation of a glaze free from lead.[7]

[1] *Manchester Mem.*, 1785, ii, 67.   [2] *Ib.*, 1785, ii, 419.
[3] *Ib.*, 1785, ii, 439.   [4] Gmelin, (1), ii, 655, 697; Poggendorff, (1), ii, 282.
[5] *Chemischer Lehrbegriff nach Spielmann's Grundsätzen ausgearbeitet und mit den neuesten Erfahrungen bereichert*, Leipzig, 1787.
[6] *Versuch einer natürlichen Geschichte des Spiesglases*, Halle, 1786; *Geschichte des Zinks . . . und seiner Anwendung auf Arzneywissenschaft und Künste*, Erfurt, 1788; *Geschichte des Braunsteins*, Jena, 1791; *Versuch einer Uebersicht der chymischen Litteratur*, Altenburg, 1785.
[7] Gmelin, iii, 541, 795; Ferguson, i, 295.

SYMBOLS WITH THEIR MEANINGS

Ref. No.	Meaning
1	tio, ⊙tio solutio
2	re praecipitare
3	io fusio
4	re vaporare
5	re digerere
6	tio digestio
7	re coquere
8	re incinerare
9	re pulverisare
10	re fundere
11	re calcinare
12	destillare
13	re sublimare
14	aa, aaa ana
15	aaa, ȧȧȧ amalgama
16	arena
17	minera
18	MB balneum maris
19	VB vaporis balneum
20	retorta
21	recipiens
22	cucurbita
23	alembicus
24	crucibulum
25	SSS stratum super stratum
26	pulver
27	libra
28	drachma
29	uncia
30	scrupulus
31	dies, nox
32	hora
33	mensis
34	corpora volatilia
35	corpora fixa
36	sublimatum, spiritus
37	caput mortuum
38	ignis
39	aer
40	aqua
41	terra
42	sales
43	c sal communis
44	ia, salia
45	sal neutrum, salsum, enixum
46	borax
47	alcalia
48	sal ammoniacus
49	tartarus
50	acida, acetum
51	acetum destillatum
52	crystalli
53	silex
54	alumen
55	nitrum
56	sulphur
57	phosphorus
58	phlogiston
59	oleum
60	tinctura
61	sapo
62	urina
63	vitrum
64	regulus
65	aurum, sol
66	argentum
67	cuprum, aes
68	ferrum
69	chalybs
70	stannum
71	plumbum
72	mercurius
73	mercurius sublimatus corrosivus
74	mercurius praecipitatus
75	antimonium
76	orichalcum
77	magnesium (manganese)
78	zincum
79	bismuthum
80	arsenicum
81	regulus niccoli
82	regulus cobalti
83	platinum
84	uranium
85	auripigmentum
86	cinnabaris
87	cancer (crab)
88	c.c. cornu cervi
89	calx (lime)
90	calx viva
91	aqua calcis
92	magnes
93	magnesia, terra muriatica
94	sal amarus
95	argilla
96	terra ponderosa
97	sal alcalinus
98	p sal alc. purus (causticus)
99	v potassinum
100	m natrum
101	sal neutralis
102	sal metallicus
103	alcalia fixa
104	alcalia volatile
105	sal tartari
106	vitriolum
107	vitriolum cupri
108	vitriolum ferri
109	vitriolum zinci
110	viride aeris, aerugo
111	cinis, cineres clavellati
112	acidum carbonicum
113	acidum vitriolicum
114	acidum nitricum
115	spiritus vitrioli
116	spiritus nitri
117	spiritus vini
118	spiritus tartari
119	ae spiritus urinae
120	aqua fortis
121	aqua regis
122	sal sedativum
123	acidum boracicum
124	acidum tartarosum
125	acidum phosphoricum
126	acidum urinae, phosphori
127	acidum salis
128	acidum arsenici
129	acidum fluoricum
130	acidum oxalicum
131	acidum benzoicum
132	acidum formicarum
133	acidum prussicum
134	acidum succinicum
135	m acidum minerale
136	acidum vegetabile
137	a acidum animale
138	oleum vitrioli
139	oleum empyreumaticum
140	isatus tartar tartarisatus
141	oleum essentiale
142	aether
143	saccharum
144	resina
145	gummi

INDEX OF NAMES

(Pages containing biographical notices or full treatments are in heavy type)

2C

INDEX OF SUBJECTS

PRINTED IN GREAT BRITAIN
BY ROBERT MACLEHOSE AND CO. LTD
THE UNIVERSITY PRESS, GLASGOW